ANNUAL REVIEW OF PHYSIOLOGY

ANNUAL REVIEW OF PHYSIOLOGY

ERNST KNOBIL, *Editor*
University of Pittsburgh School of Medicine

RALPH R. SONNENSCHEIN, *Associate Editor*
University of California, Los Angeles

I. S. EDELMAN, *Associate Editor*
University of California School of Medicine, San Francisco

VOLUME 39

1977

ANNUAL REVIEWS INC.   4139 EL CAMINO WAY   PALO ALTO, CALIFORNIA 94306

REPRINTS

The conspicuous number aligned in the margin with the title of each article in this
volume is a key for use in ordering reprints. Available reprints are priced at the
uniform rate of $1 each, postpaid. The minimum acceptable reprint order is 10
reprints and/or $10.00, prepaid. A quantity discount is available.

CONTENTS

ANNUAL REVIEWS INC. is a nonprofit corporation established to promote the advancement of the sciences. Beginning in 1932 with the *Annual Review of Biochemistry,* the Company has pursued as its principal function the publication of high quality, reasonably priced Annual Review volumes. The volumes are organized by Editors and Editorial Committees who invite qualified authors to contribute critical articles reviewing significant developments within each major discipline.

Annual Reviews Inc. is administered by a Board of Directors whose members serve without compensation.

Annual Reviews are published in the following sciences: Anthropology, Astronomy and Astrophysics, Biochemistry, Biophysics and Bioengineering, Earth and Planetary Sciences, Ecology and Systematics, Energy, Entomology, Fluid Mechanics, Genetics, Materials Science, Medicine, Microbiology, Nuclear Science, Pharmacology and Toxicology, Physical Chemistry, Physiology, Phytopathology, Plant Physiology, Psychology, and Sociology. The *Annual Review of Neuroscience* will begin publication in 1978. In addition, two special volumes have been published by Annual Reviews Inc.: *History of Entomology* (1973) and *The Excitement and Fascination of Science* (1965).

Ann. Rev. Physiology 1977. 39:1–18

MY SCIENTIFIC ODYSSEY ❖1161

John C. Eccles

Ann. Rev. Physiology 1977. 39:1–18

MY SCIENTIFIC ODYSSEY ♦1161

John C. Eccles

Contra (Ticino), CH-6611 Switzerland

I have been a wanderer over the world for more than 50 years of active scientific life. Except for my beginning at Oxford, I have not carried out even one scientific experiment as a guest in a laboratory. And after the first few months at Oxford I had, from 1928 onward, my own research room—later rooms. I have never had the good fortune in my wanderings to come to an institute with even primitive scientific equipment that could be used for my initial experiments. Like Odysseus, I have traveled the oceans carrying my own equipment with me like a snail with his house on his back. At each "port of call" I have had to set up and develop research rooms. I have left around the world a trail of elaborately designed shielded research rooms stripped of equipment! But I have been fortunate to discover expert technical and engineering assistance at each of my five ports of call after Oxford; otherwise my scientific life would have faltered. Electronics rapidly outstripped my under-standing, but I always have maintained that the technical equipment must be the best; this criterion held right up to my last experiments in Buffalo in 1975. My indebtedness to my associates is immeasurable.

I recently had the opportunity to give an account of some aspects of my scientific life (8, 9). I have tried here to minimize repetition of my story, but necessarily some key events must be retold. Both of these earlier accounts ended with the years 1954–1955, which takes us no more than about halfway through the present story.

My first university training was in Melbourne, where I graduated in Medicine at the beginning of 1925, just after my twenty-second birthday. I was fortunate to be elected to a Rhodes Scholarship, and after some months as a house physician I left for Oxford, arriving at Magdalen College in October 1925 to study under Sir Charles Sherrington, the one man in the world whom I wished to have as my master. After two years in the Final Honour School of Natural Sciences (physiology and biochem-istry) with a First Class and a Christopher Welch Scholarship, I was appointed, toward the end of 1927, to a Junior Research Fellowship of Exeter College, just as I was starting on my first research project. Apparently I was taken on promise. Exeter College was my delightful academic home for the next seven years. We were a small band of Fellows, but in their association I was able to mature culturally in

1

that natural manner characteristic of Oxford at its best. There were at Exeter famous scholars such as Farnell, Marrett, Madariaga, Dawkins, Soddy, Barber, Balfour, and Tolkien, but the closest associates were my contemporaries: Neville Coghill, John Wolfenden, Dacre Balsdon, Bill Kneale, and Jim Bessant who represented, respectively, the fields of English, chemistry, classics, philosophy, and theology!

Meanwhile I was inducted into research on the cerebellum by Denny–Brown and Liddell and on spinal inhibition by Creed. Thanks to the generosity of Creed, I inherited his modest research room. I was there joined by Ragnar Granit who arrived from Helsingfors at the beginning of 1928. At first the equipment was restricted to optical isometric myographs and a plate camera plus induction coils for single and repetitive nerve stimulation. We also had a massive antique pendulum for giving accurate timing for two induction shocks (to 0.1 msec). In 1928 Sherrington fitted up the research room with a string galvanometer—the height of luxury in those far-off days—and also with a Lucas spring pendulum. We began our collaboration studying first the motor unit and then the excitatory and inhibitory mechanisms of spinal reflexes from 1928 to 1931. That was for me a wonderful and intimate association, not restricted to neuroscience, for during our experiments the conversation ranged widely over literature, history, and art.

I have told elsewhere (7) of my first experimental success—demonstrating that the "angle" of the isometric muscle twitch was an artifact due to friction in the bearing of the recording myograph. The angle was an established dogma at Oxford. The isometric twitch was displayed with a rather flat summit and the angle occurred in the sharp onset of relaxation from this summit. I too believed in its authenticity. In fact the quality cf an optical myograph was guaranteed by the sharpness with which it displayed the angle! In order to investigate the viscoelastic properties of the muscle before, during, and after the angle, I had constructed a myograph that would subject the muscle to a vibratory stretch at a fairly high frequency. For this purpose I had to redesign the support of the torsion rod, making it a friction-free knife edge instead of a V-shaped slot. This poor design had been accepted because the myographs delivered good angles! To my consternation, the new myograph failed to deliver angles, although with the same muscle the old myographs gave good angles. Superposition of the two mechanical traces revealed that the angle was a friction artifact. The summit of the twitch was recorded as flat because of the "hold" by friction which continued during the early stage of relaxation until it could "hold" no longer, the sudden "give" being registered as the angle. This discovery was the occasion of my first appearance (in December 1929) before the Physiological Society of which I had just become a member, and I now had won recognition.

One day in 1930 Sherrington announced that the Clarendon Press had persuaded him to write a book on the researches of the Oxford School. He accepted the invitation on the condition that it would be a conjoint effort, the chosen team of his associates being Creed, Denny Brown, Liddell, and I. I was much excited by the prospect of contributing to a book at so young an age and proceeded forthwith to write my three chapters. My associates generously criticized my amateurish efforts, but themselves wrote nothing for a year or so. I meanwhile was having the experience of writing and rewriting my chapters two or three times. Eventually all was completed; *The Reflex Activity of the Spinal Cord* (3) was published in 1932. I think the printing number was only 1000 and it did not sell out for many years—an indication of the small population of neuroscientists in those days.

England, in my time there (1925–1937), was a delightful and stimulating place for a young academic, although by present standards the laboratory facilities were primitive. There were almost no research grants and no secretarial assistance even for Sherrington. We had to type our papers and service and organize our equipment, which gradually became more complicated with string galvanometers giving place to oscilloscopes, cathode-ray oscilloscopes in 1933, and valve amplifiers. But in research the competition was not severe. The world literature was unbelievably small, so that one could easily survey the total publications, not only on the nervous system, central and peripheral, but also on all types of muscle and all types of sensory systems. Furthermore, one met personally almost all the great figures, for they came to visit Sherrington at Oxford. And we physiologists of Great Britain were united by our membership in the Physiological Society, which, I think, was then in one of its great periods. It was distinguished by the critical discussions that followed each paper. These criticisms were often severe, but it was an unwritten rule of the society that all criticism had to be accepted in a sporting manner. Under no account must it be taken personally. In the period of severe controversy of electrical versus chemical transmission for neuromuscular junctions and for sympathetic ganglia, it was a surprise to overseas visitors to find that I was throughout on the friendliest terms with Dale, Feldberg, Gaddum, and Brown. I have recently written at length on this theme in my lecture on the occasion of the Dale centenary (9). As a junior member of the Society I have the happiest memories of these meetings with their characteristic egalitarian style and of the warm friendliness of the senior members. I believe it to be the best of all scientific societies. And at that time it rejoiced in the award of three Nobel Prizes to its members: Sherrington and Adrian in 1932 and Dale in 1936.

In 1934 I had achieved a permanent position at Oxford with a Tutorial Fellowship at Magdalen College and a University Demonstrationship, but shortly afterwards Sherrington retired, and the Oxford Physiological Laboratory seemed to deteriorate after his departure. Then in the late 1930s there was the ominous rise of Hitler against the unprepared western alliance. So I decided—perhaps unwisely—to return to what seemed the security of Australia. There was the opportunity to create in Sydney a research institute matching the Hall Institute at Melbourne Hospital with Kellaway and Burnet. In 1937, on the advice of Kellaway, I accepted the Directorship of the Kanematsu Institute at Sydney Hospital. In retrospect I feel I should have stayed in England and weathered the storm, but instead I embarked on my Odyssean journeyings, never to return to my beloved England. It was a fateful choice.

Sydney was of course a lovely place to live, but the academic isolation was severe. The Sydney University Medical School was a very dim place, being little more than a teaching institution. Unbelievably, it was completely locked up by guards at 5 PM, even the professors had to scurry out to avoid imprisonment for the night! The Institute I was to direct was simply the routine pathology department of a large general hospital in the city some three miles from the University. Nevertheless, with good help from the Institute Committee and the Hospital Board, I was able to construct research laboratories on the top floor, utilizing for a start the equipment that Professor John Mellanby had kindly allowed me to bring from my two research laboratories at Oxford. I decided to study the electrophysiology of neuromuscular transmission in muscles of the cat hind limb because I thought that it could lead to results of clinical interest.

The academic wilderness soon blossomed. In 1938 Stephen Kuffler arrived in Sydney as a refugee from Austria, and by good fortune I heard of this young pathologist in search of a position. So he became a neurobiologist in the Kanematsu Institute, a novice with almost no background knowledge of the nervous system! In 1939 I managed to attract Bernard Katz from England on a Carnegie Fellowship. Thus in this way, through the machinations of Hitler, we three were sheltering securely in remote Australia and studying neuromuscular transmission in cats and frogs. There was criticism of our activities from some clinicians because this research on curarized muscles and anticholinesterases seemed so remote from clinical usefulness. Ironically it was soon to find an important application in the use of relaxants during surgical operations.

The security of our academic life in Sydney lasted until Japan entered the war. Then for two years I was deeply involved in various wartime projects, and the Kanematsu Institute became the Australian center for blood serum preparation and for applied research on such acoustic problems as noise protection and communication in the high noise levels of tanks and planes. Kuffler continued with his exquisite researches on the isolated single neuromuscular junction, while Katz was chosen to become a radar expert and rendered most distinguished service.

With all this scientific and war-oriented activity I thought my position in the Kanematsu Institute of Sydney Hospital was secure; however under new management Sydney Hospital proceeded in 1943 to make my position untenable. Unbeknown to me, living quarters for hospital residents were to be constructed on top of my Institute, preventing any postwar development, and there was no academic position for me in the Australian universities. I declined an invitation from Liverpool University to return to England, which seemed so bleak at that time; fortunately I was able to accept appointment as professor of physiology at the only medical school in New Zealand, which was an integral part of the University of Otago in Dunedin. So the next stage of my odyssey was to cross the Tasman Sea to New Zealand at the end of 1943, so that I should be ready to start the academic year in 1944. The happy and fruitful collaboration of the Kanematsu trio was broken; Kuffler was already in process of going to the United States at Ralph Gerard's invitation, and, on demobilization after the war, Katz returned to A. V. Hill's department at University College London.

The 6½ years at Sydney were notable for all three of us because of the lifelong friendships created. In these enduring friendships we were linked both on scientific and on personal grounds, even playing tennis together on my court almost every weekend! It is noteworthy that Katz and Kuffler have been closely associated ever since by the exchange of numerous graduate and postdoctoral students. For me that linkage has been less developed, but Paul Fatt came from Katz to me with the great successes I describe later, and Miledi was with me as a Rockefeller Fellow before he went on to develop his brilliant career with Katz. All through my 6½ years in Sydney, the academic isolation persisted, so that we three seemed to be huddled together in an alien world. Relieving features for me were the close wartime collaboration with Archie McIntyre, and the friendship with the distinguished biochemist, Rudolph Lemberg, who remained for 40 years in a hospital laboratory in Sydney with no official recognition by Sydney University. Katz, Kuffler, and I also had no official recognition, but we did function in an honorary capacity, giving lectures on neurobiology to the medical classes. There is an historic photograph of the three of us in 1942 determinedly walking in Sydney to catch the tram to the University. In 1972 we three were photographed again walking, but in a more relaxed manner, in the grounds of St. Catherine's College, Oxford. Mounted together, the two photographs provide a commentary on changed life styles!

In summary, our scientific discoveries were the end plate potential, both its pharmacology and its role in generating the discharge of impulses along the muscle fibers. This research was undertaken without knowledge of the work of Schäfer in Germany and Feng in China. Communications had become very bad. The action of anticholinesterases in increasing and prolonging the end plate potential finally convinced me in 1942 that acetylcholine was the sole transmitter. I wrote a letter of capitulation to Sir Henry Dale, which has recently been published along with Dale's reply (9). This period of collaboration in Sydney was the beginning of the magnificent contributions of Katz and Kuffler and their numerous distinguished associates on the biophysics of neuromuscular transmission.

And so my odyssey continued to the remote university in the south of the South Island of New Zealand, the closest university to the South Pole. Even there, I found stimulating challenges and the opportunity to develop scientifically. After my ten years of teaching at Oxford I was enthusiastic to attempt a similar program of lectures, practical classes, and discussion classes despite the greatly restricted facilities. In this I was fully supported by Norm Edson, an inspired teacher of biochemistry in the modern form that he had learned from Krebs. So the medical students were subjected to this intensive modernization of physiology and biochemistry. The hours available were adequate in the two years of the course that were entirely devoted to anatomy, physiology, and biochemistry, but our staff was most inadequate, no more than two or three in each subject. So in my first year in Dunedin I lectured to the second-year medical class in the whole of physiology—75 lectures in all, and I also did much of the first-year course. With the practical and discussion classes I found my total teaching time was 20 hours a week for 25 weeks. In addition, I had to spend many hours each week learning the whole of modern physiology, so that I could lecture on it with authority.

My research virtually came to an end during the first year when I was learning physiology for my lectures and also creating a completely new practical course with its specialized equipment. But this extreme operation has to be evaluated against the world situation; in 1944 and 1945 research had virtually came to an end for all except a few who were fortunately sheltered, as for example, Lloyd, Renshaw, and

Lorente de Nó at the Rockefeller Institute. Their publications at that time seemed to have come from another world. Meanwhile I was greatly encouraged by the excellent students in my classes. Many have become medical scientists and form the majority of the senior faculty of the newly founded medical school at Auckland University. In retrospect I feel I was almost fanatical in my zeal and ambition to develop model teaching methods for physiology, but it saved me from the narrowness that seems to be so common today, where a senior member of a teaching staff can for example lecture to medical students only on the biophysics of the node of Ranvier!

The year 1944 was important in my scientific life above all my post-Sherrington years because my intimate association with Karl Popper dates from that time. I had heard from Edson about the great stir that Popper was making among the scientists of Canterbury University College about 200 miles to the north in the city of Christchurch, so we invited him to give five University lectures on the philosophy of science. They were an enormous success among the staff and student body, and there were also two special seminars, one to physical scientists, the other to biological scientists. Many people, including myself, had our scientific lives changed by the inspiring new vision of science that Popper gave us. Our association has been intimate since that time and now we have collaborated in a book *The Self and Its Brain* (14).

Briefly the message we got in those memorable lectures was that science is not inductive, but deductive. A scientific project starts as a problem, for example with a theory that appears deficient or inadequate. New hypotheses are developed and tested experimentally, either to be falsified or corroborated, but the claim of verification should never be made. Thus there are two aspects of a scientific investigation: first, the development of a hypothesis using creative imagination; second, the rigorous experimental testing of this hypothesis in its most vulnerable aspects in an attempt at falsification. Thus the outcome may be rejection of the new hypothesis, or modification and further experimental testing, or, at best, corroboration and the possibility of further testing. Thus creative imagination is given the star role in scientific investigation. Even though an hypothesis is falsified, it can be counted as a scientific success in that it led to experimental testing with the discovery that the truth lies elsewhere. I was much encouraged, as I was concerned at the fate that seemed to be threatening my electrical hypothesis of synaptic transmission. Already I had given it up for neuromuscular transmission, and a similar fate seemed likely for ganglionic transmission. So the synapses of the central nervous system were the final haven for the hypothesis of electrical synaptic transmission. Anyway I was urged by Popper to formulate the electrical hypotheses of synaptic excitation and inhibition in models that invited experimental testing and falsification.

It was certainly a crisis in my life when the intracellular recording from motoneurons in the cat spinal cord was employed to test these two hypotheses. We were encouraged to attempt this intracellular recording by the successes of Nastuk & Hodgkin (13) and Fatt & Katz (12) in recording from skeletal muscle. With the expert assistance of Brock and Coombs we managed in my last year in Dunedin (1951) to discover the essential features of the postsynaptic electrical events produced by excitatory and inhibitory synaptic transmission (1, 2), and to falsify the electrical hypothesis of synaptic inhibition. Hence, belatedly, I was converted to the Dale hypothesis of chemical synaptic transmission even in the central nervous system. A detailed account of this story is given in my Dale Centenary Lecture (9).

During my latter years in Dunedin I had come to realize that the heavy teaching program seriously handicapped me in competition with the new wave of intensive neurobiology that was developing, particularly in America. There the teaching loads were much lighter and the financial support of research much greater. Dunedin was an acceptable home for me during the war and in the period of worldwide disorganization and reconstruction that followed, but I could foresee my failure in world class if I continued there. Fortunately a most ambitious project of a research university was being planned in Canberra, with Howard Florey as the advisor on the medical section. It was therefore with enthusiasm that in 1951 I accepted the Professorship of Physiology at the Australian National University in Canberra. At that time the University had a large grassy wooded tract of land on which there were two army huts for administrators. But there was good financial support by the Australian government and great enthusiasm!

So it was time for the next stage of my odyssey. However, it was to take 15 months before I could start experimenting in Canberra. Part of the time was filled in by travel to the United States, then to England, and finally back via the United States to Australia. After my departure from England in 1937 to the Antipodes I had only been briefly in America in early 1946 for two meetings of the New York Academy of Sciences (my first visit to the United States), so it was with great anticipation that I left the Antipodean isolation at the end of 1951 to return to England after 14½ years and to spend five months in residence at Magdalen College Oxford giving the Waynflete Lectures and preparing them for publication by the Clarendon Press, Oxford. The title both of the lectures and of the book was *The Neurophysiological Basis of Mind: Principles of Neurophysiology* (4).

A special feature of my return to England was that I came as a neophyte with my newfound enthusiasm for chemical transmission at both excitatory and inhibitory synapses in the central nervous system. In February 1952 there was a Ciba symposium on the spinal cord and also a Royal Society Symposium. At the Royal Society I had the pleasure of signing the Fellows Book some eleven years after my election in 1941—still the same book that Newton had signed. It was a strenuous period with my travel around England and much entertainment and good discussion. I had the feeling that England was at the beginning of a magnificent new postwar era. Certainly I was not misled in my estimate of the great scientific successes. Hodgkin, Huxley, and Keynes in Cambridge and Fatt and Katz in London were leading the world in neurobiology, and that lead has been maintained —as evidenced by the Nobel awards to Hodgkin, Huxley, and Katz. But, as a power in the world and as a great industrial country, England has declined in a way not anticipated in 1952.

I would have liked to return to England at that time, because the Antipodean prospects were as yet a matter of faith and hope. There were by then some centers of achievement in Australia, in particular in radio astronomy and in microbiology, but Australia was at a provincial level in other sciences. This had motivated Florey to work for a research university that was entirely postgraduate, giving only doctoral degrees. So in June 1952 I returned to Australia after a brief interlude in America attending the Cold Spring Harbor Symposium on the neuron. There was much discussion on intracellular recording. Woodbury and Patton had also succeeded with motoneurons, but Lloyd was severely critical of the whole project, which he thought could only lead to a vast and misleading literature on damaged and dying neurons! This attitude of Lloyd's was more than I could have hoped for, and aroused Bob Morison to compose two limericks which were regarded as unprintable in the published symposium! I realized that, with his superb technique and penetrating insight, Lloyd could have made great progress in intracellular recording in the study of excitatory and inhibitory synapses during the long latent period which necessarily would occur in the resumption of my research career. It was to take much time and travail before I could establish laboratories in the temporary buildings then being constructed in Canberra. Meanwhile, I had brought from New Zealand four magnificent electrical stimulating and recording units (ESRU), designed by Jack Coombs and built in New Zealand. At that time and for many years to come—in fact until the transistor era—they were the best general research instruments for electrophysiology in the world. Some were still in use in David Curtis's department until 1976, and I used the original ESRU until 1968. Without doubt the successes of our department in the Canberra period were dependent on the excellence of the ESRU's. For me it was very frustrating to have to wait month after month before I could resume the intracellular studies on motoneurons that had been interrupted in December 1951 on my departure from New Zealand. Paul Fatt had come to Canberra in the latter part of 1952 to continue with motorneurons the intracellular recording that had been such a success in the study with Bernard Katz on the neuromuscular junction. In the first months before the laboratories were ready he was intensely occupied in a critical appraisal of the literature on spinal motoneurons and came up with challenging ideas that helped to guide our research in those early Canberra years.

So in March 1953 the active Canberra phase of my life began and continued for over 13 years. Without doubt it was the high point of my research career. Koketsu from Japan joined Fatt and me in our study of Renshaw cells, which was one of my most satisfying research projects. The cholinergic excitation of these cells by collaterals from motoneuron axons was a striking vindication of Dale's principle (cf 9), namely that for the synapses formed by all axonal branches of a neuron there is the same chemical transmitter.

Other members of our research team during the first five years were Jack Coombs from New Zealand, Sven Landgren from Sweden, Bill Liley from New Zealand, my daughter Rose, Vernon Brooks from Canada, David Curtis from Melbourne, Anders Lundberg from Sweden, Ben Libet, Bob Young, and Kris Krnjevic from the United States, Ricardo Miledi from Mexico, and Arthur Buller from England. Already the department was taking on the international complexion that was to become so characteristic in later years. During these earlier years we worked in the rather limited facilities of the temporary hut. The grandiose permanent building was longer in coming than we had hoped. But somehow much research was accomplished in the three research rooms.

I felt very much the urgency of showing by our achievement that this extraordinary foundation by the Australian government and by the Prime Minister, Sir Robert Menzies, was delivering the academic goods. Menzies was one of the really great men I have been privileged to know. Canberra in those early days was a very small "city" for a capital, and very short on social amenities. Menzies advised that the first permanent building to be erected would be the residential college and faculty club, called University House. He rightly sensed that a university is a community of scholars and that there had to be good facilities for cross-cultural meeting in a faculty club. University House provided faculty club facilities rivaling any other such club in the world. I spent much time in those earlier Canberra years on the governing body of University House. Two Cambridge associates, Trendall and Oliphant, and I tried to give University House the style of Cambridge and Oxford, but appropriate for an entirely postgraduate college and in harmony with the international culture that was the hope of the postwar world. It was quite a challenge to mold the style and tradition of the past so that it would be assimilated by the young academics. Some were very raw material on arrival, but most became civilized without appearing to notice the transformation. We kept our satisfaction confidential.

I have dwelt long on this aspect of Canberra because I believe most American universities, particularly those financed by state governments, are miserly in their appropriations for cultural amenities for faculty. By contrast the student body is well catered for. The state university system of New York is a notable example of this absurd unbalance. As a consequence I spent the last seven years of my academic life in Buffalo in virtual isolation from my colleagues in other departments. The university was more like a trade school—and much of it was so oriented.

A remarkable feature of the Australian National University was its international orientation. No preference was made to Australians, and there were unrivaled facilities for overseas scholars. For example, if appointed to a research scholarship, the travel to Canberra of the scholar plus wife and children was fully paid and his emoluments dated from the time of departure. The emolument and the scholarship was about twice that for basic living and housing costs in Canberra, and furnished houses were provided for scholars with children. Married and single scholars lived in University House. There were no university or degree fees, and the return journey was also fully paid. The more senior staff had fellowships at appropriate levels, again with all travel costs paid and housing provided. These generous arrangements explain why there was such an international complex in this remote Australian university. This international generosity was encouraged by Menzies, who remarked that at last Australia was in the position to pay off some of the "academic debts" incurred during its growing and maturing stages, when Europe and America had been so extraordinarily generous in their help to young Australian scholars, as I for one well remembered from my years in England. Cynics may remark that it was an attempt to attract scholars from abroad to settle in Australia, but very few did outstay their appointments in Canberra. However, Australia did gain enormously in two respects. First, there was a transformation from the academic isolation of the prewar years that I had experienced on arrival in Sydney in 1937, and many Australian scholars returned to Australia, often after long sojourns overseas. Second, the new generation of young Australians had the great advantage of association in Australia with scholars from overseas. The academic renaissance spread through the whole university structure of Australia. Australian science is now in top world class, a remarkable achievement for a middle-sized country (13 million) so remote from the great centers of the world.

At this stage I should make reference to another of the activities to which I devoted great enthusiasm in those early Canberra years. Despite the existence of many scientific societies, Australia had been lacking a prestigious scientific body that could speak with authority to the government, to industry, and to the country. What we needed was a foundation playing a role in Australia equivalent to that of the Royal Society of London. Sir Mark Oliphant was the leading spirit in furthering this project. In order to give the new foundation adequate credentials, the Fellows of the Royal Society resident in Australia, together with a few senior scientists they nominated, petitioned the Crown for the foundation of the Australian Academy of Science, which would be modeled on the Royal Society of London. In this project we were most enthusiastically supported by the Royal Society. All went well, and in 1954 Her Majesty Queen Elizabeth II founded the Australian Academy of Science in Canberra. It was the second time in history that a British monarch had founded a scientific society, the first being the Royal Society of London by Charles II in 1660! Oliphant was the first president from 1954–1957, and I succeeded him in 1957–1961. Those were early creative years with many problems in the travail of birth pains. But the Academy has flourished and has contributed notably to Australian scientific advancement and to the influence that science plays in Australian affairs. A striking symbol of Australian science was the remarkable edifice of unique style, built by the Academy for its headquarters in Canberra. Oliphant initiated this project with great insight and courage and, in my period as president, the building was completed to the great joy of the Fellows and the amazement of the local inhabitants. It displayed an extremely simple geometrical form, an enormous copper-covered dome, a section of a sphere, broken only by the arches rising in scalloped form from some 16 "feet" immersed in a circular moat. I think the design was superb and the interior had excellent facilities, particularly the central meeting hall. I have most happy memories of the many great occasions associated with those early years of the Australian Academy of Science.

But I should return to the Australian National University with the department of physiology as an integral part of the John Curtin School of Medical Research. At last in 1957 the grandiose new building was completed. We had done so well in the temporary hut that I was somewhat overawed by the new magnificence and the greatly extended facilities. I had only one floor of one wing, but managed to plan the space so that there were six research laboratories and at least 12 studies. It was my belief that each research worker should have his own study, no matter how small, in order to have the privacy for working up his data, measuring, writing, and typing. The alternative of having several junior research workers sharing a larger space is almost universal. At Oxford I had this experience in my first year, 1928, where Denny Brown, Granit, Olmsted, Marcu, and I shared a large disused laboratory; but in 1929 I managed to acquire my own study, and since then I have almost always been able to provide separate studies for all of my associates. The increased accommodation of the new laboratories and the many applicants, particularly from overseas, resulted in a large expansion of research staff, particularly during the last half of my Canberra period—1959–1966. It was quite an organizational task to arrange for the coming and going so that there would be maximum occupancy and yet no overcrowding. In those years there were always more than 20 research workers and as many technical and support staff. Of course I did not personally supervise so many. I had by then a semi-autonomous section. Macfarlane had developed his own research group in endocrinology and climatology. Curtis had his group in neuropharmacology and neurochemistry, and Hubbard had a group in the biophysics and electron microscopy of neuromuscular transmission.

My own research interests had developed far from the initial intensive study of the biophysics of the motoneuron and the action of excitatory and inhibitory synapses thereon. There was so much that this new technique could be used for at the spinal level that I stayed almost a "prisoner" in the cat spinal cord for many years —in fact until 1962. As I look back on those years I can hardly imagine how we dared to attempt so much! The opportunity to present in an integrated form the initial stages of our work at Canberra was provided by the invitation to give the Herter Lectures at Johns Hopkins Medical School in 1955. These lectures were eventually published as *The Physiology of Nerve Cells* (5) by the Johns Hopkins Press.

Patterns of organization in the spinal cord provided the challenge for studies that Lundberg in part developed independently in 1956 and 1957. The inputs from muscle receptors by groups Ia, Ib, and II were studied in detail, particularly in relationship to the functions of the muscles supplied by the motoneurons—those that are homonymous or heteronymous and synergic, and those that are heteronymous and antagonistic. In this study we were carrying the pioneering work of Sherrington to the new level of enquiry made possible by intracellular recording.

In 1957 my colleagues, Ben Libet and Bob Young (11) from America and I utilized intracellular recording from axonotomized motoneurons to account for the enigmatic reflex responses of these chromatolyzed motoneurons that had been observed many years earlier. It was of special interest because of the finding that synaptic excitation resulted in dendritic spike potentials that were transitional to the generation of impulse discharges down the motor axon. There was also an investigation of the electrical properties of the chromatolyzed motoneurons and a full explanation of the earlier observations on reflex responses. I mention this paper because it has been undeservedly overlooked by later investigators and reviewers. These later papers have very little additional to report and the illustrations and measurements of our 1958 paper are superior to those of the later papers published in the 1970s. It seems that papers published more than a decade ago are ignored, regardless of content or merit!

Cross-union of various peripheral muscle nerves was attempted in 1957 in order to discover if it would result in some central reconstruction of connectivities by a kind of plastic response. Sperry had failed to find any significant changes many years earlier, but intracellular recording made it possible to do a more refined and quantitative study. Already we had amassed control studies on monosynaptic inputs using intracellular recording from many hundreds of identified motoneurons. However the first experiment completely changed our plans. I had cross-united in young kittens the nerve to the pale flexor, gracilis, with that to the red extensor, crureus. After a period of several weeks in order to allow time for regeneration, we proposed to see if there were changed connectivities to the respective motoneurons in the light of their transposed functions. For example, did crureus motoneurons now supplying gracilis muscle receive some connectivities appropriate to knee flexors? But, on exposing the muscles, there was an incredible display. The pale gracilis now innervated by crureus motoneurons had become bright red, the other gracilis showing the normal pallor. So we immediately set up mechanical recording and found to our delight that the red color of gracilis was matched by its much slower contraction. And, complementarily, the slow crureus innervated by gracilis motoneurons had become much faster relative to the control muscle on the other side. Arthur Buller had just arrived from England, so there was one year of intensive study on the influence of motoneurons in determining muscle contraction time. Not only did we study cross-union of various muscle nerves after a wide range of post-operative times, but we also studied the time courses of muscle contraction from birth onwards. Investigations in many laboratories have stemmed from these initial studies, not only mechanical (Buller, Close, and associates), but also electrophysiological, biochemical, histological, and pharmacological. The aborted study on central connectivities and cross-union was later taken up. Some changes were found, but even just after birth there was little evidence of the plasticity in the spinal cord that has now been shown to be so prominent at higher levels of the central nervous system.

Another good story began in 1959 when following up preliminary reports by Frank and Fuortes on presynaptic inhibition. The dorsal root potential and the dorsal root reflex had been known since the work of Barron and Matthews and Toennies in the 1930s and was studied by us in Dunedin in the 1940s, but the functional significance had remained an enigma. An intensive study for some two years in collaboration with Krnjevic, Schmidt, and Willis revealed the story that has been corroborated and enhanced by much subsequent work in other laboratories. It was postulated that there are special axon-axonic synapses on presynaptic terminals that act to depolarize these terminals and so to reduce the action potential and thus the emission of transmitter. Electromicroscopy first by Gray and later notably by Saito has displayed these axon-axonic synapses much as we diagrammed them, and recent work by Nishi, Nicoll, and associates has corroborated our suggestion that GABA is the transmitter. The main thrust of these investigations was a systematic topographic and modality study in the effort to define the way in which presynaptic inhibition was employed physiologically.

I was only partially associated with the refined biophysical studies that were carried out in 1959–1963 largely by the Japanese team of Ito, Araki, and Oshima. I was particularly happy at the finding that in an investigation of 34 species of anions the inhibitory transmitter was found to open up in the postsynaptic membrane gates that allow the passage of all anions regardless of species, provided that in the hydrated state their diameter is smaller than a critical size (2.9 Å). The only exception was formate that passed through despite being slightly larger than this critical size for the other 10 species of anions. It looked as if we had a simple model for the mode of action of the inhibitory transmitter. Unfortunately the investigations on cationic permeability of the inhibitory postsynaptic membrane were much more enigmatic, and the question of potassium permeability is still debated. Parenthetically, it may be noted that the ionic mechanisms of postsynaptic inhibition in hippocampal pyramidal cells was my last experimental study (until May 1975).

It was at this stage of my Canberra life that I received the Nobel award (1963) for the ionic mechanisms of synapses, and my Nobel Lecture was on the ionic mechanisms of postsynaptic inhibition. Earlier in that year I felt that the time was ripe for an extensive review of the whole field of synaptic mechanisms. This proved a heavier task than I had anticipated, but it appeared as *The Physiology of Synapses* (6) that was published just in time to be on display in Stockholm at the time of the Prize festivities in December 1963. The publishers (Springer Verlag) made an unprecedented effort in speed of publication in order to effect this felicitous timing. All was finally printed and in order for binding except for the subject index. The typescript reached the Heidelberg office on Monday, December 2. On Sunday December 8, I received in Stockholm some six bound copies by airmail special delivery, and, on Monday, the booksellers of Stockholm had display copies, and copies for sale were available on December 10, the day of the Prize award.

After some ten years of intracellular recording in the spinal cord I was happy to move into the much more complex and challenging problems presented by higher levels of the nervous system. The change occurred gradually. At first there were investigations led by Olov Oscarsson on the cells of origin of the spinocerebellar tracts. Cells of origin of another ascending pathway were also studied. Meanwhile Tom Sears was carrying out his refined studies on the control of respiratory movements by employing intracellular recording from motoneurons supplying intercostal muscles. At this time also stimulation of the motor cortex was shown to produce presynaptic inhibition in the spinal cord. However the decisive change occurred with studies on neurons of the brain stem under the leadership of Per Andersen.

Firstly, there was synaptic transmission in the cuneate nucleus with ascending actions from the spinal cord and descending from the cerebral cortex. The neuronal machinery involved in these actions was studied in detail. Next came the ventrobasal nucleus of the thalamus on the projection line to the cerebral cortex from the cuneate nucleus. There was study of the neuronal machinery and the role of inhibition in setting the rhythmic activity of the thalamocortical circuits, a theme that Andersen was later to develop so well.

The most important study was on the hippocampus, using the new techniques of intracellular recording and field potential analysis. Andersen already had extensive experience on the hippocampus, so good progress was assured. The most interesting discovery was that the basket cells of the hippocampus gave a very large and prolonged inhibitory postsynaptic potential of the hippocampal pyramids. It had been known since the time of Ramón y Cajal that the basket cells formed a dense terminal plexus (or basket) around the somata of pyramidal cells, which he believed to exert an intense excitatory action. The combination of depth profile and intracellular studies convincingly demonstrated that the action was an intense inhibition. So for the first time an inhibitory cell with its synaptic terminals had been identified histologically. At that time Renshaw cells had not yet been recognized histologically.

Having accomplished that identification so satisfactorily, I asked: where else are there basket cells? The answer being the cerebellum, we (Andersen, Voorhoeve, and myself) immediately in early 1963 changed our attention to the cerebellum. It was a more complex study than the hippocampus; nevertheless the clear answer came that the basket cells there are also inhibitory, this again being shown by depth profile and intracellular recording. Per Andersen had to return to Norway, so we made a pact. He was to have the hippocampus for his field, and I and my associates, the cerebellum. I regret to report that in 1975 I broke the pact by again working on the hippocampus, in a final electrophysiological study on the ionic mechanism of postsynaptic inhibition. It was an appropriate and very successful termination of my experimental life with my colleagues Allen, Nicoll, Oshima, and Rubia.

The beautifully organized structural pattern of the cerebellum was a great opportunity for an analytical study of the mode of operation of the two input lines, by mossy fibers and by climbing fibers, and of the five species of neurons. Of particular importance was Szentágothai's evidence for the origin of climbing fibers from the inferior olive. Remarkably clean results were obtained by stimulating through an electrode inserted into the inferior olive. The mossy fiber input gave a more complex picture, but, by utilizing various sites of stimulating together with depth profile recording and intracellular recording from Purkinje cells, a satisfactory picture emerged that enabled us to make models of the mode of operation of the neuronal machinery in the cerebellar cortex. With but minor variations this model still holds, so the comprehensive book published in 1967 with Ito and Szentágothai, *The Cerebellum as a Neuronal Machine* (10) still does not need extensive revision. This analysis of the neuronal operation in the cerebellum was greatly aided by a principle that I had proposed as early as 1954: that all the synapses formed by a neuron in the mammalian central nervous system have not only the same transmitter (Dale's Principle), but also the same action, either excitatory or inhibitory, there being no ambivalent neurons. So we could generalize from our analytical experiments and propose models of circuits that displayed the essential features of operation in all the complex interactions of the neuronal machinery.

Troubling me in my later years at Canberra was the early retirement age of 65 that was soon to overtake me. I had hoped to get this age extended to 68, but the administrators prevented this. I already knew the very impoverished conditions that would be my lot after 65—half salary renewable year by year and one laboratory with almost no support for staff or assistants. So I realized that soon my odyssey would take me from Australia across the Pacific. There were only two choices at that time: the University of British Columbia and the newly established Institute of Biomedical Research in Chicago. Both offered far more generous support than I would have in Australia, and there was provision for extension of my position for up to 70 years and even beyond. I was impressed by the grandiose plans for Chicago, and so, unwisely as it turned out, I accepted this position, which was the first I had ever been offered in the United States.

This decision relieved the Australian National University of what was clearly an embarassment—to have me there as an impoverished worker—and there was much ceremony on my departure, including an attractive portrait of me by Miss Judy Casab and a witty cartoon by Frith. Both were unveiled at the farewell banquet and there was a most generous speech by Lord Florey who was in Canberra on one of his numerous visits as Chancellor of the Australian National University. In my reply I alluded with approval to his frequent public statements that the value of the John Curtin School of Medical Research was not to be judged by the kilograms of publications, but by the value of its scientific discoveries for the people of Australia and of the whole world. Just to emphasize the point I displayed an official document prepared by my head technician, Lionel Davis, who was a Justice of the Peace, to the effect that the total publications of the department of physiology over 13 years weighed 10.8 Kg! The cost per Kg certainly would be discouragingly high for a business man.

Some more statistics for my 14 years at Canberra are that there were in the department of physiology 74 research workers from 20 different countries, and 411 scientific papers and 4 books were published. This is a tribute to the Australian government for supporting the Australian National University so generously, particularly in respect of overseas visitors. Another "human dividend" from this Canberra period were the excellent personal relationships that developed between the families of my visitors, no doubt fostered by the isolation in Canberra. After all these years they still feel members of a supranational society of Canberrans who had dared to adventure to the Antipodes!

The next stage of my wanderings was the briefest, the least successful, and the most unhappy of my research career. There were several reasons. Although at the start there was good material support in Chicago and a most prestigious governing body, it quickly became evident to me and to the Director of the Institute for Biomedical Research, that the American Medical Association was not enthusiastic —quite the contrary. When the retirement age was lowered to 68 years, contrary to our agreement, I realized it was time to look elsewhere. But there were severe internal problems within my own group, as well. It was time to go, and fortunately I had one chance. It was an invitation from the State University of New York at Buffalo with very generous financial support of a unit to be created for me as a Distinguished Professor of Physiology and Biophysics.

So the next stage in my journey was across land—not strictly Odyssean, across the ocean as heretofore. I have been often asked why I chose to go to Buffalo. The answer is very simple—I had nowhere else to go. My age of 65 was not encouraging to universities who may have been considering me as an associate. But in any case the Buffalo appointment was very generous so far as support and salary were concerned and President Meyerson and the University agreed to retirement at 70 to be revised upward from year to year thereafter. So everything started well, again in a temporary building, pending the construction of the grandiose new university.

I was happy with the temporary accommodation which was soon fitted with the best research facilities I had ever had. It was of course on a much smaller scale than Canberra, which was a good thing. The unhappy experience of Chicago had warned me of the problems of personality. So I had a small carefully selected group of research associates and some of my associates of former times came back to join me for periods in Buffalo with the happiest results: Robert Schmidt from Germany, Tomakazu Oshima (for two periods) from Japan.

After the debacle of Chicago, I had begun to wonder if I had lost the personal touch that had given me such good relationships with all my associates at all previous "ports of call." So it was very reassuring to find that at Buffalo I was again associated with a delightful group, not only the scientists and their families, but also the secretarial and technical staff. In all, counting my wife and myself, there were 30 scientists from 11 different countries. As this seven-year period came to an end with my voluntary retirement in 1975 at the age of 72, it was with great sadness that my wife and I said farewell. So the happiest group of my research career was dissolved, with tears from the ladies!

But of course outside our charmed circle we had had all the turmoil of the University revolt with threatened destruction by dissident students. Buffalo was one of the centers of the storm, and lacked leadership at a critical juncture. I felt that the only course of action was to continue actively in research, come what may. And that we did, being helped by the isolation of our temporary laboratory from the main campus.

At the end of the Canberra section of this story I told briefly of our success in being able to construct models for the mode of operation of the neuronal machinery of the cerebellar cortex. But such models have to be built into the wider picture of the input and output paths if they are to be used in providing explanations of the mode of operation of the cerebellum in the control of movement. Despite the emotional troubles we already had some good successes in this study when at Chicago. But at Buffalo we were much better equipped for this ambitious task, with on-line computers, digitimers, and, most importantly, a most versatile mechanical stimulator. This latter instrument was of the greatest importance in the study we made on the role of cutaneous sensing in cerebellar control. Robert Schmidt's experience with cutaneous receptors was of vital importance in this systematic study of cutaneous inputs onto cerebellar Purkinje cells. Hitherto it had been generally believed that muscle receptors were of more importance for cerebellar inputs than those of skin. In previous studies cutaneous stimulation had been crude: touching, brushing, squeezing, etc. With the instrumentation provided by our stimulator and an averaging computer, there was revealed the remarkable effectiveness of the cutaneous inputs particularly by the foot pads. Muscle receptors were much less effective, but the study of joint receptors awaits the development and application of good instrumentation. Suffice it to say that we were much impressed by the effectiveness of cutaneous inputs, and began somatotopic studies in the attempt to define better the way in which the cerebellar machinery was employed in controlling movement. This study on the vermis and pars intermedia of the anterior lobe of the cerebellum led on to sequential studies of the pathways from the cerebellum through the cerebellar nuclei and then by the next relay nuclei (the red nucleus and the medial reticular nucleus) on the pathway down the spinal cord to motoneurons. Our work was of course closely related to the comprehensive anatomical studies of the Norwegian school, but in conclusion it must be stated that as yet we are far from understanding the mode of operation even of the cerebellar anterior lobe onto spinal motoneurons.

In the latter two years I had encouraged Gary Allen to attempt the very difficult task of relating cerebral cortex to the cerebellar hemispheres. He had good success with the cat, and then proceeded to the primate, where these studies would be of the greatest importance attempting to understand how in man the cerebrum and cerebellum interact in the control of movement. About 88% of the human cerebellum is oriented exclusively to the contralateral cerebrum. Allen and his associates had made very good progress, and there was a good report of the whole project in *Physiological Reviews* (November 1974), yet his application for a National Institute of Health grant in 1975 was not funded. Since I was to continue as an adviser with frequent visits to Buffalo for this purpose, my plans for the continuance of my American association were thus terminated. This project of Allen's was almost unique in the world. Only at Kyoto is there the beginnings of a comparable study by Sasaki of the detailed topography of the cerebro-cerebellar connectivities in the primate, with a study also of the relay nuclei involved in this cerebro-cerebellar transaction.

So my active scientific life came to an end in 1975 and to my regret I feel that, after nine years of intense scientific effort in America I have left there no successors who would be continuing in the projects that we opened up. There was considerable scientific achievement as can be recognized from the more than 140 papers published from the Buffalo laboratory. But I was disappointed that so few young Americans came to work in Buffalo in the seven years I was there, altogether only five. Fortunately I had many co-workers from other countries: eight from Japan, four from Germany, two from Canada, two from Italy, two from England, and one each from Australia, Czechoslovakia, France, Lebanon, and Sweden. I have the feeling that the scientific fashion is for analytical work, and that there is far too little interest in synthesis, particularly when it involves the complex neuronal machinery of the brain. But, in biology, the findings of analysis achieve scientific meaning only when they are synthesized into principles of functional operation. In the final synthesis, models can be constructed that provide the basis for understanding some performance of the whole organism. For example the analytical success in disclosing the mode of operation of the neural machinery of the cerebellar cortex requires level after level of synthesis before it can provide a basis for understanding the cerebellar control of movement and posture.

The last journey of my odyssey is now ended, again across the ocean to Europe, where I live in Switzerland in idyllic mountain surroundings; I have here all my books and journals—many thousands of volumes and a large collection of reprints, so that I can continue my academic life, concentrating on the field that lured me into neurophysiology over 50 years ago—the mind-brain problem. I believe that the great successes of recent years in the study of the brain, and particularly of the human brain, have opened up exciting new prospects for limited successes in this problem that has perplexed mankind since the Greeks, and particularly since Descartes. I have had several attempts in this field since my Waynflete Lectures in 1952, but now realize their inadequacy. Surprisingly I was too timid! I have now developed a much stronger dualistic-interactionist philosophy and it is incorporated in a book that is being published conjointly with Sir Karl Popper, *The Self and Its Brain*. This is the first fruit of my life of retirement. I have much more planned because I realize that the present predicament of mankind results from the continuous process of denigration that has proceeded too far—far beyond the limits justified by our scientific understanding of the cosmos, of evolution, of genetics, and of the brain. Scientists and philosophers share the guilt of being dogmatic in promulgating claims to a knowledge and understanding that devolves from their inflated self-esteem. Mankind has been misled by these spurious claims. I see my task as twofold: to deflate this dogmatism, based not upon science, but on a this-worldly religion of materialist-monism often allied with Marxism; to help in building a new philosophy of man which recognizes that he is a creature that has transcended his animal origin through the building of culture and particularly of language, the World 3 of Popper. We academics have to be humble in our discussion of the nature of man, recognizing the ultimate mystery of the personal existence of a conscious self.

Literature Cited

1. Brock, L. G., Coombs, J. S., Eccles, J. C. 1951. Action potentials of motoneurones with intracellular electrode. *Proc. Univ. Otago Med. School* 29: 14–15
2. Brock, L. G., Coombs, J. S., Eccles, J. C. 1952. The recording of potentials from motoneurones with an intracellular electrode. *J. Physiol. London* 117:431–60
3. Creed, R. S., Denny-Brown, D., Eccles, J. C., Liddell, E. G. T., Sherrington, C. S. 1932. *Reflex Activity in the Spinal Cord.* London: Oxford Univ. Press
4. Eccles, J. C. 1953. *The Neurophysiological Basis of Mind: The Principles of Neurophysiology.* Oxford: Clarendon
5. Eccles, J. C. 1957. *The Physiology of Nerve Cells.* Baltimore, Maryland: Johns Hopkins Univ. Press
6. Eccles, J. C. 1964. *The Physiology of Synapses.* Berlin, Göttingen, Heidelberg: Springer
7. Eccles, J. C. 1970. Alexander Forbes and his achievement in Electrophysiology. *Persp. Biol. Med.* 13:388–404
8. Eccles, J. C. 1975. Under the spell of the synapse. *The Neurosciences: Paths of Discovery,* ed. F. G. Worden, J. P. Swazey, G. Adelman. pp. 158–79. Cambridge, Mass: MIT Press
9. Eccles, J. C. 1976. From electrical to chemical transmission in the central nervous system. *Notes and Records. R. Soc.* 30:219–230
10. Eccles, J. C., Ito, M., Szentágothai, J. 1967. *The Cerebellum as a Neuronal Machine.* Heidelberg, Berlin, Göttingen, New York: Springer
11. Eccles, J. C., Libet, B., Young, R. R. 1958. The behaviour of chromatolysed motoneurones studied by intracellular recording. *J. Physiol.* 143:11–40
12. Fatt, P., Katz, B. 1970. Membrane potentials at the motor end-plate. *J. Physiol.* 111:46–47P
13. Nastuk, W. L., Hodgkin, A. L. 1950. The electrical activity of single muscle fibres. *J. Cell. Comp. Physiol.* 35:39–74
14. Popper, K. R., Eccles, J. C. 1977. *The Self and Its Brain.* Heidelberg, New York, London: Springer. In press

Ann. Rev. Physiol. 1977. 39:19–49
Copyright © 1977 by Annual Reviews Inc. All rights reserved

ION TRANSPORT IN MEMBRANES: ❖1162
Incorporation of Biological
Ion-Translocating Proteins
in Model Membrane Systems

Juan I. Korenbrot

Departments of Physiology and Biochemistry, School of Medicine,
University of California, San Francisco, California 94143

INTRODUCTION

The flow of ions across cell membrane is many orders of magnitude faster than would be predicted by the low solubility of ions in lipids (140). Whereas lipid phase:aqueous phase partition coefficients predict the rate of membrane transport of non-electrolyte molecules, the small partition coefficients measured for ions grossly underestimate their transport rate (34, 140). This anomaly led at the beginning of the century to the suggestion that ions cross biological membranes through some form of hydrophilic discontinuity in the otherwise uniform "oil-like" structure of membranes. Similar arguments led Danielli & Davson (26) to modify their original model of the biological membrane from a uniform continuous lipid bilayer to one interrupted by hydrophilic discontinuities. In the more detailed current models of the structure of biological membranes, it has been proposed that these dielectric discontinuities in the lipid bilayers are made of proteins (175). Only over the past few years, however, has direct unequivocal confirmation that ion fluxes indeed occur through proteins embedded in the lipid bilayers been obtained. Such confirmation has come about by the development of model systems consisting of lipid bilayers into which single proteins of interest are incorporated. These "reconstituted" membranes are the main subject of this review.

Interest in reconstituted membranes of ion-transporting proteins goes beyond that of demonstrating that the given protein is indeed an ion translocator. Proteins are integral components of biological membranes and are intimately associated with the membrane lipids. These lipid-protein interactions are critical not only from a purely structural aspect, but also from a functional one: the activity of the protein is dependent on the physico-chemical characteristics of its lipid environment. The

19

classification, definition, and understanding of these interactions have become major interests in membrane biology, and reconstituted membranes in which the lipid components can be defined in purity, composition, and physical state are now fundamental tools in the study of lipid-protein interactions. Finally, reconstituted membranes provide direct access to the molecular machinery of ion transport and a means of investigating molecular mechanisms of ion transport.

In this chapter, membranes reconstituted with four different proteins are discussed: Ca-ATPase, Na-K-ATPase, bacteriorhodopsin, and rhodopsin. These are but a few of the many proteins used in reconstitution experiments and recently surveyed in a complete review by Montal (128). These four proteins were selected because they are involved in ion transport and are excellent representatives of the state of the art. As might be expected in a newly emerging field, the results obtained with reconstitution of these proteins are not without controversy, but the results to date clearly set patterns and standards worth studying. Limits in the ability of the reviewer and in the availability of space make it impossible to discuss all the outstanding work done even on these four proteins. More information, however is available in recent extensive reviews on three of these proteins: Ca-ATPase (81, 118), Na-K-ATPase (25, 177), and rhodopsin (39, 130).

Methods of Reconstitution

In the process of membrane reconstitution with a single protein, three distinct methodological steps must be followed: 1. solubilization and purification of the protein; 2. biochemical and biophysical characterization of the solubilized protein to establish its functional and structural state; and 3. reassembly of the protein into a model membrane. The proteins discussed in this chapter are all membrane integral proteins (175) and can thus only be solubilized with detergent. The detergents used for solubilization should ideally meet the following criteria: 1. solubilize without denaturing the protein, which may in some cases require that phospholipids remain associated with the protein in the detergent micelles; 2. allow purification of the protein in their presence; and 3. be readily removable. An excellent review on detergents used in membrane biology has recently appeared (61). The properties of the isolated protein should resemble those of the protein in the intact membrane. For most of the proteins discussed here, the biochemical properties in detergents are quantitatively but not qualitatively different than those in the intact membrane (74, 117, 142, 198). Such differences can be rationalized as resulting from differences in the physical environment of the membrane from that in the detergent, as discussed below. The method of reassembly of the protein into a model membrane will depend on the type of model system desired. In general, three model systems have been used: 1. vesicles limited by a single or multiple lipid bilayer (liposomes) (69, 74, 152, 156, 157); 2. monolayers formed at air-water or organic solvent-water interface (11, 78); and 3. planar lipid bilayers, either black lipid membranes (BLM) (168, 171) or lipid bilayers (126, 129). Liposomes are formed by the simultaneous assembly of protein and lipid. Their formation generally requires removal, in the presence of excess phospholipid, of the detergent in which the protein has been solubilized. Detergent can be removed by slow dialysis (87) or simply by dilution (152). However, liposomes can also be formed in the absence of detergent by sonication (151), and it has recently been possible to incorporate proteins into preformed liposomes by some form of fusion (40). BLM's are formed by depositing a mixture of lipid in nonvolatile solvent on a hydrophobic aperture between two aqueous phases (132). Planar bilayers are formed by apposing two lipid monolayers across an aperture on a hydrophobic support (131). To incorporate proteins in these membranes, the general method followed has been to allow the protein to partition into the membrane from the aqueous phase (168, 170, 171). In some cases it has been possible to form BLM's with a protein suspension in the organic solvent (36). A new approach has recently been developed which depends on the incorporation of protein into monolayers, from which bilayers are then formed (126). Unfortunately, in practical terms, incorporation into planar membranes has had very limited success, as discussed below. The choice of reconstitution method should be made partly on the basis of the experiments to be carried out. Liposomes are stable and best suited for studies of tracer fluxes (69, 75, 156), spectroscopy (109), and resonance (73, 74). Planar films are best suited for measurements of transmembrane potentials and ionic conductances (126, 127, 171). More complete technical details may be found in a recent review (160).

Each of the following sections briefly describes the properties of the chosen proteins in their intact environment, what is known about their lipid-protein interactions, and the properties of their reconstituted membranes.

Ca-ATPase

In muscle cells, the interactions of the contractile proteins with each other and with ATP are regulated by the concentration of free ionized calcium in the cytoplasm (38). The cytoplasmic concentration of free Ca, in turn, is regulated by the sarcoplasmic reticulum (SR), a network of membranes with a continuous inside space which surrounds the muscle fibrils (145). When the muscle is stimulated, Ca stored inside the SR space is released into the cytoplasm, increasing the free Ca concentration and producing contraction (81). At the termination of the stimulus Ca is removed from the cytoplasm and stored again within the SR (81). The depletion of cytoplasmic Ca by the SR is Ca, Mg, and ATP dependent and is the result of an active transport mechanism located in the SR membrane (53). Hasselbach and his collaborators (53) suggested that the active transport mechanism is the Ca-Mg–activated ATPase (EC 3.16.13 ATP phosphohydrolase) found in the SR membrane, since ATPase activity and Ca transport into the SR were strictly correlated under various experimental conditions. In particular, ATPase activity and Ca transport: (*a*) require identical optimum concentrations of Ca, Mg, ATP, and H (53, 111, 211); (*b*) have the same kinetics (53); (*c*) have the same binding constants for Ca (0.1–1 μm) and ATP (5–20 μM) (53, 118, 211); (*d*) have the same activation energies (23–26 Kcal/mole) (84); and (*e*) are inhibited in parallel by ADP and sulfhydryl-reagents (56). The mole ratio of Ca transported to ATP molecules hydrolyzed (Ca/ATP $\simeq 0.2$) is constant over a range of ATP concentrations (55) independent of the ionic gradient (200). Proof that the Ca-ATPase is indeed the active Ca translocator has been obtained through the reconstitution experiments discussed below.

Organization of the Intact Membranes

Ca-ATPase is an integral protein of the SR membrane, and comprises about 65% by weight of the total protein in the SR (122). It has a molecular weight of about 102,000 as determined in SDS gel electrophoresis (117, 122), and does not appear to have any subunit structure, at least when analyzed by polyacrylamide gel electrophoresis under denaturing conditions (117, 122). Ca-ATPase hydrolyzes ATP in the presence of Ca and Mg. In the mechanism of this reaction, the enzyme catalyzes an ATP-ADP exchange (56, 191) as well as an ATP-Pi exchange (150). During the course of the reaction, the enzyme becomes transiently phosphorylated by the terminal phosphate of ATP (110, 211). The phosphorylation of the protein is Ca dependent (110, 211), whereas its dephosphorylation is Mg dependent (89). Current data suggest that a single phosphorylation site exists in each enzyme molecule (120, 122). The Ca-ATPase binds cations and, interestingly, the value of the binding constant for Ca and Mg depends on the functional state of the protein. In the process of phosphorylation, the equilibrium dissociation constants for Ca and Mg are 0.35 μM and 10.6 mM, respectively, that is K_d (Ca)/K_d (Mg) is 1/30,000. In the dephosphorylation process, however, the protein does not distinguish Ca from Mg nearly as well: the ratio of these binding constants K_d' (Ca)/K_d' (Mg) is only 1/2.5 (210). The Ca-dependent ATP hydrolysis is reversible. When a Ca gradient is established across the SR membrane under adequate conditions, the ATPase molecule synthesize ATP from ADP and Pi (88, 112).

The ATPase molecule as an integral protein of the SR membrane is surrounded by lipids, which are organized as a bilayer (37). The lipids represent about 40% of the dry weight of the membrane (42). The chemical composition of the lipids in rabbit skeletal muscle, the most common source of SR membranes, is presented in Table 1. There are about 75 phospholipid molecules per ATPase molecule. The phospholipid composition in the rabbit SR is remarkably similar to that in rat skeletal SR (43) and human skeletal SR (183). The fatty acid chains in the phos-

Table 1   Lipid composition

		Rabbit[a] SR (118)	Na-K-ATPase[b] dogfish rectal gland (142)	Purple membrane[a] (99)	Bovine[a] disc membrane (24)
Phosphatidyl choline	PC	51	50.4	—	41
Phosphatidyl ethanolamine	PE	13.5	35.5	—	39
Phosphatidyl serine	PS	1.6	8.4	—	12.9
Phosphatidyl inositol	PI	6.9	0.5	—	2.3
Sphingomyelin	Sph	3	5.7	—	3.6
Phosphatidyl glycerol	PG	—	—	4.5	—
Phosphatidyl glycerophosphate	PGP	—	—	52	—
Phosphatidyl glycerosulfate	PGS	—	—	4.8	—
Cholesterol		21	?	—	2
Neutral lipids		0.8	?	6.1	—
Glycolipids		—	—	29.6	—

[a] As percent of total lipid dry weight.
[b] As percent of phospholipid dry weight.

pholipids are generally long (> 14 C) and unsaturated. In rat SR, the three most common fatty acids are 22:6, 20:4, and 18:2 (43). This composition would predict that the SR membrane is highly fluid at 36°C, most of the fatty acid chains being above their phase transition temperature. Indeed, NMR spectroscopy (28, 29) and ESR spectroscopy of spin labels introduced in the bilayer of the SR are consistent with a low-viscosity liquid crystal environment (77, 165, 166). Recent evidence suggests that phospholipids are asymmetrically distributed in the SR membrane as they are in other membranes (57).

The shape and molecular structure of the Ca-ATPase in the SR membrane remain unknown. If spherical, however, the molecular weight of Ca-ATPase would correspond to a diameter of 60 Å and a cross-sectional area of 3×10^3 Å^2. Inesi (81) suggested that about ⅓ of the surface of the SR membrane is occupied by the ATPase. This corresponds to a packing density of 1 molecule per 9×10^3 Å^2. X-ray diffraction patterns at 16-Å resolution (37) indicate that protein in the SR membrane, 65% of which is ATPase, is asymmetrically distributed with a higher electron density in the cytoplasmic leaflet of the lipid bilayer. Freeze-fracture replicas of the SR membrane (30) show particles of 80–90 Å diameter embedded in the lipid bilayer. These occur in the cytoplasmic leaflet at a higher density than in the intravesicular leaflet of the bilayer, again suggesting an asymmetric distribution of Ca-ATPase with a higher concentration in the cytoplasmic leaflet. Evidence supporting the identity of most of these particles as Ca-ATPase comes from the observation that phospholipid vesicles containing only Ca-ATPase show 80-Å particles under freeze-fracture while the same vesicles without protein do not (120). Thus Ca-ATPase molecules may have a higher fraction of their mass on the cytoplasmic side of the SR membrane. Ca-ATPase may also span the entire thickness of the membrane, as expected from functional and physical similarities to other transport proteins, such as Na-K-ATPase; a protein that has been shown to span the bilayer (103, 163). Although direct evidence that Ca-ATPase spans the membrane has not appeared, strong evidence exists that Ca-ATPase is accessible from one surface of the membrane and not the other. It would be logical to expect that a protein involved in a vectorial transport would be oriented to interact with its ligand on the "correct" side of the membrane barrier. The orientation of Ca-ATPase in the membrane is suggested by two morphological observations: 1. Ikemoto et al (80) found that negatively stained SR membranes have 40-Å diameter particles projecting about 60 Å above the surface on one membrane surface, but not the other. Identical observations have been made on phospholipid bilayer vesicles containing only the Ca-ATPase (179). Furthermore, in both membrane systems the particles were removed by trypsin digestion (80, 82, 179). 2. Hasselbach & Elfvin (54) found that azoferritin specifically reacted with Ca-ATPase, and the ferritin label was detected with the electron microscope on one surface of the SR membrane, but not the other. These results imply that some specific reactive site of the protein is accessible from one side of the membrane but not the other.

LIPID-PROTEIN INTERACTIONS   The Ca-ATPase molecule, like the other molecules discussed in this chapter, is amphiphilic and simultaneously interacts with the hydrophobic core of the lipid bilayer and the aqueous environment of the membrane. This amphiphilic characteristic, as further described below, is fundamental to the function of the protein. The enzymatic activity of the protein is operational only when the protein finds itself in its "proper" amphiphilic environment. It remains a challenge to describe and interpret this "proper" environment in quantitative thermodynamic terms. At this point we are limited to empirical observations of how different amphiphilic molecules satisfy the environmental requirements for the protein. It may then be possible in the future to analyze this information to understand these interactions in the more rigorous thermodynamic terms of free energy changes in an effort similar to that undertaken recently by Tanford for much simpler systems (187). In the SR membrane, cholesterol, phospholipids, and fatty acids define the amphiphilic environment of the Ca-ATPase. They are required first to maintain a permeability barrier to Ca. Thus membranes made leaky to Ca by mild treatment with diethyl ether (83) or with phospholipase A (42) show Ca-dependent ATPase activity without net Ca transport. Complete phospholipid depletion from SR membranes by treatment with organic solvents (113), or some detergents such as Triton X-100 (194) and cholate, under some conditions (58, 122) leads to irreversible inactivation of the Ca-ATPase. On the other hand, partial depletion of phospholipids produces a complete, but reversible, loss of ATPase activity. For example, treatment of SR membranes with phospholipase A, followed by albumin to remove the products of hydrolysis from the membrane, completely inhibits ATPase activity. This ATPase activity is restored by incubation with lysolecithin and phosphatidyl choline (PC) (113) or fatty acids to 50–70% of the original activity (42, 189). To effectively restore the ATPase activity the fatty acids must: 1. be unsaturated, 2. be at least 14 carbons long, 3. have a double bond in the middle of the chain (58, 189). However, functional reactivation is partial: the hydrolytic activity of the molecule is restored, but the ATP to ADP phosphoryl transfer reaction is not, and the phosphorylation reaction is only minimally restored (58). Thus the reactivated Ca-ATPase-lipid complex is functionally degenerated and some but not all of its functions can be recovered. This observation is most important since it reveals the complexity and delicacy of lipid-protein interactions: the function of the protein has been divided into components according to whether these components can or cannot be fully reactivated by lipids. Along this line, Martonosi et al (114) found that phospholipid depletion selectively inhibits the dephosphorylation reaction of the ATPase molecule to an extent commensurate with the inhibition of ATPase activity, but does not affect the rate of phosphorylation. This further illustrates that the functional state of the protein exquisitely detects its amphiphilic environment.

Solubilization and Purification

The Ca-ATPase used in reconstitution experiments is solubilized from the SR membrane with the use of detergents. Two basic approaches have been followed to solubilize and purify the enzyme. The first one uses preparations of SR membranes that have been purified to only a limited extent. The ATPase is extracted from these membranes with the anionic detergent deoxycholate (DOC) or cholate. This soluble ATPase is then purified further by ammonium acetate precipitation (117) or high-speed centrifugation in detergent-free sucrose gradient (197). The second method depends on the preparation of highly purified SR membranes and removal from these membranes of weakly associated proteins with the use of low concentrations of cholate or deoxycholate (122). The purity of the Ca-ATPase obtained has been established by three criteria: (a) specific activity (15–30 μmoles Pi/mg·min), (b) formation of phosphoenzyme (7–9 nmoles Pi/mg protein), (c), SDS polyacrylamide gel patterns. In addition, the solubilized enzyme resembles the membrane-bound form with respect to 1. ionic requirements for activation (117), 2. sensitivity to inhibitors (117), 3. specificity for triphosphonucleotides (117, 175), 4. catalysis of exchange reactions, both ATP-ADP (117) and ATP-Pi (150), and 5. formation of phosphorylated intermediates (117, 122).

The use of DOC to solubilize Ca-ATPase illustrates the importance of careful control of solubilization conditions. As discussed above, Ca-ATPase requires a "proper" environment for its function. DOC solubilizes functional protein by creating such an environment, and, at high concentrations, can completely replace the endogenous phospholipids surrounding the protein (122, 198). Low concentrations of DOC are not effective in solubilizing the enzyme; very high concentrations substitute all endogenous phospholipids, thus "denaturing" the enzyme and producing an irreversible loss of function (122, 198). The adequate concentration of DOC must be established empirically. McLennan (117) obtained a soluble Ca-ATPase with a phospholipid content essentially identical to that of the intact SR membrane. Warren et al (197, 199), on the other hand, obtained soluble Ca-ATPase in which, by varying the cholate to SR lipid mole ratio, complete experimental control of the endogenous phospholipid to Ca-ATPase mole ratio was achieved. The practical importance of these observations cannot be stressed too strongly: the kind of detergent and the concentration used for protein solubilization are critical for functional reconstitution. Not only must the detergent be removable by one of the several methods available, ideally it should also allow control of the amphiphilic environment of the protein.

Reconstitution

Isolated and purified Ca-ATPase has been incorporated successfully into single bilayer phospholipid vesicles. These reconstituted membranes, hereafter referred to as Ca-ATPase liposomes, carry out both Ca- and Mg-dependent hydrolysis of ATP and ATP-dependent transport of Ca ions, demonstrating unequivocally that Ca-ATPase is an energy-dependent ion translocator. Racker (150) first reported the formation of Ca-ATPase liposomes using cholate dialysis. Vesicles were formed with a 20–100:1 added lipid:protein weight ratio with the enzyme still containing endogenous phospholipids. These Ca-ATPase liposomes show several biochemical functions similar to those observed in intact SR membranes, although they are sometimes quantitatively different, as discussed below. These functions include: 1. ATP- and Mg-dependent active accumulation of Ca (96, 119, 150, 197), 2. Mg- and Ca-dependent ATP hydrolysis (96, 119, 150, 197), 3. Ca-dependent formation of a phosphorylated intermediate (96), 4. ATP-Pi exchange (96, 150), 5. synthesis of ATP from ADP and Pi under a Ca concentration gradient (96). The efficiency of the Ca transport, measured as the mole ratio of Ca transported to ATP, hydrolyzed in these liposomes has been found to be variable, irreproducible, and generally less than that in SR membranes (96, 119, 150, 197). This variability may arise in part from the experimental conditions of reconstitution and from the various lipids used in reconstitution since, as discussed above, the Ca permeability of the membranes affects transport efficiency. A more important source of variability, however, has recently been reported (154). The Ca-ATPase molecule isolated by McLennan (117) and used in the experiments referred to above includes not only the 102,000 mol wt protein but variable amounts of a second protein of about 12,000 mol wt. The 12,000 mol wt protein is soluble in chloroform-methanol and contains 1 or 2 moles of fatty acid per mole of ATPase covalently bound (121). This proteolipid has been tentatively identified as a "coupling factor" which, added to the ATPase preparation during formation of Ca-ATPase liposomes, produces vesicles with Ca-transport efficiencies (Ca/ATP $\sim$ 1.7), almost as high as those in intact membranes. The mechanism of action of the coupling factor is unknown, however the coupling factor releases Ca from lipid vesicles (154) but the isolated and purified proteolipid does not increase ionic permeability in black lipid membranes (168).

Another approach to reconstituting Ca-ATPase membranes has been followed by Meissner & Fleischer (123, 124). SR membranes were dissolved under carefully controlled conditions through the use of DOC. The solubilized protein contained endogenous phospholipid of the same concentration and composition as the intact SR membrane. The soluble fraction was reconstituted into particulate liposomes by dialysis under carefully controlled conditions without adding excess phospholipid. The resulting vesicles had a density and structure similar to that of intact SR membrane vesicles and showed the same rate of formation of phosphorylated intermediate. Surprisingly, however, ATP hydrolysis and Ca transport became uncoupled; the Ca-ATPase activity was fourfold higher than that in native membranes, whereas the Ca transport in the presence of oxalate was only half that in native membranes. These observations remain unexplained: are they simply a consequence of changes in the leakiness of the reconstituted membrane to Ca; is the proteolipid absent in the reconstituted vesicles; or has the change in the protein amphiphilic environment or the possible lack of proteolipid resulted in a true uncoupling of functions within the macromolecule?

Ca-ATPase liposomes have also been reconstituted by sonication in the absence of detergent (153) and by simple dilution of detergent (152). These methods of reconstitution, as well as those described above, have all used a preparation in which the Ca-ATPase was associated with its endogenous phospholipids. Warren et al (197, 198) found that endogenous phospholipids can be removed from the Ca-ATPase from the original 80:1 (phospholipid:protein) mole ratio in the intact SR membrane down to 30:1 without loss of ATPase activity. However, below the 30:1 ratio, enzymatic activity decreases linearly with the decrease in the value of this ratio and is irreversibly lost for values less than 15:1. Thirty is the minimum number of phospholipid molecules needed to form a bilayer to surround a cylinder of 40-Å diameter. Warren et al (195) suggested that the functional stability of ATPase only at mole ratios higher than 30:1 is the result of the structural need of the protein to be surrounded in the membrane by a one molecule thick cylindrical "shell" of phospholipid bilayer to remain functionally active. The presence of immobilized phospholipid around Ca-ATPase has been inferred by the use of ESR probes [quoted in (118, 198)]. To investigate the effects of varous lipids on ATP hydrolysis and Ca transport by Ca-ATPase, Warren et al (195, 197, 198) developed a method for lipid exchange. This method is unique in that it allows complete control of the lipid environment of a protein without depleting lipids from around the protein. The method depends on the equilibration of endogenous lipids with a pool of excess added lipid in the presence of cholate. Over 99% of the endogenous lipid can be substituted by known lipids. Using a "native" structural state of Ca-ATPase by keeping a mole ratio of about 30:1 phospholipid:protein and using different lipids, Warren et al found that ATP hydrolysis by the ATPase is regulated by specific interactions between protein and phospholipid. These interactions are specified by the fatty acid moiety in the phospholipid and not by the polar heads. Thus dioleoyl PC and dioleoyl phosphatidyl ethanolamine (PE) have about the same effect of the ATPase. But dioleoyl PC (di 18:1) is more effective in supporting ATPase activity than distearoyl PC (di 18:0), and both are more effective than dimiristoyl PC (di 14:0). Fatty acids must in all cases be longer than 12 carbons to support ATPase activity. An interesting observation is that in the presence of cholesterol, ATPase activity is reversibly inhibited at phospholipid:protein ratios less than 15:1, whereas the inhibition is irreversible in the absence of cholesterol (196). This observation led to the suggestion that in the presence of phospholipid, cholesterol is excluded from the immediate amphiphilic environment of the protein. The ATPase activity is also regulated by the "fluidity" of its amphiphilic environment (104, 198). The concept of fluidity in the context of lipid-protein interaction has not been well defined. It must include not only the concepts of rotational and translational freedom, but also the notion of lateral compressibility (143) and clustering (16) (see below).

The effect of phospholipids on the Ca transport function of the ATPase is less clear. Some experimental disagreement exists: Warren et al (197) reported that Ca-ATPase liposomes formed from dioleoyl PC transport calcium in the presence of ATP, but Racker et al did not obtain the same results (156). Procedural differences, for example, the high salt concentrations used by Warren et al, but not by Racker, may be responsible for some of the disagreement. Using a preparation of Ca-ATPase with endogenous phospholipids, Knowles et al (95) found that Ca-ATPase liposomes transport Ca only when formed with soybean PE, and that acetylation of the PE inhibited transport. Transport could then be reactivated by adding stearylamine or oleylamine and, less effectively, by adding myristoylamine or laurylamine. Although endogenous lipids were not removed before reconstitution, these results are significant since the chemically defined lipids were added in excess in the presence of cholate. Under these conditions endogenous lipids equilibrate with added lipids (197). In short, the Ca transport function of the ATPase appears to be defined, in part, by the nature of the polar head of the phospholipids. But as stated above, ATP hydrolysis is not specifically modified by the polar head of the phospholipids. Two different functions of the same macromolecule therefore appear to be regulated with different specificities by the amphiphilic environment.

Intact native Ca-ATPase has so far not been incorporated into planar bilayer membranes. Shamoo & McLennan (168) reported that an insoluble form of Ca-ATPase, denatured by complete removal of detergent and phospholipid, is incorporated in BLM's when it is succinylated or digested by trypsin. Even though denatured, this protein can increase the conductance of BLM's in the presence of divalent cations. Analysis of tryptic digests indicated that a 20,000 mol wt fragment, a product of digestion, itself increased conductance (171). Sulfhydryl reagents that inhibited Ca-ATPase activity of the protein did not inhibit the increase in ionic conductance (169). The meaning of these results is not clear as yet; the fragment that increases cationic conductance could indeed be a structural component responsible for ion translocation, but on the other hand it could simply represent a fragment of the protein with a divalent ion binding site which, upon interaction with the lipids of the membrane, produces dielectric discontinuities.

Na-K-ATPase

Active transport of Na and K is a property of the membrane of all animal cells. This coupled transport serves several functions: maintenance of cell volume and electrolyte gradients, absorption processes, regulation of water flow, thermogenesis, and maintenance of electrical excitability (5). Coupled Na for K transport is linked to the metabolism of the cell and is dependent on ATP and Mg. Skou (176, 177) proposed that the mechanism for this active transport was the Mg-Na-K–activated ouabain-sensitive ATPase (E C 3.6.1.3 ATP phosphohydrolase), since ATP hydrolysis and Na-K transport were correlated under various experimental conditions. This suggestion has been reinforced by findings that ATP hydrolysis and Na-K transport: 1. require identical optimum concentrations of Na, K, Mg, and ATP (147, 204); 2. have the same ionic selectivity (4, 5); 3. are both inhibited by cardiotonic steroids and show the same structure-activity relationship with these compounds (1); and 4. Na and ATP activate both functions only from inside the cell, whereas K^+ and cardiotonic steroids affect them only from the outside (141, 203, 204). In the red blood cell and in the squid axon, where the data are most accurate, it has been found that 3 Na ions are moved outward and 2 K inward for every ATP molecule hydrolyzed (45, 133). Proof that indeed the Na-K-ATPase is the active Na and K translocator has been obtained through the reconstitution experiments discussed below.

Organization of the Intact Membrane

Na-K-ATPase hydrolyzes ATP in the presence of Na, K, and Mg. The requirement for Na is absolute, but various cations can substitute for K^+, the order of effectiveness being $K > Ru > NH_4 > Cs > Li$ (4). In the mechanism of ATP hydrolysis, the enzyme is transiently phosphorylated by the terminal phosphate of the ATP (148). The phosphorylation reaction is Na and Mg dependent, whereas dephosphorylation is K dependent (146, 148). Na-K-ATPase binds ATP, and the binding is regulated by monovalent cations (59). The protein also binds monovalent cations, and the characteristics of this binding seem to vary with the functional state of the protein. However, despite elegant efforts by various investigators, direct evidence correlating changes in cation affinities with cation effects on the various steps in the reaction sequence is still lacking (25).

Na-K-ATPase is an integral membrane protein. The protein has been isolated and purified from several tissues: electric organ of the eel (142), beef brain synaptosomes (190), dog kidney (100), and dogfish rectal gland (71, 142). The enzyme purified from these tissues appears to be the same macromolecule. X-ray inactivation analysis (91) indicates that the molecular weight of the protein is about 250,000. SDS gel electrophoresis reveals that purified enzyme is composed of two subunits with apparent molecular weights of about 90,000 [range 84,000 in dog kidney (102) to 97,000 in dogfish rectal gland], and about 53,000 [range 47,000 in the eel electric organ (142) to 55,000 in dogfish rectal glands (94,100)]. The heavier subunit in dog kidney appears to have a molecular weight of about 140,000 when determined by guanidium chloride gel filtration (102). The uncertainty in the true molecular weight of the subunits has led to some disagreement as to the molar ratio of the subunits in the complete protein, whereas Hokin and collaborators (70, 142) proposed that rectal gland and electric organ Na-K-ATPase contain 2 large subunits and 1 small one, Kyte (102) proposed that dog kidney ATPase contains 1 large subunit and 2 small ones. The small subunit is a glycoprotein, and contains a high percent by weight of both neutral and charged carbohydrate (70, 102, 142). Interestingly, the carbohydrate composition is different in the different Na-K-ATPases, and removal of up to 100% of the sialic acid in electric organ ATPase has no effect on its enzymatic activity (70, 142). The large subunit is referred to as the catalytic subunit because it contains a single site, which becomes sequentially phosphorylated and dephosphorylated during the hydrolysis of ATP (70, 101, 142), and a single binding site for ouabain (70, 102, 142).

In the intact membrane, the Na-K-ATPase molecule is surrounded by lipids. The Na-K-ATPase isolated from dogfish rectal gland with over 95% purity is associated with phospholipids in a mole ratio of about 120:1 phospholipid:protein (142). The phospholipid composition of this protein is presented in Table 1. X-ray diffraction studies of this preparation show a 4.3 Å band, typical of lipid bilayers (174). The ESR spectrum of nitroxide-labeled stearic acid incorporated in the same preparation confirms that the lipids are organized as a fluid bilayer (174). ESR data suggest further that the lipids in the bilayer immediate environment of the ATPase are more ordered than the overall lipid bilayer (49).

The shape and molecular structure of the Na-K-ATPase in the membrane remain unknown. However, if it were spherical, its molecular weight would suggest a diameter of 85 Å and a cross-sectional area of about 6×10^3 Å^2. There exists a wide variation in the membrane-packing density of ATPase molecules, from about 1 μm^{-2} in the erythrocyte up to 1500 μm^{-2} in the brain (6). In contrast, the measured enzymatic turnover rates per molecule in a large variety of tissue are within the narrow range of $3.5-15 \times 10^3$ min^{-1} (6). This relative constancy of turnover rates suggests that the molecular mechanism of the ATPase in different tissues is similar. That the Na-K-ATPase is asymmetrically oriented in the bilayer is implied by 1. the observation that both ATPase activity and ion transport are activated by Na and

ATP only from the inside of the membrane, whereas K and ouabain act only from the outside (141, 203, 204), and 2. that the catalytic subunit reacts with ferritin-labeled antibodies only on the inside surface of the membrane (103). The Na-K-ATPase molecule, or at least its catalytic subunit, spans the lipid bilayer membrane. Ruoho & Kyte (163) found that a ouabain analog photoaffinity labeled the catalytic subunit presumably from outside the membrane surface, while Kyte (103) found that a specific antibody to the same subunit labeled it only from inside the membrane surface. The catalytic subunit thus can be selectively and specifically labeled from both inside and outside the membrane surface, and therefore spans the membrane.

LIPID-PROTEIN INTERACTIONS   The Na-K-ATPase reaction requires the presence of phospholipids. When phospholipids are completely depleted from a soluble or membrane-bound ATPase preparation by treatment with organic solvents (162) or phospholipase (48), irreversible inactivation of the ATPase results. On the other hand, partial depletion of phospholipids produces a complete inactivation of the ATPase that can be reversed by adding phospholipids. There has been some disagreement, however, on the specificity of the phospholipids required for reactivation of the ATP hydrolysis activity. This disagreement points out again the very strong dependence of the structural and functional state of the protein on its amphiphilic environment (discussed below). Preparations of soluble Na-K-ATPase in which only a small fraction of the endogenous membrane lipid remain associated with the protein have a different specificity for reactivation by added phospholipids than do soluble enzyme preparations rich in endogenous lipids. Furthermore, the specificity for reactivation of solubilized enzyme differs from that of membrane bound enzyme. Na-K-ATPase isolated with DOC from various tissues [beef brain (186, 202), rat brain (41), rabbit brain (41), rabbit kidney (93), rat kidney (41)], according to the method of Tanaka & Strickland (186), yielded a soluble preparation with less than 10% of the endogenous lipid still associated with the protein (93, 149, 185). Reactivation by phospholipids of the ATPase activity of this preparation had a high degree of chemical specificity, both with respect to polar head and to hydrocarbon tail. PS and phosphatidyl glycerol were the most effective activators (41, 93, 186, 202); other negative phospholipids such as PI also activated, but much less effectively (93). Neutral phospholipids such as PC and PE were generaly ineffective (41, 93, 185, 202), except for lysophosphatidyl choline (185). Mono- and dialkyl phosphates also reactivated this preparation. Their effectiveness was a function of chain length; both were most active with a 10 carbon chain (184). In a very interesting series of reports, Kimelberg & Papahadjopoulos (93, 94) showed that the ability of phosphatidyl glycerol to reactivate ATPase activity in this preparation was a function of temperature and was correlated with the state of fluidity of the hydrocarbon tails: the enzyme was more active in the fluid environments above the phase transition temperature. Kimelberg (92) also found that cholesterol and magnesium inhibited PS-activated ATPase; he explained this observation as resulting from a decrease in fluidity of the environment around the protein produced by cholesterol. This observation is important since it suggests that the state of order of the amphiphilic environment defines the structural and functional state of this protein. In contrast to the relatively high lipid specificity for reactivation found in the Tanaka-Strickland preparation, ATPase isolated under conditions in which most of the endogenous lipids remain associated with the protein have far less specificity for reactivation. Hokin & Hexum (72) noted that soluble enzyme preparations rich in endogenous lipids were partially depleted of phospholipids by treatment with phospholipase A and were reactivated equally well by various negatively charged phospholipids such as PS and PI, but not by neutral phospholipids such as PC. Since the phospholipid specificity for Na-K-ATPase reactivation seems to be a function of the environment in which the macromolecule finds itself, the results discussed above cannot be extrapolated to the properties of the ATPase in an intact membrane. Indeed, De-Pont et al (33) found that selective treatment of brain microsomes with an enzyme that converted all endogenous PS to PE without removing any phospholipid from the membranes did not inhibit ATPase activity, whereas experiments in solubilized preparations, discussed above, indicated a specific requirement for PS to preserve enzymatic activity.

Solubilization and Purification

The Na-K-ATPase used in reconstitution experiments has been solubilized with the use of detergents. Two basic approaches have been followed in extraction and purification of the enzyme. The first uses the non-ionic detergent Lubrol to solubilize the protein and zonal centrifugation and ammonium acetate precipitation to purify it. This method yields protein over 90% pure, from dogfish rectal gland and eel electric organ (142). The second uses DOC at low salt concentrations to remove extrinsic proteins followed by higher DOC concentrations at high salt concentrations to solubilize the ATPase. Gel chromatography or high-speed centrifugation are used to purify the enzyme (47, 100). This method yields over 90% pure ATPase from dog kidney. The purity of the enzyme has been established by 1. a specific ATPase activity (15–25 μmole Pi mg^{-1}min^{-1}) and 2. SDS polyacrylamide gel patterns. The purified enzymes resemble the membrane bound form in various physiological parameters (70, 142). Most important is that the purified enzyme prepared by either method retains its endogenous phospholipids.

Reconstitution

Purified Na-K-ATPase has been incorporated into single bilayer phospholipid vesicles. These reconstituted membranes, hereafter referred to as Na-K-ATPase liposomes, carry out Na-, K-, Mg-dependent hydrolysis of ATP and active transport of Na, demonstrating that this macromolecule is an energy-dependent ion translocator. Hilden, Rhee & Hokin (67, 69) reported the formation of Na-K-ATPase liposomes by the cholate dialysis method using dogfish rectal gland ATPase with all its endogenous lipid complement. Vesicles were formed with a 20:1 weight ratio of added egg PC to protein. These Na-K-ATPase liposomes show several biochemical functions identical to those observed in intact membranes: 1. ouabain-sensitive Na-, K-, Mg-, and ATP-dependent ATP hydrolysis and active transport of Na; 2. specificity for phosphate trinucleotides; 3. coupled Na-K transport, which requires

Na specifically but which will transport Rb instead of K^+, and Na-Na or K-K coupled transport under adequate conditions. The stoichiometry of transport in these vesicles, measured as the mole ratio of K or Na transported to ATP split, is about half that seen in intact membranes. This discrepancy may be the result of differences in the passive ion leak in liposomes compared to natural membranes. More important, however, is that the ratio of Na to K transported per ATP hydrolyzed (1.43:1) is almost the same as that in intact membranes (1.5:1). The Na-K-ATPase in these vesicles has lost the orientational asymmetry it shows in intact membranes. Thus the protein is still inhibited by ouabain on the opposite surface from where Na and ATP activate it, but there are ouabain binding sites both in the inside and outside surfaces of the vesicle.

A relatively impure Na-K-ATPase from dog brain has also been reconstituted by cholate dialysis (181). The resulting liposomes show Na:K transport (1.2:1), which is ATP dependent and inhibited by ouabain present on the surface opposite to the ATP activation site. In these vesicles Cl is also transported along with Na to an extent just sufficient to maintain electroneutrality in the liposome. In contrast, Goldin & Tong (47) reported formation of Na-K-ATPase liposomes from dog kidney membranes by cholate dialysis. These vesicles showed ATP-dependent Na-Cl coupled flux, but not Na-K coupled flux. The authors argued that the chloride transport is indeed active since it is larger than would be expected were it simply driven by the voltage gradient generated by Na active transport alone. This result, although apparently anomalous with respect to the known behavior of the Na-K-ATPase in several tissues, may be consistent with recent electrophysiological data in the kidney (46).

No systematic investigation has been made yet of the effects of lipid variation on the structure-function of the Na-K-ATPase in the liposomes. ESR-labeled Na-K-ATPase has suggested that indeed protein structure is a function of the phospholipid composition since the spectrum of spin-labeled maleimide-treated enzyme changes upon lipid removal (174). A surprising and important observation was recently made by Hilden & Hokin (68): using the method of lipid substitution of Warren et al (197), they replaced over 99% of the intrinsic phospholipid of the dogfish rectal gland ATPase with egg PC without at any point depleting phospholipids from the protein. They then formed Na-K-ATPase liposomes, which showed ATP-dependent ouabain-sensitive Na transport. This result is surprising since, as discussed above, it has been generally found that PC alone does not reactivate ATPase activity in molecules initially deactivated by partial phospholipid depletion. In this context, it is worth noting that Kimelberg & Papahadjoupulos (94) formed Na-K-ATPase liposomes that transported Na, even though ATPase activity was recovered when they used a preparation in which the ATPase molecule had been at one point depleted of phospholipids down to 10% of the original amount. It appears therefore that two different functions of the same protein may have different specificities with respect to their amphiphilic requirements for reactivation, and that this may depend in part on the history of the preparation.

Intact native Na-K-ATPase has not been incorporated in planar bilayers so far. A rat-brain synaptosome preparation was reported to show an ATP-dependent, ouabain-sensitive, transmembrane flux of Na^+ when added to BLM's (85). However, this behavior was seen in only 20% of the preparations, and was not present in preparations of at least six other Na-K-ATPase–rich tissues (85). On the other hand, Shamoo and his collaborators (167, 170, 171) reported that 1-hr tryptic digests of eel electric organ membranes rich in Na-K-ATPase interacted with BLM's in the presence of Na^+ to produce an increase in conductance. If the membranes were digested for 24 hr, the ability to decrease membrane resistance was preserved, but the Na^+ requirement for interaction was lost. The peptides produced by the tryptic digestion were separated by column chromatography and a 2000 mol wt fragment was found to induce the resistance change in the BLM. Shamoo and collaborators also reported that the 55,000 mol wt component of the ATPase molecule isolated under denaturing conditions with SDS increased the conductance of BLM's. These results are interesting since they show that particular peptides can interact with membranes to modify their conductance. However, it is difficult at this stage to correlate these findings with the mechanism of Na-K-ATPase ion translocation since the active peptides were obtained under conditions that destroyed the structure of "native" ATPase.

BACTERIORHODOPSIN

Bacteriorhodopsin (BRh) is a light-absorbing protein localized in the cell membrane of halophilic bacteria (9, 137). Under aerobic conditions, these bacteria synthesize ATP by consuming oxygen and do not contain BRh (138). When bacteria are grown at low O_2 concentrations, BRh is synthesized and inserted into the plasma membrane to form distinct patches with a crystalline planar hexagonal lattice structure (9, 138). These patches absorb light with a maximum near 570 nm and, because of the resultant color, have been named "purple membrane" (137, 139). At low O_2 tensions, halophilic bacteria synthesize ATP in the light, but not in the dark (134, 138). Oesterhelt & Stoeckenius (138) proposed that BRh generates an electrochemical proton gradient across the bacteria cell membrane by operating as a light-driven proton pump. The energy stored in this electrochemical potential difference, is presumably used to synthesize ATP, in accordance with Mitchell's hypothesis of energy coupling (125). This proposal was based on the observations that bacteria grown at low O_2 concentration: 1. inhibit their oxygen consumption in the presence of light with an action spectrum which matches the absorption spectrum of BRh (135, 138); 2. show light-dependent proton release, that is reversed in the dark (109, 134, 138); 3. show light-dependent ATP synthesis which is reversed in the dark and inhibited by agents that make the membrane permeable to protons (27, 134). That BRh is a light-driven proton pump has been demonstrated by the reconstitution experiments discussed below.

Organization of the Intact Membrane

Bacteriorhodopsin is the only protein found in purple membrane of Halobacterium halobium (137) or Halobacterium cutirubrum (99). It comprises 75% of the dry weight of the membrane (99, 137), has a molecular weight of about 25,000, and migrates as a single band in SDS polyacrylamide gels (12). BRh has a characteristic absorption spectrum in the visible range with a single absorption band with a maximum at 570 nm (103, 134, 137). This maximum reversibly shifts to 560 nm following long incubation in the dark (136). The absorption band of BRh is the result of the covalent attachment of the chromophore retinal in a 1:1 molar ratio with BRh. The chromophore is the all-*trans* isomer when λ_{max} is 570 and 13-*cis* isomer when λ_{max} is 560 m (136, 137). BRh undergoes fast cyclic color changes upon absorption of light. At least five spectroscopically distinct intermediates have been distinguished in this cycle, which lasts about 8 msecs at room temperature (32, 98, 109). Simultaneous with the color changes, BRh sequentially releases and takes up protons (98, 109, 134).

Bacteriorhodopsin is unique as an integral membrane protein in that it exists in a rigid two-dimensional crystal (9). X-ray diffraction patterns of purple membrane indicate that the membrane components are packed in a P3 hexagonal lattice with about 3 proteins per unit cell, all oriented in the same sense across the membrane (8, 63). Furthermore, model calculation analysis of the diffraction data suggests that BRh spans the thickness of the membrane (8). Also the X-ray diffraction data suggest that BRh has a high content of α-helical structure (8, 63). Recently Henderson & Unwin (64) elegantly applied image reconstruction methods to electron micrographs of unstained specimens of purple membrane and proposed that BRh contains seven closely packed α-helical segments that extend perpendicular to the plane of the membrane for most of its thickness. Lipid bilayer occupies the spaces between the protein molecules. The protein is proposed to be about 45 Å long, and 25 Å and 35 Å in the other dimensions.

Bacteriorhodopsin is embedded in a lipid bilayer of unusual chemical composition compared to that of other cell membranes (Table 1). The sharp in-plane hexagonal reflections detected in the X-ray diffraction pattern suggest that BRh cannot rotate freely, nor can there be much rotational disorder in the membrane. Indeed, spectroscopic experiments (133a) and the spectra of lipid ESR probes incorporated in purple membrane (18) have indicated that both protein and lipids in the membrane are in an extremely rigid environment compared to that of other cell membranes. This appears to be important to the structure of the protein, since disturbance of this environment, for example by detergents such as CTAB (hexadecyl trimethyl ammonium bromide), denatures the protein (137).

Solubilization and Purification

Bacteriorhodopsin has not yet been isolated as a soluble protein. Attempts to solubilize the protein with the use of detergents has generally resulted either in denaturation, e.g. with CTAB (137), or in formation of micelles containing fragments of purple membrane with the protein still in a crystalline lattice, as seen with cholate or deoxycholate (180). Because of these limitations, all reconstituted model systems studied to date deal with the incorporation of fragments of purple membrane into bilayers. The fragments, although small, are not isolated protein. Fragments of the purple membrane have been isolated from halophilic bacteria by lysis of the cells in low salt concentration. The purple membrane fragments have been extensively purified by differential centrifugation and high-speed centrifugation in continuous sucrose gradient (139).

Reconstitution

Bacteriorhodopsin, or rather purple membrane, has been successfully incorporated in various model systems, all of which confirm that it functions as a light-dependent proton pump. Reconstitution in spherical bilayers, hereafter referred to as BRh liposomes, was first accomplished by Racker (151) using sonication in phospholipids in a high salt solution in the absence of detergent. Racker & Stoeckenius (157) used sonication as well as cholate dialysis to form BRh liposomes. BRh liposomes showed light-dependent uptake of protons, which was reversed in the dark and inhibited by proton carriers (134, 151, 157, 180). It may be remembered that intact bacteria release protons in the light. The change in direction of transport is believed to be the result of misorientation of BRh in the liposomes. Freeze-fracture studies, taking advantage of the very distinct fracture faces of the purple membrane, confirmed that purple membrane patches were preferentially oriented inside-out in the liposomes (79, 180). Interestingly, it has been found that the extent of misorientation of the purple membrane in a liposome was a function of the lipids used for reconstitution (153). Curiously, purple membrane lipids did not produce preferential orientation of purple membrane in liposomes (79, 151). Racker & Stoeckenius (157) also reported that the rate, and sometimes the extent, of proton transport in the BRh liposomes is increased by valinomycin in the presence of K. This suggested that the proton transport is electrogenic, and valinomycin-K collapses the electrical potential generated by proton transport. Indeed, measurements of transmembrane voltage indicated the generation of voltage gradients upon illumination of BRh liposome (90, 155). In very important experiments, the light-generated electrochemical potential in BRh liposomes has been shown to drive ATP synthesis by either mitochondrial (157) or bacterial (212) ATPase molecules in the same liposomes. Further, ATP synthesis is inhibited by agents which make the liposomes leaky to protons. Thus, BRh, when illuminated, transports protons across membranes and generates on energy gradient detectable by changes in pH and membrane voltage. Most importantly, an associated ATPase apparently detects these gradients and catalyzes ATP synthesis.

The data on the effect of variation in amphiphilic environment on BRh function are inconclusive. Racker & Hinkle (155) concluded that BRh proton transport function in liposomes was nearly insensitive to variations in hydrocarbon chain length of phospholipid and to the state of fluidity of these chains. These experiments however, were done with intact purple membrane where no attempt was made to remove endogenous lipids associated with the protein. Recently Hwang & Stoeckenius (79, 180) adapted the method used by Warren et al (197) and substituted about 90% of endogenous lipid from the purple membrane with defined phospholipids. In this case, protein function varied with the state of fluidity of hydrocarbon tail. The effect of specificity of polar heads has not been investigated in this preparation. Knowles et al (95) have shown in BRh liposomes prepared without removal of endogenous lipids that acetylation of PE in the liposomes did not affect BRh function.

Bacteriorhodopsin has been incorporated in black lipid membranes (BLM) by simply mixing purple membrane with the membrane-forming solution of phospholipid and hydrocarbon (36). These membranes generate potential differences when illuminated, and these potentials disappear in the presence of proton carriers. However, the photopotentials are of variable sign and magnitude, suggesting that under these conditions BRh is arbitrarily oriented in the membrane. Nonetheless, electrogenicity of proton transport was apparent. Along the same line, Drachev et al (35) reported that BRh liposomes "fused" with black lipid membranes and generated photovoltages due to electrogenic proton transport. The results discussed above point out a critical problem in reconstitution in planar systems: not only must the method succeed in incorporating a functional protein, but the protein should either be totally oriented or at least there should be a measure of the extent of orientation. In some cases it may be possible, of course, to induce functional asymmetry by simply providing impermeant substrates on one surface and not the other.

The lack of control of orientation in BRh model systems has been particularly disappointing since it has severely limited quantitative analysis. The search for means to orient purple membrane prompted the development of purple membrane films on the surface of water. The large potential difference at the air-water interface might orient membrane fragments if they had small charge or dipole difference between their two surfaces. Indeed, films with over 85% orientation of BRh have been formed on the surface of clean water (78). These films have spectroscopically intact and functional BRh (78, 180). BRh films have also been formed at an octane-water interface by absorption from the aqueous subphase. The extent of orientation in these particular films has not been quantified, but must be high since large potentials were recorded upon illumination (11). Interestingly, the generated photopotentials drove enzymatic synthesis of ATP by ATPase incorporated at the interface (209). An important practical tool may be derived from these results: a high degree of orientation may be accomplished when incorporation of proteins is carried out under voltage gradients. This may also be significant in membrane biosynthesis since, after all, highly oriented proteins are incorporated in membranes which generally sustain voltage gradients of the order of 10^4V/cm.

RHODOPSIN

Rhodopsin (Rh) is a light-absorbing protein localized in the membranes of the outer segment of rod photoreceptors in the vertebrate retina (86). The outer segments consist of a stack of between 1000 and 2000 discs all surrounded by a plasma membrane (19). The discs are free floating and are structurally (20) and electrically (164) disconnected from the plasma membrane. Absorption of a single photon of light by Rh in the discs is sufficient to trigger an electrical response in the receptor cell, the result of a change in the ionic conductance of the plasma membrane of the outer segment (50, 130). The mechanism by which the absorption of light in the disc membrane is coupled to the electrical event in the plasma membrane is unknown. Hagins & Yoshikami (50, 51, 213), recently proposed the following hypothesis for this mechanism. Rhodopsin molecules, upon absorption of light, increase the Ca permeability of disc membranes, allowing Ca ions to flow out of the disc. The resulting increase in the concentration of Ca in the space outside the disc, but still within the plasma membrane, produces the observed change in conductance of the plasma membrane. This hypothesis, which uses Ca as an internal messenger, was proposed on the basis of the following observations: 1. Topology of the outer segment: Rh in the discs regulates a function of the plasma membrane, from which it is physically separated; 2. Numerical gain: a single Rh molecule regulates the flux of as many as 10^7 ions in the plasma membrane (52, 97); 3. Changes in the concentration of Ca both outside (13, 50, 97, 213) and inside (51, 206) the plasma membrane mimic the effects of light, variations in the concentration inside the cell being much more effective than those outside. Support for this hypothesis has come from some recent reports of light-regulated flux of Ca across disc membranes (65, 66, 107, 116, 182, 201). The results are not conclusive, however, since they do not agree on the stoichiometry of the flux and the kinetics of the Ca flux have not yet been investigated. The possibility exists that Rh may regulate the Ca permeability of the disc membrane by functioning as a light-activated ion translocator. Results with reconstituted membranes containing Rh, as discussed below, make this a distinct possibility.

Organization of the Intact Membrane

Rhodopsin in the rod disc membrane in several species comprises 80–90% of the integral protein of the disc [frog (161), cattle (60)]. It has a molecular weight of about 37,000 (105) and does not appear to have any subunit structure as analyzed in SDS gel electrophoresis (60, 161). Rh is a glycoprotein containing a 6-residue covalently bound oligosacharride (62). Rh has a characteristic absorption spectrum in the visible range with a single major absorption maximum at 498–502 nm, and a minor absorption maximum at 350 nm (76). The visible absorption band is the result of the covalent attachment in a 1:1 mole ratio of a chromophore, 11-*cis* retinal, to the protein (14). Upon absorption of light, the chromophore isomerizes to the all-*trans* configuration. The photo-isomerization of the chromophore produces a sequence of spectroscopically distinct conformational states which are in thermal equilibrium with each other. At the end point of the photoreaction, all-*trans* retinal separates from the protein moiety of Rh (2, 76).

Rh is an integral protein of the disc membrane surrounded by lipids organized as a bilayer (10, 23, 207). The chemical composition of these lipids is very similar in several species (24), and the lipid composition of the bovine disc membrane is shown in Table 1. There are about 80–100 mole of phospholipid per mole of Rh in the membrane. The fatty acid chains in the phospholipids are generally long (>14 C) and unsaturated. The three most common fatty acids in frog discs are 22:6, 18:0, and 16:0 (115). From this composition it can be predicted that disc membranes at room temperature are highly fluid, since most of the lipids exist above their phase transition temperature. Indeed, ESR spectra of probes incorporated in disc membranes indicated a highly fluid environment and, interestingly, implied light-dependent changes in fluidity (31, 192). Also, Rh has been shown to be free to both rotate (21) and diffuse laterally (108, 144) in the plane of the disc membrane at rates commensurate with a low viscosity environment of 1–10 poise.

Several physical techniques have been used to elucidate the shape of Rh and its position in the disc membrane. Microspectrophotometry (106) and X-ray diffraction (7) indicate that Rh is uniformly packed in the plane of the membrane with a density of about 2.5×10^4 Rh μm^{-2}. Energy transfer experiments suggest that Rh is a long and narrow molecule about 75 Å by 35 Å (208), and extends into the aqueous phase on the cytoplasmic surface of the disc. The disc has been labeled by hydrophilic reagents from the cytoplasmic side (158, 178). Freeze-etch studies of the disc membrane show that Rh is closely associated with the monolayer on the cytoplasmic surface of the disc (17, 158). However, it is likely that Rh spans the thickness of the membrane. Chen & Hubbell (17) observed, following deep etching of freeze-fracture replicas of disc membranes, the formation of "holes" in the otherwise smooth replica of the monolayer facing the intradisc space. They interpreted these holes as the result of the sublimation of ice from below the membrane through gaps remaining where Rh was "pulled away" from the intradisc monolayer. Regardless of its precise shape and position, Rh is highly oriented in the membrane. This is indicated by the high linear dichroism shown by the outer segments: the dipole of absorption of its chromophore is parallel to the plane of the disc (193). Orientation of Rh is also indicated by the detection of charge displacement in the protein upon illumination (the early receptor potential), lost when Rh is disoriented by heating (22). Rh in the disc membrane, then, is asymmetrically localized, may span the lipid bilayer, and is strongly oriented. The amphiphilic environment of Rh is important to the structural state of the protein. Some functional characteristics of the protein are affected by variations in its lipid environment:

1. The ability of the protein moiety of Rh to recombine with 11-*cis* retinal, referred to as regenerability, was reversibly inhibited when phospholipids were partially depleted from disc membranes, although the absorption spectrum of the protein was unaffected (172, 214). This loss of regenerability has been attributed to possible variations in the rigidity of the Rh environment, but definitely not to the specific absence of phospholipids since regenerability was seen in phospholipid-free digitonin micelles of Rh (74).

2. Rh was less thermally stable in partially delipidated disc membranes than in intact membranes (173).

3. The rate of formation of one of the photoproducts of Rh was slowed by partial loss of lipids from the disc membrane and restored to its original value by adding PE (205). The effects of other lipids on this reactivation have not yet been reported.

As with the other proteins discussed here, the functional state of the protein is strongly dependent on the dynamic state of its environment, defined by subtle physico-chemical factors that are not simply determined by chemical specificity.

Solubilization and Purification

Rhodopsin has been isolated with the use of detergents. Two basic methods have been followed: In one, Rh, with its endogenous phospholipids and some small fraction of contaminating proteins, was extracted with detergent and, without further purification, used in reconstitution (127). In the other method, Rh, with endogenous phospholipids and contaminating proteins, was extracted with detergent and then purified by chromatographic procedures that remove contaminating proteins and also phospholipids, thereby reducing the phospholipid: Rh mole ratio to less than one (3, 73). The form of the absorption spectrum of Rh prepared by either method is the same, but purified Rh has a smaller ratio of absorbances at 278 nm, i.e. the peak due to aromatic amino acids, to the main peak at 500 nm. This $A^{278}:A^{500}$ ratio is used as a criterion of Rh purity, the lowest ratios reported to date being in the range of 1.6–1.7 (3, 73).

Reconstitution

Isolated and purified Rh has been successfully incorporated into single bilayer phospholipid vesicles, hereafter referred to as Rh-liposomes. Hong & Hubbell (73, 74) first reported formation of Rh-liposomes by dialysis of Rh-detergent micelles in the presence of phospholipid. The structure of the Rh-liposomes, investigated with freeze-fracture electron microscopy and X-ray diffraction, indicates that the Rh interacts with the hydrophobic core of the bilayer and that its distribution in the plane of the membrane is a function of the bilayer fluidity (15, 17). Also, at a given temperature, and for some specific phospholipids, illumination affects the distribution of Rh in the membrane in a manner similar to that seen when the temperature is raised (17). Rh in these liposomes has an absorption spectrum identical to that in the intact membrane and is regenerated with 11-*cis* retinal, a function lost in the presence of detergent. The function of regenerability has been used to investigate the specificity of lipid-protein interaction of Rh. It has been concluded that this function of the protein requires an "adequate" amphiphilic environment not provided by detergent micelles alone, but provided by lipids, although lipids with various polar heads or fatty acids are equally adequate, as long as their fatty acids are longer than 10 carbons (17). This lipid specificity is defined only for the regenerability function of Rh and, as was demonstrated by the Ca-ATPase, different functions of the same macromolecule may have differing lipid specificities. Applebury et al (3) investigated the effects of phospholipids on the rate of formation of Rh protoproducts in Rh-liposomes and found that egg PC slightly accelerated the rate of formation of one photo-intermediate (Meta II), compared to the rate in intact discs. On the other hand, solubilizing Rh in detergent, even in the presence of endogenous phospholipid increased this rate by a factor of over 100.

Rh-liposomes have been used to test the hypothesis that Rh is a light-activated ion translocator by measuring the effects of illumination on ionic fluxes across the liposome membrane. Hong & Hubbell (75), using Rh-liposomes formed with purified Rh by dialysis of detergent, and Montal (127), using Rh-liposomes formed with unpurified Rh by sonication after partial removal of detergent, have both described light-dependent release of trapped Ca from these liposomes. Further, Montal (127) has noted that this ion release was not selective; both mono- and divalent ions were released by light. These studies demonstrate one of the major attributes as well as one of the major limitations of reconstitution experiments: a light-dependent ion-translocator function of Rh has been found, but they also raise the question of whether the function observed is present in the intact membrane or was created by the manipulations of reconstitution. If the function detected in the model system is a "native" one, its primary characteristics in both native and model systems should agree quantitatively. For the ion-translocating function of Rh, these characteristics include kinetics, photon-sensitivity, light-energy dependence, and action spectrum. These parameters remain to be tested. In this context, it should be noted that Rh in the liposomes made by the method of Hong & Hubbell (74) have several chemical characteristics identical to those of Rh in intact membranes, among them reactivity to sulfhydryl reagents and to proteolytic enzymes (W. Hubbell, personal communication).

Rhodopsin has been incorporated in planar lipid bilayers. These bilayers have been formed by the opposition of Rh-containing monolayers formed by spreading an hexane suspension of Rh and lipid (129). Montal (127) reported a light-dependent increase in ionic conductance in these bilayers; this increase appears as discrete steps of a constant unitary value. Unfortunately, the increase in conductance in these membranes occurs several seconds after illumination, much slower than the delay in the photo-response of the cell, which is only of the order of milliseconds (50). It is probable that the state of Rh in this model system is not the same as that in the disc membrane. Nevertheless improvements in technique may overcome these problems and confirm that Rh forms a light-dependent ion channel in the disc membrane.

CONCLUSION

The physiological characteristics of model membranes containing phospholipids and biological ion-translocating proteins have conclusively demonstrated that the active and passive transport of ions across membranes occurs through proteins. The transporting proteins discussed in this chapter share several physical characteristics in intact membranes: 1. a strong interaction with the hydrocarbon core of the lipid bilayer; 2. a high degree of orientation; 3. an asymmetry in their accessibility to reactants from the two surfaces of the membrane; and 4. they may all extend across the entire thickness of the membrane, although this has not yet been demonstrated in all cases. These characteristics may in the future be recognized as common to all ion-translocating proteins.

Transporting proteins, both in native and in reconstituted membranes, show an exquisite dependence on the physico-chemical characteristics of their lipid environment. Understanding the nature of this dependence is one of the challenging areas of future investigation in reconstituted membranes. For example, it is clear now that protein function can vary with the degree of rotational and translational freedom of the lipids surrounding the macromolecule. However, current evidence also suggests that the transporting proteins are surrounded by a relatively immobile "shell" of lipids at least one molecule thick. The variation in protein function with lipid fluidity must therefore be the result of intricate lipid-lipid as well as lipid-protein interactions. Furthermore, single phospholipid systems, even at temperatures well above their phase-transition temperature, show coexistence of regions of high and low fluidity rather than a completely uniform high-fluidity state (104). This concept of coexistence of high- and low-fluidity states, referred to as *clustering* in single phospholipid systems (104) or *lateral phase separation* (16) in mixed phospholipid systems, may be paramount in understanding the functional state of transporting proteins. Chemical parameters regulating ion transport, such as hormones, may exert their action through modification of the amphiphilic environment of the transporting proteins.

Finally, reconstituted membranes have opened the possibility of direct investigation of the molecular mechanisms of ion transport. One of the most exciting prospects in reconstitution work is the possibility of understanding ion transport in relatively simple physico-chemical terms.

ACKNOWLEDGMENTS

I wish to thank Dr. Carol Korenbrot for her patient help and advice and B. Hansen, M. J. Pramik, and D. Roof for helpful discussions.

Literature Cited

1. Abeles, A. L. 1969. Structure-activity relationship of several cardiotonic steroids with respect to inhibition of ion transport in frog muscle. *J. Gen. Physiol.* 54:268–85
2. Abrahamson, E. W. 1973. The kinetics of early intermediate processes in the photolysis of visual pigments. In *Biochemistry and Physiology of Visual Pigments,* ed. H. Langer. Berlin:Springer. 325 pp.
3. Applebury, M. L., Zuckerman, D. M., Lamola, A. A., Jovin, T. M. 1974. Rhodopsin purification and recombination with phospholipids assayed by the Metarhodopsin I Metarhodopsin II transition. *Biochemistry* 13:3448–58
4. Baker, P. F. 1965. Phosphorus metabolism of intact crab nerve and its relation to the active transport of ions. *J. Physiol.* 180:383–423
5. Baker, P. F. 1972. The sodium pump in animal tissues and its role in the control of cellular metabolism and function. *Metab. Pathways* 6:243–68
6. Baker, P. F., Willis, J. S. 1972. Binding of the cardiac glycoside ouabain to intact cells. *J. Physiol.* 224:441–62
7. Blasie, J. K., Worthington, C. R. 1969. Planar liquid-like arrangement of photopigment molecules in frog retinal receptor disk membranes. *J. Mol. Biol.* 39:417–39
8. Blaurock, A. E. 1975. Bacteriorhodopsin: A trans-membrane pump containing α-helix. *J. Mol. Biol.* 93:139–58
9. Blaurock, A. E., Stoeckenius, W. 1971. Structure of the purple membrane. *Nature New Biol.* 233:152–54
10. Blaurock, A. E., Wilkins, M. H. F. 1972. Structure of retinal photoreceptor membranes. *Nature* 236:313–14
11. Boguslavsky, L. I., Kondrashin, A. A., Kozlov, I. A., Metel'skii, S. T., Skulachev, V. P., Volkov, A. G. 1975. Charge transfer between water and octane phases by soluble mitochondrial ATPase (F_1), bacteriophodopsin and respiratory chain enzymes. *FEBS Lett.* 50:223–26
12. Bridgen, J. A., Walker, I. D. 1976. Photoreceptor protein from the purple membrane of *Halobacterium halobium.* Molecular weight and retinal binding site. *Biochemistry* 15:792–98
13. Brown, J. E., Pinto, L. H. 1974. Ionic mechanism for the photoreceptor potential of the retina of *Bufo marinus. J. Physiol.* 236:575–91
14. Bownds, D. 1967. Site of attachment of retinal in rhodopsin. *Nature* 216:1178–80
15. Chabre, M., Cavaggioni, A., Osborne, H. B., Gulik-Krzywicki, T., Olive, J. 1972. A rhodopsin-lipid-water lamellar system: Its characterization by X-ray diffraction and electron microscopy. *FEBS Lett.* 26:197–201
16. Chapman, D. 1975. Phase transitions and fluidity characteristics of lipids and cell membranes. *Q. Rev. Biophys.* 8:185–235
17. Chen, Y. S., Hubbell, W. L. 1973. Temperature and light-dependent structural changes in rhodopsin-lipid membranes. *Exp. Eye Res.* 17:517–32
18. Chignell, C. F., Chignell, D. A. 1975. A spin label study of purple membranes from *Halobacterium halobium. Bio-*

chem. Biophys. Res. Commun. 62: 136–43

19. Cohen, A. I. 1963. Vertebrate retinal cells and their organization. *Biol. Rev.* 38:427–59
20. Cohen, A. I. 1970. Further studies on the question of the potency of saccules in outer segments of vertebrate photoreceptors. *Vision Res.* 10:445–53
21. Cone, R. A. 1972. Rotational diffusion of rhodopsin in the visual receptor membrane. *Nature New Biol.* 236:39–43
22. Cone, R. A., Brown, P. K. 1967. Dependence of the early receptor potential on the orientation of rhodopsin. *Science* 156:536
23. Corless, J. 1972. Lamellar structure of bleached and unbleached rod photoreceptor membrane. *Nature* 237:229–31
24. Daemen, F. J. M. 1973. Vertebrate rod outer segment membranes. *Biochim. Biophys. Acta* 300:255–88
25. Dahl, J. L., Hokin, L. E. 1974. The sodium-potassium adenosine triphosphatase. *Ann. Rev. Biochem.* 43:327–56
26. Danielli, J. F. 1975. The bilayer hypothesis of membrane structure. In *Cell Membranes,* ed. G. Weissman, R. Claiborne. New York: H. P. Publishing. 283 pp.
27. Danon, A., Stoeckenius, W. 1974. Photophosphorylation in *H. halobium. Proc. Natl. Acad. Sci. USA* 71:1234–38
28. Davis, D. G., Inesi, G. 1971. Proton nuclear magnetic resonance studies of sarcoplasmic reticulum membranes. *Biochim. Biophys. Acta* 241:1–8
29. Davis, D. G., Inesi, G., Gulik-Krzywicki, T. 1976. Lipid molecular motion and enzyme activity in sarcoplasmic reticulum membranes. *Biochemistry* 15:1271–76
30. Deamer, D. W., Baskin, R. J. 1969. Ultrastructure of sarcoplasmic reticulum preparations. *J. Cell Biol.* 42:296–307
31. Delmelle, M., Pontus, M. 1975. Light induced change in rod outer segment membrane fluidity. *Vision Res.* 15:145–47
32. Dencher, N., Wilms, M. 1975. Flash photometric experiments on the photochemical cycle of Bacteriorhodopsin. *Biophys. Struct. Mech.* 1:259–71
33. DePont, J. J. H. H. M., Van Prooijen-Van Eeden, A., Bonting, S. L. 1973. Studies on (Na⁺-K⁺)-activated ATPase. *Biochim. Biophys. Acta* 323:487–93
34. Diamond, J., Wright, E. M. 1969. Biological membranes: Physical basis of ion and non-electrolyte selectivity. *Ann. Rev. Physiol.* 31:582–645
35. Drachev, L. A., Jasaitis, A. A., Kaulen, A. D., Kondrashin, A. A., Liberman, E. A., Nemecek, I. B., Ostroumov, S. A., Semenov, A. Y., Skulachev, V. P. 1974. Direct measurement of electric current generation by cytochrome oxidase, H⁺-ATPase and Bacteriorhodopsin. *Nature* 249:321–24
36. Drachev, L. A., Kaulen, A. D., Ostroumov, S. A., Skulachev, V. P. 1974. Electrogenesis by Bacteriorhodopsin incorporated in a planar phospholipid membrane. *FEBS Lett.* 39:43–45
37. DuPont, Y., Harrison, S. C., Hasselbach, W. 1973. Molecular organization in the sarcoplasmic reticulum membrane studied by X-ray diffraction. *Nature* 244:555–58
38. Ebashi, S., Endo, M., Ohtsuki, I. 1969. Control of muscle contraction. *Q. Rev. Biophys.* 2:351–84
39. Ebrey, T. G., Honig, B. 1975. Molecular aspects of photoreceptor function. *Q. Rev. Biophys.* 8:129–84
40. Eytan, E., Matheson, M. J., Racker, E. 1975. Incorporation of biologically active proteins into liposomes. *FEBS Lett.* 57:121–25
41. Fenster, L. J., Copenhaver, J. H. 1967. Phosphatidyl serine requirement of (Na⁺-K⁺)-activated ATPase from rat kidney and brain. *Biochim. Biophys. Acta* 137:406–8
42. Fiehn, W., Hasselbach, W. 1970. The effect of phospholipase A on the Ca transport and the role of unsaturated fatty acids in ATPase activity of sarcoplasmic vesicles. *Eur. J. Biochem.* 13:510–18
43. Fiehn, W., Peter, J. B., Mead, J. F., Gan-Elepano, M. 1971. Lipids and fatty acids of sarcolemma, sarcoplasmic reticulum and mitochondria from rat skeletal muscle. *J. Biol. Chem.* 246:5617–20
44. Fiehn, W., Seiler, D. 1975. Alteration of erythrocyte (Na⁺K)-ATPase by replacement of cholesterol by desmosterol in the membrane. *Experientia* 31:773–74
45. Garrahan, P. J., Glynn, I. M. 1967. The stoichiometry of the sodium pump. *J. Physiol.* 192:217–35
46. Goldin, S. M., Sweadner, K. J. 1975. Reconstitution of active transport by kidney and brain. (Na⁺-K⁺)ATPase. *Ann. NY Acad. Sci.* 264:387–97
47. Goldin, S. M., Tong, S. W. 1974. Reconstitution of active transport catalyzed by the purified Na and K ion

stimulated ATPase from canine renal medulla. *J. Biol. Chem.* 249:5907–15

48. Goldman, S. S., Albers, R. W. 1973. Na-K activated ATPase. The role of phospholipids. *J. Biol. Chem.* 248: 867–74

49. Grisham, C. M., Barnett, R. E. 1972. The interrelationship of membrane and protein structure in the functioning of the (Na$^+$K)-activated ATPase. *Biochim. Biophys. Acta* 266:613–24

50. Hagins, W. A. 1972. The visual process; excitatory mechanisms in the primary receptor cells. *Ann. Rev. Biophys. Bioeng.* 1:131–58

51. Hagins,W. A., Yoshikami, S. 1974. A role for Ca^{2+} in excitation of retinal rods and cones. *Exp. Eye Res.* 18:299–306

52. Hagins, W. A., Yoshikami, S. 1975. Ionic mechanisms in excitation of photoreceptors. *Ann. NY Acad. Sci.* 264:314–25

53. Hasselbach, W. 1964. Relaxing factor and the relaxation of muscle. *Progr. Biophys. Biophys. Chem.* 14:167–222

54. Hasselbach, W., Elfvin, L. G. 1967. Structural and chemical asymmetry of the calcium-transporting membranes of the sarcotubular system as revealed by electron microscopy. *J. Ultrastruct. Res.* 17:598–622

55. Hasselbach, W., Makinose, M. 1961. Die Calciumpumpe der "Erschlaffungsgrana" des Muskels und ihre Abhangigkeit von der ATP-spaltung. *Biochem. Z.* 333:518–28

56. Hasselbach, W., Makinose, M. 1962. ATP and active transport. *Biochem. Biophys. Res. Commun.* 7:132–36

57. Hasselbach, W., Migala, A. 1975. Arrangement of proteins and lipids in the sarcoplasmic membrane. *Z. Naturforsch.* 30:681–83

58. Hasselbach, W., Suko, J., Stromer, M. H., The, R. 1975. Mechanism of calcium transport in sarcoplasmic reticulum. *Ann. NY Acad. Sci.* 264:335–49

59. Hegyvary, C., Post, R. L. 1971. Binding of ATP to Na and K ion-stimulated ATPase. *J. Biol. Chem.* 246:5234–40

60. Heitzman, H. 1972. Rhodopsin is the predominant protein of rod outer segment membranes. *Nature New Biol.* 235:114

61. Helenius, A., Simons, K. 1975. Solubilization of membranes by detergents. *Biochim. Biophys. Acta* 415:29–79

62. Heller, J., Lawrence, M. A. 1970. Structure of the glycopeptide from bovine visual pigment 500. *Biochemistry* 9: 864–69

63. Henderson, R. 1975. The structure of the purple membrane from *Halobacterium halobium:* Analysis of the X-ray diffraction pattern. *J. Mol. Biol.* 93:123–38

64. Henderson, R., Unwin, P. N. T. 1975. Three dimensional model of purple membrane obtained by electron microscopy. *Nature* 257:28–32

65. Hendricks, T., Daemen, F. J. M., Bonting, S. L. 1974. Biochemical aspects of the visual process. XXV. Light-induced calcium movements in isolated frog rod outer segments. *Biochim. Biophys. Acta* 345:468–73

66. Hemminki, K. 1975. Light-induced decrease in calcium binding to isolated bovine photoreceptors. *Vision Res.* 15: 69–72

67. Hilden, S., Hokin, L. E. 1975. Active K$^+$ transport coupled to active Na$^+$ transport in vesicles reconstituted from purified Na and K ion activated ATPase from the rectal gland of *Squalus acanthias. J. Biol. Chem.* 250:6296–6303

68. Hilden, S., Hokin, L. E. 1977. *Biochem. Biophys. Res. Commun.* In press

69. Hilden, S., Rhee, H. M., Hokin, L. E. 1974. Sodium transport by phospholipid vesicles containing purified sodium and potassium ion-activated adenosine triphosphatase. *J. Biol. Chem.* 249:7432–40

70. Hokin, L. E. 1974. Purification and properties of the (Na$^+$-K$^+$) activated ATPase and reconstitution of Na$^+$ transport. *Ann. NY Acad. Sci.* 242: 12–23

71. Hokin, L. E., Dahl, J. L., Deupree, J. D., Dixon, J. F., Hackney, J. F., Perdue, J. F. 1973. Studies on the characterization of the Na$^+$-K$^+$ transport adenosine triphosphatase. *J. Biol. Chem.* 248:2593–2605

72. Hokin, L. E., Hexum, T. D. 1972. Studies on the characterization of the Na-K transport adenosine triphosphatase. *Arch. Biochem. Biophys.* 151:453–63

73. Hong, K., Hubbell, W. L. 1972. Preparation and properties of phospholipid bilayers containing rhodopsin. *Proc. Natl. Acad. Sci. USA* 69:2617–21

74. Hong, K., Hubbell, W. L. 1973. Lipid requirement for rhodopsin regenerability. *Biochemistry* 12:4517–23

75. Hong, K., Hubbell, W. L. 1977. *Proc. Natl. Acad. Sci. USA* In press

76. Hubbard, R., Bownds, D., Yoshizawa, T. 1965. The chemistry of visual

photoreception. *Cold Spring Harb. Symp. Quant. Biol.* 30:301–15

77. Hubbell, W. L., McConnell, H. M. 1968. Spin-label studies of the excitable membranes of nerve and muscle. *Proc. Natl. Acad. Sci. USA* 61:12–16

78. Hwang, S. B., Korenbrot, J. I., Stoeckenius, W. 1977. Light-dependent proton transport by bacteriorhodopsin incorporated in an interface film. *J. Supramol. Struct.* In press

79. Hwang, S. B., Stoeckenius, W. 1977. Incorporation of bacteriorhodopsin in phospholipid vesicles. In preparation

80. Ikemoto, N., Sreter, F. A., Nakamura, A., Gergely, J. 1968. Tryptic digestion and localization of calcium uptake and ATPase activity in fragments of sarcoplasmic reticulum. *J. Ultrastruct. Res.* 23:216–32

81. Inesi, G. 1972. Active transport of calcium ion in sarcoplasmic membranes. *Ann. Rev. Biophys. Bioeng.* 1:191–210

82. Inesi, G., Asai, H. 1968. Trypsin digestion of fragmented sarcoplasmic reticulum. *Arch. Biochem. Biophys.* 126:469–77

83. Inesi, G., Goodman, J., Watanabe, S. 1967. Effect of diethyl ether on ATPase activity and the Ca uptake of fragmented sarcoplasmic reticulum of rabbit skeletal muscle. *J. Biol. Chem.* 242:4637–43

84. Inesi, G., Watanabe, S. 1967. Temperature dependence of ATP hydrolysis and Ca uptake by fragmented sarcoplasmic membranes. *Arch. Biochem. Biophys.* 121:665–71

85. Jain, M. K., White, F. P., Strikholm, A., Williams, E. 1972. Studies concerning the possible reconstitution of an active cation pump across an artificial membrane. *J. Membr. Biol.* 8:363–88

86. Jan, L. Y., Revel, J. P. 1974. Ultrastructural localization of rhodopsin in the vertebrate retina. *J. Cell Biol.* 62:257–73

87. Kagawa, Y., Racker, E. 1971. Partial resolution of the enzymes catalyzing oxidative phosphorylation. *J. Biol. Chem.* 246:5477–87

88. Kanazawa, T., Yamada, S., Tonomura, Y. 1970. ATP formation from ADP and a phosphorylated intermediate of Ca-dependent ATPase in fragmented sarcoplasmic reticulum. *J. Biochem. Tokyo* 68:593–95

89. Kanazawa, T., Yamada, S., Yamamoto, T., Tonomura, Y. 1971. Reaction mechanism of the Ca-dependent ATPase of sarcoplasmic reticulum from skeletal muscle. *J. Biochem. Tokyo* 70:95–123

90. Kayushin, L. P., Skulachev, V. P. 1974. Bacteriorhodopsin as an electrogenic proton pump: Reconstitution of bacteriorhodopsin proteoliposomes generating $\Delta\psi$ and Δ pH. *FEBS Lett.* 39:39–42

91. Kepner, G. R., Macey, R. I. 1968. Membrane enzyme systems molecular size determination by radiator inactivation. *Biochim. Biophys. Acta* 163:188–203

92. Kimelberg, H. K. 1975. Alterations in phospholipid-dependent (Na-K) ATPase activity due to lipid fluidity. Effects of cholesterol and Mg. *Biochim. Biophys. Acta* 413:143–56

93. Kimelberg, H. K., Papahadjopoulos, D. 1972. Phospholipid requirements for (Na-K) ATPase activity: Head group specificity and fatty acid fluidity. *Biochim. Biophys. Acta* 282:277–92

94. Kimelberg, H. K., Papahadjopoulos, D. 1974. Effects of phospholipid acyl chain fluidity, phase transitions and cholesterol on (Na+K) stimulated ATPase. *J. Biol. Chem.* 249:1071–80

95. Knowles, A. F., Kandrach, A., Racker, E., Khorana, H. G. 1975. Acetyl phosphatidyl ethanolamine in the reconstitution of ion pumps. *J. Biol. Chem.* 250:1809–13

96. Knowles, A. F., Racker, E. 1975. Properties of a reconstituted calcium pump. *J. Biol. Chem.* 9:3538–44

97. Korenbrot, J. I., Cone, R. A. 1972. Dark ionic flux and the effects of light in isolated rod outer segments. *J. Gen. Physiol.* 60:20–45

98. Kung, M., DeVault, D., Hess, B., Oesterhelt, D. 1975. Photolysis of bacterial rhodopsin. *Biophys. J.* 15:907–10

99. Kushwaha, S. C., Kates, M., Martin, W. G. 1975. Characterization and composition of the purple and red membrane from *Halobacterium cutirubrum.* *Can. J. Biochem.* 53:284–92

100. Kyte, J. 1971. Purification of the Na and K dependent adenosine triphosphatase from canine renal medulla. *J. Biol. Chem.* 246:4157–65

101. Kyte, J. 1971. Phosphorylation of a purified (Na+K) adenosine triphosphatase *Biochem. Biophys. Res. Commun.* 43:1259–65

102. Kyte, J. 1972. Properties of the two polypeptides of Na- and K-dependent ATPase. *J. Biol. Chem.* 247:7642–49

103. Kyte, J. 1974. The reactions of Na and K ion activated ATPase with specific antibodies. *J. Biol. Chem.* 249:3652–60

104. Lee, A. G., Birdsall, N. J., Metcalfe, J. C., Toon, P. A., Warren, G. B. 1974. Clusters in lipid bilayers and the interpretation of thermal effects in biological membranes. *Biochemistry* 13:3699–3705

105. Lewis, M. S., Krieg, L. C., Kirk, W. 1974. The molecular weight and detergent binding of bovine rhodopsin. *Exp. Eye Res.* 18:29–40

106. Liebman, P. A. 1972. Microspectrophotometry of photoreceptors. *Handb. Sensory Physiol.* 7:481–528

107. Liebman, P. A. 1974. Light-dependent Ca content of rod outer segment disc membranes. *Invest. Ophthalmol.* 13:700–1

108. Liebman, P. A., Entine, G. 1974. Lateral diffusion of visual pigment in photoreceptor disk membranes. *Science* 185:457–59

109. Lozier, R. H., Bogomolni, R. A., Stoeckenius, W. 1975. Bacteriorhodopsin: A light driven proton pump in *Halobacterium halobium*. *Biophys. J.* 15:955–62

110. Makinose, M. 1969. The phosphorylation of the membranal protein of the sarcoplasmic vesicles during active Ca transport. *Eur. J. Biochem.* 10:74–82

111. Makinose, M., Hasselbach, W. 1965. Der Einflub von Oxalat auf den Ca-transport Isolierter Vesikel des Sarcoplamatischen Reticulum. *Biochem. Z.* 343:360–82

112. Makinose, M., Hasselbach, W. 1971. ATP synthesis by the reverse of the sarcoplasmic calcium pump. *FEBS Lett.* 12:271–72

113. Martonosi, A., Donley, J., Halpin, R. A. 1968. Sarcoplasmic reticulum. The role of phospholipids in the ATPase activity and Ca transport. *J. Biol. Chem.* 243:61–70

114. Martonosi, A., Lagwinska, E., Oliver, M. 1974. Elementary processes in the hydrolysis of ATP by sarcoplasmic reticulum membranes. *Ann. NY Acad. Sci.* 227:549–67

115. Mason, W. T., Fager, R. S., Abrahamson, E. W. 1973. Lipids and fatty acid composition of frog photoreceptor outer segments. *Biochemistry* 12:2147–50

116. Mason, W. T., Fager, R. S., Abrahamson, E. W. 1974. Ion fluxes in disk membranes of retinal rod outer segments. *Nature* 247:562–63

117. McLennan, D. H. 1970. Purification and properties of an adenosine triphosphatase from sarcoplasmic reticulum. *J. Biol. Chem.* 245:4508–18

118. McLennan, D. H., Holland, P. C. 1975. Calcium transport in sarcoplasmic reticulum. *Ann. Rev. Biophys. Bioeng.* 4:377–404

119. McLennan, D. H., Ostwald, T. J., Stewart, P. S. 1974. Structural components of the sarcoplasmic reticulum membrane. *Ann. NY Acad. Sci.* 227:527–36

120. McLennan, D. H., Seeman, P., Iles, G. H., Yip, C. C. 1971. Membrane formation by the adenosine triphosphatase of sarcoplasmic reticulum. *J. Biol. Chem.* 246:2702–10

121. McLennan, D. H., Yip, C. C., Iles, G. H., Seeman, P. 1972. Isolation of sarcoplasmic reticulum proteins. *Cold Spring Harbor Symp. Quant. Biol.* 37:469–78

122. Meissner, G., Conner, G. E., Fleischer, S. 1973. Isolation of sarcoplasmic reticulum by zonal centrifugation and purification of Ca^{++} pump and Ca^{++} binding proteins. *Biochim. Biophys. Acta* 298:246–69

123. Meissner, G. Fleischer, S. 1973. Ca uptake in reconstituted sarcoplasmic reticulum vesicles. *Biochem. Biophys. Res. Commun.* 52:913–20

124. Meissner, G., Fleischer, S. 1974. Dissociation and reconstitution of functional sarcoplasmic reticulum vesicles. *J. Biol. Chem.* 249:302–9

125. Mitchell, P. 1972. Chemiosmotic coupling in energy transduction: A logical development of biochemical knowledge. *J. Bioenerg.* 3:5–24

126. Montal, M. 1974. Lipid-protein assembly and the reconstitution of biological membranes. In *Perspectives in Membrane Biology*, ed. S. Estrada-O, G. Gitler. New York: Academic. 670 pp.

127. Montal, M. 1975. Rhodopsin in experimental membranes: An approach to elucidate its role in the process of phototransduction. In *Molecular Aspects of Membrane Phenomena*, ed. H. R. Kaback, G. K. Radda, H. Neurath. New York: Springer; Berlin: Heidelberg

128. Montal, M. 1976. Experimental membranes and mechanisms of bioenergy transductions. *Ann. Rev. Biophys. Bioeng.* 5:119–75

129. Montal, M., Korenbrot, J. I. 1973. Incorporation of Rhodopsin proteolipid into bilayer membranes. *Nature* 246:219–21

130. Montal, M., Korenbrot, J. I. 1976. Rhodopsin in cell membranes and the process of phototransduction. *The Enzymes of Biological Membranes*, ed. A.

Martonosi, 4:365–405. New York: Plenum

131. Montal, M., Mueller, P. 1972. Formation of bimolecular membranes from lipid monolayers and a study of their electrical properties. *Proc. Natl. Acad. Sci. USA* 69:3561–66

132. Mueller, P., Rudin, D. O., Tien, H. T., Wescott, W. C. 1963. Methods for the formation of single bimolecular lipid membranes in aqueous solution. *J. Phys. Chem.* 67:534–35

133. Mullins, L. J., Brinley, F. J. 1969. Potassium fluxes in dialyzed squid axons. *J. Gen. Physiol.* 53:704–40

133a. Naqvi, K. Razi, Gonzalez-Rodriguez, J., Cherry, R. J., Chapman, D. 1973. Spectroscopic technique for studying protein rotation in membranes. *Nature New Biol.* 245:249–51

134. Oesterhelt, D. 1976. Bacteriorhodopsin as an example of a light-driven proton pump. *Angew. Chem.* 15:17–24

135. Oesterhelt, D., Krippahl, G. 1973. Light-inhibition of respiration in *Halobacterium halobium*. *FEBS Lett.* 36:72–76

136. Oesterhelt, D., Meetzen, M., Schuhmann, L. 1973. Reversible dissociation of the purple complex in bacteriorhodopsin and identification of 13-*cis* and all-*trans*-retinal as its chromophores. *Eur. J. Biochem.* 40:453–63

137. Oesterhelt, D., Stoeckenius, W. 1971. Rhodopsin-like protein from the purple membrane of *Halobacterium halobium*. *Nature New Biol.* 233:149–52

138. Oesterhelt, D., Stoeckenius, W. 1973. Function of a new photoreceptor membrane. *Proc. Natl. Acad. Sci. USA* 70:2853–57

139. Oesterhelt, D., Stoeckenius, W. 1974. Isolation of the cell membrane of Halobacterium halobium and its fraction into red and purple membrane. In *Methods in Enzymology: BioMembranes*, Vol. 31, ed. S. Fleischer, R. Estabrook. New York: Academic. 956 pp.

140. Parsegian, A. 1969. Energy of an ion crossing a low dielectric membrane: Solutions to four relevant electrostatic problems. *Nature* 221:844–46

141. Perrone, J. R., Blostein, R. 1973. Asymmetric interaction of inside-out and right-side-out erythrocyte membrane vesicles with ouabain. *Biochim. Biophys. Acta* 291:680–89

142. Perrone, J. R., Hackney, J. F., Dixon, J. F., Hokin, L. E. 1975. Molecular properties of purified (Na+K) activated ATPases and their subunits from the

rectal gland of *S. acanthias* and the electric organ of *E. electricus*. *J. Biol. Chem.* 250:4178–84

143. Phillips, M. C., Graham, D. E., Hauser, H. 1975. Lateral compressibility and penetration into phospholipid monolayers and bilayer membranes. *Nature* 254:154–56

144. Poo, M., Cone, R. A. 1974. Lateral diffusion of rhodopsin in the photoreceptor membrane. *Nature* 247:438–41

145. Porter, K. R. 1961. The sarcoplasmic reticulum. *J. Biophys. Biochem. Cytol.* 10(Suppl.):219–26

146. Post, R. L., Kume, S., Tobin, T., Orcutt, B., Sen, A. K. 1969. Flexibility of an active center in Na^+K adenosine triphosphatase. *J. Gen. Physiol.* 54:306s–26s

147. Post, R. L., Merritt, C. R., Kinsolving, C. R., Albright, C. D. 1960. Membrane ATPase as participant in the active transport of Na and K in the human erythrocyte. *J. Biol. Chem.* 235:1796–1802

148. Post, R. L., Sen, A. K., Rosenthal, A. S. 1965. A phosphorylated intermediate in ATP-dependent Na and K transport across kidney membranes. *J. Biol. Chem.* 240:1437–45

149. Priestland, R. N., Whittam, R. 1972. Temperature dependence of activation by phosphatidylserine of the Na pump ATPase. *J. Physiol.* 220:353–61

150. Racker, E. 1972. Reconstitution of a calcium pump with phospholipids and a purified Ca^{++}-adenosine triphosphatase from sarcoplasmic reticulum. *J. Biol. Chem.* 247:8198–8200

151. Racker, E. 1973. A new procedure for the reconstitution of biological active phospholipid vesicles. *Biochem. Biophys. Res. Commun.* 55:224–30

152. Racker, E., Chien, T. F., Kanrach, A. 1975. A cholate-dilution procedure for the reconstitution of the Ca^{++} pump, P-ATP exchange and oxidative phosphorylation. *FEBS Lett.* 57:14–18

153. Racker, E., Eytan, E. 1973. Reconstitution of an efficient calcium pump without detergents. *Biochem. Biophys. Res. Commun.* 55:174–78

154. Racker, E., Eytan, E. 1975. A coupling factor from sarcoplasmic reticulum required for the translocation of Ca^{++} ions in a reconstituted Ca^{++}-ATPase pump. *J. Biol. Chem.* 250:7533–34

155. Racker, E., Hinkle, C. 1974. Effect of temperature on the function of a proton pump. *J. Membr. Biol.* 17:181–88

156. Racker, E., Knowles, A. F., Eytan, E. 1975. Resolution and reconstitution of ion-transport systems. *Ann. NY Acad. Sci.* 264:17–31

157. Racker, E., Stoeckenius, W. 1974. Reconstitution of purple membrane vesicles catalyzing light-driven proton uptake and adenosine triphosphate formation. *J. Biol. Chem.* 249:662–63

158. Raubach, R. A., Nemes, P. P., Dratz, E. A. 1974. Chemical labeling and freeze fracture studies on the localization of rhodopsin in the rod outer segment disk membrane. *Exp. Eye Res.* 18:1–12

159. Deleted in proof.

160. Razin, S. 1972. Reconstitution of biological membranes. *Biochem. Biophys. Acta* 265:241–96

161. Robinson, W. E., Gordon-Walker, A., Bownds, D. 1972. Molecular weight of frog rhodopsin. *Nature New Biol.* 235:112–14

162. Roelofsen, B., Zwaal, R. F. A., Van Deenen, L. L. M. 1971. Lipoprotein integrity and enzymatic activity of the erythrocyte membrane. *Adv. Exp. Med. Biol.* 14:209–28

163. Ruoho, A., Kyte, J. 1974. Photoaffinity labeling of the ouabain-binding site in (Na+K) ATPase. *Proc. Natl. Acad. Sci. USA* 71:2352–56

164. Ruppel, H., Hagins, W. A. 1973. Spatial origin of the fast photovoltage in retinal rods. In *Biochemistry and Physiology of Visual Pigments,* ed. H. Langer. New York: Springer. 325 pp.

165. Scandella, C. J., Devaux, P., McConnell, H. H. 1972. Rapid lateral diffusion of phospholipids in rabbit sarcoplasmic reticulum. *Proc. Natl. Acad. Sci. USA* 69:2056–60

166. Seelig, J., Hasselbach, W. 1971. A spin label study of sarcoplasmic vesicles. *Eur. J. Biochem.* 21:17–21

167. Shamoo, A. E., Albers, R. W. 1973. Na-selective material derived from electric organ and kidney membranes. *Proc. Natl. Acad. Sci. USA* 70:1191–94

168. Shamoo, A. E., McLennan, D. H. 1974. A Ca^{++}-dependent and -selective ionophore as part of the Ca^{++}, Mg^{++} dependent adenosintriphosphatase of sarcoplasmic reticulum. *Proc. Natl. Acad. Sci. USA* 71:3522–26

169. Shamoo, A. E., McLennan, D. H. 1975. Separate effects of mercurial compounds on the ionophoric and hydrolytic functions of the Ca+Mg ATPase of sarcoplasmic reticulum. *J. Membr. Biol.* 25:65–74

170. Shamoo, A. E., Myers, M. M., Blumenthal, R., Albers, R. W. 1974. Ionophoric material derived from eel membrane preparation. *J. Membr. Biol.* 19:129–40

171. Shamoo, A. E., Ryan, T. E. 1975. Isolation of ionophores from ion transport systems. *Ann. NY Acad. Sci.* 264:83–97

172. Shichi, H. 1971. Biochemistry of visual pigments. *J. Biol. Chem.* 246:6178–82

173. Shichi, H. 1973. Conformational aspects of rhodopsin associated with disc membranes. *Exp. Eye Res.* 17:533–43

174. Simpkins, H., Hokin, L. E. 1973. Studies on the characterization of the Na-K transport adenosintriphosphatase. *Arch. Biochem. Biophys.* 159:897–902

175. Singer, S. J. 1971. The molecular organization of biological membranes. In *Structure and Function of Biological Membranes,* ed. L. Rothfield. New York: Academic. 486 pp.

176. Skou, J. C. 1957. The influence of some cations on an adenosine triphosphate from peripheral nerves. *Biochim. Biophys. Acta* 23:394–401

177. Skou, J. C. 1975. Identification and isolation of the components of the sodium pump. *Q. Rev. Biophys.* 7:401–34

178. Steinemann, A., Wu, C. W., Stryer, L. 1973. Conformational aspects of rhodopsin and retinal disc membranes. *J. Supramol. Struct.* 2:348–53

179. Stewart, P. S., McLennan, D. H. 1974. Surface particles of sarcoplasmic reticulum membranes. *J. Biol. Chem.* 249:985–93

180. Stoeckenius, W., Hwang, S. B., Korenbrot, J. I. 1977. Proton translocation by bacteriorhodopsin in model systems. *Nobel Symp.* 34: In press

181. Sweadner, K. J., Goldin, S. M. 1975. Reconstitution of active ion transport by the Na and K ion stimulated ATPase from canine brain. *J. Biol. Chem.* 250:4022–24

182. Szuts, E. Z., Cone, R. A. 1974. Rhodopsin: Light activated release of calcium. *Abstr. Biophys. Soc.* 1974:1471

183. Takagi, A. 1971. Lipid composition of sarcoplasmic reticulum of human skeletal muscle. *Biochim. Biophys. Acta* 248:12–20

184. Tanaka, R., Sakamoto, T. 1969. Molecular structure in phospholipid essential to activate (Na+K+Mg) dependent ATPase and (K+Mg)-dependent phosphatase of bovine cerebral cortex. *Biochim. Biophys. Acta* 193:384–93

185. Tanaka, R., Sakamoto, T., Sakamoto, Y. 1971. Mechanisms of lipid activation of Na, K, Mg activated ATPase and K, Mg activated phosphatase of bovine cerebral cortex. *J. Membr. Biol.* 4:42–51

186. Tanaka, R., Strickland, K. P. 1965. Role of phospholipid in the activation of the Na K-activated ATPase of beef brain. *Arch. Biochem. Biophys.* 111: 583–92

187. Tanford, C. 1973. *The Hydrophobic Effect: Formation of Micelles and Biological Membranes.* New York: Wiley. 200 pp.

188. Taniguchi, K., Tonomura, Y. 1971. Inactivation of Na+K dependent ATPase by phospholipase treatment and its reactivation by lipids. *J. Biochem. Tokyo* 69:543–57

189. The, R., Hasselbach, W. 1973. Unsaturated fatty acids as reactivators of the Ca-dependent ATPase of delipidated sarcoplasmic membranes. *Eur. J. Biochem.* 39:63–68

190. Uesugi, S., Dulak, N. C., Dixon, N. C., Hexum, J. F., Dahl, T. D., Perdue, J. F., Hokin, L. E. 1971. Studies on the characterization of the Na-K transport adenosine triphosphatase. *J. Biol. Chem.* 246:531–43

191. Ulbrecht, M. 1962. Der austausch und die abspaltung des α-phosphates des adenosin-triphosphates durch sarkosomen und kleine grana des kaninchenmuskels. *Biochim. Biophys. Acta* 57: 455–74

192. Verma, S. P., Berliner, L. J., Smith, I. C. P. 1973. Cation-dependent light-induced structural changes in visual receptor membranes. *Biochem. Biophys. Res. Commun.* 55:704–9

193. Wald, G., Brown, P. K., Gibbons, I. R. 1963. The problem of visual excitation. *J. Opt. Soc. Am.* 53:20–35

194. Walter, H., Hasselbach, W. 1973. Properties of the Ca-independent ATPase of the membranes of the sarcoplasmic reticulum delipidated by the non-ion detergent Triton X-100. *Eur. J. Biochem.* 36:110–19

195. Warren, G. B., Birdsall, N. J. M., Lee, A. G., Metcalfe, J. C. 1974. Lipid substitution: The investigation of functional complexes of single species of phospholipid and a purified calcium transport protein. In *Membrane Proteins in Transport and Phosphorylation,* ed. G. Azzone, M. Klingenberg, E. Quagliariello, N. Siliprandi. Amsterdam: North-Holland. 120 pp.

196. Warren, G. B., Houslay, M. D., Metcalfe, J. C., Birdsall, N. J. M. 1975. Cholesterol is excluded from the phospholipid annulus surrounding an active calcium transport protein. *Nature* 255:684–87

197. Warren, G. B., Toon, P. A., Birdsall, N. J. M., Lee, A. G., Metcalfe, J. C. 1974. Reconstitution of a calcium pump using defined membrane components. *Proc. Natl. Acad. Sci USA* 71:622–26

198. Warren, G. B., Toon, P. A., Birdsall, N. J. M., Lee, A. G., Metcalfe, J. C. 1974. Reversible lipid transition of the activity of pure adenosine triphosphatase-lipid complexes. *Biochemistry* 13: 5501–7

199. Warren, G. B., Toon, P. A., Birdsall, N. J. M., Lee, A. G., Metcalfe, J. C. 1974. Complete control of the lipid environment of membrane-bound proteins: Application to a Ca transport system. *FEBS Lett.* 41:122–24

200. Weber, A., Herz, R., Reiss, I. 1966. Study of the kinetics of Ca transport by isolated fragments of sarcoplasmic reticulum. *Biochem. Z.* 345:329–69

201. Weller, M., Virmaux, N., Mandel, P. 1975. Role of light and rhodopsin phosphorylation in control of permeability of retinal rod outer segment disks to Ca^{2+}. *Nature* 256:68–70

202. Wheller, K. P., Whittam, R. 1970. The involvement of phosphatidylserine in ATPase activity of the sodium pump. *J. Physiol.* 207:303–28

203. Whittam, R. 1962. The asymmetrical stimulation of a membrane ATPase in relation to active cation transport. *Biochem. J.* 84:110–18

204. Whittam, R., Ager, M. E. 1964. Vectorial aspects of ATPase activity in erythrocyte membranes. *Biochem. J.* 93:337–48

205. Williams, T. P., Baker, B. N., McDowell, J. H. 1974. The influence of lipids on dynamic properties of Rhodopsin. *Exp. Eye Res.* 18:69–76

206. Wormington, C. M., Cone, R. A. 1975. Ca and H dependence, and ionic selectivity of the light-regulated Na channel in rod outer segments. *Abstr. Biophys. Soc. Meet., 1975,* p. 171a

207. Worthington, C. R. 1974. Structure of photoreceptor membranes. *Ann. Rev. Biophys. Bioeng.* 3:58–80

208. Wu, C. W., Stryer, L. 1972. Proximity relationships in rhodopsin. *Proc. Natl. Acad. Sci. USA* 69:1104–8

209. Yagauzhinsky, L. S., Boguslavsky, L. I., Volkov, A. G., Rakhmainova, A. B.

1976. Synthesis of ATP coupled with action of membrane protonic pumps at the octane-water interface. *Nature* 259:494–96

210. Yamada, S., Tonomura, Y. 1972. Reaction mechanisms of the Ca-dependent ATPase of sarcoplasmic reticulum from skeletal muscle. *J. Biochem. Tokyo* 72:417–25

211. Yamamoto, T., Tonomura, Y. 1967. Reaction mechanisms of the Ca^{++}-dependent ATPase of sarcoplasmic reticulum from skeletal muscle. *J. Biochem. Tokyo* 62:558–75

212. Yoshida, M., Sone, N., Hirata, H., Kagawa, Y., Takeuchi, Y., Ohno, K. 1975. ATP synthesis catalysed by purified DCCD-sensitive ATPase incorporated into reconstituted purple membrane vesicles. *Biochem. Biophys. Res. Commun.* 67:1295–1300

213. Yoshikami, S., Hagins, W. A. 1973. Control of the dark current in vertebrate rods and cones. In *Biochemistry and Physiology of Visual Pigment,* ed. H. Langer. Berlin: Springer. 325 pp.

214. Zorn, M., Futterman, S. 1971. Properties of rhodopsin dependent on associated phospholipid. *J. Biol. Chem.* 246:881–86

Ann. Rev. Physiol. 1977. 39:51–71

BIOPHYSICAL ANALYSES OF BLOOD VESSEL WALLS AND BLOOD FLOW

❖1163

Margot R. Roach

Departments of Biophysics and Medicine, University of Western Ontario,
London, Ontario N6A 5C1, and Department of Medicine, University Hospital,
London, Ontario, Canada

INTRODUCTION

Our knowledge of hemodynamics, or the physics of blood flow, has expanded exponentially in the last 10 or 15 years, so the task of providing a comprehensive review in a finite length of time is impossible, at least for me. Thus I have accepted the editor's invitation to write primarily on those aspects of the subject which intrigue me.

McDonald's book, *Blood Flow in Arteries* (133), which appeared in 1960, began the phase of rapid growth of the field of hemodynamics. Attinger's 1964 book *Pulsatile Flow in Arteries* (9) summarized developments until that time. Bergel's two-volume edition *Cardiovascular Fluid Dynamics* (23), which appeared in 1972, updated the literature as seen by the contributors. McDonald's second edition (134) came out in 1974 (published posthumously) and provides a more comprehensive survey of the field, although with a bias toward his own work and that of his former students. The text by Strandness & Sumner (214), while designed for surgeons, provides a useful review of hemodynamics for physiologists as well. A recent NATO symposium in Houston was published late in 1976 (114) and, like Bergel's text, summarizes developments in the selected areas of interest of the contributors. While I have access to some chapters in manuscript form, others are not available. Many of the papers were of more surgical than physiological interest.

A survey of the literature from 1972 to 1975 inclusive suggests that the major developments have come from better instrumentation, and more extensive use of mathematical and physical models. We still do not know precisely what determines the blood velocity at any one point in any artery. Both the elastic properties of the arterial wall and the fluid factors governing the blood flow are involved. Now we can determine incremental elastic properties of arteries and also have a better understanding of the role of vascular smooth muscle (contracted or relaxed) in

51

altering these properties. The concept of impedance (or dynamic resistance) has helped in the understanding of reflections at bifurcations. Finally, in vivo elasticity can be measured, at least in some laboratories.

Knowledge of fluid dynamics has grown more slowly. Most engineering studies have been done with steady flow (66) and mathematical ones with two-dimensional flow. Recently both have been extended to tubes with curves and branches. However, we still have better models for the flow in the whole circulation (203) than for velocity at any one location in a particular vessel.

Another interesting development in the last eight years has been the rapid growth in experimentation on hemodynamic factors in atherosclerosis. While these studies are primarily of pathological interest, current work is based largely on a desire to understand how physiological differences in flow near bifurcations predispose certain parts of the wall to atherosclerosis. Thus I consider the early atherosclerotic lesion as a marker of flow differences near the wall, and discuss this briefly.

ELASTICITY

The nonlinearity of the elastic curve for arteries has been known since the turn of the century. However, only in the last ten years has detailed analysis of the precise nature of the curve been possible. The major advances in the last five years are associated with improved measurement techniques, in situ and in vivo studies (175), analysis of the role of muscle and ground substance, and more detailed realistic mathematical and physical models. A number of recent reviews (24, 87, 165, 166, 218) discuss these in some detail, and so I concentrate mainly on developments since 1972.

Good evidence now exists that the arterial wall is anisotropic (13, 47, 54, 55, 57, 124), probably because of the different orientations and elastic properties of elastin and collagen. This has been demonstrated both with strips cut in different directions (124) and by analysis of trains of superimposed pulse waves (106, 148). The detailed analysis of Patel and his colleagues (224) has shown that $S_\theta > S_z > W > S_r$ when S_θ = circumferential stress, S_z = axial stress, S_r = radial stress, and W = strain-energy-density. All of these increase with an increase in intraluminal pressure, but S_θ is most affected. In addition, they (164) found that the elastic modulus (E') and viscous modulus (E'') also were anisotropic. In the physiological range, $E_z' > E_\theta' > E_r'$ and $E_z'' > E_r'' > E_\theta''$. Note that both E' and E'' are largest in the longitudinal direction, and greater in vivo.

The elastic properties of any structure are due both to the properties of the materials that make up the structure and to the way they are woven together.

Digestion studies (143) and histological studies (49, 99, 109, 124, 170) confirmed earlier work by Roach & Burton (183) and Wolinsky & Glagov (235) on other vessels that elastin causes the low strain part of the curve, while collagen is stressed at higher strains. Hayashi and co-workers (99, 100, 216) developed a microphotometer method to determine the ratio of wall components, and applied the results to the interpretation of their elastic diagrams. The collagen probably prevents premature rupture at weak points in the elastic network by distributing deformation throughout the tissue.

For many years it was assumed that muscle played no role in the static elastic properties of tissues and little role in the viscoelastic behavior. Recent work with better techniques shows this postulate is erroneous (56, 84, 97, 156, 167). Herlihy & Murphy (101) found that medial strips of hog carotid artery, which were about 60% muscle, developed a load-bearing capacity of 2.22×10^6 dyn/cm^{-2} at L_0 and fell off on either side of this. With a Hill model (102), they proposed that the maximum power output of these strips occurred at $0.28\ P_0$, where P_0 is the maximum isometric force developed at the optimum muscle length, L_0.

Dobrin (63) found, in dog carotids, that the maximum active smooth muscle isometric stress was 1.1×10^6 dyn/cm^{-2} for the whole vessel, or 2.4–3.5×10^6 dyn/cm^{-2} if corrected for muscle mass. Excitation at pressures above 120 mm Hg, or circumferential strains above 0.70, depressed the curves. At large initial strains, isometric contraction caused greater attenuation of active stress than did isobaric contraction. With various drug trials in these arteries, Dobrin (62, 64) concluded that either the series elastic element (SEE) underwent mechanical yielding at high stresses or else was an integral part of the force-generating apparatus. Dobrin & Canfield then compared the role of the various elements in the Voigt and Maxwell models[1] (65) and found that the SEE stiffness depended on the applied stress, but not on the muscle length as long as the muscle was excited at initial strains of less than 0.70.

Viscoelastic behavior implies time dependence. This may be studied either with quick-stretch or quick-release experiments, or by sinusoidally forcing the tissue and studying the phase lag (172). Histand, Anliker, and their colleagues (106, 148) used the last method to assess the marked anisotropic behavior of arteries in situ. In situ results are often different from those in vitro (91, 92, 165).

The elastic properties of arteries are different in different parts of the vascular tree, (14, 88, 128, 215, 217), with the aorta being most distensible (159). There are also well-known differences with age (57, 90, 131, 150), disease (19, 193, 219, 231–234, 237), and species (27, 28).

There is still no good way to assess the elastic properties of arteries in intact man. The Moens-Korteweg formula, which correlates pulse wave velocity and Young's modulus, assumes the tube is long, straight, nontapering, and nonbifurcating. However, the formula has been widely applied, and does give semiquantitative results (174). The Moens-Korteweg formula states that $c_o = \sqrt{\frac{E.h}{2R\rho}}$, where c_0 = wave velocity, E = Young's modulus in the circumferential direction, h = wall thickness, R = radius, and ρ = density. Mirsky (144) showed theoretically that taper and curvature should not alter the results significantly. Posey (174) found, in dog aortae, that predicted moduli were lower than measured ones. Others (159) found that changes in the mean aortic pressure did not modify the results.

Noninvasive local in vivo measurements are now appearing. Ultrasound can give diameter values that can be coupled with pressure changes to give local pressure-

---

[1]A *Voigt model* consists of a contractile element (CE) attached in parallel with an elastic element (PE), and then both connected in series with a second elastic element (SE).

A *Maxwell model* consists of an elastic element (PE) connected in parallel with another elastic element (SE), which is connected in parallel with a contractile element (CE).

diameter curves (12, 162, 163, 196). Angiographic data can be used in the same way (42, 91). Wall thickness also has been measured as a function of pressure in one series, and found to decrease between diastole and systole by 100 μm in human carotid arteries (162). Another series (137) found no significant difference.

A number of physical and mathematical models have been developed to interpret the results of stress-strain measurements under a variety of circumstances (35, 44, 45, 48, 53, 68, 83, 223, 228). While the simpler ones are easiest to test, biological data are now good enough that comparisons can be made between the different models.

Little work has been done on veins, which also show nonlinear elastic behavior (31, 32, 227). At low pressures (physiological ones), the veins are elliptical, and so models must include a change in shape as well as in strain. Veins, like arteries, are viscoelastic (171, 240), but few mechanical studies have been done to determine the importance of the muscular component.

Studies on the components of the arterial wall are lacking (221). The technique developed by Gow & Vaishnav (89) to assess the intima is promising. It can perhaps be modified to study other layers of the arterial wall, and perhaps even bifurcations.

ARTERIAL SMOOTH MUSCLE

Vascular smooth muscle has been little studied in comparison with skeletal muscle. Two major reasons are probably 1. the muscle of arteries and veins is usually found in association with elastin, and often collagen, so that its mechanical properties are difficult to assess, and 2. the syncytial arrangement of vascular smooth muscle makes it harder to study than the well-organized myofibrils of skeletal muscle. Many pharmacological studies have been done in the past four years, but this review is restricted to studies commenting on the role of the muscle in the mechanical behavior of vessels.

Since the arrangement of the sarcomeres of arterial smooth muscle is unknown, information on the mechanism of contraction is not available. However, Bohr (33) has observed that the actin and myosin are similar to those in skeletal muscle, and proposed that the mechanism of contraction probably is explained by some modification of the Huxley sliding filament theory. Contraction can be initiated electrically or non-electrically, and actomyosin ATPase activity appears to be the rate-limiting mechanism.

Ashton et al (7) studied rabbit portal-anterior mesenteric veins with intermediate high-voltage stereo electron microscopy, and showed that the thick filaments are 2.2 μm long with tapered ends, while the intermediate (10 nm diameter) filaments are associated with dense bodies. Actin filaments are inserted on both cytoplasmic and plasma membrane-bound dense bodies. The greater length, and more parallel arrangement of thick filaments in these muscles may partially explain their ability to develop equal or greater tension than striated muscle, even though the concentration of myosin is lower.

Muscle contraction in arterioles is known to alter the peripheral resistance, but the role of muscle in large vessels is less well understood. The orientation of the muscle and its location in the arterial wall determine the effect of contraction on lumen diameter. For mechanical reasons (180), longitudinal muscle is more important in vessel closure (for example in the umbilical artery) and circular muscle in vessel narrowing. By changing the wall thickness: lumen diameter ratio by muscle contraction, the equilibrium muscle load is shifted, even though the transmural pressure is unaltered (205).

The umbilical artery is a useful source of vascular smooth muscle (181). It contains little elastin, and less collagen, and is non-innervated. The different muscle bundles (longitudinal, circular, and helical) appear to respond to different stimuli (2, 5, 181) and may have different physiological roles. These observations are important as they suggest that all vascular smooth muscle is not identical and that differences in physiological response may be due either to differences in innervation (the classical concept) or to differences in the muscle itself. Studies by Graham & Keatinge (93) on sheep carotid artery support this hypothesis, although they observed differences in innervation as well.

Altura (4) reviewed his own work and that of others on some of the pharmacological responses of vascular smooth muscle, and pointed out (3) that magnesium plays both a direct and indirect role in the contraction. Vasopressin (1) also appears to be a potent vasoconstrictor for both macroscopic and microscopic vessels.

Muscular hypertrophy occurs in the arterioles with both systemic and pulmonary hypertension, but can occur also in the small arteries (121, 236) and may vary with sex and age (121). The muscle response varies both with the type of hypertension, and also with the artery studied (34, 111). The quantitative effects of this on the dynamic elastic properties of the arteries have not been determined yet.

IMPEDANCE

Impedance is the pulsatile flow equivalent of resistance, and is determined both by the vessel wall and by the fluid. The phase is negative when flow leads pressure, and positive when pressure leads flow (80, 134). The major work on physiological impedance was done more than 10 years ago, and Taylor (218) concluded in 1973 that further analysis of wave motion was unlikely to provide further physiological insight. Attinger & Attinger (10) pointed out that the input impedance is made up of a longitudinal impedance which is a function of the inertial and viscous properties of the blood, and a transverse impedance due to the mechanical properties of the vessel wall. The vessel radius, R, is the most important variable since the viscous part of the impedance varies with R^4, the inertial part with R^2, and the transverse impedance as R^3. Milnor (141) suggested that the arterial impedance is equivalent to ventricular afterload. The "characteristic" impedance is produced by the physical properties of the artery, the "input" impedance by reflected pressure, and flow waves are generated distally. Proximal occlusions alter the input impedance (229), which is usually frequency dependent. Various experimental methods have been used to determine the impedance (142, 155, 206, 229). Matching is important in determining the amplitude of the reflected wave (157, 158). Antegrade reflections may occur from the aortic valve (38).

Mathematically (226), reflections are the major factor in determining the shape and distal amplification of the pressure wave, while geometric taper does little except to attenuate the proximal transmission of reflected waves.

Physically, impedance can be modeled as an electrical transmission line (218), or as a fluid-filled system with a closed end (176). Pressure transmission depends mainly on the ratio of tube length: wavelength (176), and resonances may develop. If the arterial system is modeled by three unbranched tubes in series (20), the frequency-dependent damping alters both the pulse contour and the input impedance. The work of Westerhof et al (230) suggests that reflections occur both at the aorto-iliac bifurcation and in the peripheral arterioles in the dog. Conversely (58), major reflections appear insignificant in the aortic arch.

I agree with Taylor (218) that the major work on impedance has been done. However, I would hope that as we gain more understanding of how different types of bifurcations modify the pressure and flow waves, we may be able to use measurements of impedance to assess the characteristics of the bifurcation. The work of Newman and co-workers (155, 158) suggests this should be possible.

BIFURCATIONS

The branching pattern of arteries is essential for the role of the circulation in distributing oxygen and nutrients to all parts of the body. However, we have virtually no knowledge as yet about their embryological development, their postnatal growth and/or change in shape and size, their elastic properties, and the flow patterns produced by them (71).

Spasmodically (182) a number of authors have considered whether optimality principles[2] might determine embryologic branching patterns. Zamir recently tackled this theoretically and suggested (243) that shear might be minimized if the branch: trunk ratio, β, and the apical branching angle, Θ, were appropriate. He (244) then combined the four hypotheses of minimum surface area, total volume, work or power, and drag, and found a small region of overlap with $\beta = 1.1 - 1.4$, and $\Theta = 75-100°$. He claimed that most bifurcations (except the side branches from the aorta) fall within this range. I have been unable to find hard data to support this statement, either in adult or in fetal (105) life. The information should be available if vigorously sought experimentally.

The exact structure of bifurcations remains to be determined. The mapping of wall components in bifurcations as described by Canham et al (40) should provide more information during the next few years, at least for muscle. It seems more likely to me that fiber orientations will be determined from the scanning electron microscope once the artifacts associated with it have been worked out (103, 104, 110). Berry (25) described two elastic patterns in the aortic bifurcations of rats, and proposed that they are related to the tension acting on the wall. With angles of $< 100°$, elastic lamellae insert into an irregular raphe, and the number of lamellar units is reduced in the wall of the smaller branch. If the angle is over 100°, the number of lamellar units is progressively and gradually reduced as units fuse with

---

[2]Optimality principles use mathematics to either minimize or maximize variables to obtain the most desirable situation.

one another. Our own studies (unpublished) on larger animals such as the dog, suggest that this pattern may not be universal. More work must be done to assess this, and there may be species differences (26).

Area ratios have been determined by casting (39) and radiologically, particularly for the aorto-iliac bifurcation, which is planar. Values vary from 0.7 in old age (126) to 1.15 in young humans. A decrease may be associated with premature atherosclerosis (86, 125). The shape and area may change in a complex way near the junction (206), and may be modified by the presence of intimal cushions (116, 210). Results differ in vivo and in situ (21), so conclusions must be based on the method of measurement. Presumably, flow switching at bifurcations in vivo depends primarily on the peripheral resistance. However, fluidic theory would suggest that switching of streamlines should be more frequent if the resistances and impedances are comparable. Anemometers are still too large to obtain accurate measurements in small branches, and no good Doppler studies have been done to my knowledge. Thus conclusions are based on model studies.

Glass model studies (72, 136, 185, 208) show that a stagnation zone occurs at the apex, and zones of flow separation at the lateral angles. This zone, at least with some geometries, receives rapidly moving streams deflected from the apex (136). The exact pattern depends on the geometry, which may be complex (207). Vortex shedding and unsteadiness are common in the branches (136, 185, 208) and increase with the angle of the branch and with decreasing Reynolds number in both closed and open channels (113).

Shear stress patterns near bifurcations are complex, and can be estimated from flow birefringence studies (60, 186) or with hot film anemometers (37). The α-parameter and Strouhal number (37, 188, 189) must be considered if the flow is pulsatile (see below).

The development of the laser anemometer (220) allows flow measurements near the wall if the tube is translucent. Refraction is a problem if the walls are not smooth. This technique should provide results in the near future.

The elastic properties of bifurcations are still unknown. Macfarlane (135) found, with a light-pipe technique, that the internal radius of curvature of cerebral arterial bifurcations changed much more than the external radius of curvature at the apex in response to pressure. The strains were larger than those in the cylindrical parts of the artery, so that assuming the bifurcation is rigid may produce significant errors.

Mathematical models of bifurcation flow are discussed below. Since we still have little biological information, the main use of these models is to separate major from minor variables, so that measurements can be made even with the available instrumentation.

MODELS

Models are important tools to study complex situations. They are useful only if they are simple and testable. We have already discussed the role of models in the interpretation and calculation of the anisotropic viscoelastic behavior of arteries. These models, on the whole, have been tested because biological information is available.

Flow models have been developed rapidly in the last few years, with most emphasis on flow at bifurcations. Unfortunately, as discussed above, we have as yet little biological information with which to design them, and even less with which to test them.

Physical models can be made either two-dimensional (channel flow) or three-dimensional (tube flow). The exact geometry, the branch: trunk ratio, the angle of the bifurcation, and the Reynolds number are important variables. With pulsatile flow, the α-parameter described by Womersley (238) and the Strouhal number must be used. The Reynolds number, $Re = \rho \cdot v \cdot d / \eta$ where Re = Reynolds number, ρ = density, v is mean velocity, d = diameter and η = viscosity, is used to determine dynamic similarity with steady flow in geometrically similar situations. The α-parameter equals $R(\omega/\nu)^{1/2}$ where R = radius, ω = angular frequency, and ν = kinematic viscosity. The Reynolds number has been widely used by biologists to normalize pulsatile flow situations. The other nondimensional parameter that can be used is the Strouhal number, $St = f \cdot R / v$ where f = frequency, R = radius, and v = average velocity across the pipe. The Strouhal number has been used by Bellhouse and others interested in pulsatile flow. As McDonald (134) pointed out, the three nondimensional parameters can be shown to be related since

$$\alpha^2 = R^2 \cdot \frac{2\pi f}{\nu} = \pi \cdot Re \cdot St.$$

If we knew the exact geometry of biological bifurcations, and if they were rigid, we could obtain reliable results by matching our physical and mathematical models with the nondimensional parameters.

Mathematical models in general have been two-dimensional and work best if designed to answer specific questions. For example, we (242) studied a two-dimensional bifurcation with a zero angle and steady flow, but variable Reynolds numbers, and found that high shear forces occurred at the apex, while regions of sluggish or even reversed flow occurred at the lateral angle. The latter varied more with flow rate than the former. The more detailed analysis of Ehrlich (69, 74, 75), with angles and pulsatile flow, showed that both spatial and temporal variations occurred. The highest values occurred at the convex corner on the outer wall of the branch and near the flow divider tip. These affected mural flux and wall concentration of materials such as lipids (75). Three-dimensional studies are needed (212).

In straight tubes, the calculations are simpler, and results with pulsatile flow agree reasonably well with experimental data (118, 129, 138). The tubes are usually considered as rigid. For practical purposes this does not produce large errors in the physiological range (127, 191). In anisotropic arteries of various geometries, the circumferential elastic modulus is the dominant one, and the cylindrical tube formula can be applied to tapered and curved tubes as well (11, 144). However, to get reasonable strain energy density[3] functions, one must use seven constitutive constants plus the third degree expression for the strain energy density function (223).

---

[3]Strain-energy-density, as defined by Patel et al (166), is the recoverable energy stored in a unit volume of tissue.

The tangential stresses are much higher at the inner wall of the blood vessel if it is considered to be a nonlinear system with molecular anisotropy (44, 201).

More complex models of circulatory beds (43, 50, 203) can be used to separate primary from secondary stimuli on overall response.

In general, the models used to date seem to have produced less useful information than one might expect. A likely reason is the lack of sound biological data with which to test them.

INSTRUMENTATION

In order to develop adequate models of flow in selected parts of the cardiovascular system, it is essential to be able to measure volume flow (66), velocity, and shear stress accurately.

Accurate pressure measurements have been possible for years. Fry (76) discussed the importance of measuring the frequency response of the transducers, and Gabe (77) discussed the various types of transducers.

Plethysmography is one of the oldest forms of measuring flow, and is particularly useful to study the volume flow into a limb. A variety of techniques are available (98, 161, 197, 198), and the limitations of each method should be considered before selecting one of them.

Electromagnetic flowmeters were invented about 20 years ago, and provide the best available measurement of volume flow in the vessel. Wyatt (239) and Mills (140) reviewed these recently. There are a number of potential artifacts (78, 222, 225), which depend to some extent on the type of probe used (222). They cannot be used to get velocities unless modified.

The ultrasonic flowmeter has been introduced within the last decade. Its chief advantage is that it is noninvasive, and so in vivo velocities can be obtained (18, 61, 81, 117, 120, 132, 140, 149, 168, 169, 175, 213, 214). The results compare favorably with those from electromagnetic flowmeters whether the artery is exposed or not (107). With careful range-gating, pulsed Doppler can be used to obtain velocity profiles (81, 117). Directional results have been obtained only recently (18, 160, 169, 213). Volume flow can be obtained with special precautions, and can be compared with results from electromagnetic flowmeters (177).

Laser Doppler anemometry (123, 202) is a powerful new technique to determine velocity profiles. Refractive problems at bifurcations make measurements there difficult, and the vessels must be translucent. Measurements with a microscope improve the resolution (122, 145–147).

Hot film anemometers have been used to assess velocity profiles (22). Their chief disadvantage is their size. However, reasonable results now have been obtained in the aorta (70, 151, 153, 154, 195) and show that the profile is blunt with a narrow boundary layer. Progress is rapid with this technique, and major developments should occur in the near future.

Radiologically, flow rate can be measured in selected arteries with videodensitometry (59, 115, 190, 200). This is the least accurate of the available methods, but may be helpful if arteriography is done for other reasons. Streaming can produce artifacts.

There still is no good technique for measuring wall shear stress in arteries because of the size of the probes. The best method, at present, is the indirect one of mapping biological "lesions." This has been done most in association with studies on atherosclerosis.

MARKERS OF FLOW DISTURBANCE IN ARTERIES

Atherosclerosis is a patchy disease that occurs primarily at bends and bifurcations (29, 82, 209). It is generally considered to be a pathological process, and so should have little place in a physiological review. However, since we have no good way at present of measuring velocity or shear profiles near bifurcations, we can use the localization of lesions to determine which areas of the wall near a bifurcation are subjected to different hemodynamic processes. Patel et al (166) discussed this approach in detail, concentrating on how different stresses can produce different responses in the arterial wall. Little work on this aspect of the subject has appeared since their review, and so I concentrate on the means of localizing the lesions to determine what the flow fields are. Interested readers should turn also to the CIBA Symposium on atherosclerosis (173), the NATO Symposium proceedings edited by Hwang (114), and to other shorter reviews (82, 209).

A number of "markers" can be assessed at bifurcations. Sudanophilic lesions are assumed to be the earliest lesions, and have been extensively studied in rabbits and some other species. Cornhill (51) devised a polar coordinate technique to map the exact size of these lesions on the aortic wall around the orifices of branches. He noted that most lesions were distal to the orifices, but the coronary lesions completely surrounded these orifices. In a group of five rabbits, we (52) found that the size of the lesion was roughly correlated to the size of the orifice (and hence presumably to the flow into the branch). The lesions around the first four pairs of intercostals were skewed, with larger lesions beyond the first and second orifices on the right, but beyond the third and fourth orifices on the left.

Anemometer studies (46, 194), suggest that the velocity profile is flat in the aorta, with a large inertial core, and a thin boundary layer. This is almost certainly because the flow is "inlet flow"[4] rather than fully developed flow. In the aortic arch, there is still a large inertial core, but the profile is skewed (139, 187). Our results (52) suggest this skewing may persist to the level of the fifth intercostals in the rabbit. In the femoral artery, by contrast, velocity profiles are nearly symmetrical except near bends and bifurcations (108).

Roach & Fletcher (184) noted that lesions on the aortic wall distal to the renal orifices were skewed, and proposed that this was due to skewing of the velocity profile in the aorta because of extraction of blood into the large branches in this region. After unilateral nephrectomies in cholesterol-fed rabbits, lesions developed

---

[4]*Inlet flow* or the inlet region is the zone where the velocity gradient is changing along the long axis of the tube.

both proximal and distal to the blind stump. Lesions around the left (distal) renal orifice were modified by right nephrectomy, but those around the right (proximal) renal orifice were unaltered by left nephrectomy.

Schwartz and co-workers (41, 204), did extensive studies with Evans Blue injections in a variety of species. Their "lesions" look comparable in location to ours, but no mapping has been done. Because these studies are in pre-atherosclerotic animals with normal blood viscosity, in contrast to studies on sudanophilic lesions usually found in animals with hyperlipidemia and possible alteration in blood viscosity, they may provide a more realistic idea of flow differences, since no staining occurs unless the dye is allowed to circulate for some time.

Endothelial cell mapping with nuclear orientation has been done by Flaherty et al (73), who demonstrated clearly that the orientation responds to the flow field in the vicinity. Gutstein et al (95) found that the sites of predilection for atherosclerosis in the aorto-iliac region of hogs are associated with highly disturbed flow patterns and with loss of endothelial cell viability. Silkworth et al (199) found, with the Häutchen technique, that the long axis of the endothelial cell was usually parallel to the direction of flow, but that not all cells were spindle-shaped. Cells about branches were often polygonal and had stigmata, stomata, and heavy silver staining, especially near the flow divider.

We still are sadly lacking in mapping techniques for the complex geometry that exists around a bifurcation (182). It is essential to do these studies with in vivo pressure, and preferably with the vessels in situ, since tethering may cause important changes (172). Our renal artery experiments (184) suggested that tethering is important since lesions in sham-operated animals are different from those in controls. Endothelial cell studies should be done near bifurcations after the flow into the branch has been modified.

UNIQUE FEATURES OF THE CORONARY CIRCULATION

The coronary circulation is unique (30), as the vessels pass through an organ which contracts around them with pressures comparable to intraluminal pressures. General agreement exists that endocardial pressures must be higher than epicardial ones in systole, but Baird and co-workers (15–17) and Archie (6) believe endocardial pressures equal intraventricular ones, while others (79) believe they are up to 30% above the ventricular ones. The latter seems unlikely to me, but I cannot determine what was wrong experimentally. In diastole, epicardial pressures are higher (15), thus providing uniform perfusion if it is averaged over the whole of the cardiac cycle (67).

Because of the intramyocardial pressure gradient, the exact position and direction of the coronary vessels are important. Casts (94, 112, 119, 192) showed that the large epicardial vessels run along the surface, and give off branches which travel at right angles through the myocardial layers. Sinusoidal networks exist in some species (130), but their role is unknown. The arterioles vary in diameter with contraction (179), and the intercapillary tissue is changed from 17 μm in the normal heart to about 11 μm in the hypoxic one (36). The size of the major coronary arteries appears roughly related to the area of the heart they supply (211), although this varies with the sex and age of the patient (178).

Most studies of coronary flow have been done with electromagnetic flowmeters on the large vessels. Recently ultrasonic probes have been used (96), but must be glued in place to maintain a constant angle (241). Labeled microspheres have been used for studying regional flow, and Nerem (152) has recently produced the first anemometer studies suggesting the velocity profile is skewed in the large arteries, but generally laminar, although fluctuating widely. They found significant systolic flows in the epicardial vessels.

Two mathematical models of the coronary circulation (8, 85), provide a means for testing biological postulates before doing the complex experiments. Flow is regulated to a large extent by myocardial function, discussed elsewhere.

CONCLUSIONS

With the development of better methods for measuring velocity of blood flow, and the help of mathematical and physical models, we now seem ready to tackle the important physiological problem of flow at bifurcations. If the detailed knowledge we have of the viscoelastic properties of cylindrical arteries can be extrapolated to the bifurcation region, major advances in our understanding of this area should be made in the next few years.

ACKNOWLEDGMENTS

Mrs. Dorothy Elston and Miss Joan Fletcher have obtained and filed my reprints for several years, and their efficiency has made my task of literature review much easier. Mrs. Vera Jordan typed the manuscript, and she and Mrs. Joan Francis typed the references. Mrs. Eva Borda, of our Medical Library, checked them. My grateful thanks to all of these people for their help.

My colleagues in Biophysics have provided much helpful discussion.

My research has been supported by the Ontario Heart Foundation, the Medical Research Council of Canada, and the Ontario Thoracic Society.

Literature Cited

1. Altura, B. M. 1973. Significance of amino acid residues in position 8 of vasopressin on contraction in rat blood vessels. *Proc. Soc. Exp. Biol. Med.* 142:1104–10
2. Altura, B. M. 1972. Comparative contractile actions of different kinins on human umbilical arteries and veins. *Eur. J. Pharmacol.* 19:171–79
3. Altura, B. M. 1975. Magnesium-neurohypophyseal hormone interactions in contraction of vascular smooth muscle. *Am. J. Physiol.* 228:1615–20
4. Altura, B. M. 1974. Effects of local anesthetics, antihistamines, and glucocorticoids on peripheral blood flow and vascular smooth muscle. *Anesthesiology* 41:197–214
5. Altura, B. M., Malaviya, D., Reich, C. F., Orkin, L. R. 1972. Effects of vasoactive agents on isolated human umbilical arteries and veins. *Am. J. Physiol.* 222:345–55
6. Archie, J. P. Jr. 1973. Determinants of regional intramyocardial pressure. *J. Surg. Res.* 14:338–46
7. Ashton, F. T., Somlyo, A. V., Somlyo, A. P. 1975. The contractile apparatus of vascular smooth muscle: Intermediate

high voltage stereo electron microscopy. *J. Mol. Biol.* 98:17–29

8. Atabek, H. B., Ling, S. C., Patel, D. J. 1975. Analysis of coronary flow fields in thoracotomized dogs. *Circ. Res.* 37: 752–61

9. Attinger, E. O., ed. 1964. *Int. Symp. Pulsatile Blood Flow. 1st, Philadelphia, 1963.* New York: McGraw-Hill. 462 pp.

10. Attinger, E. O., Attinger, F. M. L. 1973. Frequency dynamics of peripheral vascular blood flow. *Ann. Rev. Biophys. Bioeng.* 2:7–36

11. Azuma, T., Oka, S. 1974. Circumferential tension in the wall of bent blood vessels. *Microvasc. Res.* 7:10–18

12. Baan, J., Szidon, J. P., Noordergraaf, A. 1974. Dynamic local distensibility of living arteries and its relation to wave transmission. *Biophys. J.* 14:343–62

13. Bagshaw, R. J., Attinger, F. M. L. 1972. Two directional delayed compliance in the canine abdominal aorta. *Experientia* 28:803–4

14. Bagshaw, R. J., Attinger, F. M. L. 1974. Longitudinal stress relaxation in the canine aorta. *Experientia* 30:1046–47

15. Baird, R. J., Adiseshiah, M., Okumori, M. 1976. The gradient in regional myocardial tissue pressure in the left ventricle during diastole: Its relationship to regional flow distribution. *J. Surg. Res.* 20:11–16

16. Baird, R. J., Dutka, F., Okumori, M., De La Rocha, A., Goldbach, M. M., Hill, T. J., MacGregor, D. C. 1975. Surgical aspects of regional myocardial blood flow and myocardial pressure. *J. Thorac. Cardiovasc. Surg.* 69:17–29

17. Baird, R. J., Goldbach, M. M., De La Rocha, A. 1972. Intramyocardial pressure. *J. Thorac. Cardiovasc. Surg.* 64:635–46

18. Baker, D. W., Jorgensen, J. E., Campau, D. N. 1975. The characteristics of the pulsed ultrasonic Doppler flowmeter. In *Flow: Its Measurement and Control in Science and Industry,* ed. W. E. Vannah, H. Wayland. 1:1389–1400. Pittsburgh: Instrum. Soc. Am. 1493 pp.

19. Band, W., Goedhard, W. J. A., Knoop, A. A. 1973. Comparison of effects of high cholesterol intake on viscoelastic properties of the thoracic aorta in rats and rabbits. *Atherosclerosis* 18:163–71

20. Bauer, R. D., Pasch, Th., Wetterer, E. 1973. Theoretical studies on the human arterial pressure and flow pulse by means of a non-uniform tube model. *J. Biomech.* 6:289–98

21. Beales, J. S. M., Steiner, R. E. 1972. Radiological assessment of arterial branching coefficients. *Cardiovasc. Res.* 6:181–86

22. Bellhouse, B. J., Bellhouse, F. H. 1968. Thin-film gauges and the measurement of velocity or skin friction in air, water, or blood. *J. Sci. Instrum.* (Ser. 2) 1:1211–13

23. Bergel, D. H., ed. 1972. *Cardiovascular Fluid Dynamics.* London & New York: Academic. 763 pp.

24. Bergel, D. H., Schultz, D. L. 1971. Arterial elasticity and fluid dynamics. *Prog. Biophys. Mol. Biol.* 22:1–36

25. Berry, C. L. 1973. The establishment of the elastic structure of arterial bifurcation and branches. *Atherosclerosis* 18: 117–27

26. Berry, C. L. 1974. The growth and development of large arteries. *Exp. Embryol. Teratol.* 1:34–64

27. Berry, C. L., Germain, J., Lovell, P. 1974. Comparison of aortic lamellar unit structure in birds and mammals. *Atherosclerosis* 19:47–59

28. Berry, C. L., Germain, J., Newman, D. L., Greenwald, S. E. 1974. Comparative morphological and functional aspects of the aorta of the major vertebrate classes. *Lab. Anim.* 8:279–89

29. Bhagwat, A. G., Robertson, A. L. Jr. 1973. Distribution and severity of atherosclerotic lesions in the human thoracic aorta. *Angiology* 24:181–90

30. Bing, R. J. 1972. New aspects of the coronary circulation. *Arch. Fisiol.* 69: 1–19

31. Bocking, J. K., Roach, M. R. 1974. The effects of hydrostatic pressure on the elastic properties of cat veins. *Can. J. Physiol. Pharmacol.* 52:148–52

32. Bocking, J. K., Roach, M. R. 1974. The elastic properties of the human great saphenous vein in relation to primary varicose veins. *Can. J. Physiol. Pharmacol.* 52:153–57

33. Bohr, D. F. 1973. Vascular smooth muscle updated. *Circ. Res.* 32:665–72

34. Bohr, D. F. 1974. Reactivity of vascular smooth muscle from normal and hypertensive rats: Effect of several cations. *Fed. Proc.* 33:127–32

35. Botwin, M. R. 1973. Determination of viscoelastic moduli of arteries. *J. Biomech.* 6:711–18

36. Bordeau-Martini, J., Odoroff, C. L., Honig, C. R. 1974. Dual effect of oxygen on magnitude and uniformity of coronary intercapillary distance. *Am. J. Physiol.* 226:800–10

37. Brech, R., Bellhouse, B. J. 1973. Flow in branching vessels. *Cardiovasc. Res.* 7:593–600

38. Busse, R., Wetterer, E., Bauer, R. D., Pasch, Th., Summa, Y. 1975. The genesis of the pulse contours of the distal leg arteries in man. *Pfluegers Arch.* 360:63–79

39. Buxton, B. F., Wukasch, D. C., Cooley, D. A. 1972. The dimensions of the aorto-ilio-femoral arterial segment. *Aust. NZ J. Surg.* 42:204–6

40. Fourth International Congress for Stereology. 1976. *National Bureau of Standards Special Publication 431,* pp. 415–18. Wash. DC: US Gov. Printing Office

41. Caplan, B. A., Gerrity, R. G., Schwartz, C. J. 1974. Endothelial cell morphology in focal areas of in vivo Evans Blue uptake in the young pig aorta. *Exp. Mol. Pathol.* 21:102–17

42. Carroll, F. E., Weisbrod, G., Greenspan, R. H. 1974. Radiographic measurement of volume changes of tantalum-labeled pulmonary arterial segments—a new approach to in vivo evaluation of pulmonary arterial dynamics. *Invest. Radiol.* 9:425–33

43. Chao, J. C., Hwang, N. H. C. 1972. Functional dynamics of the circle of Willis. *TIT J. Life Sci.* 2:81–88

44. Cheung, J. B., Hsiao, C. C. 1972. Nonlinear anisotropic viscoelastic stresses in blood vessels. *J. Biomech.* 5:607–19

45. Chu, B. M., Oka, S. 1973. Influence of longitudinal tethering on the tension in thick walled blood vessels in equilibrium. *Biorheology* 10:517–25

46. Clark, C., Schultz, D. L. 1973. Velocity distribution in aortic flow. *Cardiovasc. Res.* 7:601–13

47. Cohen, J., Litwin, S. B., Aaron, A., Fine, S. 1972. The rupture force and tensile strength of canine aortic tissue. *J. Surg. Res.* 13:321–33

48. Collins, R., Hu, W. C. L. 1972. Dynamic deformation experiments on aortic tissue. *J. Biomech.* 5:333–37

49. Cook, T. A., Yates, P. O. 1972. A critical survey of techniques for arterial mensuration. *J. Pathol.* 108:119–27

50. Corey, P. D., Wemple, R. R., Vander Werff, T. J. 1975. A combined left ventricular/systemic arterial model. *J. Biomech.* 8:9–15

51. Cornhill, J. F., Roach, M. R. 1974. Quantitative method for the evaluation of atherosclerotic lesions. *Atherosclerosis* 20:131–36

52. Cornhill, J. F., Roach, M. R. 1976. A quantitative study of the localization of atherosclerotic lesions in the rabbit aorta. *Atherosclerosis* 23:489–501

53. Cox, R. H. 1972. A model for the dynamic mechanical properties of arteries. *J. Biomech.* 5:135–52

54. Cox, R. H. 1974. Three-dimensional mechanics of arterial segments in vitro: Methods. *J. Appl. Physiol.* 36:381–84

55. Cox, R. H. 1975. Anisotropic properties of the canine carotid artery in vitro. *J. Biomech.* 8:293–300

56. Cox, R. H. 1975. Arterial wall mechanics and composition and the effects of smooth muscle activation. *Am. J. Physiol.* 229:807–12

57. Cox, R. H., Jones, A. W., Fischer, G. M. 1974. Carotid artery mechanics, connective tissue, and electrolyte changes in puppies. *Am. J. Physiol.* 227:563–68

58. Cox, R. H., Pace, J. B. 1975. Pressure-flow relations in the vessels of the canine aortic arch. *Am. J. Physiol.* 228:1–10

59. Crepeau, R. L., Silverman, N. R. 1973. Video densitometric vascular flow rate measurement. Some error considerations. *Med. Biol. Eng.* 11:319–25

60. Crowe, W. J. Jr., Krovetz, L. J. 1972. Studies of arterial branching in models using flow birefringence. *Med. Biol. Eng.* 10:415–26

61. De Jong, D. A., Megens, R. H. A., De Vlieger, M. 1975. A directional quantifying Doppler system for measurement of transport velocity of blood. *Ultrasonics* 13:138–41

62. Dobrin, P. B. 1973. Isometric and isobaric contraction of carotid arterial smooth muscle. *Am. J. Physiol.* 225:659–63

63. Dobrin, P. B. 1973. Influence of initial length on length-tension relationship of vascular smooth muscle. *Am. J. Physiol.* 225:664–70

64. Dobrin, P. B. 1974. Vascular muscle series elastic element stiffness during isometric contraction. *Circ. Res.* 34:242–50

65. Dobrin, P. B., Canfield, T. R. 1973. Series elastic and contractile elements in vascular smooth muscle. *Circ. Res.* 33:454–64

66. Dowdell, R. B., ed. 1974. *Flow: Its Measurement and Control in Science and Industry.* Pittsburgh: Instrum. Soc. Am. 1493 pp.

67. Downey, J. M., Downey, H. F., Kirk, E. S. 1974. Effects of myocardial strains

on coronary blood flow. *Circ. Res.* 34:286–92

68. Doyle, J. M., Dobǔn, P. B. 1973. Stress gradients in the walls of large arteries. *J. Biomech.* 6:631–39

69. Ehrlich, L. W. 1974. Digital simulation of periodic fluid flow in a bifurcation. *Comput. Fluids* 2:237–47

70. Falsetti, H. L., Kiser, K. M., Francis, G. P., Belmore, E. R. 1972. Sequential velocity development in the ascending and descending aorta of the dog. *Circ. Res.* 31:328–38

71. Ferguson, G. G. 1972. Physical factors in the initiation, growth, and rupture of human intracranial saccular aneurysms. *J. Neurosurg.* 37:666–77

72. Ferguson, G. G., Roach, M. R. 1972. Flow conditions at bifurcations as determined in glass models, with reference to the focal distribution of vascular lesions. See reference 23, 2:141–55

73. Flaherty, J. T., Pierce, J. E., Ferrans, V. J., Patel, D. J., Tucker, W. K., Fry, D. L. 1972. Endothelial nuclear patterns in the canine arterial tree with particular reference to hemodynamic events. *Circ. Res.* 30:23–33

74. Friedman, M. H., Ehrlich, L. W. 1975. Effect of spatial variations in shear on diffusion at the wall of an arterial branch. *Circ. Res.* 37:446–54

75. Friedman, M. H., O'Brien, V., Ehrlich, L. W. 1975. Calculations of pulsatile flow through a branch: Implications for the hemodynamics of atherogenesis. *Circ. Res.* 36:277–85

76. Fry, D. L. 1960. Physiologic recording by modern instruments with particular reference to pressure recording. *Physiol. Rev.* 40:753–88

77. Gabe, I. T. 1972. Pressure measurement in experimental physiology. See reference 23, 1:11–50

78. Gasking, J. 1972. The design of a new pulsed-field electromagnetic flowmeter. *Biomed. Eng.* 7:474–80

79. Gerke, E., Juchelka, W., Mittmann, U., Schmier, J. 1975. Intramyocardial pressure at various depths, during aortic constriction and myocardial ischemia in the dog. *Basic Res. Cardiol.* 70:537–46

80. Gessner, U. 1972. Vascular input impedance. See reference 23, 1:315–48

81. Gill, R. W., Meindl, J. D. 1974. An integrated circuit implantable pulsed Doppler ultrasonic blood flowmeter. *Biotelemetry* 1:85

82. Glagov, S. 1973. Mechanical stresses on vessels and the non-uniform distribution of atherosclerosis. *Med. Clin. North Am.* 57:63–77

83. Goedhard, W. J. A., Knoop, A. A. 1973. A model of the arterial wall. *J. Biomech.* 6:281–88

84. Goedhard, W. J. A., Knoop, A. A., Westerhof, N. 1973. The influence of vascular smooth muscle contraction on elastic properties of pig's thoracic aortae. *Acta Cardiol.* 28:415–30

85. Gordon, R. J. 1974. A general mathematical model of coronary circulation. *Am. J. Physiol.* 226:608–15

86. Gosling, R. G., Newman, D. L., Bowden, N. L. R., Twinn, K. W. 1971. The area ratio of normal aortic junctions. Aortic configuration and pulsewave reflection. *Br. J. Radiol.* 44:850–53

87. Gow, B. S. 1972. The influence of vascular smooth muscle on the viscoelastic properties of blood vessels. See reference 23, 2:65–110

88. Gow, B. S., Schonfeld, D., Patel, D. J. 1974. The dynamic elastic properties of the canine left circumflex coronary artery. *J. Biomech.* 7:389–95

89. Gow, B. S., Vaishnav, R. N. 1975. A microindentation technique to measure rheological properties of the vascular intima. *J. Appl. Physiol.* 38:344–50

90. Gozna, E. R., Marble, A. E., Shaw, A., Holland, J. G. 1974. Age-related changes in the mechanics of the aorta and pulmonary artery of man. *J. Appl. Physiol.* 36:407–11

91. Gozna, E. R., Shaw, A. J., Marble, A. E., Winter, D. A. 1972. Distension and geometric taper of the thoracic aorta. *Can. J. Surg.* 15:1–5

92. Gozna, E. R., Marble, A. E., Shaw, A. J., Winter, D. A. 1973. Mechanical properties of the ascending thoracic aorta of man. *Cardiovasc. Res.* 7:261–65

93. Graham, J. M., Keatinge, W. R. 1975. Responses of inner and outer muscle of the sheep carotid artery to injury. *J. Physiol.* 247:473–82

94. Grayson, J., Davidson, J. W., Fitzgerald-Finch, A., Scott, C. 1974. The functional morphology of the coronary microcirculation in the dog. *Microvasc. Res.* 8:20–43

95. Gutstein, W. H., Farrell, G. A., Armellini, C. 1973. Blood flow disturbance and endothelial cell injury in preatherosclerotic swine. *Lab. Invest.* 29:134–49

96. Hartley, C. J., Cole, J. S. 1974. An ultrasonic pulsed Doppler system for

measuring blood flow in small vessels. *J. Appl. Physiol.* 37:626–29

97. Hasegawa, M., Azuma, T. 1973. Contribution of the main vascular components to the viscoelasticity of peripheral arterial walls. *J. Physiol. Soc. Jpn.* 35:423–24

98. Hayashi, H., Arita, A., Takeda, M. 1973. Practical and theoretical considerations in the photoelectric plethysmography. *J. Physiol. Soc. Jpn.* 35:424

99. Hayashi, K., Sato, M., Handa, H., Moritake, K. 1973. Biomechanical study of vascular walls (testing apparatus of mechanical behavior of vascular walls and measurement of volume fraction of their structural components). *Proc. Sixteenth Jpn. Congr. Mater. Res. Kyoto, Jpn: Soc. Mater. Sci.* pp. 240–44

100. Hayashi, K., Sato, M., Handa, H., Moritake, K. 1974. Biomechanical study of the constitutive laws of vascular walls. *Exp. Mech.* 14:440–44

101. Herlihy, J. T., Murphy, R. A. 1973. Length-tension relationship of smooth muscle of the hog carotid artery. *Circ. Res.* 33:275–83

102. Herlihy, J. T., Murphy, R. A. 1974. Force-velocity and series elastic characteristics of smooth muscle from the hog carotid artery. *Circ. Res.* 34:461–66

103. Heywood, J. A. 1975. Towards quantitative scanning electron microscopy. *Microscope* 23:47–53

104. Hilliard, J. E. 1972. Quantitative analysis of scanning electron micrographs. *J. Microsc.* 95:45–58

105. Hislop, A., Reid, L. 1972. Intra-pulmonary arterial development during fetal life-branching pattern and structure. *J. Anat.* 113:35–48

106. Histand, M. B., Anliker, M. 1973. Influence of flow and pressure on wave propagation in the canine aorta. *Circ. Res.* 32:524–29

107. Histand, M. B., Miller, C. W. 1972. A comparison of velocity profiles measured in unexposed and exposed arteries. *Biomed. Sci. Instrum.* 9:121–24

108. Histand, M. B., Miller, C. W., McLeod, F. D. Jr. 1973. Transcutaneous measurement of blood velocity profiles and flow. *Cardiovasc. Res.* 7:703–12

109. Ho, K. J., Lin, C. Y., Galysh, F. T., Patel, A. S., Liu, L. B., Taylor, C. B. 1972. Aortic compliance. Studies on its relationship to aortic constituents in man. *Arch. Pathol.* 94:537–46

110. Hollenberg, M. J., Erickson, A. M. 1973. The scanning electron microscope: potential usefulness to biologists. A review. *J. Histochem. Cytochem.* 21:109–30

111. Holloway, E. T., Bohr, D. F. 1973. Reactivity of vascular smooth muscle in hypertensive rats. *Circ. Res.* 33:678–85

112. Hood, J. H. 1973. Anatomy of the coronary arteries. *Semin. Roentgenol.* 8:3–17

113. Hugh, A. E., O'Malley, A. W. 1974. Correlation of intra-arterial contrast stasis with flow patterns at constrictions, branches and bends: An experimental model. *Clin. Radiol.* 25:505–16

114. Hwang, N. H. C., Normann, N. A., eds. 1977. *Cardiovascular Flow Dynamics and Measurements.* Baltimore: Univ. Park Press. In press

115. Itzchak, Y., Yerushalmi, S., Deutsch, V. 1975. Blood flow measurements in the iliac arteries by an improved angiographic cinedensitometric technique. *Invest. Radiol.* 10:1–9

116. Jellinger, K. 1974. Intimal cushions in ciliary arteries of the dog. *Experientia* 30:188–89

117. Jethwa, C. P., Kaveh, M., Cooper, G. R., Saggio, F. 1975. Blood flow measurements using ultrasonic pulsed random signal Doppler system. *IEEE Trans. Sonics Ultrason.* 22:1–11

118. Jones, A. S. 1972. Wall shear in pulsatile flow. *Bull. Math. Biophys.* 34:79–86

119. Jönsson, L. 1975. A microangiographic study of the normal intramural vascular pattern of the porcine heart. *J. Am. Vet. Radiol. Soc.* 16:13–17

120. Jorgensen, J. E., Campau, D. N., Baker, D. W. 1973. Physical characteristics and mathematical modelling of the pulsed ultrasonic flowmeter. *Med. Biol. Eng.* 11:404–21

121. Kay, J. M., Smith, P. 1973. The small pulmonary arteries in rats at simulated high altitude. *Pathol. Microbiol.* 39:270–75

122. Kotas, T. J., Le Fevre, E. J. 1975. An optical technique for measuring the velocity of a fluid. *J. Mech. Eng. Sci.* 17:65–70

123. Kreid, D. K., Goldstein, R. J. 1974. Measurement of velocity profiles in simulated blood by the laser-Doppler technique. In *Flow: Its Measurement and Control in Science and Industry,* ed. W. E. Vannah, H. Wayland, 1:1377–87. Pittsburgh: Instrum. Soc. Am. 1493 pp.

124. Lake, L. W., Armeniades, C. D. 1972. Structure-property relations of aortic

tissue. *Trans. Am. Soc. Artif. Intern. Organs* 18:202–8

125. Lallemand, R. C., Brown, K. G. E., Boulter, P. S. 1972. Vessel dimensions in premature atheromatous disease of aortic bifurcation. *Br. Med. J.* 2:255–57

126. Lallemand, R. C., Gosling, R. G., Newman, D. L. 1973. Role of the bifurcation in atheromatosis of the abdominal aorta. *Surg. Gynecol. Obstet.* 137:987–90

127. Ling, S. C., Atabek, H. B. 1972. A nonlinear analysis of pulsatile flow in arteries. *J. Fluid Mech.* 55:493–511

128. Litwin, S. B., Cohen, J., Fine, S. 1973. Effects of sterilization and preservation on the rupture force and tensile strength of canine aortic tissue. *J. Surg. Res.* 15:198–206

129. Lou, Y. S. 1975. Two-dimensional finite amplitude theory of arterial blood flow. *J. Biomech.* 8:57–63

130. Lunkenheimer, P. P., Merker, J. 1974. Morphology and function of an intramyocardial sinusoidal flow net. (In German) *Thoraxchir. Vask. Chir.* 22:26–35

131. McCloskey, D. I., Cleary, E. G. 1974. Chemical composition of the rabbit aorta during development. *Circ. Res.* 34:828–35

132. McCarty, K., Woodcock, J. P. 1975. Frequency modulated ultrasonic Doppler flowmeter. *Med. Biol. Eng.* 13:59–64

133. McDonald, D. A. 1960. *Blood Flow in Arteries.* London: Arnold. 328 pp. 1st ed.

134. McDonald, D. A. 1974. *Blood Flow in Arteries.* Baltimore: Williams & Wilkins. 496 pp. 2nd ed.

135. Macfarlane, T. W. R. 1975. *The geometry of cerebral arterial bifurcations and its modification with static distending pressure.* MSc thesis. Univ. Western Ontario, London, Canada. 236 pp.

136. Malcolm, A. D. 1976. *Flow phenomena at bifurcations and branches in relation to human atherogenesis: A study in a family of glass models.* MSc thesis. Univ. Western Ontario, London, Canada. 203 pp.

137. Marble, A. E., MacDonald, A. S., Holland, J. G., Hilliard, W., Miller, C. H., Winter, D. A. 1973. Measurement of aortic-wall thickness in living dogs. *Med. Biol. Eng.* 11:39–42

138. Melbin, J., Gopalakrishnan, R., Noordergraaf, A. 1975. Three dimensional laminar flow in distorting, axisymmetric, axially varying vessels. *Bull. Math. Biol.* 37:489–504

139. Miller, C. W., Nealeigh, R. C., Histand, M. B. 1972. The effect of arterial location upon arterial velocity distributions. *Biomed. Sci. Instrum.* 9:129–32

140. Mills, C. J. 1972. Measurement of pulsatile flow and flow velocity. See reference 23, 1:51–90

141. Milnor, W. R. 1975. Arterial impedance as ventricular afterload. *Circ. Res.* 36:565–70

142. Milnor, W. R., Nichols, W. W. 1975. A new method of measuring propagation coefficients and characteristic impedance in blood vessels. *Circ. Res.* 36:631–39

143. Minns, R. J., Soden, P. D. 1973. The role of the fibrous components and ground substance in the mechanical properties of biological tissues: A preliminary investigation. *J. Biomech.* 6:153–65

144. Mirsky, I. 1973. Pulse velocities in cylindrical, tapered and curved anisotropic elastic arteries. *Bull. Math. Biol.* 35:495–511

145. Mishina, H., Asakura, T. 1975. Measurement of velocity fluctuations in laser Doppler microscope by the new system employing the time-to-pulse height converter. *Appl. Phys.* 5:351–59

146. Mishina, H., Koyama, T., Asakura, T. 1975. Velocity measurements of blood flow in the capillary and vein using a laser Doppler microscope. *Appl. Opt.* 14:2326–27

147. Mishina, H., Tokui, S., Ushizaka, T., Asakura, T., Nagai, S. 1975. A laser Doppler microscope—its signal-analyzing systems. *Jpn. J. Appl. Phys.* 14:323–28

148. Moritz, W. E., Anliker, M. 1974. Wave transmission characteristics and anisotropy of canine carotid arteries. *J. Biomech.* 7:151–54

149. Morris, R. L., Histand, M. B., Miller, C. W. 1973. The resolution of the ultrasound pulsed Doppler for blood velocity measurements. *J. Biomech.* 6:701–710

150. Mozersky, D. J., Sumner, D. S., Hokanson, D. E., Strandness, D. E. 1972. Transcutaneous measurement of the elastic properties of the human femoral artery. *Circulation* 46:948–55

151. Nerem, R. M., Rumberger, J. A. Jr., Gross, D. R., Hamlin, R. L., Geiger, G. L. 1974. Hot-film anemometer velocity measurements of arterial blood flow in horses. *Circ. Res.* 34:193–203

152. Nerem, R. M., Rumberger, J. A. Jr., Gross, D. R., Muir, W. W., Geiger, G. L. 1976. Hot film coronary artery velocity measurements in horses. *Cardiovasc. Res.* 10:301–13

153. Nerem, R. M., Seed, W. A. 1972. An in vivo study of aortic flow disturbances. *Cardiovasc. Res.* 6:1–14

154. Nerem, R. M., Seed, W. A., Wood, N. B. 1972. An experimental study of the velocity distribution and transition to turbulence in the aorta. *J. Fluid Mech.* 52:137–60

155. Newman, D. L., Bowden, N. L. R. 1973. Effect of reflection from an unmatched junction on the abdominal aortic impedance. *Cardiovasc. Res.* 7: 827–33

156. Newman, D. L., Bowden, N. L. R., Gosling, R. G. 1975. The dynamic and static elastic response of the abdominal aorta of the dog. *Cardiovasc. Res.* 9:679–84

157. Newman, D. L., Gosling, R. G. 1973. Influence of peripheral vascular state on pressure pulse changes due to total occlusion of the aorta. *J. Appl. Physiol.* 35:786–89

158. Newman, D. L., Gosling, R. G., Bowden, N. L. R., King, D. H. 1973. Pressure amplitude increase on unmatching the aortic-iliac junction of the dog. *Cardiovasc. Res.* 7:6–13

159. Nichols, W. W., McDonald, D. A. 1972. Wave-velocity in the proximal aorta. *Med. Biol. Eng.* 10:327–35

160. Nimura, Y., Matsuo, H., Hayashi, T., Kitabatake, A., Mochizuki, S., Sakakibara, H., Kato, K., Abe, H. 1974. Studies on arterial flow patterns—instantaneous velocity spectrums and their phasic changes—with directional ultrasonic Doppler technique. *Br. Heart J.* 36:899–907

161. Nyboer, J. 1972. Workable volume and flow concepts of bio-segments by electrical impedance plethysmography. *TIT J. Life Sci.* 2:1–13

162. Olson, R. M. 1974. Human carotid artery wall thickness, diameter, and blood flow by a noninvasive technique. *J. Appl. Physiol.* 37:955–60

163. Olson, R. M., Shelton, D. K. Jr. 1972. A nondestructive technique to measure wall displacement in the thoracic aorta. *J. Appl. Physiol.* 32:147–51

164. Patel, D. J., Janicki, J. S., Vaishnav, R. N., Young, J. T. 1973. Dynamic anisotropic viscoelastic properties of the aorta in living dogs. *Circ. Res.* 32:93–107

165. Patel, D. J., Vaishnav, R. N. 1972. The rheology of large blood vessels. See reference 23, 2:1–64

166. Patel, D. J., Vaishnav, R. N., Gow, B. S., Kot, P. A. 1974. Hemodynamics. *Ann. Rev. Physiol.* 36:125–54

167. Peiper, U., Schmidt, E., Laven, R., Griebel, L. 1973. Length tension relationships in resting and activated vascular smooth muscle fibres. *Pfluegers Arch.* 340:113–22

168. Peronneau, P., Hinglais, J., Pellet, M., Léger, F. 1970. Vélocimètre sanguin par effet Doppler à émission ultra-sonore pulsée. *Onde Électr.* 50:369–89

169. Peronneau, P. A., Pellet, M. M., Xhaard, M. C., Hinglais, J. R. 1974. Pulsed doppler ultrasonic blood flowmeter. Real time instantaneous velocity profiles. In *Flow: Its Measurement and Control in Science and Industry,* ed. W. E. Vannah, H. Wayland, 1:1367–76. Pittsburgh: Instrum. Soci. Am. 1493 pp.

170. Pesonen, E., Martimo, P., Rapola, J. 1974. Histometry of the arterial wall. A new technique with the aid of automatic data processing. *Lab. Invest.* 30:550–55

171. Peterson, J. W., Paul, R. J. 1974. Effects of initial length and active shortening on vascular smooth muscle contractility. *Am. J. Physiol.* 227:1019–24

172. Plowman, F., Young, J. T., Janicki, J. S. 1975. An instrument for dynamic measurement of longitudinal stresses and strains in a blood vessel in situ. *Biorheology* 12:21–25

173. Porter, R., Knight, J., eds. 1973. *Atherogenesis Initiating Factors. Ciba Found. Symp.* Amsterdam: Assoc. Sci. Publishers

174. Posey, J. A. Jr., Geddes, L. A. 1973. Measurement of the modulus of elasticity of the arterial wall. *Cardiovasc. Cent. Bull.* 11:83–103

175. Rader, R. D., Meehan, J. P., Henriksen, J. K. C. 1973. An implantable blood pressure and flow transmitter. *IEEE Trans. Biomed. Eng.* BME-20:37–43

176. Renaudeaux, J. P. 1972. Propagation des ondes de pression dans les tuyaux souples. Application à la circulation du sang dans les artères. *J. Physiol. Paris* 64:517–29

177. Reneman, R. S., Clarke, H. F., Simmons, N., Spencer, M. P. 1973. In vivo comparison of electromagnetic and Doppler flowmeters: With special attention to the processing of the analogue Doppler flow signal. *Cardiovasc. Res.* 7:557–66

178. Restrepo, C., Eggen, D. A., Guzman, M. A., Tejada, C. 1973. Postmortem dimensions of the coronary arteries in different geographic locations. *Lab. Invest.* 28:244–51

179. Reuse-Blom, S., Platteborse, R. 1974. Etude cinematographique de la microcirculation coronaire chez le lapin in vivo. *Acta Cardiol. Brux* 29 (Suppl. 19): 129–34

180. Roach, M. R. 1970. Role of vascular wall elastic tissue in hemostasis. *Thromb. Diath. Haemorrh. Suppl.* 40:59–77

181. Roach, M. R. 1973. A biophysical look at the relationship of structure and function in the umbilical artery. In *Foetal and Neonatal Physiology,* ed. K. S. Comline, K. W. Cross, G. S. Dawes, P. W. Nathanielsz, pp. 141–63. Cambridge: Cambridge Univ. Press

182. Roach, M. R. 1977. The effect of bifurcations and stenoses on arterial disease. In *Cardiovascular Flow Dynamics and Measurements,* ed. N. H. C. Hwang, N. A. Normann. Baltimore: Univ. Park Press. In press

183. Roach, M. R., Burton, A. C. 1957. The reason for the shape of the distensibility curves of arteries. *Can. J. Biochem. Physiol.* 35:681–90

184. Roach, M. R., Fletcher, J. 1976. Effect of unilateral nephrectomy on the localization of aortic sudanophilic lesions in cholesterol-fed rabbits. *Atherosclerosis.* 24:327–33

185. Roach, M. R., Scott, S., Ferguson, G. G. 1972. The hemodynamic importance of the geometry of bifurcations in the Circle of Willis (glass model studies). *Stroke* 3:255–67

186. Rodbard, S., Farbstein, M. 1972. Stress concentrations induced by flow. *Cardiovasc. Res.* 6:562–68

187. Rodkiewicz, C. M. 1975. Localization of early atherosclerotic lesions in the aortic arch in the light of fluid flow. *J. Biomech.* 8:149–56

188. Rodkiewicz, C. M., Howell, D. H. 1971. Fluid dynamics in a large arterial bifurcation. *AIAA J.* 9:2284–86

189. Rodkiewicz, C. M., Roussel, C. L. 1973. Fluid mechanics in a large arterial bifurcation. *Trans. Am. Soc. Mech. Eng. J. Fluids Eng.* 95:108–12

190. Rutishauser, W., Steiger, U., Simon, R., Harlander, W., Wellauer, J. 1974. Roentgendensitometry: An indicator-dilution technique for blood flow measurement after contrast-medium injection. *Biomed. Eng.* 9:472–77

191. Saito, G. E., Vander Werff, T. J. 1975. The importance of viscoelasticity in arterial blood flow models. *J. Biomech.* 8:237–45

192. Schaper, W. 1971. *The Collateral Circulation of the Heart.* Amsterdam: North-Holland. 276 pp.

193. Schimmler, W. 1975. A longitudinal study of the relationship between the pulse wave velocity in the aorta-iliaca vessel and the blood pressure. (In German). *Basic Res. Cardiol.* 70:46–57

194. Schultz, D. L. 1972. Pressure and flow in large arteries. See reference 23, 1:287–314

195. Seed, W. A., Wood, N. B. 1972. Application of constant temperature anemometry in measurement of intra-arterial blood flow velocity. *Int. J. Eng. Sci.* 10:1009–21

196. Shelton, D. K. Jr., Olson, R. M. 1972. A nondestructive technique to measure pulmonary artery diameter and its pulsatile variations. *J. Appl. Physiol.* 33: 542–44

197. Sigdell, J. E. 1975. Venous occlusion plethysmography. Part 1: Basic principles and applications. *Biomed. Eng.* 10:300–2

198. Sigdell, J. E. 1975. Venous occlusion plethysmography. Part 2: Methods. *Biomed. Eng.* 10:342–49

199. Silkworth, J. B., Stehbens, W. E. 1975. The shape of endothelial cells in en face preparations of rabbit blood vessels. *Angiology* 26:474–87

200. Silverman, N. R., Intaglietta, M., Tompkins, W. R. 1973. A videodensitometer for blood flow measurement. *Br. J. Radiol.* 46:594–98

201. Simon, B. R., Kobayashi, A. S., Strandness, D. E., Wiederhielm, C. A. 1972. Reevaluation of arterial constitutive relations. A finite-deformation approach. *Circ. Res.* 30:491–500

202. Simpson, R. L., Barr, P. W. 1975. Laser Doppler velocimeter signal processing using sampling spectrum analysis. *Rev. Sci. Instrum.* 46:835–37

203. Skalak, R. 1972. Synthesis of a complete circulation. See reference 23, 2:341–76

204. Somer, J. B., Schwartz, C. J. 1972. Focal [³H] cholesterol uptake in the pig aorta. II. Distribution of [³H] cholesterol across the aortic wall in areas of high and low uptake in vivo. *Atherosclerosis* 16:377–88

205. Speden, R. N. 1975. Muscle load and constriction of the rabbit ear artery. *J. Physiol.* 248:531–53

206. Sperling, W., Bauer, R. D., Busse, R., Körner, H., Pasch, Th. 1975. The resolution of arterial pulses into forward and backward waves as an approach to the determination of the characteristic impedance. *Pfluegers Arch.* 355:217–27

207. Stehbens, W. E. 1974. Changes in the cross-sectional area of the arterial fork. *Angiology* 25:561–75

208. Stehbens, W. E. 1975. Flow in glass models of arterial bifurcations and berry aneurysms at low Reynolds numbers. *Q. J. Exp. Physiol.* 60:181–92

209. Stehbens, W. E. 1975. The role of hemodynamics in the pathogenesis of atherosclerosis. *Prog. Cardiovasc. Dis.* 18:89–103

210. Stehbens, W. E., Ludatscher, R. M. 1973. Ultrastructure of the renal arterial bifurcation of rabbits. *Exp. Mol. Pathol.* 18:50–67

211. Stelmasiak, M., Osemlak, J. 1972. Relations of the coronary arteries and areas of the heart supplied by them in man. (In Polish). *Folia Morphol. Warsaw* 31:515–26

212. Stoltz, J. F., Larcan, A., Lefort, M., Wackenheim, E. 1973. Etude théorique et expérimentale du concept de zone d'influence à une bifurcation du lit vasculaire. *Angiologica* 10:1–9

213. Strandness, D. E. Jr., Sumner, D. S. 1972. Current research review. Noninvasive methods of studying peripheral arterial function. *J. Surg. Res.* 12:419–30

214. Strandness, D. E., Sumner, D. S. 1975. *Hemodynamics for Surgeons.* New York: Grune & Stratton. 698 pp.

215. Strano, J. J., Welkowitz, W., Fich, S. 1972. Measurement and utilization of in vivo blood-pressure transfer functions of dog and chicken aortas. *IEEE Trans. Biomed. Eng.* BME-19:261–71

216. Taira, S., Hayashi, K., Sato, M., Handa, H., Moritake, K. 1974. Biomechanical study of vascular walls. (Stress analysis of vascular walls by finite element method.) (In Japanese.) *J. Soc. Mater. Sci.* 23:437–43

217. Tanaka, T. T., Fung, Y. C. 1974. Elastic and inelastic properties of the canine aorta and their variation along the aortic tree. *J. Biomech.* 7:357–70

218. Taylor, M. G. 1973. Hemodynamics. *Ann. Rev. Physiol.* 35:87–116

219. Thind, G. S. 1974. Blood vessel wall characteristics in experimental hypertension. *Angiology* 25:752–63

220. Tomm, D. 1975. Determination of velocity distributions in models for arterial bifurcations by laser-Doppler-anemometry. *Proc. 5th Over the Water Meet. Biol. Eng. Soc. London in Aachen June 18–20, 1975. Biol. Eng.* (Special ed.)

221. Trelstad, R. L. 1974. Human aorta collagens: Evidence for three distinct species. *Biochem. Biophys. Res. Commun.* 57:717–25

222. Uther, J. B., Peterson, K. L., Shabetai, R., Braunwald, E. 1974. Measurement of the ascending aortic flow waveform in man using an electromagnetic flow catheter. *Clin. Exp. Pharmacol. Physiol. Suppl.* 1:67–77

223. Vaishnav, R. N., Young, J. T., Janicki, J. S., Patel, D. J. 1972. Nonlinear anisotropic elastic properties of the canine aorta. *Biophys. J.* 12:1008–27

224. Vaishnav, R. N., Young, J. T., Patel, D. J. 1973. Distribution of stresses and of strain-energy density through the wall thickness in a canine aortic segment. *Circ. Res.* 32:577–83

225. Weissenhofer, W., Schmidt, R., Schenk, W. G. Jr. 1973. Technique of electromagnetic blood flow measurements: Notes regarding a potential source of error. *Surgery* 73:474–77

226. Wemple, R. R., Mockros, L. F. 1972. Pressure and flow in the systemic arterial system. *J. Biomech.* 5:629–41

227. Wesly, R. L. R., Vaishnav, R. N., Fuchs, J. C. A., Patel, D. J., Greenfield, J. C. Jr. 1975. Static linear and nonlinear elastic properties of normal and arterialized venous tissue in dog and man. *Circ. Res.* 37:509–20

228. Wesseling, K. H., Weber, H., de Wit, B. 1973. Estimated five component viscoelastic model parameters for human arterial walls. *J. Biomech.* 6:13–24

229. Westerhof, N., Elzinga, G., Van den Bos, G. C. 1973. Influence of central and peripheral changes on the hydraulic input impedance of the systemic arterial tree. *Med. Biol. Eng.* 11:710–23

230. Westerhof, N., Sipkema, P., Van den Bos, G. C., Elzinga, G. 1972. Forward and backward waves in the arterial system. *Cardiovasc. Res.* 6:648–56

231. Wolinsky, H. 1972. Effects of estrogen and progestogen treatment on the response of the aorta of male rats to hypertension. Morphological and chemical studies. *Circ. Res.* 30:341–49

232. Wolinsky, H. 1972. Effects of androgen treatment on the male rat aorta. *J. Clin. Invest.* 51:2552–55

233. Wolinsky, H. 1973. Effects of estrogen treatment on the oophorectomized

female rat aorta. *Proc. Soc. Exp. Biol. Med.* 144:864–67

234. Wolinsky, H. 1973. Comparative effects of castration and antiandrogen treatment on the aortas of hypertensive and normotensive male rats. *Circ. Res.* 33:183–89

235. Wolinsky, H., Glagov, S. 1964. Structural basis for the static mechanical properties of the aortic media. *Circ. Res.* 14:400–13

236. Wolinsky, H., Goldfischer, S., Schiller, B., Kasak, L. E. 1973. Lysosomes in aortic smooth muscle cells. Effects of hypertension. *Am. J. Pathol.* 73:727–32

237. Wolinsky, H., Goldfischer, S., Schiller, B., Kasak, L. E. 1974. Modification of the effects of hypertension on lysosomes and connective tissue in the rat aorta. *Circ. Res.* 34:233–41

238. Womersley, J. R. 1957. The mathematic analysis of the arterial circulation in a state of oscillatory motion. *Wright Air Develop. Cent. Tech. Rep.* WADC-TR56-614

239. Wyatt, D. G. 1977. Electromagnetic blood flowmetry. In *Cardiovascular Flow Dynamics and Measurements,* ed. N. H. C. Hwang, N. A. Normann. Baltimore: Univ. Park Press. In press

240. Yates, W. G., Anliker, M. 1974. Active and passive behavior of the canine vena cava in vivo. *Am. J. Physiol.* 227:24–30

241. Zakharzhevskiĭ, V. V., Grinblat, M. P. 1974. Silicon organic cold setting compounds for coating transducers implanted on the coronary artery of dog heart. (In Russian). *Biull. Eksp. Biol. Med.* 78:122–23

Ann. Rev. Physiol. 1977. 39:73–95

LYMPH FORMATION AND FLOW

❖1164

Paul A. Nicoll

Department of Medical Science, Physiology Group, Indiana University Medical School, Bloomington, Indiana 47401

Aubrey E. Taylor

Department of Physiology and Biophysics, University of Mississippi Medical School, Jackson, Mississippi 39216

INTRODUCTION

It is now recognized that the physiological roles of lymphatic vessels and lymphoid tissues may be considered separately. Getti et al (16), in a recent review, focused on the complicated topic of lymphoid tissues and immune reactions, aspects of the lymphatic system not considered here. An earlier review by Allen (1) discussed lymph formation in some peripheral sites and problems of clinical interest arising from disorders in this mechanism. Witte & Witte (60) reviewed the role lymphatics perform in the regulation of interstitial fluid volume and considered how disorders in this process lead to tissue edema. In the same series of papers, Taylor et al (57) considered in detail how Starling forces are involved in lymph formation and how interstitial fluid enters the lymphatic capillaries. In a symposium held at Bad Bürkheim in 1972, the major factors involved in capillary-interstitum-lymphatic exchanges were reviewed in considerable detail. The proceedings of this conference (17) give a concise and readable overview of the structures and activities involved in these exchanges and provide excellent bibliographies for the different topics considered.

The present review is divided into two parts. The first portion deals with contributions to lymph formation and lymph flow from studies at the microscopic level of the peripheral lymphatics mainly as found in the thin wing membrane of some bat species. The remaining section reviews the recent contributions implicating lymph formation and flow as a significant basic factor in the fluid exchange between blood and interstitium.

Sites in mammals where the initial elements or capillary units of the lymphatic system are available for direct observation and study are few. These initial lymphatics are minute; in any direct study of their activity, techniques with significant optical magnification are required. Lymph formation must be explored in the same area where it arises as a by-product of the local exchange reactions between blood and cells. Lymph flowing in the large transport channels, such as those in the mesentery, does not reflect in its composition any balance between itself and the immediate environment. The mammalian site that best fulfills these requirements is the extensive thin membrane comprising the wings in various species of bats.

LYMPHATICS OF BAT WINGS

In 1944, Webb & Nicoll (58) reported in considerable detail the structural characteristics and functional activity of the lymphatics in the wing, body skin, and mesentery in three genera and several species of insectivorous bats common in many areas of the United States. Most of this work was carried out on *Myotis lucifugus* and *M. sodalis,* where the wing size and degree of transparency offer ideal sites for observation. The structural and functional characteristics of the lymphatics in *Eptecicus fuscus* are similar, but the connective tissue of the wings tends to obscure the microvessels. However, their large size makes them ideal for study of mesenteric lymphatics.

Pipistrellus subflavus also shows identical wing lymphatics, but the wing coloration tends to be dark and less desirable for translumination. Their small size makes mesenteric study impractical, but their calvarium is so thin that pial microvessels, cerebral surface vessels, and other intracranial vascular elements may be observed and studied through the intact calvarium after the overlying skin is reflected. Although no lymphatics occur here, exchange between blood and interstitial fluid can be studied. Micropipettes may easily be inserted into this interstitial space beneath the calvarium and above the brain surface without disturbing the microvascular supply. Dye infusions into the interstitial space indicate that the fluid drains, at least in part, upward through the canniculi of the calvarium and must eventually drain away through superficial veins or lymphatic elements. Details of its final disposition have not been studied.

The lymphatics and microvascular organization in other bats have been observed, and similar lymphatic organization have been noted in the red bats, *Lasiurus borealis* and *L. cinereus* (P. A. Nicoll, unpublished). A strikingly clear and extensive thin wing membrane exhibiting comparable blood and lymphatic systems in a free-tailed species was observed during some time spent in Karachi, Pakistan. This was probably *Rhinopoma hardwickei,* but identification was not made at the time, and circumstances prevented any detailed study of the specimens available.

During a year spent in Canberra, Australia, three local species were used for lymphatic investigations (8). The most rewarding specimens were members of the genus *Mineopterus,* mainly *schreibersi,* but a few *M. australis* were also studied (41). Two rather different species also possess wing lymphatics basically similar to the type pattern seen in *Myotis* and *Mineopterus.* One was the medium-sized leaf nose bat, *Rhinolophus megaphyllus,* and a similarly organized but significantly reduced pattern was found in the thin delicate wing of *Nyctophilus timoriensis.* One may generalize somewhat even on the basis of the relatively few specimens studied that the lymphatic organization and activity observed in *Myotis* and *Miniopterus* are present in wings of most insectivorous bats. The degree of development correlates with the amount of skeletal muscle, which forms thin bands distributed throughout the wing area. This muscular development in turn is associated with that species' pattern of flight. *Myotis* and *Miniopterus* are vigorous flyers, as are most of the others studied, while *Nyctophilus* has poorly developed wing membranes with scant muscle and seems to flutter rather than exhibit vigorous flight.

Unfortunately it has not been possible to study the lymphatics in many species of nectar- or fruit-eating bats or in any blood-eaters. The medium-sized common fruit-eater of Central and South America, *Artibeus jamaicensis,* has transport channels that show moderate contraction, but no study of their collecting ducts and initial capillaries has been reported. The nectar-feeding bat, *Leptonycteris sanborni,* a native of Arizona, has rather long narrow wings that are only fairly transparent but allow reasonable observation of the blood microvasculature. The blood microvessels are interesting and seem to be distributed much as those in the insectivores. They exhibit very strong vasomotion, especially the veins and venules, and flow into capillary nets is regulated for the most part by vasomotion of the terminal arterioles. The vascular system is distributed throughout the major wing area, paralleling the distribution of the muscle bands, which are richly supplied with capillaries in the usual pattern. Other capillary nets that supply the intermuscular surfaces are clearly evident and carry a vigorous flow of blood most of the time. Lymphatic transport channels and some branches could be identified by their contractions paralleling the major blood vessels, but no lymphatics comparable to collecting ducts or expanded capillaries could be identified.

In *L. sanborni* a few indistinct pouches occur along some of the major transport channels. The pouches exhibited vigorous contractions and emptied their contents into the transport channels with each systole, but during the ensuing diastolic phase much of the fluid returned into the pouch as it dilated. There were apparently no valves to prevent this retrograde lymph flow. In some instances, contracting walls that appeared to be either dividing into branches or starting to form a pouch simply faded from view and no details could be identified. All attempts to infuse saline or saline-trypan blue solutions were completely ineffectual in demonstrating any network of lymphatic collecting ducts or enlarged capillary elements. Obviously further study is required to resolve the lymphatic supply and its activity in the wing membranes of *L. sanborni.*

Some years ago the lymphatics in the wing membrane of the larger fruit-eater *Carollia perspicallata* were studied in some detail. The wings were irregular in thickness, but portions of the surface could be studied by translumination without surgery. The collecting and transport lymphatics were well developed and showed strong contractions associated with unidirectional valves. However, even at sites along the collecting ducts where a valve indicated entrance of lymph, no structurally delineated initial element could be found. Infusion of dye into the area where an initial structure was suspected simply resulted in outward diffusion of the dye into the surrounding interstitium. Additional studies in this species should be carried out, however, before any conclusion is reached that interstitial fluid flows directly into the collecting ducts through valved openings. Another difference in the lymphatic organization of *Corallia* is that transport lymphatics, although extensive and supplying all areas, do not parallel the arterial and venous distribution but run throughout the area independently.

ORGANIZATION OF WING LYMPHATICS

The organization and activities of the wing lymphatics are readily observed in unanesthetized specimens, especially in *Myotis* and *Mineopterus* species. In their original report, Webb & Nicoll (58) described the lymphatic system in *Myotis* (*M. lucifugus* and *M. sodalis*) as made up of three functional divisions, each with characteristic structures and activities: 1. the enlarged bulbous capillaries or initial elements where lymph is formed; 2. a complex network of relatively narrow collecting ducts interspaced, particularly at duct junctions, by enlarged sinuses where the valve cusps that prevent retrograde flow are located; and 3. a coalescing arborization of transport channels that receive the lymph from the collecting ducts and eventually drain the major portion of the wing lymph into the axillary region. No nodes are present in the wing region itself, although presumably the usual axillary nodes exist. In the mesentery, all of the transport channels converge on the single large mesenteric node or "pancreas of Aselli" where they empty into a single peripheral sinus region.

The wing lymphatics in a typical area of *Myotis lucifugus* as sketched from a living specimen are shown in Figure 1. The comparable organization of the three lymphatic elements in *M. schreiberse* is shown in Figure 2. In *Mineopterus* the capillary bulb chains are more extensive on the average than in *Myotis*. It is interesting that with *Mineopterus*, when the capillary bulb chains become lengthy with 5 or more individual units, the terminal bulbs which are the largest do not exhibit contraction. In *Myotis* these longer chains are frequently branched; the end bulbs, that are also the largest, contract only in the small area adjacent to their junction with the bulb ahead. Except for the terminal bulb, or bulbs, the remaining units of the chains contract, often vigorously, if the conditions are correct to induce activity. Occasionally, when little lymph is being formed and these initial units are not distended, their walls are invisible and their presence is indicated, if at all, only by their activity.

More often than otherwise, when a wing of a normal animal is mounted for study, especially with *Myotis*, many of the microvascular beds are shut down due to high tone along the terminal arterioles. In such a preparation, usually no lymphatic capillary bulbs are evident and only an occasional active sinus along a collecting duct or a major transport channel can be observed. The ducts and channels are nearly empty and appear collapsed with minimal activity and show minimal lymph flow. Occasionally the converse is found with vigorous blood flow in the majority of minute vascular beds, along with fully distended lymphatic bulbs, ducts, and channels, all exhibiting vigorous contractions. This great difference in the ability to find the lymphatic capillaries and collecting ducts is associated with the presence or absence of a vigorous flow through the blood microvasculature. It seems reason-

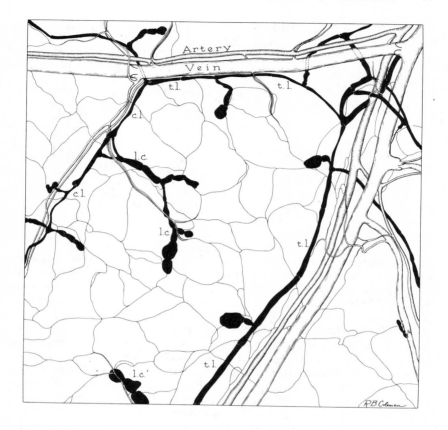

Figure 1   Blood and lymphatic vessels in a small area near the center of major wing surface in *Myotis*. Major blood vessels are shaded, and blood microvessels represented by single lines. Lymphatic vessels are solid black. lc = lymphatic collecting ducts; tl = lymphatic transport channels; capillary bulbs are the enlarged black units. [From (58) by permission of the publisher: The Wistar Institute of Anatomy and Biology, Philadelphia, Pennsylvania.]

able to assume without quantitative proof that convective shifts of fluid from blood to interstitium under ordinary conditions are directly dependent on the flow and pressure conditions in the blood exchange beds. Therefore, with vigorous flow the convective fluid shift to the interstitium should increase. Since under these conditions one may readily observe the lymphatic capillaries and collecting ducts, they must be full of lymph and by their contractions move the lymph out of the area.

It is readily possible to hydrate a local interstitial area by infusion of a few cubic microns of a slightly hypotonic (260–280 milliosmolar) saline adjusted to a pH value of 7.2 – 7.4. The infused fluid simulates an increased convective loss from the blood exchange vessels, and, within minutes, the lymphatic capillaries and collecting ducts

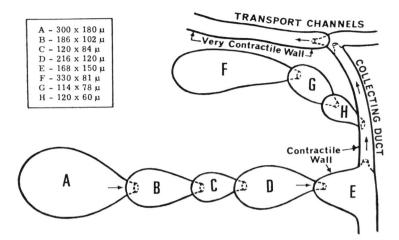

A – 300 x 180 μ
B – 186 x 102 μ
C – 120 x 84 μ
D – 216 x 120 μ
E – 168 x 150 μ
F – 330 x 81 μ
G – 114 x 78 μ
H – 120 x 60 μ

Figure 2 Lymphatic capillary bulbs, collecting ducts, and transport channel sketched from life as observed in central wing area of *Mineopterus*. Note variations of size and number of bulbs in chains A–D and F–H. [From (8) by permission of the publisher: E. & S. Livingstone, Edinburgh and London.]

become filled and active, and lymph flow out of the area is markedly increased. This infusion probably modifies the local tissue ionic environment (43), perhaps by lowering the [Ca^{2+}], and brings about the arteriolar relaxation with vigorous microvascular flow leading to a temporary increase in interstitial fluid production. The excess interstitial fluid enters the lymphatics, they fill and become active, and lymph flow from the area is increased. Following a single infusion into the interstitial site, within 5–10 min, the microvascular blood flow reverts toward a quiescent condition and lymph formation is reduced. The convective fluid loss from the blood returns to negligible amounts, and the extra infused solutions either diffuse into the surrounding interstitial spaces or are carried out of the injection site. For some time thereafter, the collecting ducts and transport channels appear to contain lymph but show reduced activity. Since the area affected by each infusion is only a small fraction of the total wing, changes in lymph flow in major transport channels may not reflect the action observed at the infused site.

LYMPHATIC CONTRACTIONS

As noted (58), contractions of all lymphatics, but especially the enlarged initial bulbs, displace the surrounding area because of the numerous anchoring filaments attached to the lymphatics and radiating outward into the interstitial fiber meshwork. This is readily observed at all optical magnifications, and, with oil, one can follow individual filaments from lymphatic to interstitial regions. Casley-Smith & Florey (5) noted these in their early electronmicroscopic (EM) study and thought they attached directly to the endothelial cells. Leak & Burke (35) studied these filaments further in fixed preparations, and suggested their involvement in a rather elaborate scheme for opening and closing passageways into initial lymphatics especially during edema (17). The filaments obviously serve as wall stabilizers, preventing collapse of the vessels, especially the thin-walled bulbous capillaries. Recoil of these attachment threads and the connective tissue network where they anchor would also aid in returning the bulbs to resting volume following relaxation of the contracting elements. Direct observation of this activity does not lend much support to the proposal, at least in bat wing lymphatics, that the contraction or distortion of the filaments opens potential orifices in the endothelial cell membrane.

The way in which lymph enters the initial units is further examined by direct infusion into the bulb lumen from a micropipette filled with isotonic Berlin blue solution (8). The dye particles, which can barely be seen as discrete entities, are observed first to slowly drift a very short distance away from the tip, and then appear to whisk quickly towards the surrounding wall. The dye particles do not escape the bulb but are absorbed on its inner surface. Initially, small rosettes of blue surrounding a minute unstained spot become visible all over the inner surface. Except in end bulbs these rosettes are distributed rather regularly over the surface. In the end bulb, the blind terminal region may become completely covered, and some dye particles appear to be outside the bulb wall. Continued infusion eventually covers the entire wall surface, and the rosette pattern and central spot are obliterated. The particles of the so-called soluble Berlin blue do not remain in suspension in dilute salt solutions, so within the lymphatic capillary agglutinated clumps of dye form and are carried downstream into the collecting ducts and transport channels. In these vessels, the particles tend to adhere to the valve sites and may occasionally block lymph flow. Except for the valve cusps, no evidence of preferential sites for adherence of small clumps in the sinus or other portions of ducts and channels is seen. This indicates that pores or other places where convective loss or gain of lymph could occur are not found beyond the capillary bulb.

If mineral oil is infused into the bulbs, no escape site into the surrounding interstitium is observed. The oil fills the bulbs and, with continued infusion, flows down into the bulbs and ducts ahead. If infusion pressure is raised slightly, one or more areas in the wall bulges outward and then ruptures with loss of oil into the surrounding tissue. If the infusion is stopped before rupture, the contractions of the bulb and duct walls will knead and shove the oil about, and after several hours the oil will be pushed into the transport channels and carried away. Somewhat similar observations can be made if small volumes of air are introduced into a bulb. Eventually the air seems to be reabsorbed rather than move down into the transport channels. At low infusion pressures, adequate to fill a chain of bulbs, no air is observed to leak into the interstitium.

Using bulb chains from *Mineoptarus* wing membranes previously infused with Berlin blue, Cliff & Nicoll (8) found a few apparently patent openings in the endothelium up to 2.5 μm wide. But even in these cases the Berlin blue did not leak out, apparently because of an ill-defined precipitated layer. These gaps could be the sites noted above in which convective loss of infused saline occurs and Berlin blue particles are retained within the bulb. No EM pictures of an end-bulb terminal wall have yet been made. The permeability of various lymphatics largely based on EM studies and infusion of various sized particles has been reviewed by Allen (1), Kato (30), Leak (34), and Casley-Smith (3). Several other initial lymphatics have been shown to offer little resistance to entrance of large particles and even cells, and, for the most part, the bulbous capillaries in the bat wing seem to behave similarly. Additional observations are needed to evaluate the actual mechanism of fluid entrance into these initial units of the collecting system.

Collecting ducts have characteristically enlarged sinus-like structures where the unidirectional valve leaflets occur, interconnected by varying lengths of narrow tubes. The sinuses are usually located at tubular junctions, and their walls exhibit the most vigorous contractions. Intersinus sections, however, also do constrict and could aid in propulsion of lymph. Occasionally these intersinus segments are markedly enlarged, thus appearing somewhat similar to the initial elements. Whether or not convective exchanges can occur across the sinus and occasional expanded intersinus walls has not been fully resolved.

Studies (42) with water soluble dyes such as trypan blue or vital new red appear to support the idea that collecting ducts in bat lymphatics do not exchange fluid with the surrounding interstitium. When lymph, colored by trypan blue upstream from the observation site, enters a nondyed area, no color loss can be detected across the collecting duct walls. If, on the contrary, the dye is carefully infiltrated in the immediate space surrounding a duct segment away from capillary elements, no color inflow into the duct can be detected.

Immediately beyond the entrance of some capillary chains a sinus-like structure may be found along the duct which has no valve but has markedly thicker walls and exhibits very strong contractions. No duct branch occurs at these sinuses, and the contractions seem to start at the capillary end, thus occluding the duct lumen and preventing retrograde flow. This mechanism then would function as a directional lymph pump. Of course with their energetic contractions and unidirectional valves, the typical valved sinuses must also contribute to lymph flow.

The problem of convective permeability along the collecting duct system tugs at the very roots of the question of how lymph forms and moves centripetally. Visual observations of bat wing lymphatics following infusion of water soluble dyes that do not bind with proteins (such as vital new red or trypan blue) do not indicate a detectable exchange of the dyes in either direction along collecting ducts (see above). Such studies, of course, suffer from the inherent problem of observing movements of minute amounts of chromogens across the microlymphatic vessel wall. Unfortunately, no other practical method of detecting such movement exists. Purely objective approaches tend to confound the issue because they are extremely difficult to apply to such minute areas with the vanishingly small volumes involved. In addition, the question of whether or not the objective technique distorts or alters the system concerned is always present. Although other lymphatics differ from bat wing lymphatics to varying degrees, and so may behave in another manner, it seems justifiable to conclude that neither the sinuses or intersinus segments of bat wing collecting ducts exhibits convective exchange with the surrounding interstitium. This does not, of course, rule out diffusive exchange of any permeable substance that has or develops a concentration difference in either direction between duct lymph and interstitium. Such diffusive exchange could also occur when no concentration difference exists. However, since normally lymph arises as excess interstitial fluid in the locale of the collecting ducts, it seems unlikely that such diffusive exchanges play a significant role in establishing lymph composition.

The third division is the coalescing system of transport channels that gathers the lymph from the collecting ducts and forms a large single channel that leaves along with the major entering artery and draining vein at the axilla. These transport channels are the lymphatics usually noted by casual observers; they are frequently evident and active with some flowing lymph when the collecting ducts and bulbous capillaries are not visible because little lymph is being formed. The transport channels show characteristic structures somewhat resembling the larger veins they accompany. They are organized in a segmental manner with each segment originating at a slightly enlarged sinus into which protrudes the valved structure connecting that segment with the segment or segments next peripheral. Each segment then extends centrally for some distance to where it joins the sinus of the upstream segment through an outlet valve. Each segment apparently contracts as a unit, forcing most of its diastolic volume through the valve and into the segment ahead.

LYMPH FLOW

The intrinsic rhythmic alteration of contraction and relaxation of lymphatic trunks has been discovered anew by quite a few observers over the last hundred years or so, and has been proposed as the major force propelling lymph along the system from initial vessel to the junction of the major trunks with the great veins. The clearest quantitative support for the contribution of intrinsic contractions to lymph flow in mammals is the study on sheep by Hall et al (24), who measured peak "systolic" pressures up to 25 mm Hg in efferent trunks from mesenteric and popliteal nodes in unanesthetized sheep. When outflow was blocked down stream, pressures reached as high as 50 mm Hg. External forces such as respiratory or limb movements produced only minor pressure changes under similar conditions. Wiederhielm et al (59) recorded peak pressures of 10 mm Hg in bat wing transport channels. Zweifach & Prather (64) found slightly higher pressure pulses in mesenteric lymphatic trunks of rats and guinea pigs that reached 13 mm Hg. Mislin (37), impressed by the segmental character of mesenteric lymphatics, suggested each segmental unit functioned as a pump with definite systolic and diastolic phases, and termed the units "Lymphagions." Hargens & Zweifach (26) demonstrated that under normal conditions, infusion of fluid into the mesentery trunk elevated "diastolic" pressure to some critical value that triggered contraction.

In the bat wing lymphatics, unlike most mesenteric or omental lymphatics, all elements from capillary to transport channels exhibit contraction. Infusion of saline at any site increases frequency of downstream units. Depending on resting rates, infusion or an increase in normal flow elevates frequency two to three times. As discussed above, the improbability of convective exchanges occurring across the transport channel walls implies that the forces exerted by wall contraction must be used to move lymph along the vessels. This is clearly supported by the experiment reported by Webb & Nicoll (58). They observed the function of convergent transport branches when one carried trypan blue–stained lymph and the other clear lymph. At their convergence, white and blue lymph alternately filled the downstream segment, in each case coinciding with the active contractions of the respective contributing branch. This type of experiment has been repeated in *Mineopterus* and in several other bat wings, and could no doubt be carried out with mesenteric lymphatics, since a similar action can be detected from lymph containing red cells in the mesenteric branches of *M. eptericus*.

Some lymphatics have not been observed to contract spontaneously, and forward flow in such vessels must result from the combination of unidirectional valve structures and an external force, such as muscle contraction or respiratory movements. Zweifach & Prather (64) reported they could not, by any means, excite contractions in the nonspontaneously active mesenteric lymphatics of cats and rabbits. They suggested an absence of smooth muscle cells in the walls of such lymphatics, but histological confirmation is lacking. Boggon & Palfrey (2) described smooth muscle cells in human transport channels scattered along the vessel either circularly or longitudinally, with little or no orientation. They did not mention whether these human lymphatic vessels could or did exhibit contractions when observed in situ. It would be useful to explore the histological details or various noncontractile lymphatic vessels.

Lymphatic contractions are also interesting relative to lymph formation. Intrinsic contractions and the unidirectional valves could establish pressure gradients leading to the movement of interstitial fluid into initial lymphatics and on into the collecting and transport vessels. Reddy et al (49) attempted to mathematically define the conditions for such activity. Unfortunately it is almost impossible to obtain accurate values for the various factors needed to support their theoretical proposals. They also assumed various relationships between initial lymphatic vessels where lymph formation takes place and the segmentally organized transport channels not found in known systems.

LYMPH FORMATION

The large lymphatic bulbar capillaries or initial vessels of the bat wing lymphatics do exhibit active contractions that could supply pressure gradients essential for lymph formation. For really efficient operation, the downstream resistance should be considerably less than resistance to retrograde flow. Unfortunately, adequate data do not yet exist to evaluate these flow resistances. Such information needs to be obtained both in the bat wing and other initial lymphatic sites. From simple direct observation, as discussed earlier, contraction apparently does result in lymph flow centripetally away from the bulbs. It is always possible that in inactive tissues the system is actually not efficient and the bulbar contractions result in an ebb and flow, through patent pores, of fluid between the interstitium and bulb lumen, and only a small fraction of the initial bulbar fluid is actually drained off as lymph with each contraction. Any elevation of interstitial fluid pressure resulting from increased convective loss of fluid from the vascular exchange bed would decrease the pressure head between the bulb and interstitium, thus decreasing fluid movement from the bulb into the interstitium. Therefore lymph flow increases down the drainage path. This mechanism is regulated by the very source of lymph, i.e. the convective shift of fluid into the interstitium, and does not require any sort of anatomical change in pore size or other elaborate physical adjustment. Lymph formation and centripetal movement, then, are adjusted to the need within the limits of the various parameters involved. Further consideration of lymph formation is discussed later.

Unfortunately, many initial lymphatic vessels are not available for direct observational study. In some cases, surgical preparation will expose a limited portion of the initial lymphatics in a tissue or area, but may also alter their natural environmental condition. Although many lymphatic trunks have been observed to exhibit contraction, some do not, and certainly some initial lymphatics apparently do not or cannot contract. In the mechanism proposed above, variations to flow resistance downstream and retrograde out of lymphatic capillaries, associated with intrinsic contractions, determine lymph formation and flow. If the vessels do not exhibit intrinsic activity, the necessary pressure variations responsible for flow into the initial lymphatics and downstream must arise from some external sources. Otherwise, the mechanism suggested could function in exactly the same manner as proposed for the active initial lymphatic bulbs of the bat wing.

Casley-Smith (4) proposed in a series of papers a rather elaborate and cumbersome mechanism for lymph formation based on EM observations and other data. He used the concept of a large difference between inflow and retrograde flow resistance out of the initial lymphatics and provided a mechanism by which strong osmotic gradients are established between lymph and interstitium. These gradients are proposed to operate downstream from the initial vessels and lead to larger influxes of water into the collecting and transport lymphatic channels. At present, the available data do not seem to support any protein-concentrating phenomena in the lymphatic system (39, 40).

That many lymphatic vessels exhibit active contractions is well established, and the activity is associated with the presence of unstriated muscle cells in their walls. These muscle cells have many responses similar to those shown by vascular smooth muscle, but they also exhibit some differences. Their spontaneous contractions are not regulated by autonomic nerves, since none are present (2). Some mesenteric lymphatic contractions do not respond the same to various autonomic drugs as shown by blood vessels, which must indicate some differences between their cellular components (64). Mesenteric lymphatic activity is not markedly sensitive to specific ion concentrations, although free Ca^{2+} is required for contraction of the bat wing lymphatics (43). The action of many substances known to modify or block specific cellular activities has not yet been studied on lymphatic activity; these studies are certainly warranted.

LYMPH AND INTERSTITIAL FLUID REGULATION

The preceding portion of this review discussed the anatomy and functional characteristics of lymphatic systems that can be visualized and manipulated in specialized capillary beds such as the bat wing or mesentery. This portion presents the recent lymphatic flow measurements in a variety of mammalian tissues that may be used to evaluate the lymphatics' role in the overall regulation of interstitial fluid volume.

STARLING FORCES AND LYMPH FLOW

Over 100 years ago, Ludwig (36) realized the importance of the lymphatic system in removing fluids from the interstitium. Later, Starling (53, 54) experimentally demonstrated the importance of plasma colloid osmotic pressure and capillary pressure as determinants of capillary filtrate and consequently of lymph flow. Drinker (13), Rusznyak, Földi & Szabo (52), and Yoffey & Courtice (62) summarized the extensive investigations of the lymphatic system as related to regulation of tissue fluid volume. Normally, the fluid and protein movement out of the capillary into the interstitium can be described by two equations developed by Kedem & Katchalsky (31) and discussed extensively by Katchalsky & Curran (29).

$$J_v = K_{F,C} [(P_C - P_T) - \sigma_P (\Pi_C - \Pi_T)],$$ 1.

and

$$J_P = \bar{C}_P(1 - \sigma_P)J_v + PS(C_P - C_T).$$ 2.

The first equation relates net volume movement (J_V) to the filtration coefficient ($K_{F,C}$) and the sum of the forces acting across the capillary membrane, i.e. capillary hydrostatic pressure (P_C), tissue fluid hydrostatic pressure (P_T), colloid osmotic pressure (or oncotic pressure) of plasma (π_C), and tissue colloid osmotic pressure (π_T). The reflection coefficient, σ_P, indicates the permeability of plasma proteins relative to the capillary membrane. $\sigma_P = 1$ if the molecule cannot permeate the capillary and $\sigma_P = 0$ if the molecule is freely permeable. The experimental determinations of σ_P are still quite controversial, but evidence is accumulating that indicates that σ_P for total protein has a value between 0.7 and 0.95 for a variety of mammalian capillary beds (11, 50, 55).

A rigorous description of the volume movement across the capillary into the interstitium should include a reflection coefficient (σ) for each plasma protein; during large filtrations, the reflection coefficients of small molecules may also be a factor. Perl (46, 48) recently published an excellent discussion of the problem of sieving of small molecules. Here, for simplification, we consider only a single σ_P that relates the calculated total colloid osmotic pressure to the effective colloid osmotic pressure acting across the capillary wall (33), and assume that sieving of small molecules is not a problem in a steady state.

Even without knowing the true value of each parameter in equation 1, it is still certain that lymph normally forms in most tissue regions as a result of imbalances in P_C, P_T, and σ_P $(\pi_C - \pi_T)$. However, there are very specialized fluid exchange systems, such as that within the brain and eye that do not possess a lymphatic system. But, these fluid systems do have very specialized draining mechanisms with which to prevent excessive build-up of their internal fluids (9, 10). When an in vivo tissue is in a steady state with respect to tissue volume, J_V net equals lymph flow (J_L), and equation 1 reduces to:

$$J_V = J_L = K_{F,C}\Delta P, \hspace{4cm} 3.$$

where ΔP is the algebraic sum of the Starling forces acting across the capillary membrane.

Equation 2 describes the net protein movement across the vascular exchange bed caused by bulk or convective flow (first term) and diffusive flow (second term) and equals the lymphatic protein flux in a steady state, i.e. lymph flow times the concentration of protein in the lymph equals lymphatic flux of protein. The bulk flow term consists of volume flow across the capillary wall (J_V) multiplied by $(1 - \sigma_P)$ and the average concentration difference $\overline{C}_P$, which equals $(C_P - C_T)[\log_e(C_P/c_T^{-1})]^{-1}$, where C_P and C_T refer to the protein concentrations of plasma and tissue respectively. If C_P is very near C_T, then $\overline{C}_S$ can be estimated by a series expansion, and the first term can be used to approximate $\overline{C}_S$ which equals: $(C_P + C_T)/2$. The diffusional term contains the permeability surface area product (PS) and the protein concentration gradient across the capillary. Collected lymph samples have been used extensively to study the transport properties of several capillary beds, using equation 2 and similar equations derived by Renkin and co-workers (15, 50, 51). In fact, most lymph flow measurements have dealt solely with capillary permeability determinations, and little inference as to the underlying mechanisms responsible for lymph formation has been made.

The remainder of this review is concerned only with volume removed by the lymphatics, but the protein flux equation was described here to emphasize that a major function of the lymphatic system is removal of tissue proteins. If the lymphatics did not remove proteins that leaked from the capillaries, then the only steady state tissue volume that could occur would be when $P_T = P_C$, which is now known to be possible only in a state of severe edema (23).

EDEMA SAFETY FACTOR

Several years ago, Guyton (20) introduced the concept that edema resistivity existed in each tissue. This safety factor is the tissue's ability to buffer increases in capillary filtration forces and prevent large changes in tissue hydration. When net volume movement (J_V) tends to increase as a result of elevated capillary pressure, it is now apparent that tissue fluid pressure can increase, tissue protein concentration can decrease, plasma colloid osmotic pressure can increase, and lymph flow can increase to oppose the increased filtration force. These compensatory changes in forces have collectively been termed the edema safety factor. Several recent publications (6, 12,

18, 38) have extensively discussed the changes in these various forces as edema develops; however, considerable controversy and confusion remain concerning the contribution of the lymphatics to the regulation of interstitial fluid volume.

Equation 3 can be rearranged to yield the imbalance in Starling forces,

$$\Delta P = \frac{J_L}{K_{F,C}}.$$ 4.

If total lymph flow and the filtration coefficient are measured in the same steady-state experimental condition, then ΔP can be calculated by this relationship. Equation 4 states that the lymphatic system can remove a certain amount of volume that can be related to the imbalance in Starling forces, across the capillary wall. Note that the numerical value has the dimensions of force, not flow. All capillary beds that possess lymphatics always have a basal rate of lymph flow, which indicates that ΔP is greater than 0 at normal tissue hydration states and ΔP always increases when P_C is elevated, i.e. lymph flow always increases with increased filtration pressures and the lymphatic system actually removes filtered volume equivalent to ΔP times the filtration coefficient.

$K_{F,C}$'s have been measured in individual capillaries, isolated hind limbs, perfused intestinal loops, isolated lungs, omentum, and isolated muscles using the classical micropipette approach introduced by Landis (32) and the isogravimetric procedure developed by Pappenheimer & Soto-Rivera (45). Equation 4 can be used to determine $K_{F,C}$ provided that the tissues are in a steady state and all Starling forces comprising ΔP are independently measured. It is essential that the total lymph flow draining the area for which ΔP was calculated be determined when making a comparison between $K_{F,C}$'s determined using equation 4 and those obtained by classical approaches.

FORMATION OF LYMPH

The manner in which lymph forms is still a matter of controversy. Some investigators propose that a protein-free filtrate enters the tissue across the arterial end of the capillary and that protein and fluid leak at the venular end, i.e. filtration occurs across the entire length of the capillary (27, 63). This fluid and protein enter the lymphatics through pores between the endothelial cells of the initial lymphatics and are propelled away from the tissues by active lymphatic propulsion and/or some other force.

Another group of investigators theorize that a large amount of protein-poor fluid is filtered at the arterial end of the exchange vessels and most of this fluid is reabsorbed at the venular end (33, 37). Protein extravasation may occur across the capillary either through "leaky" sites or by cytopempsis (50). Both exchange schemes can easily be visualized as operative in the exchange vessels, but we do not know how the pressure drop occurs along the length of the capillary. A large drop down the capillary favors the possibility that fluid will be reabsorbed at the venular end; however, if only a slight pressure drop occurs, then the capillary should filter its entire length. Experimental evidence has been presented in support of both theories of fluid movement across the capillary.

Another possible explanation for fluid and protein movement across the capillary is that flowing capillaries filter, while nonflowing ones absorb, and in either instance a small amount of protein leaks into the interstitium. What is observed as a final lymph flow is a result of changes occurring in the vasoactive capillary beds and represents an average functional value not representative of individual capillary-tissue interactions (63).

Casley-Smith (4) recently presented an interesting argument concerning reabsorption of tissue proteins at the venular end of the capillary. He proposed that large pores (10 μm in diameter) allow an osmotic pull of fluid containing proteins out of the interstitium into the capillaries. This theory will not stand a critical physical analysis because when pores are large (10 μm) then virtually no osmotic pressure can be exerted across their interface by plasma proteins. However, filtration should occur into the interstitium through these pores because venous pressure exceeds tissue pressure. Perl's recent analysis (47) indicates that protein reentry at the venous end of the capillary is possible in pores smaller than those proposed by Casley-Smith, but the hydrostatic forces operative across the venular end of the capillary would also tend to oppose any osmotic pull through pores; as pores become smaller, diffusion of protein predominates and this force is outward not inward. The process is possible but physically not very probable and in any case would only account for a relatively small component of the net protein flux that finally enters the lymphatic system.

METHODS USED TO ESTIMATE ΔP

One approach for evaluating ΔP is to measure or determine all the forces in equation 1, i.e. P_C, P_T, π_C, and π_T. This assumes that $\pi_T = \pi_L$, and a lymphatic sample must be obtained from the preparation to determine the values of π_L. This approach has been used by Erdmann et al (14), Drake & Taylor (12), Hargens & Zweifach (25), and Chen et al (6) to determine ΔP when it is not certain whether or not total lymph flow was truly measured from the organ or the preparation. However, if a reasonable estimate of total lymph flow can be obtained from the preparation, then a capillary $K_{F,C}$ can be estimated by equation 4. This approach was used by Erdmann et al and Hargens & Zweifach for determining $K_{F,C}$'s in lung and mesentery tissues, respectively.

For this calculation of ΔP, all Starling forces must be measured, and from the four cited references only that of Chen et al actually measured all the forces in a single preparation. In the other cited references P_T was assumed to be equal to zero, i.e. the algebraic sum of P_C, π_C, and π_L was equated to the "normal" ΔP (designated in Table 1 as ΔP_N). The capillary filtration pressures were then altered in each preparation and ΔP was again calculated using the same assumptions (ΔP_I). The assumption that $P_T \simeq$ to zero can lead to either over- or underestimates of ΔP depending on whether P_T is negative or positive in a particular preparation.

Table 1 Calculation of normal and elevated imbalance in Starling forces

Tissue	Species (type of preparation)	ΔP_N[a] $(K_{F,C})$	ΔP_I[a] $(K_{F,C})$	References
Lung	Dog (isolated)	0.8 (0.250)	5.0 (0.250)	Drake & Taylor (11, 12)
	Sheep (intact)	0.51–12.0 (0.005)	3.3–19.0 (0.003)	Erdmann et al (14)
Intestine	Dog (isolated)	0.2[b] —	6.8[b] —	Yablonski & Lifson (61)
	Cat (isolated)	0.2 (0.405)	4.3 (0.083)	Mortillaro & Taylor (38)
Mesentery	Cat (in vivo)	12.0[c] (0.0018)	18.0[c] (0.0031)	Hargens & Zweifach (26)
Hindpaw	Dog (isolated)	0.50 —	6.3 (0.028)	Chen et al (6)
	Dog (in vivo)	0.30[d] —	6.0[d] —	Gibson (18)

[a] Units of control ΔP, ΔP_N, and altered capillary filtration forces, ΔP_I, are mm Hg and units of $K_{F,C}$ are ml (min · 100 g · mm Hg)$^{-1}$, dashes represent preparations for which $K_{F,C}$'s were not measured, ΔP_I's were calculated for maximum ΔP observed in the preparation.

[b] Calculated assuming $K_{F,C}$'s were identical to those measured in dog intestine by Johnson & Hanson (28).

[c] These authors present several ΔP calculations; we chose the norepinephrine experimental group because this represents a preparation with an increase in capillary pressure.

[d] $K_{F,C}$'s were not measured but can be estimated from those obtained by Chen et al (6) and Renkin (15).

Hargens & Zweifach actually calculated negative ΔP's in some preparations because the capillaries were absorbing not filtering, which does not provide any force information related to lymphatic function. When ΔP is calculated by summing the Starling forces, the tissues must be in a steady state or the calculation will be time dependent because the capillary and tissue forces are adjusting due to the increased filtration. However, a ΔP related to lymphatic function can be estimated for either normal or control conditions by determining lymph flow and the Starling forces when the tissues are in a steady state, and this ΔP can be related to lymphatic function in terms of the effectiveness of the lymphatic system in opposing increases in capillary filtration forces.

Without total lymph flow measurements, the assumption that all lymphatics behave similarly allows ΔP_I to be calculated if ΔP_N has been measured and the change in lymph flow assessed following elevations of filtration pressures. For example, if ΔP_N was 1 mm Hg, and lymph flow increased 10-fold following the increase in filtration forces, then ΔP at the latter state of tissue hydration would be 10 mm Hg. Inherent in this particular calculation, where the Starling forces are not measured at the increased filtration pressures, is the assumption that $K_{F,C}$ is not altered by the increased filtration rate. This approach is useful when determining maximum lymphatic "safety factors" in tissues such as lung and intestine when double membranes in series complicate interpretation of experimental results.

The second method of obtaining ΔP is to measure $K_{F,C}$ by gravimetric procedures (28, 44, 45) and obtain total lymph flow from the organ under study. This has been done by Mortillaro & Taylor (38) and can also be applied to the data of Yablonski & Lifson (61) in isolated intestinal tissue by using published values for $K_{F,C}$'s. Basically, this method of estimating ΔP consists of measuring total lymph flow and $K_{F,C}$'s at different tissue steady states; the lymphatics' ability to remove fluid can be calculated at each state of tissue hydration. This approach is necessary if $K_{F,C}$ is altered by experimental conditions such as drug infusion or the Bayliss (myogenic) effect, which is observed as venous pressure is elevated in intestinal preparations (28).

ΔP CALCULATIONS

Lung Tissue

The data of Erdmann et al (14) represent a calculation of ΔP achieved by measuring or determining all Starling forces and assuming $P_T = 0$ at normal (ΔP_N) and elevated (ΔP_I) capillary pressures. Although a range of ΔP's are shown in Table 1, the average ΔP_N was about 4 mm Hg, and when capillary hydrostatic pressure was increased, the average ΔP_I increased to about 12 mm Hg. This indicates that the sheep pulmonary lymphatic system has a high safety factor capable of opposing even larger changes in capillary pressure since the elevated capillary pressure studies did not produce intra-alveolar edema. The work of Drake (11) indicates that only a small ΔP_N exists across isolated dog lung tissues, using the same assumptions used by Erdmann et al when calculating "normal" values. As capillary pressures were increased in a range to produce intra-alveolar edema, ΔP_I increased to 5 mm Hg in Drake's study. This ΔP_I calculation assumed that all lymphatics draining the lung behave similarly to the cannulated lymphatic, with respect to changes in lymph flows, and ΔP_I was calculated by multiplying the ΔP_N times the change in lymph flow relative to normal. Drake & Taylor (12) also calculated that ΔP_I was 2–3 mm Hg by measuring $K_{F,C}$ and estimating maximum total lung lymph flow obtained during intra-alveolar edema formation (13). The two ΔP_I calculations are in excellent agreement, even when different methods were used to calculate the lymphatic safety factor. The lungs of both dog and sheep possess a substantial lymphatic edema safety factor; however, sheep lungs appear to possess a more efficient lymphatic system.

Intestine

Mortillaro & Taylor (38) measured the total steady-state lymph flows and $K_{F,C}$'s at different levels of venous pressure; therefore, ΔP could be calculated at each lymph flow which represents several states of tissue hydration. However, the calculated ΔP's shown in Table 1 for this work were calculated at a venous pressure of 5 mm

Hg for ΔP_N and 30 mm Hg for ΔP_I. In the work of Yablonski & Lifson (61) there were no measurements of $K_{F,C}$, but Johnson & Hanson (28) measured these parameters for dog small intestine, and these values of $K_{F,C}$ were used to calculate ΔP_N and ΔP_I in Table 1 from Yablonski & Lifson's data. The lymphatic safety factor appears to be very similar in both dog and cat intestinal preparations, amounting to 4–6 mm Hg maximally. Because the intestinal capillary filtration decreases with increasing pressure, a calculation of ΔP_I is not possible by using ΔP_N times relative change in lymph flow, since lymph flow had only increased 6–7-fold maximally in these preparations, i.e. ΔP_N X relative increase in lymph flow $= 0.2 \times 7 = 1.4$ mm Hg, a value considerably lower than the ΔP_I calculated using equation 4.

Mesentery

Recently, Hargens & Zweifach (25) measured terminal lymphatic pressures, capillary pressure, plasma colloid osmotic pressure, and lymph colloid osmotic pressure in isolated mesentery tissue and calculated ΔP_N and a number of ΔP_I's following alterations in filtration forces. We choose here to present only their data obtained by using norepinephrine infusions, since this was an experimental perturbation that demonstrated predominately an increase in capillary pressure. It appears that mesenteric capillaries have a normally large imbalance of Starling forces. The largest increase in ΔP_I observed by these authors for perturbations of capillary filtration forces was approximately 8 mm Hg. Although the approach used in these experiments is excellent, and no doubt the approach of the future, the results are difficult to interpret because the capillary-lymphatic system may not be in a steady state and the Starling force calculation may be problematic because of problems of assessing π_T using lymph of mixed origin.

Peripheral Studies

Chen et al (6) were able to measure all the Starling forces in a dog hindpaw preparation. They calculated ΔP at three levels of venous pressure and the difference between the measured imbalance in Starling forces and the increase in filtration pressure at a steady state must equal ΔP. Table 1 shows a normal P_N of only 0.5 mm Hg, and ΔP_I increased to 6.3 mm Hg when venous pressure was elevated to 35 mm Hg. Unfortunately, the total lymph flow could not be measured in the preparation and no comparison can be made between the values measured by calculating Starling forces and by using equation 4.

Interestingly, Gibson (18) obtained an equivalent ΔP_N by assuming that the $K_{F,C}$ of dog hindpaw was similar to that determined in hind-limb preparations, and his calculated ΔP_I increased to levels similar to those obtained by Chen et al. These studies indicate that the lymphatic flow safety factor can contribute a maximum of 6 mm Hg in preventing excessive build-up of tissue fluid in subcutaneous tissue.

TRANSIENT ANALYSIS OF LYMPH FLOW

Figures 3A and 3B represent lymph transients for dog hindpaw (7) and cat small intestinal (18a) preparations, respectively. Note that lymph flow increases immedi-

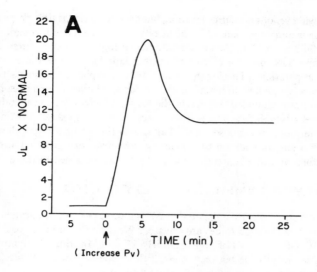

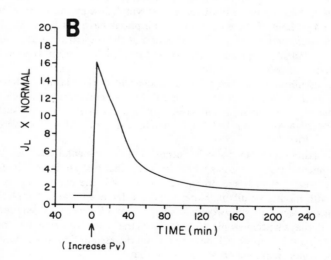

Figure 3   *A* Plot of relative change in lymph flow as a function of time following elevation of venous pressure to 35 mm Hg, from the work of Chen et al (7) in a dog hindpaw preparation. *B* Plot of relative changes in lymph flow as a function of time obtained from an isolated loop of cat ileal tissue (18a).

ately following venous pressure elevation, but flow decreases as time progresses. This observation is more pronounced in the intestine, but here a double membrane exists and since fluid moves into the intestinal lumen at high venous pressures, the lowering of lymph flow may not be caused by the same factor(s) as those operative in hindpaw preparations. The importance of these lymphatic transients is that one would expect lymph flow to remain high, but for some unexplained reason, the high flow rate is not maintained. Whatever the cause, ΔP could be considerably higher, based on peak lymph flow values, than observed in steady states. Again, we must await techniques that can assess what happens in the lymphatic system when transient flows occur, in addition to evaluating the alterations in tissue and capillary forces, before we can adequately explain the results obtained in these studies.

SUMMARY OF LYMPHATIC SAFETY FACTOR

The data of Table 1 clearly indicate that ΔP is always positive in normal conditions and increases as filtration forces are elevated. We have found in the past that most tissues have safety factors of approximately 15 mm Hg; thus the lymphatic flow would appear to provide between one-fourth to one-half of the tissues' ability to withstand alterations in capillary filtration pressures.

However, many assumptions must be made when ΔP is calculated by either summing the Starling forces or dividing total lymph flow by the filtration coefficient (equation 4). Many of these necessary assumptions have not been experimentally verified and are under extensive investigation at the present time. But, since these assumptions do affect our interpretation of ΔP's, it is important to point them out explicitly to the reader:

1. The assumption that the reflection coefficient of the plasma proteins (σp) is equal to 1 will cause an overestimate of ΔP. For skeletal muscle and subcutaneous tissue, this may not constitute any great problem, but in other tissues, such as lung and intestine where σp may be 0.7–0.8, then the calculated ΔP will be overestimated at least 20–30%.

2. The assumption that $\pi_T = \pi_L$ needs to be experimentally verified. Although no experimental evidence exists which indicates that lymphatic protein concentrations are greater than tissue protein levels (39, 40), the controversy is far from settled, with models predicting either a large difference between lymph and tissue fluids with respect to plasma protein or no apparent difference between the two fluids (22, 56). Perhaps with micropipette techniques this controversy can be settled in the near future; until then, we will have to rely on the assumption that lymph draining a specific region represents tissue fluids in that area.

3. When determining all Starling forces, some measurement of P_T must be made for each preparation. A recent review article addresses the problem of P_T measurements and this problem is not discussed further here, except to emphasize that P_T must be determined by some direct means in order to determine the Starling forces (21).

4. To apply any thermodynamic equations for calculation of ΔP, the tissue must be in a steady state with respect to tissue volume, lymph flow, and tissue protein.

For example, if capillary pressure is suddenly increased, ΔP as calculated by summing the Starling forces will initially be large because now ΔP represents the net capillary filtration pressure; but as the tissue and capillary forces adjust, the calculated ΔP will decrease until it finally equals a steady-state value that can be related to lymphatic function. Any calculation of ΔP obtained by the addition of Starling forces calculated in a nonsteady-state condition must be interpreted with considerable caution.

5. When calculating $K_{F,C}$ or ΔP from equation 4, total lymph draining the organ must be collected.

Even with the obvious problems that complicate ΔP calculations, this concept is still the only available means for assessing the lymphatics' ability to remove volume from any given tissue.

Literature Cited

1. Allen, L. 1967. Lymphatics and lymphoid tissues. *Ann. Rev. Physiol.* 29:197–224
2. Boggon, R. P., Palfrey, A. J. 1973. The microscopic anatomy of human lymphatic trunks. *J. Anat.* 114:398–405
3. Casley-Smith, J. R. 1972. The role of the endothelial intercellular junctions in the functioning of the initial lymphatics. *Angiologica* 9:106–31
4. Casley-Smith, J. R. 1975. A theoretical support for the transport of macromolecules by osmotic flow across a leaky membrane against a concentration gradient. *Microvasc. Res.* 9:43–48
5. Casley-Smith, J. R., Florey, H. W. 1961. The structure of normal small lymphatics. *Q. J. Exp. Physiol.* 46:101–6
6. Chen, H. I., Granger, H. J., Taylor, A. E. 1976. Interaction of capillary interstitial and lymphatic forces in the canine hind paw. *Circ. Res.* 38:245–54
7. Chen, H. I., Granger, H. J., Taylor, A. E. 1977. Lymph flow transients following elevation of venous pressure in the dog's hind paw. In *Advances in Lymphology*, ed. R. C. Mayall, M. Witte. New York: Plenum. In press
8. Cliff, W. J., Nicoll, P. A. 1970. Structure and function of lymphatic vessels of the bat's wing. *Q. J. Exp. Physiol.* 55:112–21
9. Davson, H. 1955. A comparative study of the aqueous humor and cerebrospinal fluid in the rabbit. *J. Physiol.* 129:111–33
10. Davson, H. 1960. Intracranial and intraoccular fluids. In *Handb. Physiol.,* Sect. 1, Vol. III, ed. H. W. Magoun, P.

761. Wash. DC: *Am. Physiol. Soc.* Williams & Wilkins
11. Drake, R. E. 1975. *Changes in the Starling forces during the formation of pulmonary edema.* PhD thesis. Univ. Miss. Med. Cent. Jackson, Miss.
12. Drake, R. E., Taylor, A. E. 1977. The effect of decreased tissue proteins in opposing pulmonary edema formation. See Ref. 7
13. Drinker, C. K. 1945. *Pulmonary Edema and Inflammation.* Cambridge: Harvard Univ. Press
14. Erdmann, A. J. III, Vaughan, T. R. Jr., Brigham, K. L., Woolverton, W. C., Staub, N. C. 1975. Effect of increased vascular pressure on lung fluid balance in unanesthetized sheep. *Circ. Res.* 37:271–84
15. Garlick, D. G., Renkin, E. M. 1970. Transport of large molecules from plasma to interstitial fluid and lymph in dogs. *Am. J. Physiol.* 219:1595–1605
16. Gatti, R. A., Stutman, O., Good, R. A. 1970. The lymphoid system. *Ann. Rev. Physiol.* 32:529–46
17. Gauer, O. H., ed. 1972. Proceedings of a symposium on capillary exchange and the interstitial space. *Pfluegers Arch. Suppl.* 336:s1–s98
18. Gibson, H. W. 1976. *Dynamics of lymph flow, tissue pressure and protein exchange in subcutaneous tissue.* PhD thesis. Univ. Miss. Med. Cent., Jackson, Miss.
18a. Granger, D. N., Mortillaro, N. A., Taylor, A. E. 1977. Interactions of intestinal lymph flow and secretion. *Am. J. Physiol.* In press
19. Guyton, A. C. 1963. A concept of negative interstitial pressure based on pres-

sures in implanted perforated capsules. *Circ. Res.* 12:399–414

20. Guyton, A. C., Coleman, T. G. 1968. Regulation of interstitial fluid volume. *Ann. NY Acad. Sci.* 150:537–47

21. Guyton, A. C., Granger, H. J., Taylor, A. E. 1971. Interstitial fluid pressure. *Physiol. Rev.* 51:527–63

22. Guyton, A. C., Taylor, A. E., Drake, R. E., Parker, J. C. 1976. Dynamics of subatmospheric pressure in the pulmonary interstitial fluid. In *Lung Liquids: Ciba Found. Symp.* pp. 77–100. North-Holland: Amsterdam; Elsevier: Excerpta Medica

23. Guyton, A. C., Taylor, A. E., Granger, H. J. 1975. *Circulatory Physiology: Dynamics of Body Fluids.* Philadelphia: Saunders

24. Hall, J. G., Morris, B., Woolley, G. 1965. Intrinsic rhythmic propulsion of lymph in the unanesthetized sheep. *J. Physiol.* 180:336–49

25. Hargens, A. R., Zweifach, B. W. 1976. Transport between blood and peripheral lymph in intestine. *Microvasc. Res.* 11:89–101

26. Hargens, A. R., Zweifach, B. W. Personal communication

27. Intaglietta, M., Zweifach, B. W. 1974. Microcirculatory basis of fluid exchange. *Adv. Biol. Med. Phys.* 15:111–59

28. Johnson, P. C., Hanson, K. M. 1966. Capillary filtration in small intestine of dog. *Circ. Res.* 19:766–73

29. Katchalsky, A., Curran, P. F. 1965. *Nonequilibrium Thermodynamics in Biophysics.* Cambridge, Mass: Harvard Univ. Press

30. Kato, F. 1966. The fine structure of the lymphatics and the passage of China ink particles through their walls. *Nagoya Med. J.* 12:221–46

31. Kedem, O., Katchalsky, A. 1958. Thermodynamic analysis of biological membranes to nonelectrolytes. *Biochim. Biophys. Acta* 27:299–346

32. Landis, E. M. 1934. Capillary pressure and capillary permeability. *Physiol. Rev.* 14:404–81

33. Landis, E. M., Pappenheimer, J. R. 1963. Exchange of substances through the capillary wall. In *Handb. Physiol., Circulation, Sect. 2, Vol. II,* ed. W. F. Hamilton, P. Dow, pp. 961–1034. Wash. DC: Am. Physiol. Soc.

34. Leak, L. V. 1970. Electron microscopic observations on lymphatic capillaries and the structural components of the connective tissue-lymph outerface. *Microvasc. Res.* 2:361–91

35. Leak, L. V., Burke, J. F. 1968. Ultrastructural studies on the lymphatic anchoring filaments. *J. Cell Biol.* 36:129–49

36. Ludwig, C. 1858. *Lehrbuch der Physiologie des Menchen.* Leipzig: Winter

37. Mislin, H. 1971. Die kontraktilen Eigenschaften der Lymphgefässe. *Angiologica* 8:206–11

38. Mortillaro, N. A., Taylor, A. E. 1976. Interactions of capillary and tissue forces in the cat small intestine. *Circ. Res.* 39:348–58

39. Nicolaysen, G., Nicolaysen, A., Staub, N. C. 1975. A quantitative radioautographic comparison of albumin concentration in different sized lymph vessels in normal mouse lung. *Microvasc. Res.* 10:138–52

40. Nicolaysen, G., Staub, N. C. 1975. Time course of albumin equilibration in interstitium and lymph of normal mouse lungs. *Microvasc. Res.* 9:29–37

41. Nicoll, P. A. 1969. Peripheral lymphatic activity and permeability in the bat wing. *Microvasc. Res.* 1:312

42. Nicoll, P. A. 1973. Formation and flow of lymph and lymphatic permeability. In *Regulation and Control in Physiological Systems,* ed. A. S. Iberall, A. C. Guyton, pp. 122–26. Pittsburgh, Penn: Instrum. Soc. Am.

43. Nicoll, P. A. 1975. Excitation-contraction of single vascular smooth muscle cells and lymphatics *in vivo. Immunochemistry* 12:511–15

44. Pappenheimer, J. R., Renkin, E. M., Borrero, L. M. 1951. Filtration, diffusion and molecular sieving through peripheral capillary membranes. A contribution to the pore theory of capillary permeability. *Am. J. Physiol.* 167:13–46

45. Pappenheimer, J. R., Soto-Rivera, A. 1948. Effective osmotic pressure of the plasma proteins and other quantities associated with the capillary circulation in the hind limbs of cats and dogs. *Am. J. Physiol.* 152:471–91

46. Perl, W. 1973. A friction coefficient, series-parallel channel model for transcapillary flux of nonelectrolytes and water. *Microvasc. Res.* 6:169–93

47. Perl, W. 1975. Convection and permeation of albumin between plasma and interstitium. *Microvasc. Res.* 10:83–94

48. Perl, W., Chowdhury, P., Chinard, F. P. 1975. Reflection coefficients of dog lung endothelium to small hydrophilic solutes. *Am. J. Physiol.* 228:797–809

49. Reddy, N. P., Krouskop, T. A., Newell, P. H. Jr. 1975. A note on the mechanism of lymph flow through the terminal lymphatics. *Microvasc. Res.* 10: 214–16

50. Renkin, E. M. 1964. Transport of large molecules across the capillary walls. *Physiologist* 7:13–28

51. Renkin, E. M., Carter, R. D., Joyner, W. L. 1974. Mechanisms of the sustained action of histamines and bradykinin on transport of large molecules across capillary walls in the dog paw. *Microvasc. Res.* 7:49–60

52. Rusznyak, I., Földi, M., Szabo, G. 1967. *Lymphatics and Lymph Circulation.* Oxford: Pergamon. 2nd ed.

53. Starling, E. H. 1896. On the absorption of fluids from the connective tissue spaces. *J. Physiol. London* 19:312–26

54. Starling, E. H. 1898. *Textbook of Physiology,* ed. E. A. Schafer. Edinburgh & London: Pentland

55. Staub, N. C. 1974. Pulmonary edema. *Physiol. Rev.* 54:687–811

56. Taylor, A. E., Gibson, W. H. 1975. Concentrating ability of the lymphatic vessels. *Lymphology* 8:43–49

57. Taylor, A. E., Gibson, W. H., Granger, H. J., Guyton, A. C. 1973. The interaction between intracapillary and tissue forces in the overall regulation of interstitial fluid volume. *Lymphology* 6:192–208

58. Webb, R. L., Nicoll, P. A. 1944. Behavior of lymphatic vessels in the living bat. *Anat. Rec.* 88:351–67

59. Wiederhielm, C. A., Weston, B. V. 1973. Microvascular, lymphatic, and tissue pressures in the unanesthetized mammal. *Am. J. Physiol.* 225:992–96

60. Witte, M. H., Witte, C. L. 1973. Physiology 301 (Clinical Correlation Lectures): Lymph formation > lymph absorption: The formula of edema. A second experiment in the teaching of lymphology to medical students. *Lymphology* 6:101–9

61. Yablonski, M. E., Lifson, N. 1976. Mechanism of production of intestinal secretion by elevated venous pressure. *J. Clin. Invest.* 57:904–15

62. Yoffey, J. M., Courtice, F. G. 1970. *Lymphatics, Lymph and Lymphomyeloid Complex.* London: Academic

63. Zweifach, B. W. 1973. Microcirculation. *Ann. Rev. Physiol.* 35:117–50

64. Zweifach, B. W., Prather, J. W. 1975. Micromanipulation of pressure in terminal lymphatics in the mesentery. *Am. J. Physiol.* 228:1326–35

Ann. Rev. Physiol. 1977. 39:97–134
Copyright © 1977 by Annual Reviews Inc. All rights reserved

ACTIONS OF HORMONES ON THE KIDNEY

❖1165

Adrian I. Katz and Marshall D. Lindheimer

Departments of Medicine and Obstetrics and Gynecology, The University of Chicago
Pritzker School of Medicine, Chicago, Illinois 60637

INTRODUCTION

Endocrinologists and renal physiologists (unfortunately seldom working together) have long been intrigued by the interaction between hormones and the kidney. Within one year, three special journal issues (39, 202, 265) were devoted to reviews of the many recent publications dealing with the actions of hormones on the kidney, the renal disposition of hormones, the kidney as an endocrine organ, and the effect of renal failure on hormone metabolism. In these symposia contributors had the luxury to devote their entire review to a single hormone. Here, space constraints preclude a comprehensive review of "renal endocrinology," and the present article deals only with the actions of hormones on kidney function. Even within this topic a selective approach was necessary, and we chose to review less frequently surveyed hormones, a choice which in part also reflects our own research interests. Reluctantly, we had to omit certain hormones for which the kidney is a primary target organ, such as parathyroid hormone, aldosterone, and vasopressin, each of which could have easily occupied the entire space available to us. Readers interested in the contribution of the kidney to the peripheral metabolism of hormones, in endocrine abnormalities in renal failure, or in humoral substances not included in this article are referred to the three symposia listed above. These provide a rich source of further reference to the topics not covered here.

The literature survey for this review was concluded in April 1976.

THYROID HORMONES

Thyroid hormones (thyroxine, T_4; triiodothyronine, T_3) play an important role in kidney growth and in the maintenance of many of its functions. In general, most parameters of renal function are enhanced in hyperthyroid patients and depressed in hypothyroidism. These alterations are corrected when patients become euthyroid, and can be reproduced in animals by administering thyroid hormones or by surgical

97

or chemical thyroid ablation. While the mechanisms that mediate the effects of thyroid hormones on the kidney are incompletely understood, it should be noted that T_3 binds specifically to kidney nuclei (85, 232), and nuclear binding is an important step in the initiation of hormonal action in susceptible tissues (89, 231).

The renal effects of thyroid hormones are often modified by their extrarenal actions, chiefly on intermediary metabolism and systemic hemodynamics. In addition, thyroid hormones alter mineral metabolism and the distribution of water and electrolytes between fluid compartments which indirectly also affect renal function. Comprehensive reviews of the interaction between the thyroid and the kidney have been published recently (41, 154), and the following discussion is addressed primarily to the direct renal effects of thyroid hormones.

Kidney Growth and Morphology

T_4 treatment increases kidney weight and the mitotic index, indicative of both hypertrophy and hyperplasia (240), whereas thyroid deficiency interferes with normal kidney growth in young rats (307) and decreases the kidney size of adult animals (156, 315). Compensatory kidney growth after unilateral nephrectomy does occur in hypothyroid rats (315), but to a somewhat lesser extent than in euthyroid animals (156). Thyroid deficiency is also accompanied by morphologic alterations in both the developing and the adult kidney (268).

Renal Hemodynamics

Renal plasma flow (RPF) and glomerular filtration rate (GFR) increase substantially in hyperthyroid patients (105, 137) and in animals treated with thyroid hormones (92, 127, 156). Administration of T_3 and T_4 also increases RPF and GFR in hypothyroid patients (137), but seems to have only a modest effect on renal hemodynamics in normal subjects (105). In contrast, RPF and GFR are depressed by approximately one-third in hypothyroid humans (81, 105, 137, 154) and animals (40, 95, 140, 156, 208, 311). Since these changes in renal hemodynamics parallel similar alterations in cardiac output and blood flow in other vascular beds, they probably do not reflect specific effects of thyroid hormones on the renal vasculature.

Tubular Function

Tubular secretory (T_mPAH or T_m diodrast) and reabsorptive (T_m glucose) maxima are augmented in spontaneous and experimental hyperthyroidism, roughly in proportion to the increase in RPF and GFR (92, 105, 127, 137), while tubular transport capacity is consistently below normal in myxedematous patients (105, 137) and in hypothyroid animals (311). It is not clear to what extent these alterations are a result of changes in the metabolic machinery involved in tubular transport or reflect the striking changes in tubular mass seen with thyroid hormone excess or deficit.

Thyroid extracts increase urine flow in man and laboratory animals [reviewed in (154)]. Most of this increment is apparently free water, since T_4 injections enhance the ability of the kidney to excrete a water load (164) and protect the animals from water intoxication (110). Despite this, patients with uncomplicated hyperthyroidism have at most a mild concentrating defect that becomes significant only when there is renal structural damage due to superimposed nephrocalcinosis (154). On the other hand, both urine dilution and, to a lesser extent, concentrating ability are impaired in thyroid deficiency (84, 154). Hypothyroid patients frequently exhibit a delayed diuretic response to a water load and occasionally present with severe dilutional hyponatremia (68, 70, 81, 120, 305). The mechanism involved in the limited ability of the kidney to generate free water in hypothyroidism is disputed. Defective adrenocortical hormone production (305), inappropriate secretion of antidiuretic hormone (ADH) (120), impaired Na reabsorption in the loop of Henle (210), and decreased delivery of filtrate to the diluting segment (81) have all been suggested. This question has been investigated in our laboratory (95): thyroidectomized rats excreted a smaller fraction of a water load and had decreased absolute free water clearance (CH_2O) and distal Na delivery, but when corrected for the lower GFR these measurements were similar to those obtained in intact animals. Furthermore, fractional sodium reabsorption in the diluting segment of hypothyroid rats was normal, and when distal delivery was increased, fractional CH_2O was even greater than in controls. These results suggest that in hypothyroid animals the sodium reabsorptive capacity of the diluting segment is preserved and favor the view that the impaired water excretion is due primarily to decreased delivery of filtrate to this site. Essentially similar results were obtained in hypothyroid rats with congenital diabetes insipidus, negating a role for ADH in the pathogenesis of the diluting effect.

Electrolyte Excretion

Thyroid hormones increase the urinary excretion of Ca and PO_4 both by acting on the kidney and indirectly through their effects on bone metabolism: the hypercalciuria and hyperphosphaturia often seen in hyperthyroid patients are due chiefly to the enhanced skeletal turnover and in part to the hormone-induced increments in GFR (3, 14, 59, 168). The effect of thyroid hormones on the tubular handling of mineral ions is less clear, however, since Ca reabsorption decreases while the reabsorption of PO_4 seems to be enhanced in uncomplicated hyperthyroidism (3, 31, 98, 126). These changes probably reflect the reduction in parathyroid hormone (PTH) levels produced by the increased ionized Ca rather than a direct effect of thyroid hormones on the renal tubule (98, 154). Magnesium excretion is also increased in hyperthyroidism (152).

Whereas plasma levels and the urinary excretion of Na and K are little affected by excess thyroid hormone, Na metabolism is markedly altered in thyroid-deficient humans and animals. In myxedematous patients, total exchangeable Na is increased, although plasma Na tends to be low because of concomitant water retention (5, 291). The accumulation of excess body Na implies a limitation of the kidney's ability to excrete Na in proportion to intake, which could be a result of the reduced GFR, or increased tubular Na reabsorption (T_{Na}) caused by the contracted plasma volume, or both. It is also possible that part of the retained Na is bound to tissue mucopolysaccharides in a way that makes it unavailable to the volume-sensing mechanisms governing renal excretion (235).

In contrast to humans, hypothyroid rats exhibit a defect in Na conservation, manifested by salt wasting when eating Na-deficient diets and by an exaggerated natriuretic response to saline loading (109, 140, 208). The mechanism responsible for this "sodium leak" is not agreed upon. Decreased secretion of, or renal sensitivity to, mineralocorticoids has been proposed (109) and denied (140). An intriguing explanation for this phenomenon has been proposed by Bradley et al (40), who found that the glomerular size was similar in normal and hypothyroid rats, while the proximal tubules were shorter in the latter. This anatomic glomerulotubular imbalance results in a higher filtrate velocity which, in these authors' view, accounts for the impaired T_{Na} in hypothyroid rats. Decreased rates of aerobic and glycolytic metabolism in kidney slices from hypothyroid rats (141) also raise the possibility that the reabsorptive defect is due to insufficient energy for active Na transport, but results obtained in slices in vitro may have limited relevance to the situation in the filtering and reabsorbing kidney in vivo.

A mild defect in urinary acidification has been recently reported in hypothyroid rats; the authors suggest that the defect reflects impaired H^+ secretion in the distal tubule (209).

Effect on Na Transport and Renal Na-K-ATPase

Edelman and co-workers proposed that an important part of the thermogenic action of thyroid hormones is due to the stimulation of active Na transport in responsive tissues through regulation of membrane of Na-K-ATPase via induction protein synthesis (89). Thus, Ismail-Beigi & Edelman found decreased oxygen consumption (QO_2) in slices and lower Na-K-ATPase in homogenates of kidneys from hypothyroid rats, while both ouabain-sensitive QO_2 and Na-K-ATPase were stimulated by the administration of T_3 (147). The relation between thyroid status and renal function was further studied by the authors (156), who confirmed the decreased Na-K-ATPase activity in kidneys of hypothyroid rats and enhanced levels in T_3-treated animals. In all the experimental situations tested, Na-K-ATPase specific activity closely paralled the net T_{Na}, and Na-K-ATPase of thyroid-deficient rats could be restored to normal by increasing T_{Na} (through increments in GFR produced by contralateral nephrectomy or the administration of methylprednisolone) despite the persistence of hypothyroidism. These results led to the conclusion that changes in renal Na-K-ATPase in altered thyroid states represent primarily adaptive responses to changing reabsorptive Na loads rather than being the result of lack or excess of thyroid hormone per se. However, as suggested by Edelman (90), it is possible that both an adaptive response to increase Na loads and direct induction of Na-K-ATPase operate together in mediating the effect of thyroid hormones on Na transport in the kidney.

CALCITONIN

Calcitonin inhibits bone resorption (10, 197, 238, 261) and increases the urinary excretion of numerous solutes, including sodium (7, 11, 12, 18, 32, 33, 58, 123, 159, 233, 241, 252, 267, 280, 283, 284, 312), chloride (7, 11, 12, 32), calcium (7, 11, 18, 32, 33, 58, 123, 214, 233, 280, 284), phosphate (8, 11, 18, 32, 33, 58, 123, 160, 213, 214, 233, 241, 252, 260, 280, 283, 284), citrate (107), and uric acid (34). Plasma Ca and PO_4 concentrations are decreased by calcitonin through its dual effect on bone and kidney. The skeletal action is usually dominant, and when bone turnover is rapid it may obscure the renal effect of the hormone on Ca and PO_4 excretion, whereas the renal action comes to the fore when the rate of bone resorption is low (58, 123, 260, 261, 312).

Interpretation of the renal effects of calcitonin is complicated by the fact that its administration results in hypocalcemia which secondarily stimulates parathyroid hormone release. Thus, proof of the effects of calcitonin on electrolyte excretion has been most convincingly demonstrated in parathyroidectomized animals and hypoparathyroid humans where it is generally accepted that they result from a direct action of calcitonin on the renal tubule. This view is strongly supported by the demonstration of renal receptors specific for calcitonin in an anatomical distribution different from that of PTH receptors (199, 200).

The biological activity of calcitonin varies both with the source of the hormone and with the species tested. Salmon calcitonin is by far the most potent preparation, due in part to its high affinity for calcitonin receptors and in part to its slower degradation rate when given in vivo (200, 312). Calcitonin is calciuric, phosphaturic, and saluretic in most mammalians tested except the dog (57, 266), but does not affect kidney function appreciably in elasmobranchs (131). In this respect it is of interest that CT stimulates renal adenylate cyclase in the rat (199, 200) but not in nonmammalian vertebrates (88). Purified and synthetic calcitonin produce results similar to the crude hormone (18, 123, 267, 283), and oxidation of calcitonin with performic acid completely abolishes its biological effects (18, 241, 312).

Renal Hemodynamics

Calcitonin had no significant effect on GFR as measured by the clearance of inulin in dogs (266) pigs (266), rabbits (267), and humans (11, 233). Similarly, neither the exogenous creatinine clearance in the dog (57), nor the endogenous creatinine clearance in healthy (34) and hypoparathyroid (123) subjects or in parathyroidectomized rats (107) was affected by the hormone. [In one study the creatinine clearance increased after calcitonin in some subjects, but the clearance of inulin measured in other individuals did not change (233).] The hormone produced a significant increase in RPF in the rabbit (267), but did not affect PAH clearance in the dog and pig (266).

Sodium, Chloride, and Potassium Excretion

Calcitonin has a potent natriuretic effect in rat (7, 159, 241, 252, 283, 312), rabbit (267), sheep (18), and man (11, 12, 32, 33, 58, 233, 280, 284). Although most studies reported acute effects obtained with pharmacologic doses of the hormone, calcitonin affects electrolyte excretion similarly when given in more physiological amounts and over extended periods of time. For example, the circulating levels of calcitonin in humans receiving a constant infusion for 6–39 days (!) were in the range normally seen in healthy individuals who receive intravenous calcium (32), and prolonged administration of calcitonin was associated with polyuria, salt loss, and volume contraction in both rats (159) and humans (32). The increment in Na excretion is linearly related to the log dose of calcitonin (159, 312), and as little as 6–9 ng salmon calcitonin produced a natriuretic response in rats (159). Both salmon (7, 18, 159) and porcine (32, 58, 241, 267, 280, 284) calcitonin increase the excretion of sodium considerably more than that of other electrolytes.

Since GFR appears unaffected, the natriuresis produced by calcitonin is probably due to decreased tubular reabsorption. This effect is independent of the changes in PTH levels, since it occurs both in parathyroidectomized animals (18, 241, 252, 283) and in hypoparathyroid patients (11, 12, 123, 233, 280, 284). It is also unrelated to changes in mineralocorticoid secretion because a similar natriuresis occurred in subjects pretreated with spironolactone or receiving a continuous infusion of aldosterone (12, 233). Because of the known relationship between Na and Ca transport in the kidney it has been proposed that the increased excretion of Na after calcitonin is somehow related to the calciuric effect of the hormone (159). Observations that the excretion of Na and of Ca were neither statistically (12) nor temporally (32) correlated conflict with this view.

While the precise mechanism whereby calcitonin increases Na excretion has not been clarified, it probably represents a direct effect on the tubular cell, possibly mediated through the adenylate cyclase system. One site of calcitonin action appears to be the proximal tubule, from two lines of indirect evidence: First, calcitonin increases the excretion of amino acids (which are reabsorbed in the proximal tubule) and of Na in parallel (32) and second, proximal fluid delivery ($C_{Na}+C_{H_2O}/GFR$) increases significantly after calcitonin in normal subjects undergoing a sustained water diuresis (233).

The natriuresis produced by calcitonin is accompanied by a parallel chloruresis (7, 11, 12, 32). Calcitonin also increases K excretion in the rabbit (267) and sheep (18), but results in the rat are conflicting (7, 159, 241, 252, 283). Calcitonin both increased (33, 123) and produced only slight or inconsistent changes in K secretion in acute studies in humans (11, 58, 233, 280). Prolonged administration of the hormone resulted in a definite kaliuresis in 11 patients studied by Bijvoet et al (32), probably due to the increase in aldosterone secretion secondary to the preceding NaCl loss.

Phosphate Excretion

The phosphaturic effect of calcitonin, first demonstrated with a crude preparation in the rat (160), has been amply documented in numerous studies using various calcitonin preparations in several animal species. Administration of calcitonin is followed by a prompt and substantial rise in PO_4 excretion in rats (214, 241, 283), sheep (18), and humans (11, 32, 33, 58, 233, 280), which is sustained when the hormone is given over longer periods (8, 18, 283). A smaller phosphaturic effect of calcitonin is also seen in pigs (266). Since calcitonin usually decreases serum Ca and thus secondarily stimulates PTH secretion, its phosphaturic effect may be mediated by the parathyroid glands. A number of studies, however, demonstrate the same phosphaturic effect in parathyroidectomized or thyroparathyroidectomized rats (8, 213, 214, 241, 252, 260, 283) and sheep (18), as well as in hypoparathyroid patients (11, 123, 233, 280, 284). However, in the dog, calcitonin increased PO_4 excretion only in intact animals (65, 234), and not in those thyroparathyroidectomized (57, 234, 266) or in animals receiving Ca infusions to suppress endogenous PTH secretion (57). The reason for this discrepancy is not clear but may represent a true species difference since, in the dog, calcitonin also does not affect electrolyte excretion even when infused into the renal artery (57, 266).

The mechanism responsible for the phosphaturic effect of calcitonin is unknown. Early suggestions that the phosphaturia is perhaps due to impurities rather than to calcitonin (52) were unfounded since the same effect has been obtained later with synthetic calcitonin (18, 241, 283). Rasmussen et al (252) were able to increase PO_4 excretion by infusing a calcium chelator (EGTA) and proposed that the increased PO_4 excretion produced by calcitonin is secondary to its hypocalcemic effect. However, the phosphaturic effect of calcitonin is also seen when serum Ca remains stable (11, 280) or is increased by infusion (233). Moreover, when calcitonin was infused into the renal artery of pigs the phosphaturia was greater in the infused kidney. This result cannot be explained by systemic hypocalcemia, which should affect both kidneys equally (266).

There is now general agreement that the increased phosphate excretion is mediated by a direct action of calcitonin on the renal tubule. Studies using distal nephron blockade with diuretics suggest that the phosphaturic effect of calcitonin is due to decreased PO_4 reabsorption in the proximal tubule (233).

Calcium Excretion

Unlike the natriuretic and phosphaturic effects of calcitonin which are consistent and reproducible, its action on renal Ca excretion is more controversial. While most investigators describe a calciuric effect of calcitonin [in humans (11, 32, 33, 58, 123, 233, 280, 284), rats (7, 214), and sheep (18)], others noted only insignificant changes (213, 267) or even decrements in Ca excretion (159, 238, 252, 283, 312). Some of the latter effects, seen in rats, may have been related to the dose or duration of calcitonin administration, as the decreased calciuria occurred only transiently (283) or when lower doses of the hormone were utilized (159, 312).

It is now clear that calcitonin depresses tubular reabsorption of Ca as it does that of other ions and that the divergent results reported in the past can be reconciled if the dual effect of the hormone on bone and kidney is taken into account. By decreasing bone resorption, calcitonin lowers serum Ca (18, 33, 58, 65, 122, 197, 214, 233, 312) and consequently the filtered Ca load. The effect of the hormone on Ca excretion represents the algebraic sum of the changes in filtration and reabsorption, and therefore calcitonin may either increase or decrease Ca excretion depending on the relative magnitude of its effect on bone and on kidney. This, in turn, is determined by the state of bone remodeling. In situations in which bone turnover is fast, such as in patients with Paget's disease or in young animals, the effect on bone predominates and may obscure that on the kidney, whereas the renal effect is more evident in adults or parathyroidectomized animals where skeletal Ca turnover is slow (33, 58, 123, 260, 261, 312).

As in the case of Na and PO_4, the increment in Ca excretion produced by calcitonin was demonstrated in parathyroidectomized animals (18) and in hypoparathyroid humans (11, 123, 233, 280 284), and is therefore independent of parathyroid hormone. The calciuria is also unrelated to the concomitant increase in PO_4 excretion because it could not be duplicated by an infusion that produced a phosphaturia similar to that seen after calcitonin (123). Since GFR does not change and plasma Ca usually decreases, the calciuric action of calcitonin is due to a direct effect of the hormone on the renal tubule. This view is supported by the observation that calcitonin inhibits active Ca transport in kidney cells grown in culture (38).

Other Actions

Reports on the effect of calcitonin on Mg excretion are conflicting. However, a reduction in Mg excretion was noted in animals [rat (7, 159, 238, 252, 312), sheep (18), and dog (65)], whereas in man calcitonin either had no effect (11, 58, 280) or increased Mg excretion (123, 233, 284). Both the increase and the reduction in Mg excretion have occurred both in the presence and absence of the parathyroid glands. The hypothesis that Mg and Ca share a common reabsorptive mechanism has been invoked to explain changes in Mg excretion in either direction, and therefore does not clarify the issue.

Calcitonin does not affect urinary pH or the excretion of titratable acid and ammonia in a reproducible way (13).

Renal Calcitonin Receptors and Stimulation of Adenylate Cyclase

Calcitonin attaches to receptors on renal plasma membranes and stimulates the adenylate cyclase activity of the kidney in vivo and in vitro[1] (170, 199, 200). ^{125}I-calcitonin binds to high-affinity receptors present on the brush border as well as on the basal cell membrane (201), and the interaction of calcitonin with its specific receptor is required for the activation of adenylate cyclase (198).

Calcitonin stimulates adenylate cyclase similarly in the renal cortex and outer medulla of the rat kidney, but has little effect on the enzyme from the papilla (199, 200), suggesting that the anatomic distribution of the calcitonin receptors differs from that of the receptors for PTH and vasopressin (198). This observation, coupled with the fact that the effects of calcitonin and PTH on cAMP generation are additive (133, 188), indicates that different cell populations may be involved in the response to each hormone (200).

The stimulation of renal cortical adenylate cyclase shows a log-linear dose response with both salmon and porcine calcitonin (133). The effect of salmon calcitonin, however, is 20 times greater than that of porcine calcitonin, analogous to the difference in the affinity of the two hormones for the calcitonin receptor (133, 188, 200). Thus the affinity of calcitonins from different species for the renal receptor parallels their relative potency in stimulating adenylate cyclase in vitro, and both correspond to the biological activity of the various calcitonins in vivo; a correlation which strongly suggests that the renal actions of calcitonin are mediated through the adenylate cyclase–cAMP system (198).

[1]Despite this, calcitonin has little effect on the urinary excretion of cAMP (32, 52, 170).

Physiological Role of the Calcitonin Effects on the Kidney

Despite the influence of calcitonin on the excretion of a variety of electrolytes, the physiological significance of these effects is not entirely clear. The calciuria and phosphaturia produced by calcitonin undoubtedly contribute to the reduction in the plasma concentrations of Ca and PO_4 but are not essential for this effect of the hormone in normal animals since both the hypocalcemic (122, 261) and the hypophosphatemic (261, 294) effect of calcitonin occur after nephrectomy. In contrast, the renal effect accounts for most of the decrement in plasma Ca and PO_4 when bone turnover is slow, e.g. in parathyroidectomized animals in which the hypophosphatemic action of calcitonin is prevented by nephrectomy (261). Calcitonin decreases renal Ca content (160) and appears to protect the kidney from PTH-induced nephrocalcinosis in rats (253).

Because of its pronounced natriuretic and diuretic effect, calcitonin has been postulated to play a major role in sodium and volume regulation, and even to be the elusive "natriuretic hormone" (32). However, Na depletion is not a prominent feature of calcitonin-producing medullary carcinomas, nor is deficiency of calcitonin in thyroidectomized animals and humans clearly associated with impaired Na excretion. The concept of calcitonin as a regulatory hormone of Na excretion, although intriguing, needs to be substantiated.

CATECHOLAMINES

Both α- and β-adrenergic receptors and a specific dopamine receptor are present in the kidney (43, 119, 195), and all three endogenous catecholamines (epinephrine, norepinephrine, and dopamine) influence renal hemodynamics and function. Because of their profound cardiovascular effects, however, it is often difficult to distinguish between their direct renal actions and those produced by participation of the kidneys in the systemic response to catecholamines. Since the type of adrenergic stimulation (α, β, or mixed) and the preponderance of local or systemic effects depend on the dose used and on the route of administration (119, 195, 237), it is not surprising that the renal actions of sympathetic amines remain a subject of controversy.

Effects of Systemic Administration of Catecholamines on Kidney Function

The renal effects of norepinephrine given intravenously include decreased RPF and usually GFR, Na retention, and increased free water formation (15, 237, 271). Intravenous infusion of β-adrenergic agonists generally produces an antidiuresis, while their effect on renal hemodynamics and Na excretion is variable and depends on whether the blood pressure decreases or not (35, 178, 237, 272).

The dose dependence of the renal actions of catecholamines administered systemically is best exemplified by dopamine, the immediate metabolic precursor of norepinephrine. This compound is used clinically to improve renal perfusion in circulatory insufficiency and acute vasomotor nephropathy. In small doses, dopamine substantially increases renal blood flow (RBF), GFR, and Na excretion, whereas in higher doses α-adrenergic effects predominate and result in vasoconstriction and reduced RBF (1, 119, 205, 207).

Direct Renal Effects of Catecholamines

Direct renal effects of catecholamines differ from those reported after systemic administration. Infusion of low doses of norepinephrine into the renal artery of the dog produces vasoconstriction and decrements in RBF and Na excretion independently of an effect of the catecholamine on blood pressure (17, 237). The effect on GFR is variable and depends on the relative degree of vasoconstriction of the afferent and efferent arterioles (271). Prolonged intrarenal infusion of high doses of norepinephrine has been utilized to produce acute unilateral oliguric renal failure in the dog, with ultrastructural evidence of morphologic alterations in the glomerular epithelial cells (62). Norepinephrine may increase T_{Na} in the proximal tubule since it produced a unilateral decrease in urine flow and C_{H_2O} in dogs undergoing a water diuresis (117). In these experiments GFR remained unchanged and the authors suggested that norepinephrine has a direct tubular effect, possibly mediated by increased intratubular generation of cyclic GMP (117, 118).

The effects of β-adrenergic stimulation on renal function (based on studies using isoproterenol as the β agonist) are generally the opposite of those observed with α stimulation. Pearson & Williams (237) demonstrated an increase in RBF and Na excretion after infusion of isoproterenol into the renal artery of the dog, and ascribed this unilateral natriuresis to a direct renal effect of the drug. Gill & Casper (115) reported an ipsilateral decrease in proximal Na reabsorption (estimated from the increase in urine volume and C_{H_2O} during water diuresis) when dogs received isoproterenol into the renal artery during α blockade with phenoxybenzamine The decrement in T_{Na} occurred without significant changes in mean blood pressure, GFR, RPF, or intrarenal blood flow distribution, and was therefore attributed to a direct tubular effect of isoproterenol. The increased Na delivered into the distal nephron was completely reabsorbed since Na excretion was unchanged, suggesting that the effect of β stimulation is limited to the proximal tubule.

The foregoing conclusions regarding a direct proximal tubular effect of both α- and β-adrenergic stimulation were based on urine flow and free water clearance determinations during water diuresis. However, more direct measurements with micropuncture techniques yielded different results. Blendis et al (36) studied the effect of β stimulation (isoproterenol) during α blockade and of α stimulation (norepinephrine) during β blockade in dogs, and found no significant changes in the ratio of inulin concentrations in the proximal tubular fluid and plasma, $[(TF/P)_{In}]$, or in absolute proximal T_{Na} in either experiment. These authors concluded that neither α- nor β-adrenergic agents have a significant effect on proximal T_{Na} when infused in doses that do not alter renal hemodynamics. Other investigators have also been unable to demonstrate an effect of either α- (222) or β- (287) adrenergic stimulation on proximal reabsorption.

The reasons for the divergent results obtained with clearance and with micropuncture techniques are not clear. Besides the obvious methodological differences, alterations in distal water permeability or in intrarenal distribution of blood flow during water diuresis have been suggested (36, 289). The possibility that catecholamines influence Na reabsorption by an effect on the tubule is indirectly supported by in vitro studies of their action in other tissues: epinephrine and isoproterenol stimulate active Na transport in amphibian (130) and mammalian (101) muscle [in the latter associated with stimulation of Na-K-ATPase (53)], and norepinephrine increases the short-circuit current (SCC) in the toad bladder (124) and frog skin (218). Additional evidence favoring a direct tubular effect of catecholamines is provided by studies of renal nerve stimulation. Adrenergic nerve fibers are in direct contact with the basement membrane of proximal and distal tubules (219), and low levels of renal nerve stimulation result in an ipsilateral decrease in Na excretion in the absence of changes in GFR, RBF, or intrarenal distribution of blood flow (282). Similar results were recently reported in a study using micropuncture techniques in which, in addition, proximal Na and water reabsorption during sympathetic nerve stimulation were found to be increased (23).

Effects on Renal Adenylate Cyclase

The activity of adenylate cyclase in homogenates of isolated renal cortical tubules is stimulated by epinephrine and inhibited by propranolol (206), and an isoproterenol-sensitive adenylate cyclase was demonstrated in plasma membranes from both the cortex and medulla of rat kidneys (199). Beta stimulation with either epinephrine or isoproterenol also increased cAMP concentration in slices from the renal cortex and the outer and inner medulla of the dog kidney (22) and in homogenates of human renal medulla (220). Since dibutyryl cAMP injected into the canine renal artery increased urine flow and C_{H_2O} without increasing Na excretion and without altering either GFR or total or regional RPF—a response essentially identical to that produced by isoproterenol—it was suggested that β-adrenergic stimulation decreased proximal T_{Na} by a direct tubular effect mediated through the generation of cAMP (116). However, Chabardès et al (49) demonstrated with an elegant microdissection technique that isoproterenol stimulated adenylate cyclase in the distal convoluted and cortical collecting tubule of the rabbit nephron, but had no effect on the enzyme in the proximal tubule.

Interaction with Vasopressin and Effect on Water Excretion

Intravenous infusion of norepinephrine is associated with a water diuresis (15, 104, 163) and that of isoproterenol with an antidiuresis (163, 177, 178, 272), which can be abolished by α and β blockade, respectively. Since both effects occur without changes in GFR or solute excretion (15, 104, 271, 272) and are the opposite of what is expected from the known direct tubular actions of α- (117) and β- (115) adrenergic stimulation on water excretion, considerable interest in the elucidation of their mechanism has been generated. Schrier and his colleagues have approached this problem in a methodical way and in a series of reports spanning the last five years have contributed significantly to its clarification (26–28, 271, 272).

The effects of norepinephrine and isoproterenol on water excretion occur independently of changes in systemic blood pressure and of the sympathetic innervation of the kidney (271, 272). The possibility of a direct renal effect of adrenergic stimulation on osmotic water movement was suggested by observations that norepinephrine interferes with ADH-induced cAMP generation (124, 169), while isoproterenol stimulates cAMP production (22, 49), as well as by the demonstration of an antidiuretic effect of isoproterenol in rats with congenital diabetes insipidus (178). Schrier et al, however, could not duplicate the effects of iv catecholamines on water excretion by infusing these compounds into the renal artery (271, 272) and concluded that adrenergic stimulation alters water excretion by extrarenal mechanisms, specifically by alterations in endogenous ADH release. This conclusion was supported by the failure of both α and β stimulation to alter water excretion in hypophysectomized dogs (271, 272) or in patients with diabetes insipidus (28).

The mechanism whereby adrenergic stimulation alters vasopressin secretion is not entirely clear. Angiotensin II may stimulate ADH release, but this mechanism is unlikely because although both α- and β-adrenergic stimuli enhance renin production (254, 300, 302–304, 306), their effects on water excretion are diametrically opposite. Neither α- nor β-adrenergic agents influenced water excretion when injected into the carotid artery, but their renal effects were abolished by denervation of arterial baroreceptors. These results led to the conclusion that the effects of adrenergic stimulation on vasopressin release are mediated through alterations in arterial baroreceptor tone (26, 27).

Effects of Catecholamines on Renin Release

It is well established that both α- and β-adrenergic agents provide a potent stimulus for renin release, probably through a direct intrarenal effect. Epinephrine (302), norepinephrine (300, 302), and isoproterenol (151, 254, 300) all increase renin secretion when given intravenously. Infusion of epinephrine (306) and norepinephrine (47, 306, 313) into the renal artery also stimulates renin secretion, whereas an effect of intra-arterial isoproterenol was demonstrated by some (151, 313), but not by others (47, 254). Isoproterenol, epinephrine, and norepinephrine increase renin secretion by the isolated perfused rat kidney (303, 304).

The demonstration that epinephrine and norepinephrine, as well as cAMP, increased renin production in a kidney cell preparation in vitro has raised the possibility of a direct cellular effect of catecholamines, presumably mediated by cAMP (211). This hypothesis was supported by subsequent reports of β-adrenergic stimulation of renin release in kidney slices (308) and by the study of Winer et al (313) who showed that cAMP, norepinephrine, and isoproterenol injected into the renal artery increased renin secretion independently of changes in blood pressure, GFR, and Na excretion. These authors suggested that cAMP acts within the kidney as an intracellular mediator of renin release (313). Further evidence for an intrarenal effect of catecholamines mediated by β receptors was provided by Vandongen and colleagues (303, 304) who demonstrated that isoproterenol, epinephrine, and norepinephrine stimulated renin release by the isolated rat kidney in the absence of changes in perfusion pressure and flow, and by Johnson et al (151) who reported similar results with isoproterenol in the dog kidney. It has been proposed that the β receptors responsible for the effect of catecholamines on renin release are located in the juxtaglomerular cells (151), which are well supplied by adrenergic nerve fibers.

In contrast to the aforementioned studies, Reid et al were unable to demonstrate an effect of isoproterenol injected into the renal artery, but they observed a significant increase in renin secretion in response to the same dose given intravenously and concluded that the effect of isoproterenol on renin release is mediated through extrarenal mechanisms (254). This view is at variance with the weight of evidence favoring a direct renal effect, but a recent report from the same laboratory also supports a direct intrarenal effect of β stimulation on renin release (293).

Dopamine

As mentioned above, small doses of dopamine increase RBF, GFR, and Na excretion. The effects on GFR and on Na excretion appear to be separate since marked increments in filtration rate may occur with little change in Na excretion, and a natriuresis has been observed when GFR was unchanged or decreased (185). The increment in Na excretion produced by dopamine has therefore been attributed to a direct tubular effect (76, 119) and to redistribution of blood flow (125), A physiologic role of endogenous dopamine is suggested by the observation that its urinary excretion rises when salt intake is increased in man (9).

INSULIN

In contrast to the important role of the kidney in the metabolism of insulin in man (50) and animals (157, 247), the renal effects of insulin are modest[2] and their physiological significance uncertain. Interpretation of earlier reports is complicated by the difficulty in separating the direct renal effects of insulin from those caused by its hypoglycemic action. This is particularly true of the renal handling of glucose and Na, since insulin-induced hypoglycemia affects solute excretion by decreasing the amount of glucose filtered and reabsorbed and, at the same time, alters the concentration of adrenal corticoids and other hormones affecting renal function. This problem has been circumvented in several recent studies in which the concentration of glucose was maintained constant (78, 224, 285).

Sodium Excretion

It has been known for a long time that diabetic patients treated with insulin frequently retain Na, occasionally in amounts sufficient to cause edema. Studies in diabetic humans (270) and rats (37) indicate that the retention of Na under these circumstances can be dissociated from the cocomitant decrements in glucose and ketone excretion, and exceeds the amounts required to replace previous deficits. Furthermore, the natriuresis observed in nonglucosuric fasting subjects is abolished

---

[2]The rapid inactivation of insulin by the kidney may be in part responsible for the limited effects of the hormone in this organ: Thus insulin enhances the utilization of glucose and pyruvate by kidney slices from alloxan-treated rats in which insulin degradation is impaired, but has no effect in slices from untreated animals (193).

by carbohydrate (155, 309), an effect attributed by some to the increased insulin secretion accompanying refeeding (167, 224). Taken together, these observations suggest that insulin enhances Na reabsorption by acting directly on the kidney, a hypothesis strongly supported by the recent work of Nizet et al with the isolated kidney of the dog (224) and of DeFronzo et al in man (78). In both studies, plasma glucose was maintained at a constant level, and a significant increment in T_{Na} was found at insulin concentrations close to the physiologic range. In addition, aldosterone concentration was unaltered in the human study, and hormonal changes were precluded by the experimental design in the isolated dog kidney. It is evident therefore that the decrease in Na excretion was due to a direct effect of insulin on the kidney and, as GFR and filtered Na did not change, this effect occurred in the renal tubule. Since K excretion was similarly reduced (37, 78, 224), insulin probably does not act in the most distal nephron where K secretion occurs. The increase in C_{H_2O} produced by insulin during water diuresis indicates that the proximal tubule is not the site of insulin action and suggests that this hormone increases T_{Na} in the diluting segment (78).

Some insight into the mechanism of insulin action on the kidney tubule may be gained by examination of its effect on other cell membranes. Insulin stimulates Na transport across the amphibian skin (64, 135), colon (64), urinary bladder (64), and skeletal muscle (121, 217), but pharmacological concentrations (> 100 mU•ml^{-1}) are required for these in vitro effects. The stimulation of Na efflux from frog muscle treated with insulin was accompanied by increased ouabain binding, indicating an increase in the number of active Na pumping sites. Since the increase in ouabain binding was not affected by cycloheximide, it was suggested that insulin acts by unmasking latent pump sites rather than by synthesizing new enzyme (121). In another study, insulin stimulated the activity of Na-K-ATPase of frog muscle in a manner quantitatively similar to the increment in Na efflux it produced in intact muscle cells (113). The authors attributed this effect to an increase in the affinity of the enzyme for one or more of its substrates and suggested that the Na-K-ATPase enzyme system is the "transducer between the binding of insulin to its receptor on the plasma membrane and the cellular actions of insulin" (113). Insulin also increased Na extrusion from rat skeletal muscle (316) but did not stimulate the Na-K-ATPase in this tissue (263).

Effect on Renal Hemodynamics and on Water and Electrolyte Excretion

Insulin does not affect RBF or GFR in dogs (166, 176) or in humans (78, 215, 216, 221, 285). Insulin decreased urine flow in normal (216, 221) and diabetic (221, 270) subjects and in animals (37, 224), but this effect was not found in two studies in which plasma glucose was maintained constant (78, 285). Since the insulin antidiuresis was blunted by alcohol and could not be demonstrated in a patient with diabetes insipidus, it was attributed to an increase in endogenous ADH release (221). However, this explanation is not consistent with the later observation that insulin decreases water excretion (albeit modestly) in an isolated kidney preparation (224).

Doses of insulin within the physiological range of plasma concentrations decrease K excretion (37, 78, 216, 224). In the study of DeFronzo et al the decrease in K excretion was associated with a decrease in plasma K (78), but the same effect was observed in the isolated perfused dog kidney when plasma K and GFR remained constant (224), suggesting a direct effect of insulin on the tubular transport of K. The mechanism underlying this effect is obscure, since if insulin acts on the renal tubular cell as it does on muscle (113, 316) it should increase intracellular K, and this effect would be expected to facilitate rather than reduce K secretion. The role of insulin in the renal excretion of other ions has scarcely been studied; in normal humans undergoing a water diuresis, insulin increased urinary Ca and reduced urinary PO_4 excretion (78).

Role of Insulin in Glucose Reabsorption

Earlier studies suggested that insulin has the paradoxical effect of slightly decreasing the tubular reabsorptive maximum of glucose (Tm_G) in both normal (215) and diabetic (102) subjects. However, recent reports indicate that in concentrations ranging between 17 and 1560 $\mu U \cdot ml^{-1}$, insulin has no effect on the Tm_G in dogs (176), and that in diabetics in whom plasma glucose concentration is kept constant, insulin actually decreases urinary glucose excretion (285). Clearly, insulin is not required for the reabsorption of glucose from the glomerular filtrate since Tm_G in diabetics is the same or even higher than in normal subjects (102).

GLUCAGON

In pharmacologic doses, glucagon increases the excretion of Na (51, 71, 75, 93, 179, 181, 246, 286, 288), K (51, 71, 75, 93, 246, 286), Cl (71, 75, 93, 246, 286), PO_4 (93, 246, 286), Ca (51, 246), and Mg (246), as well as glucose (246) and uric acid (94). The increments in electrolyte excretion are substantial, often averaging several times the control measurements, and are independent of the hyperglycemic effect of the hormone (93, 286). The renal actions of glucagon have been demonstrated in dogs (71, 179, 181, 246, 286, 288), rats (75), and humans (93, 94, 269), and occur whether glucagon is administered intramuscularly (93, 94), intraperitoneally (75, 275), intravenously (71, 93, 179, 180, 181, 286, 288), or into the renal artery (179, 181, 246, 288). Inactivated glucagon is devoid of renal effects (93, 286). The natriuretic effect of glucagon has also been observed at physiologic plasma levels (such as seen during fasting) in humans, but at these concentrations the hormone did not affect the urinary excretion of K, Ca, and PO_4 (269).

Renal Hemodynamics and Sodium Excretion

Glucagon increases renal blood flow (74, 288) and effective renal plasma flow (PAH clearance) in dogs (275) and humans (93), and its vasodilating effect on the renal vasculature has been demonstrated with renal arteriography (74). On the other hand, measurements of GFR under the influence of glucagon have yielded conflicting results. Serrato & Earle (275) reported a significant increase of 25% in GFR in the dog, and Broadus et al (42) noted a moderate increase in inulin clearance in two healthy men, but others found that in both dogs and humans glucagon produced inconsistent changes or only small increments in GFR which were of borderline statistical significance (71, 93, 94, 269, 286, 288). Pullman et al (246) infused glucagon into the renal artery of dogs and found a transient GFR increase in the infused kidney, followed by a more sustained but modest bilateral rise. Since there was no difference in GFR between the two kidneys but only the infused kidney showed a striking natriuresis, the authors concluded that glucagon acts directly on the renal tubule to decrease Na reabsorption. In contrast, Levy (179, 181) demonstrated a substantial increase in GFR of about 30% in dogs receiving glucagon intravenously or into the renal artery. As the concomitant natriuresis amounted only to a small fraction of the increased filtered Na load, and clamping the renal artery abolished both the rise in GFR and the increased Na excretion, Levy concluded that the glucagon natriuresis is caused largely by increments in filtered Na load. It is not clear whether the conflicting reports on the effect of glucagon on GFR reflect the use of glucagon preparations of variable purity or methodologic differences (181).

Although glucagon enhances renin secretion by the isolated perfused rat kidney (304), the glucagon-induced increase in RBF is thought to be due to renal vasodilatation rather than to increased cardiac output (181). The GFR increments observed by Levy were not prevented by renal denervation, thyroparathyroidectomy, or by blockade of adrenergic, cholinergic, dopaminergic, or histaminergic receptors (179). It is noteworthy that glucagon also exerted its hemodynamic and natriuretic effects in pathological conditions characterized by renal hypoperfusion such as constriction of the inferior vena cava (181), hemorrhagic hypotension, or barbiturate overdosage (180).

Mechanism of Increased Solute Excretion

While the increased excretion of Na and other ions produced by glucagon could probably be explained in large part by its effect on GFR, the conflicting views on the hemodynamic effects of the hormone have prompted alternative explanations. Stowe & Hook, for example, attributed the natriuretic action of glucagon to the concomitant increase in RBF since both effects were abolished by previous maximal renal vasodilatation with mannitol or reserpine (288). In addition, a direct effect of glucagon on the renal tubule was repeatedly proposed by investigators who could not demonstrate a consistent change in GFR (71, 93, 246, 269, 286), and was not excluded even by proponents of the hemodynamic hypothesis (181, 288). However, neither the site in the nephron where such an effect might occur nor its mechanism has been defined. The proximal tubule does not seem to be involved, since in recollection micropuncture experiments the end proximal (TF/P) inulin was not changed by glucagon (181). The suggestion that the natriuresis produced by glucagon is due to its induction of tubular resistance to aldosterone (269), implying a distal effect, is negated by the strong kaliuretic action of the hormone. Finally, Stowe & Hook concluded that glucagon does not act in the diluting segment or in the proximal tubule, but examination of their results reveals an appreciable downward trend of C_{H_2O} during water diuresis, which raises the possibility of an effect on the diluting segment. In this context, it is of interest that recent evidence points to the existence of a glucagon-sensitive adenylate cyclase in the renal medulla (220).

Glucagon also stimulates adenylate cyclase in isolated renal cortical tubules (206), but its effect on the urinary excretion of cAMP is less clear. Although the hormone produced a striking increase in cAMP excretion in normal men, this could be accounted for entirely by increased plasma levels of the nucleotide from extrarenal sources (42). Glucagon did not affect cAMP excretion when infused directly in the renal artery of dogs (179).

PROGESTERONE

In 1955 Landau and colleagues (173) demonstrated that progesterone increases sodium excretion in man. Despite this, renal physiologists who have been assiduously pursuing natriuretic factors for at least two decades have neglected this hormone, perhaps because of the problems inherent in attempts to elucidate its direct renal effects. Progesterone is itself a substrate for the biosynthesis of a number of hormones (e.g. aldosterone, cortisol, desoxycorticosterone, testosterone, and estrogen), and there are considerable species differences in its renal actions. For instance, progesterone appears to influence volume homeostasis quite differently in man and in two commonly utilized laboratory animals, the dog and the rat.

Renal Hemodynamics

GFR, RPF, and plasma levels of progesterone increase markedly during human pregnancy. In an attempt to reproduce the renal hemodynamic changes of gestation, investigators have used doses of progesterone high enough to produce levels similar to those found in pregnancy. In doses of 4–7 mg/day for 14–20 days, progesterone did not affect the clearance of inulin or PAH in either anesthetized or awake rats (184, 203). Progesterone, however, stimulates the tubular secretion of creatinine in female rats and increases the creatinine/inulin clearance ratios 20% above unity (129). Since in female rats eating freely, this steroid is also anabolic and increases renal mass (136, 184), RPF and GFR per unit kidney weight actually decrease (184, 203).

Progesterone had no effect on either total blood flow or its intrarenal distribution in dogs (19), although the same author noted dilatation of vasa recta and papillary vessels when the kidneys were fixed by the rapid injection of silicone rubber. In contrast, both the acute and chronic (3 days) administration of progesterone in doses ranging from 100–300 mg consistently increased PAH clearance in humans (54, 230). In acute experiments, GFR is unaffected (230), but small increases in filtration rate frequently occur with chronic administration of the hormone (54).

Electrolyte Excretion

The observation that pregnancy delayed lethal volume depletion in adrenalectomized animals (262) led to studies of the salt-retaining effects of several pregnancy-associated steroids, including progesterone. Crystalline progesterone was shown to prolong the life of adrenalectomized ferrets and mice (111, 112). Thorn & Engel (295) observed transient decrements in urinary Na when large doses of this steroid were given to normal or adrenalectomized dogs. O'Connell et al (228) and Johnson et al (149) could not confirm any salt-retaining action of progesterone in this species, but examination of their data suggests a small antinatriuretic effect that might have reached statistical significance had more animals been studied.

Data in rats are inconclusive. In short-term experiments, low doses of progesterone had little effect (153), while both antinatriuretic and diuretic properties have been reported with higher doses of the hormone (80, 153, 250, 274). Many of these studies had shortcomings in their design or were poorly controlled. In a better designed protocol, progesterone produced acute Na retention in adrenalectomized rats in a manner similar to that observed with equivalent doses of desoxycorticosterone (103). Chronic administration of progesterone to female rats or mice leads to salt retention, as evidenced by increases in extracellular water (136) and inulin space (184), and by the observation of an immediate diuresis when the drug is discontinued. However, progesterone-treated rats were able to excrete infused Na as well as untreated controls (184).

While its action in the dog and rat is equivocal, there is little doubt that progesterone is natriuretic in man, an effect demonstrated in classical metabolic balance studies by Landau et al (173, 175) and confirmed by others (171, 229). Progesterone also decreases exchangeable sodium (67), and if this reflects a decrement in extracellular volume, it could be one reason that the hormone also increases renin activity (66, 229, 230, 281). Since the saluretic effect of the hormone was apparent only in the presence of normal adrenal function or in adrenalectomized subjects receiving replacement therapy, it was originally ascribed to competitive inhibition of aldosterone (173, 174). Inhibition by progesterone of the Na-retaining effect of infused aldosterone or desoxycorticosterone in adrenal-deficient patients and in rats is consistent with this hypothesis (153, 174). However, recent observations by Oparil et al (230) suggest that the acute natriuretic action of progesterone is in part independent of aldosterone inhibition. These authors measured osmolal clearance, free water generation, and Na excretion in progesterone-treated men undergoing a maximal water diuresis. Their data suggest that progesterone inhibits Na reabsorption at proximal as well as distal nephron sites. Furthermore, Na excretion increased more in subjects ingesting high-salt (low endogenous aldosterone levels) than in those receiving low-salt diets (high endogenous aldosterone levels), and the increment in excretion was minimal in volunteers who had "escaped" from the Na-retaining effects of exogenous desoxycorticosterone. Such data are in accord with a saluretic action of progesterone independent of its ability to competitively inhibit aldosterone.

Reports of the effects of progesterone on K excretion are conflicting (103, 153, 171, 173, 183, 229, 230), which is surprising in view of the spironolactone-like action of this hormone. Inhibition of distal K secretion can be overridden by the increased delivery of Na from proximal sites and the increased K load secondary to the catabolic effect of this steroid in man. However, Ehrlich & Lindheimer (91) have adduced evidence suggesting that progesterone may be the K-sparing hormone in human pregnancy, a situation marked by high endogenous aldosterone levels and the delivery of substantial quantities of Na to distal nephron sites.

Effect on Active Sodium Transport

Progesterone has no in vitro or in vivo effect on the specific activity of Na-K-ATPase in rat or guinea pig kidney microsomes (139, 184). This hormone has been reported to decrease the SCC in frog skin (298, 299) but not in the toad bladder (63, 139, 243). In the latter tissue, progesterone blocks the ability of aldosterone to increase SCC and Na transport (63, 243, 276, 277), but Porter et al (242) noted that large doses were necessary to produce this effect, and were unable to inhibit the aldosterone-induced increment in SCC with physiologic amounts of progesterone. Furthermore, using radioautographic techniques, these authors demonstrated that labeled aldosterone had an affinity for the nuclear region of the cell, but ^{3}H-progesterone was located diffusely throughout the cytoplasm. Finally, while progesterone has been used as a displacing steroid in a number of experiments designed to demonstrate renal steroid receptors, it appears that no thorough search has been made for a progesterone receptor in the kidney.

ESTROGENS

Effects of estrogens on renal salt and water excretion and volume homeostasis, both in pregnancy and during the menstrual cycle, were described during the 1930s and 1940s. More recently, synthetic estrogens and oral contraceptives have been linked to edema, hypertension, and alterations in the renin-angiotensin system. Nevertheless, an extensive review published in late 1974 contained this sobering introductory paragraph: "This paper presents a review of the major anatomical, biochemical, and physiological effects of estrogen upon the kidney. The field awaits a careful and comprehensive study" (55).

Renal Hemodynamics

Estrogens have little if any influence on renal hemodynamics in the dog. Many studies performed in the 1940s and 1950s [reviewed in (55)] are subject to considerable criticism on methodological grounds. More recently, Johnson and colleagues (148, 150) performed serial measurements of GFR and RPF during the continuous administration of 17-β-estradiol to adrenalectomized bitches maintained with replacement mineralocorticoids and glucocorticoids. Transient and barely significant increments in exogenous creatinine and PAH clearances were noted on day 2 but were not sustained during the remaining 6 days of therapy. Similarly, Barnes (19) found no acute or chronic effects of estrogen on RBF measured by the krypton washout technique.

There is little information on renal hemodynamics in estrogen-treated rodents, and data in humans are also scarce. In the few references to inulin or endogenous creatinine clearance performed in rats (128, 225, 250) and guinea pigs (212), the methods are either inadequately described or seem erroneous, and the results are inconclusive. Similarly unrevealing are studies of exogenous creatinine and PAH clearances in estrogen-treated rabbits (227).

Intravenous estradiol had no effect on the clearances of inulin and PAH in postmenopausal women (83), and a 3-day course of oral estrogens did not influence renal hemodynamics in females of childbearing age (54). Also, there were no differences in GFR and RPF measured before, 6 hr after starting therapy, and after the continued administration of 2 mg of estradiol benzoate im daily for 3–9 days to normal male volunteers receiving constant diets (M. D. Lindheimer and S. Oparil, unpublished observations). A recent study by Hollenberg and colleagues (138) in which RBF was measured by the xenon washout technique in women being evaluated as kidney transplant donors is intriguing. Normotensive healthy subjects consuming a variety of estrogen- and progestin-containing oral contraceptives had RBF measurements 25% below those of age-matched nonpill users who were ingesting diets of similar Na content. The authors attributed these findings to increments in circulating angiotensin II.

Tubular Function

Estrogens may inhibit the uptake of PAH in renal cortical slices (145) and decrease the T_mPAH in the dog (258). However, tubular maxima of both glucose and PAH were unaffected by estrogens in the few studies performed on humans (77). Of interest is the observation that estrogens decrease the tubular reabsorption of ascorbic acid in both dogs and man (77, 273). In the dog, excretion of vitamin C approaches its filtered load and prolonged estrogen therapy causes a bleeding diathesis and anemia. In human pregnancy, which is marked by high estrogen levels, the excretion of ascorbic acid increases twofold (146).

Electrolyte Excretion

Estrogens decrease Na excretion in normal and adrenalectomized dogs (55, 73, 148–150, 295, 296). Johnson et al (148–150) performed careful metabolic studies and assayed the Na-retaining properties of 17 β-estradiol and estriol in normal animals. They demonstrated that estradiol is antinatriuretic in dogs with arteriovenous fistulae, in adrenalectomized bitches maintained with replacement doses of cortisol or cortisol and desoxycorticosterone (DOC), and following DOC "escape." Potassium excretion was unaffected. Dance et al (73) injected stilbestrol, a nonsteroid estrogen, into trained conscious dogs subsequently given oral water loads. They noted decrements in both urine flow and Na excretion compared to measurements in control studies. Since GFR appeared to increase, the results suggest that stilbestrol-induced antinatriuresis may occur primarily in the proximal tubule.

Data concerning electrolyte excretion in estrogen-treated rodents are difficult to interpret. Evaluation of short-term actions of the hormone has been restricted to monitoring electrolyte excretion for 3–7 hr following injection of estrogens into adrenalectomized male rats. With one exception (80), such studies have failed to reveal any immediate effects of estrogens on either Na or K excretion (87, 103, 279).

Reductions in Na excretion have occurred in adrenalectomized male (82) and intact female (250) rats treated with estradiol or estriol for several days, but the significance of such reports is obscure in the absence of data describing dietary intake. When balance studies have been performed on rats of both sexes (225, 297) and on male guinea pigs (212) eating ad lib, estrogens consistently decreased food intake but did not alter the fractional excretion of ingested Na. In these studies the fractional turnover of K was also unaltered in the rat, but the fate of this cation in the guinea pig was more complex. Studies performed on animals eating at will, are deficient because several variables change simultaneously. In one study in which treated and control animals were pair-fed, ovariectomized rats receiving large doses of stilbestrol excreted less Na and K than their controls (225). On the other hand, Na and K excretion were similar in male rats receiving estradiol and in their pair-fed controls (106).

Sodium is retained with little change in K excretion when estrogens are chronically administered to adrenalectomized (295) and normal (55, 83, 165, 172, 254) human subjects. The positive Na balance usually continues for several days after which Na excretion returns to control levels in a manner similar to that seen during "escape" from the salt-retaining effects of aldosterone or DOC. Crane & Harris (67) noted a mean increase of 226 mEq in the ^{22}Na space of women receiving 0.05 mg of ethynyl estradiol daily for three months; smaller increments occurred with conjugated estrogens and stilbestrol. Others have shown that plasma volume and inulin spaces increase while the hematocrit decreases during periods of estrogen treatment (6, 314).

The mechanism of estrogen-induced Na retention is unclear. Dignam and colleagues (83) were unable to detect any acute effects of intravenous estrogens in humans, and we could not demonstrate a consistent change in urinary Na excretion 6 hr after injection of large doses of estradiol benzoate (M. D. Lindheimer, S. Oparil, unpublished observations). More intriguing is the report of Katz & Kappas (158) that extremely high doses of estrogens in humans were initially natriuretic, and salt retention occurred only on the second or third day of treatment. Such studies raise the question whether estrogens have direct renal antinatriuretic actions or cause salt retention by extrarenal mechanisms (e.g. anabolic changes, enhanced aldosterone secretion, or Na storage in bone, mucopolysaccharides, or "sexual" skin). The studies of Johnson et al in the dog (148, 150) are cited as those which most strongly suggest a direct renal antinatriuretic effect of estrogen. It should be noted, however, that estrogens may promote binding of corticoids to steroid receptors in the kidney (292) and "replacement" doses of steroids were administered to the adrenalectomized rats studied by Johnson et al (148, 150). Finally, estrogens increase SCC in the anuran skin (298).

Estrogen Receptors in the Kidney

Receptors with high affinity for estrogens have been demonstrated in kidneys of hamsters (182), rats (82, 162), mice (46), and fetal guinea pigs (236). They are described as specific estradiol-macromolecular complexes different from those formed with aldosterone, and are found both in the cytosol and nuclei. These receptors may be located in the proximal tubule [(161), and C. A. Villee, discussion following (236)], the site where the majority of estrogen-induced ultrastructural changes have been described (55). DeVries et al (82) suggested a role for these receptors in mediating the antinatriuretic effect of estrogens in the rat. In addition,

Matthews et al (204) have described estrogen-dependent tumors in hamsters, but the relationship between these neoplasms and renal estrogen receptors is not clear.

Other Actions

Estrogens decrease the urinary excretion of Ca and PO_4 in humans (255), probably secondary to their anabolic properties, while in the rat they have a phosphaturic effect (106).

Hemodilution accompanied by small decrements in serum Na and osmolality and increased urine osmolality in randomly collected samples have been noted in post-menopausal women ingesting estrogens when compared with age-matched controls (6). It is not clear whether this observation reflects an estrogen-vasopressin interaction, since this aspect is only now beginning to be studied in humans (301), and data in animals are inconclusive (56, 73, 79, 225–227).

A number of biochemical effects of estrogens on renal tissue and the literature concerning effects of estrogens on the renin-angiotensin-aldosterone systems have been reviewed by Christy & Shaver (55) and by others (66, 138). The general opinion is that estrogens act primarily on the liver where they enhance the production of renin substrate. This leads to increments in angiotensin I and II and, when appropriate feedback control is operative, the increased levels of angiotensin directly or indirectly decrease the renal synthesis or release of renin.

PROLACTIN

Prolactin is phylogenetically the oldest polypeptide hormone secreted by the pituitary and has an important role in maintaining volume homeostasis and osmoregulation in lower vertebrates. A vast literature on this subject, too detailed for this review, has been summarized by others (16, 29, 96, 223), but we note with special interest that this hormone is renotropic, decreases renal Na excretion while enhancing urine flow (96), and stimulates renal Na-K-ATPase in certain teleosts (239). Furthermore, prolactin may enhance active Na transport in the toad bladder (72).

In contrast to the many reports dealing with lower vertebrates, research on the renal actions of prolactin in mammals has been sparse. Interest in the action of this hormone on the mammalian kidney is increasing, however, in part because of the recent controversy regarding the role of prolactin in human osmoregulation (4, 25, 44, 45). When evaluating the actions of prolactin, one should be mindful of the uncertainty regarding the purity of the hormone, which may be contaminated with other pituitary substances, and of the fact that prolactin influences the secretion of, or interacts with, other hormones affecting renal function, such as estrogens and aldosterone.

Renal Hemodynamics

Prolactin has no immediate effect on inulin clearance (190) or creatinine excretion (187), but sustained administration of this hormone may increase GFR and RPF in rats (203). The hormone does not affect renal hemodynamics in the perfused cat kidney (186). Data in dogs are not consistent; the intravenous administration of prolactin caused marked increments in both inulin and PAH clearance in awake animals (192) while infusion of the hormone into the renal artery of anesthetized dogs was without effect (259). A report that ovine prolactin increases GFR and RPF in man requires substantiation (21).

Water and Electrolyte Excretion

Lockett & Nail (187) reported that prolactin rapidly decreased Na, K, and water excretion in the rat. Somewhat contrasting, however, are the results of Lucci et al (190) who were unable to demonstrate any immediate renal actions of the hormone in hydropenic animals but found that prolactin blunted the natriuretic effects of subsequent saline loading. Prolactin-induced decrements in Na, K, and water excretion have also been observed in the perfused cat kidney (186) and in man (142). The hormone may also be antidiuretic and antinatriuretic in sheep, but the validity of these observations is difficult to evaluate because of the complexity of the protocols employed (48, 143, 144).

Results in dogs conflict, perhaps due to differences in experimental conditions. MacCallum et al (192) administered prolactin intravenously and observed a significant natriuresis in awake dogs during water diuresis. Analysis of free water and solute excretion suggested that intrarenal Na handling was unaltered and that the natriuresis resulted from the simultaneous increase in GFR. In contrast, infusion of the hormone into the renal artery of anesthetized animals had no influence on either Na or water excretion and as stated before, renal hemodynamics did not change (259). A calciuric effect of prolactin in humans has been reported (21).

Osmoregulation in Mammals

A flurry of excitement followed reports which attributed a role for prolactin in osmoregulation in man (44, 45) and in the rat (256). Water loading or hypotonic saline infusions decreased, while hypertonic saline increased prolactin levels in both species (44, 45, 256). In the rat, dehydration resulted in decreased pituitary levels (97) and increased both the serum concentrations and renal binding of the hormone (196, 257). Furthermore, prolactin may increase renal medullary adenylate cyclase activity in a manner which mimics the action of vasopressin (100). However, Adler et al (4) as well as Berl et al (25) failed to detect any influence of either water loads or the infusion of hypotonic or hypertonic saline on prolactin levels in normal volunteers, and the former authors commented that the effects observed by others are at variance with those expected from studies in lower vertebrates. In the single study demonstrating an antidiuretic effect of prolactin in water-loaded man (142), the authors did not eliminate convincingly the possibility that their preparation may have been contaminated with vasopressin (194).

Renal Receptors

There are conflicting reports on the presence of specific prolactin receptors in the kidney. Frantz et al (108) described membrane-rich particulate fractions in mouse kidney which bound prolactin in a manner consistent with the presence of specific receptors. Marshall et al (196) also demonstrated specific renal binding in the rat kidney, the activity of which could be altered by water deprivation or salt loading. Posner and colleagues (244), however, were unable to demonstrate renal receptors in this species. Furthermore, the localization of injected hormone within the kidney (which should presumably include receptor sites) is also disputed. Two groups of investigators (86, 251) noted that prolactin binding is confined only to the proximal tubule, and it was proposed (189) that the hormone may change the renal response to Na loading by inhibiting the dilatation of the lateral intercellular spaces in the proximal tubule. In contrast, Evan et al (100) found with autoradiographic techniques that ^{125}I prolactin bound selectively and for long periods of time in the loops of Henle, distal tubules, and collecting ducts, with little activity present in the proximal tubule, and that the hormone activates adenylate cyclase in broken cell preparations from the renal medulla, but not the cortex. These discrepancies are hard to explain but suggest that the hormone may act at several locations in the nephron.

GROWTH HORMONE

Many of the renal actions ascribed to growth hormone (GH) must now be reassessed, since the hormonal preparations used in earlier experiments were most likely contaminated with other pituitary substances (20, 248, 249). The older literature, reviewed only in selected references, can be summarized as follows:

In the dog, GH increased GFR, RPF, and the Tm of glucose, SO_4 and PO_4 (2, 61, 310). In man injection of the hormone increased the clearances of creatinine and inulin, and the TmPAH (21, 60, 114, 310), in agreement with observations of elevated GFR, RPF, TmPAH, and Tm glucose in acromegalic patients (310). Effects of GH on electrolyte excretion include Na and K retention in the rat (69, 187, 191, 278), cat (186), and man (24, 30, 134); decreased PO_4 excretion in dogs and humans (2, 60, 61); and increased urinary Ca in man (21, 60). Data from micropuncture experiments demonstrate enhanced proximal tubular Na reabsorption in GH-treated rats (278), and the antinatriuretic action of this hormone was blocked by actinomycin (191). GH also enhanced water flux and SCC in the anuran skin (132). It should be noted that this summary is a simplified synthesis of many studies, some of which required dietary and surgical manipulation, as well as interaction with other hormones, to demonstrate the reported effect. Furthermore, some of these results were not reproducible, and many authors, aware of the possibility of contamination, showed appropriate caution in interpreting their results.

Highly purified human growth hormone is now available and some of the observations described above have already been disputed. Rabkin et al (249) have demonstrated convincingly that the action of GH on the anuran skin was due to vasopressin, and that the purified hormone had no effect. The same group failed to observe changes in electrolyte or water excretion when their purified human preparation was administered to rats or human volunteers (248).

Growth hormone has been indirectly linked to renin secretion, among other reasons because acromegalics demonstrate a high renin activity relative to their volume status (290). However, purified human growth hormone given to normal volunteers had no effect on plasma renin activity (99). Finally, much has been written on the role of hypophysectomy and GH in compensatory renal hypertrophy after uninephrectomy. This question remains to be resolved (264).

ACKNOWLEDGMENTS

We thank Ms. Victoria Armstrong, Ms. Mary Knutsen, and Ms. Gail Sims for assistance in preparing the manuscript. Authors' work reviewed here was supported by grants AM13601, HD05572, HD07110, and RR55 from the National Institutes of Health and by the Chicago and Illinois Heart Associations.

Literature Cited

1. Abrahamsen, A. M., Storstein, L., Westlie, L., Storstein, O. 1974. Effects of dopamine on hemodynamics and renal function. *Acta Med. Scand.* 195:365–73
2. Abramow, M., Corvilain, J. 1967. Effect of growth hormone on tubular reabsorption of glucose and phosphate. *Nature* 213:85–86
3. Adams, P. H., Jowsey, J., Kelly, P. J., Riggs, B. L., Kinney, V. R., Jones, J. D. 1967. Effects of hyperthyroidism on bone and mineral metabolism in man. *Q. J. Med.* 36:1–15
4. Adler, R. A., Noel, G. L., Wartofsky, L., Frantz, A. G. 1975. Failure of oral water loading and intravenous hypotonic saline to suppress plasma prolactin in man. *J. Clin. Endocrinol. Metab.* 41:383–89
5. Aikawa, J. K. 1956. The nature of myxedema. Alterations in the serum electrolyte concentrations and radiosodium space and in the exchangeable sodium and potassium contents. *Ann. Intern. Med.* 44:30–39
6. Aitken, J. M., Lindsay, R., Hart, D. M. 1974. The redistribution of body sodium in women on long-term oestrogen therapy. *Clin. Sci. Mol. Med.* 47:179–87
7. Aldred, J. P., Kleszynski, R. R., Bastian, J. W. 1970. Effects of acute administration of porcine and salmon calcitonin on urine electrolyte excretion in rats. *Proc. Soc. Exp. Biol. Med.* 134:1175–80
8. Aldred, J. P., Stubbs, R. K., Hermann, W. R., Zeedyk, R. A., Bastian, J. W. 1970. Effects of porcine calcitonin on some urine electrolytes in the rat. *Acta Endocrinol.* 65:737–50
9. Alexander, R. W., Gill, J. R. Jr., Yamabe, H., Lovenberg, W., Keiser, H. R. 1974. Effects of dietary sodium and of acute saline infusion on the interrelationship between dopamine excretion and adrenergic activity in man. *J. Clin. Invest.* 54:194–200
10. Aliapoulios, M. A., Goldhaber, P., Munson, P. L. 1966. Thyrocalcitonin inhibition of bone resorption induced by parathyroid hormone in tissue culture. *Science* 151:330–31
11. Ardaillou, R., Fillastre, J. P., Milhaud, G., Rousselet, F., Delaunay, F., Richet, G. 1969. Renal excretion of phosphate, calcium and sodium during and after a prolonged thyrocalcitonin infusion in man. *Proc. Soc. Exp. Biol. Med.* 131:56–60
12. Ardaillou, R., Milhaud, G., Rousselet, F., Vuagnat, P., Richet, G. 1967. Effet de la thyrocalcitonine sur l'excrétion rénale du sodium et du chlore chez l'homme normal. *C. R. Acad. Sci. Ser D* 264:3037–40
13. Ardaillou, R., Vuagnat, P., Milhaud, G., Richet, G. 1967. Effets de la thyrocalcitonine sur l'excrétion rénale des phosphates, du calcium et des ions H+ chez l'homme. *Nephron* 4:298–314
14. Aub, J. C., Bauer, W., Heath, C., Ropes, M. 1929. Studies of calcium and phosphorus metabolism III. The effects of the thyroid hormones and thyroid disease. *J. Clin. Invest.* 7:97–137
15. Baldwin, D. S., Gombos, E. A., Chasis, H. 1963. Changes in sodium and water excretion induced by epinephrine and l-norepinephrine in normotensive and hypertensive subjects. *J. Lab. Clin. Med.* 61:832–57
16. Ball, J. N. 1969. Prolactin and osmoregulation in teleost fishes: A review. *Gen. Comp. Endocrinol. Suppl.* 2:10–25
17. Barger, A. C., Muldowney, F. P., Liebowitz, M. R. 1959. Role of the kidney in the pathogenesis of congestive heart failure. *Circulation* 20:273–85

18. Barlet, J. P. 1972. Effect of porcine, salmon and human calcitonin on urinary excretion of some electrolytes in sheep. *J. Endocrinol.* 55:153–61
19. Barnes, A. B. 1973. The effect of oxytocin on renal blood flow and its distribution in the dog. *Nephron* 11:40–57
20. Baumann, G., Rayfield, E. J., Rose, L. I., Williams, G. H., Dingman, J. F. 1972. "Trace" contamination of corticotropin and human growth hormone with vasopressin—clinical significance. *J. Clin. Endocrinol. Metab.* 34:801–4
21. Beck, J. C., Gonda, A., Hamid, M. A., Morgen, R. O., Rubinstein, D., McGarry, E. E. 1964. Some metabolic changes induced by primate growth hormone and purified ovine prolactin. *Metabolism* 13:1108–34
22. Beck, N. P., Reed, S. W., Murdaugh, H. V., Davis, B. B. 1972. Effects of catecholamines and their interaction with other hormones on cyclic 3', 5'-adenosine monophosphate of the kidney. *J. Clin. Invest.* 51:939–44
23. Bello-Reuss, E., Trevino, D. L., Gottschalk, C. W. 1976. Effect of renal sympathetic nerve stimulation on proximal water and sodium reabsorption. *J. Clin. Invest.* 57:1104–7
24. Bergenstal, D. M., Lipsett, M. B. 1960. Metabolic effects of human growth hormone and growth hormone of other species in man. *J. Clin. Endocrinol. Metab.* 20:1427–46
25. Berl, T., Brautbar, N., Ben-David, M., Czaczkes, W., Kleeman, C. 1975. Osmotic control of prolactin (PRL) release and the effect of the hormone on renal excretion of water in man. *Kidney Int.* 8:468
26. Berl, T., Cadnapaphornchai, P., Harbottle, J. A., Schrier, R. W. 1974. Mechanism of suppression of vasopressin during alpha adrenergic stimulation with norepinephrine. *J. Clin. Invest.* 53:219–27
27. Berl, T., Cadnapaphornchai, P., Harbottle, J. A., Schrier, R. W. 1974. Mechanism of stimulation of vasopressin release during beta adrenergic stimulation with isoproterenol. *J. Clin. Invest.* 53:857–67
28. Berl, T., Harbottle, J. A., Schrier, R. W. 1974. Effect of alpha and beta adrenergic stimulation on renal water excretion in man. *Kidney Int.* 6:247–53
29. Bern, H. A., Nicoll, C. S. 1968. The comparative endocrinology of prolactin. *Recent Prog. Horm. Res.* 24:681–720
30. Biglieri, E. G., Watlington, C. O., Forsham, P. H. 1961. Sodium retention with human growth hormone and its subfractions. *J. Clin. Endocrinol. Metab.* 21:361–70
31. Bijvoet, O. L. M. 1969. Relation of plasma phosphate concentration to renal tubular reabsorption of phosphate. *Clin. Sci.* 37:23–36
32. Bijvoet, O. L. M., van der Sluys Veer, J., de Vries, H. R., van Koppen, A. T. J. 1971. Natriuretic effect of calcitonin in man. *N. Engl. J. Med.* 284:681–88
33. Bijvoet, O. L. M., van der Sluys Veer, J., Jansen, A. P. 1968. Effects of calcitonin on patients with Paget's disease, thyrotoxicosis, or hypercalcemia. *Lancet* 1:876–81
34. Blahos, J., Osten, J., Mertl, L., Kotas, J., Gregor, O., Reisenauer, R. 1975. The uricosuric effect of calcitonin. *Horm. Metab. Res.* 7:445–46
35. Blake, W. D. 1955. Pathways of adrenaline action on renal function with observations on a blood pressure reflex regulating water and electrolyte excretion. *Am. J. Physiol.* 181:399–416
36. Blendis, L. M., Auld, R. B., Alexander, E. A., Levinsky, N. G. 1972. Effect of renal beta- and alpha-adrenergic stimulation on proximal sodium reabsorption in dogs. *Clin. Sci.* 43:569–76
37. Blumenthal, S. A. 1975. Observations on sodium retention related to insulin treatment of experimental diabetes. *Diabetes* 24:645–49
38. Borle, A. B. 1969. Effects of thyrocalcitonin on calcium transport in kidney cells. *Endocrinology* 85:194–99
39. Bradley, S. E., ed. 1974. Hormones and the kidney. *Kidney Int.* 6:261–376
40. Bradley, S. E., Bradley, G. P., Stéphan, F. 1972. Role of structural imbalance in the pathogenesis of renal dysfunction in the hypothyroid rat. *Trans. Assoc. Am. Physicians* 85:344–52
41. Bradley, S. E., Stéphan, F., Coelho, J. B., Réville, P. 1974. The thyroid and the kidney. *Kidney Int.* 6:346–65
42. Broadus, A. E., Kaminsky, N. I., Northcutt, R. C., Hardman, J. G., Sutherland, E. W., Liddle, G. W. 1970. Effects of glucagon on adenosine 3',5'-monophosphate and guanosine 3',5'-monophosphate in human plasma and urine. *J. Clin. Invest.* 49:2237–45
43. Brotzu, G. 1970. Inhibition by chlorpromazine of the effects of dopamine on the dog kidney. *J. Pharm. Pharmacol.* 22:664–67

44. Buckman, M. T., Kaminsky, N., Conway, M., Peake, G. T. 1973. Utility of L dopa and water loading in evaluation of hyperprolactinemia. *J. Clin. Endocrinol. Metab.* 36:911–19
45. Buckman, M. T., Peake, G. T. 1973. Osmolar control of prolactin secretion in man. *Science* 181:755–57
46. Bullock, L. P., Bardin, C. W. 1975. The presence of estrogen receptor in kidneys from normal and androgen insensitive tfm/y mice. *Endocrinology* 97:1106–11
47. Bunag, R. D., Page, I. H., McCubbin, J. W. 1966. Neural stimulation of release of renin. *Circ. Res.* 19:851–58
48. Burstyn, P. G., Horrobin, D. F., Manku, M. S. 1972. Saluretic action of aldosterone in the presence of increased salt intake and restoration of normal action by prolactin or oxytocin. *J. Endocrinol.* 55:369–76
49. Chabardès, D., Imbert-Teboul, M., Montégut, M., Clique, A., Morel, F. 1975. Catecholamine sensitive adenylate cyclase activity in different segments of the rabbit nephron. *Pfluegers Arch.* 361:9–15
50. Chamberlain, M. J., Stimmler, L. 1967. The renal handling of insulin. *J. Clin. Invest.* 46:911–19
51. Charbon, G. A., Hoekstra, M. H., Schuckink Kool, D. 1963. The influence of glucagon on the urinary excretion of water, sodium, potassium, calcium, magnesium, chloride and inorganic phosphate. *Acta Physiol. Pharmacol. Neerl.* 12:48–56
52. Chase, L. R., Aurbach, G. D. 1967. Parathyroid function and the renal excretion of 3′,5′-adenylic acid. *Proc. Natl. Acad. Sci. USA* 58:518–25
53. Cheng, L., Rogus, E., Zierler, K. L. 1976. Catechol, a structural requirement for Na, K-ATPase stimulation in rat skeletal muscle membrane. *Fed. Proc.* 35:835
54. Chesley, L. C., Tepper, I. H. 1967. Effects of progesterone and estrogen on the sensitivity to angiotensin II. *J. Clin. Endocrinol. Metab.* 27:576–81
55. Christy, N. P., Shaver, J. C. 1974. Estrogens and the kidney. *Kidney Int.* 6:366–76
56. Cizek, L. J., Nocenti, M. R., Oparil, S. 1966. Sex difference in fluid exchange during food deprivation in the rabbit. *Endocrinology* 78:291–96
57. Clark, J. D., Kenny, A. D. 1969. Hog thyrocalcitonin in the dog: Urinary calcium, phosphorus, magnesium and sodium responses. *Endocrinology* 84:1199–1205
58. Cochran, M., Peacock, M., Sachs, G., Nordin, B. E. C. 1970. Renal effects of calcitonin. *Br. Med. J.* 1:135–37
59. Cook, P. B., Nassim, J. R., Collins, J. 1959. The effects of thyrotoxicosis upon the metabolism of calcium, phosphorus and nitrogen. *Q. J. Med.* 28:505–29
60. Corvilain, J., Abramow, M. 1962. Some effects of human growth hormone on renal hemodynamics and on tubular transport in man. *J. Clin. Invest.* 41:1230–35
61. Corvilain, J., Abramow, M. 1964. Effect of growth hormone on tubular transport of phosphate in normal and parathyroidectomized dogs. *J. Clin. Invest.* 43:1608–12
62. Cox, J. W., Baehler, R. W., Sharma, H., O'Dorisio, T., Osgood, R. W., Stein, J. H., Ferris, T. F. 1974. Studies on the mechanism of oliguria in a model of unilateral acute renal failure. *J. Clin. Invest.* 53:1546–58
63. Crabbé, J. 1964. Decreased effectiveness of aldosterone on active sodium transport by the isolated toad bladder in the presence of other steroids. *Acta Endocrinol.* 47:419–32
64. Crabbé, J., François, B. 1967. Stimulation par l'insuline du transport actif de sodium à travers les membranes épithéliales du crapaud, *Bufo marinus*. *Ann. Endocrinol.* 28:713–15
65. Cramer, C. F., Parkes, C. O., Copp, D. H. 1969. The effect of chicken and hog calcitonin on some parameters of Ca, P, and Mg metabolism in dogs. *Can. J. Physiol. Pharmacol.* 47:181–84
66. Crane, M. G., Harris, J. J. 1974. Effects of estrogens and gestagens on the renin-aldosterone system. In *Oral Contraceptives and High Blood Pressure*, ed. M. J. Fregly, M. S. Fregly, pp. 100–19. Gainesville, Florida: Dolphin. 375 pp.
67. Crane, M. G., Harris, J. J. 1974. Effectiveness of estrogens and gestagens on exchangeable sodium. See Ref. 66, pp. 159–82
68. Crispell, K. R., Parson, W., Sprinkle, P. 1954. A cortisone-resistant abnormality in the diuretic response to ingested water in primary myxedema. *J. Clin. Endocrinol. Metab.* 14:640–44
69. Croxatto, H., Swaneck, G., LaBarca, E. 1968. The renotropic effect of growth hormone. In *Growth Hormone*, ed. A. Pacile, S. S. Müller, pp. 332–48. Amsterdam: Excerpta Medica

70. Curtis, R. H. 1956. Hyponatremia in primary myxedema. *Ann. Intern. Med.* 44:376–85

71. Dalle, X., Tanghe, J., Gryspeerdt, W. 1959. Influence du glucagon sur l'excrétion rénale des électrolytes. *Arch. Int. Pharmacodyn. Ther.* 70:505–7

72. Dalton, T., Snart, R. S. 1969. Effect of prolactin on the active transport of sodium by the isolated toad bladder. *J. Endocrinol.* 43:vi-vii

73. Dance, P., Lloyd, S., Pickford, M. 1959. The effects of stilboestrol on the renal activity of conscious dogs. *J. Physiol.* 145:225–40

74. Danford, R. O. 1970. The effect of glucagon on renal hemodynamics and renal arteriography. *Am. J. Roentgenol.* 108:665–73

75. David, M. A., Horváth, I. W., Kovács, K. 1960. Uber die Wirkung des Glukagons auf den Wasser-und-Elektrolyt-Stoffwechsel. *Endokrinologie* 39:138–49

76. Davis, B. B., Walter, M. J., Murdaugh, H. V. 1968. The mechanism of the increase in sodium excretion following dopamine infusion. *Proc. Soc. Exp. Biol. Med.* 129:210–13

77. Dean, A. L., Abels, J. C., Taylor, H. C. 1945. The effects of certain hormones on the renal function of man. *J. Urol.* 53:647–51

78. DeFronzo, R. A., Cooke, C. R., Andres, R., Faloona, G. R., Davis, P. J. 1975. The effect of insulin on renal handling of sodium, potassium, calcium, and phosphate in man. *J. Clin. Invest.* 55:845–55

79. Deis, R. P., Lloyd, S., Pickford, M. 1963. The effects of stilboestrol and progesterone and of renal denervation on the response of the kidneys to vasopressin and oxytocin. *J. Physiol.* 165:348–57

80. Deming, Q. B., Luetscher, J. A. Jr. 1950. Bioassay of deoxycorticosterone-like material in the urine. *Proc. Soc. Exp. Biol. Med.* 73:171–75

81. DeRubertis, F. R., Michelis, M. F., Bloom, M. E., Mintz, D. H., Field, J. B., Davis, B. B. 1971. Impaired water excretion in myxedema. *Am. J. Med.* 51:41–53

82. DeVries, J. R., Ludens, J. H., Fanestil, D. D. 1972. Estradiol renal receptor molecules and estradiol-dependent antinatriuresis. *Kidney Int.* 2:95–100

83. Dignam, W. S., Voskian, J., Assali, N. S. 1956. Effects of estrogens on renal hemodynamics and excretion of electrolytes in human subjects. *J. Clin. Endocrinol.* 16:1032–42

84. DiScala, V. A., Kinney, M. J. 1971. Effects of myxedema on the renal diluting and concentrating mechanism. *Am. J. Med.* 50:325–35

85. Docter, R., Visser, T. J., Stinis, J. T., van den Hout-Goemaat, N. L., Hennemann, G. 1976. Binding of L-triiodothyronine to isolated rat liver and kidney nuclei under various circumstances. *Acta Endocrinol.* 81:82–95

86. Donatsch, P., Richardson, B. 1975. Localization of prolactin in rat kidney tissue using a double-antibody technique. *J. Endocrinol.* 66:101–16

87. Dorfman, R. I. 1949. Influence of adrenal cortical steroids and related compounds on sodium metabolism. *Proc. Soc. Exp. Biol. Med.* 72:395–98

88. Dousa, T. P. 1974. Effects of hormones on cyclic AMP formation in kidneys of nonmammalian vertebrates. *Am. J. Physiol.* 226:1193–97

89. Edelman, I. S. 1974. Thyroid thermogenesis. *N. Engl. J. Med.* 290:1303–8

90. Edelman, I. S. 1975. Thyroidal regulation of renal energy metabolism and (Na^+ + K^+)-activated adenosine triphosphatase activity. *Med. Clin. North Am.* 59:605–14

91. Ehrlich, E. N., Lindheimer, M. D. 1972. Effect of administered mineralocorticoids or ACTH in pregnant women. Attenuation of kaliuretic influence of mineralocorticoids during pregnancy. *J. Clin. Invest.* 51:1301–9

92. Eiler, J. J., Althausen, T. L., Stockholm, M. 1944. The effect of thyroxin on the maximum rate of transfer of glucose and diodrast by the renal tubules. *Am. J. Physiol.* 140:699–707

93. Elrick, H., Huffman, E. R., Hlad, C. J. Jr., Whipple, N., Staub, A. Smith, A. E., Yearwood-Drayton, V. 1958. Effects of glucagon on renal function in man. *J. Clin. Endocrinol. Metab.* 18:813–24

94. Elrick, H., Whipple, N., Aray, Y., Hlad, C. J. Jr. 1959. Further studies on the renal action of glucagon. *J. Clin. Endocrinol. Metab.* 19:1274–81

95. Emmanouel, D. S., Lindheimer, M. D., Katz, A. I. 1974. Mechanism of impaired water excretion in the hypothyroid rat. *J. Clin. Invest.* 54:926–34

96. Ensor, D. M., Ball, J. N. 1972. Prolactin and osmoregulation in fishes. *Fed. Proc.* 31:1615–23

97. Ensor, D. M., Edmondson, M. R., Phillips, J. G. 1972. Prolactin and dehydration in rats. *J. Endocrinol.* 53:lix–lx

98. Epstein, F. H. 1968. Calcium and the kidney. *Am. J. Med.* 45:700–14

99. Epstein, S., Le Roith, D., Rabkin, R. 1976. The effect of different preparations of human growth hormone on plasma renin activity in normal males. *J. Clin. Endocrinol. Metab.* 42:390–92

100. Evan, A. P., Palmer, G. C., Lucci, M. S., Solomon, S. 1977. Prolactin-induced stimulation of rat renal adenylate cyclase and autoradiographic localization to the distal nephron. *Nephron.* In press

101. Evans, R. H., Smith, J. W. 1973. Mode of action of catecholamines on skeletal muscle. *J. Physiol.* 232:81P–83P

102. Farber, S. J., Berger, E. Y., Earle, D. P. 1951. Effect of diabetes and insulin on the maximum capacity of the renal tubules to reabsorb glucose. *J. Clin. Invest.* 30:125–29

103. Fimognari, G. M., Fanestil, D. D., Edelman, I. S. 1967. Induction of RNA and protein synthesis in the action of aldosterone in the rat. *Am. J. Physiol.* 213:954–62

104. Fisher, D. A. 1968. Norepinephrine inhibition of vasopressin antidiuresis. *J. Clin. Invest.* 47:540–47

105. Ford, R. V., Owens, J. C., Curd, G. W. Jr., Moyer, J. H., Spurr, C. L. 1961. Kidney function in various thyroid states. *J. Clin. Endocrinol. Metab.* 21:548–53

106. Forland, M. 1968. Effect of estradiol on phosphorus excretion in intact and hypophysectomized rats. *Endocrinology* 83:516–20

107. Franklin, R., Costello, L. C., Stacey, R., Stephens, R. 1973. Calcitonin effects on plasma and urinary citrate levels in rats. *Am. J. Physiol.* 225:1178–80

108. Frantz, W. L., MacIdoe, J. H., Turkington, R. W. 1974. Prolactin receptors: Characteristics of the particulate fraction binding activity. *J. Endocrinol.* 60:485–97

109. Fregly, M. J., Brimhall, R. L., Galindo, O. J. 1962. Effect of the antithyroid drug propylthiouracil on the sodium balance of rats. *Endocrinology* 71:693–700

110. Gaunt, R., Cordsen, M., Liling, M. 1944. Water intoxication in relation to thyroid and adrenal function. *Endocrinology* 35:105–11

111. Gaunt, R., Hays, H. W. 1938. Life-maintaining effect of crystalline progesterone in adrenalectomized ferrets. *Science* 88:576–77

112. Gaunt, R., Nelson, W. O., Loomis, E. 1938. Cortical hormone-like action of progesterone and non-effect of sex hormones on water intoxication. *Proc. Soc. Exp. Biol. Med.* 39:319–22

113. Gavryck, W. A., Moore, R. D., Thompson, R. C. 1975. Effect of insulin upon membrane bound ($Na^+ + K^+$)-ATPase extracted from frog skeletal muscle. *J. Physiol.* 252:43–58

114. Gershberg, H. 1960. Metabolic and renotropic effects of human growth hormone in disease. *J. Clin. Endocrinol. Metab.* 20:1107–19

115. Gill, J. R. Jr., Casper, A. G. T. 1971. Depression of proximal tubular sodium reabsorption in the dog in response to renal beta adrenergic stimulation by isoproterenol. *J. Clin. Invest.* 50:112–18

116. Gill, J. R. Jr., Casper, A. G. T. 1971. Renal effects of adenosine 3',5'-cyclic monophosphate and dibutyryl adenosine 3',5'-cyclic monophosphate. Evidence for a role for adenosine 3',5'-cyclic monophosphate in the regulation of proximal tubular sodium reabsorption. *J. Clin. Invest.* 50:1231–40

117. Gill, J. R. Jr., Casper, A. G. T. 1972. Effect of renal alpha-adrenergic stimulation on proximal tubular sodium reabsorption. *Am. J. Physiol.* 223:1201–5

118. Gill, J. R. Jr., Tate, J., Kelly, G. 1971. Evidence that guanosine-3',5'-cyclic monophosphate (CGMP) but not guanosine 5'-monophosphate (5'-GMP) increases sodium reabsorption by the proximal tubule. *Fourth Ann. Meet. Am. Soc. Nephrol. Wash. DC* p. 26

119. Goldberg, L. I. 1972. Cardiovascular and renal actions of dopamine: Potential clinical applications. *Pharmacol. Rev.* 24:1–29

120. Goldberg, M., Reivich, M. 1962. Studies on the mechanism of hyponatremia and impaired water excretion in myxedema. *Ann. Intern. Med.* 56:120–30

121. Grinstein, S., Erlij, D. 1974. Insulin unmasks latent sodium pump sites in frog muscle. *Nature* 251:57–58

122. Gudmundsson, T. V., MacIntyre, I., Soliman, H. A. 1966. The isolation of thyrocalcitonin and a study of its effect in the rat. *Proc. R. Soc. London Ser. B* 164:460–77

123. Haas, H. G., Dambacher, M. A., Guncaga, J., Lauffenburger, T. 1971. Renal effects of calcitonin and parathyroid extract in man. Studies in hyperparathyroidism. *J. Clin. Invest.* 50:2689–2702

124. Handler, J. S., Bensinger, R., Orloff, J. 1968. Effect of adrenergic agents on toad bladder response to ADH, 3',5'-

AMP, and theophylline. *Am. J. Physiol.* 215:1024–31

125. Hardaker, W. T. Jr., Wechsler, A. S. 1973. Redistribution of renal intracortical blood flow during dopamine infusion in dogs. *Circ. Res.* 33:437–44

126. Harden, R. M., Harrison, M. T., Alexander, W. D., Nordin, B. E. C. 1964. Phosphate excretion and parathyroid function in thyrotoxicosis. *J. Endocrinol.* 28:281–88

127. Hare, K., Phillips, D. M., Bradshaw, J., Chambers, G., Hare, R. S. 1944. The diuretic action of thyroid in diabetes insipidus. *Am. J. Physiol.* 144:187–95

128. Harvey, A. M., Malvin, R. L. 1965. Comparison of creatinine and inulin clearances in male and female rats. *Am. J. Physiol.* 209:849–52

129. Harvey, A. M., Malvin, R. L. 1966. The effect of androgenic hormones on creatinine secretion in the rat. *J. Physiol.* 184:883–88

130. Hays, E. T., Dwyer, T. M., Horowicz, P., Swift, J. G. 1974. Epinephrine action on sodium fluxes in frog striated muscle. *Am. J. Physiol.* 227:1340–47

131. Hayslett, J. P., Epstein, M., Spector, D., Myers, J. D., Murdaugh, H. V. 1972. Lack of effect of calcitonin on renal function in the elasmobranch, *Squalus acanthias*. *Comp. Biochem. Physiol. A* 43:223–26

132. Heblock, H. J., Sauls, H. S., Reynaldo, J. W., Brown, D. H. 1971. Effects of human growth hormone preparations on sodium transport in isolated frog skin. *J. Clin. Endocrinol. Metab.* 33:903–7

133. Heersche, J. N. M., Marcus, R., Aurbach, G. D. 1974. Calcitonin and the formation of 3',5',-AMP in bone and kidney. *Endocrinology* 94:241–47

134. Henneman, P. H., Forbes, A. P., Moldawer, M., Dempsey, E. F., Carroll, E. L. 1960. Effects of human growth hormone in man. *J. Clin. Invest.* 39:1223–38

135. Herrera, F. C., Whittembury, G., Planchart, A. 1963. Effect of insulin on short-circuit current across isolated frog skin in the presence of calcium and magnesium. *Biochim. Biophys. Acta* 66:170–72

136. Hervey, E., Hervey, G. R. 1967. The effects of progesterone on body weight and composition in the rat. *J. Endocrinol.* 37:361–84

137. Hlad, C. J. Jr., Bricker, N. S. 1954. Renal function and I^{131} clearance in hyperthyroidism and myxedema. *J. Clin. Endocrinol. Metab.* 14:1539–50

138. Hollenberg, N. K., Williams, G. H., Burger, B., Chenitz, W., Hoosmand, I., Adams, D. F. 1976. Renal blood-flow and its response to angiotensin II, an interaction between oral contraceptive agents, sodium intake, and the renin-angiotensin system in healthy young women. *Circ. Res.* 38:35–40

139. Hollowell, J. G., Frazer, J. W., Gardner, L. I. 1968. Inhibition of toad bladder sodium transport and $Na^+ + K^+$ stimulated adenosinetriphosphatase by extracts of human urine: Studies of patients with virilizing adrenal hyperplasia. *J. Clin. Endocrinol. Metab.* 28:492–502

140. Holmes, E. W. Jr., DiScala, V. A. 1970. Studies on the exaggerated natriuretic response to a saline infusion in the hypothyroid rat. *J. Clin. Invest.* 49:1224–36

141. Holmes, E. W. Jr., DiScala, V. A. 1971. Oxygen consumption, glycolysis, and sodium reabsorption in the hypothyroid rat kidney. *Am. J. Physiol.* 221:839–43

142. Horrobin, D. F., Lloyd, I. J., Lipton, A., Burstyn, P. G., Durkin, N., Muiruri, K. L. 1971. Actions of prolactin on human renal function. *Lancet* 2:352–54

143. Horrobin, D. F., Manku, M. S., Burstyn, P. G. 1973. Saluretic action of aldosterone in the presence of excess cortisol: Restoration of salt-retaining action by prolactin. *J. Endocrinol.* 56:343–44

144. Horrobin, D. F., Manku, M. S., Robertshaw, D. 1973. Water-losing action of antidiuretic hormone in the presence of excess cortisol: Restoration of normal action by prolactin or by oxytocin. *J. Endocrinol.* 58:135–36

145. Huang, K. C., McIntosh, B. J. 1955. Effect of sex hormones on renal transport of *p*-aminohippuric acid. *Am. J. Physiol.* 183:387–90

146. Hytten, F. E. 1973. The renal excretion of nutrients in pregnancy. *Postgrad. Med. J.* 49:625–29

147. Ismail-Beigi, F., Edelman, I. S. 1971. The mechanism of the calorigenic action of thyroid hormone. Stimulation of $Na^+ + K^+$-activated adenosine triphosphatase activity. *J. Gen. Physiol.* 57:710–22

148. Johnson, J. A., Davis, J. O. 1976. The effect of estrogens on renal sodium excretion in the dog. In *Hypertension in Pregnancy*, ed. M. D. Lindheimer, A. I.

Katz, F. P. Zuspan, pp. 239–48. New York: Wiley.

149. Johnson, J. A., Davis, J. O., Baumber, J. S., Schneider, E. G. 1970. Effect of estrogens and progesterone on electrolyte balances in normal dogs. *Am. J. Physiol.* 219:1691–97

150. Johnson, J. A., Davis, J. O., Brown, P. R., Wheeler, P. D., Witty, R. T. 1972. Effects of estradiol on sodium and potassium balances in adrenalectomized dogs. *Am. J. Physiol.* 223:194–97

151. Johnson, J. A., Davis, J. O., Gotshall, R. W., Lohmeier, T. E., Davis, J. L., Braverman, B., Tempel, G. E. 1976. Evidence for an intrarenal beta receptor in control of renin release. *Am. J. Physiol.* 230:410–18

152. Jones, J. E., Desper, P. C., Shane, S. R., Flink, E. B. 1966. Magnesium metabolism in hyperthyroidism and hypothyroidism. *J. Clin. Invest.* 45:891–900

153. Kagawa, C. M. 1958. Blocking urinary electrolyte effects of desoxycorticosterone with progesterone in rats. *Proc. Soc. Exp. Biol. Med.* 99:705–7

154. Katz, A. I., Emmanouel, D. S., Lindheimer, M. D. 1975. Thyroid hormone and the kidney. *Nephron* 15:223–49

155. Katz, A. I., Hollingsworth, D. R., Epstein, F. H. 1968. The influence of carbohydrate and protein upon sodium excretion during starvation and refeeding. *J. Lab. Clin. Med.* 72:93–104

156. Katz, A. I., Lindheimer, M. D. 1973. Renal sodium- and potassium-activated adenosine triphosphatase and sodium reabsorption in the hypothyroid rat. *J. Clin. Invest.* 52:796–804

157. Katz, A. I., Rubenstein, A. H. 1973. Metabolism of proinsulin, insulin and C-peptide in the rat. *J. Clin. Invest.* 52:1113–21

158. Katz, F. H., Kappas, A. 1967. The effects of estradiol and estriol on plasma levels of cortisol and thyroid hormone-binding globulins on aldosterone and cortisol secretion rates in man. *J. Clin. Invest.* 46:1768–77

159. Keeler, R., Walker, V., Copp, D. H. 1970. Natriuretic and diuretic effects of salmon calcitonin in rats. *Can. J. Physiol. Pharmacol.* 48:838–41

160. Kenny, A. D., Heiskell, C. A. 1965. Effect of crude thyrocalcitonin on calcium and phosphorus metabolism in rats. *Proc. Soc. Exp. Biol. Med.* 120:269–71

161. King, R. J. B. 1967. Fixation of steroids to receptors. *Arch. Anat. Microsc. Morphol. Exp.* (Suppl. 3–4) 56:570–82

162. King, R. J. B., Mainwaring, W. I. P. 1974. *Kidney in Steroid-Cell Interactions,* p. 247. Baltimore, Maryland: Univ. Park

163. Klein, L. A., Liberman, B., Laks, M., Kleeman, C. R. 1971. Interrelated effects of antidiuretic hormone and adrenergic drugs on water metabolism. *Am. J. Physiol.* 221:1657–65

164. Klisiecki, A., Pickford, M., Rothschild, P., Verney, E. B. 1933. The absorption and excretion of water by the mammal. II. Factors influencing the response of the kidney to water ingestion. *Proc. R. Soc. London* 112:521–47

165. Knowlton, K., Kenyon, A. T., Sandiford, I., Lotwin, G., Fricker, R. 1942. Comparative study of metabolic effects of estradiol benzoate and testosterone propionate in man. *J. Clin. Endocrinol.* 2:671–84

166. Knox, F. G., Riggs, D. S. 1963. Effects of insulin on renal hemodynamics. *Proc. Soc. Exp. Biol. Med.* 114:826–28

167. Kolanowski, J., Pizarro, M. A., deGasparo, M., Desmecht, P., Harvengt, C., Crabbé, J. 1970. Influence of fasting on adrenocortical and pancreatic islet response to glucose loads in the obese. *Eur. J. Clin. Invest.* 1:25–31

168. Krane, S. M., Brownell, G. L., Stanbury, J. B., Corrigan, H. 1956. The effect of thyroid disease on calcium metabolism in man. *J. Clin. Invest.* 35:874–87

169. Kurokawa, K., Massry, S. G. 1973. Interaction between catecholamines and vasopressin on renal medullary cyclic AMP of rat. *Am. J. Physiol.* 225:825–29

170. Kurokawa, K., Nagata, N., Sasaki, M., Nakane, K. 1974. Effects of calcitonin on the concentration of cyclic adenosine 3',5'-monophosphate in rat kidney *in vivo* and *in vitro. Endocrinology* 94:1514–18

171. Laidlaw, J. C., Ruse, J. L., Gornall, A. G. 1962. The influence of estrogen and progesterone on aldosterone excretion. *J. Clin. Endocrinol. Metab.* 22:161–71

172. Landau, R. L., Berganstal, D. M., Lugibihl, K., Dimick, D. F., Rashid, E. 1957. The relationship of estrogen and of pituitary hormones to the metabolic effects of progesterone. *J. Clin. Endocrinol.* 17:177–85

173. Landau, R. L., Berganstal, D. M., Lugibihl, K., Kascht, M. E. 1955. The metabolic effects of progesterone in man. *J. Clin. Endocrinol.* 15:1194–1215

174. Landau, R. L., Lugibihl, K. 1958. Inhibition of the sodium-retaining influence

of aldosterone by progesterone. *J. Clin. Endocrinol.* 18:1237–45

175. Landau, R. L., Lugibihl, K., Bergenstal, D. M., Dimick, D. F. 1957. The metabolic effects of progesterone in man: Dose response relationships. *J. Lab. Clin. Med.* 50:613–20

176. Lecomte, M. J. H., Lefèbvre, P., Luyckx, A. 1972. Insulinémie et travail maximal de réabsorption tubulaire du glucose chez le chien anesthésié. *Arch. Intern. Physiol. Biochim.* 80:97–106

177. Lees, P. 1968. The influence of beta-adrenoceptive receptor blocking agents on urinary function in the rat. *Br. J. Pharmacol.* 34:429–44

178. Levi, J., Grinblat, J., Kleeman, C. R. 1971. Effect of isoproterenol on water diuresis in rats with congenital diabetes insipidus. *Am. J. Physiol.* 221:1728–32

179. Levy, M. 1975. Further observations on the response of the glomerular filtration rate to glucagon: Comparison with secretin. *Can. J. Physiol. Pharmacol.* 53:81–85

180. Levy, M. 1975. The effect of glucagon on glomerular filtration rate in dogs during reduction of renal blood flow. *Can. J. Physiol. Pharmacol.* 53:660–68

181. Levy, M., Starr, N. L. 1972. The mechanism of glucagon-induced natriuresis in dogs. *Kidney Int.* 2:76–84

182. Li, J. J., Talley, D. J., Li, S. A., Villee, C. A. 1974. An estrogen binding protein in the renal cytosol of intact, castrated and estrogenized golden hamsters. *Endocrinology* 95:1134–41

183. Liddle, G. W. 1961. Specific and nonspecific inhibition of mineralocorticoid activity. *Metabolism* 10:1021–30

184. Lindheimer, M. D., Koeppen, B., Katz, A. I. 1976. Renal function in normal and hypertensive pregnant rats. See reference 148, pp. 217–27

185. Lindheimer, M. D., Lalone, R. C., Levinsky, N. G. 1967. Evidence that an acute increase in glomerular filtration has little effect on sodium excretion in the dog unless extracellular volume is expanded. *J. Clin. Invest.* 46:256–65

186. Lockett, M. F. 1965. A comparison of the direct renal actions of pituitary growth and lactogenic hormones. *J. Physiol.* 181:192–99

187. Lockett, M. F., Nail, B. 1965. A comparative study of the renal actions of growth and lactogenic hormones in rats. *J. Physiol.* 180:147–56

188. Loreau, N., Lepreux, C., Ardaillou, R. 1975. Calcitonin-sensitive adenylate cyclase in rat renal tubular membranes. *Biochem. J.* 150:305–14

189. Lucci, M. S., Evan, A., Bengele, H. H., Solomon, S. 1974. Altered effect of saline loading on the lateral intercellular spaces of the proximal tubule during prolactin infusion. *Fed. Proc.* 33:368

190. Lucci, M. S., Bengele, H. H., Solomon, S. 1975. Suppressive action of prolactin on renal response to volume expansion. *Am. J. Physiol.* 229:81–85

191. Ludens, J. H., Bach, R. R., Williamson, H. E. 1969. Characteristics of the antinatriuretic action of growth hormone. *Proc. Soc. Exp. Biol. Med.* 130:1156–58

192. MacCallum, G. C., Simpson, A., Auld, R. B. 1975. Effects of prolactin (Prl) on canine renal function. *Clin. Res.* 23:652A

193. Mahler, R. J., Szabo, O. 1968. Metabolic effects of insulin in rat kidney after inhibiting degradation of the hormone. *Endocrinology* 83:1166–72

194. Manku, M. S., Horrobin, D. F., Burstyn, P. G. 1972. Prolactin and A.D.H. release. *Lancet* 1:1243

195. Mark, A. L., Eckstein, J. W., Abboud, F. M., Wendling, M. G. 1969. Renal vascular responses to isoproterenol. *Am. J. Physiol.* 217:764–67

196. Marshall, S., Gelato, M., Meites, J. 1975. Serum prolactin levels and prolactin binding activity in adrenals and kidneys of male rats after dehydration, salt loading, and unilateral nephrectomy. *Proc. Soc. Exp. Biol. Med.* 149:185–88

197. Martin, T. J., Robinson, C. J., MacIntyre, I. 1966. The mode of action of thyrocalcitonin. *Lancet* 1:900–2

198. Marx, S. J., Aurbach, G. D. 1975. Renal receptors for calcitonin: Coordinate occurrence with calcitonin-activated adenylate cyclase. *Endocrinology* 97:448–53

199. Marx, S. J., Fedak, S. A., Aurbach, G. D. 1972. Preparation and characterization of a hormone-responsive renal plasma membrane fraction. *J. Biol. Chem.* 247:6913–18

200. Marx, S. J., Woodard, C. J., Aurbach, G. D. 1972. Calcitonin receptors of kidney and bone. *Science* 178:999–1001

201. Marx, S. J., Woodward, C., Aurbach, G. D., Glossmann, H., Keutmann, H. T. 1973. Renal receptors for calcitonin. Binding and degradation of hormone. *J. Biol. Chem.* 248:4797–802

202. Massry, S. G., ed. 1975. Symposium on kidney and hormones. *Nephron* 15:165–408

203. Matthews, B. F. 1963. Effects of hormones, placental extracts and hypophysectomy on inulin and paraaminohippurate clearances in the anaesthetized rat. *J. Physiol.* 165:1–9
204. Matthews, V. S., Kirkman, H., Bacon, R. L. 1947. Kidney damage in the golden hamster following chronic administration of diethylstilbestrol in sesame oil. *Proc. Soc. Exp. Biol. Med.* 66:195–96
205. McDonald, R. H. Jr., Goldberg, L. I., McNay, J. L., Tuttle, E. P. Jr. 1964. Effects of dopamine in man: Augmentation of sodium excretion, glomerular filtration rate, and renal plasma flow. *J. Clin. Invest.* 43:1116–24
206. Melson, G. L., Chase, L. R., Aurbach, G. D. 1970. Parathyroid hormone-sensitive adenyl cyclase in isolated renal tubules. *Endocrinology* 86:511–18
207. Meyer, M. B., McNay, J. L., Goldberg, L. I. 1967. Effects of dopamine on renal function and hemodynamics in the dog. *J. Pharmacol. Exp. Ther.* 158:186–92
208. Michael, U. F., Barenberg, R. L., Chavez, R., Vaamonde, C. A., Papper, S. 1972. Renal handling of sodium and water in the hypothyroid rat. *J. Clin. Invest.* 51:1405–12
209. Michael, U. F., Chavez, R., Cookson, S. L., Vaamonde, C. A. 1976. Impaired urinary acidification in the hypothyroid rat. *Pfluegers Arch.* 361:215–20
210. Michael, U. F., Kelley, J., Alpert, H., Vaamonde, C. A. 1976. Role of distal delivery of filtrate in impaired renal dilution of the hypothyroid rat. *Am. J. Physiol.* 230:699–705
211. Michelakis, A. M., Caudle, J., Liddle, G. W. 1969. *In vitro* stimulation of renin production by epinephrine, norepinephrine, and cyclic AMP. *Proc. Soc. Exp. Biol. Med.* 130:748–53
212. Middleton, E., Williams, P. C. 1974. Electrolyte and fluid appetite and balance in male guinea-pigs: Effects of stilboestrol treatment and renal function tests. *J. Endocrinol.* 61:381–99
213. Milhaud, G., Moukhtar, M. S. 1966. Antagonistic and synergistic actions of thyrocalcitonin and parathyroid hormone on the levels of calcium and phosphate in the rat. *Nature* 211:1186–87
214. Milhaud, G., Moukhtar, M. S., Cherian, G., Pérault, A. M. 1966. Effet de l'administration de thyrocalcitonine sur les principaux paramètres du métabolisme du calcium chez le rat normal et du rat thyroparathyroidectomisé. *C.R. Acad. Sci. Ser. D* 262:511–14
215. Miller, J. H. 1953. Effect of insulin on maximal rate of renal tubular uptake of glucose in non-diabetic humans. *Proc. Soc. Exp. Biol. Med.* 84:322–24
216. Miller, J. H., Bogdonoff, M. D. 1954. Antidiuresis associated with administration of insulin. *J. Appl. Physiol.* 6:509–12
217. Moore, R. D. 1973. Effect of insulin upon the sodium pump in frog skeletal muscle. *J. Physiol.* 232:23–45
218. Morel, F., Jard, S. 1971. Cyclic AMP and sodium transport in frog skin. *Ann. NY Acad. Sci.* 185:351–62
219. Müller, J., Barajas, L. 1972. Electron microscopic and histochemical evidence for a tubular innervation in the renal cortex of the monkey. *J. Ultrastruct. Res.* 41:533–49
220. Mulvehill, J. B., Hui, Y. S., Barnes, L. D., Palumbo, P. J., Dousa, T. P. 1976. Glucagon-sensitive adenylate-cyclase in human renal medulla. *J. Clin. Endocrinol. Metab.* 42:380–84
221. Murdaugh, H. V. Jr., Robinson, R. R., Doyle, E. M. 1959. The mechanism of insulin antidiuresis. *J. Lab. Clin. Med.* 53:569–71
222. Myers, B. D., Deen, W. M., Brenner, B. M. 1975. Effects of norepinephrine and angiotensin II on the determinants of glomerular ultrafiltration and proximal tubule fluid reabsorption in the rat. *Circ. Res.* 37:101–10
223. Nicoll, C. S., Bern, H. A. 1972. On the actions of prolactin amongst the vertebrates: Is there a common denominator? In *Lactogenic Hormones,* ed. G. E. W. Wolstenholme, J. Knight, pp. 299–317. Edinburgh: Churchill-Livingstone
224. Nizet, A., Lefebvre, P., Crabbé, J. 1971. Control by insulin of sodium potassium and water excretion by the isolated dog kidney. *Pfluegers Arch.* 323:11–20
225. Nocenti, M. R., Cizek, L. J. 1964. Influence of estrogens on electrolyte and water exchanges in the ovariectomized rat. *Am. J. Physiol.* 206:476–82
226. Nocenti, M. R., Cizek, L. J. 1970. Effects of hydrocortisone acetate and estradiol in normal and adrenalectomized salt deficient rabbits. *Endocrinology* 87:1140–46
227. Nocenti, M. R., Cizek, L. J. 1973. Influence of estrogen on renal function and water intake in male rabbits rendered polyuric-polydipsic by food deprivation. *Endocrinology* 93:925–31
228. O'Connell, J. M. B., Boonshaft, B., Hayes, J. M., Schreiner, G. E. 1969. Metabolic effects of progesterone in the

dog. *Proc. Soc. Exp. Biol. Med.* 132:862–64

229. Oelkers, W., Schöneshöfer, M., Blümel, A. 1974. Effects of progesterone and four synthetic progestagens on sodium balance and the renin-aldosterone system in man. *J. Clin. Endocrinol. Metab.* 39:882–90

230. Oparil, S., Ehrlich, E. N., Lindheimer, M. D. 1975. Effects of progesterone on renal sodium handling in man: Relation to aldosterone excretion and plasma renin activity. *Clin. Sci. Mol. Med.* 49:139–47

231. Oppenheimer, J. H. 1975. Initiation of thyroid-hormone action. *N. Engl. J. Med.* 292:1063–68

232. Oppenheimer, J. H., Koerner, D., Schwartz, H. L., Surks, M. I. 1972. Specific nuclear triiodothyronine binding sites in rat liver and kidney. *J. Clin. Endocrinol. Metab.* 35:330–33

233. Paillard, F., Ardaillou, R., Malendin, H., Fillastre, J. P., Prier, S. 1972. Renal effects of salmon calcitonin in man. *J. Lab. Clin. Med.* 80:200–16

234. Pak, C. Y. C., Ruskin, B., Casper, A. 1970. Renal effects of porcine thyrocalcitonin in the dog. *Endocrinology* 87:262–70

235. Papper, S., Lancestremere, R. G. 1961. Certain aspects of renal function in myxedema. *J. Chron. Dis.* 14:495–506

236. Pasqualini, J. R., Sumida, C., Gelly, C. 1974. Steroid hormone receptors in fetal guinea-pig kidney. *J. Steroid Biochem.* 5:977–85

237. Pearson, J. E., Williams, R. L. 1968. Analysis of direct renal actions of alpha and beta adrenergic stimulation upon sodium excretion compared with acetylcholine. *Br. J. Pharmacol. Chemother.* 33:223–41

238. Pechet, M. M., Bobadilla, E., Carroll, E. L., Hesse, R. H. 1967. Regulation of bone resorption and formation. *Am. J. Med.* 43:696–710

239. Pickford, G. E., Griffith, R. W., Torretti, J., Hendler, E., Epstein, F. H. 1970. Branchial reduction and renal stimulation of (Na⁺,K⁺)-ATPase by prolactin in hypophysectomized killifish in fresh water. *Nature* 228:378–79

240. Pisi, E., Cavalli, G. 1955. Teneur en acide desoxyribonucléique et activité mitotique dans le rein du rat blanc dans diverses conditions expérimentales. *Arch. Biol. Paris* 66:439–82

241. Pors Nielsen, S., Buchanan-Lee, B., Matthews, E. W., Moseley, J. M., Williams, C. C. 1971. Acute effects of synthetic porcine calcitonins on the renal excretion of magnesium, inorganic phosphate, sodium, and potassium. *J. Endocrinol.* 51:455–64

242. Porter, G. A., Bogoroch, R., Edelman, I. S. 1964. On the mechanism of action of aldosterone on sodium transport: The role of RNA synthesis. *Proc. Natl. Acad. Sci. USA* 52:1326–33

243. Porter, G. A., Edelman, I. S. 1964. The action of aldosterone and related corticosteroids on sodium transport across the toad bladder. *J. Clin. Invest.* 43:611–20

244. Posner, B. I., Kelly, P. A., Shiu, R. P. C., Friesen, H. G. 1974. Studies of insulin, growth hormone and prolactin binding: Tissue distribution, species variation and characterization. *Endocrinology* 95:521–31

245. Preedy, J. R. K., Aitken, E. H. 1956. Effect of estrogen on water and electrolyte metabolism. I. The normal. *J. Clin. Invest.* 35:423–29

246. Pullman, T. N., Lavender, A. R., Aho, I. 1967. Direct effects of glucagon on renal hemodynamics and excretion of inorganic ions. *Metabolism* 16:358–73

247. Rabkin, R., Colwell, J. A. 1969. The renal uptake and excretion of insulin in the dog. *J. Lab. Clin. Med.* 73:893–900

248. Rabkin, R., Epstein, S., Swann, M. 1975. Effect of growth hormone on renal sodium and water excretion. *Horm. Metab. Res.* 7:139–42

249. Rabkin, R., Swann, M., Shapiro, D. J., Issacson, L. C. 1974. Effect of growth hormone on sodium transport and osmotic water flow across toad skin. *Horm. Metab. Res.* 6:129–32

250. Radev, A. I. 1973. Effect of consecutive use of estriol and progesterone on urinary sodium and potassium excretion and their renal tissue levels. *Probl. Endokrinol.* 19:91–96

251. Rajaniemi, H., Oksanen, H., Vanha-Perttula, T. 1974. Distribution of ¹²⁵I-prolactin in mice and rats. Studies with whole-body and microautoradiography. *Horm. Res.* 5:6–20

252. Rasmussen, H., Anast, C., Arnaud, C. 1967. Thyrocalcitonin, EGTA, and urinary electrolyte excretion. *J. Clin. Invest.* 46:746–52

253. Rasmussen, H., Tenenhouse, A. 1967. Thyrocalcitonin, osteoporosis and osteolysis. *Am. J. Med.* 43:711–26

254. Reid, I. A., Schrier, R. W., Earley, L. E. 1972. An effect of extrarenal beta adrenergic stimulation on the release of renin. *J. Clin. Invest.* 51:1861–69

255. Reifenstein, E. C. Jr., Albright, F. 1947. The metabolic effects of steroid hormones in osteoporosis. *J. Clin. Invest.* 26:24–56

256. Relkin, R. 1974. Effects of alterations in serum osmolality on pituitary and plasma prolactin levels in the rat. *Neuroendocrinology* 14:61–64

257. Relkin, R., Adachi, M. 1973. Effects of sodium deprivation on pituitary and plasma prolactin, growth hormone and thyrotropin levels in the rat. *Neuroendocrinology* 11:240–47

258. Richardson, J. A., Houck, C. R. 1951. Renal tubular excretory mass and the reabsorption of sodium, chloride and potassium in female dogs receiving testosterone propionate or estradiol benzoate. *Am. J. Physiol.* 165:93–101

259. Riley, A. L., Hagen, T. C., Stefaniak, J. 1975. Is kidney a target organ for prolactin? *Clin. Res.* 23:508A

260. Robinson, C. J., Martin, T. J., MacIntyre, I. 1966. Phosphaturic effect of thyrocalcitonin. *Lancet* 2:83–84

261. Robinson, C. J., Martin, T. J., Matthews, E. W., MacIntyre, I. 1967. Mode of action of thyrocalcitonin. *J. Endocrinol.* 39:71–79

262. Rogoff, J. M., Stewart, G. N. 1927. Studies on adrenal insufficiency: III. The influence of pregnancy upon the survival period in adrenalectomized dogs. *Am. J. Physiol.* 79:508–35

263. Rogus, E., Price, T., Zierler, K. L. 1969. Sodium plus potassium-activated. ouabain-inhibited adenosine triphosphatase from a fraction of rat skeletal muscle, and lack of insulin effect on it. *J. Gen. Physiol.* 54:188–202

264. Ross, J., Goldman, J. K. 1970. Compensatory renal hypertrophy in hypophysectomized rats. *Endocrinology* 87:620–24

265. Rubin, A. L., Cheigh, J. S., Stenzel, K. H., eds. 1975. Symposium on endocrine functions of the kidney. *Am. J. Med.* 58:1–75

266. Russell, R. G. G., Fleisch, H. 1968. The renal effects of thyrocalcitonin in the pig and dog. In *Calcitonin. Proc. Symp. Thyrocalcitonin and the C Cells*, ed. S. Taylor, pp. 297–305. London: Heinemann

267. Salako, L. A., Smith, A. J., Smith, R. N. 1971. The effects of porcine calcitonin on renal function in the rabbit. *J. Endocrinol.* 50:485–91

268. Salomon, M. I., DiScala, V., Grishman, E., Brener, J., Churg, J. 1967. Renal lesions in hypothyroidism: A study based on kidney biopsies. *Metabolism* 16:846–52

269. Saudek, C. D., Boulter, P. R., Arky, R. A. 1973. The natriuretic effect of glucagon and its role in starvation. *J. Clin. Endocrinol. Metab.* 36:761–65

270. Saudek, C. D., Boulter, P. R., Knopp, R. H., Arky, R. A. 1974. Sodium retention accompanying insulin treatment of diabetes mellitus. *Diabetes* 23:240–46

271. Schrier, R. W., Berl, T. 1973. Mechanism of effect of alpha adrenergic stimulation with norepinephrine on renal water excretion. *J. Clin. Invest.* 52:502–11

272. Schrier, R. W., Lieberman, R., Ufferman, R. C., Harbottle, J. A. 1972. Mechanism of antidiuretic effect of beta adrenergic stimulation. *J. Clin. Invest.* 51:97–111

273. Selkurt, E. E., Talbot, L. J., Houck, C. R. 1943. Effect of estradiol on urinary excretion of ascorbic acid in the dog. *Proc. Soc. Exp. Biol. Med.* 53:96–98

274. Selye, H., Bassett, L. 1940. Diuretic effect of progesterone. *Proc. Soc. Exp. Biol. Med.* 44:502–4

275. Serrato, M., Earle, D. P. 1959. Effect of glucagon on renal functions in the dog. *Proc. Soc. Exp. Biol. Med.* 102:701–4

276. Sharp, G. W. G., Komack, C. L., Leaf, A. 1966. Studies on the binding of aldosterone in the toad bladder. *J. Clin. Invest.* 45:450–59

277. Sharp, G. W. G., Leaf, A. 1964. Biological action of aldosterone *in vitro*. *Nature* 202:1185–88

278. Simone, P. G., Solomon, S. 1970. Aldosterone and growth hormone: Influence of diet and hypophysectomy on rat renal response. *Proc. Soc. Exp. Biol. Med.* 133:786–89

279. Simpson, S. A., Tait, J. F. 1952. A quantitative method for the bioassay of the effect of adrenal cortical steroids on mineral metabolism. *Endocrinology* 50:150–61

280. Singer, F. R., Woodhouse, N. J. Y., Parkinson, D. K., Joplin, G. F. 1969. Some acute effects of administered porcine calcitonin in man. *Clin. Sci.* 37:181–90

281. Sjundsford, J. A. 1971. Plasma renin activity and aldosterone excretion during prolonged progesterone administration. *Acta Endocrinol.* 67:483–90

282. Slick, G. L., Aguilera, A. J., Zambraski, E. J., DiBona, G. F., Kaloyanides, G. J. 1975. Renal neuroadrenergic transmission. *Am. J. Physiol.* 229:60–65

283. Sørensen, O. H., Hindberg, I. 1972. The acute and prolonged effect of porcine

calcitonin on urine electrolyte excretion in intact and parathyroidectomized rats. *Acta Endocrinol.* 70:295–307

284. Sørensen, O. H., Hindberg, I., Friis, T. 1972. The renal effect of calcitonin in hypoparathyroid patients. *Acta Med. Scand.* 191:103–6

285. Spathis, G. S. 1971. Insulin and glycosuria. *Diabetologia* 7:247–51

286. Staub, A., Springs, V., Stoll, F., Elrick, H. 1957. A renal action of glucagon. *Proc. Soc. Exp. Biol. Med.* 94:57–60

287. Stein, J. H., Osgood, R. W., Ferris, T. F. 1972. The effect of beta adrenergic stimulation on proximal tubular sodium reabsorption. *Proc. Soc. Exp. Biol. Med.* 141:901–5

288. Stowe, N. T., Hook, J. B. 1970. Role of alterations in renal hemodynamics in the natriuretic action of glucagon. *Arch. Int. Pharmacodyn. Ther.* 183:65–74

289. Strandhoy, J. W., Schneider, E. G., Willis, L. R., Knox, F. G. 1974. Intrarenal effects of phenoxybenzamine on sodium reabsorption. *J. Lab. Clin. Med.* 83:263–70

290. Strauch, G., Vallotton, M. B., Touitou, T., Bricaire, H. 1972. The renin-angiotensin-aldosterone system in normotensive and hypertensive patients with acromegaly. *N. Engl. J. Med.* 287:795–99

291. Surveyor, I. 1969. Sodium, potassium and water metabolism in myxedema. *Postgrad. Med. J.* 45:659–63

292. Swaneck, G. E., Highland, E., Edelman, I. S. 1969. Stereospecific nuclear and cytosol aldosterone-binding proteins of various tissues. *Nephron* 6:297–316

293. Taher, M. S., McLain, L. G., McDonald, K. M., Schrier, R. W. 1976. Effect of beta adrenergic blockade on renin response to renal nerve stimulation. *J. Clin. Invest.* 57:459–65

294. Talmage, R. V., Anderson, J. J. B. 1972. The effect of calcitonin on ^{32}p disappearance from plasma in parathyroidectomized and nephrectomized rats. *Proc. Soc. Exp. Biol. Med.* 141:982–85

295. Thorn, G. W., Engel, L. L. 1938. The effect of sex hormones on the renal excretion of electrolytes. *J. Exp. Med.* 68:299–312

296. Thorn, G. W., Harrop, G. A. 1937. The "sodium retaining effect" of the sex hormones. *Science* 86:40–41

297. Thornborough, J. R., Passo, S. S. 1975. The effects of estrogens on sodium and potassium metabolism in rats. *Endocrinology* 97:1528–36

298. Tomlinson, R. W. S. 1971. The action of progesterone derivatives and other steroids on the sodium transport of isolated frog skin. *Acta Physiol. Scand.* 83:407–11

299. Tomlinson, R. W. S. 1971. The action of progesterone on the sodium transport of isolated frog skin. *Acta Physiol. Scand.* 83:463–72

300. Ueda, H., Yasuda, H., Takabatake, Y., Iizuka, M., Iizuka, T., Ihori, M., Sakamoto, Y. 1970. Observations on the mechanism of renin release by catecholamines. *Circ. Res.* 26, 27 (Suppl. 2):195–200

301. Vallotton, M. B., Dubied, M. C., Gaillard, R., Merkelbach, U. 1976. Influence of angiotensin II (AII) and estrogen (E) on responsiveness of vasopressin (AVP) to salt loading (SL) in man. *Clin. Res.* 24:280A

302. Vander, A. J. 1965. Effect of catecholamines and the renal nerves on renin secretion in anesthetized dogs. *Am. J. Physiol.* 209:659–62

303. Vandongen, R., Greenwood, D. M. 1975. The stimulation of renin secretion by non-vasoconstrictor infusions of adrenaline and noradrenaline in the isolated rat kidney. *Clin. Sci. Mol. Med.* 49:609–12

304. Vandongen, R., Peart, W. S., Boyd, G. W. 1973. Adrenergic stimulation of renin secretion in the isolated perfused rat kidney. *Circ. Res.* 32:290–96

305. Vogt, J. H. 1960. Impaired water excretion capacity in primary myxedema improved by corticosteroids, corticotropin and thyroid substitution. *Acta Endocrinol.* 35:277–92

306. Wathen, R. L., Kingsbury, W. S., Stouder, D. A., Schneider, E. G., Rostorfer, H. H. 1965. Effects of infusion of catecholamines and angiotensin II on renin release in anesthetized dogs. *Am. J. Physiol.* 209:1012–24

307. Weil, A. 1941. The chemical constitution of brain, kidneys and heart of white rats in experimental hypothyroidism. *Endocrinology* 29:919–26

308. Weinberger, M. H., Aoi, W., Henry, D. P. 1975. Direct effect of beta-adrenergic stimulation on renin release by the rat kidney slice *in vitro*. *Circ. Res.* 37:318–24

309. Weinsier, R. L. 1971. Fasting—A review with emphasis on the electrolytes. *Am. J. Med.* 50:233–40

310. Wesson, L. G. Jr. 1961. Hormonal influences on renal function. *Ann. Rev. Med.* 12:77–92

311. White, H. L., Heinbecker, P., Rolf, D. 1947. Some endocrine influences on renal function and cardiac output. *Am. J. Physiol.* 149:404–17

312. Williams, C. C., Matthews, E. W., Moseley, J. M., MacIntyre, I. 1972. The effects of synthetic human and salmon calcitonins on electrolyte excretion in the rat. *Clin. Sci.* 42:129–37

313. Winer, N., Chokshi, D. S., Walkenhorst, W. G. 1971. Effects of cyclic AMP, sympathomimetic amines, and adrenergic receptor antagonists on renin secretion. *Circ. Res.* 29:239–48

314. Witten, C. L., Bradbury, J. T. 1951. Hemodilution as a result of estrogen therapy: Estrogenic effects in the human female. *Proc. Soc. Exp. Biol. Med.* 78:626–29

315. Zeckwer, I. T. 1946. Compensatory growth of the kidney after unilateral nephrectomy in thyroidectomized rats. *Am. J. Physiol.* 145:681–84

316. Zierler, K. L., Rogus, E., Hazlewood, C. F. 1966. Effect of insulin on potassium flux and water and electrolyte content of muscles from normal and from hypophysectomized rats. *J. Gen. Physiol.* 49:433–56

Ann. Rev. Physiol. 1977. 39:135–58
Copyright © 1977 by Annual Reviews Inc. All rights reserved

GASTROINTESTINAL HORMONES AND THEIR FUNCTIONS

❖1166

Leonard R. Johnson

Department of Physiology, University of Texas Medical School, Houston, Texas 77030

INTRODUCTION

The mucosa of the gastrointestinal tract is the largest endocrine organ in the body. Long ignored by peptide chemists, the number of hormones and peptides present which may eventually gain hormonal status has become apparent only during the past several years. Three long-standing gastrointestinal hormones—gastrin (47), secretin (80), and CCK (79) (cholecystokinin)—were identified and chemically purified during the 1960s. Four intestinal peptides—motilin (20), GIP (17) (gastric inhibitory polypeptide), VIP (109) (vasoactive intestinal peptide), and chymodenin (1)—have been chemically defined. One of these, GIP, qualifies as gastrointestinal hormone number four. Two other hormones have been immunologically identified in the intestinal mucosa—glucagon and somatostatin (4). Whether they function physiologically as gastrointestinal hormones remains to be determined. In contrast to the above peptides is a group whose members have no chemical credentials but have been postulated to exist on the basis of physiological evidence. This group includes incretin, enterogastrone, villikinin, duocrinin, enterocrinin, gastrone, entero-oxyntin, sialogastrone, and bulbogastrone (50). In each case a crude mucosal extract has been shown to mimic the action of the putative hormone. This group of "hormones," discovered and named between 1906 and 1967, epitomizes the so-called physiological era of gastrointestinal hormone research. During this time, any crude intestinal extract producing an action on secretion or motility of the digestive tract was thought to contain a distinct hormone. The substance was named and dutifully recorded in our literature. Only time will tell how many members of this group will be preserved by chemical identification. This review deals only with the actions of the proven gastrointestinal hormones plus those peptides that have been chemically defined and have interesting pharmacological (physiological?) or pathological effects on the gastrointestinal tract.

The gastrointestinal hormones and related peptides are located in endocrine cells scattered throughout the gastrointestinal mucosa from the stomach through the

135

colon. Cells containing individual hormones are not clumped together but are dispersed throughout the epithelia. The nature of this distribution makes it virtually impossible to surgically remove the source of a gastrointestinal hormone and examine the effect of its absence in the classical manner. The distribution of endocrine cells over extensive areas of mucosa ensures that hormone release is regulated by an integrated sampling of mixed luminal contents rather than by a specific stimulus which might exist transiently at only one point.

The endocrine cells of the gut are members of a widely distributed system of "clear cells" (enterochromaffin, argyrophil, argentaffin) which produces amines as well as peptides. Pearse and co-workers (103, 104) developed the unifying concept that all peptide hormone-producing cells are embryologically derived from neuroectoderm. This group of cells is known by the acronym, APUD (Amine Precursor Uptake and Decarboxylating), which refers to its members' most interesting biochemical characteristics.

The concept of chemical messengers as we know it was first postulated in 1902 with the discovery of secretin by Bayliss & Starling (6). Edkins (39) wrote a preliminary report on the chemical mechanism of gastric secretion in 1905 in which the word gastrin was used. In 1928 Ivy & Oldberg (58) described a hormone which stimulated gallbladder evacuation and named it cholecystokinin. Harper & Raper (56) found that extracts of duodenal mucosa contained a stimulant for pancreatic enzyme secretion which they called pancreozymin. It was not until these extracts were purified by Jorpes & Mutt (79) in the 1960s that cholecystokinin and pancreozymin were found to be identical. This hormone is called cholecystokinin in reference to the first of its actions to be discovered.

In order to establish the existence of a gastrointestinal hormone a number of steps are required. First, one must demonstrate that a physiological stimulus (one which would be present normally during the ingestion and digestion of a meal) applied to one part of the gut changes the activity in another part; second, the effect must persist after all nervous connections between the two parts have been interrupted; third, one must isolate a substance from the site of application of the stimulus which, when injected into the bloodstream, mimics the effect of the stimulus; and fourth, one must identify the substance chemically and confirm its structure by synthesis. The first 60 years of gastrointestinal endocrinology were spent almost entirely on the first two criteria. The biochemical epoch in the history of gastrointestinal hormones began in the 1960s, and in 1964 Gregory and co-workers (47) proved the existence of gastrin. Shortly thereafter Jorpes & Mutt isolated and determined the structures of secretin (80) and cholecystokinin (79). Thus the three original gastrointestinal hormones were finally identified.

The availability of pure hormones and other peptides originating from the digestive tract opened up areas of precise gastrointestinal endocrine research that were impossible 15 years ago. It became possible to inject a hormone and ascribe the effects to a specific substance. This in itself led to the realization that each hormone affected almost every function of every target organ or gland in the gastrointestinal tract. The problem now, and the primary subject of this review, is to discern which of these effects are physiologically significant.

GENERAL CHARACTERISTICS OF GASTROINTESTINAL HORMONES AND PEPTIDES

The gastrointestinal hormones and most related peptides can be divided into two structurally homologous families. The first consists of gastrin and CCK. All of the biological activity of gastrin can be reproduced by the C-terminal tetrapeptide (47), which is therefore the minimal active fragment of gastrin. The entire gastrin molecule contains 17 amino acids and is about 6 times as potent as the tetrapeptide. The sixth amino acid from the C-terminus is tyrosine, which may (gastrin II) or may not (gastrin I) be sulfated (47). Both hormones occur with equal frequency in nature and have equal biological activity in most systems (47).

CCK has 33 amino acids and contains a sulfated tyrosyl residue in position 7 from the C-terminus (78). Qualitatively the actions of gastrin and CCK are identical, although each hormone is more potent at its own receptors than those of its homologue. CCK is always sulfated in nature, and desulfation results in a peptide with the gastrin pattern of activity. The minimal active fragment of CCK is, therefore, the C-terminal heptapeptide. In summary peptides belonging to the gastrin–CCK group having a tyrosyl residue in position 6 from the C-terminus or, unsulfated and in position 7 possess the gastrin pattern of activity-strong stimulation of gastric acid secretion with little or no effect on gallbladder contraction (75). Those peptides having a sulfated residue in position 7 have CCK potency and are weak stimulators of acid secretion in most species and potent stimulants of gallbladder contraction. Obviously, the tetrapeptide itself and all fragments less than 7 amino acids long possess the gastrin pattern of activity. In general the important actions of these two hormones are on gastric acid secretion, enzyme secretion, motility, and growth of the pancreas and gastrointestinal mucosa.

The second group of intestinal peptides is homologous to secretin and includes VIP, GIP, and glucagon in addition to secretin. Secretin has 27 amino acids, all of which are required for activity. Pancreatic glucagon has 29 amino acids, 14 of which are identical to those of secretin. Glucagon-like immunoactivity has been found in the small intestine (117), but the significance of this "enteroglucagon" has not been established (110). Glucagon has no active fragment and, like secretin, the entire molecule is required for activity. There is evidence that secretin exists as a helix; thus the entire molecule may be necessary to form the active tertiary structure. VIP (109) (28 amino acids) and GIP (17) (43 amino acids) each has 9 amino acids identical to those of secretin. In general, this group of peptides inhibits gastric acid secretion, stimulates pancreatic and biliary fluid and bicarbonate secretion, stimulates intestinal secretion, and alters insulin release. Not all of these actions apply to each hormone, nor are they necessarily physiological for any hormone in the group.

A list of the general types of actions of gastrointestinal hormones and peptides is shown in Table 1. Most of these are the classical effects on the digestive activity of the gut. Two categories, however, have been discovered only since the availability of pure gastrointestinal peptides: the stimulation of growth of gastrointestinal mucosa and the exocrine pancreas, and the influences on the release of hormones. Both of these new categories emphasize an important and usually neglected point

Table 1   General categories of gastrointestinal hormone effects

Water and electrolyte secretion			
stomach	pancreas	liver	gut
Enzyme secretion			
stomach	pancreas		
Trophic effects			
stomach	pancreas	gut	
Endocrine secretion			
GI hormones	insulin	glucagon	calcitonin
Motility			
stomach	gut	sphincters	
Intestinal absorption			
water	electrolytes	nutrients	

—the gastrointestinal hormones do not comprise an independent system of regulators; some of their actions are identical to and integrated with those of the rest of the endocrine system.

Table 2 lists many specific targets of gastrointestinal hormones and peptides and the effect each of the three classical hormones has on each activity. Note that there are no blank spaces. If we added GIP and VIP to the list, there would only be a few blanks, primarily because the effect has not been tested. Our problem then is to sort through this myriad of effects and identify those likely to have physiological significance. In order for an effect to be considered physiological several criteria must be met. First, the effect should occur in response to an exogenous dose of the hormone which does not increase the serum level of the hormone over the increment

Table 2   Effects of three "classical" gastrointestinal hormones

Action	Hormone		
	Gastrin	CCK	Secretin
Gastric acid secretion	S	S	I
Gastric emptying	I	I	I
Pancreatic bicarbonate secretion	S	S	S
Pancreatic enzyme secretion	S	S	S
Biliary bicarbonate secretion	S	S	S
Gallbladder contraction	S	S	S
Gastric motility	S	S	I
Intestinal motility	S	S	I
Insulin release	S	S	S
Mucosal growth	S	S+	I

S—stimulates; I—inhibits; S+—stimulates pancreatic growth.

resulting from normal physiological release. The only way to rigidly satisfy this criterion is to measure serum hormone levels during continuous infusion of a low dose of the hormone and compare the occurrence of the effect with the serum concentration of the hormone. In the case of hormones, such as CCK, for which there is not yet a reliable immunoassay, the D_{50} for the primary effect of the hormone is a satisfactory guideline. That is, the effect in question should occur in response to an exogenous dose of the hormone equal to or less than the dose needed to produce half the maximal response of the primary effect of the hormone (i.e. gallbladder contraction for CCK). A second criterion is that the effect be shown to occur in response to endogenous hormone. Gastrin released in response to a meal should produce all of the effects of exogenous gastrin considered to be physiological. This criterion eliminates the effects of any peptide, such as VIP, whose stimuli for release are unknown, from the physiological realm. The actions of the gastrointestinal hormones which I consider physiological are shown in Table 3. Most of the effects listed in Table 2 are pharmacological and are seen only with relatively large doses of hormone.

Another characteristic of gastrointestinal hormones is that their effects are often species dependent. Thus it is impossible to experiment on one species and draw valid conclusions for another. The effects of CCK on acid secretion are a good case in point. In the cat CCK is a full agonist producing the same rate of gastric secretion as gastrin (35). In the dog it is a potent competitive inhibitor of gastrin (70), although low doses will weakly stimulate. Its actions in man lie in between those in the cat and dog (13).

GASTRIC SECRETION

In discussing gastric secretion and the other targets of gastrointestinal hormones I concentrate on proven physiological actions of the hormones, areas of controversy, and recent studies pertaining to the significance of the more widely accepted actions. Except when they pertain to a question of the physiological significance of a hormonal effect I do not discuss mechanisms of hormone release. This area was reviewed in this series by Andersson (3) in 1973. The actions of the chemically identified intestinal peptides that have not achieved hormonal status are reviewed briefly here. Research concerning these substances is popular and proceeding rapidly.

Table 3 Physiological actions[a] of gastrointestinal hormones

Gastrin:	Gastric acid secretion, gastrointestinal mucosal growth
Secretin:	Pancreatic and biliary bicarbonate secretion, potentiation of CCK-stimulated pancreatic enzyme secretion
CCK:	Gallbladder contraction, pancreatic enzyme secretion, potentiation of secretin-stimulated pancreatic bicarbonate secretion, inhibition of gastric emptying, growth of exocrine pancreas
GIP:	Inhibition of gastric acid secretion, insulin release

[a] Stimulatory unless stated otherwise.

Stimulation of Acid Secretion

There are four naturally occurring chemical agents capable of stimulating gastric acid secretion. These are gastrin, histamine, acetylcholine, and digested protein. The latter stimulates when topically applied to the gastric mucosa (34). The status of gastrin and acetylcholine as physiological regulators of gastric acid secretion is secure. The role of histamine, however, remains uncertain. Most of the physiological evidence argues against histamine as a mediator for gastric acid secretion (59), although recent pharmacological studies with histamine H_2-receptor antagonists suggest the involvement of a histamine receptor in acid secretion (54). The specificity of this new group of blocking agents, however, has not been proven.

Debas & Grossman (34) have recently shown that digested protein stimulated Heidenhain pouch acid secretion to 80% of the maximal histamine response. The response was not blocked by either metiamide or atropine. Since the pouch did not contain antral mucosa, acid secretion was the result of a direct chemical stimulation by the topical protein. Until this report, the release of gastrin was the only recognized mechanism by which chemicals in the stomach stimulate acid secretion. However, since atropine and metiamide almost totally inhibit acid secretion from normal vagally innervated mucosa, there is reason to doubt whether this new mechanism operates under physiological conditions (34).

Acetylcholine is released at the parietal cell by postganglionic nerves activated by long (vagal) and short (local or intramural) reflexes. In addition to directly stimulating the parietal cell, acetylcholine is released at the gastrin-containing cell (G-cell), causing gastrin release. Vagal stimulation is therefore ultimately mediated by both acetylcholine and gastrin (101).

Gastrin is the most potent gastric secretagogue known. On a molar basis it is at least 1500 times more potent than histamine both in vivo and in vitro. The final physiological proof of the gastrin mechanism for gastric secretion was provided in 1948 by Grossman et al (55) who showed that distention of the canine antrum stimulated acid secretion from a denervated stomach. In recent years most research on gastrin and acid secretion has dealt with direct measurement of gastrin in the serum in response to various stimuli.

The availability of synthetic gastrin led to McGuigan's (95) development of a highly sensitive radioimmunoassay. Yalow & Berson (127) demonstrated that circulating gastrin consisted of two major forms: G-17, the heptadecapeptide analogous to that isolated by Gregory from porcine antral mucosa, and G-34, consisting of G-17 plus another 17 amino acid peptide split off by tryptic digestion. In the dog feeding increases serum gastrin to a peak of about 160 pg (G-17 equivalent) per ml serum. This increase is about three-fourths G-34 and one-fourth G-17 on a molar basis. These amounts represent approximately one-third of the blood level of G-34 and about two-thirds of the amount of G-17 needed for half-maximal acid secretion (124). G-17 I and II, G-34 I and II, and pentagastrin produce similar maximal acid responses (124).

The potency of a hormone can be defined two ways: in terms of the exogenous dose, or in terms of the endogenous increments in serum concentration. If two compounds produce equal increments in serum concentration when infused at equimolar rates, and if they have the same efficacies, it makes no difference whether exogenous doses or endogenous serum concentrations are compared. This is the case for G-17 I and II (124). However, under steady-state conditions, molar serum concentrations of G-34 about 5 times higher than those of G-17 are required to produce equal rates of acid secretion. Equal exogenous doses of G-17 and G-34 produce equal rates of secretion, because the serum half-life of G-34 is approximately 5 times greater than that of G-17 (124).

Recent work by Soll (113) provides excellent evidence that gastrin stimulates parietal cells directly. Pentagastrin, but not histamine, stimulated oxygen uptake in a preparation of canine gastric mucosal cells. Further studies demonstrated that isolated mammalian parietal cells also increased oxygen uptake in response to gastrin (114). Histamine was effective only in the presence of isobutyl methylxanthine, a phosphodiesterase inhibitor. Companion studies demonstrated that stimulated parietal cells underwent morphological transformations characteristic of those that occur during the stimulation of acid secretion. These studies have as yet not been published as full papers. Nevertheless, if I have interpreted them correctly, they add the final proof to the conclusion that histamine is not the final common mediator of acid secretion nor even the mediator of gastrin-stimulated acid secretion (59, 64).

Inhibition of Acid Secretion

As early as 1886, Ewald & Boas (42) demonstrated that the addition of olive oil to a meal inhibited gastric emptying in human subjects. In 1926 Farrell & Ivy (43) showed that fat inhibited the motility of a transplanted fundic pouch, and, in 1929, Feng et al (44) demonstrated the same effect on acid secretion. Kosaka & Lim (82) showed that crude intestinal extracts inhibited gastric acid secretion, and named the active principle enterogastrone. *Enterogastrone* literally means hormone from the small intestine that inhibits gastric secretion and/or motility.

There are several hormones or peptides that, in the general meaning of the word, qualify as enterogastrones, including secretin, CCK, VIP, and GIP. Secretin released by duodenal acidification is a potent inhibitor of acid secretion in the dog, but it is unlikely that sufficient secretin is released physiologically to function as an inhibitor in other species. Andersson has obtained evidence that acid releases an inhibitor from the duodenal bulb, separate and distinct from secretin and CCK, which he has named bulbogastrone (112). On the other hand, Konturek & Johnson (81) could demonstrate inhibition only when innervation was preserved. This discrepancy is unresolved and will remain so until bulbogastrone is chemically identified and shown to be released into the blood in response to a meal and in sufficient quantities to inhibit acid secretion.

CCK, which is released by fat, is a potent competitive inhibitor of gastrin-stimulated acid secretion in the dog (70) but is a partial (13) or full (35) agonist of acid secretion in other species. At this point in time there is no good radioimmunoassay of CCK, but on the basis of current evidence it is unlikely that CCK contributes significantly to the physiological inhibition of acid secretion.

Johnson & Grossman (68) showed that neither CCK nor secretin inhibited histamine-stimulated acid secretion. In the same experiments, the introduction of fat into the duodenum strongly inhibited histamine-stimulated acid secretion from the Heidenhain pouch. On the basis of this evidence we speculated that fat released a separate inhibitory hormone and that neither secretin nor CCK was the "enterogastrone" of Kosaka and Lim.

Both VIP (11) and GIP (105) inhibit histamine-stimulated acid secretion. VIP, however, has not been shown to be released into the blood by a meal, and its physiological significance is unknown. By using a highly specific radioimmunoassay, Kuzio et al (83) have shown that following a meal the levels of GIP in human serum quickly rise from 237 pg/ml to over 1000 pg/ml. The release of GIP followed a biphasic pattern, and evidence indicates that the early peak response was due to release by glucose and the later more prolonged plateau was due to the fat present in the meal (19). As little as 0.25 μg GIP/kg-hr inhibited pentagastrin-stimulated acid secretion, and 90% inhibition was reached with a dose of 1.0 μg/kg-hr (105). This higher dose of GIP caused serum levels to increase no further than 1000 pg/ml, a level easily reached in response to a meal. Since it is released by fat and inhibits histamine-stimulated secretion, GIP may well be the enterogastrone first described by Feng et al (44) and Kosaka & Lim (82). GIP is the only gastrointestinal hormone proven to have a physiological role as an inhibitor of acid secretion. This effect satisfies the physiological criteria needed to admit GIP to full hormonal status.

Pepsin Secretion

Two gastrointestinal hormones, secretin and gastrin, stimulate pepsinogen secretion. Secretin and duodenal acidification have been shown to strongly stimulate pepsin secretion in dog, cat (116), and man (15). Due to the relatively small amounts of secretin released by a meal, it is unlikely that this is a physiological effect in any of the species tested. Secretin has been nicknamed "nature's antacid" since it stimulates pancreatic and biliary bicarbonate secretion and inhibits gastrin release and gastric acid secretion. Therefore, the pepsigogic action of secretin is interesting in itself, since this is one of the few actions of this hormone that does not decrease the amount of acid in the duodenum.

Stimulants of acid secretion also stimulate pepsin secretion, and gastrin is no exception (28, 40). In 1972, however, Dutt & Magee (38) reported that pepsin secretion could not be stimulated in vagally denervated canine pouches by endogenous gastrin, pentagastrin, or tetragastrin. Gastrin was an effective stimulator of pepsin secretion from vagally innervated stomachs in the same dogs. The only difference between earlier studies demonstrating increased pepsin output from Heidenhain pouches in response to gastrin (28, 40) and this negative one was that Dutt & Magee used a washout technique employing 0.9% saline to ensure complete collection from the Heidenhain pouches.

This apparent discrepancy was resolved by demonstrating that the gastric mucosa contains receptors sensitive to hydrogen ion, which, when activated, trigger a cholinergic reflex stimulating pepsin secretion (60). This hypothesis was tested by comparing Heidenhain pouch pepsin responses to various secretagogues during irrigation with 0.1 N HCl and PO_4 buffer. Phosphate buffer shifted the dose-response curves to the right for histamine, urecholine, and secretin, and completely abolished the response to pentagastrin (61). Acid by itself significantly stimulated pepsin output. Thus the entire pepsigogic response to gastrin may be due to the stimulation produced from these receptors by concurrently produced acid. Although they did not use a buffer, Dutt & Magee (38) apparently diluted the acid secreted in response to gastrin below the threshold for stimulation of pepsin secretion. This acid-sensitive reflex has been shown to be present in innervated human stomach as well (21). Thus it appears that physiological amounts of none of the gastrointestinal hormones directly stimulate pepsin secretion independently of their acid-stimulatory effects.

PANCREATIC SECRETION

Pancreatic secretion has two components. The so-called primary action of secretin is the stimulation of the aqueous component mainly consisting of water and sodium bicarbonate. One of the primary actions of cholecystokinin is the stimulation of the enzymatic component of pancreatic secretion. It appears now that the actual pancreatic response to a meal is due to interactions between these two hormones. Each enhances the primary effect of the other (Table 3).

In 1970 Grossman (48) proposed the hypothesis that CCK, gastrin, and secretin act on one receptor with two interacting sites, one for CCK and gastrin and one for secretin. The hypothesis was based on the following observations: 1. CCK and gastrin are structurally related and have the same spectrum of actions, 2. secretin is chemically different but alters the effects of the other two hormones, 3. CCK competitively inhibits gastrin-stimulated acid secretion in the dog (70), and 4. secretin noncompetitively inhibits gastrin-stimulated acid secretion in the dog (69). This hypothesis predicts that gastrin and CCK acting on the same receptor site will produce competitive inhibition if their efficacies (V_{max}) differ for that site, competitive augmentation if their efficacies are equal. It further predicts that secretin will produce noncompetitive inhibition (decreased V_{max}) of a gastrin or CCK effect, if it inhibits the target in question when given by itself. Similarly secretin will potentiate (noncompetitive augmentation, increased V_{max}) an effect of CCK or gastrin, if it stimulates the specific target when given alone. The reverse is also true for CCK and gastrin interactions with secretin effects.

Meyer et al (97) found that the maximal pancreatic bicarbonate response to secretin was significantly increased by either exogenous CCK or infusion of phenylalanine into the duodenum (endogenous CCK). This indicates that CCK potentiates the pancreatic response to secretin, increasing the V_{max}. Perhaps more important physiologically, CCK caused a significant shift of the secretin dose-response curve to the left, so that at low secretin doses the addition of CCK resulted in high pancreatic bicarbonate responses. Secretin also augmented the response to CCK but the effect was not as dramatic.

Secretin is released when the duodenal pH drops below 4.5 (98). However, the pH of the contents of most of the duodenum rarely falls below the threshold for secretin release. Gastric chyme enters the duodenum at a pH around 3.0, which rises above 4.5 before it has traversed 10 cm beyond the pylorus (14). Only in the duodenal bulb does significant acidification occur for any length of time. These studies raised doubts over whether the amount of acid in the duodenum after a meal was sufficient to stimulate pancreatic bicarbonate secretion. Grossman & Konturek (53) found that when the intragastric pH was kept at 7.0 pancreatic bicarbonate secretion was low and enzyme output moderate, a response characteristic of CCK acting alone. The high rates of bicarbonate secretion seen after a meal did not occur if the pH of the meal was held above 4.5. At pH 5.0 a subthreshold dose of secretin in combination with the meal produced a bicarbonate response equal to 65% of maximal. The range of gastric pH that caused augmentation of bicarbonate secretion, pH 4.5 or lower, also significantly increased pancreatic protein output, indicating that secretin potentiates the response to CCK. The authors concluded that, following a meal, acid significantly contributes to both pancreatic enzyme and bicarbonate secretion (53). This study was, however, indirect, and the question remains: do serum secretin concentrations increase significantly in response to a meal?

Several secretin radioimmunoassays have been developed during the past few years. Many of these have had sensitivity problems, but these have apparently been resolved by most laboratories. Boden et al (12) found no increase in serum secretin following the infusion of amino acid, fatty acid, sugar, or hyper- and hypotonic solutions into the canine duodenum. HC1 did release immunoactive secretin. The animals, however, were anesthetized, and the sensitivity of their assay was only 70 pg secretin/ml serum. In a similar group of experiments in conscious dogs and humans, Chey et al (26) showed no increase in immunoactive secretin following a meal unless the meal were acidified. Plasma gastrin levels increased significantly in the same experiments. They concluded that pancreatic bicarbonate responses to a meal were due either to small amounts of secretin interacting with CCK or to VIP. I know of no evidence to implicate VIP in the physiological regulation of pancreatic secretion. P. L. Rayford and J. C. Thompson (personal communication) agree with the above report in that they have not been able to detect increases in serum secretin following a meal in the dog. Their secretin assay has a sensitivity of 10 pg/ml serum.

At the present time, a fair assessment of the hormonal regulation of pancreatic secretion is that small amounts of secretin probably interact with relatively large amounts of CCK to stimulate bicarbonate output. Since a reliable immunoassay for CCK has not been developed we do not know the actual amounts released. However, the presence of amino acids and fatty acids throughout the upper small intestine during the course of a meal ensures sufficient serum CCK concentrations to potentiate the pancreatic bicarbonate response to whatever secretin is released and to stimulate pancreatic enzyme secretin. I do not mean to rule out the possibility that secretin does not contribute to the pancreatic bicarbonate response to a meal; this remains to be proven one way or the other. However, pancreatic secretion rises and falls in response to duodenal acidification, secretin is the only intestinal hormone released by physiological amounts of acid, and secretin is the only peptide that can stimulate pancreatic secretion maximally—a potent argument in favor of secretin.

BILIARY SECRETION

There have been comparatively few studies of the hormonal regulation of bile secretion. The results of these studies are typical of the actions of the gastrointestinal hormones on other targets in that all hormones stimulate bile flow. The effect in most cases, however, occurs only at pharmacological doses.

Bayliss & Starling (6) recognized the choleretic effect of duodenal extracts in their original report. Secretin was proven to be the choleretic agent present in duodenal extracts by showing that pure natural and pure synthetic secretin are equal in choleretic potency (121). In the dog secretin stimulated bile flow at doses as low as 0.06 unit/kg-hr and bicarbonate output at 0.12 unit/kg-hr (76). Secretin is considered a physiological stimulator of bile flow since these doses are no greater than those required for pancreatic secretion. As in the case with pancreatic secretion it remains to be demonstrated that significant secretin is released following a meal to drive biliary secretion.

Members of the gastrin family of peptides also stimulate bile flow (77, 129). CCK is more potent than gastrin (77), but the maximal response to CCK is considerably less than that seen with secretin. Again the situation is analogous to pancreatic bicarbonate secretion in that CCK may potentiate the effect of secretin.

MOTILITY

Classical physiological studies of gastrointestinal motility led to the discovery of one hormone, cholecystokinin (58). Following the isolation and purification of the gastrointestinal hormones it was demonstrated that all three either stimulate or inhibit the motor activity of the esophagus, stomach, small and large bowel, biliary tract, and the sphincters. The following discussion is confined to recently discovered effects that have a good chance of being physiological or those over which controversy exists and the evidence is incomplete.

One of the hottest controversies in gastrointestinal physiology concerns the role of gastrin in the function of the lower esophageal sphincter (LES). The debate has been both educational and entertaining. Giles et al (46) found that 0.005 unit gastrin/kg increased LES pressure in human subjects. Pentagastrin (0.6 μg/kg-hr) given as a continuous infusion had the same effect in three out of five subjects. Introduction of meat extract into the stomachs of four subjects also increased sphincter pressure. Castell & Harris (22) found that sphincter pressure closely paralleled gastric acid secretion. Acid itself, however, lowered pressure while alkalinization of the stomach increased it. They suggested that alkalinization was responsible for gastrin release and found that peptone broth (supposedly by virtue of gastrin release) increased pressure, as did subcutaneous injection of gastrin.

Following these observations, there was a rapid proliferation of papers describing the effects of gastrin on the LES. Using circular smooth muscle strips from the opossum LES, Lipshutz & Cohen (88) demonstrated development of tension at a 10^{-12} M concentration of gastrin I. The LES proved to be much more sensitive to gastrin than to either acetylcholine or norepinephrine. Although these studies were done in vitro, the authors concluded that these findings suggest an important physiological role for gastrin in the regulation of LES pressure in vivo. The gastrin response appeared to be nerve mediated, for it could be blocked by atropine, ganglionic blocking agents, and tetrodotoxin (91). The dose-response curve to gastrin was shifted to the right by the addition of secretin (89). Secretin proved to be a competitive inhibitor in this preparation. The case for gastrin was further strengthened by the demonstration that injection of gastrin antiserum lowered resting LES pressure 70% in the opossum (90). The theory that gastrin was the major determinant of LES pressure became widely accepted when it was shown that feeding a protein meal in man caused an increase in LES pressure, which was prevented by acidification (100). These responses were presumably caused first by gastrin release in response to a meal and then inhibition of release by antral acidification. The teleological interpretation of these data was that gastrin prevented acid reflux during a meal.

Recent studies have not found a correlation between serum gastrin levels and LES pressure. These plus the failure to demonstrate increased sphincter pressure in response to a continuous infusion of gastrin have changed the status of gastrin in LES physiology from having "top billing" to being a "has been." Dodds et al (36) studied LES pressure and serum gastrin levels in 30 healthy subjects without finding a correlation, which led them to conclude that gastrin is not a major determinant of LES tone in humans. While their results certainly do not support the gastrin hypothesis, in my opinion they cause no harm either. There are wide variations in normal for both basal serum gastrins and LES tone, and to suppose that a positive correlation should exist between the two is asking a lot. Furthermore most basal circulating gastrin has been shown to be "big-big" gastrin, which is biologically inactive (128).

The most damaging evidence against a major role for gastrin in LES function is the finding that constant intravenous infusion of pentagastrin in doses ranging from 0.004 to 12 μg/kg-hr failed to increase sphincter pressure while evoking maximal acid secretion in normal subjects (123). However, continuous infusion of synthetic human gastrin I has recently been shown to increase both LES pressure and acid secretion. Serum gastrin levels did not exceed those normally found in response to a meal (45).

The foregoing discussion over the role of gastrin in the control of the LES has perhaps been inordinately long. Nevertheless, this controversy illustrates the problems involved in sorting through the various effects of gastrointestinal hormones to determine which are physiological (27, 49, 51). At this time the evidence regarding gastrin and the LES is incomplete, and the best view is an open-minded one.

The D_{50} of CCK required for the stimulation of gallbladder contraction and pancreatic enzyme secretion has been used as a guideline to test the physiological significance of the other effects of this hormone. The D_{50} for 20% pure CCK is approximately 1000 ng/kg-hr, and the D_{50} for the synthetic C-terminal octapeptide of CCK is 130 ng/kg-hr (33). Since there is no reliable sensitive radioimmunoassay for CCK, we can only assume that the D_{50} for continuous infusion of the hormone is a valid indicator of endogenous levels following a meal. There is good evidence that this is the case (53).

To my knowledge the only effect of a gastrointestinal hormone on motility, other than CCK on gallbladder contraction, that has been thoroughly tested for physiological significance and found to be significant is the inhibition of gastric emptying by CCK (32). The D_{50}'s of 20% pure CCK and of the octapeptide of CCK for inhibition of gastric emptying were found to be about the same as their D_{50}'s for gallbladder contraction and pancreatic enzyme secretion. Pure CCK was also a potent inhibitor of emptying. Tryptophan, which releases CCK, inhibited gastric emptying at the same time it stimulated gallbladder contraction and pancreatic enzyme secretion (32). Although both gastrin (57) and pentagastrin (29) inhibit gastric emptying, the doses required proved to be much higher than the D_{50}'s for acid secretion (32).

The so-called enterogastrone effect of various substances in the duodenum includes the inhibition of gastric emptying as well as the inhibition of gastric secretion. The hormonal mediator of the secretory effect, as discussed previously, is GIP, but the mediator of the effect on emptying has not been determined. A recent study by Valenzuela (122) examined the effect of a number of duodenal peptides on intragastric pressure. The pressure within the stomach influences emptying and would be expected to vary directly with the rate of transfer of gastric contents to the duodenum. Intravenous infusion of CCK, VIP, and secretin produced dose-related decreases in intragastric pressure, which reached 40% at higher doses. Glucagon and GIP had lesser effects. CCK and secretin had large and significant effects in doses equal to their D_{50}'s for pancreatic enzyme and bicarbonate secretion, respectively, and Valenzuela suggested that decreased intragastric pressure may be a physiological effect of these hormones (122). GIP significantly decreased pressure at a dose of 500 ng/kg-hr, which is the D_{50} for the inhibition of gastric acid secretion. Inhibition of gastric emptying could therefore also be a significant action of GIP. The effect, however, was much smaller than that seen with either CCK or secretin. The response to VIP occurred at high doses. In the same study glucagon also decreased intragastric pressure, but it is likely that all of the biologic actions of pancreatic glucagon on the gut are pharmacological (9).

One of the difficulties in determining which actions of the gastrointestinal peptides on motility are physiological is the lack of an objective criterion for motility. While one can quantitatively measure gastric emptying and LES pressure, this is not the case for gastric and intestinal motility in general. Two effects that occur at low doses and may prove to be physiological are the stimulation of antral motility by gastrin (25) and intestinal motility by CCK (8).

HORMONE RELEASE

Many hormones and especially those from the pituitary exert primary effects on the release of other hormones. Realization that gastrointestinal hormones influence the release of each other and the release of other endocrines substances, and in turn have their release influenced by other hormones, occurred shortly after the development of a sensitive radioimmunoassay for gastrin. Here again the chemical purification of gastrointestinal hormones which took place in the 1960s was entirely responsible for a whole new field of study.

Both secretin (119) and glucagon (7) inhibit antral gastrin release as well as the effect of gastrin on the parietal cell. Although these effects occur with relatively high doses and are not likely to be important physiologically, they are important clinically. Patients with Zollinger-Ellison syndrome or gastrinoma have high circulating gastrin levels of tumor origin. These individuals usually present with severe duodenal ulcer disease due to overproduction of gastric acid. The operation of choice is total gastrectomy since the tumor is relatively slow growing and usually cannot be resected. Basal serum gastrin levels are not always elevated sufficiently to differentiate between gastrinoma and normal duodenal ulcer. Secretin and glucagon, however, stimulate tumor gastrin release in contrast to their effects on antral release of the hormone. These tests have proved to be useful tools in the diagnosis of this disease (120).

In 1930 La Barre and his co-workers (84, 85) suggested that crude secretin contained two active principles: "excretin," which stimulated the exocrine pancreas, and "incretin," which stimulated insulin release. The word incretin has since been used to designate any substance from the duodenum that stimulated insulin release. The impetus to search for enteric factors stimulating insulin release was provided by the development of the insulin radioimmunoassay and the demonstration that insulin levels increased more following oral glucose than after intravenous glucose despite the smaller increase in serum glucose levels (96). Subsequently gastrin, CCK, and secretin were shown to stimulate insulin release (107). The insulin-releasing effects of the three "classical" gastrointestinal hormones, however, do not appear to be physiological (31), and none are released by glucose.

Both VIP (111) and GIP (37) release insulin. Since VIP is destroyed in the liver and since no releasing agent has yet been identified for it, it is not a likely candidate for incretin. GIP potentiated insulin release in response to an intravenous glucose infusion and improved glucose tolerance in man (37). This effect was obtained with 1 μg GIP/min for 30 min, and peak serum levels did not exceed 1 ng/ml, levels often seen following a meal. GIP release is stimulated by oral glucose in man and the resultant serum levels are sufficient to release insulin (23). In the dog, pure GIP in a dose as low as 0.25 μg/kg was a potent stimulant of insulin release without glucose loading (106). Thus the release of insulin appears to be the second proven physiological effect of the new hormone, GIP. Furthermore, since it is released by glucose, GIP may be the long sought-after incretin.

TROPHIC EFFECTS

Definitions of the word *hormone* usually include the phrase: "bloodborne mediator of metabolism and/or secretion." As we have seen in the previous part of this review, the obvious actions of the gastrointestinal hormones, the actions leading to their discovery and for which they are named, are their effects on secretion and motility of the digestive tract. Metabolic regulation is almost universally regarded as the realm of the other endocrine substances. This dichotomy of actions has resulted in a separation, placing gastrointestinal hormones within the confines of the field of physiology known as digestion and excluding them from that area known as endocrinology. Recent evidence, however, suggests that this separation is completely spurious. I have already reviewed data demonstrating that gastrointestinal hormones regulate the release of other hormones and vice versa. The dramatic effect of GIP on the release of insulin, the primary hormonal regulator of carbohydrate metabolism, is an excellent example. It has recently been clearly established that gastrointestinal hormones directly regulate the growth of a number of digestive tract tissues (62, 63).

As is often the case the preliminary experiments had already been done in nature. Several years after antrectomy, a popular surgical "cure" for ulcer disease, the remaining gastric mucosa atrophies. Vagotomy, which like antrectomy reduces acid secretion about 60%, has no such effect. The opposite picture, mucosal hyperplasia, occurs in patients with hypergastrinemia due to gastrinoma. Clinically, therefore, overproduction of gastrin is associated with gastrointestinal mucosal growth and lack of the hormone with mucosal atrophy. These observations suggested that gastrin exerted a trophic influence on the mucosa of the oxyntic gland area of the stomach and led us to examine the effect of pentagastrin on protein synthesis (66). A dose of pentagastrin submaximal for acid secretion stimulated protein synthesis in the mucosa of both the oxyntic gland portion of the stomach and the duodenum. Protein synthesis was not stimulated in either the liver or skeletal muscle. Histamine had no stimulatory effect in any tissue. We concluded that gastrin stimulated protein synthesis specifically in gastrointestinal tissues, and that this stimulation was unrelated to acid secretion. In addition we hypothesized that gastrin was a trophic hormone regulating the growth of gastrointestinal mucosa (66).

Chronic injection of large doses of pentagastrin stimulated parietal cell hyperplasia (30) and enlargement of the exocrine pancreas (93) and duodenum (93) in rats. Chronic injection of pentagastrin also prevented the deleterious effects of hypophysectomy on the pancreas, stomach, and duodenum, but had no effect on restoring the growth of any nongastrointestinal tissue (94).

Trophic hormones influence a number of biochemical processes related to growth of their target tissues. These include stimulation of protein, RNA and DNA synthesis, increased amino acid uptake, and decreased protein catabolism. Collectively this reaction to a growth hormone is termed the pleiotypic response. Stimulation of RNA, DNA, and protein synthesis have all been demonstrated in response to gastrin (62, 63).

Gastrin or pentagastrin stimulated DNA synthesis in mucosa of the oxyntic gland region of the stomach, the duodenum, the ileum (71) and the colon (62). It does not appear to have trophic effects on the esophagus or antrum (62). Although gastrin is a potent trophic hormone for mucosa on either side of the antrum, it is not surprising that it has no effect on the antrum itself. Hormones as a rule do not influence the growth of their tissues of origin. The trophic effects of gastrin appear to be restricted to the mucosa, at least in the stomach and duodenum (65). There have been no trophic effects described for gastrin in any tissue outside the gastrointestinal tract. Those examined include liver, skeletal muscle, kidneys, spleen, and testes (63).

A number of basic questions can be asked about the mechanism of action of any hormone. First, does the hormone act directly or does it trigger the release of another hormone or factor which in turn is responsible for the effect in question? Second, are the metabolic effects secondary to another action of the hormone such as, in the case of gastrin, the stimulation of secretion? Third, what biochemical mechanism is primarily triggered by the hormone?

The best evidence that a hormone acts directly is the demonstration of its effects in vitro. Such data, of course, do not eliminate the involvement of a second messenger such as one of the cyclic nucleotides. They do, however, mean that the hormone does not trigger the release of a second hormone transported via the blood to react with receptors on the target cells. The trophic actions of gastrin have been demonstrated in both tissue and organ culture preparations. Miller et al (99) found that pentagastrin was necessary to maintain tissue cultures of rat and human oxyntic gland epithelial cells. At confluency, the mitotic rate of pentagastrin-treated cultures was more than twice that of controls. Gastrin-treated subcultures contained significantly more protein than control subcultures derived from identical primary cultures. Cells present in gastrin-treated cultures were largely epithelial with numerous junctional complexes visible by electronmicroscopy, while the control cultures were primarily fibroblasts. Lichtenberger et al (87) obtained essentially the same results with cultured duodenal mucosal cells. In addition pentagastrin-treated cultures had a shorter doubling time, 19.5 hr, compared to 31.5 hr for saline-treated controls. This was attributed in part to the greater percentage of cells in the proliferative population in the hormone-treated cultures, 73% in comparison to the controls, 36%. This latter measurement was made by the autoradiographic determination of ^{3}H thymidine uptake into nuclei. Using organ cultures of rabbit gastric mucosa, Sutton & Donaldson (118) found that a number of pepsigogues, including pentagastrin, stimulated pepsinogen synthesis and secretion. Pentagastrin, however, was the only agent that stimulated synthesis of protein which was not secreted into the medium but retained as part of the cell.

Since the secretory or effector cells are not usually the proliferative cells, one must assume that separate receptors are involved in the trophic action. There appears to be total agreement between different studies that the trophic action of gastrin is independent of its secretory function. The in vitro studies mentioned above support this conclusion in that all systems were buffered, therefore eliminating the possibility that exposure to acid might account for the trophic effects. Many tissues besides the stomach show a growth response to gastrin, and gastrin has no prominent secretory effect on these. Acid secretory effects have been most often controlled by the use of histamine. The results of these studies have been unanimous in that metabolic actions of gastrin were not duplicated by histamine. These studies have involved gastrin-stimulated parietal cell hyperplasia (30); pancreatic cell hyperplasia (93); gastric and duodenal protein synthesis (66); gastric and duodenal RNA synthesis (24); gastric, duodenal, and ileal DNA synthesis (71); and DNA synthesis by cultured duodenal cells (87). Since these studies were done in rats, and the rat does not respond well to histamine, it can be argued that the involvement of acid secretion in the trophic response to gastrin was not ruled out. For this reason, the study by Willems et al (125) in the dog is noteworthy. They infused either gastrin or histamine over a period of 4 hr in doses producing nearly identical rates of acid secretion.

Thymidine uptake into gastric mucosal cells and cell division were significantly stimulated in the animals receiving gastrin and unchanged in those infused with histamine.

Further evidence that the trophic effect of gastrin is independent of the secretory effect comes from studies of inhibitors of acid secretion. Secretin inhibited gastrin-stimulated DNA synthesis (72), but metiamide (72) and 16, 16-dimethyl prostaglandin E_2 (73), in amounts which inhibit the secretory action of gastrin, had no effect on its trophic action.

Our major criterion for determining whether the action of a hormone is physiological has been that the effect must occur in response to levels of the hormone normally occurring in the blood. In the present discussion this has meant the normal increment in the serum hormone concentration following a meal. However, it could also mean the normal continuing presence of the hormone. A constant background of hormone would be important in the case of a permissive effect or an effect which requires repeated or continuing exposure to the hormone. There is general agreement that the trophic action of gastrin is physiological and that it may be the most important effect of the hormone (52).

Alterations in endogenous gastrin levels are associated with changes in growth which support the gastrin hypothesis. In the rat antrectomy resulted in significant decreases in gastric and duodenal mucosal RNA and DNA content. Injection of pentagastrin largely prevented these changes (67). At the time of weaning the rat small intestine undergoes major developmental changes. Maltase, sucrase, and trehalase activities increase, and lactase decreases; the gut becomes heavier with respect to body weight, and the RNA content of the gut increases. At the same time antral gastrin concentration increased from 1–3 μg/g to adult levels of 15–20 μg/g (86). None of these changes occurred when weaning was prevented. In animals prevented from weaning injection of pentagastrin for 10 days significantly increased the gut weight to body weight, RNA to body weight, and protein to body weight ratios over those found in saline-injected controls (116). Ingestion of a meal is followed by increases in DNA synthesis and mitotic index of canine fundic mucosa (126). This pattern was reproduced by a 4-hr infusion of gastrin, suggesting that gastrin is one of the factors responsible for postprandial cell renewal (125). In a recent study we maintained a group of rats for two weeks by total parenteral nutrition (74). Half of this group received a continuous infusion of pentagastrin in a dose equal to less than D_{25} for acid secretion. A control group was fed the nutrient solution orally. Serum as well as antral gastrin concentrations decreased significantly (70–80% decrease). Weights of the oxyntic gland area, small intestine, and pancreas decreased significantly in all parenterally fed rats except those receiving pentagastrin. Weights of the antrum, liver, spleen, and kidneys were not affected by the absence of food from the gut or by gastrin. Disaccharidase activities decreased as much as 75% in parenterally fed animals. These enzyme changes did not occur in the parenterally nourished rats receiving pentagastrin. These data indicated that the oral ingestion of food and its presence in the gastrointestinal tract are necessary to maintain endogenous gastrin, and that the trophic effect of gastrin is essential to maintain the structural and hence the functional integrity of the gut (74).

Viewed as one body of evidence, the parallels between endogenous gastrin levels and growth of gastrointestinal tissues are striking. In each case, decreased endogenous gastrin was associated with decreased growth, and the addition of exogenous gastrin significantly increased growth. In the study involving parenterally fed animals the exogenous dose of gastrin was well below that considered physiological (74). The dramatic effects of this study indicate that the continuing presence of a low level of the hormone is more effective in stimulating growth than periodic fluctuations in serum hormone concentrations. In summary the evidence that gastrin is a physiological regulator of gastrointestinal tissue growth is strong—perhaps as strong as similar evidence for any action of a gastrointestinal hormone.

As mentioned earlier, CCK is related to gastrin both structurally and functionally. Rothman & Wells (108) found that CCK stimulated pancreatic protein synthesis, but they did not relate this finding to trophic activity. Mainz et al (92) demonstrated that CCK increased RNA, protein, and DNA content of the pancreas. Other stimulants of pancreatic enzyme synthesis had no effect on pancreatic DNA content or synthesis. We found that low doses of CCK octapeptide stimulated pancreatic DNA synthesis but did not have a trophic action on gastrin or duodenal mucosa (113). Thus CCK appears to be a physiological regulator of the growth of the exocrine pancreas but not of the gastrointestinal mucosa.

Current evidence indicates that secretin can inhibit the trophic action of exogenous gastrin. Injection of secretin in combination with pentagastrin over a 2-week period prevented parietal cell hyperplasia and increased acid secretory capacity found in rats treated with pentagastrin alone (115). Animals receiving secretin alone had slightly lower secretory capacities and parietal cell counts than did saline-injected controls. Secretin also inhibited DNA synthesis stimulated by pentagastrin (72), thus providing a biochemical basis for the effects of chronically administered secretin on secretory capacity and parietal cell number. Whether secretin inhibits mucosal growth directly or whether it only inhibits the action of gastrin is not known. However, Pansu et al (102) found that secretin suppressed the labeling and mitotic indices of rat jejunal mucosal cells. This could have been either a direct action of secretin or inhibition of the effects of endogenous gastrin. Since the effects of endogenous secretin have not been investigated and uncertainties surround the amounts of secretin released and circulating in the blood, it is impossible to draw conclusions regarding the physiological role of this hormone in the growth of gastrointestinal tract tissues.

The realization that the functions of the gastrointestinal hormones include those normally reserved for other endocrine substances makes it necessary to discover the relationships which must certainly exist between these two groups of hormones. Pentagastrin, for example, prevented atrophy of the pancreas, duodenum, and oxyntic gland region of the stomach in hypophysectomized rats (94). In this study the mean body weights of saline- and pentagastrin-injected groups were not statistically different, but the oxyntic gland and duodenal weights of the gastrin-treated rats were 100 mg heavier than the saline controls and essentially the same as the weights of corresponding organs from intact rats. In addition there is strong evidence that the pituitary and, in particular, growth hormone may regulate gastrin synthesis and release. Serum and antral gastrin levels are depleted in hypophysectomized rats, and restored to nearly normal by growth hormone (41, 47). For the 70 years we have assumed that gastrointestinal hormones had no interactions with the other endocrines. The time has arrived to treat gastrointestinal hormones as an integral part of endocrinology.

OTHER INTESTINAL PEPTIDES

From time to time I have mentioned VIP, motilin, and chymodenin. These are peptides isolated from the intestinal mucosa which have pronounced effects on the gastrointestinal tract. They have not, however, satisfied the physiological criteria necessary for hormonal status. Nevertheless, some of their actions should be mentioned for the sake of completeness and because research involving these peptides is progressing rapidly.

VIP belongs to the secretin family of intestinal peptides and possesses the major action of each of the other members of the group. Like GIP, it inhibits acid secretion and stimulates insulin release. It stimulates pancreatic secretion like secretin and has the gluconeogenic and glycogenolytic actions of glucagon on the liver. Since it possesses all of these activities, VIP may be a primitive hormone from which the more specialized peptides evolved during the course of biological evolution. One of the more interesting effects of VIP is its stimulation of intestinal secretion (5). It has recently been discovered to be responsible for pancreatic cholera or the water diarrhea syndrome associated with non-insulin–secreting islet cell adenomas of the pancreas (10). This and the role of gastrin in Zollinger-Ellison syndrome are the only known examples of direct involvement by gastrointestinal peptides in abnormal clinical conditions. As mentioned previously, the physiological role of VIP is uncertain because it is significantly destroyed by passage through the liver, and it has not been shown to be released by any of the stimuli tested.

Motilin is a 22-amino-acid peptide discovered and isolated by Brown (16, 18). This peptide stimulates antral and fundic motor activity without affecting gastric secretion. Motilin is released by duodenal alkalinization, but it is doubtful whether the pH ever rises sufficiently (pH 10) under normal circumstances to stimulate its release.

Chymodenin is a basic polypeptide isolated and purified from porcine duodenum. Its amino acid sequence has not been published. Adelson & Rothman (1) found that chymodenin elicited the enzyme-specific secretion of chymotrypsinogen from the pancreas. A possible physiological role for chymodenin in promoting nonparallel secretion of chymotrypsinogen depends upon the outcome of the controversy over whether such nonparallelism does in fact occur (2). The peptide still has to be demonstrated in the blood following a meal or other appropriate stimulus in amounts sufficient to produce its effect.

SUMMARY

The past 10 years of gastrointestinal hormone research have clarified the significance of many actions of this group of peptides. In general, there have been two major realizations. First, only a few of the myriad of effects on the digestive tract are physiological. Second, two new types of physiological actions, the trophic action and hormone-releasing action, have emerged, linking the functions of the gastrointestinal hormones to those of the other endocrine substances.

It is interesting to speculate on the teleological significance of gastrointestinal hormones. Gastrointestinal motility is largely under neural regulation. Absorption is seemingly unregulated, depending only on the presence of absorbable material in the lumen. Some aspects of secretion are also regulated by extrinsic nerves and intramural reflexes. The canine Heidenhain pouch will, in fact, secrete maximally in response to topical stimulation by liver extract (34). Gastrin is not involved in this response. A viable, rapidly renewing population of mucosal cells, however, is necessary for the production of intrinsic factor, digestive enzymes, and the absorption of nutrients. Thus the metabolic effects of the gastrointestinal hormones may be their most important and, although only recently discovered, their primary actions. In any event, the gastrointestinal hormones can no longer be considered as a separate system of "digestive" regulators, but must be treated as an integral part of endocrinology.

Literature Cited

1. Adelson, J. W., Rothman, S. S. 1974. Selective pancreatic enzyme secretion due to a new peptide called chymodenin. *Science* 183:1087–89
2. Adelson, J. W., Rothman, S. S. 1975. Chymodenin, a duodenal peptide: Specific stimulation of chymotrypsinogen secretion. *Am. J. Physiol.* 229:1680–86
3. Andersson, S. 1973. Secretion of gastrointestinal hormones. *Ann. Rev. Physiol.* 35:431–52
4. Arimura, A., Sato, H., Dupont, A., Nishi, N., Schally, A. V. 1975. Abundance of immunoreactive GH-release inhibiting hormone in the stomach and pancreas of the rat. *Fed. Proc.* 34:273
5. Barbezat, G. O., Grossman, M. I. 1971. Intestinal secretion: Stimulation by peptides. *Science* 174:422–24
6. Bayliss, W. M., Starling, E. M. 1902. The mechanism of pancreatic secretion. *J. Physiol. London* 28:325–53
7. Becker, H. D., Reeder, D. D., Thompson, J. C. 1973. Effect of glucagon on circulating gastrin. *Gastroenterology* 65:28–35
8. Bertaccini, G., Agosti, A. 1971. Action of caerulein on intestinal motility in man. *Gastroenterology* 60:53–63
9. Bloom, S. R. 1974. Glucagon: Pancreatic and enteric. In *Endocrinology of the Gut,* ed. W. Y. Chey, F. P. Brooks, pp. 88–102. Thorofare, New Jersey: Slack. 373 pp.
10. Bloom, S. R., Polak, J. M. 1975. The role of VIP in pancreatic cholera. In *Gastrointestinal Hormones,* ed. J. C. Thompson, pp. 635–42. Austin, Texas: Univ. Texas Press. 666 pp.
11. Bodanszky, M., Klausner, Y. S., Said, S. I. 1973. Biological activities of synthetic peptides corresponding to fragments of and to the entire sequence of the vasoactive intestinal peptide. *Proc. Natl. Acad. Sci. USA* 70:384–85
12. Boden, G., Essa, N., Owen, O. E. 1975. Effects of intraduodenal amino acids, fatty acids and sugars on secretin concentrations. *Gastroenterology* 68:722–27
13. Brooks, A. M., Agosti, A., Bertaccini, G., Grossman, M. I. 1970. Inhibition of gastric acid secretion in man by peptide analogues of cholecystokinin. *N. Engl. J. Med.* 282:535–38
14. Brooks, A. M., Grossman, M. I. 1970. Postprandial pH and neutralizing capacity of the proximal duodenum in dogs. *Gastroenterology* 59:85–89
15. Brooks, A. M., Isenberg, J. I., Grossman, M. I. 1969. The effect of secretin, glucagon, and duodenal acidification on pepsin secretion in man. *Gastroenterology* 57:159–62
16. Brown, J. C. 1967. Presence of a gastric motor-stimulating property in duodenal extracts. *Gastroenterology* 52:225–29
17. Brown, J. C. 1971. A gastric inhibitory polypeptide. I. The amino acid composition and tryptic peptides. *Can. J. Biochem.* 49:255–61.

18. Brown, J. C., Cook, M. A., Dryburgh, J. R. 1972. Motilin, a gastric motor activity stimulating polypeptide: The complete amino acid sequence. *Can. J. Biochem.* 51:533–37

19. Brown, J. C., Dryburgh, J. R., Pederson, R. A. 1974. Gastric inhibitory polypeptide (GIP). See Ref. 9, pp. 76–82

20. Brown, J. C., Mutt, V., Dryburgh, J. R. 1971. The further purification of motilin, a gastric motor activity stimulating polypeptide from mucosa of the small intestine of hogs. *Can J. Physiol. Pharmacol.* 29:399–405

21. Bynum, T. E., Johnson, L. R. 1975. Stimulation of human pepsin output by topical hydrochloric acid. *Am. J. Dig. Dis.* 20:607–12

22. Castell, D. P., Harris, L. D. 1970. Hormonal control of gastro-esophageal sphincter strength. *N. Engl. J. Med.* 282:886–89

23. Cataland, S., Crockett, S. E., Brown, J. C., Mazzaferri, E. L. 1974. Gastric inhibitory polypeptide (GIP) stimulation by oral glucose in man. *J. Clin. Endocrinol. Metab.* 39:223–28

24. Chandler, A. M., Johnson, L. R. 1972. Pentagastrin-stimulated incorporation of ^{14}C orotic acid into RNA of gastric and duodenal mucosa. *Proc. Soc. Exp. Biol. Med.* 141:110–13

25. Chey, W. Y., Gutierrez, J., Yoshimori, M., Hendricks, J. 1974. Gut hormones on gastrointestinal motor function. See Ref. 9, pp. 194–211

26. Chey, W. Y., Tai, H. H., Rhodes, R., Lee, K. Y., Hendricks, J. 1975. Radioimmunoassay of secretin: Further studies. See Ref. 10, pp. 269–81

27. Cohen, S. 1974. What is "physiological"? An answer! *Gastroenterology* 66:479–80

28. Cooke, A. R. 1967. Acid and pepsin responses to gastrin in Heidenhain pouch dogs following bilateral adrenalectomy. *Gut* 8:588–91

29. Cooke, A. R., Chvasta, T. E., Weisbrodt, N. W. 1972. Effect of pentagastrin on emptying and electrical motor activity of the dog stomach. *Am. J. Physiol.* 223:934–38

30. Crean, G. P., Marshall, M. W., Rumsey, R. D. E. 1969. Parietal cell hyperplasia induced by the administration of pentagastrin (ICI 50, 123) to rats. *Gastroenterology* 57:147–56

31. Creutzfeldt, M. 1974. Insulin-releasing factors of the gastrointestinal mucosa (incretin). *Gastroenterology* 67:748–50

32. Debas, H. T., Farooq, O., Grossman, M. I. 1975. Inhibition of gastric emptying is a physiological action of cholecystokinin. *Gastroenterology* 68:1211–17

33. Debas, H. T., Grossman, M. I. 1973. Pure cholecystokinin: Pancreatic protein and bicarbonate response. *Digestion* 9:469–81

34. Debas, H. T., Grossman, M. I. 1975. Chemicals bathing the oxyntic gland area stimulate acid secretion in dog. *Gastroenterology* 69:654–59

35. Deveney, K., Way, L. W. 1972. Effect of fat in the duodenum on gastric acid secretion in cats. *Gastroenterology* 62:405–11

36. Dodds, W. J., Hogan, W. J., Miller, W. N., Barrera, R. F., Arndofer, R. C., Stef, J. J. 1975. Relationship between serum gastrin concentration and lower-esophageal sphincter pressure. *Am. J. Dig. Dis.* 20:201–7

37. Dupre, J., Ross, S., Watson, D., Brown, J. C. 1973. Stimulation of insulin secretion by gastric inhibitory polypeptide in man. *J. Clin. Endocrinol.* 37:826–28

38. Dutt, B., Magee, D. F. 1972. Pepsin secretion by Heidenhain pouches in dogs. *Am. J. Physiol.* 223:480–83

39. Edkins, J. S. 1905. On the chemical mechanism of gastric secretion. *Proc. R. Soc. Lond. Ser. B.* 76:376

40. Emas, S., Grossman, M. I. 1967. Effect of truncal vagotomy on acid and pepsin response to histamine and gastrin in dogs. *Am. J. Physiol.* 212:1007–12

41. Enochs, M. R., Johnson, L. R. 1976. Effect of hypophysectomy and growth hormone on serum and antral gastrin levels in the rat. *Gastroenterology* 70:727–32

42. Ewald, C. A., Boas, J. 1886. Beitrage zur Physiologie und Pathologie der Verdauung. *Virchows Arch. A* 104:271–305

43. Farrell, J. I., Ivy, A. C. 1926. Studies on the motility of the transplanted gastric pouch. *Am. J. Physiol.* 76:227–28

44. Feng, T. P., Hou, H. C., Lim, R. K. S. 1929. On the mechanism of the inhibition of gastric secretion by fat. *Clin. J. Physiol.* 3:371–80

45. Freeland, G. R., Higgs, R. H., Castel, D. O., McGuigan, J. E. 1975. Lower esophageal sphincter (LES) and gastric acid (GA) response to intravenous infusion of synthetic human gastrin heptadecapeptide I (HGH). *Gastroenterology* 68:894 (Abstr.)

46. Giles, G. R., Mason, M. C., Humphries, C., Clark, C. G. 1969. Action of gastrin

on the lower esophageal sphincter in man. *Gut* 10:730–34

47. Gregory, R. A., Tracy, H. J. 1964. The constitution and properties of two gastrins extracted from hog antral mucosa. *Gut* 5:103–17

48. Grossman, M. I. 1970. Gastrin, cholecystokinin, and secretin act on one receptor. *Lancet* 1:1088–89

49. Grossman, M. I. 1973. What is physiological? *Gastroenterology* 65:994

50. Grossman, M. I. 1974. Candidate hormones of the gut. *Gastroenterology* 67:730–55

51. Grossman, M. I. 1974. What is physiological: Round 2. *Gastroenterology* 67:766–67

52. Grossman, M. I. 1975. Trends in gut hormone research. See Ref. 10, pp. 3–10

53. Grossman, M. I., Konturek, S. J. 1974. Gastric acid does drive pancreatic bicarbonate secretion. *Scand. J. Gastroenterol.* 9:299–302

54. Grossman, M. I., Konturek, S. J. 1974. Inhibition of acid secretion in dog by metiamide a histamine antagonist acting on H_2-receptors. *Gastroenterology* 66:517–21

55. Grossman, M. I., Robertson, C. R., Ivy, A. C. 1948. Proof of a hormonal mechanism for gastric secretion—the humoral transmission of the distention stimulus. *Am. J. Physiol.* 153:1–9

56. Harper, A. A., Raper, H. S. 1943. Pancreozymin, a stimulant of the secretion of pancreatic enzymes in extracts of the small intestine. *J. Physiol. London* 102:115–25

57. Hunt, J. N., Ramsbottom, N. 1967. Effect of gastrin-II on gastric emptying and secretion during a test meal. *Br. Med. J.* 4:386–87

58. Ivy, A. C., Oldberg, E. 1928. A hormone mechanism for gallbladder contraction and evacuation. *Am. J. Physiol.* 86:599–613

59. Johnson, L. R. 1971. The control of gastric secretion: No room for histamine? *Gastroenterology* 61:106–18

60. Johnson, L. R. 1972. Regulation of pepsin secretion by topical acid in the stomach. *Am. J. Physiol.* 223:847–50

61. Johnson, L. R. 1973. Effect of gastric mucosal acidification on the action of pepsigogues. *Am. J. Physiol.* 225:1411–15

62. Johnson, L. R. 1974. Gut hormones on growth of gastrointestinal mucosa. See Ref. 9, pp. 163–77

63. Johnson, L. R. 1976. The trophic action of gastrointestinal hormones. *Gastroenterology* 70:278–88

64. Johnson, L. R. 1977. Histamine and gastric secretion. In *Handbook of Experimental Pharmacology*, Vol. 28, ed. M. Roche e Silva. Berlin: Springer. In press

65. Johnson, L. R., Aures, D., Hakanson, R. 1969. Effect of gastrin on the in vivo incorporation of ^{14}C leucine into protein of the digestive tract. *Proc. Soc. Exp. Biol. Med.* 132:996–98

66. Johnson, L. R., Aures, D., Yuen, L. 1969. Pentagastrin induced stimulation of the in vitro incorporation of ^{14}C leucine into protein of gastrointestinal tract. *Am. J. Physiol.* 217:251–54

67. Johnson, L. R., Chandler, A. M. 1973. RNA and DNA of gastric and duodenal mucosa in antrectomized and gastrin-treated rats. *Am. J. Physiol.* 224:937–40

68. Johnson, L. R., Grossman, M. I. 1969. Effects of fat, secretin, and cholecystokinin on histamine-stimulated gastric secretion. *Am. J. Physiol.* 216:1176–79

69. Johnson, L. R., Grossman, M. I. 1969. Characteristics of inhibition of gastric secretion by secretin. *Am. J. Physiol.* 217:1401–14

70. Johnson, L. R., Grossman, M. I. 1970. Analysis of inhibition of acid secretion by cholecystokinin in dogs. *Am. J. Physiol.* 218:550–54

71. Johnson, L. R., Guthrie, P. D. 1974. Mucosal DNA synthesis: A short term index of the trophic action of gastrin. *Gastroenterology* 67:453–49

72. Johnson, L. R., Guthrie, P. D. 1974. Secretin inhibition of gastrin-stimulated deoxyribonucleic acid synthesis. *Gastroenterology* 67:601–06

73. Johnson, L. R., Guthrie, P. D. 1976. Effect of cholecystokinin and 16,16-dimethyl PGE$_2$ on RNA and DNA of gastric and duodenal mucosa. *Gastroenterology* 70:59–65

74. Johnson, L. R., Lichtenberger, L. M., Copeland, E. M., Dudrick, S. J., Castro, G. A. 1975. Action of gastrin on gastrointestinal structure and function. *Gastroenterology* 68:1184–92

75. Johnson, L. R., Stening, G. F., Grossman, M. I. 1970. The effect of sulfation on the gastrointestinal actions of caerulein. *Gastroenterology* 58:208–16

76. Jones, R. S., Grossman, M. I. 1969. Choleretic effects of secretin and histamine in the dog. *Am. J. Physiol.* 217:532–35

77. Jones, R. S., Grossman, M. I. 1970. Choleretic effects of cholecystokinin,

gastrin II, and caerulein in the dog. *Am. J. Physiol.* 219:1014–18

78. Jorpes, J. E. 1968. The isolation and chemistry of secretin and cholecystokinin. *Gastroenterology* 55:157–64

79. Jorpes, J. E., Mutt, V. 1966. Cholecystokinin and pancreozymin, one single hormone? *Acta Physiol. Scand.* 66:196–202

80. Jorpes, J. E., Mutt, V. 1970. On the biological activity and amino acid composition of secretin. *Acta Chem. Scand.* 15:513–519

81. Konturek, S. J., Johnson, L. R. 1971. Evidence for an enterogastric reflex for the inhibition of acid secretion. *Gastroenterology* 61:667–74

82. Kosaka, T., Lim, R. K. S. 1930. Demonstration of the humoral agent in fat inhibition of gastric secretion. *Proc. Soc. Exp. Biol. Med.* 27:890–91

83. Kuzio, M., Dryburgh, J. R., Malloy, K. M., Brown, J. C. 1974. Radioimmunoassay for gastric inhibitory polypeptide. *Gastroenterology* 66:347–64

84. La Barre, J. 1932. Sur les possibilités d'un traitement élu diabète par l'incretine. *Bull. Acad. R. Med. Belg.* 12:620–34

85. La Barre, J., Still, E. V. 1930. Studies on the physiology of secretin. III. Further studies on the effects of secretin on the blood sugar. *Am. J. Physiol.* 91:649–53

86. Lichtenberger, L., Johnson, L. R. 1974. Gastrin in the ontogenic development of the rat small intestine. *Am. J. Physiol.* 227:390–95

87. Lichtenberger, L., Miller, L. R., Erwin, D. N., Johnson, L. R. 1973. The effect of pentagastrin on adult rat duodenal cells in culture. *Gastroenterology* 65:242–51

88. Lipshutz, W., Cohen, S. 1971. Physiological determinants of lower esophageal sphincter function. *Gastroenterology* 61:16–24

89. Lipshutz, W., Cohen, S. 1972. Interaction of gastrin I and secretin on gastrointestinal circular muscle. *Am. J. Physiol.* 222:775–81

90. Lipshutz, W., Hughes, W., Cohen, S. 1972. The genesis of lower esophageal sphincter pressure: Its identification through the use of gastrin antiserum. *J. Clin. Invest.* 51:522–29

91. Lipshutz, W., Tuch, A. F., Cohen, S. 1971. A comparison of the site of action of gastrin I on lower esophageal sphincter and antral circular smooth muscle. *Gastroenterology* 61:454–60

92. Mainz, D. L., Black, O., Webster, P. D. 1974. Hormonal control of pancreatic growth. *J. Clin. Invest.* 52:2300–4

93. Mayston, P. D., Barrowman, J. A. 1971. The influence of chronic administration of pentagastrin on the rat pancreas. *Q. J. Exp. Physiol.* 56:113–22

94. Mayston, P. D., Barrowman, J. A. 1973. Influence of chronic administration of pentagastrin on the pancreas in hypophysectomized rats. *Gastroenterology* 64:391–99

95. McGuigan, J. E. 1968. Immunochemical studies with synthetic human gastrin. *Gastroenterology* 54:1005–11

96. McIntyre, N., Holdsworth, C. D., Turner, D. S. 1964. New interpretation of oral glucose tolerance. *Lancet* 2:20–21

97. Meyer, J. H., Spingola, L. J., Grossman, M. I. 1971. Endogenous cholecystokinin potentiates exogenous secretin on pancreas of dog. *Am. J. Physiol.* 221:742–47

98. Meyer, J. H., Way, L. W., Grossman, M. I. 1970. Pancreatic response to acidification of various lengths of proximal intestine in the dog. *Am. J. Physiol.* 219:971–77

99. Miller, L. R., Jacobson, E. D., Johnson, L. R. 1973. Effect of pentagastrin on gastric mucosal cells grown in tissue culture. *Gastroenterology* 64:254–67

100. Nebel, O. T., Castell, D. O. 1972. Lower esophageal sphincter pressure changes after food ingestion. *Gastroenterology* 63:778–83

101. Nilsson, G., Simon, J., Yalow, R. S., Berson, S. A. 1972. Plasma gastrin and gastric acid responses to sham feeding and feeding in dogs. *Gastroenterology* 63:51–59

102. Pansu, D., Berard, A., Dechelette, M. A., Lambert, R. 1974. Influence of secretin and pentagastrin on the circadian rhythm of cell proliferation in the intestinal mucosa of rats. *Digestion* 11:266–74

103. Pearse, A. G. E., Polak, J. M. 1971. Neural crest origin of the endocrine polypeptide (APUD) cells of the gastrointestinal tract and pancreas. *Gut* 12:783–88

104. Pearse, A. G. E., Polak, J. M., Heath, C. M. 1973. Development, differentiation and derivation of the endocrine polypeptide cells of the mouse pancreas. *Diabetologia* 9:120–29

105. Pederson, R. A., Brown, J. C. 1972. The inhibition of histamine-, pentagastrin-, and insulin-stimulated gastric secretion

by pure gastric inhibitory polypeptide. *Gastroenterology* 62:393–400

106. Pederson, R. A., Schubert, H. E., Brown, J. C. 1975. The insulinotropic action of gastric inhibitory polypeptide. *Can. J. Physiol. Pharmacol.* 53:217–23

107. Rehfeld, J. F. 1972. Gastrointestinal hormones and insulin secretion. *Scand. J. Gastroenterol.* 7:289–92

108. Rothman, S. S., Wells, H. 1967. Enhancement of pancreatic enzyme synthesis by pancreozymin. *Am. J. Physiol.* 213:215–18

109. Said, S. I., Mutt, V. 1970. Polypeptide with broad biological activity: Isolation from small intestine. *Science* 169:1217–18

110. Sasaki, H., Faloona, G. R., Unger, R. H. 1974. Enteroglucagon. *Gastroenterology* 67:746–48

111. Schebalin, M., Brooks, A. M., Said, S. I., Makhloaf, G. M. 1974. The insulinotropic effect of vasoactive intestinal peptide (VIP): Direct evidence from in vitro studies. *Gastroenterology* 66:772 (Abstr.)

112. Sjodin, L., Andersson, S. 1972. Inhibition of gastric secretion by acidification of the duodenal bulb before and after transection of the pylorus. *Scand. J. Gastroenterol.* 7:151–56

113. Soll, A. H. 1975. Isolated canine gastric mucosal cells: Stimulation of oxygen uptake by pentagastrin and acetylcholine. *Physiologist* 18:3 (Abstr.)

114. Soll, A. H. 1976. The isolated mammalian parietal cell: Actions and interactions of secretagogues. *Gastroenterology* 70:974 (Abstr.)

115. Stanley, M. D., Coalson, R. E., Grossman, M. I., Johnson, L. R. 1972. Influence of secretin and pentagastrin on acid secretion and parietal cell number in rats. *Gastroenterology* 63:264–69

116. Stening, G. F., Johnson, L. R., Grossman, M. I. 1969. A comparison of the effect of secretin on acid and pepsin secretion in the cat and dog. *Gastroenterology* 56:468–75

117. Sutherland, E. W., DeDuve, V. 1948. Origin and distribution of hyperglycemic-glycogenolytic factor of pancreas. *J. Biol. Chem.* 175:663–74

118. Sutton, D. R., Donaldson, R. M. Jr. 1975. Synthesis and secretion of protein and pepsinogen by rabbit gastric mucosa in organ culture. *Gastroenterology* 69:166–74

119. Thompson, J. C., Reeder, D. D., Buchman, H. H., Becker, H. D., Brandt, E. N. 1972. Effect of secretin on circulating gastrin. *Ann. Surg.* 176:384–93

120. Thompson, J. C., Reeder, D. D., Viller, H. V., Fender, H. R. 1975. Natural history and experience with diagnosis and treatment of the Zollinger-Ellison syndrome. *Surg. Gynecol. Obstet.* 140:721–39

121. Vagne, M., Stening, G. F., Brooks, F. P., Grossman, M. I. 1968. Synthetic secretin: Comparison with natural secretin for potency and spectrum of physiological actions. *Gastroenterology* 55:260–67

122. Valenzuela, J. E. 1977. Effect of intestinal hormones and peptides on intragastric pressure in dogs. *Gastroenterology* In press

123. Walker, C. O., Frank, S. A., Manton, J., Fordtran, J. S. 1975. Effect of continuous infusion of pentagastrin on lower esophageal sphincter pressure and gastric acid secretion in normal subjects. *J. Clin. Invest.* 56:218–25

124. Walsh, J. H., Debas, H. T., Grossman, M. I. 1974. Pure human big gastrin: Immunochemical properties, disappearance half time, and acid stimulating action in dogs. *J. Clin. Invest.* 54:477–85

125. Willems, G., Van steenkiste, Y., Limbosch, J. M. 1972. Stimulating effect of gastrin on cell proliferation kinetics in canine fundic mucosa. *Gastroenterology* 62:385–89

126. Willems, G., Vansteenkiste, Y., Smets, P. H. 1971. Effects of food ingestion on the cell proliferation kinetics in the canine fundic mucosa. *Gastroenterology* 61:323–27

127. Yalow, R. S., Berson, S. A. 1970. Size and charge distinctions between endogenous human plasma gastrin in peripheral blood and heptadecapeptide gastrins. *Gastroenterology* 65:609–15

128. Yalow, R. S. Berson, S. A. 1972. And now, "big-big" gastrin. *Biochem. Biophys. Res. Commun.* 48:391–95

129. Zaterka, S., Grossman, M. I. 1966. The effect of gastrin and histamine on the secretion of bile. *Gastroenterology* 50:500–5

Ann. Rev. Physiol. 1977. 39:159–84
Copyright © 1977 by Annual Reviews Inc. All rights reserved

HETEROGENEITY OF NEPHRON FUNCTION

❖1167

Norbert H. Lameire, Meyer D. Lifschitz, and Jay H. Stein[1]
Department of Medicine, University of Texas Health Science Center,
San Antonio, Texas 78284

INTRODUCTION

The dictionary (151) gives several different definitions of the word heterogeneous, but the following seems the most appropriate for this topic: "made up of parts or elements that are not uniform, compatible or proportionate." This definition is quite suitable for the primary subject of this review: the evidence, pro and con, that subpopulations of nephrons differ in structure and function. In addition, however, many observations have recently been published which demonstrate that heterogeneity exists along a given proximal or distal tubule of the same nephron. In other words, a given anatomical segment of the same nephron may have functional and structural differences between its parts. This review primarily evaluates the evidence for heterogeneity of function between different nephron populations. The available data on heterogeneity of proximal and distal tubular transport in the same nephron are discussed in a later section. Two points should be noted: First, we have not attempted to discuss or quote every paper ever addressed to this subject, and have primarily utilized data published in the past five years. Second, the data accumulated in this particular field are contradictory. When possible, the reviewers attempt to explain the apparent discrepancies. There are issues, however, which are totally unsettled at the present time.

Studies by Goodyer & Jaeger (60) and Barger and associates (17, 142) have led to the current interest in evaluating the hemodynamic and functional characteristics of different nephron populations within the kidney. Goodyer & Jaeger (60) found that hemorrhage of a degree that did not significantly alter mean arterial pressure,

[1]This work was supported in part by NIH grants AM 17387-03 and AM18485-02, and a NATO grant 1975 N15516.

159

GFR, or renal blood flow markedly reduced sodium excretion. The authors suggested that this finding might be due to a redistribution of blood flow and glomerular filtrate to inner cortical nephrons. No measurement of regional blood flow or nephron GFR was obtained in this study. Subsequently, Barger and his group modified the inert gas washout technique of Kety (83) to attempt to measure regional blood flow distribution in the kidney. Their results concurred with Goodyer & Jaeger's view that inner cortical nephrons had a greater sodium reabsorptive capacity when compared to the shorter outer cortical nephrons. Although the results of these studies popularized the view that blood flow redistribution was an important regulator of sodium balance, the inert gas method has been severely criticized for numerous technical and theoretical reasons (134). In addition, until recently, no methods were available to compare the intrinsic transport characteristics of different nephron populations. Thus when the original redistribution hypothesis was formulated, there was no evidence that superficial and juxtamedullary nephrons had different transport characteristics. Major technical advances, however, have recently occurred. A technique has become available that makes measuring the distribution of cortical blood flow (the radioactive microsphere method) (100, 136) and the transport characteristics of different nephron populations (isolated tubular perfusion method) possible (32). In addition, the problem of measurement of individual nephron GFR by micropuncture has become better appreciated, and the use of the Hanssen technique (68, 69) (vida infra) has been established. Thus the following sections summarize the newer findings relating to heterogeneity of nephron function with special reference to the regulation of sodium balance. First, however, certain anatomical considerations are worthy of note.

ANATOMICAL CONSIDERATIONS

Anatomical nephron heterogeneity has been documented in many mammalian species by Sperber (130). A number of classifications of nephron subpopulations have been made. One group of investigators classified the nephron subpopulations of the rabbit kidney into four groups according to their location in the renal cortex and the anatomical characteristics of their efferent arteriole as follows (15). G_1: Glomeruli from the most superficial part of the cortex and with an efferent arteriole rising towards the kidney surface before it branches. G_2: Other glomeruli (G_1 excluded) from the superficial half of the cortex. G_3: Glomeruli of the deep half of the cortex except the G_4 type glomeruli. G_4: Glomeruli whose efferent arteriole provides vasa recta which descend into the medulla.

Although this classification has some utility, we prefer the more widely used division into superficial, intermediate, and juxtamedullary nephron populations. For the purpose of this discussion, these three nephron subpopulations, based upon their site of origin, are defined as follows (109, 130): 1. Superficial cortical nephrons have some portion extending to the surface of the kidney. These are the nephrons accessible to routine micropuncture. 2. Juxtamedullary nephrons have glomeruli situated

in the innermost portion of the cortex, have long medullary loops extending into the papilla, and constitute the smallest fraction (<10%) of the nephron population.
3. The remaining nephrons do not touch the surface of the kidney or extend into the papilla and are thus not accessible to micropuncture. For the purposes of this discussion, they are called intermediate nephrons (58, 120).

The main anatomical characteristics of glomerular and tubular structures in these different types of nephrons are summarized in Table 1. These data are derived from postmortem microdissection and silicone rubber injection techniques which subject the kidney to maceration processes in which distortion of shape and dimensions are inevitable.

Based upon the data in Table 1, the main anatomical differences between superficial and juxtamedullary nephrons can be summarized as follows:

1. In nearly all species studied, the juxtamedullary glomerulus has a larger volume and is connected to a longer proximal tubule than in the superficial nephron. In the rabbit, the diameters of both the afferent and efferent arterioles in the superficial and juxtamedullary nephron are dissimilar. In superficial nephrons, the afferent arteriole is ± 18.3 μm and the efferent arteriole is ± 11.5 μm, while in juxtamedullary nephrons the afferent and efferent arteriole are 20.8 μm and 28.0 μm in diameter, respectively.

2. Superficial nephrons have a shorter loop of Henle than juxtamedullary nephrons, at least in rat and dog. In the rat, the loop of Henle of superficial nephrons turns in the outer medulla (120, 147), while in the dog the bend is located in the inner medulla (22, 130). Juxtamedullary nephron loops in the rat kidney extend for a variable distance into the inner medullary zone, with one third of the total reaching

Table 1 Summary of anatomical characteristics of nephron subpopulations

	Superficial	Intermediate	Juxtamedullary	Species	Reference
Diameter	148	152	185	Rabbit	14
glomerulus (μm)	181		190	Dog	34
	150	165	184	Child (6 months)	55
	287	280	283	Adult human	55
Volume (10^{-5} mm^3)	193	236	356	Rat	11
Glomerulus	98		118	Rat	40
	26	54	68	Psammomys	11
Afferent arteriole diameter (μm)	18.3	18.6	20.8	Rabbit	14
Efferent arteriole diameter (μm)	11.5	12.1	28.0	Rabbit	14
Proximal tubule (mm)	9.3	10.8	12.2	Rat	11
length	6.5	8.1	12.2	Mouse	11
	3.9	5.0	6.5	Psammomys	11
	13.2	15.2	23.1	Dog	22
	4.8	6.0	6.7	Child (6 months)	55
	21.5	19.4	17.8	Adult human	55
Henle's loop (mm)	4.4		12.2	Rat	88
length	10	11	12.5	Dog	22

the tip of the papilla (89). In the rat at least, the loop of Henle of superficial nephrons lacks a thin ascending limb (7).

Further extensive anatomical studies by Beeuwkes & Bonventre (22) have demonstrated that the efferent arteriolar vessels are quite different in the superficial, midcortical, and juxtamedullary regions of the dog kidney. Only in the superficial cortex does the efferent arteriole from a given glomerulus exclusively supply the tubule of the parent nephron. In the midcortex, efferent arterioles may be directed toward either the superficial or the deep regions of the cortex, ultimately surrounding tubules quite distant in origin from the parent nephron. In juxtamedullary nephrons there are two main types of efferent arterioles, as noted by Edwards (53) and Smith (128). The so-called corticomedullary efferent arteriole is a thin-walled vessel which divides into a capillary network in the area of the corticomedullary junction and the outer medullary area. The medullary efferent arteriole is a larger vessel, which contains smooth muscle and divides into multiple vasa recta.

Enzymatic differences between superficial and deep nephrons have been demonstrated for several important enzyme systems. It has been shown that there is a stratification of renin content in the renal cortex with the amount being greatest in outer cortical and least in inner cortical nephrons. This has been demonstrated in rabbit, dog, and rat kidney (30, 56, 57, 72, 118). The renin content per juxtaglomerular apparatus was inversely proportional to the NaCl intake of the animal (56, 57, 118). In addition, the renin gradient noted disappeared in animals on a high salt intake (56) and was also abolished by manipulating the carotid arteries (56). The authors of this latter study suggested that this artifact resulting from carotid artery manipulation could explain the failure of some investigators to find this renin gradient from outer to inner cortex in the rat kidney (61). Schmidt & Dubach (122, 123) described other important enzymatic differences between superficial and juxtamedullary nephrons. These authors noted that Na^+K-ATPase activity was higher in the proximal tubules of juxtamedullary nephrons than in superficial nephrons.

Anatomical nephron heterogeneity may be the result of the centrifugal pattern of maturation of nephron populations in which juxtamedullary nephrons are the first to form. There also seem to be different rates of glomerular and tubular growth in the developing kidney with a glomerular preponderance (4, 55, 98). Except for man and guinea pig, the development of the superficial renal cortex is incomplete at birth in most mammals. During the first weeks of extrauterine life, impressive functional changes in glomerular filtration rate, renal plasma flow, glomerular differentiation, and intrarenal blood flow distribution occur (12, 74, 79, 107, 131).

DISTRIBUTION OF SINGLE NEPHRON GLOMERULAR FILTRATION RATE (SNGFR)

In addition to morphological differences among nephrons, functional heterogeneity exists as well. The filtration rate differs in superficial and juxtamedullary nephrons. Two experimental approaches have been used to delineate this difference: a micropuncture method and a microdissection technique originally developed by Hanssen (68, 69). The direct micropuncture studies involve comparing nephron

GFR determined from proximal tubules of superficial nephrons with values obtained by puncturing the loops of Henle of juxtamedullary nephrons accessible to study after exposure of the renal papilla.

The methodological limitations and technical problems of the determination of nephron GFR have been reviewed by Orloff & Burg (108), Wright & Giebisch (155), and in the proceedings of a recent micropuncture workshop (59).

A number of studies have also been performed where superficial SNGFR was compared to total kidney GFR before and after a given experimental maneuver. This indirect evaluation of the behavior of nephrons inaccessible to micropuncture must be considered with caution since it involves a comparison of measurements obtained by two techniques each having its own source of errors and may be totally insensitive to discerning a major distributional change in a small subpopulation of nephrons.

Micropuncture of the loop of Henle with a quantitative collection of the tubular fluid is particularly difficult, due to the movement of the papilla and the possible contamination of samples with collecting duct fluid (73). Another disadvantage of the measurement of SNGFR by micropuncture is the limited number of nephrons studied in each experiment. It has been found, at least in the rat, that the juxtamedullary nephron population is composed of a mixture of both large and small glomeruli, indicating considerable morphological and presumably functional heterogeneity (18). The SNGFR measured at the bend of Henle's loop is therefore not necessarily representative of all juxtamedullary nephrons. In addition, all direct measurements of juxtamedullary nephron SNGFR have been obtained from young rats or desert rodents since the extrarenal part of the papilla is more readily accessible to micropuncture in the immature animal than in the adult. Whether these values are similar in adult rats has been evaluated with more indirect estimates of SNGFR.

The microdissection technique described by Hanssen and its subsequent modifications have recently been discussed by Chabardès et al (35) and in (59). This method relies on the use of ferrocyanide ions associated with a microdissection technique. Ferrocyanide has an extracellular volume of distribution and behaves like a glomerular indicator. Various modifications of this basic technique have been used, and the results obtained depend strongly on the method used to administer the ferrocyanide. The first technique originally developed by Hanssen consists of a pulse injection of concentrated ferrocyanide into the circulation. Approximately 10–12 seconds after injection, the pedicle is ligated and the kidney removed. The ferrocyanide is subsequently precipitated as Prussian blue, and the proximal tubules are individually dissected. The measured distance between the glomerulus and the distal front of the precipitated bolus was assumed to be proportional to the nephron filtration rate. An improvement of the technique consisted of the use of [14C]-labeled ferrocyanide instead of unlabeled ferrocyanide. An elegant modification of this technique has been developed by de Rouffignac and his co-workers (119) which makes it possible to quantitatively estimate SNGFR. [14C]-sodium ferrocyanide is injected at a constant rate and, at equilibrium, a short pulse of nonradioactive ferrocyanide is injected as a bolus. The portion of each tubule containing the nonradioactive ferrocyanide is dissected and the total radioactivity determined. The nephron filtration rate is calculated from the total radioactivity per unit time divided by the plasma radioactivity. Another modification of the Hanssen technique has been presented by Coehlo et al (40), who infused the labeled ferrocyanide intravenously and ligated the renal pedicle 12 seconds after the beginning of the infusion. After microdissection, the proximal tubules were cut at the front of the [^{14}C]-ferrocyanide precipitate and the distal tubules containing no intraluminal radioactivity were used to determine the radioactivity per mm of tubule due to extraluminal contamination. The radioactivity in the proximal tubule can then be corrected for extraluminal contamination.

It has been suggested that the use of a single pulse injection of labeled ferrocyanide may lead to erroneous results especially in circumstances associated with extracellular volume expansion (35). This phenomenon is discussed in more detail subsequently.

A summary of recent data on the distribution of SNGFR in the different nephron subpopulations under normal conditions of hydropenia is given in Table 2. All the micropuncture data were obtained in very young animals (<200 g) while the microdissection results were generally obtained in adult animals. Despite relatively wide differences in the absolute values, there is agreement that the SNGFR is higher in the juxtamedullary nephrons. The ratio of superficial to juxtamedullary SNGFR (S:J ratio) is 0.5 or less in all micropuncture studies with the exception of one (8), while the ratio is approximately 0.8, with the microdissection technique in all animals, except *Psammomys*. The reason for this quantitative discrepancy in the ratio of superficial to juxtamedullary SNGFR in the rat is not totally clear. The majority of microdissection studies were performed in rats considerably older than in the micropuncture studies. Thus differences in the ages of the rats studied with micropuncture versus the Hanssen technique may explain this discrepancy.

When both the micropuncture and microdissection techniques were applied in the same laboratory, a reasonable agreement between the SNGFR values for superficial and juxtamedullary nephrons in both *Psammomys* (117) and rat (8) was obtained. No study, however, has been performed in which both techniques were used simultaneously in the same animal.

Based upon the recent data by Bankir et al (15, 16) in the rabbit, it can be calculated that the SNGFR ratio between superficial (G_1) and juxtamedullary nephrons (G_4) is 0.80, while the glomerular surface ratio between G_1 and G_4 is 0.64, indicating that the ratio of SNGFR to glomerular surface area is lower in the juxtamedullary than in superficial nephrons. In the rat, Coelho et al (40) calculated the surface ratio between superficial and juxtamedullary nephron as 0.89, while the SNGFR ratio was 0.84. In this species, therefore, there seems to be a relative constant ratio of SNGFR to glomerular surface area in superficial and juxtamedullary nephrons.

Considerable attention has recently been given to the effect of antidiuretic hormone (ADH), renal perfusion pressure, and alterations in extracellular fluid volume on the distribution of SNGFR. Controversy exists on the effect of ADH on the distribution of SNGFR. Jamison & Lacy (78) measured nephron GFR in rats with

Table 2 Summary of distribution of SNGFR during hypropenia

A. Micropuncture method

Species	Superficial	Juxtamedullary nl/min g or nl/min	S:JM	Reference
Rat	23.5	58.2	0.40	73
Rat (180–200 g)	30.5	59.7	0.51	140
Rat (55–95 g)	25.6	60.2	0.42	76
Rat (<100 g)	30.3	64.9	0.47	77
Rat (80–115 g)	29.2[a]	39.3[a]	0.74	8
Psammomys	9.0[a]	21.4[a]	0.42	121

B. Ferrocyanide method

Species	Superficial	Intermediate nl/min	Juxtamedullary nl/min	S:JM	Reference
Rat (173–218 g)	32	38	49	0.65	11
Rat (200 g)	27.9	33.3	38.5	0.72	116
Rat	27.7	27.0	35.3	0.78	119
Rat (160–230 g)	32.7	—	40.6	0.80	25
Rat (230–355 g)	39.9	38.7	47.7	0.84	40
Rat	24.5	—	30.1	0.87	47
Rat	36	45	70	0.50	141
Rat	30.6	—	38.0	0.80	8
Rat (conscious) (189 g)	39	—	49.4	0.79	110
Psammomys	8.4	16.2	28.2	0.30	11
Rabbit	24.7	—	30.9	0.80	16
Dog	60	—	72	0.84	31

[a] Studies measuring SNGFR in nl/min.

hereditary diabetes insipidus during water diuresis and ADH-induced antidiuresis in superficial and juxtamedullary nephrons. The calculated distribution ratio (S:JM) was 0.48 during water diuresis and 0.69 after ADH, indicating a possible disproportionate rise in superficial nephron GFR. Using the ferrocyanide technique, Davis & Schnermann (46) found a redistribution of filtrate towards the juxtamedullary nephrons in diabetes insipidus rats given vasopressin. The latter findings are indirectly supported by Baines who found, using the same method, a slight rise in the S:JM SNGFR ratio after induction of chronic water diuresis (9). Whether these conflicting results (78) versus (9, 45) are due to the different methods used is not clear.

Abundant evidence should be available on the effect of renal perfusion pressure (RPP) on the distribution of nephron GFR. Surprisingly, however, only limited data have been reported in the literature dealing with this problem. No definite conclusion can be drawn from the studies comparing superficial SNGFR measured by micropuncture versus total kidney GFR in circumstances in which RPP has been lowered either by hemorrhagic hypotension, phentolamine administration, or aortic constriction. A proportionately greater reduction in the superficial SNGFR than in the simultaneously determined total kidney GFR was reported in both dogs (97) and rats (26) by some investigators, while others found no change in distribution (27, 42, 86, 114).

In only one study has direct measurement of both superficial and juxtamedullary SNGFR been made before and after a reduction in renal perfusion pressure by aortic constriction. Both the superficial and juxtamedullary SNGFR remained relatively stable in the autoregulatory range (70–130 mmHg) and decreased in parallel below this range (25). Coelho et al (42) utilizing the Hanssen technique also found no redistribution in both hydropenic and saline-loaded rats when the renal perfusion pressure was reduced by hemorrhagic hypotension.

It has been known for several years that acute elevations in the renal perfusion pressure result in a parallel increase in the urinary excretion of sodium even when the filtered load of sodium is maintained constant (3, 13, 44, 52, 87, 125, 126, 144). Recently, Lameire & Kunau (92) showed that this natriuresis could not be attributed to enhanced sodium delivery from the late distal tubule of superficial nephrons but could have been due to greater delivery of sodium out of more inner cortical nephrons. It is therefore, particularly relevant to note that de Rouffignac et al (115), using the ferrocyanide method, observed a constancy of SNGFR of both superficial and juxtamedullary nephrons after acute elevation of the RPP to 175 mmHg after bilateral carotid clamping. A constant relationship between the change in superficial SNGFR and total kidney GFR has also been found after acute elevation of the renal perfusion pressure in both dog (97) and rat (27). Studies on the effect of chronic hypertension, induced by chronic unilateral renal ischemia, also reveal conflicting results. By direct cortical and papillary micropuncture, Stumpe et al found a constant superficial SNGFR and an increase in the juxtamedullary SNGFR indicating redistribution to the juxtamedullary nephrons (140). With the ferrocyanide technique, however, de Rouffignac et al (115) found exactly the opposite pattern of filtrate distribution.

A number of investigators have evaluated the relationship between changes in extracellular fluid volume and the distribution of SNGFR. This relationship may be of major physiologic significance since it has been suggested that alterations in filtrate and blood flow distribution may modify urinary sodium excretion (17).

These studies are summarized in Table 3. Included are only studies where both superficial and juxtamedullary SNGFR's were measured and attention has been given to the different protocols used to induce changes in sodium balance (sodium

Table 3 Effect of changes in Na$^+$ balance on distribution of SNGFR

A. Micropuncture method (nl/min g kidney)

	Superficial	Juxtamedullary	Conclusions	Species	Reference
Chronic salt restriction	23.5	58.3	Red JM	Rat	73
Chronic salt load	38.1	16.5	Red Sup	(100 g)	—
Control	24.0	58.3	—	Rat	77
Acute salt load	35.3	75.4	Red Sup	(60–80 g)	—

B. Ferrocyanide method (P = pulse injection; I = infusion technique) (nl/min)

Study no.			Superficial	Intermediate	Juxtamedullary	Conclusions	Species	Reference
1	P	Control	27.9	33.3	38.5		Rat	116
		Chronic salt load	52.4	51.7	52.7	Red Sup		
2	P	Chronic salt load	—	—	—	Red Sup	Rat	10
		Acute salt load	—	—	—	Red Sup		
3	P	Control	—	—	—		Rat	42
		Acute salt load	—	—	—	Red Sup		
		Chronic salt load	—	—	—	Red Sup		
4	P	Control	—	—	—		Rat	37
		Acute salt load	—	—	—	No Red	(conscious)	
5	I	Control	29.0	27.0	35.9		Rat	116
		Chronic salt load	44.7	42.8	49.0	Red Sup		
6	I	Control	40.4	38.7	48.6		Rat	38
		Chronic salt load	44.9	45.1	57.6	No Red		
7	I	Control	39.0	—	49.4		Rat	110
		Chronic salt load + Acute salt load	50.8	—	66.9	No Red		
8	I	Chronic salt load	—	—	—	No Red	Rat (conscious)	39
9	I	Control	—	—	—		Dog	34
		Acute salt load	—	—	—	No Red		
10	I	Control	60	—	72		Dog	31
		Acute salt load	74	—	65	Red Sup		
11	P	Control	27.9	33.3	38.5		Rat	116
		Chronic salt restriction	32.1	42.8	49.1	No Red		
12	P	Chronic salt restriction				No Red	Rat	10
13	I	Control	40.4	38.7	48.6		Rat	38
		Chronic salt restriction	37.7	—	53.7	No Red		
14	I	Chronic salt restriction	—	—	—	No Red	Rat (conscious)	39

Abbreviations: P = Pulse injection
I = Infusion method
No Red = No redistribution
Red JM = Redistribution towards juxtamedullary nephrons
Red Sup = Redistribution towards superficial nephrons

restriction or loading, acute or chronic). From inspection of Table 3, it is obvious that the issue has not yet been resolved. Surprisingly enough, to our knowledge, only two micropuncture studies have been performed where the effect of changes in sodium balance on the distribution of SNGFR was directly examined by measuring both superficial and juxtamedullary nephron filtration rates (73, 78). Both studies showed a redistribution of the filtrate toward the superficial nephrons. In the acute saline loading study, however, the changes were quite small (78), and there was considerable scatter in the data. In addition, the "shift" in SNGFR distribution is quantitatively different, with the S:JM ratio being 2.30 after chronic salt loading and only 0.47 in the acute study. As pointed out before, these studies were performed in young animals.

The indirect micropuncture studies comparing the change in superficial SNGFR and total kidney GFR after acute volume expansion are also quite disparate (5, 20, 27, 124, 132). Moreover, in the dog, redistribution of filtrate to outer cortical nephrons was noted when a previously punctured tubule was restudied during acute volume expansion (132). In contrast, no redistribution was found when a freshly punctured tubule was utilized (99, 138). This phenomenon is presumably due to artifactual alterations in intratubular dynamics in the repunctured tubule. A similar artifact has not been noted in the rat (2, 27, 43).

Numerous studies of the distribution of SNGFR after changes in sodium balance have been studied with the ferrocyanide technique. In Table 3, these studies are listed in relation to the method used for the administration of the glomerular marker, either a pulse injection (P) or an infusion method (I). With a few exceptions, whenever the glomerular indicator was injected as a pulse, a superficial redistribution of SNGFR was observed after both chronic or acute salt loading. With the infusion method, redistribution was rarely noted. Recently, Charbardès and associates (35) attributed this discrepancy to a possible artifactual "streaming" effect of the pulse injection of ferrocyanide during extracellular volume expansion. However, exceptions should be noted: Two recent studies performed in the dog after acute volume expansion in which the infusion method was utilized yielded conflicting results. In one (34), no redistribution was noted while in the other (31), a redistribution of the filtrate to the superficial nephrons was found. Furthermore, despite the use of a bolus injection, Clausen & Tysseboth (37) did not observe a redistribution in conscious rats. Finally, Baines (9, 10) using the ferrocyanide method found a redistribution of SNGFR after acute volume expansion only in young rats, while no redistribution was detected in larger rats (>250 gm). He suggested that structural changes with age may modify the response of SNGFR distribution to volume expansion.

Recently, attention was given to a possible redistribution of SNGFR in two experimental models of chronic salt retention in rats. Stumpe et al (141), using the ferrocyanide infusion method, found an unchanged ratio of superficial to juxtamedullary SNGFR after induction of heart failure. On the other hand, Yarger (156) with the same method, found a redistribution of filtrate to outer cortical nephrons, 4–10 days after ligation of the common bile duct.

INTRARENAL DISTRIBUTION OF BLOOD/PLASMA FLOW

From studies utilizing the inert gas washout method, Barger and associates predicted that a natriuresis will occur with a redistribution of blood flow to outer cortical nephrons while the converse will be seen in salt-retaining states (17). Results obtained with the radioactive microsphere method, a technique which measures more directly regional blood flow in the renal cortex, seemingly conflict with data obtained with the inert-gas washout method. Before reviewing these results, it seems necessary to evaluate critically both the inert-gas washout and the radioactive microsphere method. Other techniques used to evaluate intrarenal distribution of blood flow have been recently reviewed elsewhere (134).

With the inert gas method, a bolus of a radioactive gas such as ^{85}Kr or ^{133}Xe is injected into the renal artery. An index of renal blood flow is obtained by measurement of the removal rate of the radioactive gas, using the following formula: $F/V = K\lambda/e$, where F equals blood flow in ml/min, V is the distribution volume of the gas, K is the disappearance rate of the gas, λ is the partition coefficient of the gas between renal tissue and blood, and e is the specific gravity of the tissue. The washout curve is obtained with an external detector placed above the kidney. As first shown by Thorburn et al (142), the washout curve obtained from the kidney is multiexponential indicating an undefined number of compartments with differing flow rates. In this regard, autoradiographic comparison has been used to correlate the different components of the curve with specific anatomical areas of the kidney (142).

The most important theoretical and practical considerations concerning the washout method in general and its application to the measurement of intrarenal distribution of blood flow in particular can be summarized as follows: 1. This method does not measure blood flow, but flow per volume and K may be unchanged in spite of marked changes in flow if the volume of a given area is not constant. 2. The use of a given partition coefficient (λ) in various experimental conditions has not been validated. 3. There are experimental data indicating that complete equilibration of the gas does not occur (24). 4. The use of the washout method is further complicated by the inability to define what component of the curve is related to the blood flow in a given anatomical area of the renal parenchyma. In a comparison with radioactive microspheres, two groups of investigators (94, 127) were unable to correlate the second component of the curve with any specific cortical area. Therefore a precise profile of regional cortical flow rates cannot be obtained with the inert gas method.

In recent years, synthetic radiolabeled microspheres with a specific gravity varying from 1.1 to 1.6, have been used to measure the intrarenal distribution of blood flow. After injection of 15 μm spheres into the arterial circulation (left ventricle or left atrium), the particles are almost exclusively trapped in the glomerular capillary bed. Extensive experience has accumulated with this method in a number of laboratories and it seems that the microsphere method serves as an index of the glomerular perfusion rate (91, 100, 127, 136). Several investigators have found, in the hydropenic dog, that approximately 75% of total renal blood flow was distributed in the outer half of the renal cortex and approximately 25% in the inner half of the cortex (91, 100, 136). Cutting the renal cortex into four equidistant sections permits an even more precise estimation of the intracortical blood flow distribution. If the innermost fourth of the renal cortex primarily contains juxtamedullary nephrons whose efferent arterioles supply the medulla, the flow rate in this zone may be used as an index of total medullary blood flow, since it has been shown that virtually no microspheres can be detected in the medulla, indicating that the blood flow to this area first goes through a glomerular capillary (136). According to the data of Stein et al (136), the flow in this zone represents approximately 10% of total renal blood flow.

Because of the unique arborization of the renal circulation, the possible effect of axial streaming of the microspheres must be considered. It is very unlikely that a significant intrarenal streaming of erythrocytes occurs, since superficial nephron filtration fraction calculated from either efferent arteriolar hematocrit or protein concentration was not significantly different in both the dog (85, 135) and the rat (29). Further evidence that the distribution of microspheres within the dog kidney is not altered by axial streaming has been summarized by Stein et al (134). In addition, Baehler and associates compared the fractional distribution of renal cortical blood flow with radioactive microspheres and labeled frog red cells, a particle which has the same density as a dog erythrocyte (6). There was no difference in cortical blood flow distribution between the markers in control animals, during acetylcholine administration, or during hemorrhagic hypotension. These results clearly demonstrated that the density of the microspheres did not artifactually alter the distribution of renal cortical blood flow obtained with this method.

The most pertinent results obtained with radioactive microspheres in various experimental settings is summarized in Table 4. Several comments can be made concerning these results. First, the change in fractional distribution of blood flow noted is seemingly primarily dependent on the concomitant change in renal resistance. In virtually all of the models associated with a redistribution of blood flow to inner cortical nephrons (acetylcholine, bradykinin, dopamine, PGE, SQ20881, minoxodil, saline diuresis in anesthetized dogs, elevated ureteral pressure, elevated renal venous pressure, and aortic constriction), renal resistance fell. The only excep-

Table 4 Summary of regional blood studies in the dog as determined by the radioactive microsphere method

Model	Sodium excretion (uEq/min)	Renal blood flow (ml/min)	Renal resistance (mmHg/ml/min)	Fractional cortical blood flow (%) Z_1	Z_4	Reference
1 Acetylcholine	↑	↑	↓	↓	↓	136
2 Bradykinin	↑	↑	↓	↓	↑	136
3 Dopamine	↑	↑	↓	↓	↑	70
4 PGE	↑	↑	↓	↓	↑	112
5 SQ 20881	↑	↑	↓	↓	↑	7
6 Saline diuresis, anesthetized	↑	↑	↓	↓	↑	23, 138
7 Saline diuresis, conscious	↑	=	=	↑		65
8 Furosemide	↑	↑	↓	↓	↓	96, 137
9 Minoxodil	↓	=	↓	↓	↑	157
10 Elevated ureteral pressure	↓	↑	↓	↓	↑	1, 21, 91
11 Elevated renal venous pressure	↓	=	↓	↓	↑	1
12 Aortic constriction	↓	=	↓	↓	↑	90, 100, 133
13 Hemorrhagic hypotension	↓	↓	=↑	↓	↑	91, 111
14 Chlorothiazide	↑	=↓	=↑	=	=	137
15 Ethacrynic acid	↑	↑	↓	↑	=	101
16 Mannitol	↑	↑	↓	=	=	91, 101
17 Norepinephrine	↓	↓	↑	=	=	91, 111
18 Angiotensin	↓	↓	↑	=	=	91, 111
19 Sympathetic nerve stimulation	↓	↓	↑	=	=	133
20 Prostaglandin inhibition	=↓	↓	↑	↑	↓	80, 84, 93

Abbreviations; Z_1 = outer cortical zone 1; Z_4 = inner cortical zone 4; ↓ = decrease; ↑ = increase; = = no change; =↓ = no change or decrease.

tion was seen with furosemide administration (96, 137), and this may relate to a greater rise in medullary interstitial pressure in this setting which would increase resistance in the post-glomerular circulation of juxtamedullary nephrons. In hemorrhagic hypotension, a similar redistribution of blood flow to inner cortical nephrons was noted (133). It was suggested that with hemorrhage, the fall in perfusion pressure initiates an autoregulatory renal vascular response, but that renal resistance was set at a higher level due to the concomitant release of humorally mediated vasoconstrictor substances plus enhanced sympathetic nerve activity. Table 4 also illustrates that most of the models associated with renal vasoconstriction have no alteration in cortical blood flow distribution (91, 111, 133). The exceptions are the inhibitors of prostaglandin synthesis which preferentially decrease juxtamedullary blood flow (80, 84, 93). Second, there is no correlation between the changes in regional blood flow distribution and urinary sodium excretion. Although a number of the natriuretic models are associated with inner cortical redistribution, antinatriuresis is also noted in other settings with the same alteration in regional blood flow (i.e. elevated ureteral pressure, elevated renal venous pressure, aortic constriction, minoxodil administration) (1, 21, 90, 91, 100, 133, 157). Thus, from these data, no strong case can be made for a relationship between the distribution of renal blood flow and the excretion of sodium in the urine.

The mechanism of the redistribution of cortical blood flow seen with renal vasodilatation is not clear. This change does not correlate with renal venous renin release or the delivery of sodium to the early distal tubule (134, 136). As suggested previously (133), it seems more likely that this phenomenon is due to intrinsic differences in the vascular tone of the various subpopulations of nephrons. The resistance in outer cortical nephrons may be set at a minimum level so that the absolute flow through these nephrons may be pressure dependent. In contrast, the more inner cortical nephrons may have a higher basal resistance and are therefore able to respond appropriately to drug-induced vasodilatation, a reduction in renal perfusion pressure, and other stimuli which reduce renal resistance.

Although several groups have demonstrated a redistribution of blood flow to inner cortical nephrons during acute extracellular expansion in the anesthetized dog (23, 138), contradictory results have been found in the conscious dog (65) and anesthetized rat (148). The findings in the unanesthetized dog are surprising and deserve further evaluation. The behavior of the rat in response to an acute saline load could be due to species difference although adequate rheologic evaluation of microspheres in this species has not been performed as yet.

Recently, Migdal and associates examined the mechanism of cortical blood flow redistribution during acute saline loading in the dog (102). Hemodilution without volume expansion or with intravascular volume expansion alone resulted in a superficial redistribution of blood flow. This effect was attributed to a fall in hematocrit per se. They concluded that the opposite pattern of regional blood flow distribution seen during acute saline loading was a consequence of expansion of the intrarenal interstitial volume.

Table 5 summarizes results from three different microsphere studies that examined the effects of chronic alterations in sodium balance on the distribution of

Table 5 Effect of chronic changes in sodium balance on distribution of intracortical blood flow as determined by the radioactive microsphere method

Species	Salt intake		Outer cortex (ml/min g)	Inner cortex (ml/min g)	Conclusions	Reference
Rat	Low	3 weeks	8.10	3.41	—	95
	Normal		8.65	3.60	No Red	
	High		8.85	3.76	No Red	
Rabbit	Low	1 week	5.7	2.3	Red JM	103
	Normal		7.2	2.8	—	
	High		9.8	3.6	Red Sup	
			ml/min	ml/min		
Rabbit	Low	1 week	71.6	32.2	Red JM	150
	Normal		88.2	35.6	—	

Abbreviations: No Red = No redistribution

Red JM = Redistribution towards juxtamedullary nephrons

Red Sup = Redistribution towards superficial nephrons

cortical blood flow (95, 103, 150). As can be noted from the table, a species difference again seems to be present. In the rat, there was no significant difference in the ratio of outer to inner cortical blood flow between normal rats and those that had been on either a low or high salt diet for three weeks (95). In contrast, two separate studies in the rabbit demonstrate an increase in the OC:IC ratio as sodium intake was increased in animals either on a low or normal sodium intake (103, 150). In both of these latter studies, the authors suggested that an increase in sodium intake preferentially decreased renin release in outer cortical nephrons.

On the basis of the consistent results found in the anesthetized dog during acute extracellular expansion (redistribution of blood flow to inner cortical nephrons), at least two separate mechanisms, which involve heterogeneity of nephron function, capable of modulating sodium excretion in this setting may be devised: 1. a selective decrease in filtration fraction in inner cortical nephrons, and 2. washout of medullary solutes.

In studies in the cat, Nissen calculated the filtration fraction from the protein concentration of the post-glomerular circulation of the superficial and inner cortical nephrons. He found that the filtration fraction of plasma entering the inner cortex is less than that of plasma entering the outer cortex in control conditions (105). The same investigator subsequently observed a greater fall of the filtration fraction in the inner cortex than in the outer cortex after loading with either mannitol or Ringer's solution (106). Micropuncture studies in the rat by Daugharty et al (45) and by Barratt and associates (18) also indicated that the filtration fraction fell to a greater extent in inner cortical nephrons during loading with Ringer's solution. Finally, Bruns and associates (31), using dogs, measured both glomerular blood flow and nephron filtration rate in the same animal, and from these data, nephron filtration fraction was calculated. The superficial nephron filtration fraction remained unchanged at 0.31 in both hydropenia and after acute volume expansion; in contrast, the juxtamedullary nephron filtration fraction decreased from 0.34 in hydropenia to 0.24 after volume expansion.

Assuming a direct relationship between peritubular capillary oncotic pressure and proximal tubule sodium reabsorption (28, 29, 54, 85), a greater fall in filtration fraction in juxtamedullary nephrons could lead to a greater increase in distal sodium delivery in these nephrons during extracellular volume expansion. Of possible relevance, Stein, Osgood & Kunau (139) recently compared the delivery of sodium to the end of the distal tubule of superficial nephrons with the delivery to the base of the papillary collecting duct during Ringer loading. The fractional sodium delivery to the papillary base was greater than the fractional delivery to the end of the distal tubule of superficial nephrons (12% versus 8% of the filtered load). These findings suggest that the deeper nephrons deliver more sodium to the collecting duct in this setting.

Earley & Friedler proposed an alternative mechanism whereby an increase in inner cortical and presumably medullary blood flow could influence sodium excretion (50, 51). They suggested that an increase in medullary blood flow, as occurs with saline loading (129), will produce a marked reduction in medullary interstitial hypertonicity. If it is assumed that the reabsorption of sodium by the ascending limb of Henle's loop proceeds to a minimal concentration, then the net sodium delivery to the distal tubule would be highly dependent upon the volume of fluid entering the ascending limb. Washout of the high solute concentration of the medullary interstitium by increased medullary blood flow would reduce the osmotic movement of water out of the descending limb. A larger volume of tubular fluid with the same amount of sodium, but at a lower sodium concentration, would enter the water-impermeable ascending limb. Reabsorption of sodium to the same minimal concentration in the ascending limb would result in the delivery of a larger volume of fluid and an increased total amount of sodium beyond the loop of Henle. This alteration would be most marked in the inner cortical nephrons whose loops descend to the tip of the papilla and are therefore normally surrounded by the most hypertonic milieu. This mechanism could also explain the recent data obtained by Stein et al, who showed a higher fractional sodium delivery to the base of the papilla than to the superficial late distal tubule (139) after acute Ringer loading.

DIFFERENCES IN TRANSPORT CHARACTERISTICS OF SUPERFICIAL AND JUXTAMEDULLARY NEPHRONS

To this point, the discussion has focused on evidence pro and con that blood flow and glomerular filtrate are redistributed in various experimental models. In addition, two hemodynamic mechanisms have been proposed that might lead to disproportionate reduction in sodium transport in juxtamedullary nephrons: 1. a greater fall in filtration fraction in deep nephrons; and 2. washout of medullary solute. It might seem surprising that no comment has been made concerning the possible differences in the intrinsic transport properties of superficial and juxtamedullary nephrons. Very little information, however, is available on this issue. Kawamura et al (81) recently demonstrated major electrophysiologic differences between these two nephron populations. Utilizing the isolated perfused straight proximal tubule of the rabbit, these investigators found no difference in fluid reabsorption, transtubular potential difference (PD) during perfusion with an artificial ultrafiltrate of plasma, or in the response to ouabain. Yet, with addition of a tubular perfusate containing a high chloride concentration, disparate PD's were found in superficial and juxtamedullary tubules, +1.6 and −1.3 mV, respectively. These differences, although small, were highly significant. From these experiments and isotopic permeability studies, the authors concluded that the superficial straight tubule is twice as permeable to chloride as sodium while the converse was true in juxtamedullary nephrons. Subsequent studies from the same laboratory have shown that this difference in permselectivity in superficial and juxtamedullary nephrons is also generally present in the convoluted portion of the proximal tubule (75).

Some evidence exists that an important fraction of proximal tubular reabsorption may be driven by passive chloride flux down a chemical gradient from lumen to blood generated by selective (active) reabsorption of $NaHCO_3$ (190). If correct, then the overall amount of filtrate reabsorbed by proximal tubules could depend in part on the passive permeability to chloride. As noted above (81), the pars recta of juxtamedullary nephrons may be less permeable to Cl than the pars recta of superficial nephrons. If so, then a larger fraction of filtrate may escape reabsorption in deeper nephrons and studies of superficial tubules may underestimate delivery of tubular fluid distally during maneuvers that increase filtration rate and/or depress proximal tubular reabsorption. Such reabsorptive heterogeneity could influence overall excretion of sodium without necessitating heterogeneity of blood flow or nephron filtration rates per se.

Warnock & Burg (149) recently demonstrated heterogeneity of bicarbonate transport in superficial and juxtamedullary nephrons. These investigators also used the isolated tubular perfusion technique and found that the steady-state total CO_2 concentration was considerably higher in superficial than in juxtamedullary nephrons, 16 versus 9 mM. They further noted that the pump rate was the same in both segments while the leak rate-constant was three times greater in superficial nephrons.

Thus, differences in the functional properties of superficial and juxtamedullary nephrons have now been established. What relationship these findings may have to overall nephron transport of sodium and its attendant anions is not clear. Yet, continued investigation in this area may establish major differences in transport between superficial and juxtamedullary nephrons which have important implications with respect to the regulation of electrolyte transport.

HETEROGENEITY OF FUNCTION WITHIN THE SAME NEPHRON SEGMENT

Proximal Tubule

Virtually all information concerning heterogeneity of function has been obtained with the isolated tubule technique. Probably the first demonstration of heterogeneity of function within a given nephron segment was reported by Tune, Burg, & Patlak in 1969 (145). They evaluated the transport of the organic acid, para-aminohippurate (PAH) in the proximal convoluted tubule and pars recta of the rabbit, and found that fluid absorption was approximately twofold greater in the convoluted portion of the proximal tubule but that PAH secretion was almost four times greater in the pars recta. This observation was subsequently confirmed by Grantham and his associates (62). Recently, Woodhall et al (153) further evaluated this finding. They compared the transport and histologic characteristics of different segments of the pars recta of superficial (SF) and juxtamedullary (JM) nephrons and found that the SF pars recta was approximately four times as long as the JM segment in the New Zealand white rabbit. Light and electron microscopy revealed that the cell structure in the upper third of the SF straight segment was markedly different from that of the lower third of SF straight segments. JM straight segments contained only one cell type which was similar to that in the lower third of the SF straight segment. In addition, PAH secretion in the upper third of the SF pars recta was 1393×10^{-15} mole mm^{-1} min^{-1} compared with 318 and 248×10^{-15} mole mm^{-1} min^{-1} in the lower third of SF and in JM pars recta respectively. These findings, therefore, represent an example of heterogeneity in different nephron populations as well as in the same portion of a given nephron.

Chonko, Lowe, & Grantham (36) compared uric acid transport in various nephron segments. They noted that net secretion of uric acid occurred only in the pars recta of the isolated perfused rabbit nephron, and that it did not occur in the proximal convoluted tubule. Tune et al (146) also compared glucose transport in the convoluted and straight portion of the proximal tubule and found that transport was markedly greater in the convoluted portion. In addition, a preliminary report has suggested that net secretion of urea occurs in the pars recta, and not in the convoluted portion of the proximal tubule (82). Thus there are several major examples of differences in transport between the convoluted and straight portion of the proximal tubule.

In addition, recent evidence has also been presented which suggests heterogeneity within a given proximal convoluted tubule. Hamburger, Lawson, & Dennis (66) compared fluid absorption in the early and late portions of the proximal convoluted tubule and found the values to be quite different, 1.6 versus 0.5 nl mm^{-1} min^{-1} respectively. In addition, these investigators subsequently demonstrated that parathyroid hormone only altered fluid absorption in the early portion of the proximal tubule (67). Recently, Jacobson & Kokko (75) have further characterized differences between various segments of the proximal convoluted tubule. In the first mm of the superficial proximal tubule, the permeability to sodium was greater than to chloride while in the remainder of this segment the reverse was true. In the juxtamedullary nephrons, the permeability to sodium was greater throughout the entire segment.

Distal Tubule

It is now becoming clear that the distal tubule is really a transitional area between the thick ascending limb and the cortical collecting tubule. Wright first described the increasing magnitude of the transepithelial potential difference (PD) along the distal convoluted tubule with values averaging –9 mV (lumen negative) in the early distal tubule and –52 mV in the late distal tubule (154). Recently, Barratt et al (19) even found a positive PD in the early distal tubule of the Munich-Wistar rat. They concluded that this segment had functional characteristics similar to that of the thick ascending limb.

Woodhall & Tisher (152) found morphologic differences in the response to vasopressin in early and late distal tubules of the rat. Cell swelling and dilatation of intercellular spaces, morphologic findings indicative of vasopressin responsiveness, were observed in the latter portion of the distal tubule and cortical collecting tubules but not in the early distal tubule. As these investigators noted, the epithelium of the late distal tubule is also quite distinct from that in the early distal tubule, and resembles the cortical collecting duct epithelium. In this regard, de Bermudez & Windhager (48) further evaluated the electrical differences between early and late distal tubules. They noted that the transverse specific electrical resistance fell along the length of the distal convoluted tubule of the hydropenic rat concomitant with the increasing magnitude of the PD. They also provided convincing evidence that the decrease in resistance along the distal tubule was primarily due to the increase in osmolality of late distal tubular fluid. In fact, there was a direct correlation between the osmolality of distal tubular fluid and the transepithelial conductance.

Gross, Imai & Kokko (64) noted that vasopressin increased water movement in the isolated cortical collecting tubule but not in the distal convolution. In addition, these same authors also compared several other functional characteristics of the distal tubule and cortical collecting tubule of the rabbit (64). In rabbits on a regular sodium intake, the PD of the distal convoluted tubule was consistently greater (–40 mV) than that of the cortical collecting tubule, which was approximately 0 in this setting. When the animal was placed on either a low salt diet or a high potassium diet plus a mineralocorticoid, the PD in the cortical collecting tubule was markedly increased to approximately –35 mV while no change occurred in the PD of the distal tubular segment. The authors concluded from these data that mineralocorticoids were the primary determinants of the electrogenic properties of the cortical collecting tubule but not the distal convoluted tubule. It should be emphasized, however, that the measurement of PD may not be analogous to the transport of sodium across a given nephron segment. This has been clearly shown by Cardinal and associates (33) in the isolated rabbit proximal convoluted tubule. In addition, there is excellent micropuncture data indicating that mineralocorticoids alter sodium transport along the distal tubule (71).

Recently, Morel and his group (104) developed a sophisticated and extremely sensitive assay to measure adenyl cyclase activity at the level of the individual tubular segment. Utilizing a microdissection technique, they found that the distal convoluted tubule in the rabbit can be divided into four components, from both the morphologic and functional standpoint. They measured basal adenyl cyclase activity and the response to parathyroid hormone (PTH), arginine vasopressin (AVP), and isoproterenol (ISO) in these microdissected subunits of the distal tubule. The very first portion, designated DCTa, was located immediately after the macula densa, and had the appearance of a thick ascending limb. Adenyl cyclase in this segment was greatly stimulated by PTH, slightly by AVP, and not at all by ISO. The second portion had a brilliant appearance and was therefore called the bright portion of the distal tubule (DCTb); adenyl cyclase was stimulated by sodium fluoride but not by PTH, AVP, or ISO. The third portion, which was granular in appearance (DCTg) and resembled the arched portion of the cortical collecting tubule, had a high basal adenyl cyclase level and responded markedly to PTH and ISO. The fourth portion was light in appearance (DCTl) and resembled what the authors called the light portion of the cortical collecting tubule. It was present only in the superficial cortex and responded well to AVP, moderately to ISO, and was not altered by PTH. Thus these beautiful studies clearly demonstrate the structural and functional correlation of heterogeneous function within a given nephron segment.

Collecting Duct

In the previous section, we described the complexities of functional and structural heterogeneity within the so-called distal convoluted tubule and why the late distal tubule might be more appropriately called the first portion of the cortical collecting tubule. It should be emphasized, however, that the cortical collecting tubule has several functional characteristics distinct from the more distal portions of the collecting duct system. First, urea permeability is much lower in the cortical collecting tubule than in the medullary collecting duct (113). Second, Tisher & Yarger (143) demonstrated that the permeability to lanthanum across the tight junction is much less in the cortical collecting tubule than in the more distal segments. Third, Grantham and associates (63) noted net addition of potassium along the isolated cortical collecting tubule of the rabbit, while in micropuncture studies of the papillary collecting duct, either no net transport or reabsorption of potassium has been noted in a variety of models (49, 139). Thus this segment of the nephron also has clearly defined heterogeneous properties.

CONCLUSIONS

Although extensive studies have been performed in many laboratories throughout the world, utilizing a variety of techniques to measure SNGFR, the change in this parameter in various pathophysiologic states is still not well delineated.

It seems certain that the juxtamedullary SNGFR is higher than the superficial SNGFR during hydropenia. During either acute or chronic alterations in sodium balance, the results are variable. This may relate to methodologic problems and/or the particular design of individual studies. From these data one might conclude, however, that alteration in the distribution of glomerular filtrate per se is unlikely to be a major determinant of the regulation of sodium balance in these models.

On the other hand, measurement of regional blood flow with the radioactive microsphere method, at least in the dog, has produced more consistent results. In virtually all models associated with a fall in renal resistance, there is a redistribution of blood flow to inner cortical nephrons. This hemodynamic alteration may modify sodium excretion by causing a disproportionate fall in filtration fraction in more inner cortical nephrons and/or reducing the medullary interstitial hypertonicity.

With the development of the isolated tubular perfusion method, it is now possible to compare the transport properties of segments of superficial and juxtamedullary nephrons. These types of experiments should help to determine whether there are physiologically significant intrinsic differences between various populations of nephrons.

Literature Cited

1. Abe, Y., Kishimoto, T., Yamamoto, K., Ueda, J. 1973. Intrarenal distribution of blood flow during ureteral and venous pressure elevation. *Am. J. Physiol.* 224:746–51

2. Andreucci, V. E., Herrera-Acosta, J., Rector, F. C. Jr., Seldin, D. W. 1971. Measurement of single-nephron glomerular filtration rate by micropuncture: Analysis of error. *Am. J. Physiol.* 221:1551–59

3. Aperia, A. C., Broberger, C. G. O., Söderlund, S. 1971. Relationship between renal artery pressure and tubular sodium reabsorption. *Am. J. Physiol.* 220:1205–12

4. Arataki, M. 1926. On the postnatal growth of the kidney with special reference to the number and size of the glomeruli (albino rat). *Am. J. Anat.* 36:399–436

5. Auld, R. B., Alexander, E. A., Levinsky, N. G. 1970. Nephron filtration and proximal reabsorption during saline infusion, arterial clamping, and hemorrhage in the dog. *J. Clin. Invest.* 59:5a (Abstr.)

6. Baehler, R. W., Catanzaro, A., Stein, J. H., Hunter, W. 1973. The radiolabelled frog red blood cell: A new marker of cortical blood flow distribution in the kidney of the dog. *Circ. Res.* 32:718–24

7. Bailie, M. D., Barbour, J. A. 1975. Effect of inhibition of peptidase activity on distribution of intrarenal blood flow. *Am. J. Physiol.* 228:850–53

8. Baines, A. D. 1971. Effect of extracellular fluid volume expansion on maximum glucose reabsorption rate and glomerulo-tubular balance in single rat nephrons. *J. Clin. Invest.* 50:2414–25

9. Baines, A. D. 1972. SNGFR redistribution: A structurally determined phenomenon in young rats. *Int. Congr. Nephrol., Mexico, 5th,* p. 7. (Abstr.)

10. Baines, A. D. 1973. Redistribution of nephron function in response to chronic and acute sodium loads. *Am. J. Physiol.* 224:237–44

11. Baines, A. D., de Rouffignac, C. 1969. Functional heterogeneity of nephrons. II. Filtration rates, intraluminal flow velocities and fractional water reabsorption. *Pfluegers Arch.* 308:260–76

12. Baker, J. T., Kleinman, L. I. 1973. Glucose reabsorption in the newborn dog kidney. *Proc. Soc. Exp. Biol. Med.* 142:716–19

13. Bank, N., Aynedjian, H. S., Bansal, V. K., Goldman, D. M. 1970. Effect of acute hypertension on sodium transport by the distal nephron. *Am. J. Physiol.* 219:275–80

14. Bankir, L., Farman, N. 1973. Hèterogèneité des glomerules chez le lapin. *Arch. Anat. Microsc. Morphol. Exp.* 62:287–91

15. Bankir, L., Farman, N., Grünfeld, J. P., Huet de la Tour, E., Funck-Brentano, J. L. 1973. Radioactive microsphere distribution and single glomerular blood flow in the normal rabbit kidney. *Pfluegers Arch.* 342:111–23

16. Bankir, L., de Rouffignac, C., Grünfeld, J. P., Sabto, J., Funck-Brentano, J. L. 1975. Single glomerular blood flow and single glomerular filtration rate in the hydropenic rabbit kidney. In *Radionuclides in Nephrology,* ed. K. ZumWinkel, M. D. Blaufox, J. L. Funck-Brentano, pp. 2–8. Stuttgart: Thieme

17. Barger, A. C. 1961. Renal hemodynamic factors in congestive heart failure. *Ann. N.Y. Acad. Sci.* 139:276–84

18. Barratt, L. J., Wallin, J. D., Rector, F. C. Jr., Seldin, D. W. 1973. Influence of volume expansion on single-nephron filtration rate and plasma flow in the rat. *Am. J. Physiol.* 224:643–50

19. Barratt, L. J., Rector, F. C. Jr., Kokko, J. P., Tisher, C. C., Seldin, D. W. 1975. Transepithelial potential difference profile of the distal tubule of the rat kidney. *Kidney Int.* 8:368–75

19a. Barratt, L. J., Rector, F. C. Jr., Kokko, J. P., Seldin, D. W. 1974. Factors governing the transepithelial potential difference across the proximal tubule of the rat kidney. *J. Clin. Invest.* 53:454–64

20. Bartoli, E., Earley, L. E. 1971. The relative contribution of reabsorptive rate and redistributed nephron filtration rate to changes in proximal tubular fractional reabsorption during acute saline infusion and aortic constriction in the rat. *J. Clin. Invest.* 50:2191–2203

21. Bay, W. H., Stein, J. H., Rector, J. B., Osgood, R. W., Ferris, T. F. 1972. Redistribution of renal cortical blood flow during elevated ureteral pressure in the dog. *Am. J. Physiol.* 222:33–37

22. Beeuwkes, R., Bonventre, J. V. 1975. Tubular organization and vascular-tubular relations in the dog kidney. *Am. J. Physiol.* 229:695–713

23. Blantz, R. C., Katz, M. A., Rector, F. C. Jr., Seldin, D. W. 1971. Measurement of intrarenal blood flow: II. Effect of saline diuresis in the dog. *Am. J. Physiol.* 220:1914–20

24. Bolme, P., Edwall, L. 1970. Disappearance of ^{133}Xe and ^{125}I from skeletal muscle of the anesthetized dog during sympathetic cholinergic vasodilatation. *Acta Physiol. Scand.* 78:28–38

25. Bonvalet, J. P., Bencsath, P., de Rouffignac, C. 1972. Glomerular filtration rate of superficial and deep nephrons during aortic constriction. *Am. J. Physiol.* 222:599–606

26. Brenner, B. M., Bennett, C. M., Berliner, R. W. 1968. The relationship between glomerular filtration rate and sodium reabsorption by the proximal tubule of the rat nephron. *J. Clin. Invest.* 47:1358–74

27. Brenner, B. M., Daugharty, T. M., Ueki, I. F., Troy, J. L. 1971. Quantitative assessment of proximal tubule function in single nephrons of the rat kidney. *Am. J. Physiol.* 220:2058–67

28. Brenner, B. M., Falchuk, K. H., Keimowitz, R., Berliner, R. W. 1969. The relationship between peritubular capillary protein concentration and fluid reabsorption by the renal proximal tubule. *J. Clin. Invest.* 48:1519–31

29. Brenner, B. M. Galla, J. H. 1971. Influence of postglomerular hematocrit and protein concentration on rat nephron fluid transfer. *Am. J. Physiol.* 220: 148–61

30. Brown, J. J., Davies, D. L., Lever, A. F., Parker, R. A., Robertson, I. S. 1965. The assay of renin in single glomeruli in the normal rabbit and the appearance of the juxtaglomerular apparatus. *J. Physiol. London* 176:418–28

31. Bruns, F. J., Alexander, E. A., Riley, A. L., Levinsky, N. G. 1974. Superficial and juxtamedullary nephron function during saline loading in the dog. *J. Clin. Invest.* 53:971–79

32. Burg, M. B., Grantham, J. J., Abramow, M., Orloff, J. 1966. Preparation and study of fragments of single rabbit nephrons. *Am. J. Physiol.* 210:1293–98

33. Cardinal, J., Lutz, M. D., Burg, M. B., Orloff, J. 1975. Lack of relationship of potential difference to fluid absorption in the proximal renal tubule. *Kidney Int.* 7:94–102

34. Carrière, S., Boulet, P., Mathieu, A., Brunette, M. G. 1972. Isotonic saline loading and intrarenal distribution of glomerular filtration in dogs. *Kidney Int.* 2:191–96

35. Chabardès, D., Poujeol, P., Deiss, S., Bonvalet, J. P., de Rouffignac, C. 1974. Intrarenal glomerular filtration rate distribution in salt loaded rats: A study of different techniques using ferrocyanide ions. *Pfluegers Arch.* 349:191–202

36. Chonko, A. M., Lowe, C. M., Grantham, J. J. 1975. Uric acid secretion in isolated perfused rabbit kidney tubules: Comparison of proximal convoluted, proximal straight and cortical collecting segments. *Clin. Res.* 23:358A (Abstr.)

37. Clausen, G., Tysseboth, I. 1973. Intrarenal distribution of glomerular filtration in conscious rats during isotonic saline infusion. *Acta Physiol. Scand.* 89:289–95

38. Coelho, J. B. 1973. Effect of dietary sodium intake on the intrarenal distribution of nephron glomerular filtration rates in the rat. *Circ. Res.* 33:547–54

39. Coelho, J. B. 1974. Sodium metabolism and intrarenal distribution of nephron glomerular filtration rates in the unanesthetized rat. *Proc. Soc. Exp. Biol. Med.* 146:225–31

40. Coelho, J. B., Chien, K. C. H., Bradley, S. E. 1972. Measurement of single nephron glomerular filtration rate without micropuncture. *Am. J. Physiol.* 223: 832–39

41. Coelho, J. B., Chien, K. C. H., Stella, S. R., Bradley, S. E. 1971. Relationship of extraluminal tubular deposition of ferrocyanide to peritubular perfusion rate in cortical and medullary nephron seg-

ments of the rat kidney. *Circ. Res.* 29:21–28

42. Coelho, J. B., Stella, S. R., Chien, K. C. H., Bradley, S. E. 1970. Glomerular filtration rate in superficial and juxtamedullary nephrons during salt loading and hemorrhagic hypotension. *Clin. Res.* 18:496 (Abstr.)

43. Davidman, M., Lalone, R. C., Alexander, E., Levinsky, N. G. 1971. Some micropuncture techniques in the rat. *Am. J. Physiol.* 221:1110–14

44. Daugharty, T. M., Belleau, L. J., Martino, J. A., Earley, L. E. 1968. Interrelationship of physical factors affecting sodium reabsorption in the dog. *Am. J. Physiol.* 215:1442–47

45. Daugharty, T. M., Ueki, I. F., Nicholas, D. P., Brenner, B. M. 1972. Comparative renal effects of isoncotic and colloid-free volume expansion in the rat. *Am. J. Physiol.* 222:225–32

46. Davis, J. M., Schnermann, J. 1971. The effect of antidiuretic hormone on the distribution of nephron filtration rates in rats with hereditary diabetes insipidus. *Pfluegers Arch.* 330:323–34

47. Davis, J. M., Schnermann, J. 1972. Juxtamedullary filtration rate and urinary concentrating ability. *Int. Congr. Physiol.* 9:132 (Abstr.)

48. de Bermudez, L., Windhager, E. E. 1975. Osmotically induced changes in electrical resistance of distal tubules of rat kidney. *Am. J. Physiol.* 229:1536–46

49. Diezi, J., Michoud, P., Aceves, J., Giebisch, G. 1973. Micropuncture of electrolyte transport across papillary collecting duct of the rat. *Am. J. Physiol.* 224:623–34

50. Earley, L. E., Friedler, R. M. 1965. Changes in renal blood flow and possibly the intrarenal distribution of blood during the natriuresis accompanying saline loading in the dog. *J. Clin. Invest.* 44:929–41

51. Earley, L. E., Friedler, R. M. 1965. Studies on the mechanism of natriuresis accompanying increased renal blood flow and its role in the renal response to extracellular volume expansion. *J. Clin. Invest.* 44:1857–65

52. Earley, L. E., Friedler, R. M. 1966. The effects of combined renal vasodilatation and pressor agents on renal hemodynamics and the tubular reabsorption of sodium. *J. Clin. Invest.* 45:542–51

53. Edwards, J. G. 1956. Efferent arterioles of glomeruli in the juxtamedullary zone of human kidney. *Anat. Rec.* 125:521–29

54. Falchuk, K. H., Brenner, B. M., Tadokoro, M., Berliner, R. W. 1971. Oncotic and hydrostatic pressures in peritubular capillaries and fluid reabsorption by proximal tubule. *Am. J. Physiol.* 220:1427–33

55. Fetterman, G. H., Shuplock, N. A., Philipp, F. J., Gregg, H. S. 1965. The growth and maturation of human glomeruli and proximal convolutions from term to adulthood. *Pediatrics* 35:601–19

56. Flamenbaum, W., Hamburger, R. J. 1974. Superficial and deep juxtaglomerular apparatus renin activity of the rat kidney. *J. Clin. Invest.* 54:1373–81

57. Gavras, H., Brown, J. J., Lever, A. F., Robertson, J. I. S. 1970. Changes of renin in individual glomeruli in response to variations of sodium intake in the rabbit. *Clin. Sci.* 38:409–14

58. Ghouse, A. M., Schubert-Braun, G., Gertz, K. H., Boyland, J. W. 1969. The number of surface nephrons in the rat kidney. *Int. Congr. Nephrol. Congr. 4th* 1:103 (Abstr.)

59. Giebisch, G. 1972. Renal micropuncture techniques: A symposium. *Yale J. Biol. Med.* 45:187–456

60. Goodyer, A. V. N., Jaeger, C. A. 1955. Renal response to nonshocking hemorrhage. Role of the autonomic nervous system and of the renal circulation. *Am. J. Physiol.* 180:69–74

61. Granger, P., Dahlheim, H., Thurau, K. 1972. Enzyme activities of the single juxtaglomerular apparatus in the rat kidney. *Kidney Int.* 1:78–88

62. Grantham, J. J., Qualizza, P. B., Irwin, R. L. 1974. Net fluid secretion in proximal straight renal tubules in vitro, role of PAH. *Am. J. Physiol.* 226:191–97

63. Grantham, J. J., Burg, M. B., Orloff, J. 1970. The nature of transtubular sodium and potassium transport in isolated rabbit renal cortical tubules. *J. Clin. Invest.* 49:1815–26

64. Gross, J. B., Imai, M., Kokko, J. P. 1975. A functional comparison of the cortical collecting tubule and the distal convoluted tubule. *J. Clin. Invest.* 55:1284–94

65. Gutman, R. A., Applegate, C. W. 1975. Renal intracortical blood flow distribution, function and sodium excretion in response to saline loading of anesthetized and unanesthetized dogs. *Am. Soc. Nephrol.* p. 81 (Abstr.)

66. Hamburger, R. J., Lawson, N. L., Dennis, V. W. 1974. Effects of cyclic adeno-

sine nucleotides on fluid absorption by different segments of proximal tubules. *Am. J. Physiol.* 227:396–401

67. Hamburger, R. J., Lawson, N. L., Schwartz, J. H. 1975. Functional heterogeneity of superficial proximal tubules: Fluid absorption and response to parathyroid hormone. *Int. Congr. Nephrol., 6th,* p. 126 (Abstr.)

68. Hanssen, O. E. 1961. The relationship between glomerular filtration and length of the proximal convoluted tubule in mice. *Acta Pathol. Microbiol. Scand.* 53:265–79

69. Hanssen, O. E. 1963. Method for comparison of glomerular filtration in individual rat nephrons. *Int. Congr. Nephrol., 2nd,* p. 527 (Abstr.)

70. Hardaker, W. T. Jr., Wechsler, A. S. 1973. Redistribution of renal intracortical blood flow during dopamine infusion in dogs. *Circ. Res.* 33:437–44

71. Hierholzer, K., Wiederholt, W., Holzgreve, H., Giebisch, G., Klose, R. M., Windhager, E.E. 1965. Micropuncture study of renal transtubular concentration gradients of sodium and potassium in adrenalectomized rats. *Pfluegers Arch.* 285:193–210

72. Horiuchi, K., Tanaka, H., Yamamoto, K., Ueda, J. 1971. Distribution of renin in the dog kidney. *Life Sci.* 10:727–34

73. Horster, M., Thurau, K. 1968. Micropuncture studies on the filtration rate of single superficial and juxtamedullary glomeruli in the rat kidney. *Pfluegers Arch.* 301:162–81

74. Horster, M., Valtin, H. 1971. Postnatal development of renal function: Micropuncture and clearance studies in the dog. *J. Clin. Invest.* 50:779–95

75. Jacobson, H. R., Kokko, J. P. 1975. Intrinsic differences in various segments of proximal convoluted tubules. *Clin. Res.* 23:431A (Abstr.)

76. Jamison, R. L. 1970. Micropuncture study of superficial and juxtamedullary nephrons in the rat. *Am. J. Physiol.* 218:46–55

77. Jamison, R. L. 1972. Evidence for functional intrarenal heterogeneity obtained by micropuncture technique. *Yale J. Biol. Med.* 45:254–62

78. Jamison, R. L., Lacy, F. B. 1971. Effect of saline infusion on superficial and juxtamedullary nephrons in the rat. *Am. J. Physiol.* 221:690–97

79. Jose, P. A., Logan, A. G., Slotkoff, L. M., Lilienfield, L. S., Caleagno, P. L., Eisner, G. M. 1971. Intrarenal blood flow distribution in canine puppies. *Pediatr. Res.* 5:335–44

80. Kaloyanides, G. J., Ahrens, R. E., Shepherd, J. A., DiBona, G. F. 1976. Inhibition of prostaglandin E_2 secretion: Failure to abolish autoregulation in the isolated dog kidney. *Circ. Res.* 38:67–73

81. Kawamura, S., Imai, M., Seldin, D. W., Kokko, J. P. 1975. Characteristics of salt and water transport in superficial and juxtamedullary straight segments of proximal tubules. *J. Clin. Invest.* 55:1269–77

82. Kawamura, S., Kokko, J. P. 1975. Urea secretion by the straight segment of the proximal tubule. *Am. Soc. Nephrol.* p. 86 (Abstr.)

83. Kety, S. S. 1951. The theory and applications of the exchange of inert gas at the lungs and tissues. *Pharmacol. Rev.* 3:1–41

84. Kirschenbaum, M. A., White, N., Stein, J. H., Ferris, T. F. 1974. Redistribution of renal cortical blood flow during inhibition of prostaglandin synthesis. *Am. J. Physiol.* 227:801–5

85. Knox, F. G., Willis, L. R., Strandhoy, J. W., Schneider, E. G., Navar, L. G., Ott, C. E. 1972. Role of peritubule Starling forces in proximal reabsorption following albumin infusion. *Am. J. Physiol.* 223:741–49

86. Knox, F. G., Wright, F. S., Howards, S. S., Berliner, R. W. 1969. Effect of furosemide on sodium reabsorption by proximal tubule of the dog. *Am. J. Physiol.* 217:192–98

87. Koch, K. M., Aynedjian, H. S., Bank, N. 1968. Effect of acute hypertension on sodium reabsorption by the proximal tubule. *J. Clin. Invest.* 47:1696–1709

88. Kriz, W. 1967. Der architektonische und funktionelle Aufbau der Rattenniere. *Z. Zellforsch. Mikrosk. Anat.* 82:495–535

89. Kriz, W., Schnermann, J., Koepsell, H. 1972. The position of short and long loops of Henle in the rat kidney. *Z. Anat. Entwicklungsgesch.* 138:301–9

90. Lameire, N. H. 1974. Effect of autoregulation on the intracortical distribution of renal blood flow. *Arch. Int. Physiol. Biochem.* 82:410–13

91. Lameire, N. H. 1975. Onderzoekingen over de Aanpassingen van de Doorbloedings-Verdeling in de Nierschors. Phd thesis. Univ. Ghent, Belgium. 395 pp.

92. Lameire, N. H., Kunau, R. T. 1976. Renal perfusion pressure and sodium excretion. *Clin. Res.* 24:56A (Abstr.)

93. Lameire, N. H., Ringoir, S. 1974. Effect of prostaglandin synthesis inhibition with indomethacin on intracortical blood flow distribution during autoregulation of renal blood flow. *IRCS Libr. Compend.* 2:1433

94. Lameire, N. H., Ringoir, S. 1975. Comparison of the xenon washout method, the electromagnetic flowmeter, and radioactive microspheres for the measurement of renal blood flow. *Rein et Foie, Maladies de la Nutrition* 16:107–111

95. Lameire, N. H., Ringoir, S. 1975. Influence de différents apports sodés sur la distribution intracorticale du flux sanguin rénal. Etude avec microsphères chez le rat. *J. Urol. Nephrol.* 81:703–6

96. Lameire, N. H., Ringoir, S. 1974. The influence of furosemide on the distribution of renal blood flow in the normal and hypotensive dog. *Kidney Int.* 5:455 (Abstr.)

97. Liebau, G., Levine, D. Z., Thurau, K. 1968. Micropuncture studies on the dog kidney. I. The response of the proximal tubule to changes in systemic blood pressure within and below the autoregulatory range. *Pfluegers Arch.* 304:57–68

98. Ljungqvist, A. 1963. Fetal and postnatal development of intrarenal arterial pattern in man. *Acta Paediatr.* 52:443–64

99. Mandin, H., Israelit, A. H., Rector, F. C. Jr., Seldin, D. W. 1971. Effect of saline infusions on intrarenal distribution of glomerular filtrate and proximal reabsorption in the dog. *J. Clin. Invest.* 50:514–22

100. McNay, J. L., Abe, Y. 1970. Pressure-dependent heterogeneity of renal cortical blood flow in dogs. *Circ. Res.* 27:571–87

101. McNay, J. L., Abe, Y. 1970. Redistribution of cortical blood flow during renal vasodilatation in dogs. *Circ. Res.* 27:1023–32

102. Migdal, S., Alexander, E. A., Bruns, F. J., Riley, R. L., Levinsky, N. G. 1975. Effect of hemodilution on the distribution of renal blood flow. *Circ. Res.* 36:71–75

103. Mimran, A., Guiod, L., Hollenberg, N. K. 1974. The role of angiotensin in the cardiovascular and renal response to salt restriction. *Kidney Int.* 5:348–55

104. Morel, F., Chabardès, D., Imbert, M. 1976. Functional segmentation of the rabbit distal tubule by microdetermination of hormone-dependent adenylate cyclase activity. *Kidney Int.* 9:264–77

105. Nissen, O. I. 1966. The filtration fractions of plasma supplying the superficial and deep venous drainage area of the cat kidney. *Acta Physiol. Scand.* 68:275–85

106. Nissen, O. I. 1968. Changes in the filtration fractions in the superficial and deep venous drainage area of the cat kidney due to fluid loading. *Acta Physiol. Scand.* 73:320–28

107. Olbing, H., Blaufox, M. D., Aschinberg, L. C., Silkalns, G. I., Bernstein, J., Spitzer, A., Edelmann, C. M. Jr. 1973. Postnatal changes in renal glomerular blood flow distribution in puppies. *J. Clin. Invest.* 52:2885–95

108. Orloff, J., Burg, M. 1971. Kidney. *Ann. Rev. Physiol.* 33:83–130

109. Pai, H. C. 1935. Dissections of nephrons from the human kidney. *J. Anat.* 69:344–49

110. Poujeol, P., Chabardès, D., Bonvalet, J. P., de Rouffignac, C. 1975. Glomerular filtration rate and microsphere distributions in single nephron of rat kidney. *Pfluegers Arch.* 357:291–301

111. Rector, J. B., Stein, J. H., Bay, W. H., Osgood, R. W., Ferris, T. F. 1972. Effect of hemorrhage and vasopressor agents on distribution of renal blood flow. *Am. J. Physiol.* 222:1125–31

112. Riley, R. L. 1974. Effects of acute changes in renal cortical blood flow distribution on renal function in dogs. In *Recent Advances in Renal Physiology and Pharmacology,* ed. L. G. Wesson, G. M. Fanelli Jr., pp. 149–63. Baltimore: Univ. Park. 388 pp.

113. Rocha, A. S., Kokko, J. P. 1974. Permeability of medullary nephron segments to urea and water: Effect of vasopressin. *Kidney Int.* 6:379–87

114. Rodicio, J., Herrera-Acosta, J., Sellman, J. C., Rector, F. C. Jr., Seldin, D. W. 1969. Studies on glomerulotubular balance during aortic constriction, ureteral obstruction and venous occlusion in hydropenic and saline-loaded rats. *Nephron* 6:437–56

115. de Rouffignac, C., Berjal, G., Bencsath, P., Bonvalet, J. P. 1972. Relationship between some morphological and physiological factors and the single nephron glomerular filtration rate. In *Recent Advances in Renal Physiology,* pp. 207–24. Basel, Switzerland: Karger. 298 pp.

116. de Rouffignac, C., Bonvalet, J. P. 1970. Etude chez le rat des variations du debit individuel de filtration glomerulaire des nephrons superficiels et profonds en

fonction de l'apport sodé. *Pfluegers Arch.* 317:141–56

117. de Rouffignac, C., Bonvalet, J. P. 1972. Use of sodium ferrocyanide as glomerular indicator to study the functional heterogeneity of nephrons. *Yale J. Biol. Med.* 45:243–53

118. de Rouffignac, C., Bonvalet, J. P., Menard, J. 1974. Renin content in superficial and deep glomeruli of normal and salt-loaded rats. *Am. J. Physiol.* 226:150–54

119. de Rouffignac, C., Deiss, S., Bonvalet, J. P. 1970. Determination du taux individuel de filtration glomerulaire des néphrons accessible et inaccessible à la microponction. *Pfluegers Arch.* 315:273–90

120. de Rouffignac, C., Morel, F. 1967. Etude par microdissection de la distribution et de la longueur des tubules proximaux dans le rein de cinq espèces de rongeurs. *Arch. Anat. Microsc. Morphol. Exp.* 56:123–32

121. de Rouffignac, C., Morel, F. 1969. Micropuncture study of water, electrolytes, and urea movements along the loops of Henle in Psammomys. *J. Clin. Invest.* 48:474–86

122. Schmidt, U., Dubach, V. C. 1969. Differential enzymatic behavior of single proximal segments of the superficial and juxtamedullary nephron. I. Alkaline phosphatase, (Mg^{++}) ATPase and $(Na^{+}K^{+})$ ATPase. *Z. Ges. Exp. Med.* 151:93–102

123. Schmidt, U., Dubach, V. C. 1971. Differential enzymatic behavior of single proximal segments of the superficial and juxtamedullary nephron. II. Lactic-, isocitric-, malic-, glutamic- and glucose-6-phosphate dehydrogenases. *Z. Ges. Exp. Med.* 155:340–53

124. Schneider, E. G., Lynch, R. E., Dresser, T. P., Knox, F. G. 1970. Effect of saline infusion on superficial nephron filtration rate in the dog. *Physiologist* 13:303 (Abstr.)

125. Selkurt, E. E. 1951. Effect of pulse pressure and mean arterial pressure modification on renal hemodynamics and electrolyte and water excretion. *Circ. Res.* 4:541–51

126. Selkurt, E. E., Womack, I., Bailey, W. N. 1965. Mechanism of natriuresis and diuresis during elevated renal arterial pressure. *Am. J. Physiol.* 209:95–99

127. Slotkoff, L. M., Logan, A., Jose, P., D'Avella, J., Eisner, G. M. 1971. Microsphere measurement of intrarenal circulation of the dog. *Circ. Res.* 28:158–66

128. Smith, J. P. 1956. Anatomical features of the human renal glomerular efferent vessel. *J. Anat.* 90:290–92

129. Solez, K., Kramer, E. C., Fox, J. A., Heptinstall, R. H. 1974. Medullary plasma flow and intravascular leukocyte accumulation in acute renal failure. *Kidney Int.* 6:24–37

130. Sperber, I. 1944. Studies on the mammalian kidney. *Zool. Bidr. Uppsala* 22:249–431

131. Spitzer, A., Brandis, M. 1974. Functional and morphologic maturation of the superficial nephrons. *J. Clin. Invest.* 53:279–87

132. Stein, J. H., Barton, L. J., Mandin, H., Lacker, L. H., Rector, F. C. Jr., Seldin, D. W. 1969. Effect of extracellular volume expansion on proximal tubular sodium reabsorption and distribution of renal blood flow and glomerular filtrate in the dog. *Clin. Res.* 17:449 (Abstr.)

133. Stein, J. H., Boonjarern, S., Mauk, R. C., Ferris, T. F. 1973. Mechanism of the redistribution of renal cortical blood flow during hemorrhagic hypotension in the dog. *J. Clin. Invest.* 52:39–47

134. Stein, J. H., Boonjarern, S., Wilson, C. B., Ferris, T. F. 1973. Alterations in intrarenal blood flow distribution. Methods of measurement and relationship to sodium balance. *Circ. Res.* Suppl.: 1:32–33; 61–72

135. Stein, J. H., Congbalay, R. C., Karsh, D. L., Osgood, R. W., Ferris, T. F. 1972. Effect of bradykinin on proximal tubular sodium reabsorption in the dog: Evidence for functional nephron heterogeneity. *J. Clin. Invest.* 51:1709–21

136. Stein, J. H., Ferris, T. F., Huprich, J. E., Smith, T. C., Osgood, R. W. 1971. Effect of renal vasodilatation on the distribution of cortical blood flow in the kidney of the dog. *J. Clin. Invest.* 50:1429–38

137. Stein, J. H., Mauk, R. C., Boonjarern, S., Ferris, T. F. 1972. Differences in the effect of furosemide and chlorothiazide on the distribution of renal cortical blood flow in the dog. *J. Lab. Clin. Med.* 79:995–1003

138. Stein, J. H., Osgood, R. W., Ferris, T. F. 1972. Effect of volume expansion on distribution of glomerular filtrate and renal cortical blood flow in the dog. *Am. J. Physiol.* 223:984–90

139. Stein, J. H., Osgood, R. W., Kunau, R. T. Jr. 1976. Direct measurement of

papillary collecting duct sodium and potassium transport in the rat: Evidence for heterogeneity of nephron function. *Clin. Res.* 14:469A (Abstr.)

140. Stumpe, K. O., Lowitz, H. D., Ochwadt, B. 1969. Function of juxtamedullary nephrons in normotensive and chronically hypertensive rats. *Pfluegers Arch.* 313:43–52

141. Stumpe, K. O., Solle, H., Klein, H., Krück, F. 1973. Mechanism of sodium and water retention in rats with experimental heart failure. *Kidney Int.* 4:309–17

142. Thorburn, G. D., Kopald, H. H., Herd, J. A., Hollenberg, M., O'Morchoe, C. C. C., Barger, A. C. 1963. Intrarenal distribution of nutrient blood flow determined with Krypton[85] in the unanesthetized dog. *Circ. Res.* 13:290–307

143. Tisher, C. C., Yarger, W. E. 1975. Lanthanum permeability of tight junctions along the collecting duct of the rat. *Kidney Int.* 7:35–43

144. Tobian, L., Coffee, K., Ferreira, D., Meuli, J. 1964. The effect of renal perfusion pressure on net transport of sodium out of distal tubular urine as studied with the stop-flow technique. *J. Clin. Invest.* 43:118–28

145. Tune, B. M., Burg, M. B., Patlak, C. S. 1969. Characteristics of p-amminohippurate transport in proximal renal tubules. *Am. J. Physiol.* 217:1057–63

146. Tune, B. M., Burg, M. B. 1971. Glucose transport by proximal renal tubules. *Am. J. Physiol.* 221:580–85

147. Wahl, M. Schnermann, J. 1969. Microdissection study of the length of different tubular segments of rat superficial nephrons. *Z. Anat. Entwicklungsgesch.* 129:128–34

148. Wallin, J. D., Blantz, R. C., Katz, M. A., Andreucci, V. E., Rector, F. C. Jr., Seldin, D. W. 1971. Effect of saline

diuresis on intrarenal blood flow in the rat. *Am. J. Physiol.* 221:1297–304

149. Warnock, D. G., Burg, M. B. 1975. Heterogeneity of CO_2 transport in proximal straight tubules. *Kidney Int.* 8:492 (Abstr.)

150. Warren, D. J., Ledingham, J. G. G. 1975. Effects of beta-adrenergic receptor blockade on the renal vascular response to a low sodium diet in the rabbit. *Clin. Sci. Mol. Med.* 48:533–35

151. Webster, N. *The Living Encyclopedic Dictionary of the English Language.* 1975. Chicago: Engl. Lang. Inst. Am. 1158 pp.

152. Woodhall, P. B., Tisher, C. C. 1973. Response of the distal tubule and cortical collecting duct to vasopressin in the rat. *J. Clin. Invest.* 52:3095–3108

153. Woodhall, P. B., Tisher, C. C., Simonton, C. A., Robinson, R. R. 1976. Relationship between p-aminohippurate (PAH) secretion and cellular morphology in superficial and juxtamedullary straight segments of proximal tubules. *Clin. Res.* 14:40A (Abstr.)

154. Wright, F. S. 1971. Increasing magnitude of electrical potential along the renal distal tubule. *Am. J. Physiol.* 220:624–38

155. Wright, F. S., Giebisch, G. 1972. Glomerular filtration in single nephrons. *Kidney Int.* 1:201–9

156. Yarger, W. E. 1976. Intrarenal mechanisms of salt retention after bile duct ligation in rats. *J. Clin. Invest.* 52:408–18

157. Zins, G. R. 1974. Alteration in renal function during vasodilation therapy. In *Recent Advances in Renal Physiology and Pharmacology,* ed. L. G. Wesson, G. M. Fanelli Jr., pp. 165–86. Baltimore, Maryland: Univ. Park Press. 388 pp.

Ann. Rev. Physiol. 39:185–200

REGULATION OF BODY FLUIDS

♦1168

Bengt Andersson

Department of Physiology I, Karolinska Institutet, 104 01 Stockholm 60, Sweden

INTRODUCTION

The volume and the distribution of the body fluids are determined ultimately by the amounts of body water and sodium. However, the regulation of water and salt turnover is highly complex, involving multiple factors which operate both independently and in conjunction with each other. Therefore a constellation of experts in several fields of physiology and endocrinology would be needed to create a comprehensive, up-to-date review on the regulation of body fluids. Share & Claybaugh (86) realized this in 1972 when they treated the subject in this series. They skillfully avoided the problem by confining the topic to the control of endocrine factors of importance for the maintenance of body fluid homeostasis. However, they ended their excellent survey by declaring that an era had commenced in which it would be possible to study how various factors regulating body fluids are related to each other. With that statement, Share & Claybaugh optimistically handed over the arduous task of integration to the next reviewer. Limitation of competence unfortunately makes it impossible for me to pick up the gauntlet. Because of personal interest, I have instead chosen an easier way by limiting this review to a discussion of cerebral mechanisms of importance in the control of fluid balance.

In mammalian species, a dynamic balance between loss and gain normally maintains the amount of body water and the $[Na^+]$ of the extracellular fluid (ECF) within narrow limits. The homeostatic control of water balance depends on the one hand upon a sensitive regulation of antidiuretic hormone (ADH) release from the neurohypophysis, and on the other hand upon an efficient thirst mechanism, which ensures that inevitable water loss is compensated for by drinking. Hormonal and neural factors also act conjointly to maintain salt balance. Sodium depletion, accompanied by reduced ECF volume and hypovolemia, activates the renin-angiotensin system (see 31) and induces hypersecretion of sodium-retaining aldosterone (see 28). In addition, sodium depletion in many species also gives rise to specific sodium appetite which provides a motivation to seek and to ingest salt (see 32). Excessive intake of sodium, on the other hand, results in an expansion of the ECF and a brake on hormonal systems of importance for sodium conservation. This and other more or less clarified factors form the multiple cause of the ensuing natriuresis (see 67, 90). It has gradually become apparent that the CNS to a varying extent is engaged in most of these facets of the control of water and salt balances. The studies of diabetes insipidus in man originally directed attention to the involvement of the hypothalamus and the pituitary gland in the regulation of renal water excretion (47). Hypernatremia, associated with damage to the hypothalamic region of the brain, was recognized when Allot (6) observed high serum sodium in patients with hypo-thalamic lesions at autopsy. In most cases, hypernatremia due to hypothalamic disorders in man occurs concomitant with dehydration and hypovolemia, indicating that it is secondary to impaired regulation of water intake and ADH secretion (see 80). Ablation studies in experimental animals have largely confirmed the earlier clinical observations, and have provided further information about the effects on fluid balance of damage at the suprasellar level of the brain. The demonstration by Ranson and co-workers (41) that high sectioning of the pituitary stalk induces diabetes insipidus in animals made it evident that the release of ADH from the neurohypophysis is regulated by nerve impulses from the hypothalamus. That hypo-thalamic lesions may induce hypernatremia in combination with inadequate water intake in experimental animals was first demonstrated by Stevenson (91). Subse-quent animal studies have revealed complete and persistent loss of thirst after extensive forebrain damage (105). However, ablation studies of this kind do not tell whether resulting impairment of homeostatic mechanisms is due to inactivation of structures specifically sensitive to alterations in the internal environment. The part of the brain subjected to lesioning might function as a site for integration, or relay of relevant impulses from the periphery, or from other parts of the CNS, rather than as a monitor of the body fluid.

CEREBRAL CONTROL OF WATER BALANCE

Those parts of the CNS involved in the regulation of body fluids may receive information about deviations from fluid balance either via afferent impulses trans-mitted from peripheral receptors of various kinds, or by a direct influence of hu-moral agents on sensory elements located within the brain. Definitive proof of the existence of cerebral receptors important in controlling water balance was provided thirty years ago by Verney (100).

Functional Characteristics of the Receptors

SODIUM vs OSMOTIC SENSITIVITY   From the results of his ingenious studies in the non-anesthetized hydrated dog, Verney (100) concluded that hypothalamic osmoreceptors (receptors excited by a reduction of their own volume) regulate the release of ADH from the neurohypophysis. His osmoreceptor theory profoundly influenced later research in this field, and was extended to involve the regulation of water intake when it was demonstrated that injections of minute amounts of hypertonic NaCl into the anterior-medial hypothalamus elicit drinking in water-replete animals (7). Considerable evidence was later presented that provides additional support for the classic view that cerebral osmoreceptors are of fundamental importance in the control of water balance (see 22, 42, 49, 86). That the time now seems to have come for a radical modification of the osmoreceptor theory by no means depreciates Verney's fundamental contribution to our knowledge of the regulation of ADH secretion.

The application of hyperosmolal solutions of various kinds from both the inside and the outside of the blood-brain barrier [intracerebroventricular (IVT) and intracarotid infusions] affects water balance of goats in a manner that appears largely inconsistent with the osmoreceptor theory. The integrated results of these studies imply that tasks in the control of water balance, hitherto attributed to osmoreceptors, are instead executed by juxtaventricular sodium-sensitive receptors (15). The principal data supporting this viewpoint are as follows: An elevation of the [Na^+] of the cerebrospinal fluid (CSF) by slow infusion of hypertonic NaCl into the third or lateral ventricles elicits cumulative drinking in the water-replete goat, and an inhibition of the water diuresis [due to release of ADH (9)] in the hydrated animal. According to the osmoreceptor theory, a sucrose-induced elevation of the CSF osmolality would also be expected to stimulate the release of ADH and the thirst mechanism. This is apparently not the case, however (61, 69). On the contrary, IVT infusions of iso- or hypertonic saccharide solutions have been found to: (a) inhibit basic ADH secretion in nonhydrated normovolemic animals (37), (b) attenuate dehydrative drinking (71), and (c) repress the dipsogenic and antidiuretic responses to intracarotid infusions of hypertonic NaCl (70). Little or no inhibitory effect has been obtained with saccharides dissolved in isotonic saline (37, 70), indicating that IVT infusions of pure saccharide solutions attenuate drinking and ADH secretion primarily by dilution-reduction of CSF [Na^+]. However, influences of the carbohydrates on choroidal and periventricular Na transporting mechanisms must also be considered in view of more recent studies (56, 72) in which two known inhibitors of Na^+-K^+-ATPase—glycerol (5, 62) and deuterium (3)—have been administered into the CSF. These studies revealed that IVT infusions of glycerol solutions inhibit ADH release much more effectively than corresponding glucose infusions (72), and that IVT infusions of deuterium (with NaCl added to isotonicity) likewise inhibit ADH release and also attenuate dehydrative drinking (56). Like previously observed effects of hypothalamic ouabain implants (19, 46), this inhibitory effect of glycerol and deuterium indicates that excitation of cerebral receptors regulating ADH release and thirst at some stage might involve activation of Na-transporting enzyme systems.

ANGIOTENSIN SENSITIVITY   It was shown more than twenty years ago that injections of renal extracts elicit drinking in the rat (57). Subsequent studies performed in the same species by Fitzsimons and co-workers (see 42) stressed the importance of the renin-angiotensin system in the regulation of water intake, and demonstrated that intravenously inactive amounts of angiotensin II elicit drinking when injected directly into the hypothalamic region. A centrally mediated dipsogenic effect of angiotensin has since been confirmed in several other species (see 82, 84), and the octapeptide has also been shown to stimulate ADH release (24) by a central action (16, 65, 85), suggesting that renal renin release may constitute a humoral link in volumetric control of water balance. However, it still remains doubtful whether circulating angiotensin can influence the cerebral regulation of ADH release and water intake under physiological conditions. The plasma concentration of angiotensin is normally very low in comparison to the amounts of the octapeptide so far used to demonstrate its effect on the CNS (1), and the blood-brain barrier apparently restricts the access of circulating angiotensin to the CNS (82). Furthermore, IVT infusions of a competitive antagonist of angiotensin (saralasin) did not reduce dehydrative (71, 77) or hypovolemic drinking (96).

Improved knowledge about the importance of the renin-angiotensin system in cerebral control of fluid balance should develop as a consequence of: (a) the disclosure of an intrinsic cerebral renin-angiotensin system (40, 43), which appears functionally connected with Na balance (43, 89); and (b) the demonstration of central Na-angiotensin interaction (see below).

Na-ANGIOTENSIN AND Na-PGE$_1$ INTERACTION   On the basis of studies in the rat, it has been claimed that angiotensin and elevated ECF [Na] induce drinking via spatially and functionally independent cerebral mechanisms, and that no interaction exists between these two dipsogenic factors (42). However, the results of work performed over the past several years in the goat suggest quite the opposite (15). Like hypertonic NaCl, IVT infusions of relatively small amounts of angiotensin (dissolved in almost isotonic NaCl) elicit drinking and ADH release (15). A drastic augmentation of the response to each stimulus alone is obtained when both are applied together into the third ventricle. In contrast, the response to angiotensin becomes extinguished or much attenuated when the octapeptide is administered into the CSF dissolved in isotonic glucose solution. These experiments indicate that CSF Na and angiotensin act synergistically on the same juxtaventricular receptor mechanism(s). As a working hypothesis, it has been suggested that angiotensin influences local ion transport in a manner facilitating excitation of primarily Na-sensitive receptors (8). Additional data supporting this idea are the observations that (a) IVT infusions of small (in itself ineffective) amounts of angiotensin strengthen the dipsogenic and ADH-releasing effects of intracarotid infusions of hypertonic NaCl (73), and (b) brief, ineffective IVT infusions of angiotensin/glucose markedly accentuate the thirst-eliciting and antidiuretic effects of a subsequent elevation of the CSF [Na] (14).

Angiotensin stimulates transepithelial Na transport in the gut (30) and also facilitates transmembrane passage of this ion in certain other tissues (see 79). Prostaglandin E$_1$ (PGE$_1$) appears to have a similar effect on transmembrane ion transport (78). Therefore it is interesting to note that, like angiotensin, IVT infusions of PGE$_1$ (dissolved in isotonic saline) elicited thirst and stimulated the release of ADH (55). Furthermore, the dipsogenic and ADH releasing effects obtained during simultaneous IVT administration of hypertonic NaCl and PGE$_1$ are considerably stronger than the sum of the effects of each stimulus administered separately. This demonstration of central Na-PGE$_1$ interaction supports the concept of specific periventricular sensitivity to Na. However, it can by no means be taken as evidence that PGE$_1$ synthesis within the CNS plays a physiological role in the control of body fluid homeostasis. With regard to figures reported for normal PG concentration in the CSF (29), the IVT infusions of PGE$_1$ found to affect water balance ought to have raised the local PG concentration sky-high above physiological level.

COMMENTS   Sodium-sensitive receptors, the activity of which depend primarily upon the CSF [Na], seem to play an important role in the control of water balance. Angiotensin appears to lower the stimulus threshold of this sensory mechanism, eventually by effects of the octapeptide on Na-transporting mechanisms.

The concept of specific cerebral Na sensitivity gives rise to many new questions. The most pertinent appear to be, In what manner does Na excite juxtaventricular receptors? Does the degree of receptor activation depend upon the extracellular, or upon the intracellular, [Na], and is the transmembrane concentration gradient of particular importance? A possibility that deserves further attention with regard to some of the studies reviewed here (19, 46, 56, 72) is that excitation of cerebral "Na receptors" might be the manifestation of increased Na$^+$-K$^+$-ATPase activity. Future studies on IVT administration of agents with established effects on active or passive Na exchange should provide the basic information needed for the understanding of the mechanism behind excitation of cerebral receptors participating in the regulation of body fluids.

In recent years, numerous studies have been performed, especially in the rat, where IVT and hypothalamic injections of various neurotransmittors have been used to study regulation of water intake (see 42, 84). Contradictory results have been obtained, and different, more or less elaborate, models of mixed monoaminergic and cholinergic pathways in the thirst mechanism have been constructed. The results of some of these studies may need to be reevaluated in consideration of the obvious possibility that influences on periventricular Na transport may have been the ultimate cause of observed effects on water intake.

Location of the Receptors

In discovering the cerebral sensory mechanism that regulates ADH release, Verney (100) also conclusively demonstrated that receptors having this function are located in an area affected by stimuli reaching the brain via the internal carotid artery. In subsequent work with Jewell (51), Verney investigated ADH release in response to intracarotid infusions of hypertonic NaCl in a large number of dogs in which various branches of the internal carotid artery had been tied off. By elimination, they reached the conclusion that the sensitive region of the brain is the anterior hypothalamus and/or the preoptic region. However, this important work leaves open the possibility that agents administered into the carotid blood may affect the receptors indirectly via the choroid plexes and the CSF. This could explain the intricate finding by Jewell and Verney that the two dogs whose anterior hypothalamus and preoptic region were supplied exclusively with hypernatremic blood did not respond with ADH release. Since hypernatremic blood in these dogs apparently did not reach the choroid plexus, the intracarotid NaCl infusions probably did not affect the CSF [Na].

More recent attempts to localize cerebral receptors of importance in the control of water balance largely support the site postulated by Jewell and Verney, and indicate that the receptors are accessible to stimuli carried by the CSF. It has been demonstrated in the goat that infusions of hypertonic NaCl into the anterior portion of the third ventricle have considerably stronger ADH releasing and dipsogenic effects than similar infusions into its posterior portion (9), whereas equivalent infusions into the fourth ventricle neither elicit ADH release nor thirst (15). Long-term studies in goats with medially placed forebrain lesions also imply that the sensitive area is close to the anterior portion of the third ventricle (13). These studies revealed that lesions involving the entire anterior wall of the third ventricle cause persistent adipsia and lack of apparent ADH release in response to hypernatremia, plasma hyperosmolality, and to the intracarotid infusion of hypertonic NaCl and angiotensin. The acute effect of such lesions has been uncompensated temporary water diuresis, which rapidly induced pronounced hypernatremia, plasma hyperosmolality, and hypovolemia. The subfornical organ, situated in the anterior-dorsal wall of the third ventricle near the foramen of Monro, has lately received particular attention as a possible site of receptors involved in the regulation of water intake (39, 87, 88). Absence of dipsogenic response to injections of angiotensin into the lateral ventricles of rats has been observed as acute effect of lesions involving this particular periventricular structure, which has been considered the exclusive site of angiotensin-sensitive thirst receptors (88). However, subsequent studies demonstrated that drinking in response to angiotensin still can be obtained after destruction of the subfornical organ, and that the effect is probably then elicited from periventricular structures ventral to this organ (26). That the subfornical organ is not essential for the development of thirst is also made evident by the fact that it has been totally embraced by septal lesions causing hyperdipsia (13).

COMMENTS   Altogether, the results of studies performed in order to localize cerebral receptors involved in the regulation of ADH secretion and thirst indicate that such receptors are distributed along the anterior wall of the third cerebral ventricles. So far, no evidence has been presented that juxtaventricular receptors with this particular function are also present at more posterior levels of the brain. The morphological characteristics of the receptors remain unknown, but these sensory cells are obviously accessible to stimuli mediated by the CSF. However, certain structures in the anterior wall of the third ventricle are devoid of effective blood-brain barrier (4, 104). This makes it likely that sensory elements in that area also are directly accessible to blood-borne stimuli.

Reflex Volumetric Influences

Considerable evidence favors the concept that distension receptors in the heart and capacitance vessels monitoring the blood volume exert a reflex inhibitory tonus on the release of ADH from the neurohypophysis. The afferent impulses from these receptors primarily are transmitted by the vagus nerve, but the impulse propagation within the CNS remains largely unexplored. Two recent reviews in this series (44, 45) extensively and critically treated the importance of this neurohormonal reflex in the regulation of body fluid volume. Thus the present discussion is limited to some highly speculative remarks about possible organization of reflex volumetric inhibition of ADH secretion at the hypothalamic level of the brain.

The cells of the supraoptic and paraventricular nuclei constitute the final neuronal link in the regulation of hormone release from the neurohypophysis. Since cerebral receptors regulating the release apparently are located at a distance from these nuclei, reflex inhibition of ADH release may be a result either of an indirect mechanism via reduction of cerebral receptor activity, or direct inhibition of neuronal activity in the supraoptic and/or paraventricular nuclei. The latter possibility appears most plausible. Twenty years ago, Walker (103) suggested that elimination of reflex inhibitory tonus at the supraoptic level causes the inappropriate secretion of ADH that generally takes place in hydrated subjects during anesthesia. Walker presupposed the presence of spontaneous intrinsic activity in the supraoptico-neurohypophyseal system when this final neuronal link in the regulation of ADH secretion is deprived of all extrinsic influences. Subsequent electrophysiological studies have in fact demonstrated increased autonomous activity in supraoptic nuclei isolated from the remainder of the brain (95). Walker's hypothesis may explain the observation that profound forebrain cooling induces ADH release in hydrated animals (69). The theory also provides a plausible explanation for the apparently inappropriate ADH secretion observed as a consequence of hypothalamic disorders in man (17, 25), and in animals with forebrain lesions extending close to the supraoptic nuclei (13). Local brain cooling and hypothalamic lesions that cause inappropriate ADH secretion may have impaired extrinsic inhibition of autonomous supraoptic activity, and may thereby have made hydration and volume expansion less effective in blocking ADH release and inducing water diuresis. However, reflex inhibition of this kind is apparently not an absolute prerequisite for cessation of ADH secretion in response to hydration. It has been shown that cats with the ventral hypothalamus totally deafferented may still develop a water diuresis in response to excessive water loading (106).

From a teleological point of view, excitation of distension receptors monitoring the intravascular fluid volume would also be expected to affect cerebral mechanisms involved in the regulation of water intake, most likely in the form of tonic reflex inhibition of thirst, which means a contribution to volumetric regulation of water intake opposite to that ascribed to the renin-angiotensin system. The anticipated result of discontinuance in such a reflex logically should be exaggerated thirst drive and water consumption in excess of bodily needs. Harvey & Hunt (48) discovered that lesions of the septal nuclei have this effect in the rat. This hyperdipsia is not preceded by polyuria (58). Since oropharyngeal factors have been eliminated as possible causes of hyperdipsia developing in consequence of septal lesions in the rat, it has been suggested that the excessive water intake is due to removal of reflex volumetric inhibition of thirst (23). Some support for that suggestion is provided by the later observation that septal lesions also produce primary hyperdipsia in the goat, which is not a postprandially drinking species (13). However, experimental results supporting the idea that vascular stretch receptors participate in the regulation of water intake are still sparse and far from conclusive.

COMMENTS   Factors affecting ADH secretion and thirst are apparently engaged on the negative as well as on the positive side in the regulation of intravascular fluid volume. Considerable evidence supports the view that, on the negative side, hypovolemia-induced activation of the renin-angiotensin system restores blood volume by stimulating ADH secretion and evoking an urge to drink. On the positive side, hypervolemia-induced excitation of vascular stretch receptors seem to work in the opposite direction by reflexly inhibiting ADH release, and perhaps thirst, as well.

A debated question (42, 67, 93) concerning overall control of water balance is, which has the precedence when the two regulatory systems are in conflict; a regulation aimed at maintaining normal blood volume (volume regulation), or a regulation aimed at maintaining normal ECF [Na] (hitherto probably inadequately named "osmotic" regulation)? In the rat, volume regulation of water intake appears particularly well developed (42). In this species, however, hypovolemia is no longer effective as a thirst stimulus when ECF [Na] is reduced by 10% or less (92). Furthermore, rats stop drinking in response to continued IVT angiotensin stimulation much earlier when drinking water rather than isotonic saline (76). This supports the concept that one important link in volume regulation of water intake (angiotensin) affects water balance by lowering the stimulus threshold of cerebral receptors that are primarily Na sensitive (8). If this is so, the whole question of precedence between volume and "osmotic" regulations of water balance assumes a purely academic character.

CEREBRAL CONTROL OF SODIUM BALANCE

As Nashat pointed out in a recent review (67), hypo- and hypervolemia can be considered essentially as changes in total body Na, and the control of ECF fluid volume as the control of the balance between Na intake and output. Renal Na excretion constitutes the consistently most important variable in the control of Na balance. However, a complex constellation of intrinsic and extrinsic factors determines glomerular filtration rate (GFR) and renal tubular reabsorption of Na, and thus the amount of Na excreted (63, 67, 74). This makes it hard to judge which is most important in the regulation of body fluids; renal autoregulation or external influences on kidney function. Since blood pressure changes and variations in sympathetic nervous activity affect renal function, it is not surprising that neurotransmittor injection and lesions in the septal and hypothalamic regions (53, 54, 68, 81) influence renal Na excretion. On the whole, however, such experiments must be regarded as very inconclusive evidence for the presence of a cerebral sensory control of Na balance. More suggestive evidence that a cerebral sensory mechanism may be involved in the homeostatic regulation of renal Na excretion has been provided by experiments involving alterations in the [Na] of the CSF and the carotid blood (see below).

Renal Sodium Excretion

EFFECTS OF ELEVATED CSF AND CAROTID BLOOD [Na]   Experimentally induced elevation of CSF [Na] caused increased renal sodium excretion in conscious
goats (12) and sheep (60), and in anesthetized dogs (35), rats (36), and cats (27).
That this effect is due to stimulation of cerebral sodium-sensitive receptors is supported by the effects of application of a Na load to the brain via the carotid artery.
In goats (70), cats (98), and sheep (21), intracarotid infusions of hypertonic NaCl
induced more rapid and, temporarily more accentuated, natriuresis than equivalent
intravenous infusions.

Attempts to elucidate the nature of this centrally mediated effect on kidney
function have provided inconclusive results. In the goat, the natriuresis was associated with an increase in GFR (10) and some rise in the arterial blood pressure (11).
A consistent relation between vasopressor and natriuretic responses has also been
observed in the cat (27) where guanethidine blocked both effects, indicating the
involvement of increased sympathetic nerve activity. However, no changes in GFR
have been observed during natriuresis induced by IVT administration of hypertonic
NaCl in the dog (35). The increase in renal sodium excretion is apparently not
secondary to reduced aldosterone secretion, since pretreatment with this hormone
did not prevent the response (12). Nevertheless, elevated CSF [Na] seems to exert
some inhibitory influence upon aldosterone secretion. It has been demonstrated that
perfusion of the cerebroventricular system with artificial CSF, which is high in Na,
reduces aldosterone hypersecretion in Na-depleted sheep (34). The observation that
IVT infusions of hypertonic NaCl caused a drop in plasma renin concentration
indicates that elevated CSF [Na] to some extent also depresses the activity of the
renal renin-angiotensin system (38).

EFFECTS OF REDUCED CSF [Na]   A reduced CSF [Na] appears to affect renal Na
excretion and the renal renin-angiotensin system in the reverse manner to elevated
CSF [Na]. IVT infusions of pure saccharide solutions markedly attenuated the
natriuretic effect of intracarotid infusions of hypertonic NaCl in the goat (70).
Furthermore, ventriculo-cisternal perfusions with low-Na artificial CSF reduced
renal sodium excretion and elevated plasma renin concentration in dogs (66) and
sheep (64) without having a significant effect upon plasma aldosterone concentration. From the results of these experiments in the sheep, it has been concluded that
juxtaventricular tissue contains receptors sensitive to low NaCl concentration or low
osmolality, activation of which causes antinatriuresis and renin secretion. In the
reviewer's opinion, a more plausible and straightforward explanation of the results
would be inactivation of Na-sensitive receptors which to some extent are already
active at normal ECF [Na].

CENTRALLY MEDIATED NATRIURETIC EFFECT OF ANGIOTENSIN   A cen-
trally mediated pressor response to angiotensin was discovered in the dog by Bickerton & Buckley in 1961 (20). That amounts of angiotensin that are inactive
systemically produce a rise in the arterial blood pressure when administered into the
CSF or into the cerebral blood supply was later confirmed in many other mam-

malian species, including man (see 82). It has also been observed that IVT infusions of angiotensin lower plasma renin concentration (38), which vaguely suggests the existence of either a cerebral negative feedback control of renal renin release, or an inverse functional relation between the cerebral (40, 43) and the renal renin-angiotensin systems. The possibility can not be excluded, however, that this fall in plasma renin concentration might have been secondary to a rise in blood pressure induced by the IVT angiotensin infusion.

Alpha-receptor mediated sympathetic discharge appears to be the main cause of the centrally mediated pressor response to angiotensin (82). However, a pituitary factor (probably vasopressin) has been shown to contribute to the increase in arterial blood pressure elicited by injections of angiotensin into the lateral cerebral ventricle of rats (85). IVT infusions (16) and injections (83) of angiotensin have also been found to induce natriuresis, most pronounced in the hydrated, volume-expanded animal. In the goat, the natriuretic and pressor responses are well correlated in both magnitude and duration (11). Furthermore, like the ADH-releasing and dipsogenic responses, the pressor and natriuretic effects of IVT angiotensin infusions apparently are highly dependent on the CSF [Na]. Thus amounts of angiotensin, that are practically ineffective when administered dissolved in isotonic glucose solution, have moderate natriuretic and pressor effects when given in isotonic saline. These effects become markedly accentuated when angiotensin is infused into the CSF together with hypertonic NaCl. This interaction suggests that angiotensin and elevated CSF [Na] may share the same juxtaventricular sensory target(s) in eliciting a rise in arterial blood pressure and natriuresis.

LOCATION OF PRESUMPTIVE RECEPTORS   Administration of angiotensin into the vertebral artery has revealed that a blood pressure rise can be induced by action of the octapeptide on structures in the medulla oblongata where the area postrema appears to be the responsive region (52). However, investigations involving IVT administration indicate that angiotensin also elevates the arterial blood pressure by acting on periaqueductal midbrain and periventricular hypothalamic structures (see 82). It suggests that the receptors presumed to mediate a hypertensive effect of the octapeptide may be distributed widely along the cerebroventricular system. The close correlation in duration and magnitude between the pressor and natriuretic responses to IVT infusions of angiotensin (11) indicates that the increase in renal Na excretion is secondary to hemodynamic events, and that both responses may be manifestations of identical receptor stimulation. Whether elevated CSF [Na] elicits natriuresis and a rise in arterial blood pressure via the same cerebral receptors as angiotensin remains an open question. The observed interaction between the two stimuli is a hint in that direction. That, like angiotensin-sensitive structures, sensory elements mediating the natriuretic response to elevated CSF [Na] are also present at different sites along the cerebroventricular system is indicated by some recent studies in the cat. In this species, lesions involving the anterior-dorsal wall of the third ventricle attenuated the natriuretic response to intracarotid infusions of hypertonic NaCl (99), and perfusion of the fourth ventricle with high-sodium artificial CSF increased renal Na excretion (75, 97).

COMMENTS   The accumulated results of investigations in several mammalian species provide considerable evidence that a cerebral sensory mechanism, the activity of which primarily is influenced by the [Na] of the CSF, participates in the regulation of renal Na excretion. As a complement to a similar sensory system regulating ADH release and water intake, this presumed cerebral regulation of Na excretion may play an important role in the control of the volume and distribution of the body fluids. Whereas cerebral receptors regulating ADH secretion and water intake appear to be concentrated mainly near the anterior border of the third ventricle, those presumed to regulate renal Na excretion may be more widely distributed along the cerebroventricular system, from the hypothalamic region back to the surroundings of the fourth ventricle.

It is obviously much more hazardous to speculate about any physiological significance of the observed natriuretic effect of IVT-administered angiotensin. This effect appears quite inappropriate in the regulation of body fluids since activation of the renal renin-angiotensin system occurs during distortions of fluid balance (hypovolemia and hyponatremia) which demand Na retention (see 31). However, normal, or even more so, elevated CSF [Na] appears to be a prerequisite for the natriuretic response to IVT administration of angiotensin. As discussed above, the reason may be that angiotensin elicits natriuresis by influencing periventricular sodium transport in a manner that facilitates the excitation of Na sensitive receptors. That PGE_1 also interacts with CSF Na in eliciting natriuresis (55) lends some support to this novel idea.

The way in which alterations in CSF [Na] may affect renal Na excretion has been a matter of speculation. Several factors may be involved, but the underlying mechanism remains unknown.

Salt Appetite

Voluntary Na intake in human beings is apparently unrelated to Na balance, and is mainly determined by individual liking for salt, based on palatability. Specific Na appetite does not seem to be recognized by man during Na deficiency (50, 59). However, such appetite exists as a strong motivation to seek and ingest salt in Na-deficient rodents and herbivorous animals. Here, salt appetite obviously constitutes an important factor in the regulation of body fluids. Extensive investigations have been performed in the rat (see 93) and the sheep to elucidate how this specific motivation is generated. In sheep made Na deficient by salivary drainage, Denton and co-workers studied salt appetite as an integral part of fundamental research on the control of aldosterone secretion. Most of their important contributions to our knowledge of the etiology of salt appetite is included in a comprehensive handbook chapter published ten years ago (32). After considering the importance of various endocrine and afferent nervous influences on the specific motivation for salt consumption, Denton concluded by putting forward the hypothesis that the ultimate cause of salt appetite might be a subnormal intracellular Na content in cerebral receptors subserving the regulation of Na intake. He found support for this suggestion in his observation that it takes considerable time before a sudden elevation of plasma [Na] satisfies the urge to consume salt in Na depleted sheep (18). This delay could possibly reflect the slow passage of Na across the blood-brain barrier into the brain cells. The subsequent observation that intracarotid infusions of ouabain inhibit salt appetite (33) lends some support to this idea. In agreement with Denton's hypothesis is the finding that plasma volume repletion per se does not inhibit salt appetite (32, 94), and that there is a considerable lag between Na need and intake in the rat (93). On the whole, however, very little additional information has been provided in recent years regarding the causal factors and the cerebral organization of the specific appetite for salt. Like some earlier work, several studies in the rat have suggested the involvement of the hypothalamus and parts of the limbic system (93). However, these investigations do not tell anything essentially new. Hence, the cerebral mechanism underlying salt appetite largely remains to be explored.

CONCLUDING REMARKS

The heading of this article is somewhat misleading inasmuch as the discussion has been limited to cerebral mechanisms of possible importance in the regulation of body fluids. Enticed by my own research interests, I may have put too much emphasis on evidence that juxtaventricular Na-sensitive receptors play an important role in the control of body fluid homeostasis. I may also have overstressed the likelihood that the activity of such a receptor system is predominantly determined by the composition of the CSF. Since knowledge about their exact location and morphology is still lacking, the possibilities that cerebral receptors regulating body fluids to a great extent are also stimulated directly via the blood-brain barrier, or that they are located in parts of the brain which are devoid of this barrier, can by no means be excluded. However, the idea of specific periventricular sensibility is far from new. It has been known for many years that in the hypothalamic region, and also more posterior in the CNS, are neurons with dendrites protruding into the CSF (102). Over half a century ago, Agduhr (2) called attention to the possibility that these neurons may function as some kind of sense organ which is affected by certain properties of the CSF. More recently, it has been suggested that CSF influence upon the hypothalamic division of this particular cell population may play a role in the regulation of the ADH secretion and in the neurohumoral control of anterior pituitary function (101). Whatever turns out to be the function of the CSF-contacting neurons, future coordination of morphological and physiological studies will be needed to disclose the true nature of cerebral receptors involved in the regulation of body fluids.

Literature Cited

1. Abraham, S. F., Baker, R. M., Blaine, E. H., Denton, D. A., McKinley, M. J. 1975. Water drinking induced in sheep by angiotensin—a physiological or pharmacological effect? *J. Comp. Physiol. Psychol.* 88:503–18
2. Agduhr, E. 1922. Über ein zentrales Sinnesorgan (?) bei den Vertebraten. *Z. Anat. Entwicklungsgesch.* 66:223–360
3. Ahmed, K., Foster, D. 1974. Studies on the effects of ^2H_2O on Na^+, K^+-ATPase. *Ann. NY Acad. Sci.* 242:280–92
4. Akert, K. 1969. Subfornical organ and cholinergic activity. In *Zirkumventrikuläre Organe und Liquor*, ed. A. Sterba, pp. 89–93. Jena: Fischer
5. Albers, R. W., Koval, G. J. 1972. Sodium potassium activated triphosphatase. VII. Concurrent inhibition of Na^+-K^+-adenosine triphosphatase and activation of K^+nitrophenyl-phosphatase activities. *J. Biol. Chem.* 247:3088–92
6. Allot, E. N. 1939. Sodium and chlorine retention without renal disease. *Lancet* 1:1035–37
7. Andersson, B. 1953. The effect of injections of hypertonic Na Cl-solutions into different parts of the hypothalamus of goats. *Acta Physiol. Scand.* 18:188–201
8. Andersson, B. 1971. Thirst—and brain control of water balance. *Am. Sci.* 59:408–15
9. Andersson, B., Dallman, M., Olsson, K. 1969. Observations on central control of drinking and the release of antidiuretic hormone (ADH). *Life Sci.* 8:425–32
10. Andersson, B., Dallman, M., Olsson, K. 1969. Evidence for a hypothalamic control of renal sodium excretion. *Acta Physiol. Scand.* 75:496–510
11. Andersson, B., Eriksson, L., Fernández, O., Kolmodin, C. G., Oltner, R. 1972. Centrally mediated effects of sodium and angiotensin II on arterial blood pressure and fluid balance. *Acta Physiol. Scand.* 85:398–407
12. Andersson, B., Jobin, M., Olsson, K. 1967. A study of thirst and other effects of an increased sodium concentration in the 3rd brain ventricle. *Acta Physiol. Scand.* 69:29–36
13. Andersson, B., Leksell, L. G., Lishajko, F. 1975. Perturbations in fluid balance induced by medially placed forebrain lesions. *Brain Res.* 99:261–75
14. Andersson, B., Leskell, L. G., Rundgren, M. 1975. Duration of central action of angiotensin II estimated by its interaction with CSF Na^+. *Acta Physiol. Scand.* 93:472–76
15. Andersson, B., Olsson, K. 1973. On central control of body fluid homeostasis. *Cond. Reflex* 8:147–159
16. Andersson, B., Westbye, O. 1970. Synergistic action of sodium and angiotensin on brain mechanisms controlling fluid balance. *Life Sci.* 9:601–8
17. Bartter, F. C., Schwartz, W. B. 1967. The syndrome of inappropriate secretion of antidiuretic hormone. *Am. J. Med.* 42:790–813
18. Beilharz, S., Bott, E. A., Denton, D. A., Sabine, J. R. 1965. The effect of intracarotid infusions of 0.4 m-NaCl on the sodium drinking of sheep with parotid fistula. *J. Physiol. London* 178:80–91
19. Bergmann, F., Chaimovitz, M., Costin, A., Gutman, Y., Ginath, Y. 1967. Water intake of rats after implantation of ouabain into the hypothalamus. *Am. J. Physiol.* 213:328–32
20. Bickerton, R. K., Buckley, J. P. 1961. Evidence for a central mechanism in angiotensin-induced hypertension. *Proc. Soc. Exp. Biol. Med.* 106:834–36
21. Blaine, E. H., Denton, D. A., McKinley, M. J., Weller, S. 1975. A central osmosensitive receptor for renal sodium excretion. *J. Physiol. London* 244:497–509
22. Blass, E. M. 1973. Cellular-dehydration thirst: Physiological, neurological, and behavioral correlates. In *The Neurophysiology of Thirst: New Findings and Advances in Concepts*, ed. A. N. Epstein, H. R. Kissileff, E. Stellar, pp. 37–72. Wash. DC: Winston. 357 pp.
23. Blass, E. M., Hanson, D. G. 1970. Primary hyperdipsia in the rat following septal lesions. *J. Comp. Physiol. Psychol.* 70:87–93
24. Bonjour, J. P., Malvin, R. L. 1970. Stimulation of ADH release by the renin-angiotensin system. *Am. J. Physiol.* 218:1555–59
25. Brisman, R., Chutorian, A. M. 1970. Inappropriate antidiuretic hormone secretion (hypothalamic glioma in a child). *Arch. Neurol. Chicago* 23:63–69
26. Buggy, J., Fisher, A. E., Hoffman, W. E., Johnson, A. K., Phillips, M. J. 1975. Ventricular obstruction: Effect on drinking induced by intracranial injection of angiotensin. *Science* 190:72–74
27. Chiu, P. J. S., Sawyer, W. H. 1974. Third ventricular injection of hyper-

tonic NaCl and natriuresis in cats. *Am. J. Physiol.* 226:463–69

28. Coghlan, J. P., Blair-West, J. R., Denton, D. A., Scoggins, B. A., Wright, R. D. 1971. Perspectives in aldosterone and renin control. *Aust. NZ J. Med.* 2:178–97

29. Cranston, W. I., Hellon, R. F., Mitchell, D. 1975. A dissociation between fever and prostaglandin concentration in cerebrospinal fluid. *J. Physiol. London.* 253:583–92

30. Crocker, A. D., Munday, K. A. 1970. The effect of the renin-angiotensin system on mucosal water and sodium transfer in everted sacs of rat jejunum. *J. Physiol. London* 206:323–34

31. Davis, J. O., Freeman, R. H. 1976. Mechanisms regulating renin release. *Physiol. Rev.* 56:1–56

32. Denton, D. A. 1967. Salt appetite. *Handb. Physiol. Sect. 6.* 1:433–59

33. Denton, D. A. 1972. Instinct, appetites and medicine. *Aust. NZ J. Med.* 2: 203–12

34. Denton, D. A. 1973. The brain and sodium homeostasis. *Cond. Reflex* 8:125–46

35. Dorn, J. B., Levine, N., Kaley, G., Rothballer, A. B. 1969. Natriuresis induced by injection of hypertonic saline into the third cerebral ventricle of dogs. *Proc. Soc. Exp. Biol. Med.* 131:240–42

36. Dorn, J. B., Porter, J. C. 1970. Diencephalic involvement in sodium excretion in the rat. *Endocrinology* 86:1112–17

37. Eriksson, L. 1974. Effect of lowered CSF sodium concentration on the central control of fluid balance. *Acta Physiol. Scand.* 91:61–68

38. Eriksson, L., Fyhrquist, F. 1976. Effect of centrally infused angiotensin II or altered CSF Na⁺ concentraion on plasma renin activity. *Acta Physiol. Scand.* 96:3A–4A

39. Felix, D., Akert, K. 1974. The effect of angiotensin II on neurons of the cat subfornical organ. *Brain Res.* 76:350–53

40. Fischer-Ferraro, C., Nahmod, V. E., Goldstein, D. J., Finkielman, S. 1971. Angiotensin and renin in rat and dog brain. *J. Exp. Med.* 133:353–61

41. Fisher, C., Ingram, W. R., Ranson, S. W. 1938. *Diabetes Insipidus and the Neuro-hormonal Control of Water Balance.* Ann Arbor, Mich: Edward Bros.

42. Fitzsimons, J. T. 1972. Thirst. *Physiol. Rev.* 52:468–561

43. Ganten, D., Minnich, J. L., Granger, P., Hayduk, K., Brecht, H. M., Barbeau, A., Boucher, R., Genest, J. 1971.

Angiotensin-forming enzyme in brain tissue. *Science* 173:64–65

44. Gauer, O. H., Henry, J. P., Behn, C. 1970. The regulation of extracellular fluid volume. *Ann. Rev. Physiol.* 32: 547–95

45. Goetz, K. L., Bond, C. C., Bloxham, D. D. 1975. Atrial receptors and renal function. *Physiol. Rev.* 55:157–205

46. Gutman, Y., Bergmann, F., Zerachia, A. 1971. Influence of hypothalamic deposits of antidipsic drugs on renal excretion. *Eur. J. Pharmacol.* 13: 326–29

47. Hann, F. von. 1918. Über die Bedeutung der Hypophysemverännderungen bei Diabetes insipidus. *Frankfurt. Z. Pathol.* 21:337–65

48. Harvey, J. A., Hunt, H. F. 1965. Effects of septal lesions on thirst in rats as indicated by water consumption and operant responding for water reward. *J. Comp. Physiol. Psychol.* 59:49–56

49. Hayward, J. N. 1975. Neural control of the posterior pituitary. *Ann. Rev. Physiol.* 37:191–210

50. Henkin, R. I., Gill, J. R. Jr., Bartter, F. C. 1963. Studies of taste thresholds in normal man and in patients with adrenal cortical insufficiency: The role of adrenal cortical steroids and of serum sodium concentration. *J. Clin. Invest.* 42:727–35

51. Jewell, P. A., Verney, E. B. 1957. An experimental attempt to determine the site of the neurohypophysial osmoreceptors in the dog. *Philos. Trans. R. Soc. London Ser. B* 240:197–324

52. Joy, M. D., Lowe, R. D. 1970. Evidence that the area postrema mediates the central cardiovascular response to angiotensin II. *Nature* 228:1303–4

53. Keeler, R. 1959. Effect of hypothalamic lesions on renal excretion of sodium. *Am. J. Physiol.* 197:847–849

54. Keeler, R. 1975. Effect of chronic preoptic lesions on the renal excretion of sodium in rats. *Am. J. Physiol.* 228:1725–28

55. Leksell, L. 1976. Influence of prostaglandin E₁ on cerebral mechanisms involved in the control of fluid balance. *Acta Physiol. Scand.* 98:85–93

56. Leksell, L., Lishajko, F., Rundgren, M. 1976. Negative water balance induced by intracerebroventricular infusion of deuterium. *Acta Physiol. Scand.* 97: 142–44

57. Linazasoro, J. M., Jiménez Diaz, C., Castro Mendoza, H. J. 1954. The kid-

ney and thirst regulation. *Bull. Inst. Med. Res. Madrid* 7:53–61

58. Lubar, J. F., Boyce, B. A., Schaefer, C. F. 1968. Etiology of polydipsia and polyuria in rats with septal lesions. *Physiol. Behav.* 3:289–92

59. McCance, R. A. 1936. Experimental sodium chloride deficiency in man. *Proc. R. Soc. London Ser. B* 119:245–268

60. McKinley, M. J., Blaine, E. H., Denton, D. A. 1973. Stimulation of renal sodium excretion by hypertonic stimuli to the third ventricle and effects of renal denervation on this response. *Proc. Aust. Physiol. Pharmacol. Soc.* 4:66–67

61. McKinley, M. J., Blaine, E. H., Denton, D. A. 1974. Brain osmoreceptors, cerebrospinal fluid electrolyte composition and thirst. *Brain Res.* 70:532–37

62. Meyer, M., Avi-Dor, Y. 1970. Interaction of solvents with membranal and soluble potassium ion-dependent enzymes. *Biochem. J.* 116:49–54

63. Morel, F., de Rouffignac, C. 1973. Kidney. *Ann. Rev. Physiol.* 35:17–54

64. Mouw, D. R., Abraham, S. F., Blair-West, J. R., Coghlan, J. P., Denton, D. A., McKenzie, J. S., McKinley, M. J., Scoggins, B. A. 1974. Brain receptors, renin secretion and renal sodium retention in conscious sheep. *Am. J. Physiol.* 226:56–62

65. Mouw, D. R., Bonjour, J. P., Malvin, R. L., Vander, A. J. 1971. Central action of angiotensin in stimulating ADH release. *Am. J. Physiol.* 220:239–42

66. Mouw, D. R., Vander, A. J. 1970. Evidence for brain sodium receptors controlling renal sodium excretion and plasma renin activity. *Am. J. Physiol.* 219:822–32

67. Nashat, F. S. 1974. Topics in renal physiology. *Recent Advances in Physiology, No 9,* ed. R. J. Linden, pp. 191–238. London: Churchill-Livingstone

68. Novakova, A., Stevenson, J. A. F. 1971. Effect of posterior hypothalamic lesions on renal function in the rat. *Can. J. Physiol. Pharmacol.* 49:941–50

69. Olsson, K. 1969. Studies on central regulation of secretion of antidiuretic hormone (ADH) in the goat. *Acta Physiol. Scand.* 78:465–74

70. Olsson, K. 1973. Further evidence for the importance of CSF Na^+ concentration in central control of fluid balance. *Acta Physiol. Scand.* 88:183–88

71. Olsson, K. 1975. Attenuation of dehydrative thirst by lowering of the CSF $[Na^+]$. *Acta Physiol. Scand.* 94:536–38

72. Olsson, K. 1976. Efficiency of intraventricular glycerol infusions in lowering CSF $[Na^+]$ and inhibiting ADH-release. *Acta Physiol. Scand.* 96:24A–25A

73. Olsson, K., Kolmodin, R. 1974. Accentuation by angiotensin II of the antidiuretic and dipsogenic responses to intracarotid infusions of NaCl and fructose. *Acta Endocrinol.* 75:333–41

74. Orloff, J., Burg, M. 1971. Kidney. *Ann. Rev. Physiol.* 33:83–130

75. Passo, S., Thornborough, J. R., Rothballer, A. B. 1975. Natriuresis following fourth ventricle perfusion with high-sodium artificial CSF. *Can. J. Physiol. Pharmacol.* 53:363–67

76. Radio, G. J., Summy-Long, J., Daniels-Severs, A. E., Severs, W. B. 1972. Hydration changes produced by central infusion of angiotensin II. *Am. J. Physiol.* 223:1221–26

77. Ramsay, D. J., Reid, I. A. 1975. Some central mechanisms of thirst in the dog. *J. Physiol. London* 253:517–25

78. Ramwell, P. W., Shaw, J. E. 1970. Biological significance of the prostaglandins. *Recent Prog. Horm. Res.* 26:139–87

79. Regoli, D., Park, W. K., Rioux, F. 1974. Pharmacology of angiotensin. *Pharmacol. Rev.* 26:69–123

80. Ross, E. J., Christie, S. B. M. 1969. Hypernatremia. *Medicine Baltimore* 48:441–473

81. Saad, W. A., Camargo, L. A. A., Silva-Netto, C. R., Gentil, C. G., Antunes-Rodrigues, J., Covian, M. R. 1975. Natriuresis, kaliuresis and diuresis following microinjections of carbachol into the septal area. *Pharmacol. Biochem. Behav.* 3:985–93

82. Severs, W. B., Daniels-Severs, A. E. 1973. Effects of angiotensin on the central nervous system. *Pharmacol. Rev.* 25:415–49

83. Severs, W. B., Daniels-Severs, A. E., Summy-Long, J., Radio, G. J. 1971. Effects of centrally administered angiotensin II on salt and water excretion. *Pharmacology* 6:242–52

84. Severs, W. B., Summy-Long, J. 1975. The role of angiotensin in thirst. *Life Sci.* 17:1513–26

85. Severs, W. B., Summy-Long, J., Taylor, J. S., Connor, J. D. 1970. A central effect of angiotensin: Release of pituitary pressor material. *J. Pharmacol. Exp. Ther.* 174:27–34

86. Share, L., Claybaugh, J. R. 1972. Regu-

lation of body fluids. *Ann. Rev. Physiol.* 35:235–60

87. Simpson, J. B., Routtenberg, A. 1972. The subfornical organ and carbachol-induced drinking. *Brain Res.* 45:135–41

88. Simpson, J. B., Routtenberg, A. 1973. Subfornical organ: site of drinking elicitation by angiotensin II. *Science* 181:1172–75

89. Slaven, B. 1975. Influence of salt and volume on changes in rat brain angiotensin. *J. Pharm. Pharmacol.* 27:783–84

90. Stein, J. H., Reineck, H. J. 1975. Effect of alterations in extracellular fluid volume on segmental sodium transport. *Physiol. Rev.* 55:127–141

91. Stevenson, J. A. F. 1949. Effects of hypothalamic lesions on water and energy metabolism in the rat. *Recent Prog. Horm. Res.* 4:363–94

92. Stricker, E. M. 1969. Osmoregulation and volume regulation in rats: Inhibition of hypovolemic thirst by water. *Am. J. Physiol.* 217:98–105

93. Stricker, E. M. 1973. Thirst, sodium appetite, and complementary physiological contributions to the regulation of intravascular fluid volume. In *The Neurophysiology of Thirst: New Findings and Advances in Concepts,* ed. A. N. Epstein, H. R. Kissileff, E. Stellar, pp. 73–98. Wash. DC: Winston. 357 pp.

94. Stricker, E. M., Wolf, G. 1969. Behavioral control of intravascular fluid volume: Thirst and sodium appetite. *Ann. NY Acad. Sci.* 157:553–67

95. Suda, I., Koizumi, K., Brooks, C. McC. 1963. Study of unitary activity in the supraoptic nucleus of the hypothalamus. *Jpn. J. Physiol.* 13:374–85

96. Summy-Long, J., Severs, W. B. 1974. Angiotensin and thirst: Studies with a converting enzyme inhibitor and a receptor antagonist. *Life Sci.* 15:569–82

97. Thornborough, J. R., Passo, S. S. 1975. Evidence for sodium specificity of the receptor in the fourth cerebral ventricle affecting sodium excretion in the cat. *Can. J. Physiol. Pharmacol.* 53:677–79

98. Thornborough, J. R., Passo, S. S., Rothballer, A. B. 1973. Receptors in cerebral circulation affecting sodium excretion in the cat. *Am. J. Physiol.* 225:138–41

99. Thornborough, J. R., Passo, S. S., Rothballer, A. B. 1973. Forebrain lesion blockade of the natriuretic response to elevated carotid blood sodium. *Brain Res.* 58:355–63

100. Verney, E. B. 1947. The antidiuretic hormone and factors which determine its release. *Proc. R. Soc. London Ser. B* 135:25–106

101. Vigh, B. 1970. Does the paraventricular organ have a receptor function? *Ann. Endocrinol. Paris* 31:659–63

102. Vigh-Teichman, I., Vigh, B. 1974. The infundibular cerebrospinalfluid contacting neurons. *Adv. Anat. Embryol. Cell Biol.* 50(2):1–91

103. Walker, J. M. 1957. The release of vasopressin and oxytocin in response to drugs. In *The Neurohypophysis,* ed. H. Heller, pp, 221–32. London: Butterworths. 275 pp.

104. Weindl, A., Joynt, R. J. 1972. Ultrastructure of ventricular walls. Threedimensional study of regional specialization. *Arch. Neurol.* 26:420–27

105. Witt, D. M., Keller, A. D., Batsel, H. L., Lynch, J. R. 1952. Absence of thirst and resultant syndrome associated with anterior hypothalamectomy in the dog. *Am. J. Physiol.* 171:780

106. Woods, J. W., Bard, P., Bleier, R. 1966. Functional capacity of the deafferented hypothalamus: Water balance and responses to osmotic stimuli in the decerebrate cat and rat. *J. Neurophysiol.* 29:751–67

Ann. Rev. Physiol. 39:201–20

HEART: EXCITATION-CONTRACTION COUPLING

❖1169

Harry A. Fozzard[1]

Departments of Medicine and the Pharmacological and Physiological Sciences, University of Chicago, Chicago, Illinois 60637

INTRODUCTION

One of the most remarkable characteristics of heart muscle is its ability to vary its force of contraction over a large range under normal conditions and from a fixed initial length. This length-independent change in contraction force over an almost tenfold range allows the heart to adjust rapidly to varying demands of the circulation. Since the action potential does not change much in height (although it does vary in duration and shape) and the contractile proteins presumably can not change structure on a beat-by-beat basis, we generally ascribe the contractile variability of heart muscle to the step called *excitation-contraction coupling* (E-C coupling). For this review I have gathered articles that have contributed to our understanding of several aspects of E-C coupling.

This review was originally intended to cover a broader consideration of E-C coupling in striated muscle. Important progress has recently been made in the field of E-C coupling both in skeletal muscle and in heart muscle, and comparison of the two muscles promises to be advantageous. I had the opportunity to preview the excellent discussion of E-C coupling in skeletal muscle by Ebashi (21) prepared for Volume 38 of this series; in the delightful fashion that we have become accustomed to expect from him, Professor Ebashi has synthesized our understanding and progress in skeletal muscle studies. We encourage the cardiac investigator to review that article along with this one. Occasional reference to skeletal muscle studies are made in this chapter, where they assist in interpreting experiments on heart muscle.

The previous review of E-C coupling in heart muscle in Volume 35 by Langer (53) represents a starting point for this chapter. Other important reviews include one on E-C coupling by Morad & Goldman (61) and on calcium ion currents by Reuter (71). Weidmann (98) reviewed cardiac membrane electrogenesis in Volume

[1]Supported in part by USPHS grant HL-11665.

36 of this series, and Trautwein (88) summarized the results of voltage clamp studies in heart muscle. The potentially important phenomenon of Na-Ca exchange has been reviewed by Baker (3) and Blaustein (7).

The sequence of this review reflects our present understanding of the E-C coupling process, modified from Ebashi (21) into four phases: (*a*) The action potential occurs across the sarcolemma. (*b*) This depolarization releases Ca ions from the terminal cisternae of the sarcoplasmic reticulum (SR) and/or allows release or entry of Ca from outside the sarcolemma. (*c*) The Ca ions diffuse to the troponin molecules on the thin filaments and, in a complex sequence of events, permit actin-myosin interaction. (*d*) The SR reaccumulates the Ca ions, permitting dissociation of Ca from troponin and consequent relaxation. Step (*a*) is discussed in terms of the relations between transmembrane voltage and tension development and in terms of frequency of depolarization. Concern with the origin of the Ca used in troponin interaction is considered in relation to step (*b*). Several of the agents that modify contraction strength may influence steps (*c*) and (*d*). These include digitalis and the catecholamines.

Almost every aspect of cardiac physiology involves E-C coupling in some fashion, and we can only consider some of them. Reflecting my bias, I write as if the E-C coupling mechanism were the same in all kinds of heart muscle. I draw freely from studies in tissues from different parts of the heart and from different species, and I warn the reader that significant differences in E-C coupling mechanisms between these tissues would be hidden by this simplification.

THE ROLE OF MEMBRANE DEPOLARIZATION

Force-Frequency Relationship

The influence of rate and pattern of stimulation on heart muscle contraction was well described a century ago by Bowditch (10). This phenomenon is assumed to be related to the E-C coupling process in heart muscle, but the evidence has been inferential. Several recent studies have offered additional support for the idea that more frequent stimulation of action potentials causes more Ca to enter the cells and to be thereby available for release. Edman & Jóhannsson (22) "primed" rabbit papillary muscle with various stimulation rates and examined contraction strength at different times after terminating the priming series. Recovery of the contraction was found to be maximal after an interval of 0.8 sec, regardless of the rate of stimulation during priming. After this maximal value, the tension declined with increasing length of the rest interval with two time constants of 2.6 and 92 sec. They interpreted their results in terms of a commonly used model in which the Ca-uptake site for relaxation is not the same as the Ca-release site. The 0.8 sec was ascribed to the process of transfer of Ca from the uptake site to the release site. Decline with longer rest intervals was considered to be transport of Ca out of the cell by perhaps two separate mechanisms. The magnitude of the maximal response depended on the stimulus rate during priming, increasing monotonically with rate to a stimulus rate of 5/sec. Measuring the time period when the fiber was depolarized beyond -40 mV, they found a linear relationship of this depolarized time with maximal contraction. This fits into their model by assuming that the Ca available for release is linearly dependent on depolarization of the membrane, as the result of a calcium current. Steady-state force-frequency relationships represent a balance, in this explanation, between extent of prior loading of the cell with Ca and recovery between beats.

Rather similar studies were made by Allen, Jewell & Wood (2), who found the rate of decline of tension with increasing length of rest period after a single beat to vary with external concentration of Ca. Decrease in size of the second contraction with rest was markedly slowed by increasing Ca_o. The size of the "rest" contraction was influenced by both Ca_o and Na_o. Time of maximal recovery after prior stimulation by a single beat was quite variable in this experiment: 2–20 sec, rather than the constant 0.8 sec found by Edman & Jóhannsson (22). The two groups of investigators invoked similar models. A characteristic of the "rest" contractions offered to Allen, Jewell & Wood an important insight into the relation between Ca entering from the outside and that released from intracellular structures. The "rest" contraction showed a very slow time course of force development—over 400 msec to peak tension. With priming stimulation, an earlier phase of tension increased to produce a peak tension around 200 msec. They suggested that the late "rest" contraction is the result of entry of Ca from outside the cell, and the earlier peak is the result of release from a variable intracellular pool of Ca.

The voltage dependence of the staircase phenomenon was examined by Gibbons & Fozzard (34), who used a two-micropipette voltage clamp technique in short Purkinje fibers to produce trains of square voltage steps. Trains of steps of different duration between 60 msec and 1000 msec were used to simulate action potentials of different duration. The steps were at constant frequency of 0.5 sec^{-1} (but different repolarized intervals between steps) or at a constant repolarized interval of 1.5 sec. In both cases the train of 60 msec steps showed a negative staircase and the train of 1000 msec steps showed a positive staircase. There was progressive loss of staircase with depolarization of the resting or holding potential. Staircase was also strongly influenced by the amplitude of the voltage steps. Trains of steps to about –12 mV showed little staircase. Those to more negative levels resulted in negative staircases and those to more positive levels (e.g. +40 mV) resulted in strongly positive staircases. Therefore it is reasonable to conclude that one of the factors controlling staircase is voltage dependent.

Recovery or "restitution" is an important factor in determining contraction strength. The influence of duration of the first, or depleting, voltage step on the recovery rate was measured by test pulses after different periods of recovery. Recovery rate was about twice as fast after 500 msec steps as it was after 90 msec steps. At this point, these voltage clamp studies by Gibbons & Fozzard are only descriptive, but their interpretation may be possible after we understand the relation between voltage and Ca release. For example, McCans et al (59) have shown that blockage of the slow inward current by exposure of rabbit ventricular muscle to verapamil changes the positive force-frequency relationship into a negative one.

The possibility that the force-frequency relationship described above is an experimental artifact has been raised in recent years [e.g. Kavaler et al (48)]. In general, intact animal studies show little to no effect of stimulus rate on contraction strength until rates are quite high. Further observations include experiments of Baumann & Reichel (4), who studied pressure development in functionally isolated left atria of guinea pigs. Taking pains to maintain reasonably normal conditions, they found little dependence of developed pressure on frequency immediately after isolation of the tissue. With time, the contraction at lower stimulus frequencies declined, and increasing the frequency had a larger effect. They felt that the force-frequency relation usually seen in vitro preparations is the result of depletion of endogenously stored catecholamines. Carrier et al (12) found isotopic Ca exchange to be strongly dependent on time after isolating guinea pig atria. With time after isolation the tissue had a steady decrease of contraction strength, associated with a decline in Ca exchange. This "aging" effect could be reversed by cardiac glycosides.

Mahler, Yoran & Ross (58) were successful in studying the force-frequency relationship in awake, previously instrumented dogs. They found an increase in LV dP/dt_{max} (maximal rate of systolic pressure development in the left ventricle) in the face of a fall in LV end-diastolic fiber length. The relationship was not influenced by administration of a β-adrenergic blocking agent.

These conflicting studies fail to resolve the question of the physiological role of the force-frequency relation. However, it should be pointed out that time is required for recovery or "restitution" after every beat. If beats fail to decline in strength with the encroachment on their recovery time that occurs with any rate increase, then some positive inotropic effect of increased rate must have occurred. Rat myocardium is usually reported to have only a negative force-frequency relationship (decline in force with increasing steady frequency). In an interesting set of experiments, Forester & Mainwood (29) showed that a positive force-frequency relation could be seen in this tissue, if Ca_o is lowered to 1.0 mM or less. This maneuver presumably prevents the Na:Ca pump (see the section on intracellular Na and contraction, below) from removing during the interstimulus intervals all of the Ca accumulated during the action potentials.

Calcium Current and Contraction

The existence and importance of the transmembrane Ca current are probably the most important issues at this time in cardiac E-C coupling. In 1973 in this series, Langer (53) concluded that there was indeed a Ca current that flowed through a membrane channel that is separate from the Na channel. There remain certain important questions about this current that were first clearly stated by Johnson & Lieberman (41). They pointed out that much of the evidence for this current depended on interpretation of voltage clamp studies, which in heart muscle were of uncertain accuracy. In addition, the positive Ca current was influenced by other ions than Ca and it did not necessarily follow simple kinetic behavior. In the intervening years, most investigators in the field have satisfied themselves that transmembrane Ca current does exist in heart muscle, although disagreement exists regarding some kinetic properties.

Evidence for Ca currents comes from perhaps four sources—nonvoltage clamp experiments, pharmacological effects, improved voltage clamp analysis, and analogy with other tissues. In tissues depolarized with current flow or with increased K_o, action potentials occur that behave as though Ca carried the inward current. These "Ca action potentials" are thoroughly reviewed in a book by Cranefield (17). TTX does not block the Ca current, but Mn, verapamil, and D600 do block it. Evidence of differential blockage of currents is, however, sometimes difficult to interpret. For example, Kass & Tsien (45) have shown that Mn, La, and D600 influence i_x, an important potassium current. Voltage clamp studies in heart muscle have been refined and analyzed for sources of error (30), and they continue to show reproduceable currents logically ascribed to Ca. Finally, Ca currents continue to be found in such divergent tissues as embryonic skeletal muscle and pituitary cells. It seems wise to accept the conclusion that Ca current does exist in heart muscle, but to keep in mind that quantitative details of this current are still rather clouded by artifact in imperfect experiments.

The threshold for Ca current and for contraction is almost always identical (5, 33, 35, 66). For small voltage steps of increasing magnitude, the size of contraction increases linearly with Ca current (35, 90), and steady-state contraction in response to a train of steps is directly proportional to Ca current over a substantial voltage range in the experiments of Reuter (72), Trautwein, McDonald & Tripathi (90), and Trautwein (89). However, a major problem is apparent when this relationship is studied with markedly positive voltage steps. The Ca current diminishes beyond 0 mV and becomes 0 around +30 or +40 mV, yet contraction continues to increase or remains large. This has led Trautwein, McDonald & Tripathi (90) to suggest that Ca conductance is the factor related to contraction, regardless of the magnitude or direction of the current (also see section on tonic tension).

In spite of concordance between Ca current and contraction under certain circumstances, a discrepancy is seen during transitions in rate or size of voltage step. For example, during trains of voltage steps the current may be constant while contraction increases (5) or decreases (35). Efforts to calculate the amount of Ca entering the cell by the transmembrane Ca current, in order to compare it to the amount of Ca needed for reaction with contractile proteins, have been frustrated by uncertainties in the techniques, and assumptions that cannot be substantiated. A number of models of Ca movement have been formulated; two of the more elaborate have been described by Morad & Goldman (61) and by Kaufmann et al (46). However, it may be premature to attempt a synthesis of cellular Ca movements in more than general terms. A general summary statement is that voltage-dependent Ca current is used primarily to replenish or alter cellular Ca stores, which are normally released by voltage-related processes from their intracellular location. In spite of the advantages of measuring Ca current under the voltage clamp conditions, such studies give only inferential information regarding the quantity of Ca in the intracellular stores and the means by which it is regulated or released. Only by correlating these studies with others are we likely to gain a clearer picture of the Ca cycle.

Ca-Flux Studies

A more traditional way to study the role of Ca in E-C coupling is monitoring of the size and exchange rates of the cellular Ca pool by radioisotopes of Ca. This work has been difficult to interpret when it is viewed alone; for example, the cellular Ca content is many times the amount needed for full contraction, but most of it must be sequestered and not available for E-C coupling. Langer, Serena & Nudd (54) exploited a tissue culture preparation derived from hearts of newborn rats to study Ca exchange. They found that a freely or easily exchangeable fraction of cell Ca is displaced by exposure of the tissue to small quantities of other heavy metals. Specifically the displacement effectiveness provided a sequence of La > Cd > Zn > Mn > Mg, which is similar to the effects of these ions on E-C coupling. In a subsequent report, these investigators (55) showed that Mn displaced Ca and rapidly decreased contraction strength, while verapamil did not displace cellular Ca and simply prevented replenishment of the Ca as it was lost from the cell. Consistent with this displacement concept, Delahayes (19) found Mn to enter heart cells and interfere with E-C coupling in some direct fashion, in addition to blockage of the transmembrane Ca current.

Tonic Tension

Often two phases of contraction can be seen in cardiac muscle. The initial phase appears as a transient, developing to its peak value and then falling to merge with a slowly developing or steady tonic contraction. These two phases have been seen during long action potentials or during voltage steps [e.g. see Fozzard & Gibbons (31)]. Coraboeuf (16) wrote an excellent review of experimental bases for these two phases, and his discussion is not repeated here. A second article clarifying these two phases was written by Vassort (95), who showed that the phasic tension was well correlated with Ca current in frog atrial muscle. The tonic tension in his experiments was an increasing function of membrane voltage, even to values of greater than +100 mV (inside positive) where Ca current is usually outward. His experiments showed a sensitivity of the tonic tension to Na_o. When he removed Na altogether, a contraction was produced that relaxed very slowly, consistent with a slow loss of Ca, as might occur by a Na:Ca exchange pump. He has suggested that Na_i displaces Ca_i to generate this tonic tension.

The relation of this voltage-dependent tonic contraction to Na-K contractures in heart muscle is interesting. Gibbons & Fozzard (32) studied contractures due to K-depolarization. They found two phases of contracture: a transient one (lasting seconds) and a sustained one (lasting minutes). The transient phase was voltage dependent and sensitive to Na_o, prior stimulation, and other maneuvers favoring loading the cell with Ca. In many respects the transient contracture resembles the tonic tension described by Vassort. The sustained contracture was sensitive to outside Ca during the contracture, and appeared to be due to continued Ca entry into the cell. Kavaler (47) studied sustained tensions seen in frog ventricular muscle during very long voltage clamps. These tensions, which lasted many seconds, were also due to outside Ca during the voltage step. Sakai & Kurihara (76) reported a two-phased contracture as the result of cooling toad heart muscle to 0°, and it will be interesting to compare the properties of these tension phases with those produced by depolarization with current of K.

The various types of tension development do not appear to be artifacts of technique. Rather, they emphasize the complexity of contractile regulation in heart muscle. Ca can be increased in the sarcoplasm by net entry through a Ca channel, via the Na:Ca exchange system, by release from a subcellular compartment such as the SR or the mitochondria, or by unbinding from intracellular membrane sites. Recognition of these possibilities is a major step toward understanding the physiological contraction, as well as interpreting experimental observations such as the variable relationship between Ca current and tension, discussed in the previous section.

One cautionary note is perhaps warranted at this point. Interpretation of contraction is presently entirely in terms of varying sarcoplasmic Ca. The contractile apparatus is a far more complex process itself than a linear expression of Ca_i, and variation in Mg, pH, cooperative protein interactions, or other factors could have independent effects on contraction. These considerations should be remembered when investigators measure isometric tension approximately and infer the level of Ca_i.

INTRACELLULAR RELEASE OF CALCIUM

Voltage-Dependent Factors

If one step of the very complex sequence of events in E-C coupling can be considered the most important one, it is the release mechanism of Ca. Accepting that it is unlikely that all of the activating Ca comes from the extracellular solution in heart muscle, then the Ca-release problem is shared with skeletal muscle. In skeletal muscle, depolarization of the sarcolemma leads to release of Ca from the SR, perhaps via changing the conductance of the SR membrane. Some important progress has been made in developing techniques for monitoring electrical changes across the SR in skeletal muscle (21) and these are noted because of their possible analogy to E-C coupling in heart.

Chandler et al (13) have reported a dipole movement in the surface membrane upon depolarization of frog skeletal muscle that resembles gating currents. This charge movement has voltage- and time-dependent properties similar to contraction, and could represent a link between sarcolemmal depolarization and the SR. Bezanilla & Horowicz (6) stained frog skeletal muscle membrane with Nile Blue A, an agent that changes fluorescence as a function of the electric field across a membrane to which it is attached. They found fluorescence signals that behaved as one might expect of a monitor of the SR membrane potential. Further development of this optical approach to monitoring SR behavior was reported by Oetliker, Baylor & Chandler (67), who compared fluorescence signals with optical retardation. Only one attempt to record fluorescence signals from heart muscle has been reported. Salama & Morad (77) exposed frog hearts to Merocyanine 540 and were able to record optical signals that resembled transmembrane action potentials. One would not expect much signal from the SR of frog ventricle, since it is thought to be rather scanty. Application of this optical approach to the study of heart muscle will not be easy, but it appears to be a promising opportunity to obtain direct information about internal membrane behavior.

Monitoring of Sarcoplasmic Ca

Another candidate for the most important experimental measure in E-C coupling is a dynamic monitor of sarcoplasmic Ca. A number of agents have been used in various tissues to provide a useful signal proportional to Ca activity, including murexide and aequorin. This approach is particularly useful in large cells, where the indicator molecules can be injected directly. All attempts to use these indicators in heart muscle have been unsatisfactory, but the study of E-C coupling in heart would be greatly helped if a method could be devised. Perhaps more effort to develop a Ca-sensitive microelectrode comparable to those now available for Na, K, etc would be productive (14). Monitoring of Ca_i would have other investigative benefits beyond the field of muscle contraction. DeMello (20) reported that injection of Ca and Sr into the cardiac cell leads to electrical uncoupling of that cell from its neighbor. Unfortunately, we do not know if the levels needed for this effect are achievable by physiologic release or the entry of Ca that might occur during the contractile cycle.

"Skinned Fibers"

The development of a satisfactory method of removing the sarcolemma of skeletal muscle fibers has been a boon to the study of E-C coupling in that tissue. Quantitative experiments depended on the development of sufficiently sensitive transducers, the means to attach the muscle segment to the transducers, and a convenient way to change the bathing (artificial sarcoplasmic) solution [Hellam & Podolsky (37)]. Cardiac investigators sought to follow this approach by destroying the sarcolemma of multicellular bundles using glycerol or EDTA [Winegrad (100), Solaro et al (82)].

A more direct method for producing a skinned cardiac fiber has been developed by Fabiato & Fabiato (23). First, the cells are minced and then broken into small fragments in a blender. This results in cell pieces about 10 μm in diameter and 40–50 μm long. The remainder of the sarcolemma is then dissected away with a microneedle. The fiber is attached to a transducer by impaling the ends with microneedles that are then used as transducer arms. Artificial intracellular solution is made with EDTA or EGTA buffers and appropriate amounts of Mg, Ca, ATP, etc. The initial studies of these fibers showed many features similar to skinned skeletal muscle fibers, except that it was rather easy to obtain cyclic contractions and relaxations.

Fabiato & Fabiato (25) published extensive descriptions of their methods and experiments. Tonic tension was generated by raising Ca_i that was strongly buffered with EGTA. The sigmoid relation between pCa (the negative logarithm of [Ca]) and tension resembled that of skeletal muscle, with tension threshold around pCa of 6.75, and was not modified by chemical destruction of the SR. With light buffering of Ca, a small rise to pCa of 7.4 (which would not produce tension in heavily buffered solutions), produced cyclic contractions that resembled the Ca-triggered Ca release of skeletal muscle. Blockage of mitochondrial Ca binding or uptake with azide or ruthenium red did not affect this cyclic release. A reasonable explanation of these cyclic contractions is that regenerative Ca release occurred, and is repeated as soon as the Ca stores of the SR had reloaded themselves. In skeletal muscle, the regenerative Ca release is inhibited by Mg levels of 0.5 to 1 mM, which is approximately the level thought to exist in the sarcoplasm [Polimeni & Page (69)]. For this and other reasons, most investigators doubt that Ca-triggered Ca release is the physiologic process of E-C coupling in skeletal muscle. On the other hand, the experiments of the Fabiatos in heart cells show that the phenomenon occurs reliably at these Mg levels. A second objection that has been made to a physiologic role of the Ca-triggered release is that it is a regenerative (all-or-nothing) process and does not permit the fine gradations of activation that are seen in intact muscle. Fabiato & Fabiato (25) found that the Ca-triggered contraction did scale in size with the quantity of triggering Ca. This would indicate simply an amplifying effect rather than a regenerative one. No clear mechanism for this graded effect is apparent. These Ca-triggered contractions have also been seen by Kerrick & Best (49). Both groups of investigators reported that SR is quite swollen under the conditions of their experiments, and the effect of this distortion of SR geometry on experimental results is not known.

It is not yet clear to this reviewer that we must accept the conclusion that Ca-triggered Ca release is the mechanism of E-C coupling in heart muscle. This is a fascinating phenomenon, and its study will continue to provide very good insights into the E-C coupling process. Alternative explanations can be given for the phenomena seen, and there are too many uncertainties in the composition of the artificial sarcoplasmic solutions. Heart muscle has a transmembrane Ca current closely associated with contraction, but it is probably insufficient in quantity to produce the contraction (see section on Ca current and contraction). It could well be the source of trigger Ca. Therefore, the Ca-triggered release of Ca is a plausible, but not yet proved, step in cardiac E-C coupling.

A mechanism that is also seen in skeletal skinned fibers is a phasic contraction in response to changing anions in the perfusing solution. The SR appears to be permeable to Cl, but not to larger anions such as propionate. If the fiber has its SR loaded with Ca in the presence of propionate, and then the solution is changed to an identical one except for Cl in place of the propionate, the fiber undergoes a phasic contraction. This solution change is thought to result in the interior of the SR becoming more negative because of entry of Cl ions. A similar effect has been seen when K is replaced by Na or Li, so it appears to be an electrical effect on the SR rather than a specific anion effect. The physiologic role of this "electrical" release of Ca in heart muscle is not clear, but it is a reasonable competitor of Ca-triggered release as the normal E-C coupling event. This "electrical" triggering of Ca release has been shown to exist in skinned heart muscle by Kerrick & Best (49), but few details of this phenomenon have been investigated. Bloom, Brady & Langer (9) found no effect of cation substitutions on skinned mouse cells. They did not investigate anion changes.

Sarcoplasmic Reticulum

Significant progress has been made in quantitative electron microscopy using stereologic techniques to estimate organelle volume and surface area of redundant membranes. Page & McCallister (68) have determined these quantitative details of SR in rat ventricular muscle, noting differences from fast skeletal muscle. Careful studies by Solaro & Briggs (81) of Ca uptake by SR isolated from dog ventricle showed 300–400 nmoles Ca/gm wet heart weight with 10^{-5} M free Ca and about half this much with 10^{-6} M free Ca. These calculations depend on blockage of Ca binding by other cellular structures and a variety of other extrapolations from broken-cell studies. Complementary studies of Ca requirements for myofibrillar ATPase by Solaro et al (82) showed half-maximal activation at 2.4×10^{-6}M free Ca. To be achieved in muscle it would require about 22 μmoles Ca/kg wet heart weight. The relation between Ca binding to myofibrils and ATPase activity or tension was not simple, so that there must be a variety of binding sites, only some of which influence tension. It has become commonly accepted that Ca binding is to troponin, but Szent-Györgyi (83) pointed out that Ca may bind to myosin, and thereby regulate contraction in molluscan muscles. This myosin regulation of contraction is widespread in the animal kingdom, but its role in mammalian heart muscle is not clear.

A fascinating series of experiments have been accomplished with Ca ionophores. These ionophores facilitate passive ion movement across membranes, and several have been shown to release Ca from loaded SR. Schwartz et al (80) have shown a positive inotropic effect of RO2-2985 in anesthetized dogs, even when catecholamine effects were prevented by pretreatment with reserpine. Another ionophore, X-537A, was reported by de Guzman & Pressman (18) also to produce a positive inotropic effect. Both groups of investigators raise the possibility that these agents or other ionophores might find important clinical use in heart failure. They also are fascinating probes to assist in understanding membrane transport of ions, but they may not help much in sorting out the normal mechanism of Ca release from the SR. A study of Ca uptake by SR in cardiac hypertrophy and failure by Ito et al (40) suggested that these conditions might be associated with a quantitative defect in SR.

Length-Dependence of Activation

The concept of "active state," presented by A. V. Hill to assist in understanding the tension responses to quick length changes, has been with muscle physiology for 40 years. The original concept has been subject to modification in recent years, see Julian & Moss (42). Assuming that activation is constant, tension of a muscle is determined by its length; that is to say, by the overlap of its myosin and actin filaments. A major difference between skeletal and cardiac muscle was thought to be that skeletal muscle was fully activated during a twitch, whereas heart muscle was partially activated. Activation in this sense meant the extent to which all of the Ca sites of troponin were saturated by Ca. This variable activation gave heart muscle a flexibility in its contraction strength beyond that achieved by variable myosin-actin overlap. This simplified view of skeletal muscle has been challenged recently. Taylor & Rüdel (85) showed buckling of myofibrils in the center of the skeletal fiber that is activated at short lengths. This appears to be related to a decreased release of Ca at short lengths, since monitoring of light signals from injected aequorin are less at shorter lengths [Taylor (86)]. When they used a skinned skeletal fiber to investigate tension at short lengths with maximal Ca activation, Schoenberg & Podolsky (79) found much greater tension than that produced by tetanic electrical stimulation.

The part of the length-tension relationship with positive slope (short lengths) is of special importance for heart muscle, because it appears to function normally in that region. Indeed, this is an important part of the basis for the Frank-Starling relationship. Allen, Jewell & Murray (1) studied length-tension relations in intact kitten ventricular muscle. They found that the positive slope part of the relationship, when normalized for maximal contraction at optimal length, showed less tension with lower external Ca. This suggested that less Ca was released at shorter lengths, but it could be because of less transmembrane Ca current, decreased intracellular stores of Ca, some defect in release from the SR, or a change in Ca uptake by the SR. These possibilities were examined directly by Fabiato & Fabiato (27) using the skinned fiber. Tonic tension generated by heavily buffered Ca was much larger than those expected from electrically stimulated contractions at short lengths. Ca-triggered contractions were smaller than tonic contractions at equivalent lengths, and they resembled tensions produced by electrical stimulation.

This length dependence of Ca-triggered contractions could be due to poor loading of the SR or to incomplete release. Caffeine exposure leads to release of the remaining Ca, and its use showed that residual Ca was large at short lengths. The most reasonable explanation of these excellent experiments is that Ca-triggered release of Ca was less effective at short lengths, leaving larger amounts of Ca in the SR. It was not possible to be certain that uptake of Ca by the SR was normal, but changes in uptake would not explain the results. It therefore appears that the positive slope part of the length-tension curve in heart muscle is the result both of changes in myosin-actin overlap and of decreased release of Ca from the SR.

We have long been concerned that part of the complex mechanical behavior of cardiac muscle was caused by internal shortening in a muscle bundle. This could occur in a multicellular preparation by realignment of cells, but it could also occur within a cell by realignment of myofibrils. Krueger & Pollack (51) documented this realignment. They showed 7% shortening of the sarcomeres at optimal length for tension development, but more than this for shorter lengths. This internal shortening could not only change the myosin-actin overlap, but also alter Ca release from the SR during the course of a single twitch. With this increase in complexity of the events during a single cardiac excitation, one begins to wonder if any mechanical studies could provide quantitative results unless they contained the means of sarcomere length clamping.

INTRACELLULAR Na AND CONTRACTION

The original demonstration by Schatzmann (78) that cardiac glycosides block the sarcolemmal Na-K pump led eventually to the suggestion that cardiac contraction was regulated by Na_i [e.g. Gadsby, Niedergerke & Page (36)]. The contractile proteins themselves appeared to have little dependence on Na_i or K_i within reasonable limits, but cell gain of Na and/or loss of K was usually associated with increased contraction strength [e.g. see Müller (64), Langer (52)]. The ion of major importance for contraction has long been considered to be Ca, but the relation of Na_i to Ca_i was obscure. Several important facts were apparent: free Ca in the sarcoplasm is kept at a low level, below $10^{-7}M$, so that the electrochemical gradient for Ca favored its entry; maintenance of a steady cellular Ca level would require continued uphill transport out of the cell; Ca_o is essential for continued contractility; and reduction in Na_o increased contraction strength.

Recent studies of Na and Ca fluxes across membranes have led to an intriguing but incomplete picture of interdependent Na and Ca transport [Blaustein (7), Reuter (73)]. Ca appears to leave cardiac cells either in exchange for Ca or for Na. The movement into the cell of two or three Na ions passively down their electrochemical gradient leads to extrusion of one Ca ion, apparently by a membrane transport shuttle. Na and Ca compete for sites on the shuttle at the inside and outside surfaces of the membrane. This results in the following relationship. Increased Na_o favors Ca exit and increased Ca_o favors Ca:Ca exchange; increased Na_i favors Na:Na exchange and inhibits Ca exit. Inhibiting Ca exit would result in a net cell gain of Ca, but it also appears that increased Na_i favors Ca entry. Arguing from the carrier shuttle model, we can see that the carrier that moves Ca into the cell must be returned to the outside somehow, before it can reload with Ca. It is possible, by this reasoning, that increased Na_i leads to Na exit on this return trip. Complex models have been suggested in the articles mentioned (7, 73) and in other articles, but they contain at least 24–32 rate constants, and cannot be rigorously tested. One very interesting observation in noncardiac tissue is that Ca efflux is voltage dependent, with reduction in efflux on depolarization [Russell & Blaustein (75), Mullins & Brinley (65)]. Comparable observations in heart muscle have been difficult to accomplish, but Jundt et al (43) reported results of decreased Na_o on Ca exit to be the same with and without KCl depolarization (–76 mV to –12 mV). This tends to support their impression that the Na:Ca exchange in heart muscle is 2:1 and is electroneutral.

The laboratory of Reuter continued to investigate several other aspects of the Na:Ca exchange [Jundt et al (43)]. Using agents that release Ca from intracellular stores (caffeine, cyanide, and ionophore X537A) they could produce increased Ca efflux. This efflux was primarily dependent on external Na and Ca (Na:Ca exchange and Ca:Ca exchange). Under all conditions studied, the pumping ratio was two Na's for each Ca transported. The rise in Ca_i could be monitored by tension recording, and the pump could prevent tension development (keep Ca_i below about 10^{-7}M) if Na and Ca are present outside the cell. They also showed that Ca release from mitochondria is an important source of Ca_i under certain experimental, but not necessarily physiological, conditions. This latter question of the role of mitochondria in Ca uptake and release was nicely discussed in an editorial by Carafoli (11).

While these results of Jundt et al (43) support the previous description of the Na:Ca transport system in general, they point out a serious problem. Energetically, the 2:1 pump ratio is sufficient to keep Ca_i to levels of 10^{-7}M only of Na_i is 1–2 mM. Either Na_i is lower than usually estimated or some other factors must be involved in the removal of Ca from the cell. Evidence in favor of a role for ATP in achieving the gradient of Ca is not clear. A mechanism that can be suggested, but not supported experimentally, is a stepwise removal of Ca. First it is pumped into the SR by an ATP-dependent pump. Then it is transferred to the outside by the Na:Ca pump across the terminal cisterna membrane. This would also imply that the Na concentration of importance is that in the SR. However, there are reasons to believe that the SR may have a concentration of Na not very different from the external solution, so this suggested mechanism is suspect.

Only recently has the activity of internal Na been measured in heart muscle. Using glass microelectrodes made of NAS_{27-04} glass, Lee & Fozzard (57) measured intracellular activities of K and Na in resting rabbit papillary muscle and compared these with chemically determined K and Na concentrations. The activity of K was 82.6 mM, with an activity coefficient of 0.612, and the activity of Na was 5.7 mM, with an activity coefficient of 0.175. It does not come as any surprise that the activity coefficient of Na is so low, since similar results have been reported previously for *Carcinus* muscle fibers, squid giant axons, frog skeletal muscle, and other tissues. Nevertheless, it emphasizes that when interpretations of experimental studies depend on chemical concentrations of Na, they may be quite misleading. Ideally, Na activity should be measured under the experimental conditions used for Na:Ca exchange studies.

Tillisch & Langer (87) studied the effect of increased Na_o on ion fluxes and contraction strength in rabbit intraventricular septa. Increase of Na_o to 200 mM produced a fall in contraction strength as one would expect from the increase in Na_o. Rapidly thereafter, the muscle recovered its contraction strength. This recovery rate was dependent on stimulus frequency and was associated with an uptake of Na. These and other flux observations were consistent with the Na:Ca exchange mechanism described.

It is surprising to this reviewer that so few studies of the Na:Ca pump have been published in the last several years, considering its probable importance to cellular Ca balance. We are indebted to the laboratories of Reuter and Langer for almost all the studies available in heart muscle.

Weiss, Tritthart & Walter (99) found that the effects of Na withdrawal on contraction strength and on Ca-dependent action potentials had similar time courses. Cat ventricular muscles were perfused with solutions containing 14 mM K, which produced depolarization to about -50 mV, inactivating the fast Na system, and left action potentials dependent on Ca_o. If Na_o was then reduced to 50%, the action potential was rapidly reduced in area and contractions increased along a similar time course. Assuming that the contraction strength is a reasonable monitor of Ca_i, the increase in contraction indicates an increase in Ca_i and, thereby, a reduction in the Ca driving force for the action potentials. Weiss et al (99) suggested that decreased Na_o and its consequent decrease in Na_i produce the raised Ca_i. If the fiber is not stimulated for a 10-minute period, the action potentials and contractions produced by renewed stimulation are similar to those obtained before reduction of Na_o. This is explained by presuming that the membrane Ca pump can return Ca_i to its previous level with time, in spite of maintained low Na_o and Na_i. They interpret these results to indicate that the Ca channel is not influenced by Na, but that the effect of reduced Na on the transmembrane Ca gradient indirectly produces smaller action potentials. It seems equally plausible that the effect of lowering Na_o is an increased entry of Ca into the cell through the membrane channel. Almost the same current could be passing through the channel, but the proportion due to Na movement is reduced.

This would allow increased Ca entry, and overload the Ca pump during repetitive stimulation. Studies of pump transients might give us clues as to the nature of the Na influence, if it is more than an interference with Ca entry through the membrane channel.

Another sort of approach to the role of Na_i in control of contraction strength was considered by Horackova & Vassort (39). They studied the effects of veratrine on the action potential of frog atria in a double sucrose gap voltage clamp. A marked slowing of the inactivation of Na current was found that greatly increased total inward Na current sensitive to TTX. There was a concomitant increase in contraction strength, which they ascribed to an increased Na_i. No apparent effect of veratrine on the Ca current was seen. This interpretation was supported by the finding that low concentrations of TTX blocked the inotropic effect of veratrine.

INOTROPIC AGENTS

Catecholamines

Two of the most potent natural agents for increasing strength of contracture of heart muscle are epinephrine and norepinephrine. Two major effects of these hormones shown in recent years are an influence on the slow inward current channel that controls Ca current and an activation of adenyl cyclase that results in increased intracellular levels of cAMP. Some valuable experiments have been published on these subjects in the last few years.

The catecholamines raise the plateau of the cardiac Purkinje action potential, shorten the action potential duration, and accelerate the pacemaker potential. Associated with these effects is an increase in inward Ca current. In a pair of papers Tsien, Giles & Greengard (91) and Tsien (93) showed that the catecholamines also influenced potassium currents, accelerating the rate of change of I_K with voltage changes. These effects did not appear to be due to increased Ca_i, and Tsien sought to determine if they depended on increase in cAMP levels. Tsien introduced cAMP into the Purkinje fiber iontophoretically through an intracellular micropipette, and produced the same sort of changes in the action potential (92). He did not examine Ca currents directly, so he could not conclude that cAMP mediated those effects. Reuter (74) has reported a direct effect of cAMP on the Ca current. A study of Ca-mediated action potentials in depolarized or TTX-blocked guinea pig hearts showed electrical changes and increased contraction strength that correlated temporally with increased levels of cAMP measured chemically [Watanabe & Besch (97)].

The mechanism of action of cAMP on contraction could also be directly on Ca release from the SR. Kirchberger et al (50) reported that cAMP stimulation of a protein kinase results in enhanced Ca uptake by isolated SR, so the mechanism of cAMP action could be through increased SR storage capacity for Ca. In the same laboratory [Tada et al (84)] they found that epinephrine had no effect on Na-K-ATPase in isolated sarcolemma.

A direct effect of cAMP on Ca capacity of SR was reported by Fabiato & Fabiato (26). They used a skinned preparation and showed that cyclic AMP increased the size of a Ca-triggered contraction. They also saw an accelerated rate of relaxation, consistent with an increased rate of Ca uptake by the SR. No direct effect of cAMP was seen on the sensitivity of the myofibrils to Ca. Their studies lend support to the concept that cAMP influences contraction strength by its effects on the SR, but they do not rule out other additive effects, such as an influence on the Ca channel. In a series of voltage clamp studies of Ca current, Reuter (74) has developed very strong evidence that Ca current is increased in response to catecholamines by rapidly increasing the number of Ca channels in the membrane. This is an important point to sort out in the future. For example, are the channels present but only activated by catecholamines or are more channels synthesized?

The recent experiments discussed all point to a major role of cAMP in the positive inotropic effect and in some of the membrane effects of catecholamines. However, Henry, Dobson & Sobel (38) were unable to find any stimulatory effect of papaverine (a phosphodiesterase inhibitor) on contraction in guinea pig hearts, even though levels of cAMP rose substantially. On the other hand, cAMP levels did not rise when the guinea pig hearts were perfused with glucagon, even though contraction strength did increase substantially. Although most evidence favors the cAMP mechanism for the contractile effect of catecholamines, there remains sufficient conflict in the reported data to require continued study.

Digitalis Glycosides

We are approaching the 200th anniversary of the first paper describing the use of foxglove for the treatment of heart failure. The mechanism of digitalis action has challenged and frustrated the physiologist for decades. As discussed earlier (see section on intracellular Na and contraction), a major hypothesis is that digitalis inhibits the Na-K pump and produces an increase in Na_i. This in turn leads to accumulation of Ca in the cell, adding to the stores available for release. Increase in Na_i by 5 mM would have a major effect on Ca_i via the Na:Ca exchange system and be sufficient to produce the observed contractile changes (73). Alternative ideas include an influence on the membrane Ca current, a direct effect on the contractile proteins, etc. Application of our most recently developed experimental tools has added to our knowledge concerning the influence of digitalis on E-C coupling.

Several investigators have found no effect of digitalis on the Ca current under voltage clamp conditions. McDonald, Nawrath & Trautwein (60) presented their observations in cat ventricular muscle, showing an early positive inotropic effect in the absence of any change in membrane currents. After more prolonged exposure to dihydro-ouabain, they found an apparent fall in Ca current and a rise in the outward current. The reduced Ca current was seen when the fiber showed some steady tension, suggesting a rise in Ca_i. Morad & Greenspan (63) found similar results in frog ventricle, and Vassort (94) found a rise in contraction strength in frog atrial muscle without a change in Ca current. As noted before, McCans et al (59) found that verapamil did not prevent increase in contraction strength by ouabain.

It is reasonable to conclude that digitalis does not act via an increase in membrane Ca current through the slow channel described earlier. A fascinating phenomenon provoked by digitalis is a transient afterpotential. Ferrier & Moe (28) suggested that this transient afterpotential might be due to a transient influx of Ca. Its role in digitalis-induced arrhythmias is likely (56), but the ionic origin of the current is not yet clear. This effect of glycosides is associated with an increased membrane "noise" (44), which is difficult to analyze in terms of changes in channel behavior or pump sites.

Digitalis could have a direct effect on the contractile proteins. The technique of skinned cardiac cells should be appropriate to test this data. Fabiato & Fabiato (24) exposed skinned cells to strophanthidin and found no effect on cyclic or tonic contractions. It therefore seems unlikely that digitalis exerts a direct effect on contractile proteins or directly influences the SR.

The action of digitalis has also been associated with cellular K balance. Morad & Greenspan (62) suggested that digitalis might act by accelerating K loss via a Ca:K pump, thereby moving more Ca into the cell. While the literature of digitalis mechanisms is replete with studies relating inotropic effects to K loss, a few new observations have been made. Poole-Wilson & Langer (70) produced a cellular acidosis by increasing the P_{CO_2} of the perfusing solution to a rabbit ventricular preparation. During the acidosis a marked digitalis contractile effect was seen without loss of K. Cohen, Dent & Noble (15) offered some evidence that ouabain can stimulate the Na:K pump in sheep Purkinje fibers, and Blood (8) found that glycoside levels for that effect do produce increased contraction strength. They suggested that the mechanism may be via reducing K_o in a limited extracellular space. Digitalis does produce moderate depolarization of the resting potential [McDonald, Nawrath & Trautwein (60), Morad & Greenspan (63)]. It is usually assumed that this is due to a gradual K loss from the cell and Na gain. Walker (96) recorded K activity in Purkinje fibers using a liquid ion-exchanger microelectrode. He found depolarization of the resting membrane without changes in intracellular K activity after exposure to ouabain. We therefore cannot say that the depolarization is due to K loss.

We continue to find that most evidence favors action of digitalis on contracture strength by altering Na_i and secondarily Ca flux. Yet digitalis has additional membrane actions that need to be sorted out before we can be satisfied with this explanation.

SUMMARY

The study of E-C coupling in heart muscle has been facilitated by the recent availability of reasonably reliable voltage clamp techniques and a method of "skinning" cardiac cells. We have also had the introduction of several new ideas, including a Na:Ca exchange pump, metabolically controlled Ca storage capacity of the SR, and length dependence of Ca release. Consideration of the mechanism of E-C coupling in striated muscle as a general model has enabled transfer of insights gained studying fast skeletal muscle to heart muscle. On the other hand, many of the complexities of regulation of heart muscle contraction are manifested in fast skeletal muscle, as investigators explore the details of E-C coupling. On the whole, it is interesting to be an investigator in this field, as the E-C coupling mechanisms under investigation are being located in many nonmuscle cells, for such varied functions as control of cell shape during growth and excitation-secretion coupling.

The last few years have seen the establishment of the existence and importance of a channel in the membrane that admits Ca as a function of electric field. We remain uncertain, however, of the details of relation of this current to the size of contraction. We have begun to explore the characteristics and role of the Na:Ca exchange mechanism in regulating the magnitude of intracellular Ca stores. Most investigators feel that this finally represents the necessary link in understanding digitalis action. A powerful but technically demanding tool is available in the "skinned" cardiac cell, permitting direct studies of Ca release from the SR in more-or-less intact cells. One dramatic finding with that technique is the demonstration of length-dependence of Ca release. On the horizon are methods of monitoring any possible transient potentials across subcellular organelle membranes and directly determining transient changes in free Ca in the sarcoplasm. This reviewer cannot help but feel that the next three or four years will be exciting ones in this field, and that the next review of E-C coupling will make interesting reading.

Literature Cited

1. Allen, D. G., Jewell, B. R., Murray, J. W. 1974. The contribution of activation processes to the length-tension relation of cardiac muscle. *Nature* 248:606–7
2. Allen, D. G., Jewell, B. R., Wood, E. H. 1976. Studies on the contractility of mammalian myocardium at low rates of stimulation. *J. Physiol.* 254:1–18
3. Baker, P. F. 1972. Transport and metabolism of calcium ions in nerve. *Prog. Biophys. Mol. Biol.* 24:177–223
4. Baumann, K., Reichel, H. 1974. Time dependence of frequency potentiation in the isolated guinea pig's atrium. *Pfleugers Arch.* 350:69–80
5. Beeler, G. W. Jr., Reuter, H. 1970. The relation between membrane potential, membrane currents, and activation of contraction in ventricular myocardial fibres. *J. Physiol.* 207:211–29
6. Bezanilla, F., Horowicz, P. 1975. Fluorescence intensity changes associated with contractile activation in frog muscle stained with Nile Blue A. *J. Physiol.* 246:709–35
7. Blaustein, M. P. 1974. The interrelationships between sodium and calcium fluxes across cell membranes. *Rev. Physiol. Biochem. Pharmacol.* 70:33–82
8. Blood, B. E. 1975. The influence of low doses of ouabain and potassium ions on sheep Purkinje fibre contractility. *J. Physiol.* 251:69–70
9. Bloom, S., Brady, A. J., Langer, G. A. 1974. Calcium metabolism and active tension in mechanically disaggregated heart muscle *J. Mol. Cell. Cardiol.* 6:137–48

10. Bowditch, H. P. 1871. Über die Eigenthümlichkeiten der Reizbarkeit, welche die Muskelfasern des Herzens zeigen. *Ber. Ges. Wiss. Leipzeig* 23:652–89
11. Carafoli, E. 1975. Mitochondria, Ca transport and regulation of heart contraction and metabolism. *J. Mol. Cell. Cardiol.* 7:83–87
12. Carrier, G. O., Lullmann, H., Neubauer, L., Peters, T. 1974. The significance of a fast exchanging superficial calcium fraction for the regulation of contractile force on heart muscle. *J. Mol. Cell. Cardiol.* 6:333–48
13. Chandler, W. K., Schneider, M. F., Rakowski, R. F., Adrian, R. H. 1976. Charge movements in skeletal muscle. *Philos. Trans. R. Soc. London Ser. B* 270:501–5
14. Christoffersen, G. R. J., Johansen, E. S. 1976. Microdesign for a calcium-sensitive electrode. *Anal. Chim Acta* 81:191–95
15. Cohen, I., Dent, J., Noble, D. 1975. The influence of extracellular potassium ions on the action of ouabain on membrane currents in sheep Purkinje fibers. *J. Physiol.* 249:42–43P
16. Coraboeuf, E. 1974. Membrane electrical activity and double component contraction in cardiac tissue. *J. Mol. Cell. Cardiol.* 6:215–25
17. Cranefield, P. F. 1975. *The Conduction of the Cardiac Impulse.* Mt. Kisco, New York: Futura. 404 pp.
18. de Guzman, N. T., Pressman, B. C. 1974. The inotropic effects of the calcium ionophore X-537A in the anesthetized dog. *Circulation* 49:1072–77

19. Delahayes, J. F. 1975. Depolarization-induced movement of Mn₊₊ across the cell membrane in the guinea pig myocardium: Its effect on the mechanical response. *Circ. Res.* 36:713–18
20. DeMello, W. C. 1975. Effect of intracellular injection of calcium and strontium on cell communication in heart. *J. Physiol.* 250:231–46
21. Ebashi, S. 1976. Excitation-contraction coupling. *Ann. Rev. Physiol.* 38:293–313
22. Edman, K. A. P., Jóhannsson, M. 1976. The contractile state of rabbit papillary muscle in relation to stimulation frequency. *J. Physiol.* 254:565–82
23. Fabiato, A., Fabiato, F. 1972. Excitation-contraction coupling of isolated cardiac fibres with disrupted or closed sarcolemmas. Calcium dependent cyclic and tonic contraction. *Circ. Res.* 31:293–307
24. Fabiato, A., Fabiato, F. 1973. Activation of skinned cardiac cells. Subcellular aspects of cardioactive drugs. *Eur. J. Cardiol.* 1/2:143–55
25. Fabiato, A., Fabiato, F. 1975. Contractions induced by a calcium-triggered release of calcium from the sarcoplasmic reticulum of single skinned cardiac cells. *J. Physiol.* 249:469–96; 497–518
26. Fabiato, A., Fabiato, F. 1975. Relaxing and inotropic effects of cyclic AMP on skinned cardiac cells. *Nature* 253:556–58
27. Fabiato, A., Fabiato, F. 1975. Dependence of the contractile activation of skinned cardiac cells on the sarcomere length. *Nature* 256:54–56
28. Ferrier, G. R., Moe, G. K. 1973. Effect of calcium on acetylstrophanthidin-induced transient depolarization in canine Purkinje tissue. *Circ. Res.* 33:508–15
29. Forester, G. V., Mainwood, G. W. 1974. Interval dependent inotropic effects in the rat myocardium and the effect of calcium. *Pfleugers Arch.* 352:189–96
30. Fozzard, H. A., Beeler, G. W. Jr. 1975. The voltage clamp and cardiac electrophysiology. *Circ. Res.* 37:403–13
31. Fozzard, H. A., Gibbons, W. R. 1973. Action potential and contraction of heart muscle. *Am. J. Cardiol.* 31:182–92
32. Gibbons, W. R., Fozzard, H. A. 1971. High potassium and low sodium contractures in sheep cardiac muscle. *J. Gen. Physiol.* 58:483–510
33. Gibbons, W. R., Fozzard, H. A. 1971. Voltage dependence and time dependence of contraction in sheep cardiac Purkinje fibers. *Circ. Res.* 28:446–60
34. Gibbons, W. R., Fozzard, H. A. 1975. Relationships between voltage and tension in sheep Purkinje fibers. *J. Gen. Physiol.* 65:345–65
35. Gibbons, W. R., Fozzard, H. A. 1975. Slow inward current and contraction of sheep cardiac Purkinje fibers. *J. Gen. Physiol.* 65:367–84
36. Gadsby, D. C., Niedergerke, R., Page, S. 1971. Do intracellular concentrations of potassium or sodium regulate the strength of the heart beat? *Nature* 232:651–53
37. Hellam, D. C., Podolsky, R. J. 1969. Force measurements in skinned muscle fibres. *J. Physiol.* 200:807–19
38. Henry, P. D., Dobson, J. G. Jr., Sobel, B. E. 1975. Dissociations between changes in myocardial cyclic adenosine monophosphate and contractility. *Circ. Res.* 36:392–400
39. Horackova, M., Vassort, G. 1974. Excitation-contraction coupling in frog heart. *Pfleugers Arch.* 352:291–302
40. Ito, Y., Suko, J., Chidsey, C. A. 1974. Intracellular calcium and myocardial contractility. V. Calcium uptake of sarcoplasmic reticulum fraction in hypertrophied and failing rabbit hearts. *J. Mol. Cell. Cardiol.* 6:237–48
41. Johnson, E. A., Lieberman, M. 1971. Heart: Excitation and contraction. *Ann. Rev. Physiol.* 33:479–532
42. Julian, F. J., Moss, R. L. 1976. The concept of active state in striated muscle. *Circ. Res.* 38:53–59
43. Jundt, H., Porzig, H., Reuter, H., Stucki, J. W. 1975. The effect of substances releasing intracellular calcium ions on sodium-dependent calcium efflux from guinea-pig auricles. *J. Physiol.* 246:229–54
44. Kass, R. S., Lederer, W. J., Tsien, R. W. 1976. Current fluctuations in strophanthidin-treated cardiac Purkinje fibers. *Biophys. J.* 16:25a
45. Kass, R. S., Tsien, R. W. 1975. Multiple effects of calcium antagonists in plateau currents in cardiac Purkinje fibers. *J. Gen. Physiol.* 66:169–92
46. Kaufmann, R., Bayer, R., Fürniss, T., Krause, H., Tritthart, H. 1974. Calcium-movement controlling cardiac contractility. II. Analog computation of cardiac excitation-contraction coupling on the basis of calcium kinetics in a

multicompartmental model. *J. Mol. Cell. Cardiol.* 6:543–60

47. Kavaler, F. 1974. Electromechanical time course in frog ventricle: manipulation of calcium level during voltage clamp. *J. Mol. Cell. Cardiol.* 6:575–80

48. Kavaler, F., Harris, R. S., Lee, R. J., Fisher, V. J. 1971. Frequency-force behavior of in situ ventricular myocardium in the dog. *Circ. Res.* 28:533–44

49. Kerrick, W. G. L., Best, P. M. 1974. Calcium ion release in mechanically disrupted heart cells. *Science* 183:435–37

50. Kirchberger, M. A., Tada, M., Repke, D. I., Katz, A. M. 1972. Cyclic adenosine 3', 5'-monophosphate-dependent protein kinase stimulation of calcium uptake by canine cardiac microsomes. *J. Mol. Cell. Cardiol.* 4:673–80

51. Krueger, J. W., Pollack, G. H. 1975. Myocardial sarcomere dynamics during isometric contraction. *J. Physiol.* 251:627–44

52. Langer, G. A. 1968. Ion fluxes in cardiac excitation and their relation to myocardial contractility. *Physiol. Rev.* 48:708–57

53. Langer, G. A. 1973. Heart: Excitation-contraction coupling. *Ann. Rev. Physiol.* 35:55–86

54. Langer, G. A., Serena, S. D., Nudd, L. M. 1974. Cation exchange in heart cell culture: Correlation with effects on contractile force. *J. Mol. Cell. Cardiol.* 6:149–62

55. Langer, G. A., Serena, S. D., Nudd, L. M. 1975. Localization of contractile-dependent Ca: Comparison of manganese and varapamil in cardiac and skeletal muscle. *Am. J. Physiol.* 229:1003–7

56. Lederer, W. J., Tsien, R. W. 1977. Transient inward current underlying arrhythmogenic effects of cardiotonic steroids in Purkinje fibers. *J. Physiol.* In press

57. Lee, C. O., Fozzard, H. A. 1975. Activities of potassium and sodium ions in rabbit heart muscle. *J. Gen. Physiol.* 65:695–708

58. Mahler, F., Yoran, C., Ross, J. Jr. 1974. Inotropic effect of tachycardia and post-stimulation potentiation in the conscious dog. *Am. J. Physiol.* 227:569–75

59. McCans, J. L., Lindemayer, G. E., Munson, R. G., Evans, R. W., Schwartz, A. 1974. A dissociation of positive staircase (Bowditch) from ouabain-induced positive inotropism: Use of verapamil. *Circ. Res.* 35:439–47

60. McDonald, T. F., Nawrath, H., Trautwein, W. 1975. Membrane currents and tension in cat ventricular muscle treated with cardiac glycosides. *Circ. Res.* 37:674–82

61. Morad, M., Goldman, Y. 1973. Excitation-contraction coupling in heart muscle: Membrane control of development of tension. *Prog. Biophys. Mol. Biol.* 27:259–316

62. Morad, M., Greenspan, A. M. 1973. Excitation-contraction coupling as a possible site for the action of digitalis on heart muscle. In *Cardiac Arrhythmias*, ed. L. S. Dreifus, W. Likoff, pp. 479–89. New York: Grune & Stratton. 681 pp.

63. Morad, M., Greenspan, A. M. 1975. Electromechanical studies on the inotropic effects of acetylstrophanthidin in ventricular muscle. *J. Physiol.* 253:357–84

64. Müller, P. 1965. Ouabain effects on cardiac contraction, action potential and cellular potassium. *Circ. Res.* 17:46–56

65. Mullins, L. J., Brinley, F. J. Jr. 1975. Sensitivity of calcium efflux from squid axons to changes in membrane potential. *J. Gen. Physiol.* 65:135–52

66. New, W., Trautwein, W. 1972. The ionic nature of slow inward current and its relation to contraction. *Pfluegers Arch.* 334:24–38

67. Oetliker, H., Baylor, S. M., Chandler, W. K. 1975. Simultaneous changes in fluoresence and optical retardation in single muscle fibres during activity. *Nature* 357:693–96

68. Page, E., McCallister, L. P. 1973. Quantitative electron microscopic description of heart muscle cells. *Am. J. Cardiol.* 31:172–81

69. Polimeni, P. I., Page, E. 1973. Magnesium in heart muscle. *Circ. Res.* 33:367–74

70. Poole-Wilson, P. A., Langer, G. A. 1975. Glycoside inotropy in the absence of an increase in potassium efflux in the rabbit heart. *Circ. Res.* 37:390–95

71. Reuter, H. 1973. Divalent cations as charge carriers in excitable membranes. *Prog. Biophys. Mol. Biol.* 26:1–43

72. Reuter, H. 1973. Time- and voltage-dependent contractile responses in mammalian cardiac muscle. *Eur. J. Cardiol.* 1/2:177–81

73. Reuter, H. 1974. Brief review: Exchange of calcium ions in the mammalian myocardium: Mechanism and physiological significance. *Circ. Res.* 34:599–605

74. Reuter, H. 1974. Localization of beta adrenergic receptors and effects of noradrenaline and cyclic nucleotides on action potentials, ionic currents, and tension in mammalian cardiac muscle. *J. Physiol.* 242:429–51

75. Russell, J. M., Blaustein, M. P. 1974. Calcium efflux from barnacle muscle fibers. Dependence on external cations. *J. Gen. Physiol.* 63:144–67

76. Sakai, T., Kurihara, S. 1974. The rapid cooling contracture of toad cardiac muscles. *Jpn. J. Physiol.* 24:649–66

77. Salama, G., Morad, M. 1976. Merocyanine 540 as an optical probe of transmembrane electrical activity in the heart. *Science* 191:485–87

78. Schatzmann, H. J. 1953. Herzglykoside als Hemmstuffe für den aktiven Kalcium- und Natrium-transport durch die Erythrocytenmembranen. *Helv. Physiol. Pharmakol. Acta* 11:346–54

79. Schoenberg, M., Podolsky, R. J. 1972. Length-force relation of calcium activated muscle fibers. *Science* 176:52–54

80. Schwartz, A., Lewis, R. M., Hanley, H. G., Munson, R. G., Dial, F. D., Ray, M. V. 1974. Hemodynamic and biochemical effects of a new positive inotropic agent: Antibiotic ionophore RO2-2985. *Circ. Res.* 34:102–11

81. Solaro, R. J., Briggs, F. N. 1974. Estimating the functional capabilities of sarcoplasmic reticulum in cardiac muscle: Calcium binding. *Circ. Res.* 34:531–40

82. Solaro, R. J., Wise, R. M., Shiner, J. S., Briggs, F. N. 1974. Calcium requirements for cardiac myofibrillar activation. *Circ. Res.* 34:525–30

83. Szent-Györgyi, A. G. 1975. Calcium regulation of muscle contraction. *Biophys. J.* 15:707–23

84. Tada, M., Kirschberger, M. A., Iorio, J. M., Katz, A. M. 1975. Control of cardiac sarcolemmal adenylate cyclose and sodium, potassium-activated ATPase activities. *Circ. Res.* 36:8–17

85. Taylor, S. R., Rüdel, R. 1970. Striated muscle fibers: Inactivation of contraction induced by shortening. *Science* 167:882–84

86. Taylor, S. R. 1974. Decreased activation in skeletal muscle fibers at short lengths. In *The Physiological Basis of Starling's Law of the Heart*, pp. 93–108.

Ciba Found. Symp. 24 (New Ser.). Amsterdam:Elsevier

87. Tillisch, J. H., Langer, G. A. 1974. Myocardial mechanical responses and ionic exchange in high sodium perfusate. *Circ. Res.* 34:40–50

88. Trautwein, W. 1973. Membrane currents in cardiac muscle fibers. *Physiol. Rev.* 53:793–835

89. Trautwein, W. 1973. The slow inward current in mammalian myocardium. *Eur. J. Cardiol.* 1/2:169–75

90. Trautwein, W., McDonald, T. F., Tripathi, O. 1975. Calcium conductance and tension in mammalian ventricular muscle. *Pfleugers Arch.* 354:55–74

91. Tsien, R. W., Giles, W. R., Greengard, P. 1972. Cyclic AMP mediates the action of epinephrine on cardiac Purkinje fibers. *Nature New Biol.* 240:181–83

92. Tsien, R. W. 1973. Adrenaline-like effects of intracellular intophoresis of cyclic AMP in cardiac Purkinje fibres. *Nature New Biol.* 245:120–22

93. Tsien, R. W. 1974. Effects of epinephrine on the pacemaker current of cardiac Purkinje fibers. *J. Gen. Physiol.* 64:293–319

94. Vassort, G. 1973. Influence of sodium ions on the regulation of frog myocardial contractility. *Pfleugers Arch.* 339:225–40

95. Vassort, G. 1973. Existance of two components in frog cardiac mechanical activity. *Eur. J. Cardiol.* 1/2:163–68

96. Walker, J. L. 1976. Ouabain effect on membrane and potassium equilibrium potentials in sheep Purkinje fibers. *Biophys. J.* 16:31a (Abstr.)

97. Watanabe, A. M., Besch, H. R. Jr. 1974. Cyclic adenosine monophosphate modulation of slow calcium influx channels in guinea pig hearts. *Circ. Res.* 35:316–24

98. Weidmann, S. 1974. Heart: Electrophysiology. *Ann. Rev. Physiol.* 36:155–69

99. Weiss, R., Tritthart, H., Walter, B. 1974. Correlation of Na-withdrawal effects on Ca-mediated action potentials and contractile activity in cat ventricular myocardium. *Pfleugers Arch.* 350:299–307

100. Winegrad, S. 1973. Intracellular calcium binding and release in frog heart. *J. Gen. Physiol.* 62:693–706

Ann. Rev. Physiol. 39:221–51
Copyright © 1977 by Annual Reviews Inc. All rights reserved

CARDIOVASCULAR ADAPTATIONS TO PHYSICAL TRAINING[1]

❖1170

James Scheuer

Departments of Medicine and Physiology, Albert Einstein College of Medicine, Bronx, New York 10467

Charles M. Tipton

Departments of Physiology-Biophysics and Physical Education, University of Iowa, Iowa City, Iowa 52240

INTRODUCTION

The role of physical activity in cardiovascular health has received increasing attention in recent years. A large number of reports have indicated that populations or individuals with high levels of physical activity tend to have a lower prevalence of symptomatic coronary artery disease and lesser death rates from cardiovascular diseases (69, 139). Although no single report provides complete proof that physical activity has a protective effect, the evidence heavily favors that conclusion.

The extent of physical training or detraining also obviously has profound implications with regard to the ability of normal persons to participate comfortably, safely, and successfully in recreational or competitive athletic activities. This matter assumes more importance with increased participation in sports and physical exertional activity by middle-aged and older male and female populations.

Thus an understanding of the adaptations that the cardiovascular system undergoes during chronic exercise programs and the effects of different types and intensities of such programs upon cardiovascular responses have been of considerable interest to physiologists, clinicians, public health workers, and sports professionals.

This article reviews the cardiovascular adaptations that occur during exercise in experimental animals and in man and how they contribute to the trained state. Whenever possible, the mechanisms underlying these adaptations are discussed.

[1]Work related to this review was supported by US Public Health Service Research Grants 15498 and HL 14388.

221

Physical training refers to the state of adaptation that permits the organism to successfully respond to exercise loads of various types, intensities, and durations. A poorly trained or a detrained subject responds to an exercise load only with great effort, perhaps inefficiently, and cannot sustain that effort without soon developing signs of fatigue. On the other hand, a highly trained individual can respond to the same stress with much less effort and strain and can sustain the activity for a much longer period before the symptoms and signs of fatigue become limiting.

THE EVALUATION OF EXERCISE AND TRAINING EFFECTS

It is essential for investigators to establish some common reference points when designing, presenting, and evaluating results of studies on exercise and training. We prefer to consider exercise as a disruption of a homeostatic relationship that has been caused by bodily movement. The nature and the effects of the disruption can be quantified. The response to exercise is influenced by the type of muscular contraction producing the movement, i.e. concentric, eccentric (isotonic types of contraction), or isometric contraction (126). Activities such as running, swimming, bicycling, rowing, and free exercises are predominately, although not exclusively, the result of concentric or eccentric contractions. On the other hand, lifting, pushing, holding, or "tensing" movements are virtually isometric. When forearm and hand isometric contractions are performed during isotonic exercise (running), there is a dramatic increase in heart rate, blood pressure, and cardiac output, suggesting the augmentation of a neurogenic component (10, 126). At the same levels of oxygen consumption or cardiac output, arm movements elicit higher heart rates and blood pressures than do leg movements (10, 155).

The single laboratory procedure used most often to evaluate the strenuousness or intensity of an exercise bout is the measurement of oxygen consumption (10, 155). This reflects any change in cardiac output and oxygen extraction by the tissues. Strenuousness can be evaluated on an absolute (liters) basis, ml/kg units, or a percentage of the subject's maximum capacity (maximum $\dot{V}O_2$). The latter approach allows more flexibility for classification or comparative purposes. The strenuousness of an exercise requirement can be considered to be light (25% maximum), medium (50% maximum), heavy (75% maximum), or exhaustive (90–100% maximum). The linear relationship between heart rate and oxygen consumption at submaximal and near-maximal workloads permits the use of heart rates to estimate the strenuousness of exercise (10, 89). Since heart rate responses are influenced by a variety of conditions such as disease, age, sex, and level of training (10, 89, 155), it is customary in human research to use an age- and sex-predicted heart rate rather than an absolute value for evaluative purposes (89). Similar principles apply to animals, but it is very difficult to routinely measure oxygen consumption. Strenuous exercise by rats (173) and dogs (54) will elicit oxygen consumption values in the range of 90–120 ml(kg·min)$^{-1}$, although in swimming rats, these values will range between 50 and 90 (122). Because of the difficulty in measuring oxygen consumption, many investigators performing animal exercise studies utilize changes in heart rates, rectal temperatures, blood constituents, or muscle glycogen to evaluate the strenuousness of the exercise. Our experience has been that the maximal heart rates are generally between 260–320 beats/min for exercising dogs and 550–620 beats/min for exercising rats. Unfortunately, treadmill speeds are frequently the only information given in rodent exercise studies. In such cases, it is helpful to extrapolate from the studies of oxygen consumption (173), which showed that rats running in activity wheels at speeds of 16.0, 22.5, 28.5, and 39.0 m/min performed at 67%, 77%, 82%, and 93%, respectively, of their maximum oxygen consumption capacity.

To evaluate the effects of exercise, it is important to consider the frequency and duration of exercise as well as the intensity.

Adaptations to chronic exercise will be influenced by intrinsic and extrinsic factors. Intrinsic factors include age, sex, hormonal status, nutritional status, health status, distribution of muscle fiber types, level of training, and the degree of motivation. Extrinsic factors pertain to environmental conditions that may alter exercise performance. Since it is very difficult to control or standardize the multitude of factors that modify an exercise or a training effect, it is not surprising that much confusion and controversy prevail when the benefits and limitations of exercise are discussed.

Repeated bouts of exercise produce adaptations known as *training effects*. In this review, training effects refer to anatomical, biochemical, or physiological alterations that differ significantly from those seen in sedentary subjects. Although this definition allows the investigator to clearly identify an adaptation, it does not consider whether such changes have biological importance. Equally important in defining a training effect is the concept of specificity (39, 90, 142), used by exercise physiologists to indicate that the training effects will be specific to the type of movement being performed. Therefore one cannot generalize on a training effect but must describe the type of movement and the manner in which it was produced; also exercises must be carefully considered and prescribed with regard to the effects being sought.

VARIABLES AFFECTING THE TRAINING EFFECT

This section outlines how the numerous variables mentioned above may influence some training effects.

Physical Training in Humans

The species most extensively employed for studying physical training is man. The cardiovascular responses to training in man have been reviewed thoroughly (65, 155, 158).

Although all individuals will develop some training effects from chronic exercise programs, world class athletes may have added capacities over similarly trained competitors of lesser ability (81). Whether this is due to enhanced natural endowment for peak physical performance or to better training techniques is not clear. Studies using twins are promising with regard to separating genetically determined responses to training from responses solely due to the training program (105). In general, younger subjects have greater adaptations to cardiovascular training than older persons (61, 79, 85, 101), and training responses decrease with increasing age. Females have the same qualitative responses as males, but generally do not reach the same absolute levels of maximum $\dot{V}_{O_2}$ (30, 150, 157).

Isotonic training produces profound cardiovascular adaptations, whereas training with isometric exercise (i.e. weight lifting) does not markedly alter heart volume, oxygen pulse, or the heart-rate response to isotonic exercise (103). Increases in myocardial mass are seen in athletes performing isometric exercises (130).

The specific muscle groups used in the training program influence human cardiovascular responses. Swimmers become conditioned for swimming but not for running (113, 142). Highly trained oarsmen markedly increase cardiovascular responses to arm but not to leg exercise (81). If the legs are used during the conditioning program, the cardiovascular responses to maximal arm exercise may not be enhanced, whereas those due to leg exercise are markedly augmented (39). Where only one leg is used for training, the training effect is not perceived when tests using both legs are employed (47).

The frequency, duration, and intensity of individual training sessions influence the cardiovascular responses. In general, 3–4 sessions per week for 30–45 min per session at an intensity level of 60% of maximal $\dot{V}_{O_2}$ will regularly improve cardiorespiratory performances or fitness (32, 68, 147, 169). However, 2 training sessions per week have been sufficient to change submaximal heart-rate responses, endurance, maximum oxygen consumption, and other indices of a training effect in middle-aged men (146). Vigorous exercise once a week has been reported to cause a detectable effect on some of these parameters (106), as has running in place 12 min daily (184).

In general, both the intensity and the duration of a training program influence the conditioning level achieved (153, 171). There appears to be little training effect when heart rates of less than 130–150 beats per minute are achieved during the training sessions.

The pattern of steady versus intermittent exercise as a training stimulus may be important. One report indicates that steady exercise promotes changes in submaximal exercise effect (68) whereas intermittent exercise is effective in increasing maximum $\dot{V}_{O_2}$.

The total duration of the training program also influences the degree of training achieved. As few as 3 weeks of a strenuous program produces detectable effects on maximum $\dot{V}_{O_2}$ in women (4), and a gradual and progressive increase in cardiovascular fitness occurs over a 5-week period (158).

There is an inverse relationship between the training effect achieved and the prior level of physical fitness. When levels of physical activity prior to the training program have been relatively high, only slight or no alterations in $\dot{V}_{O_2}$ max are produced by the training program (155, 158).

Retention of the physical training state also depends on the factors of frequency, intensity, and duration. After 5 weeks of a daily exercise program, the degree of physical fitness achieved can be maintained if the exercise is continued 3 times weekly (32). Most of the cardiovascular training effects have been reported to be completely lost 3 weeks after cessation of exercise (153). Many years after cessation of intensive physical activity the only residual effect seems to be persistence of cardiomegaly (96, 104, 149).

Physical Training in Animals

A major problem in evaluating cardiovascular training in experimental animals is that the training effect under study is often the same one used to define the degree of training.

Resting heart rate and heart-rate responses to exercise are frequently employed (189, 195, 200). A general relation between heart mass and the natural physical activity of animals has been observed (148), and heart mass has also been used in animal experimentation as an index of the training effect.

Enzymatic analyses of changes in skeletal muscle are helpful in indicating that the animal has undergone a training effect (95), but muscle enzymes provide little information about specific effects on the cardiovascular system.

RODENTS   Studies of physical conditioning have been conducted most frequently in rats, yet the small size of the animal, its rapid resting heart rate, and the difficulty of measuring cardiac function make it less than an ideal animal for such investigations.

Both swimming and running have been used for conditioned rats. Rats may be made to swim singly or in groups, and they may have weights attached to their tails to increase the exercise load. Running can be in a voluntary wheel, in a motorized wheel, or on a treadmill with or without various physical stimuli to make the rats run. Several variables and artifacts may be introduced by both swimming and running techniques. In swimming, air can become trapped in the rat's fur, causing the rat to be more buoyant and to require less energy for swimming (48). The water temperature (33-37°C) is critical to the ease and length of swimming programs of long duration (48).

It is frequently postulated that swimming not only results in a training effect in rats, but that a concomitant psychologic stimulus may be responsible for some of the training effects. Factors such as loss of vibrissae, the number of animals swimming, conditions for housing the animals, chronic stress, and transparency of the swimming tank may all alter swimming performance, and these have been attributed to different psychological stresses (48). There appears to be a learning process in swimming programs; therefore it is important to have the rats swim only for brief periods during the early portions of the program, and to lengthen the swimming period gradually. When this precaution is taken, the rats become adept swimmers. However, no conclusive evidence has been presented to establish or to refute the possibility that some of the effects of swimming programs might be due to chronic stress reaction.

A major problem with swimming programs is that accurate estimates of energy expenditure cannot be routinely monitored. Since rats usually are made to swim in groups, and therefore interact, the swimming activity and oxygen consumption may be considerably greater than when the rat is swimming alone.

Running allows the experimenter to determine the distance the animal has traveled over a certain time period. Exercise intensity can be controlled by the speed and grade of the treadmill. In most treadmill studies, an electric grid is employed to keep the rats running, particularly during the initial training phases and when the animals approach fatigue, and although treadmill exercise is preferred by many investigators, the treadmill, like swimming, may introduce a psychologic stimulus (49).

The results obtained with both swimming and treadmill exercise in rats appear to be similar, and it seems unlikely that either produces a unique cardiovascular effect.

Rats have also been trained to climb an incline with a weight attached to the animal (121) in an attempt to produce more of an isometric load. As in humans, isometric overload results in cardiac hypertrophy.

There are numerous variables in the training of rats, including those directly related to the training program (swimming versus running), the frequency, intensity, and duration of the training sessions, and the duration of the total program. Other factors include the age at onset of the program, the sex of the animal, and the strain of rats used. Females appear to develop greater degrees of absolute cardiac hypertrophy than males (121, 135, 204), particularly with swimming programs. Males tend not to increase their food intake to cover the energy needs imposed by the exercise, and their body weights fail to follow the normal growth curve (135); females have a compensatory increase in food intake and their body weight follows a normal growth curve (135). When the food intake of sedentary control male rats is controlled so that their body weights follow a growth curve similar to exercised animals, the heart weights of the exercised males consistently exceed those of the food-regulated controls (134, 135, 204). Thus diet appears to be an important factor in the different responses to training seen in male and female rats.

Different responses to exercise may also be observed in rats of the same sex subjected to similar exercise programs. For instance it is not clear why male rats subjected to a slightly less strenuous swimming program may develop cardiac hypertrophy (26) when male rats subjected to a program of slightly greater frequency and duration do not (144). The answer may lie in subtle intraspecies differences.

Swimming and running have not been carefully compared. In one study in which swimming and running were employed in separate groups of male rats (134), running caused a more marked decrease in growth rate and lighter heart weights at the end of the exercise program. However, the ages of the swimmers and runners were not exactly the same in this study. In another study where both swimming and treadmill exercise were employed there were no systematic difference between the two (178). Thus whether one type of exercise is superior in producing a training effect is not known.

Increasing the intensity of the training program in rats does not consistently cause cardiac hypertrophy. Increasing the duration of swimming each day in males has a greater effect on body weight than on heart weight (134). Moreover, one of the regimens that most consistently produced cardiac hypertrophy in males was a swimming program of only 1 hr per day (26). Paradoxically, increased heart weight was not observed when males were made to swim 6 hr per day (135). When spontaneous running was compared with treadmill running in females, the forced running resulted in a significant increase in heart weight (121). One of the most vigorous running programs in males (15) produced cardiac hypertrophy, whereas most of the other running programs failed to do so.

The importance of frequency in achieving a training effect has not been examined in depth. However it appears that daily exercise has a more profound effect than less frequent exercise. Swimming for only 2 days a week can produce changes in the body weight of male rats and even increase heart weight in very young animals (26).

It is difficult to determine why so many inconsistencies exist in exercising rats, but the use of heart weight alone may be a poor measure of physical training since many cardiac adaptations to chronic exercise may be seen prior to the onset of hypertrophy (24, 26).

Although several other species of rodents have been used for studies of chronic exercise, there are not enough data to analyze the effects of some of the variables cited for rats. However, there are indications that both swimming and treadmill exercise in guinea pigs may provide reproducible cardiac hypertrophy (19, 82). Guinea pigs might have other advantages over rats in that they have slower heart rates, lower cardiac metabolic rates, and lower myosin ATPase activities. Therefore both cardiac biochemical and mechanical measurements might be made with greater accuracy.

DOGS   Dogs can easily learn to run on a treadmill, and a variety of training programs have been employed (99, 195, 209). These programs may produce a training effect as measured by the heart rate response and a small increase in myocardial mass (209).

The submaximal heart rate response to exercise and the resting heart rate response to intravenous atropine have been successfully employed to follow the progress of training in dogs (195).

Most of the changes induced by training in dogs are reversed by 4–5 weeks of inactivity (195). Therefore, there appear to be relatively consistent responses to training programs in dogs. Dogs provide additional advantages because they are large enough for chronic instrumentation so that repetitive monitoring of cardiovascular events can be performed while the animal is at rest and during exercise. Additional measurements, such as of regional blood flow and many other parameters, can be made in the awake unanesthetized closed-chest animal, thereby avoiding many of the possible artifacts that might be introduced in studies of smaller animals.

OTHER ANIMALS   Swine, mice, cats, and other animals have also been used for studying the effects of chronic exercise. However, the number of studies is too small to draw any conclusions about possible advantages or disadvantages of these models.

HEART RATE AND AUTONOMIC CONTROL MECHANISMS

Resting Heart Rate

Champion athletes generally have resting rates 15–20 beats per minute lower than those of the general population (29). Although the low values found in athletes may be genetically determined (72), numerous studies involving humans and animals (10, 70, 120, 167, 177, 195) indicate that the bradycardia is a biological adaptation resulting from chronic exercise.

In addition to "normal" rat groups (189), exercised rats subjected to unilateral vagotomy (189), thyroidectomy (201), hypophysectomy (192), and immunological sympathectomy (141) exhibit significantly lower resting heart rates than their non-trained controls. Similar trends have been reported for diencephalic (189) and adrenalectomized (199) trained groups. Even though not every training study involving rats (141, 189) demonstrates a significant reduction in heart rate, the conclusion seems valid that chronic exercise will usually cause a resting bradycardia in rats.

The mechanism(s) responsible for this adaptation are unclear. Most frequently cited explanations involve alterations within the autonomic nervous system. Physically trained experimental animals demonstrate less cardiac acceleration than non-trained controls when submaximal doses of atropine are administered (115, 195, 200). When maximal doses of atropine were used in dogs and rats (191, 196), there were no significant differences between heart rates in sedentary and conditioned animals. This suggests that training increased either the amount of acetylcholine in the heart or decreased the sensitivity of the heart to atropine.

After cholinesterase inhibitors were injected, unanesthetized trained rats had significantly lower resting heart rates than nontrained rats (192, 193). Since myocardial cholinesterase levels are not influenced by training (193), these findings support the concept that training causes an increase in parasympathetic activity. Although there have been conflicting reports on the role of training on myocardial (atrial) acetylcholine concentrations (93, 109), it was recently reported that trained rats had significantly more myocardial acetylcholine per gram of tissue than their nontrained controls (50). This observation is compatible with the finding that chronic exercise is associated with increased atrial choline acetyltransferase activity (66).

Changes in the parasympathetic mechanisms probably cannot occur without changes in the sympathetic system. It has generally been thought that training causes a decrease in resting sympathetic tone, although the issue remains equivocal. Animal studies in which propranolol was used to block sympathetic influences have not yielded consistent conclusions (56, 115, 196). Propranolol injections appear to cause greater declines in resting heart rate in sedentary than in conditioned animals. Similar findings were observed when isolated hearts from trained and nontrained rats were perfused with propranolol (56). These findings suggest that training caused a decrease in resting sympathetic tone and/or a change in the intrinsic rate.

Decreased, increased, or unchanged myocardial catecholamine levels have been reported in hearts of trained animals (51, 114, 137, 138), but these levels have not been closely correlated with resting heart rate. Norepinephrine uptake and turnover were found to be decreased in hearts of conditioned animals (138, 161). Resting plasma or urinary (31, 86, 87) catecholamine levels in trained humans or dogs (99) were not significantly different from control values, although trained rats had lower urinary excretion rates (138).

In studies in which simultaneous sympathetic and parasympathetic blockage was effected with pharmacologic agents in order to unmask the intrinsic heart rate, trained rats had a lesser increase in heart rates than the untrained rats (115). However, after intravenous injections of both drugs in dogs, no differences were observed between the trained and nontrained groups (196). Nonathletic subjects had a higher resting mean intrinsic heart rate than the athletes after double blockage (71). In longitudinal studies using double blockage of subjects before and after a training program, the intrinsic heart rate decreased the most in those subjects who exhibited the greatest increase in aerobic capacity (179). With short periods of training, no significant differences in intrinsic heart rate were noted (179). When spontaneous heart rates were studied in isolated hearts from trained and nontrained rats, there were no significant differences between the two populations (144, 190), suggesting that the true intrinsic heart rate was unchanged by training in these animals. This finding does not agree with studies from an isolated sino-atrial preparation of rats in which the rate for preparations from trained animals was less than that for the nontrained groups (27). Thus the question of whether training reduces the intrinsic resting heart rate remains unsettled.

A change in nodal sensitivity to cholinergic influences has also been used to explain the bradycardia of training. However, this view is derived from experiments using double blockage experiments and not from experiments employing neurophysiologic techniques in atrial tissue. Since trained populations appear to have normal resting levels of serum potassium and lower than normal mean blood pressures, it is unlikely that the resting bradycardia of training could be explained by ionic or baroreceptor mechanisms.

It is doubtful that an increased cardiac volume would cause a reduced heart rate by increasing tension on pacemaker cells. Although a reduction in heart rate could accompany an increase in stroke volume, the reduction in heart rate is probably the primary cause for the increased stroke volume.

In summary, the enigma of the resting bradycardia of training continues. From the evidence reviewed, training apparently increases parasympathetic activity to the heart with a concomitant reduction in resting sympathetic activity. Future studies are needed that include more neurophysiological and electrophysiological measurements and, perhaps, that place less reliance on pharmacologic manipulations.

Heart-Rate Responses During Exercise

Physical training in humans or animals will result in lower heart rates at submaximal work loads (10, 84, 85, 100, 177, 195). Most training studies have shown that maximal heart rates can be decreased by training (85, 117, 142, 155, 158), regardless of the exercise employed. When subjects were trained by swimming and tested on the treadmill, the maximal heart rate also was lower (117). Explanations for the rate reductions during exercise include many of those cited in the previous section related to autonomic control, circulating catecholamines, increased stroke volume, or a change in the integrating ability of the central nervous system.

There have been few studies in which the plasma concentrations of catecholamines were measured at similar submaximal or maximal work loads in the trained and untrained state. When subjects were tested before and after training at similar submaximal $\dot{V}O_2$ levels, the norepinephrine concentrations were slightly lower at the highest work load after training (86, 87, 107), but the variability was quite large. When the work tasks were altered so that the subjects exercised to exhaustion, plasma norepinephrine levels were markedly lower in the trained subjects. Under the same conditions, epinephrine values showed little differences. Others have found similar trends (206). Five to eight weeks of training, which significantly increased the submaximal work performance, was not associated with any effect on the urinary norepinephrine or epinephrine levels either after submaximal or maximal exercise tests (31, 46). In dogs exercised after coronary occlusion, a standardized treadmill test caused less of a rise in plasma epinephrine for the trained than for the control dogs (99). No group differences were noted in the norepinephrine levels.

When subjects were tested with intravenous injections of propranolol at submaximal and maximal work loads before and after training, the training effect on the exercise heart-rate response was eliminated by the beta blockade (31). The results suggested that training might have reduced the sympathetic drive to the heart during exercise. Other workers (64) came to similar conclusions after double blockage experiments with exercising trained and nontrained subjects. The findings that trained rats excrete less urinary cathecholamines (137, 138) after exercising also tend to support such a viewpoint. However, the evidence cited is indirect. Direct assessment of cardiac catecholamine levels coupled with neurophysiological evaluation of parasympathetic and sympathetic nerve traffic is essential.

Changes in baroreceptor activity during exercise and their effect on peripheral vascular resistance and heart rate could account for some of the changes in exercise heart-rate responses with training. Such a concept is yet to be evaluated in subjects before and after training. In view of the heart-rate changes that can be elicited by isometric contractions, it is uncertain what effect training may have on the afferent limb of the cardiovascular reflexes that originate in skeletal muscle (126). Training might alter the peripheral or central components of this reflex, but this has not been critically evaluated.

There is considerable uncertainty as to why training is associated with lower maximal heart rates or with lower rates at submaximal work conditions. A change in stroke volume fails to explain whether the responsible mechanisms are intrinsic or extrinsic to the myocardium. The evidence for less sympathetic activation or for a decrease in responsiveness of the beta-1 receptors of the heart is far from complete and either is indirect or has been obtained from studies in which dose-response principles were not followed. Neither do such studies take into account the role of the alpha receptors and their contributions to changes in peripheral vascular resistance. The contribution and importance of the sensory information from working muscles or from the baroreceptors and of the integrated function of the central nervous system remain to be determined.

CARDIAC DIMENSIONS

Cardiac enlargement is a well-recognized adaptation of highly conditioned athletes. It persists in previously well-trained athletes, long after other training effects have disappeared (96, 149).

However, in evaluating cardiomegaly, differentiation must be made between increased mass and increased volume. Dogs subjected to training on a treadmill had an increased in ventricular mass after 8 weeks, but no increase in end-diastolic volume (209). Echocardiographic studies in professional basketball players showed substantial increases in internal left ventricular end-diastolic dimension and in ventricular mass (152). When normal males were subjected to a 12-week program of physical training (158), radiologic evidence of increased cardiac size was found as early as 8 weeks, but there was no evidence of increased mass by electrocardiographic criteria. Electrocardiographic evidence of increased mass and radiologic evidence of increased cardiac size are uniformly found in athletes trained for endurance events (18, 62, 203). When swimmers, runners, and wrestlers were compared with normals by echocardiographic techniques, the swimmers and runners were found to have increased ventricular end-diastolic diameters at rest, whereas left ventricular wall thickness of the wrestlers was markedly increased without an increase in diastolic dimensions (130). The calculated left ventricular mass for all three groups was increased. However, it cannot be concluded from these studies in highly trained athletes that an increase in muscle mass is an obligatory component of a training effect. Training effects on heart rate and ventricular function in rats, cardiac vascularity, and increased actomyosin and myosin ATPase activities have all been observed in the absence of increased cardiac mass (24, 144, 196, 202, 209).

Changes in Cardiac Mass in Rodents

The definition of cardiac hypertrophy is controversial when applied to studies in the rat heart. Many investigators have assumed that an increase in the heart weight to body weight ratio is prima facie evidence of hypertrophy. But, since training programs cause a decrease in the body weight, particularly in male rats, this change in body weight is frequently responsible for the increase in the heart:body weight ratio. Physical training appears to cause myocardial cellular hyperplasia in young rats (26), but the capacity for myocardial cells to undergo mitosis is lost early in life in the rat as in other species. Since the number of cells is presumably constant in hearts of adult rats undergoing physical training, hearts of the same weight will have the same number of muscle cells. True hypertrophy cannot be present unless the absolute cardiac weight is increased and enlargement of myocardial cells occurs. Increased absolute heart weight is more frequently found in female than in male rats (135). When exercised males are compared with pair-weighted sedentary animals, the hearts of the trained rats are heavier than the pair-weighted controls (134, 135). This may represent a relative underdevelopment of the hearts of the pair-weighted controls, rather than a true hypertrophy in the hearts of the physically trained animals. The final resolution of this problem cannot come from intuitive arguments or from the use of regression equations derived from normal growth patterns, but must come from histological studies that define the normal myocardial cell size for a given age of the animal, and which describe any deviations from that population caused by random variation, physical training, or altered nutrition. An increase in mass is not a sensitive indicator of a training effect.

ULTRASTRUCTURAL CHANGES

No significant differences in myocardial fiber diameters have been observed in rats trained with treadmill exercise (57, 202). In young adult male rats trained by swimming, an increase in heart weight was reported, associated with mild hyperplasia of myocardial cells and increased sarcoplasmic volume per fiber (112, 113). With cessation of exercise, these changes were reversible. In younger rats, hyperplasia was a more frequent finding in association with absolute cardiac enlargement. An increase in fiber diameter has been found to be associated with an absolute increase in heart weight in trained guinea pigs (82).

In addition to changes in myofiber diameter, alterations in the membranes, intercalated discs, and other structures have been reported in exercised rats (174). Enlarged mitochondria with diminished density of the cristae and an increase in total mitochondrial mass have been described in female rats conditioned by a swimming program 140–180 hr in duration (7). However, with swimming up to 361–490 hr the relative mitochondria mass was not increased. In other studies, the total number of mitochondria was found to be increased, but this was accompanied by mitochondrial degeneration, which was prevented by the administration of digitoxin during the swimming program (2). In male rats exercised on treadmill, a shift toward smaller mitochondria was reported even when cardiomegaly was absent (60). In male rats subjected to a less arduous treadmill program no mitochondrial changes were observed (185).

Although it appears that certain microscopic alterations occur in the hearts of some physically trained rats, it is not clear how important these alterations are in the cardiac adaptations.

CARDIAC OUTPUT—STROKE VOLUME AND HEART RATE VERSUS OXYGEN NEED

Stroke volume and heart rate in relation to oxygen need have been examined almost exclusively in humans and have been reviewed recently (155). As mentioned earlier, the single most objective indication of a training effect is the increase in the maximal $\dot{V}_{O_2}$. This implies a greater oxygen utilization by the peripheral musculature at maximum stress and is associated with increased extraction of oxygen by skeletal muscles and by lower levels of blood lactate during exercise in trained subjects.

Once the movement patterns associated with exercise have been learned, the oxygen consumption for any level of exercise is not altered by mild training (179, 182). However, since maximal exercise performance is enhanced, the oxygen consumption achieved at maximal exercise is uniformly increased (63, 155, 158). Changes in cardiac output are generally proportional to changes in oxygen consumption. Therefore the submaximal cardiac output is usually the same in the trained and untrained state (158), but the maximal cardiac output is increased by physical training. A decrease in submaximal cardiac output with training has been observed by some workers (6, 62). Greater extraction of oxygen across the peripheral bed accounts for a major portion of the increased oxygen utilization by the cell. This enhanced oxygen extraction during exercise accounts for about 50% of the increased oxygen supplied to the tissue of trained subjects (155). However, in those situations where cardiac output increases minimally with training, the rise in the oxygen extraction ratio is the major factor in increased oxygen delivery. When patients with coronary artery disease are subjected to a physical training program, the increased maximal $\dot{V}_{O_2}$ depends almost entirely upon the increased peripheral extraction of oxygen (154). The mechanisms for this increased extraction include redistribution of blood from areas of low extraction such as the splanchnic bed to the working skeletal muscles, and increased extraction per se by the skeletal muscles (155). In fact, extraction may increase to such an extent in the skeletal muscles that the increment in limb blood flow may be less for any level of work in conditioned than in sedentary individuals (78, 205). Increase in peripheral oxygen extraction is therefore a highly important mechanism in physical training; the skeletal muscle adaptations that might account for this have been discussed in great detail elsewhere (95).

The heart rate at maximum $\dot{V}_{O_2}$ is usually either the same or less in the trained than in the untrained state, and the resting and submaximal heart rates are diminished (see heart rate section). Therefore stroke volume must be greater in trained than in untrained subjects both at rest and during exercise. Approximately 50% of the potential increase in oxygen delivery that results from physical training is due to the augmented stroke volume (155), and since heart rates at maximum $\dot{V}_{O_2}$ are generally similar in untrained and trained subjects, the increase in maximum cardiac output is entirely due to the change in stroke volume. This may relate to the larger ventricular volumes usually found in people who have undergone training programs. However, the change in stroke volume need not depend entirely upon bradycardia or on increased ventricular volume since, in perfused rat hearts, stroke volume was greater in hearts of conditioned rats than in sedentary controls even when heart rate and ventricular diastolic volumes were the same in the two groups (20).

BLOOD PRESSURE

Resting Blood Pressure

In recent years there has been heightened interest in the effect of chronic exercise on resting blood pressure. The majority of surveys of large populations show no significant effect of activity on blood pressure (129). However, the Tecumseh, Michigan study indicated that, regardless of age, active men had significantly lower systolic and diastolic pressures than less active men. Some comparisons between highly trained athletes and nonathletes have shown lower resting pressures in the athletes (21, 29, 125, 159). However, these cross-sectional studies are difficult to evaluate because the investigators have failed to control or to standardize numerous factors that can influence blood pressure measurements. Longitudinal studies have also not demonstrated consistent lowering of the resting pressures during training. Lowering of systolic, diastolic, and/or mean pressures with training has been reported by a variety of investigators (14, 41, 85), whereas no effects have been reported by others (63, 72, 158, 180). Although young people (less than 30 years) and persons with high initial fitness levels appear to manifest less change in blood pressure during training these factors of age and initial fitness cannot explain all the negative results. For instance, in one study 16 weeks of training resulted in a 17% increase in maximum $\dot{V}o_2$ but no change in resting pressures (63).

The effect of training on the blood pressure of hypertensive subjects is important. When normotensive, borderline, and severe hypertensive persons were subjected to exercise programs, all groups showed significant reductions in blood pressure (28, 38, 83). However not all investigators reported this change (98). It is difficult to interpret the results from hypertensive patients because comparable matched nonexercised controls were not studied, the amount of medication used varied among subjects, and the measurement procedures were not standardized.

Animal studies have not been numerous or helpful in characterizing the response of training on resting blood pressures. Normal and spontaneously hypertensive rats (SHR), both male and female, subjected to exercise had significantly lower systolic blood pressures than nontrained SHR (33, 58, 166, 194, 198), but systolic pressures was not lowered to normal control levels. Others have found no blood pressure lowering effects of exercise in SHR or in animals made hypertensive with DOCA (45, 58, 186). No differences in blood pressure were noted between anesthetized trained and nontrained dogs (196).

For animal models to be useful in elucidating the role of exercise on resting levels of blood pressure, future studies should concentrate on unanesthetized animals.

Mechanism Responsible for Resting Changes

For mean arterial pressure to decrease, central and peripheral mechanisms that will alter cardiac output and total peripheral resistance must be considered. Training has been reported to be associated with an increased (72), unchanged (131), or reduced resting cardiac output (63, 158, 180), but the decrease in cardiac output has not been associated with a fall in blood pressure. The possibility that a decrease in sympathetic tone might reduce total peripheral resistance cannot be discounted, but the evidence for such a possibility is far from complete. Injections of norepinephrine produced significantly lesser increases in systolic and diastolic pressures in athletic than in nonathletic subjects (140). No meaningful differences were noted after epinephrine injections.

Total peripheral resistance after training was increased at rest in some studies (63, 158, 180) and decreased in others (21) when compared to control values. However, we are unaware of any evidence that training reduces the sympathetic nerve traffic to the periphery. Without such information, it is difficult to ascribe a change in resting blood pressure to a decrease in peripheral resistance. Whether a reduction in resting blood pressure could be attributed to changes in baroreceptor activity is unknown. Baroreceptors of endurance-trained athletes exhibited decreased sensitivity to neck suction (175) and to lower body negative pressures (132) than those of nontrained groups. Trained rats also show less vasoconstrictor capability when subjected to progressive conditions of lower body negative pressures (141, 197).

Blood Pressures During Exercise

Intra-arterial pressures increase with increasing work loads (9, 22). At maximum $\dot{V}_{O_2}$, mean arterial pressures were significantly higher in some studies of athletes and trained subjects (21, 63), but not different (85) or slightly lower (158) in others. In one study, pulmonary arterial pressures were also significantly higher in the trained group at maximum $\dot{V}_{O_2}$ (21). With submaximal exercise in the upright position, there is very little difference in mean blood pressures before and after training (85, 180). Some studies (63, 158) are difficult to interpret because blood pressure measurements were reported for absolute heart rates or specific O_2 consumption rather than for designated work loads.

The involvement of the many reflexes regulating arterial blood pressure is even less well understood for exercising conditions in trained subjects than at rest, and definitive studies have not been conducted on the role of the arterial baroreceptors. These structures do not appear to play a major role in modulating the cardiovascular adjustments during severe exercise (22, 123).

These findings suggest that the future emphasis of studies on training should be placed on integration of afferent information and on the "local" factors (myogenic, hormonal, metabolic) operating within the vascular beds. It remains to be determined whether training can modify the blood pressure response associated with group III or IV muscle afferents involved in the isometric response (126); this area requires detailed investigation.

The influence of training is not apparent in younger subjects and active individuals, but training does seem to lower blood pressure responses in older, less fit, or hypertensive subjects. This finding has not been sufficiently investigated in animal models to determine responsible mechanisms. Experiments at rest suggest that arterial baroreceptors are reset by training, but their role in exercise responses or in the exercise-trained subjects does not appear to be extensive, and is poorly understood. Two areas neglected in training studies are the central integration of afferent information and the changes occurring within or near the vessels of active and inactive beds.

OXYGEN TRANSPORT: PULMONARY FUNCTION, BLOOD VOLUME, AND HEMOGLOBIN

In general, athletic populations are reported to have higher pulmonary diffusing capabilities than nonathletic populations (12, 17, 172), but longitudinal studies have not yielded convincing evidence for an obvious training effect (151, 158). Pulmonary diffusing capacity does not appear to be a limiting factor in the cardiovascular responses to exercise in trained subjects, and detailed analysis of adaptations in pulmonary function is beyond the scope of this review.

Despite voluminous research in this area, it is unclear whether training will result in an increased blood volume. Blood-volume measurements in athletic and nonathletic populations have yielded inconsistent results (42, 52, 128). For example, it was shown that well-conditioned middle-distance runners had blood volumes 21% higher than collective means of nonathletic populations (52). However in this study the blood volume was measured with carbon monoxide, which is a controversial technique. Using a different method but similar approach, blood volumes in varsity athletes were found to be 8.5% greater than those in sedentary subjects when expressed as ml/kg, but were 4.5% lower when expressed on the basis of fat-free weight (128). When individuals who participated in a variety of sports were compared, there were no statistically significant differences (42, 128). Training was associated with slightly increased blood volumes in dogs (128), although the time course for the change was quite variable. In humans, training has been associated with no change (16, 151) or with only a small increase (94, 159, 160). Most of the changes in blood volume can be accounted for by an increase in plasma volume (136, 159, 160). Cross-sectional studies show that athletic populations have increased plasma volumes (42, 129).

Several studies have shown lack of increase in the volume of red cells in trained subjects (136, 159, 160). Hemoglobin concentrations for athletic populations are frequently similar to or lower than the values found for control or nonathletic subjects (52). The effects of training per se are unclear, as increases (10, 93), decreases (136), or no changes (63, 151) have been reported. It would be advantageous for the trained persons to have a higher total body hemoglobin concentration because these individuals would have the potential to deliver more oxygen to the active tissue. Although reports indicate that such a change occurs with training, the negative results with hemoglobin concentrations, total blood volume, and red cell volume are sufficient to warrant caution.

A decrease in oxyhemoglobin affinity might also account for increased oxygen delivery to the tissue. Some studies show higher P_{50} (arterial oxygen tension when 50% of the hemoglobin is saturated) and 2-3-diphosphoglycerate (DPG) levels in the trained persons (181), others show elevated 2-3-DPG concentrations but no meaningful differences in P_{50}, while others find similar levels of 2-3-DPG with increased P_{50} levels. The critical question is whether the changes noted in P_{50} or 2-3-DPG are physiologically significant in the delivery of oxygen to active tissues. Unless the determination of the P_{50} value is performed under conditions approximating venous blood conditions at the time of severe exercise, it is possible to overestimate the amount of oxygen dissociated because of the shape of the dissociation curve at the lower P_{O_2} values (187).

At this time, it appears unlikely that training has a significant impact on the affinity of hemoglobin for oxygen during an exercise response. Tissue O_2 measurements are needed in addition to the other parameters normally measured in order to better understand if exercise, much less training, has more of an influence on the O_2 dissociation curve than can be predicted from the Bohr effect.

As indicated earlier, with exercise the arteriovenous O_2 difference increases (63, 131, 156). Careful studies concerned with the longitudinal effect of training indicate that the (A–V) O_2 differences at maximal exercise conditions increase with training (63, 156, 158) in younger but not older subjects (85). Initial fitness levels also appear to be important in determining whether such a change will occur (158).

Mechanisms responsible for the widening of an (A–V) O_2 difference via training involve and implicate muscle blood flow, number of capillaries, the fiber type of the muscles being recruited, alterations in the concentration and activity of aerobic enzymes in cells, plus changes in the number and function of mitochondria. Rowell (155) concluded that it is unlikely that the increase in (A–V) O_2 difference during a maximal response resulting from training was due to further vasoconstriction. Since fiber types differ in aerobic capacity, their degree of vascularity, and their pattern of recruitment during exercise (75, 76) training may have more of an effect on local and cellular events than can be detected by regional measurements or by the determination of single (A–V) O_2 values. Therefore, precise flow and O_2 utilization measurements of known fiber types are needed before and after training in order to resolve these uncertainties.

An increased extraction of oxygen by working muscle could occur by 1. a decrease in the affinity of hemoglobin for oxygen at low P_{O_2} tensions, 2. elevated myoglobin concentrations, 3. increased capillary density, or 4. changes in the number and functioning of mitochondria within active muscle cells. As mentioned earlier, there is little evidence that training modifies the affinity between hemoglobin and oxygen. Myoglobin levels do increase with training (95), and since this pigment can facilitate O_2 diffusion in a fluid matrix, an elevated concentration would be advantageous to active tissue. Animal studies concerned with capillary density and training are more numerous (37, 118, 145) and convincing than those conducted with humans (5, 92). However, trained humans have more skeletal muscle capillaries per muscle fiber than nontrained subjects (92). This fact coupled with higher muscle myoglobin concentrations may have more physiological significance than the number of capillaries per unit area (155). The recent review of Holloszy & Booth (95) carefully documents the myriad of biochemical changes that can occur from training within muscle cells of different fiber types. They documented that training will markedly increase the respiratory capability of these cells.

We must conclude at this time that it is unclear why training enhances (A–V) O_2 difference. Our biases favor events which cause adaptations at the cellular level (95).

INTRINSIC CARDIAC ADAPTATIONS

Mechanical Function

It is essential to differentiate cardiac pumping capabilities from the intrinsic mechanical properties of the myocardium since a change in one of these does not necessarily imply a change in the other. When studying cardiac performance it is also important to apply a stress to the heart, since any potential differences in mechanical performance may not be obvious when studies are conducted under baseline conditions.

Pump performance of the heart is improved by physical training, as evidenced by the greater stroke volume at rest and during submaximal and maximal exercise. The slower heart rate and greater stroke volume for any level of performance fosters more effective energy utilization by the myocardium. However, there is only suggestive evidence that mechanical performance of the myocardium, or its intrinsic contractility, is altered by physical training. In conditioned professional basketball players, echocardiographically determined left ventricular ejection fraction and mean velocity of circumferential fiber shortening (Vcf) were not increased, although pump function was enhanced (152). Unfortunately, measurements were performed only when the subjects were resting. Therefore it is possible that the negative findings were due to the insensitivity of the measuring technique, and the fact that the hearts were not adequately stressed. In another human study, there was a suggestion of increased resting contractility in cross-country runners as compared with sedentary controls when systolic time intervals were measured (208). In a preliminary report on chronically instrumented unanesthetized greyhounds with marked cardiac hypertrophy, several indices of resting contractility were found to be the same as in dogs with normal-sized hearts (35). Such inconclusive studies indicate the need to examine contractile performance more directly.

The most precise method for studying myocardial mechanics utilizes isolated papillary muscles or trabeculae carnae. A few such studies have been reported in preliminary form, and the results are contradictory. Papillary muscles from trained rats have been found to have passive and active mechanical relationships similar to those from sedentary controls (3, 80), or decreased mechanical performance (133), or increased contractile performance (127, 176). More complete reports of this type are needed.

Attempts have also been made to analyze myocardial function in hearts studied in the open chest of physically trained animals. Isometric tension development of ventricular muscle was increased in female rats made to swim for 6 hr per day (44). In that study, the increased contractile force may have been related to the greater muscle mass under the strain gauge or to the relative bradycardia of the trained animals. However, increased isovolumic pressure development was observed in hearts of physically trained rats when the heart rates were equalized (40). The difference in performance was not observed until the hearts of these rats were stressed. Others noted unchanged contractility in unstressed hearts of conditioned rats (36, 55), but enhanced contractility 24 hr after partial aortic constriction (55). In studies conducted on isolated working rat hearts (144), hearts from rats made to swim 150 min a day for 8 weeks demonstrated enhanced responses of cardiac output, stroke volume, maximum rate of left ventricular pressure rise (dP/dt), and stroke work to increasing preload, increasing afterload, or rapid atrial pacing. During isovolumic beats, systolic pressure and dP/dt were significantly higher in the hearts of conditioned rats. This provides presumptive evidence of increased contractility. Further studies in which more precise analysis of ventricular mechanics could be accomplished confirmed the increased contractile response (20). Relaxation was also faster in hearts of conditioned rats. These studies from one model of physical training in which hypertrophy is absent suggest that potential contractility of the myocardium is enhanced. However, the results should not be extrapolated to other models.

In summary, the studies of myocardial function in intact animals and man and observations on open-chest animals, isolated hearts, and isolated muscle have not firmly established the association of an increased contractile state with physical training. The differing findings of increased, decreased, or constant contractility may be due to several factors. One is the variability of the conditioning model employed. During one phase of training, contractility may be increased, during another phase it may be normal, and during a third phase it may be depressed. The models of training will have to be rigorously defined and the methods of study will have to be more precise to settle this question.

Metabolic and Biochemical Alterations

Physical training has been found to cause a large number of biochemical alterations in skeletal muscle and many of these have recently been reviewed (95). However adaptations in cardiac muscle were not as prominent (162).

ENERGY GENERATION   Very few studies have been concerned with the metabolism of exogenous substrates in physically trained animals or in man. Physically trained professional cyclists have been compared with sedentary controls of the same age, during both rest and exercise (102). Coronary arteriovenous oxygen difference was found to be similar at rest in the two groups, but did not increase as much during exercise in conditioned as in sedentary subjects. Glucose extraction by the heart decreased less in conditioned subjects during exercise than in controls and lactate extraction by the athletes' hearts was also greater despite lower arterial lactate levels for any exercise load. Free fatty acid extraction by the heart decreased in equal proportions during exercise in both groups. There was no metabolic evidence of myocardial hypoxia in either group. Since coronary flow was not measured, metabolic rates could not be calculated. In this study, the exercise load imposed was relatively light and short. There is evidence that during more prolonged exercise fatty acids become an increasingly important fuel (95).

Although studies of substrate extraction of the type cited above are useful, they do not provide precise information about metabolic activity in relation to mechanical function of the heart. Cardiac metabolism has been studied in the isolated working rat heart apparatus in which mechanical function can be controlled and measured. Perfused hearts of physically trained rats were found to increase their oxygen consumption in proportion to external cardiac work as preload or heart rate were increased (144). Although both energy utilization and energy production were increased in the conditioned hearts as compared with controls, the energy cost of external work was the same in the two groups. The increased energy delivery was related to greater coronary flow responses in hearts of conditioned rats. This greater flow reserve in hearts of conditioned rats is consistent with the evidence showing increased vascularity.

Training lowers blood triglycerides and plasma levels of free fatty acids (73, 95, 116). It is also associated in rat myocardium with lower endogenous triglyceride stores and with increased turnover of fatty acids through the triglyceride pool (73, 163). Homogenates from hearts of conditioned rats demonstrate enhanced esterification of glycerol-3-phosphate (8), and this is in concert with the general finding of a greater utilization of lipid for fuel in the physically trained subject.

There is evidence that the amount of glycogen in skeletal muscle may be a limiting factor in muscle endurance and the development of fatigue (1, 43, 91). Hearts of physically trained rodents have been shown to have increased resting glycogen stores (163, 170). Glycogen synthetase activity is increased in hearts of physically trained guinea pigs (111). After a bout of physical activity which reduces cardiac glycogen content, there is rapid resynthesis of cardiac glycogen, and this process is exaggerated in more severely exercised animals (168). Thus during physical training there are probably wide oscillations of cardiac glycogen stores with reductions during the exercise periods and marked supercompensation during the rest periods. This supercompensation could account for the high cardiac levels of glycogen cited above and would presumably confer a greater substrate reserve for cardiac activity during exertion.

There have only been a few investigations of the glycolytic pathway in hearts of physically trained animals. In isolated hearts of conditioned rats perfused in the arrested state, carbohydrate utilization was the same as in those from sedentary animals (164). Similarly, beating hearts of conditioned animals evidenced no greater carbohydrate contribution to energy formation during hypoxia than the hearts of sedentary animals (165). Studies of the glycolytic enzymes revealed no change in phosphofructokinase activity in the hearts of rats subjected to physical training, but pyruvate kinase and lactate dehydrogenase (LDH) activities were increased substantially (77, 210). An increase in the proportion of M subunits of LDH was also found (74). It is difficult to interpret the reports on glycolytic enzymes since there may be cellular hyperplasia of vascular and connective tissue in these hearts and the M-LDH may not be representative of the myocardial cells.

Mitochondria of skeletal muscles undergo major adaptations to physical training, which may be partially responsible for the enhanced capacity of trained muscles to extract oxygen during severe exercise (95). The oxidative capacities of skeletal muscle homogenates are also enhanced. Increased numbers of mitochondria, some with degenerative characteristics, have been observed in hearts of physically trained animals (7, 60). Administration of digitoxin appears to protect against some of these alterations (2). Increased fragility due to exercise has also been suspected in these mitochondria, but this phenomenon has been thought to be artifactual by at least one group of workers (185). Most biochemical studies of mitochondria from conditioned hearts have shown normal function. However, glycerol-P-dehydrogenase activity and succinic dehydrogenase activity have been reported to be increased in mitochondria from hearts of conditioned female rats (110). These findings were associated with significant increases in mitochondrial protein content in these hearts. On the other hand, studies of cardiac homogenates from male rats undergoing swimming or treadmill training failed to reveal increases in succinic dehydrogenase or cytochrome oxidase activities, or in cytochrome-C content (88, 134). Oxidation rates and ADP:O ratios for mitochondria from conditioned hearts have been reported to be unchanged (53). Therefore, as with other measures of physical training in the rat, the findings regarding mitochondrial capacities remain contradictory.

The enhanced performance and oxidative rates of conditioned hearts when they are stressed indicate that turnover of high-energy phosphate must also be greater. Normal values of creatine phosphate, adenosine triphosphate, adenosine diphosphate, adenosine monophosphate, and inorganic phosphate levels were found in hearts of conditioned rats (163). However, these hearts were not being stressed when the measurements were made. Turnover rates of high-energy phosphates have not been measured in hearts of conditioned animals.

In summary, although there are some minor alterations in pathways of carbohydrate and lipid metabolism, it appears unlikely that changes in energy production account entirely for the intrinsic cardiac adaptations found in physical training. When oxygenation in the isolated perfused rat heart was artificially limited, enhanced pump performance of the conditioned hearts persisted (36, 165). Since in some of these studies energy utilization was known to be the same in both groups, this suggests a possible change within the pathways of energy utilization.

ENERGY UTILIZATION   The increased contractile responses in hearts of conditioned rats and the finding of faster relaxation phases (20) suggest alterations in the processes of excitation-contraction coupling and of relaxation.

A good correlation has been found between the actomyosin and myosin ATPase and speed of contraction of skeletal muscle (13). The calcium ATPase activity of actomyosin studied in high KCl concentration was found to be increased both in hearts and in gastrocnemious muscle of swimming rats (24, 207). More exercise was required to produce changes in the gastrocnemius than in the heart. The elevation in calcium ATPase and magnesium ATPase activity of actomyosin was found to be proportional to the number of hours of swimming (24). Animals made to swim 100 hr over an 8-wk period had significantly higher actomyosin and myosin ATPase activities than animals made to swim 60 hr over 8 wk. These increased ATPase activities were observed both before and after the development of cardiac hypertrophy. The changes in actomyosin ATPase activity were completely reversible 13 days after cessation of the training program (119). The superprecipitation rate of actomyosin in the presence of magnesium ATP was also faster in preparations from hearts of conditioned rats (24). Thus a biochemical alteration has been demonstrated that may represent a controlling factor for contractility. Other mechanisms related to the control of actin and myosin interactions, such as alterations in the troponin sensitivity to calcium, have not been explored.

It was shown that heavy meromysin from hearts of conditioned rats had the same types of ATPase changes as those found in myosin (25). The myosin light chains appeared not to be altered in either quantity or mobility. However, several different types of biochemical measurements suggest a conformational change in the myosin molecule at or near its active site. The alteration appears to involve regulatory sulfhydryl groups that are involved in the binding of ATP (23). It is not known whether this represents new myosin formation or an alteration in the myosin already formed. However the half-time decay of the increased ATPase activity after cessation of exercise approximates the half-time for myosin replacement (119). These changes in myosin from hearts of conditioned rats are similar to those due to thyroid hormone (211). This hormone produces an increased contractile state, cardiac hypertrophy, and a rise in myosin ATPase activity that is also associated with alterations in the regulatory sulfhydryl compounds. Glycerol-phosphate dehydrogenase, which is activated by thyroxin, is increased in conditioned hearts (110). Thus the alterations in thyroid hormone metabolism found in physical training (11, 97) may be a factor in cardiac adaptive responses.

The observed increased rate of cardiac relaxation must be explained by a biochemical mechanism. Calcium transport in the heart is reportedly increased by physical training (124), and one study indicates that sarcoplasmic reticulum preparations from hearts of conditioned rats transport calcium more rapidly and to a greater extent than do preparations from hearts of sedentary controls (143). Much more intensive studies of the relaxation process must be conducted.

Increases in intracellular potassium during some phases of physical training and acute exercise have been observed, but not changes in the sodium, potassium ATPase activity (107, 108). Such a change in potassium might alter sodium exchange and thereby affect calcium exchange in myocardium.

Additional factors in the control of cardiac function such as electrophysiology of the heart, and the adenylate-cyclase–cyclic AMP system, have not been thoroughly explored. As discussed earlier there are alterations in adrenergic and cholinergic transmitters that might affect cardiac performance and metabolism (see section on heart rate and autonomic control).

Thus several adaptations in intrinsic myocardial function, myocardial metabolism, and biochemistry do occur in physical training. Most of the studies cited have been performed in rats. It is not certain how important any of these adaptations are in relation to the more obvious alterations in skeletal muscle and in factors extrinsic to the myocardium. The latter may alter responses of heart rate and stroke volume, thereby favorably affecting the relationship between myocardial oxygen consumption and cardiac output in the physically fit subject.

MYOCARDIAL VASCULARITY

One potentially important effect of physical training on the heart is the increase in myocardial vascularity. It has yet to be demonstrated that this effect provides protection against ischemic heart disease or promotes the growth of collateral vessels.

Early studies indicated that physical training could increase myocardial vascularity in dogs and guinea pigs (145, 188). Physical training has been shown by coronary cast techniques to increase the ratio of vascular space to myocardial mass in male and female rats trained by swimming or by running (49, 178, 183). It has been reported that as little as two days of exercise per week by rats is sufficient to cause increased vascularity (26, 178). In some of these studies, increased capillary density was observed in the absence of cardiac hypertrophy. The number of myocardial capillaries decreases with advancing age of rats, but the capillary:fiber ratios and the total number of capillaries are greater in conditioned animals for any age group (202). With daily or twice weekly swimming the capillary:fiber ratio increased in very young, young adult, and old rats, but in the younger rats this was due to an absolute increase in the number of capillaries and in the old rats the change was due to a decrease in the number of fibers (26). The cross-sectional areas of extracoronary collateral arteries and the major coronary arteries were also increased. With cessation of exercise, the capillary:fiber ratio and the extracoronary collateral area remained increased in hearts of previously conditioned rats, but the size of the major coronary vessels returned toward normal. These findings suggest that there may be some permanency to the myocardial vascular effects from physical training.

The possible significance of increased vascular growth has been indicated by studies in which the circumflex artery was narrowed surgically (59). After recovery the dogs were trained on a treadmill. Subsequently the circumflex artery was ligated and retrograde flow measured. Retrograde flow was increased in the animals that had been subjected to exercise. In other studies of dogs trained without prior narrowing of the circumflex artery, the maximal rate of retrograde flow after acute ligation was not different in control and exercised dogs, although total retrograde flow appeared to be greater in the physically trained animals (34). When training was begun after complete ligation of the coronary artery there was no angiographic evidence in the trained animals for increased collaterals (99). However these experiments were performed while the animals were resting.

It could be concluded from the above studies that ischemia must be present for physical training to result in increased collateral vessel formation. But there is a need for complete reevaluation of this problem with techniques that directly measure both myocardial blood flow and myocardial function while the heart is stressed.

In patients with coronary artery disease studied with coronary angiography, physical training has not been observed to increase collateral vessels (67). However, these studies performed in unstressed hearts with insensitive techniques cannot be considered conclusive.

Literature Cited

1. Ahlborg, B., Bergstrom, J., Ekelund, L.-G., Hultman, E. 1967. Muscle glycogen and muscle electrolytes during prolonged physical exercise. *Acta Physiol. Scand.* 70:129–42
2. Aldinger, E. E., Rajindar, S. S. 1970. Effects of digitoxin on the ultrastructural myocardial changes in the rat subjected to chronic exercise. *Am. J. Cardiol.* 26:369–74
3. Amsterdam, E. A., Wickmann-Coffelt, J., Choquet, Y., Kamiyama, T., Lenz, J., Zelis, R., Mason, D. T. 1972. Response of the rat heart to strenuous exercise: Physical, biochemical and functional correlates. *Clin. Res.* 20:361 (Abstr.)

4. Anderson, M. C., Furnass, B., Jenkins, R., Pang, H., Pennington, J. 1973. Effects of three weeks' strenuous exercise on the cardiovascular fitness of young women. *Med. J. Aust.* 2:966–69
5. Anderson, P. 1975. Capillary density in skeletal muscle of man. *Acta. Physiol. Scand.* 95:203–5
6. Andrew, G. M., Guzman, C. A., Becklake, M. R. 1966. Effect of athletic training on exercise cardiac output. *J. Appl. Physiol* 21:603–8
7. Arcos, J. C., Sohal, R. S., Sun, S.-C., Argus, M. F., Burch, G. E. 1968. Changes in ultrastructure and respiratory control mitochondria of rat heart

hypertrophied by exercise. *Exp. Mol. Pathol.* 8:49–65

8. Askew, E. W., Huston, R. L., Dohm, G. L. 1973. Effect of physical training on esterification of glycerol-3-phosphate by homogenates of liver, skeletal muscle, heart, and adipose tissue of rats. *Metabolism* 22:473–80

9. Astrand, P. O., Ekblom, B., Messin, R., Saltin, B., Stenberg, J. 1965. Intraarterial blood pressure during exercise with different muscle groups. *J. Appl. Physiol.* 20:253–56

10. Astrand, P. O., Rodal, K. 1970. *Textbook of Work Physiology.* New York: McGraw-Hill

11. Balsam, A., Leppo, L. E. 1975. Effect of physical training on the metabolism of thyroid hormones in man. *J. Appl. Physiol.* 38:212–15

12. Bannister, R. G., Cotes, J. E., Jones, R. S., Meade, F. 1960. Pulmonary diffusing capacity on exercise in athletes and non-athletic subjects. *J. Physiol.* 152: 66P–67P

13. Barany, M. 1967. ATPase activity of myosin correlated with speed of muscle shortening. *J. Gen. Physiol.* 50:197–220

14. Barry, A. J., Daly, J. W., Pruett, E. D. R., Steinmetz, J. R., Page, H. F., Birkhead, N. C., Rodahl, K. 1966. The effects of physical conditioning on older individuals. I. work capacity, circulatory-respiratory function, and work electrocardiogram. *J. Gerontol.* 21:182–91

15. Bartosova, D., Chvapil, M., Korecky, B., Poupa, O., Rakusan, K., Turek, Z., Vizek, M. 1969. The growth of the muscular and collagenous parts of the rat heart in various forms of cardiomegaly. *J. Physiol.* 200:285–95

16. Bass, D. E., Buskirk, E. R., Iampietro, P. F., Mager, M. 1958. Comparison of blood volume during physical conditioning heat acclimatization and sedentary living. *J. Appl. Physiol.* 12:186–88

17. Bates, D. V., Boucot, N. G., Dorner, A. E. 1955. The pulmonary diffusing capacity in normal subjects. *J. Physiol. London* 129:237–52

18. Beckner, G. L., Winsor, T. 1954. Cardiovascular adaptations to prolonged physical effort. *Circulation* 9:835–46

19. Beickert, V. A. 1954. Zur Entstehung und Bewertung der Arbeitshypertrophie des Herzens, der Nebenniere und Hypophyse. *Arch. Kreislaufforsch.* 21: 115–26

20. Bersohn, M. M., Scheuer, J. 1976. Mechanics underlying increased performance of hearts of physically trained rats. *Clin. Res.* 24 (Suppl. 3):209A

21. Bevegård, B. S., Holmgren, A., Jonsson, B. 1963. Circulatory studies in well trained athletes at rest and during heavy exercise, with special reference to stroke volume and the influence of body position. *Acta. Physiol. Scand.* 57:26–50

22. Bevegård, B. S., Shepherd, J. T. 1967. Regulation of the circulation during exercise in man. *Physiol. Rev.* 47:178–213

23. Bhan, A. K., Malhotra, A., Scheuer, J. 1975. Biochemical adaptations in cardiac muscle: Effects of physical training on sulfhydryl groups of myosin. *J. Mol. Cell. Cardiol.* 7:435–42

24. Bhan, A. K., Scheuer, J. 1972. Effects of physical training on cardiac actomyosin adenosine triphosphatase activity. *Am. J. Physiol.* 223:1486–90

25. Bhan, A. K., Scheuer, J. 1975. Effects of physical training on cardiac myosin ATPase activity. *Am. J. Physiol.* 228:1178–82

26. Bloor, C. M., Leon, A. S. 1970. Interaction of age and exercise on the heart and its blood supply. *Lab. Invest.* 22:160–65

27. Bolter, C. P., Hughson, R. L., Critz, J. B. 1973. Intrinsic rate and cholinergic sensitivity of isolated atria from trained and sedentary rats. *Proc. Soc. Exp. Biol. Med.* 144:364–67

28. Boyer, J. L., Kasch, F. W. 1970. Exercise therapy in hypertensive men. *J. Am. Med. Assoc.* 211:1668–71

29. Branwell, C., Ellis, R. 1929. Clinical observations on Olympic athletes. *Arbeitsphysiologie* 2:51–60

30. Brown, C. H., Harrower, J. R., Deeter, M. F. 1972. The effects of cross-country running on pre-adolescent girls. *Med. Sci. Sports* 4:1–5

31. Brundin, T., Cernigliaro, C. 1975. The effect of physical training on the sympathoadrenal response to exercise. *Scand. J. Clin. Lab. Invest.* 35:525–30

32. Brynteson, P., Sinning, W. E. 1973. The effects of training frequencies on the retention of cardiovascular fitness. *Med. Sci. Sports* 5:29–33

33. Burgess, L. E., Cropper, R., Gates, H. O., Thomas, J., Russ, C., Scott, M. T. 1976. Influence of exercise on resting systolic blood pressure and cardiac dysfunction of the spontaneously hypertensive rats. *Fed. Proc.* 35:796

34. Burt, J. J., Jackson, R. 1965. The effects of physical exercise on the coronary collateral circulation of dogs. *J. Sports Med. Phys. Fitness* 4:203–206

35. Carew, T. E., Dennis, C. A., Covell, J. W. 1974. Left ventricular function in exercise-induced hypertrophy. *Fed. Proc.* 33:380

36. Carey, R. A., Tipton, C. M., Lund, D. R. 1976. Influence of training on myocardial responses of rats subjected to conditions of ischaemia and hypoxia. *Cardiovasc. Res.* 10:359–67

37. Carrow, R. E., Brown, R. E., Van Huss, W. D. 1967. Fibre sizes and capillary to fibre ratios in skeletal muscles of exercised rats. *Anat. Rec.* 159:33–40

38. Choquette, G., Ferguson, R. J. 1973. Blood pressure reduction in "borderline" hypertensives following physical training. *Can. Med. Assoc. J.* 108:699–703

39. Clausen, J. P., Trap-Jensen, J., Lassen, N. A. 1970. The effects of training on the heart rate during arm and leg exercise. *Scand. J. Clin. Lab. Invest.* 26:295–301

40. Codini, M. A., Yipintsoi, T., Scheuer, J. 1977. Cardiac responses to moderate training in rats. *J. Appl. Physiol.* In press

41. Cogswell, R. C., Henderson, C. R., Berryman, C. H., Harris, S. C., Ivy, A. C., Youmans, J. B. 1946. Some observations on the effects of training on pulse rate, blood pressure and endurance, in humans using the step test (Harvard), treadmill and electrodynamic brake bicycle ergometer. *Am. J. Physiol.* 146:422–30

42. Cook, D. R., Gualtier, W. S., Galla, S. J. 1970. Body fluid volumes of college athletes and non athletes. *Med. Sci. Sports* 1:217–20

43. Costill, D. L., Gollnick, P. D., Jansson, E. D., Saltin, B., Stein, E. M. 1973. Glycogen depletion pattern in human muscle fibres during distance running. *Acta Physiol. Scand.* 89:374–83

44. Crews, J., Aldinger, E. E. 1967. Effect of chronic exercise on myocardial function. *Am. Heart J.* 74:536–42

45. Critz, J. B., Lipsey, P. 1976. Relationships between physical training and DOCA hypertension in rats. *Proc. Soc. Exp. Biol. Med.* 151:552–55

46. Cronan, T. L. III, Howley, E. T. 1974. The effect of training on epinephrine and norephinephrine excretion. *Med. Sci. Sports* 6:122–25

47. Davies, C. T. M., Sargeant, A. J. 1975. Effects of training on the physiological response to one- and two-leg work. *J. Appl. Physiol.* 38:377–81

48. Dawson, C. A., Horvath, S. 1970. Swimming in small laboratory animals. *Med. Sci. Sports* 2:51–78

49. Denenberg, D. L. 1972. The effects of exercise on the coronary collateral circulation. *J. Sports Med. Phys. Fitness* 18:76–81

50. DeSchyver, C., Mertens-Strythagen, J. 1975. Heart tissue acetylcholine in chronically exercised rats. *Experientia* 31:316–18

51. DeSchyver, C., Mertens-Strythagen, J., Becsei, I., Lammerant, J. 1969. Effect of training on heart and skeletal muscle catecholamine concentration in rats. *Am. J. Physiol.* 217:1589–92

52. Dill, D. B., Braithwaite, K., Adams, W. C., Bernauer, E. M. 1974. Blood volume of middle-distance runners: Effect of 2,300–M altitude and comparison with non-athletes. *Med. Sci. Sports* 6:1–7

53. Dohm, G. L., Huston, R. L., Askew, E. W., Weiser, P. C. 1972. Effects of exercise on activity of heart and muscle mitochondria. *Am. J. Physiol.* 223:783–87

54. Donald, D. E., Ferguson, D. 1966. Response of heart rate, oxygen consumption, and arterial blood pressure to graded exercise in dogs. *Proc. Soc. Exp. Biol. Med.* 121:626–30

55. Dowell, R. T., Cutilletta, A. F., Rudnik, M. A., Sodt, P. C. 1976. Heart functional responses to pressure overload in exercised and sedentary rats. *Am. J. Physiol.* 230:199–204

56. Dowell, R. T., Tipton, C. M. 1970. Influence of training on the heart rate responses of rats to isoproterenol and propranolol. *Physiologist* 13:182

57. Dowell, R. T., Tipton, C. M., Tomanek, R. J. 1976. Cardiac enlargement mechanisms with exercise training and pressure overload. *J. Mol. Cell. Cardiol.* 8:407–18

58. Dunne, A. P., Untermeyer, M. W., Manger, W. M., Wolff, M., Wolinsky, H., Von Estorff, I., Birkner, J., Dufton, S. 1974. Effect of exercise on spontaneously hypertensive rats (SHR). *Physiologist* 17:214

59. Eckstein, R. W. 1957. Effect of exercise and coronary artery narrowing on coronary collateral circulation. *Circ. Res.* 5:230–35

60. Edington, D. W., Cosmas, A. C. 1972. Effect of maturation and training on mitochondrial size distributions in rat hearts. *J. Appl. Physiol.* 33:715–18

61. Ekblom, B. 1969. Effect of physical

training in adolescent boys. *J. Appl. Physiol.* 27:350–55

62. Ekblom, B. 1969. Effect of physical training on oxygen transport system in man. *Acta Physiol. Scand. Suppl.* 328:5–45

63. Ekblom, B., Åstrand, P. O., Saltin, B., Stenberg, J., Wallström, B. 1968. Effect of training on circulatory response to exercise. *J. Appl. Physiol.* 24:518–28

64. Ekblom, B., Kilbom, A., Soltysiak, J. 1973. Physical training, bradycardia, and autonomic nervous system. *Sc. J. Clin. Lab. Invest.* 32:249–56

65. Ekelund, L-G. 1969. Exercise, including weightlessness. *Ann. Rev. Physiol.* 31:85–116

66. Ekstrom J. 1974. Choline acetyltransferase in the heart and salivary glands of the rat after physical training. *Q. J. Exp. Physiol.* 59:73–80

67. Ferguson, R. J., Petitclerc, R., Choquette, G., Chaniotis, L., Gauthier, P., Huot, R., Allard, C., Jankowski, L., Campeau, L. 1974. Effect of physical training on treadmill exercise capacity, collateral circulation and progression of coronary disease. *Am. J. Cardiol.* 34:764–69

68. Fox, E. L., Bartels, R. L., Billings, C. E., O'Brien, R., Bason, R., Mathews, D. K. 1975. Frequency and duration of interval training programs and changes in aerobic power. *J. Appl. Physiol.* 38:481–84

69. Fox, S. M. III, Naughton, J. P., Haskell, W. L. 1971. Physical activity and the prevention of coronary heart disease. *Ann. Clin. Res.* 3:404–32

70. Frick, M. H. 1967. Significance of bradycardia in relation to physical training. In *Physical Activity and the Heart,* ed. M. J. Karvonen, A. J. Barry, pp. 33–41. Springfield: Thomas

71. Frick, M. H., Elovainio, R. O., Somer, T. 1967. The mechanism of bradycardia evoked by physical training. *Cardiologia* 51:46–54

72. Frick, M. H., Konttinen, A., Sarajas, H. S. S. 1963. Effects of physical training on circulation at rest and during exercise. *Am. J. Cardiol.* 12:142–47

73. Fröberg, S. O. 1971. Effects of training and of acute exercise in trained rats. *Metabolism* 20:1044–51

74. Gollnick, P. D., Hearn, G. R. 1961. Lactic dehydrogenase activities of heart and skeletal muscle of exercised rats. *Am. J. Physiol.* 201:694–96

75. Gollnick, P. D., Karlsson, J., Piehl, K., Saltin, B. 1974. Selective glycogen depletion in skeletal muscle fibers of man following sustained contractions. *J. Physiol. London* 241:59–67

76. Gollnick, P. D., Piehl, K., Saltin, B. 1974. Selective glycogen depletion pattern in human muscle fibers after exercise of varying intensity and of varying pedalling rates. *J. Physiol. London* 241:45–57

77. Gollnick, P. D., Struck, P. J., Bogyo, T. P. 1967. Lactic dehydrogenase activities of rat heart and skeletal muscle after exercise and training. *J. Appl. Physiol.* 22:623–27

78. Grimby, G., Häggendal, E., Saltin, B. 1967. Local xenon 133 clearance from the quadriceps muscle during exercise in man. *J. Appl. Physiol.* 22:305–10

79. Grimby, G., Saltin, B. 1966. Physiological analysis of physically well-trained middle-aged and old athletes. *Acta Med. Scand.* 179:513–26

80. Grimm, A. F., Kubota, R., Whitehorn, W. V. 1963. Properties of myocardium in cardiomegaly. *Circ. Res.* 12:118–24

81. Hagerman, F. C., Addington, W. W., Gaensler, E. A. 1972. A comparison of selected physiological variables among outstanding competitive oarsmen. *J. Sports Med. Phys. Fitness* 12:12–22

82. Hakkila, J. 1955. Studies on the myocardial capillary concentration in cardiac hypertrophy due to training. *Ann. Med. Exp. Biol. Fenn.* 33:7–82

83. Hanson, J. S., Nedde, W. H. 1970. Preliminary observations on physical training for hypertensive males. *Circ. Res.* 26, 27 (Suppl. 1):49–53

84. Hanson, J. S., Tabakin, B. S. 1965. Comparison of the circulatory response to upright exercise in 25 "normal" men and 9 distance runners. *Br. Heart J.* 27:211–19

85. Hartley, L. H., Grimby, G., Kilbom, A., Nilsson, N. J., Åstrand, I., Bjure, J., Ekblom, B., Saltin, B. 1969. Physical training in sedentary middle-aged and older men. *Scand. J. Clin. Lab. Invest.* 24:335–44

86. Hartley, L. H., Mason, J. W., Hogan, R. P., Jones, L. G., Kotchen, T. A., Mougey, E. H., Wherry, F. E., Pennington, L. L., Ricketts, P. T. 1972. Multiple hormonal responses to graded exercise in relation to physical training. *J. Appl. Physiol.* 33:602–6

87. Hartley, L. H., Mason, J. W., Hogan, R. P. Jones, L. G., Kotchen, T. A., Mougey, E. H., Wherry, F. E., Pennington, L. L., Ricketts, P. T. 1972. Multiple hormonal responses to prolonged

exercise in relation to physical training. *J. Appl. Physiol.* 33:607–10

88. Hearn, G. R., Wainio, W. W. 1956. Succinic dehydrogenase activity of the heart and skeletal muscle of exercised rats. *Am. J. Physiol.* 185:348–50

89. Hellerstein, H. K., Hirsch, E. Z., Ader, R., Greenblott, N., Siegel, M. 1973. Principles of exercise prescription for normals and cardiac subjects. In *Exercise Testing and Exercise Training in Coronary Health Disease,* ed. J. Naughton, H. K. Hellerstein, J. C. Mohler, pp. 129–67. New York: Academic

90. Henry, F. M. 1956. Coordination and motor learning. *Proc. Coll. Phys. Ed. Assoc.* 59:68–75

91. Hermansen, L., Hultman, E., Saltin, B. 1967. Muscle glycogen during prolonged severe exercise. *Acta Physiol. Scand.* 71:129–39

92. Hermansen, L., Wachtlova, M. 1971. Capillary density of skeletal-muscle in well trained and untrained men. *J. Appl. Physiol.* 30:860–63

93. Herrlich, H. C., Raab, W., Gigee, W. 1960. Influence of muscular training and of catecholamines on cardiac acetylcholine and cholinesterase. *Arch. Int. Pharmacodyn. Ther.* 129:201–15

94. Holmgren, A., Mossfeldt, F., Sjöstrand, T., Ström, G. 1960. Effect of training on work capacity, total hemoglobin, blood volume, heart volume and pulse rate in recumbent and upright positions. *Acta Physiol. Scand.* 50:72–83

95. Holloszy, J. O., Booth, F. W. 1976. Biochemical adaptations to endurance exercise in muscle. *Ann. Rev. Physiol.* 38:273–91

96. Holmgren, A., Strandell, T. 1959. The relationship between heart volume, total hemoglobin and physical working capacity in former athletes. *Acta Med. Scand.* 163:149–60

97. Irvine, C. H. G. 1968. Effect of exercise on thyroxine degradation in athletes and non-athletes. *J. Clin. Endocrinol. Metab.* 28:942–48

98. Johnson, W. P., Grover, J. A. 1967. Hemodynamic and metabolic effects of physical training in four patients with essential hypertension. *Can. Med. Assoc. J.* 96:842–47

99. Kaplinsky, E., Hood, W. B. Jr., McCarthy, B., McCombs, L., Lown, B. 1968. Effects of physical training in dogs with coronary artery ligation. 37:556–65

100. Karvonen, M. J., Kentala, E., Mustala, O. 1957. The effects of training on heart rate. *Am. Med. Exp. Fenn.* 35:307–15

101. Kasch, F. W., Phillips, W. H., Carter, J. E. L., Boyer, J. L. 1973. Cardiovascular changes in middle-aged men during two years of training. *J. Appl. Physiol.* 34:53–57

102. Keul, J. 1971. Myocardial metabolism in athletes. In *Muscle Metabolism During Exercise,* ed. B. Pernow, B. Saltin, pp. 447–55. New York: Plenum

103. Keul, J. 1973. The relationship between circulation and metabolism during exercise. *Med. Sci. Sports* 5:209–19

104. Kilbom, Å. 1971. Physical training in women. *Scand. J. Clin. Lab. Invest.* 28:7–34

105. Klissouras, V. 1971. Heritability of adaptive variations. *J. Appl. Physiol.* 31:338–44

106. Koerner, D. R. 1973. Cardiovascular benefits from an industrial physical fitness program. *J. Occup. Med.* 15:700–7

107. Korge, P., Masso, R., Roosson, S. 1974. The effect of physical conditioning on cardiac response to acute exertion. *Can. J. Physiol. Pharmacol.* 52:745–52

108. Korge, P., Viru, A. 1971. Water and electrolyte metabolism in myocardium of exercising rats. *J. Appl. Physiol.* 31:5–7

109. Koudelkova, Z., Vlk, J. 1966. Influence of training on the vagus regulation of heart activity and on the amount of acetylcholine in heart auricle. *Plzen. Lek. Sb.* 26:35–42

110. Kraus, H., Kirsten, R. 1970. Die Wirkung von korperlichem Training auf die mitochondriale Energieproduktion im Herzmuskel und in der Leber. *Pfluegers Arch.* 320:334–47

111. Lamb, D. R., Peter, J. B., Jeffress, R. N., Wallace, H. A. 1969. Glycogen, hexokinase, and glycogen synthetase adaptations to exercise. *Am. J. Physiol.* 217:1628–32

112. Leon, A. S., Bloor, C. M. 1968. Effects of exercise and its cessation on the heart and its blood supply. *J. Appl. Physiol.* 23:485–90

113. Leon, A. S., Bloor, C. M. 1976. The effect of complete and partial deconditioning on exercise-induced cardiovascular changes in the rat. In *Adv. Cardiol.* 18:81–92

114. Leon, A. S., Horst, W. D., Spirt, N., Wiggan, E. B., Womelsdorf, A. H. 1975. Heart norepinephrine levels after exercise training in the rat. *Chest* 67:341–43

115. Lin, Y., Horvath, S. M. 1972. Autonomic nervous control of cardiac frequency in the exercise-trained rat. *J. Appl. Physiol.* 33:796–99

116. Lopez-Santolino, A., Vial, R., Balart, L., Arroyave, G. 1974. Effect of exercise and physical fitness on serum lipids and lipoproteins. *Atherosclerosis* 20:1–9

117. Magel, J. R., Foglia, F., McArdle, W. D., Gutin, B., Pechar, S., Katch, F. I. 1974. Specificity of swim training on maximum oxygen uptake. *J. Appl. Physiol.* 38:151–55

118. Mai, J. V., Edgerton, R. V., Barnard, R. J. 1970. Capillary of red, white, and intermediate fibers in trained and untrained guinea pigs. *Experentia* 26:1222–23

119. Malhotra, A., Bhan, A. K., Scheuer, J. 1976. Cardiac actomyosin ATPase activity after prolonged physical conditioning and deconditioning. *Am. J. Physiol.* 230:1622–25

120. Marsland, W. P. 1968. Heart rate response to submaximal exercise in the standardbred horse. *J. Appl. Physiol.* 24:98–101

121. Mazher Jaweed, M., Herbison, G. J., Ditunno, J. F. Jr., Gordon, E. E. 1974. Heart weight of rat in different exercises. *Arch. Phys. Med. Rehab.* 55:539–44

122. McArdle, W. D. 1967. Metabolic stress of endurance swimming in the laboratory rat. *J. Appl. Physiol.* 22:50–54

123. McRitchie, R. J., Vatner, S. F., Bolttcher, D., Heyndrickx, G. R., Patrick, T. A., Braunwald, E. 1975. Role of arterial baroreceptors in mediating cardiovascular response to exercise. *Am. J. Physiol.* 230:85–89

124. Meerson, F. Z., Kapelko, V. J., Shaginova, S. J. 1973. The contractile function of the myocardium during adaptation to physical load. *Kardiologia* 4:5–18

125. Mellerowicz, H. 1966. The effect of training on heart and circulation and its importance in preventive cardiology. In *Prevention of Ischemic Heart Disease,* ed. W. Raab, pp. 309–15. Springfield: Thomas

126. Mitchell, J. H., Wildenthal, K. 1974. Static (isometric) exercise and the heart. Physiological and clinical considerations. *Ann. Rev. Med.* 25:369–81

127. Mole, P. A., Rabb, C. 1973. Force-velocity relations in exercise-induced hypertrophied rat heart muscle. *Med. Sci. Sports* 5:69

128. Moore, R., Buskirk, E. R., 1960. Exercise and body fluids. In *Science and Medicine of Exercise and Sports,* ed. W. Johnson, pp. 207–35. New York: Harper & Row

129. Montoye, H. J., Metzner, H. L., Keller, J. B., Johnson, B. C., Epstein, F. H. 1972. Habitual physical activity and blood pressure. *Med. Sci. Sports* 4:175–81

130. Morganroth, J., Maron, B. J., Henry, W. L., Epstein, S. E. 1975. Comparative left ventricular dimensions in trained athletes. *Ann. Intern. Med.* 82:521–24

131. Musshoff, K., Reindell, H., Klepzig, H. 1959. Stroke volume, arteriovenous difference, cardiac output and physical working capacity, and their relationship to heart volume. *Acta Cardiol.* 14:427–52

132. Myhre, L., Luft, U. C., Venters, M. D. 1976. Responses of athletes and nonathletes to lower body negative pressure and acute dehydration. *Med. Sci. Sports* 8:53–54

133. Nutter, D., Fuller, E., Watt, E., Chen, H. 1975. Myocardial mechanics in exercise trained and detrained rats. *Fed. Proc.* 34:462

134. Oscai, L. B., Mole, P. A., Brei, B., Holloszy, J. O. 1971. Cardiac growth and respiratory enzyme levels in male rats subjected to a running program. *Am. J. Physiol.* 220:1238–41

135. Oscai, L. B., Mole, P. A., Holloszy, J. O. 1971. Effects of exercise on cardiac weight and mitochondria in male and female rats. *Am. J. Physiol.* 220:1944–48

136. Oscai, L. B., Williams, B. T., Hertig, B. A. 1968. Effect of exercise on blood volume. *J. Appl. Physiol.* 26:622–24

137. Ostman, I., Sjöstrand, N. O. 1971. Effect of prolonged physical training on the catecholamine levels of the heart and the adrenals of the rat. *Acta Physiol. Scand.* 82:202–8

138. Ostman, I., Sjöstrand, N. O., Swedin, G., 1972. Cardiac noradrenaline turnover and urinary catecholamine excretion in trained and untrained rats during rest and exercise. *Acta Physiol. Scand.* 86:299–308

139. Paffenbarger, R. S. Jr., Hale, W. E. 1975. Work activity and coronary heart mortality. *New Engl. J. Med.* 292:545–50

140. Pavlik, G., Frenkl, R. 1975. Sensitivity to catecholamines and histamine in the trained and in the untrained human organism and sensitivity changes during

digestion. *Eur. J. Appl. Physiol.* 34:199–204

141. Paynter, D. E., Tipton, C. M., Matthes, R. D. 1974. Response of immunosympathectomized rats to chronic exercise. *Physiologist* 17:346

142. Pechar, G. S., McArdle, W. D., Katch, F. I., Magel, J. R., DeLuca, J. 1974. Specificity of cardio-respiratory adaptation to bicycle and treadmill training. *J. Appl. Physiol.* 36:753–56

143. Penpargkul, S., Repke, D., Katz, A. M., Scheuer, J. 1977. Effect of physical training on calcium transport by rat cardiac sarcoplasmic reticulum. *Circ. Res.* In press

144. Penpargkul, S., Scheuer, J. 1970. The effect of physical training upon the mechanical and metabolic performance of the rat heart. *J. Clin. Invest.* 49:1859–68

145. Petren, T., Sjöstrand, T., Sylven, B. 1936. Der Einflub des Trainings auf die Haufigkeit der Capillaren in Herz- and Skeletmuskulatur. *Arbeitphysiologie* 9:376–86

146. Pollock, M. L., Broida, J., Kendrick, Z., Miller, H. S. Jr., Janeway, R., Linnerud, A. C. 1972. Effects of training two days per week at different intensities on middle-aged men. *Med. Sci. Sports* 4:192–97

147. Pollock, M. L., Cureton, T. K., Greninger, L. 1969. Effects of frequency of training on working capacity, cardiovascular function, and body composition of adult men. *Med. Sci. Sports* 1:70–74

148. Poupa, O., Rakusan, K., Ostadal, B. 1970. The effect of physical activity upon the heart of vertebrates. *Med. Sports* 4:202–33

149. Pyorala, K., Karvonen, M. J., Taskinen, P., Takkunen, J., Kyronseppa, H., Peltokallio, P. 1967. Cardiovascular studies on former endurance athletes. *Am. J. Cardiol.* 20:191–205

150. Raven, P. B., Drinkwater, B. L., Horvath, S. M. 1972. Cardiovascular responses of young female track athletes during exercise. *Med. Sci. Sports* 4:205–9

151. Reuschlein, P. S., Reddan, W. G., Burpee, J., Gee, J. B. L., Rankin, J. 1968. Effect of physical training on the pulmonary diffusing capacity during submaximal work. *J. Appl. Physiol.* 24:152–58

152. Roeske, W. R., O'Rourke, R. A., Klein, A., Leopold, G., Karliner, J. S. 1975. Noninvasive evaluation of ventricular hypertrophy in professional athletes. *Circulation* 53:286–92

153. Roskamm, H. 1967. Optimum patterns of exercise for healthy adults. *Can. Med. Assoc.* 96:895–900

154. Rousseau, M. F., Brasseur, L. A., Detry, J. M. R. 1973. Hemodynamic determinants of maximal oxygen intake in patients with healed myocardial infarction: Influence of physical training. *Circulation* 48:943–49

155. Rowell, L. B. 1974. Human cardiovascular adjustments to exercise and thermal stress. *Physiol. Rev.* 54:75–159

156. Rowell, L. B. 1962. *Factors affecting the prediction of the maximal oxygen intake from measurements made during submaximal work with observations related to factors which may limit maximal oxygen intake.* PhD thesis. Univ. Minnesota, Minneapolis, Minnesota. 325 pp.

157. Saltin, B., Astrand, P. O. 1967. Maximal oxygen uptake in athletes. *J. Appl. Physiol.* 23:353–58

158. Saltin, B., Blomqvist, G., Mitchell, J. H., Johnson, R. L. Jr., Wildenthal, K., Chapman, C. B. 1968. Response to exercise after bed rest and after training. *Circulation* 38(Suppl. 7):1–78

159. Saltin, B., Grimby, G. 1968. Physiological analysis of middle-aged and old former athletes. Comparison with still active athletes of the same ages. *Circulation* 38:1104–15

160. Saltin, B., Hartley, L. H., Kilbom, Å., Astrand, I. 1969. Physical training in sedentary middle-aged and older men. II. Oxygen uptake, heart rate, and blood lactate concentration at submaximal and maximal exercise. *Scand. J. Clin. Lab. Invest.* 24:323–34

161. Salzman, S. H., Hirsch, E. Z., Hellerstein, H. K., Bruell, J. H. 1970. Adaptation to muscular exercise: Myocardial epinephrine-^{3}H uptake. *J. Appl. Physiol.* 29:92–95

162. Scheuer, J. 1973. Physical training and intrinsic cardiac adaptations. *Circulation* 47:677–80

163. Scheuer, J., Kapner, L., Stringfellow, C. A., Armstrong, C. L., Penpargkul, S. 1970. Glycogen, lipid, and high energy phosphate stores in hearts from conditioned rats. *J. Lab. Clin. Med.* 75:924–29

164. Scheuer, J., Penpargkul, S., Bhan, A. K. 1973. Effect of physical conditioning upon metabolism and performance of the rat heart. In *Recent Advances in Studies on Cardiac Structure and Metabolism,* ed. N.S. Dhalla, G. Rona,

SCHEUER & TIPTON

3:145–59. Baltimore, Maryland: University Park

165. Scheuer, J., Stezoski, S. W. 1972. Effect of physical training on the mechanical and metabolic response of the rat heart to hypoxia. *Circ. Res.* 30:418–29

166. Secord, D. C., Taylor, A. W., Fielding, W. 1973. Effect of anesthetic agents on exercised, atropinized rats. *Lab. Ann. Sci.* 23:397–400

167. Sedgwick, A. W., Craig, R. J., Crouch, R., Dowling, B. 1974. The effects of physical training on the day and night long-term heart-rates of middle-aged men. *Eur. J. Appl. Physiol.* 33:307–14

168. Segel, L. D., Chung, A., Mason, D. T., Amsterdam, E. A. 1975. Cardiac glycogen in Long-Evans rats: Diurnal pattern and response to exercise. *Am. J. Physiol.* 229:398–401

169. Sharkey, B. J. 1970. Intensity and duration of training and the development of cardiorespiratory endurance. *Med. Sci. Sports* 2:197–202

170. Shelley, W. B., Code, C. F., Visscher, M. B. 1942. The influence of thyroid, dinitrophenol and swimming on the glycogen and phosphocreatine level of the rat heart in relation to cardiac hypertrophy. *Am. J. Physiol.* 138:652–58

171. Shephard, R. J. 1968. Intensity, duration and frequency of exercise as determinants of the response to a training regime. *Int. Z. Angew. Physiol. Einschl. Arbeitsphysiol.* 26:272–78

172. Shephard, R. J. 1972. Exercise and the lungs. In *Fitness and Exercise,* ed. J. F. Alexander, R. C. Serfass, C. M. Tipton, pp. 7–18. Chicago, Illinois: Athletic Inst.

173. Shepherd, R. E., Gollnick, P. D. 1976. Oxygen uptake of rats at different work intensities. *Pfluegers Arch.* 362:219–22

174. Sohal, R. S., Sun, S. C., Colcolough, H. L., Burch, G. E. 1968. Ultrastructural changes of the intercalated disc in exercised rat hearts. *Lab. Invest.* 18:49–53

175. Stegemann, J., Busert, A., Brock, D. 1974. Influence of fitness on the blood pressure control system in man. *Aerospace Med.* 45:45–48

176. Steil, E., Hansis, M., Hepp, A., Kissling, G., Jacob, R. 1975. Cardiac hypertrophy due to physical exercise—an example of hypertrophy without decrease of contractility: Unreliability of conventional estimation of contractility by simple parameters. In *Recent Advances in Studies on Cardiac Structure and Metabolism,* ed. A. Fleckenstein, N. S.

Dhalla, 5:491–96 Baltimore, Maryland: University Park

177. Steinhaus, A. H. 1933. Chronic effects of exercise. *Physiol. Rev.* 12:103–47

178. Stevenson, J. A. F., Feleki, V., Rechnitzer, P., Beaton, J. R. 1964. Effect of exercise on coronary tree size in the rat. *Circ. Res.* 15:265–69

179. Sutton, J. R., Cole, A., Gunning, J., Hickie, J. B., Seldon, W. A. 1967. Control of heart rate in healthy young men. *Lancet* 2:1398–1400

180. Tabakin, B. S., Hanson, J. S., Levy, A. M. 1965. Effects of physical training on the cardiovascular and respiratory response to graded upright exercise in distance runners. *Br. Heart J.* 27:205–10

181. Taunton, J. E., Taunton, C. A., Banister, E. W. 1974. Alterations in 2,3-DPG and P_{50} with maximal and submaximal exercise. *Med. Sci. Sports* 6:238–41

182. Taylor, H. L. 1960. Exercise and metabolism. In *Science and Medicine of Exercise,* ed. W. R. Johnson, pp. 123–61. New York: Harper & Bros. 740 pp.

183. Tepperman, J., Pearlman, D. 1961. Effects of exercise and anemia on coronary arteries of small animals as revealed by the corrosion-cast technique. *Circ. Res.* 11:576–84

184. Terjung, R. L., Baldwin, K. M., Cooksey, J., Samson, B., Sutter, R. A. 1973. Cardiovascular adaptation to twelve minutes of mild daily exercise middle-aged sedentary men. *J. Am. Geriatr. Soc.* 21:164–68

185. Terjung, R. L., Klinkerfuss, G. H., Baldwin, K. M., Winder, W. W., Holloszy, J. O. 1973. Effect of exhausting exercise on rat heart mitochondria. *Am. J. Physiol.* 225:300–5

186. Tharp, G. D. 1976. The effect of exercise training on blood pressure and aortic strip tension of normal and spontaneously hypertensive rats. *Fed. Proc.* 35:796

187. Thomson, J. M., Dempsey, J. A., Chosy, L. W., Shahidi, N. T., Reddan, W. G. 1974. Oxygen transport and oxyhemoglobin dissociation during prolonged muscular work. *J. Appl. Physiol.* 37:658–64

188. Thorner, W. 1935. Trainingsversuche an Hunden. III. Histologische Beobachtungen an Herz- und Skeletmuskeln. *Arbeitphysiologie* 8:359–70

189. Tipton, C. M. 1965. Training and bradycardia in rats. *Am. J. Physiol.* 209:1089–94

190. Tipton, C. M. 1968. Heart rate measurements from intact and isolated

preparations from trained and non-trained rats. *Proc. Int. Union. Physiol. Sci.* 7:434

191. Tipton, C. M. 1969. The influence of atropine on the heart rate responses of nontrained, trained and detrained animals. *Physiologist* 12:376

192. Tipton, C. M., Barnard, R. J., Tcheng, T. 1969. Resting heart rate investigations with trained and nontrained hypophysectomized rats. *J. Appl. Physiol.* 26:585–88

193. Tipton, C. M., Barnard, R. J., Tharp, G. D. 1966. Cholinesterase activity in trained and nontrained rats. *Int. Z. Angew. Physiol. Einschl. Arbeitsphysiol.* 23:34–41

194. Tipton, C. M., Callahan, A. K., Matthes, R. D. 1975. Influence of training on the resting systolic blood pressures of genetic hypertensive rats. *Fed. Proc.* 34:443

195. Tipton, C. M., Carey, R. A., Eastin, W. C., Erickson, H. H. 1974. A submaximal test for dogs: Evaluation of effects of training, detraining, and cage confinement. *J. Appl. Physiol.* 37:271–75

196. Tipton, C. M., Erickson, H. H. 1974. Physiologic tests to differentiate dogs with different functional capabilities. *Rep. SAM-TR-74-14, US Air Force School of Aerospace Med.* p. 56

197. Tipton, C. M., Matthes, R. D., Gross, P. M., Vailas, A. C. 1976. The effect of lower body negative pressure on blood pressure changes in rats. *Physiologist.* 19:391

198. Tipton, C. M., Matthes, R. D., Paynter, D. E., Lais, L. T., Callahan, A. K. 1973. The influence of chronic exercise on the blood pressure of rats. *Med. Sci. Sports* 5:62

199. Tipton, C. M., Struck, P. J., Baldwin, K. M., Matthes, R. D., Dowell, R. T. 1972. Response of adrenalectomized rats to chronic exercise. *Endocrinology* 91:573–79

200. Tipton, C. M., Taylor, B. 1965. Influence of atropine on heart rates of rats. *Am. J. Physiol.* 208:480–84

201. Tipton, C. M., Terjung, R. L., Barnard, R. J. 1968. Response of thyroidectomized rats to training. *Am. J. Physiol.* 215:1137–42

202. Tomanek, R. J. 1969. Effects of age and exercise on the extent of the myocardial capillary bed. *Anat. Rec.* 167:55–62

203. Van Ganse, W., Versee, L., Eylenbosch, W., Vuylsteek, K. 1970. The electrocardiogram of athletes—comparison with untrained subjects. *Br. Heart J.* 32:160–64

204. Van Liere, E. J., Northup, D. W. 1957. Cardiac hypertrophy produced by exercise in albino and in hooded rats. *J. Appl. Physiol.* 7:91–92

205. Varnauskas, E., Björntorp, P., Fahlen, M., Prerovsky, I., Stenberg, J. 1970. Effects of physical training on exercise blood flow and enzymic activity in skeletal muscle. *Cardiovasc. Res.* 4:418–22

206. Von Euler, U.S. 1974. Sympatho-adrenal activity in physical exercise. *Med. Sci. Sports* 6:165–73

207. Wilkerson, J. E., Evonuk, E. 1971. Changes in cardiac and skeletal muscle myosin ATPase activities after exercise. *J. Appl. Physiol.* 30:328–30

208. Winters, W. G., Leaman, D. M., Anderson, R. A. 1973. The effect of exercise on intrinsic myocardial performance. *Circulation* 48:50–55

209. Wyatt, H. L., Mitchell, J. H. 1974. Influences of physical training on the heart of dogs. *Circ. Res.* 35:883–89

210. York, J. W., Penney, D. G., Oscai, L. B. 1975. Effects of physical training on several glycolytic enzymes in rat heart. *Biochim. Biophys. Acta* 381:22–27

211. Yazaki, Y., Raben, M. S. 1975. Effect of the thyroid state on the enzymatic characteristics of cardiac myosin. A difference in behavior rat and rabbit cardiac myosin. *Circ. Res.* 36:208–15

Ann. Rev. Physiol. 39:253–76

GROWTH AND DEVELOPMENT
OF THE LUNG: FETAL
AND POSTNATAL

❖1171

L. B. Strang

Department of Paediatrics, University College Hospital Medical School,
London, W.C.1., England

INTRODUCTION

Lung development begins in early embryonic life and continues throughout the period of body growth. At birth a number of sudden changes take place. This review considers aspects of several related topics: lung morphology during development, the secretion and absorption of fetal lung liquid, the initiation of breathing, the development of surfactant, and changes in the pulmonary circulation. For lack of space, it omits reference to lung mechanics and gas exchange during the period of postnatal growth. Although the whole subject of lung development has not been previously covered in the *Annual Review of Physiology,* some aspects of it have; the 1974 edition contains papers making reference to surfactant metabolism during development (172) and to the pulmonary circulation of the fetus (161). In the overlapping field of comparative respiration, 1975 was marked by the publication of a monograph of rare quality (65).

MORPHOLOGY OF LUNG DEVELOPMENT

Prenatal Development

About 22–26 days after fertilization, when the human embryo is 5 mm long, the lung makes its first appearance as a shallow groove in the ventral wall of the gut just cephalad to the liver and stomach. In the human, it begins as a single pouch which later divides; in the mouse, the right and left lungs are initially separate and later fuse proximally to form the trachea (169). The epithelial component forms a sheet of cells, which grows more rapidly than the surrounding mesoderm (166) and branches repeatedly, like a growing tree. Classically, prenatal development of the lung is divided for descriptive purposes into three periods–glandular, canalicular, and alveolar (67). *Nomina Embryologica* (140) recognizes four; in the human they

253

are an "embryonic" period up to 5–6 weeks, a "pseudoglandular" period up to 17 weeks, a "canalicular" period up to 24 weeks, and a "terminal sac" period from then until term. An "alveolar" period follows after birth. Reid (156) summarized the main morphological features of these periods. Recent research has been occupied with two main topics: control of morphogenesis in the embryonic period and differentiation of the epithelium in the canalicular and terminal sac periods.

FACTORS DETERMINING MORPHOGENESIS   Morphogenesis of an epithelial organ such as the lung, salivary gland, or pancreas depends on interactions between the epithelial primordium and its underlying mesoderm. In organ culture neither component assumes its characteristic morphology when separated from the other [see Bernfield & Wessells (20)]. When the epithelium of a developing lung bud has its mesoderm scraped off, growth continues but branches stop forming; reuniting the epithelium and mesoderm makes branching begin (174). The epithelium also influences the mesoderm; in its absence the mesoderm does not develop its own structural organization (see below). The influence of mesoderm on epithelium persists even when the two tissues are separated by a porous barrier (174); it is believed to depend on an interaction between the basal surfaces of epithelial cells and polypeptide precursors of collagen, the extracellular protein produced by mesodermal cells. The collagen seems to polymerize in specific patterns that control growth and branching of the epithelial surface.

A lung rudiment will not form in an explant of mouse foregut if the mesoderm is removed before buds appear. But covering the appropriate area of epithelium with mesoderm from any part of the embryo allows the budding to take place, even when the replacement with "foreign" material is done 36 hr before the buds are due; the epithelial cells are already committed to lung development and do not need a specific mesoderm in order to make a beginning (169). Once the primitive trachea and primary branches have formed, further organogenesis depends on more specific interactions of each part with its own mesoderm. Removal of a piece overlying the tracheal epithelium and its replacement with mesoderm from the growing tip of a lung bud causes the trachea to form a supernumerary bronchus with branches (7, 178). Conversely, the branching of one lung can be stopped by replacing its covering with mesoderm from the trachea, while the other lung, covered by its own mesoderm, continues happily to ramify (178). The electron microscope shows a highly ordered structure in the mesoderm overlying the trachea and other nonbranching areas of epithelium (178). Its cells, which have a rectangular shape in section, are regularly arranged in tightly packed rows with their long axes perpendicular to the epithelial tube. An array of collagen fibers runs parallel to the axis of the airway, between the mesodermal cells and the epithelium. At the tips of the lung bud the mesodermal cells and collagen fibers are not arranged in this regular way. According to Wessells (178) and Alescio (6), growth of the epithelium is stabilized and controlled by the collagen fibers, which create a barrier to the formation of branches except at appropriate points where the collagen bundles are interrupted. Subdivision is not determined by localized epithelial overgrowth: thymidine labeling experiments did not show differential mitotic activity in epithelial cells at the cites of bud formation (178).

The importance of collagen in morphogenesis has been demonstrated by selectively destroying collagen or inhibiting its growth. In transfilter experiments (epithelium on one side, mesoderm on the other) treatment with collagenase stopped the branching without preventing epithelial growth; branches again formed when the collagenase was washed away and new mesoderm supplied (179). In a different type of experiment, Alescio (6) used an inhibitor of collagen synthesis, azetidine-2-carboxylic acid; it is an analog of proline, the main building block of collagen. In lung explants from 11-day mouse embryos, this substance, at the lowest concentration used (40 μg/ml) caused partial uncoupling of growth and branching. The lung continued to grow but few bifurcation points appeared; after incubation for 48 hr, branching was reduced by 45%, epithelial area by only 22%. The effect was attributed to incorporation of the proline analog into polypeptide precursors of collagen, distorting its polymerization in appropriate patterns.

A different mechanism for the interaction, namely passage of RNA from mesoderm to epithelium, seems unlikely. The possibility was investigated by incorporating labeled nucleosides into the macromolecular RNA of lung mesoderm incubated in isolation. Recombining the labeled mesoderm with epithelium by the transfilter method produced branching, but transfer of RNA to the epithelium was not detectable (93).

EPITHELIAL DIFFERENTIATION   In the pseudoglandular and canalicular stages, epithelial cells in the lung contain glycogen (167). At the stage of differentiation into type I and type II cells, it disappears from the epithelium but in the mesoderm persists in diminishing amounts until term. Its significance is a matter for speculation. In the embryonic and pseudoglandular periods, when epithelial cells are 5–10 μm from capillaries, they may need to hold a store of carbohydrate from which glucose can be made available at the time of cell division. In general, mitosis is not easily limited by restrictions in the supply of raw materials for new cytoplasm, but its energy demands are such that only the oxidation of glucose can provide a sufficient supply (38).

Most recent interest in the differentiation of the lung epithelium has centered on structures thought to be connected with surfactant synthesis. Most lung physiologists accept the paradigm that surfactant is synthesized in type II alveolar cells and stored in osmiophilic lamellar bodies (OLBs). [For a note on paradigms, see (66).] OLBs appear relatively late in gestation: in the mouse (181) at 18 days (term = 19 days), in the lamb (114) at 120 days (term = 147 days), in the rabbit (115) at 24 days (term = 31 days), in the human (43) at 22–26 weeks (term = 40 weeks). In the lamb at 120 days only about 10% of type II cells contain OLBs; at 125–130 days the number increases rapidly to an average of 4 per type II cell and by term to 6 per type II cell (114). Granular inclusions, probable precursors of OLBs, have been described in lung cultures from chick embryos (58). The earliest stage in OLB formation appears to be a granular body at the center of a short, partly coiled length of membranelike material. As the cell develops, a helix of osmiophilic membrane builds up and the granular center is assimilated. Transplanting a lung rudiment to an older embryo speeds up the transformation; putting it into a younger embryo slows it down (131).

Another subcellular component to show marked changes in late fetal life is the peroxisome. [Peroxisomes are dense bodies 0.2–1.0 μm in diameter containing H_2O_2-producing enzymes and catalase (148).] According to Schneeberger (162), they appear in type II cells of the mouse fetus at 15 days (before OLBs) and increase threefold before birth; their functional significance is unknown.

Structural development of the fetal lung in general and its epithelial differentiation in particular can be accelerated by injecting corticosteroids directly into the lamb, rabbit, or monkey fetus [see Avery (10) for a summary of this work]. L-Thyroxine produces a similar effect (182); hypophysectomy retards differentiation (23). In fetal rabbits, the increase in lung maturity produced by corticosteroids is brought about at the expense of cell division (44); growth however shows some evidence of catch-up after birth (125).

A reduction in the volume of the fetal thorax limits lung growth. In cases of diaphragmatic hernia, the number of bronchial branches is diminished in both lungs but more on the side of the hernia; the reduction in branching indicates interference with lung development as early as the pseudoglandular period (8). Probably the lung hypoplasia in renal agenesis [Potter's syndrome (152)] is due to chest compression, a consequence of oligohydramnios. Similar findings have been reported when the deficiency of amniotic fluid is a result of long-term leakage (73).

Postnatal Development

Thurlbeck (171) recently published a comprehensive review. Early in postnatal life the acini become subdivded by septae, and their previously smooth walls develop bumpy outcrops of new alveoli (39). According to Burri et al (40) these changes remodel the rat lung between 4 and 13 days. As a result alveolar number per ml of lung increases three times, and mean alveolar diameter decreases from 54 μm to 38 μm. Labeling of fibroblasts with [^{3}H]thymidine reaches a peak during this period, particularly at the tips of actively growing tissue septae (110). In the epithelium, 50–55 min after injection of the label, only the type II cell was labeled; hence it could be a stem cell for other epithelial components [for discussion of this point see (171)]. Lung maturation is accompanied by a fivefold increase in collagen, as a proportion of total protein (32). According to Boyden & Tompsett (31), remodeling of the acinus in man takes place in the first two months of life. Reconstructions from serial sections show that budding starts in the peripheral saccules of the acinus and spreads proximally. Estimates of alveolar number in the newborn infant, summarized by Thurlbeck (171), vary from 17×10^6 to 71×10^6; he gives an average of 376×10^6 for the adult. New alveoli continue to appear until 8–11 years (59, 68), but according to Dunnill (68) nearly 40% of the increase takes place in the first year. In the second decade growth may take place by expansion of existing units but measurements to date are insufficient to exclude the possibility that new alveoli are formed. Dunnill (68) found an increase in alveolar surface area from 2.8 m^2 in the newborn to 12.2 m^2 at 1 year and 75 m^2 in the adult; the increase is approximately linear with body surface area (68).

Two factors have been shown to influence postnatal lung growth—available space and inspired oxygen concentration. Removal of one lung is followed by compensatory growth in the other except when the vacant space is filled with plastic sponges (78) or wax (56). One week after pneumonectomy in young rats, mitotic activity and collagen synthesis per cell were at a peak and the weight of the remaining lung had already reached that of the two lungs in controls (78). Hypoxia for 3–6 weeks (41) or simulated altitude (19) caused proliferation of acini. Compensatory lung growth after pneumonectomy was increased by hypoxia, slowed by hyperoxia, unaffected by breathing CO_2 (35). The effect seems to be specific to oxygen; carbon monoxide at a concentration of 0.02% had no effect on lung growth despite an 18% increase in hematocrit (18). There is conflicting evidence as to whether or not increased oxygen consumption stimulates lung growth: Bartlett (17) found no effect of tread-mill exercise, L-thyroxine or thiouracil in young rats; but Japanese waltzing mice, whose oxygen consumption is nearly twice normal, have smaller, more numerous alveoli and larger, thinner exchange areas than normal mice (83). (These wretched animals are repeatedly set in motion at two and a half turns per second due to an inborn brain defect.)

SECRETION AND ABSORPTION OF FETAL LUNG LIQUID

The lungs of the fetal lamb contain about 30 ml of liquid per kg body weight (139); the volume is similar to the functional residual capacity (FRC) of a newborn infant (138). We can refer to it simply as "lung liquid." It is formed in situ at 2–3 ml/hr kg and leaves the lungs via the trachea to be swallowed or added to amniotic liquid (139). Jost & Policard (108) first showed it was formed locally by observing lung distension after ligation of the fetal trachea in rabbits. The liquid must be formed by transfer of solutes and water across the endothelium of lung capillaries and the epithelium of the fine air spaces. The mechanisms responsible were investigated in two stages; in the first (30, 139), passive permeabilities to macromolecules and small non-electrolytes were measured. In the second (143), ion fluxes across the epithelium were compared with predictions from measurements of electrochemical potential. The methods used in these investigations depend on taking samples from the three extracellular spaces of the lung—vascular, interstitial, and alveolar. In the exterio-rized fetal lamb, liquid can be sampled from the alveolar space through a tracheal cannula (about 15 ml/kg can be withdrawn); from the interstitital space by collect-ing lung lymph (104); and from the vascular space by cannulating a carotid artery, a pulmonary vein, or the pulmonary artery, depending on requirements. Details of the techniques and assessment of how adequately the samples represent liquids in the exchange areas are given in (104, 139, 142, 143).

Non-Electrolyte Permeability of Pulmonary Endothelium and Epithelium in the Fetus

In fetal and newborn lambs, Boyd et al (30) measured the permeability of lung capillaries to large molecules. They compared the lymph and plasma concentrations of endogenous plasma protein fractions, obtained by Sephadex gel filtration, and they also followed the penetration of labeled polyvinylpyrrolidone (PVP) from plasma to lymph. Molecules with diffusion radii between 1.7 and 11 nm passed through capillary walls, their transfer rates inversely related to molecular radius, but none of them go through the alveolar epithelium when put in either plasma or lung liquid. The permeability of the epithelial barrier was further investigated by Normand et al (139). They used trace amounts of metabolically inert polar non-electrolytes with diffusion radii between 1.39 and 0.22 nm: these were inulin (1.39 nm), sucrose (0.51 nm) mannitol (0.42 nm), erythritol (0.35 nm), and urea (0.22 nm). Permeability to [^{3}H] water was also measured. Following intravenous injection, all these tracers were rapidly transferred to lymph; sucrose, mannitol, erythritol, urea, and water also appeared in lung liquid at rates inversely related to molecular size, but no inulin got through to lung liquid. A similar orderly transfer to lymph and plasma was observed when the molecular probes were put in lung liquid, except, again, in the case of inulin and larger molecules to which the lung epithelium was completely impermeable.

Changes in the concentration of one of the impermeant tracers, put in lung liquid, provided an accurate measurement of lung liquid volume (V_L) and secretion rate (J_v). Olver & Strang (143) excluded an artifact due to mixing in the bulk of the liquid by obtaining very similar results with two impermeant tracers that differed in free diffusion coefficient by a factor of 2.5. This method gave the values of $V_L = 30$ ml/kg and $J_v = 2$–3 ml/hr kg, referred to above. Very similar results for J_v have been obtained more directly by collecting lung liquid from the chronically cannulated fetal lamb, maintained in utero (3, 149).

Analysis of the permeant tracer movements by compartmental analysis gave the following results for epithelial permeability constant (cm/sec) (139): sucrose = 4.1×10^{-9}, mannitol = 1.4×10^{-8}, erythritol = 5.9×10^{-8}, urea = 5.9×10^{-7}, [^{3}H] water = 3.3×10^{-6}. Thus a decrease in molecular radius from 0.51 nm to 0.14 nm is associated with an increase in permeability by three orders of magnitude. These results fit well with predictions for transfer through a fairly "tight" epithelium having uniform pores 0.55–0.60 nm in radius. Plainly the permeabilities of endothelium and epithelium are very different. The first allows access for large molecules such as antibodies to the interstitial space; the second limits passive penetration of even small plasma solutes and allows an osmotic gradient in favour of absorption to the interstitial space to be maintained. Normand et al (139) also showed that nonpolar (lipid soluble) substances permeate the epithelium much more readily than polar solutes. In accord with Overton's hypothesis (146), they deduced the presence of two pathways across the epithelium—one for polar substances consisting of water-filled channels between epithelial cells, the other for nonpolar substances, consisting of epithelial cell membranes. In postnatal life the latter no doubt provides an easy route for the lipid-soluble respiratory gases and some other substances such as ether and alcohol.

Ion Fluxes and the Secretion of Lung Liquid

The distinctness of lung liquid is shown by striking differences from amniotic fluid in ionic concentration, osmolality, and urea concentration. Lung liquid contains little protein (0.03 g/100 ml) but in other respects it differs from an ultrafiltrate of plasma as can be seen from the following (plasma):(lung liquid) concentration ratios measured in samples from the lamb fetus between 120 and 140 days (2, 142). [(plasma):(ultrafiltrate) ratios from Davson (60) are appended in parentheses]: Na^+ = 1.03(1.05), K^+ = 0.72(1.04), Ca^{2+} = 2.89(1.53), Cl^- = 0.68(0.96), HCO_3^- = 8.61(0.96), H^+ = 0.08.

It is difficult to explain these ratios except by active transport of one or more of the ionic species. Olver & Strang (143) investigated ion movements across the pulmonary epithelium of the fetal lamb by injecting radioactive isotopes of alkali metal, alkaline earth, and halide ions into plasma or lung liquid (sometimes both routes were used simultaneously). The results allowed calculation of one-way ion flux and of the ratio of one-way fluxes, both for ions normally present and for ions artificially introduced for experimental purposes. To decide whether or not a given ionic species was actively transported across the epithelium, its measured flux-ratio was compared with expectations for passive flux predicted from measurements of chemical and electrical potential; the chemical potential was obtained by measuring ionic concentration or isotope distribution, the electrical potential by inserting salt bridges, connected to calomel electrodes, into lung liquid and plasma; lung liquid was always electronegative to plasma by an average of 4.3 mV.

Both Na^+ and Ca^{2+} followed predictions for passive transport but a group of halides (Cl^-, Br^-, and I^-) as well as K^+ and Rb^+ satisfied stringent criteria for active transport from plasma to lung liquid. Of these the most important quantitatively is Cl^- (average one-way flux from plasma to lung liquid, 71 μeq/min compared with 5.6 μeq/min for K^+). It was also possible to calculate a minimum estimate, in electrical units, for the force supplied by active transport; it was 25.8 mV for Cl^-, 21.2 mV for Br^-, 33.9 mV for I^-, 22.7 mV for K^+, and 23.6 mV for Rb^+. These could be underestimates if exchange diffusion contributes to the tracer movements. By analogy with other transport systems there would seem to be two ion pumps at work, one for halides (69) as in the stomach, the other for K^+ and Rb^+ (165).

These findings, however, do not explain the differences in [HCO_3^-] and [H^+] between plasma and lung liquid; a potential difference of approximately 60 mV (lung liquid negative) would be needed to account for the observed concentration ratios. Bicarbonate transport was investigated by raising the unlabeled [HCO_3^-] in lung liquid to between 30 and 60 meq/kg H_2O and then measuring it repeatedly for 5–6 hr. In that time lung liquid [HCO_3^-] fell slowly to its normal level of 2–3 meq/kg H_2O while the plasma level did not change. Olver & Strang (143) attributed this result to active HCO_3^- transport from lung liquid to plasma, but they were unable to exclude an active pump for H^+ in the reverse direction causing HCO_3^- dissociation. (One-way HCO_3^- flux cannot be measured with a ^{14}C isotope because the label exchanges with CO_2.)

The secretion of fetal lung liquid is probably achieved by the active transport of Cl^- in excess of a reverse HCO_3^- flux, with Na^+ following passively down the electrical gradient set up by Cl^- movement; net water flow can be attributed to the osmotic force of NaCl. The manner in which a bulk flow of liquid is linked to solute movement in such circumstances is a controversial matter (see 112). In support of these conclusions, Olver & Strang (143) found no increase in lung liquid formation when lymph flow from the lungs was doubled by transfusing the fetus; but adding potassium cyanide to lung liquid stopped the secretion and initiated absorption, presumably by poisoning the ion pump. No information is available as to which components of the pulmonary epithelium are responsible for the ion transport. Structural studies with an eye on the long, narrow, dead-end channels, currently thought to be important in active ion transport by epithelia (145), have yet to be done. In another respiratory epithelium, the fish gill, ion transport has long been associated with the so-called chloride cells which change in number and morphology when the salt concentration of the surrounding medium is altered (113, 164). Epithelia in two other respiratory structures, the bullfrog lung (82) and the canine trachea (141), have also been shown to transport Cl⁻ actively.

Absorption of Lung Liquid at Birth

As can be detected by changes in lung weight, liquid is absorbed from the lungs in the first 5–6 hr after birth (104). During that period the interstitial spaces become distended (4) and lymph flow from the lungs increases—in the lamb from an average of 1.8 ml/hr kg to a peak of 6.2 ml/hr kg, 15–30 min after starting ventilation (104). According to Egan et al (71), the start of spontaneous breathing produces a permeability change in the pulmonary epithelium, favoring rapid absorption. They put molecular probes (PVP, inulin, sucrose, etc) in lung liquid and made the lamb breathe by pouring cold water on it, while the umbilical cord and placenta were still attached and functioning. At 20 min intervals they withdrew the cold stimulation, the lamb stopped breathing and residual liquid in the lung could be sampled. An increase in permeability allowing transfer of molecules with radii of 0.5–2.4 nm was observed. The results could be explained by molecular transfer through water-filled pathways 3.4–5.6 nm in radius. Egan et al (71) attributed the change to a six- to tenfold increase in the dimensions of pathways between epithelial cells as a result of lung expansion—a development which would greatly increase the hydraulic conductivity of the epithelium, favoring rapid absorption, while retaining a small enough pore size to prevent significant albumin penetration (albumin diffusion radius = 3.4 nm). Without the change, absorption would be intolerably slow. A similar increase in the size of paracellular pathways has been reported in corneal epithelium due to a hydrostatic pressure difference (183) and in renal tubular (29) and bladder (175) epithelium due to a difference in osmotic pressure. In neonatal lambs aged 12 hr to 2.5 days, non-electrolyte permeabilities, measured in a liquid-containing lobes at low volume, had returned close to the fetal pattern (71). In adult dogs, estimated pore radius varied from 0.9 nm at functional residual capacity (FRC) to 4.0 nm at 90% total lung capacity (TLC) (70). In all these postnatal experiments, net absorption of liquid was observed. Indeed it is very unlikely that net secretion takes place into the lung after birth; if it did there would be a tendency for the lung distal to a pathological obstruction to fill up with liquid, a result which is not observed in postnatal life, although it is in the fetus (94, 153); the ion transport system must be switched off or made ineffective in some way, how is not known. In some cases of alveolar cell carcinoma, the adult lung seems to revert partially at least to the fetal state. There are several clinical reports (102, 170) of patients with this condition who produced voluminous amounts of watery liquid from the lung, sometimes leading to whole-body electrolyte depletion. In one such case (102), the concentrations of protein and Cl⁻ resembled those found in fetal lung liquid.

ONSET AND CONTROL OF NEONATAL BREATHING

Fetal Breathing and the Changes at Birth

The onset of breathing at birth is the most remarkable of lung developments, but our understanding of what happens remains sketchy. Discussion of this topic should begin with Barcroft & Barron's descriptions of three periods in the development of fetal respiratory movements (14–16). In the first, at 40 days in the lamb (term = 147 days), stimulation of the face produced both a generalized jerk and an inspiration. In the second period (at 50 days), the respiratory response was more segregated from other movements and easier to elicit; touching any part of the body caused a burst of breathing. In the third period (at 60 days), these responses disappeared and breathing could be provoked only by umbilical cord occlusion. Brain-stem section[1] just below the pons at 60–80 days caused reversion to the 50-day pattern of easily elicited responses, but sections higher in the brain did not have that effect. (16). Hence rudimentary respiratory centers are present in the medulla and capable of function as early as 40–50 days, but at 60 days they come under inhibition from pontine centers. According to Barcroft (14), the inhibition persists until birth when it is released in some way.

This view requires some modification in the light of recent evidence on fetal breathing movements. They have been detected in the chronically catheterized lamb fetus, maintained in utero with minimal disturbance to its normal environment (64, 133). Episodes of very rapid shallow breathing lasting 10–20 min are present 40–50% of the time. Merlet et al (133) recorded rates of 70–240/min and pleural pressure deflections as low as –40 cm H_2O. Very little liquid is displaced, usually less than 1 ml (64), presumably because the liquid has a relatively high viscosity and inertia. Dawes et al (64) detected movements in lambs as young as 40 days and up to term. They are not due to asphyxia; fetal Pa_{O_2}, Pa_{CO_2}, and pHa were closely similar in breathing and nonbreathing periods (64, 133); they were abolished by anesthesia, by operating on the exposed fetus and by lowering fetal Pa_{O_2} from 25 mm Hg (a normal value) to 16 mm Hg, but not by vagotomy (64). Raising Pa_{CO_2} by 8–10 mm Hg increased the rate and depth of fetal breathing but an increase of Pa_{O_2} by a few mm Hg had no effect (64). Dawes et al (64) identified three sleep states in fetal lambs—an apparently awake condition (present 5% of the time), deep sleep (about 55% of the time), and active sleep associated both with rapid eye movements (REM) and a characteristic electrocorticograph (about 40%). Fetal breathing movements are almost entirely confined to periods of REM sleep. They also show diurnal variation with a peak in the late evening and a trough in the early

---

[1]These (16) were probably the first "chronic" fetal experiments. Barcroft & Barron did the sections without exteriorizing the fetus and allowed the pregnancy to continue for 10–14 days before testing respiratory responses. They succeeded in 11 out of 20 attempts.

hours; the peak is said to occur later in the spring than in winter (24). According to Maloney et al (130) there are changes in the pattern of respiratory frequency as gestation advances. For example, in one lamb fetus at 100–114 days, breathing rates greater than 60/min occupied 19% of the time and rates less than 2/min only 6%; but at 130–140 days the fast rate occupied only 3% of the time and the slow rate, 17%. Any residual doubt that the changes in pleural pressure and tracheal flow are associated with respiratory excursions has been removed by recordings of electrical activity in the diaphragm (130) and phrenic nerve (12). Respiratory movements can also be detected in the undisturbed human fetus by ultrasound (26), by careful palpation of the mother's abdomen (99), or by use of a force transducer (25). Even in the early years of the century Ahlfield (5) obtained good kymographic records of these movements in the human, through the mother's abdominal wall.

From these observations on fetal breathing movements we learn that the respiratory centers and other neuromuscular mechanisms responsible for breathing are present and capable of functioning from an early stage. In postnatal life, as Plum (150) pointed out, breathing movements reflect two types of influence—metabolic and behavioral; the first is typified by the response to CO_2, the second by the heavy breathing of emotional distress or sexual arousal. The association of fetal breathing with active sleep means that the respiratory center can respond to stimuli arising above the brain stem, which suggests that the pathways required for the behavioral response are working, but the link between breathing and metabolism is not yet forged. For 50–60% of the time the fetus makes no attempt to breathe, yet the arterial blood gases and pH are at levels which would stimulate maximal hyperventilation in a nonfetal animal. [The following are normal values for the fetal lamb in late gestation: Pa_{O_2} = 23 mm Hg, Pa_{CO_2} = 46–48 mm Hg (53), pHa = 7.33–7.37 (133).] It is the lack of response to these basic chemical stimuli that most characterizes the inhibition noticed by Barcroft (14). The insensitivity to chemical stimuli is not complete: according to Pagtakhan et al (147) the inhibition is breached by the following combinations of arterial gas tensions (mm Hg): Pa_{CO_2} = 40 and Pa_{O_2} = 5; Pa_{CO_2} = 41–100 and Pa_{O_2} = 6–14; Pa_{CO_2} > 100 and Pa_{O_2} = 17–20. Since occlusion of the umbilical cord rapidly produces arterial gas tensions within these ranges, it is easy to see how breathing could get started. What remains a mystery is how it is maintained when pulmonary ventilation has established blood gas tensions in the normal range. A one-way activation or removal of inhibition must occur either in the respiratory center or in the chemoreceptors. The observations on fetal breathing show that the centers are not insensitive given an appropriate stimulus (in this case REM sleep) and there is other new evidence discounting the old belief in central depression. Bystrzycka et al (42) made microelectrode recordings from respiratory neurons in the medulla of the fetal lamb; they found tonically discharging units in the nonbreathing fetus and rhythmically discharging ones in the breathing fetus. In neither case did the findings suggest medullary depression as seen in barbiturate narcosis; medullary activity, however, was remarkably unaffected by "normal" stimuli to respiration. According to Chernick et al (47) respiratory neurons in the medulla have similar threshold sensitivities to electrical stimulation in the fetal and newborn lamb.

Although the respiratory centers of the fetus are probably not depressed, there is evidence that both central and peripheral chemoreceptors are. In the fetal lamb, aortic body chemoreceptors respond to hypoxia and to cyanide but the effects are mainly on the circulation (62). Carotid body receptors in the fetus have a low sensitivity to both cyanide and hypoxia, but it is not zero; Dawes et al (63) obtained an inspiratory response to the injection of cyanide into both carotids, abolished by carotid sinus denervation. Harned et al (97) got a weak respiratory response to perfusion of one common carotid with blood having a Po_2 between 7.5 and 9.5 mm Hg. Reynolds & Mackie (159) obtained a respiratory response to cyanide only when an additional sensory input was provided by pulling on the tongue. In keeping with these blunted responses, Biscoe & Purves (22) found a very low or absent level of chemoreceptor discharge in multifiber preparations of the sinus nerve during fetal life. At birth, occlusion of the umbilical cord was followed by a great increase in efferent postganglionic sympathetic discharge before the first breath (22). Sympathetic activity is known to increase the sensitivity of arterial chemoreceptors (see 173) and could play a part in their activation at birth. Whatever the reason, even minutes after the start of breathing, Biscoe & Purves (22) found chemoreceptor activity in the sinus nerve of the lamb; it increased when Pao_2 was reduced by 5–10 mm Hg and on breathing 5% CO_2 in air; it was diminished by breathing 100% O_2. According to Harned et al (96) respiratory adaptation at birth needs intact chemoreceptors; chemodenervated lambs started breathing as soon after cord occlusion as controls but did not sustain rhythmic breathing. Quantitatively there seem to be no important differences between the newborn lamb and adult sheep in the ventilatory response to oxygen (154).

The activity of central medullary chemoreceptors (Loeschke's and Mitchell's areas) in the fetus has been difficult to investigate. Herrington et al (100) perfused the exposed ventral surface of the medulla in fetal lambs near term. Lowering pH from 7.3 to 6.8 by raising Pco_2 in the perfusate did not stimulate breathing. The surgery needed for these experiments might have blunted neural responses but, at face value, the result argues for insensitivity of the medullary chemoreceptors. Cyanide applied to the ventral surface of the medulla or injected intravenously in chemodenervated lambs did provoke an inspiratory response but the effect was probably due to direct neural stimulation and not mediated through the central chemoreceptors since it was elicited by intravenous cyanide even after destruction of the medullary surface to a depth of 2 mm (105) [the chemoreceptors lie about 0.2 mm deep to the surface (127)]. There are no important differences in CSF composition between fetal and newborn lambs (100, 101) so a given rise in $Paco_2$ should produce the same pH drop in brain extracelluar fluid. After birth the central chemoreceptors function much as in the adult; the synergism between hypoxia and hypercapnia is the same in newborn lambs aged 4 hr to 10 days as in adult sheep (155); small preterm infants, however, have a diminished CO_2 response in the presence of hypoxia (160). According to Avery et al (11) newborn infants show a bigger response to CO_2 in ventilation per kg body weight than adults; but the difference largely disappears when the responses are compared on the basis of $Wt^{0.7}$ [see Dejours (65) for a discussion of appropriate standards for physiological comparisons in subjects of differing size]. Taken together, the information on both arterial and medullary chemoreceptors suggests, but does not prove, that they are the sites of inhibition in the fetus.

Certain nonchemical stimuli also have an important effect on the initiation of breathing. Cooling the exposed fetal lamb is a powerful stimulus to breathing even when there are no changes in Pao_2, $Paco_2$, or pHa (95). According to Merlet et al (134), cooling the snout is particularly effective. Certain liquids in the upper airway of the newborn lamb inhibit breathing (106). The effect depends in a curious way on the composition of the liquid: in the lamb, breathing was not inhibited by lung liquid, sheep's milk, or NaCl solutions between 0.08 M and 0.62 M, but it was by a variety of other liquids including water, 0.01N HCl, 0.02 M quinine hydrochloride, glucose solutions, cows' milk, and allantoic fluid. Since neither osmolality nor pH seem important, Johnson et al (106) suggested that the inhibitory reflex may depend on taste-bud receptors.

Lung and Chest Wall Reflexes in the Newborn Infant

The Hering-Breuer inflation reflexes has been demonstrated in the exteriorized fetal lamb breathing liquid (151). Ponte & Purves (151) also found a surprisingly high level of vagal afferent impulses from stretch receptors in the apneic fetus; the rate of discharge was increased by liquid expansion of the lungs. In mature newborn infants the Hering-Breuer reflex is present in the first four days and then disappears (57). Olinsky et al (144) measured it by the increase in duration of an inspiration produced by occluding the airway (i.e. removing the stretch stimulus). In full-term infants the mean prolongation of inspiration was 25% ($\pm$ 15 SD) and in preterm infants at 30 weeks gestation it was 53% ($\pm$ 12 SD). With increasing postnatal age, the prolongation got less in the preterm infant and disappeared at about term. Bodegard et al (28) found a slightly different pattern; the reflex was present but weak at 32 weeks, strongest at 36 weeks, declined and disappeared at term. The inflation reflex also affects the response to CO_2 (27). At gestations below 37 weeks, frequency increased from the beginning; above that age, the adult response described by Clarke & von Euler (48) was observed—i.e. tidal volume had to reach a threshold before frequency increased. In lambs, vagal section abolished the increase in frequency (132). According to Olinsky et al (144) the Hering-Breuer reflex determines the high frequency of breathing of preterm infants and provides effective inputs when the organization of brain stem centers is still incomplete. By causing a high breathing frequency it also plays a part in maintaining lung volume because the time constant of the preterm lung is more than one second, too long to permit emptying to true FRC at high frequencies (144). Recurrent apnea of prematurity, they suggest (144), may be due to a vicious circle involving the need for stretch receptor inputs; if breathing gets interrupted, slowed, or impeded, lung volume will decrease and lead to a fall in stretch-receptor output—hence the apnea and its tendency to self-perpetuation. Whatever the validity of these conclusions, in clinical practice, preventing lung deflation by a constant positive airways pressure goes a long way to stopping recurrent apnea in preterm infants (109). Head's paradoxical reflex, which is an inspiratory response to a large lung inflation, the reverse of the Hering-Breuer inflation reflex, has also been demonstrated in the first week of life (57).

As in the fetus, sleep states affect breathing patterns in the newborn. In REM sleep, breathing frequency and minute ventilation are greater and more variable than in quiet sleep (98). A complex interaction between sleep state and the response to added respiratory loads has also been demonstrated. In quiet sleep progressive compensation was seen as in the adult, but in REM sleep the response in tidal volume and frequency was disorganized and distortion of the rib cage occurred (123, 124).

SURFACTANT

When air first enters the lung, surfactant suspended in lung liquid is adsorbed to the new interface, forming a surface film with special physical properties, necessary for the retention of air in small lung units. There are many reviews dealing with the physiology of lung surfactant and with the effects of its absence or relative insufficiency in the Respiratory Distress Syndrome (RDS) of the newborn infant. Tierney (172) recently reviewed its metabolism in these pages and there are up-to-date reviews on the composition of surfactant (116), on its nature and physical properties (91) and on its role in the pathogenesis of RDS (74). Accordingly, I refer only to some points of particular interest in lung development.

Pulmonary surfactant appears relatively late in the gestation of most species. It can be extracted from lung tissue in the mouse (37), rabbit (90), and lamb (157) at about the same gestational age as osmiophilic lamellar bodies (OLBs) are first seen. In man, the same applies; small amounts have been detected as early as 23 weeks (158). In several species it has been possible to define a period of tissue storage, followed by secretion into acini (80, 90): although first detectable at 26 days in the rabbit, surfactant does not appear in lung washings until 29 days; after that age, ventilation greatly increases the amount found in washings (90). In man, our best information about the gestational age at which surfactant is delivered to the alveolar surface comes from its detection in amniotic fluid where it arrives as a constituent of lung liquid. This approach was pioneered by Gluck and colleagues (87, 88) who detected surfactant by measuring the "L:S" ratio [i.e. the concentration ratio of acetone-precipitable phosphatidyl choline (lecithin) to sphyingomyelin—a marker for "nonsurfactant" phospholipid]. Surfactant in amniotic fluid has also been detected by measuring total unextracted phosphatidyl choline (PC) (21) and by Clements et al's "shake" test (52), which depends on physical properties of surfactant. Apart from their usefulness in predicting susceptibility to RDS [see (74) for a review], these methods agree in showing that surfactant is first secreted between the thirty-second and thirty-sixth week of human gestation and continues to increase in amount until term (52, 87). Doubt has been cast on the specificity of these tests because surface-active phospholipids are also present in fetal urine and skin secretions and can be detected in sheep amniotic fluid even when lung liquid is prevented from entering the amnion (54); it has been largely dispelled by finding parallel changes in the amniotic fluid concentration of the protein specific to surfactant (121) and by the close relationship shown to exist between phospholipid synthesis and amniotic fluid L:S ratio in the rhesus monkey (72).

Current experimental work on the biosynthesis of surfactant in the fetal lung has to be assessed in the light of recent information on its nature and composition (116). Isolation procedures based on density gradient centrifugation (117) have yielded fractions of more or less constant composition, possessing the physical properties required of surfactant (118) and enriched in dipalmitoyl phosphatidyl choline (DPPC)—the only surface-active phospholipid in a wide range of species sufficiently abundant to form a surface layer large enough to cover the whole alveolar area (51). Gil & Reiss (85) obtained three ultrastructurally "pure" fractions of surface-active material from lung washings by density gradient separation; two probably represented storage forms, the third had the ultrastructural appearance of tubular myelin—a liquid crystal thought to correspond to the physical state of surfactant in the subphase. These investigations and others (79, 81) reveal the molecular complexity of surfactant. According to King & Clements (117), it contains at least ten distinct molecular species; they include DPPC (41%) a group of monoenoic phosphatidyl cholines (25%), some other phospholipids (12%), glycerides (4%), cholesterol (8%), and protein (8%). There is no guarantee that this composition does not depend partly on the methods used for isolation (91) which could bring together components not normally associated in vivo. For example, Shelly et al (163) reported artifactual formation of lipid-protein complexes by separation steps involving precipitation of surfactant. Cell membranes, while varying considerably in composition (33), are built from basically similar molecules to those found in the surfactant fraction isolated by King & Clements (117). From our knowledge of these structures and the surface chemistry of phospholipids it is fair to assume that surfactant is like a unit membrane split in half—a supramolecular assembly consisting mainly of polar phospholipids regularly orientated with their hydrocarbon chains turned to the air and their polar heads in the aqueous phase. The physical properties of such a film can be expected to depend critically on the proportions of saturated and unsaturated fatty acids esterified to glycerol in the phospholipids, on its proportional content of cholesterol and glycerides, and on the nature and amount of the protein [see Branton & Park (33)]. As with various types of subcellular membrane, we can expect surfactant to be unique in the proportions of its main constituents, but apart from the protein, all its component molecules are to be found in most tissue cells [only in the lung, however, is DPPC present in such abundance (36, 49)]. A comprehensive description of surfactant biosynthesis would require knowledge of the synthetic pathways followed by each molecular constituent and of how and where within the cells they are brought together; assembly probably takes place in the membranous structures of OLBs [see Clements (50)] but it could occur in the subphase or at the surface [see Gil & Reiss (85)].

We are a long way from being able to provide a description of such complexity. Two components of surfactant, however, can be identified. One is the apoprotein isolated by King et al (120) (its mol wt is about 11,000 and it has a strong affinity for lipids); the other is DPPC, not unique to surfactant, but quantitatively predominant. King et al (121) detected the apoprotein in human amniotic fluid. It first appeared at 30–32 weeks and increased fivefold by 37 weeks. Since this substance can now be detected by specific immunoassay (119, 122) and localized histologically by immunofluorescence (122), we can soon expect to learn more about its appearance and distribution in the fetal lung. Metabolic pathways leading to synthesis of phosphatidyl cholines have been investigated in several species. All the enzymes needed for phospholipid synthesis are to be found in adult and fetal lungs [see Farrell & Avery (74) for summary]. Two pathways of phosphatidyl choline (PC) synthesis first described in other tissues have been identified in lung. In pathway I [Kennedy & Weiss (111)], phosphoryl choline is first formed and then attached to diglyceride. In pathway II [Bremner & Greenberg (34)], phosphatidyl ethanolamine is first formed and then methylated by stepwise additions of three terminal methyl groups (phosphatidyl dimethyl ethanolamine, PDME, is an intermediate). Pathway I is generally agreed to be the main route of PC synthesis in the lungs of all adult species and in the fetal lungs of rats (136, 168, 177). According to Gluck and colleagues (86, 89), however, pathway II has special importance early in the gestation of man and some primates; its appearance early in gestation is said to be a special feature of these species allowing the survival of preterm deliveries; but the pathway is thought to be easily inhibited by hypoxia, hypothermia, and other forms of "stress." The theory depends on detecting PDME, the pathway II intermediate, in lung washings and pharyngeal aspirates and on identifying the unusual α-palmitic (C_{16}), β-myristic (C_{14}) form of both PDME and PC. It is claimed that esterification of myristic acid to the β carbon of the glycerol component of phosphoglycerides is specific to pathway II. These conclusions have been criticized on several counts. According to Goerke & Clements (92), a film of PC in the α-palmitic, β-myristic form, at 37°C, lacks some of the physical characteristics vital for surfactant. In lung slices from the fetal rhesus monkey between 100 days and 161 days (term = 164 days), pathway I incorporated 10–50 times more precursor ([^{14}C] choline) than pathway II (detected using [^{14}C] methionine or [^{14}C] ethanolamine as precursors); and the activity of pathway I increased twofold at about 150 days, whereas pathway II did not change during gestation (72). In fetal rat lungs, pathway I enzymes, choline kinase, and choline phosphotransferase increase sharply two days before term (75).

There is a considerable body of evidence showing that surfactant synthesis is accelerated by injecting corticosteroids, ACTH, or L-thyroxine directly into the immature fetus [for a summary see (74)]. The most direct quantitative demonstration of the effect was obtained by Platzker et al (149) who measured surfactant production by collecting fetal lung liquid from chronically intubated fetal lambs. They showed a fourfold increase at 108–134 days in response to dexamethasone (400 μg/day). Cytoplasmic and nuclear glucosorticoid receptors have been found in the fetal rabbit lung (13, 84). Corticosteroids have also been shown to activate one of the enzymes in pathway I, choline phosphotransferase (76). Neither corticosteroids (135) nor L-thyroxine (182) influences the fetal lung of the rabbit when given to the pregnant mother but according to evidence from a clinical trial, fetal lung maturity can be accelerated in the human by giving dexamethasone to the mother in spontaneous premature labor at less than 32 weeks gestation (103). Whether the clinical benefits outweigh the potential risks remains controversial. The increase in endogenous cortisol production, thought to be a critical event in starting labor (128), may provide a physiological stimulus for maturation of surfactant biosynthesis. In human infants, an inverse relationship between the cortisol level in cord blood and the incidence of RDS has been reported (137). Fedrick & Butler (77) found an increased incidence of RDS in infants delivered by caesarean section before the onset of labor, which they attributed to the absence of natural corticosteriod stimulation of surfactant synthesis. An apparent decrease in RDS incidence after prolonged rupture of the fetal membranes has been attributed to a premature rise in endogenous cortisol production due to "stress," but detailed statistical analysis of a large clinical series failed to confirm a reduced incidence in these circumstances and highlighted some of the difficulties arising in the interpretation of this kind of information (107).

PULMONARY CIRCULATION

Changes in pulmonary blood flow and vascular resistance play an important part in the developments at birth. Before the start of ventilation only 7–10% of combined ventricular output passes through the lungs (161); the remaining output of the right heart reaches the systemic arteries through the ductus arteriosus and foramen ovale. These arrangements depend on a high pulmonary vascular resistance, due, in large part, to constricted vascular smooth muscle. At birth, pulmonary ventilation leads to a lowering of vascular resistance and to a ten- or fifteenfold increase in blood flow; it has also been shown recently that pulmonary blood volume increases by 43% (176). Closure of the foramen and ductus follow, the one due to a rise in left atrial pressure, the other to an increase in the Po_2 of blood perfusing the ductus. The mechanisms involved in these changes have been extensively reviewed (61, 161). More recent work has been concerned with some aspects of the microcirculation.

According to Humphreys et al (104), pulmonary lymph flow, reflecting net filtration from lung capillaries, is approximately twice as high in the mature fetal lamb (143 days) as in the 2-day-old newborn lamb. These values omit the postnatal increase due to lung liquid clearance which is completed by the age of 6 hr. Boyd et al (30) measured lung capillary permeability to macromolecules, which they interpreted in terms of pore theory. Unmodified, the results did not conform with the theory, but they did if it was assumed that all the largest molecules (diffusion radius = 11.0 nm) passed through a small number of large leaks and none through pores—a model for which there is morphological support in some vascular beds (126). Boyd et al (30) calculated a larger pore radius for the mature fetus (15 nm) than the newborn lamb (9.0 nm). Estimates for pore area per unit path length (A_p/Δ_x) were also obtained in these calculations. The value for the newborn lamb $(3.3 \times 10^3 \text{ cm})$ was about five times larger than for the mature fetus $(0.6 \times 10^3 \text{ cm})$. According to a rather speculative interpretation favored by Boyd et al (30), much of the pulmonary microcirculation in the fetus is intermittently shut off by closure of precapillary vessels—hence the small area term, A_p/Δ_x; but the open capillaries are exposed to a substantial proportion of the high inflow pressure, explaining the high net rate of filtration and also—on the bases of stretched pores—the large pore radius. In the newborn lamb the pulmonary vascular bed is no longer constricted; presumably large areas open up, hence the larger A_p/Δ_x; also, the mean inflow pressure is lower—25–30 mm Hg instead of 55–60 mm Hg—which could be reflected in a reduced capillary pressure and filtration rate. Left atrial pressure is slightly higher in the newborn lamb ($\approx$6 mm Hg) than the fetus ($\approx$3 mm Hg) (9), and cannot be related to the difference in filtration rate. Asphyxia exaggerates some of the fetal characteristics: an episode of umbilical cord occlusion for 5–10 min in the lamb causes an increase in pulmonary artery pressure by about 20 mm Hg (1), a decrease in pulmonary blood flow (46), and an approximately twofold rise in pulmonary lymph flow, maximum in the 5 min after release of the occlusion (1).

The shape of arterial pressure flow curves lends some support to the possibility that much of the microcirculation in the fetal lung is cut off and that recruitment of vessels accounts for a good part of the change in vascular resistance at birth. In the fetal lamb, these curves have a very nonlinear portion where flow approaches zero, even at substantial pulmonary artery pressures; but they also have an apparently linear segment at higher pressures (45, 55)—a pattern to be expected from a population of small vessels resembling thin-walled cellophane tubes, fully collapsible at low pressures but inelastic when open (180).

CLOSING COMMENTS

Studying prenatal development shifts the lung physiologist's perspective. The function of gas exchange no longer occupies the foreground (the placenta is the fetal gas exchanger). Interest instead centers on the assembly of structural components, on cellular functions concerned in surfactant synthesis, on the control of ion and liquid movements. The manner in which the respiratory function of the central nervous system becomes organized and activated and the adaptive changes in the lungs at birth are also major interests. The lung has its beginning as a piece of epithelium—and such it remains. Several of the functions occupying our attention in the fetal lung depend on epithelial properties; it is the epithelium that secretes lung liquid, that controls the composition of the lung interior, that synthesizes surfactant. Indeed, one approach to the study of lung physiology might begin by considering the lung as a specially adapted epithelium with properties usefully to be compared with other large epithelial surfaces such as the intestine or the renal tubule; but not until 1952 (129) was it known that the lung possesses a complete epithelium, and its functional importance has only recently received attention.

Literature Cited

1. Adamson, T. M., Boyd, R. D. H., Hill, J. R., Normand, I. C. S., Reynolds, E. O. R., Strang, L. B. 1970. Effect of asphyxia due to umbilical cord occlusion in the foetal lamb on leakage of liquid from the circulation and on permeability of lung capillaries to albumin. *J. Physiol. London* 207:493–505

2. Adamson, T. M., Boyd, R. D. H., Platt, H. S., Strang, L. B. 1969. Composition of alveolar liquid in the foetal lamb. *J. Physiol. London* 204:159–68

3. Adamson, T. M., Brodecky, V., Lambert, T. F., Maloney, J. E., Ritchie, B. C., Walker, A. 1973. The production and composition of lung liquid in the *in utero* foetal lamb. In *Foetal and Neonatal Physiology. Proc. Sir Joseph Barcroft Centenary Symp.* pp. 208–16 Cambridge, Engl: Cambridge Univ. Press. 641 pp.

4. Aherne, W., Dawkins, M. J. R. 1964. The removal of fluid from the pulmonary airways after birth and the effect on this of prematurity and prenatal hypoxia. *Biol. Neonat.* 7:214–29

5. Ahlfield, F. 1905. Die intrauterine Tatigkeit der Thorax-und Zwerch-fellmuskulatur. Intrauterine Atmung. *Monatsschr. Geburtshilfe Gynaekol.* 21:143–63

6. Alescio, T. 1973. Effect of a proline analogue acetidine-2-carboxylic acid on the morphogenesis *in vitro* of mouse embryonic lung. *J. Embryol. Exp. Morphol.* 29:439–51

7. Alescio, T., Cassini, A. 1962. Induction *in vitro* of tracheal buds by pulmonary mesenchyme grafted on tracheal epithelium. *J. Exp. Zool.* 150:83–94

8. Areechon, W., Reid, L. 1963. Hypoplasia of lung with congenital diaphragmatic hernia. *Br. Med. J.* 1:230–33

9. Assali, N. S., Morris, J. A., Beck, R. 1965. Cardiovascular hemodynamics in the fetal lamb before and after lung expansion. *Am. J. Physiol.* 208:122–29

10. Avery, M. E. 1975. Pharmacological approaches to the acceleration of fetal lung maturation. *Br. Med. Bull.* 31:13–17

11. Avery, M. E., Chernick, V., Dutton, R. E., Permutt, S. 1963. Ventilatory response to inspired carbon dioxide in infants and adults. *J. Appl. Physiol.* 18:895–903

12. Bahoric, A., Chernick, V. 1975. Electrical activity of phrenic nerve and diaphragm in utero. *J. Appl. Physiol.* 39:513–18

13. Ballard, P. L., Ballard, R. A. 1972. Glucocorticoid receptors and the role of glucocorticoids in fetal lung development. *Proc. Natl. Acad. Sci. USA* 69:2668–72

14. Barcroft, J. 1946. *Researches on Prenatal Life*, pp. 260–72 Oxford: Blackwell. 292 pp.

15. Barcroft, J., Barron, D. H. 1937. The genesis of respiratory movements in the foetus of the sheep. *J. Physiol. London* 88:56–61

16. Barcroft, J., Barron, D. H. 1937. Movements in mid foetal life in the sheep embryo. *J. Physiol. London* 91:329–51

17. Bartlett, D. Jr. 1970. Post natal growth of the mammalian lung: Influence of exercise and thyroid activity. *Respir. Physiol.* 9:50–57

18. Bartlett, D. Jr. 1975. Postnatal growth of the mammalian lung: Lack of influence by carbon monoxide exposure. *Respir. Physiol.* 23:343–50

19. Bartlett, D. Jr., Remmers, J. E. 1971. Effect of high altitude exposure on the lungs of young rats. *Respir. Physiol.* 13:116–25

20. Bernfield, M. R., Wessells, N. K. 1970. Intra- and extracellular control of epithelial morphogenesis. *Dev. Biol. Suppl.* 4:195–249

21. Bhagwanani, S. G., Fahmy, D., Turnbull, A. C. 1972. Prediction of neonatal respiratory distress by estimation of amniotic fluid lecithin. *Lancet* 1:159–62

22. Biscoe, T. J., Purves, M. J. 1965. Cervical sympathetic and chemoreceptor activity before and after the first breath of the newborn lamb. *J. Physiol. London* 181:70–71P

23. Blackburn, W. R., Travers, H., Potter, D. M. 1972. The role of the pituitary-adrenal thyroid axes in lung differentiation 1. Studies of the cytology and physical properties of anencephalic fetal rat lung. *Lab. Invest.* 26:306–18

24. Boddy, K., Dawes, G. S., Robinson, J. S. 1973. A 24-hour rhythm in the foetus. See Ref. 3, pp. 63–66

25. Boddy, K., Mantell, C. D. 1972. Observation of the fetal breathing movements transmitted through maternal abdominal wall. *Lancet* 2:1219–20

26. Boddy, K., Robinson, J. S. 1971. External method for detection of fetal breathing in utero. *Lancet* 2:1231–33

27. Bodegard, G. 1975. Control of respiration in newborn babies III. *Acta Paediatr. Stockholm* 64:684–92

28. Bodegard, G., Schwieler, G. H., Skoglund, S., Zetterstrom, R. 1969. Control of respiration in newborn babies. *Acta Paediatr. Scand.* 58:567–71

29. Boulpaep, E. L. 1972. Permeability changes of the proximal tubule of Necturus during saline loading. *Am. J. Physiol.* 222:517–31

30. Boyd, R. D. H., Hill, J. R., Humphreys, P. W., Normand, I. C. S., Reynolds, E. O. R., Strang, L. B. 1969. Permeability of lung capillaries to macromolecules in foetal and new-born lambs and sheep. *J. Physiol. London* 201:567–88

31. Boyden, E. A., Tompsett, D. H. 1965. The changing patterns in the developing lungs of infants. *Acta Anat.* 61:164–92

32. Bradley, K. H., McConnell, S. D., Crystal, R. G. 1974. Lung collagen composition and synthesis. Characterization and changes with age. *J. Biol. Chem.* 249:2674–83

33. Branton, D., Park, R. B. 1968. In *Papers on Biological Membrane Structure,* ed. D. Branton, R. B. Park, pp. 1–22. Boston, Mass: Little, Brown. 311 pp.

34. Bremer, J., Greenberg, D. M. 1961. Methyl transferring enzyme system of microsomes in biosynthesis of lecithin (phosphatidyl choline). *Biochim. Biophys. Acta.* 46:205–16

35. Brody, J. S. 1975. Time course of and stimuli to compensatory growth of lung after pneumonectomy. *J. Clin. Invest* 56:897–904

36. Brown, E. S. 1964. Isolation and assay of dipalmitoyl lecithin in lung extracts. *Am. J. Physiol.* 207:402–6

37. Buckingham, S., Avery, M. E. 1962. Time of appearance of lung surfactant in the foetal mouse. *Nature London* 193:688–89

38. Bullough, W. S. 1952. The energy relations of mitotic activity. *Biol. Rev. Cambridge Philos. Soc.* 27:133–68

39. Burri, P. H. 1974. The postnatal growth of the rat lung III. Morphology. *Anat. Rec.* 180:77–98

40. Burri, P. H., Dbaly, J., Weibel, E. R. 1974. The postnatal growth of the rat lung I. Morphometry. *Anat. Rec.* 178:711–30

41. Burri, P. H., Weibel, E. R. 1971. Morphometric estimation of pulmonary diffusion capacity II. Effect of environmental PO_2 on the growing lung. *Respir. Physiol.* 11:247–64

42. Bystrzycka, E., Nail, B. S., Purves, M. J. 1975. Central and peripheral neural respiratory activity in the mature sheep foetus and newborn lamb. *Respir. Physiol.* 25:199–215

43. Campiche, M. A., Gautier, A., Hernandez, E. I., Raymond, A. 1963. An electron microscope study of the fetal development of the human lung. *Pediatrics Springfield* 32:976–94

44. Carson, S. H., Tausch, H. W., Avery, M. E. 1973. Inhibition of lung cell division after hydrocortisone injection into fetal rabbits. *J. Appl. Physiol.* 34:660–63

45. Cassin, S., Dawes, G. S., Mott, J. C., Ross, B. B., Strang, L. B. 1964. The vascular resistance of the foetal and newly ventilated lung of the lamb. *J. Physiol. London* 171:61–79

46. Cassin, S., Dawes, G. S., Ross, B. B. 1964. Pulmonary blood flow and vascular resistance in immature foetal lambs. *J. Physiol. London* 171:80–89

47. Chernick, V., Havlicek, V., Pagtakhan, R. D.; Sklenovsky. 1973. Respiratory response to electrical stimulation of the brain stem of fetal and neonatal sheep. *Pediatr. Res.* 7:20–27

48. Clark, F. J., von Euler, C. 1972. On the regulation of depth and rate of breathing. *J. Physiol. London* 222:267–95

49. Clements, J. A. 1971. Comparative lipid chemistry of lungs. *Arch. Intern. Med.* 127:387–89

50. Clements, J. A. 1973. Composition and properties of pulmonary surfactant. In *Respiratory Distress Syndrome,* ed C. A. Villee, D. B. Villee, J. Zuckerman, pp. 77–98. New York & London: Academic. 406 pp.

51. Clements, J. A., Nellenbogen, J., Trahan, H. J. 1970. Pulmonary surfactant and evolution of the lungs. *Science* 169:603–4

52. Clements, J. A., Platzker, A. C., Tierney, D. F., Hobel, C. J., Creasy, R. K., Margolis, A. J., Thibeault, D. W., Tooley, W. H., Oh, W. 1972. Assessment of the risk of the Respiratory Distress Syndrome by a rapid test for surfactant in amniotic fluid. *New Engl. J. Med.* 286:1077–81

53. Comline, R. S., Silver, M. 1975. Placental transfer of blood gases. *Br. Med. Bull.* 31:25–31

54. Condorelli, S., Cosmi, E. V., Scarpelli, E. M. 1974. Extrapulmonary source of amniotic fluid phospholipids. *Am. J. Obstet. Gynecol.* 118:842–48

55. Cook, C. D., Drinker, P. A., Jacobson, H. N., Levison, H., Strang, L. B. 1963.

Control of pulmonary blood flow in the foetal and newly born lamb. *J. Physiol. London* 169:10–29

56. Cowan, M. J., Crystal, R. G. 1975. Lung growth after unilateral pneumonectomy: Quantitation of collagen synthesis and content. *Am. Rev. Respir. Dis.* 3:267–77

57. Cross, K. W., Klaus, M., Tooley, W. H., Weisser, K. 1960. The response of the newborn baby to inflation of the lungs. *J. Physiol. London* 151:551–65

58. Dameron, F., Marin, L. 1970. Mode de formation des inclusions lamellaires dans le poumon embryonaire du poulet. *Z. Zellforsch. Mikrosk. Anat.* 110: 72–84

59. Davies, G., Reid, L. 1970. Growth of the alveoli and pulmonary arteries in childhood. *Thorax* 25:669–81

60. Davson, H. 1956. *Physiology of the Occular and Cerebral Fluids*, p. 67. London: Churchill. 388 pp.

61. Dawes, G. S. 1968. *Foetal and Neonatal Physiology*, pp. 79–90. Chicago: Yearb. Med. 247 pp.

62. Dawes, G. S., Duncan, S. L. B., Lewis, B. V., Merlet, C. L., Owen-Thomas, J. B., Reeves, J. T. 1969. Hypoxaemia and aortic chemoreceptor function in foetal lambs. *J. Physiol. London* 201:105–16

63. Dawes, G. S., Duncan, S. L. B., Lewis, B. V., Merlet, C. L., Owen-Thomas, J. B., Reeves, J. T. 1969. Cyanide stimulation of the systemic arterial chemoreceptors in foetal lambs. *J. Physiol. London* 201:117–28

64. Dawes, G. S., Fox, H. E., Leduck, B. M., Liggins, G. S., Richards, R. T. 1972. Respiratory movements and rapid eye movement sleep in the foetal lamb. *J. Physiol. London* 220:119–43

65. Dejours, P. 1975. *Principles of Comparative Respiratory Physiology*. Amsterdam, Oxford: North Holland; New York: American Elsevier. 253 pp.

66. Diamond, J. M. 1974. Tight and leaky junctions of epithelia: A perspective on kisses in the dark. *Fed. Proc.* 33: 2220–24

67. Dubriel, G., Lacoste, A., Raymond, R. 1936. Observations sur le développement du poumon humain. *Bull. Histol. Appl. Physiol. Patnol. Microsc.* 13: 235–45

68. Dunnill, M. S. 1962. Postnatal growth of the lung. *Thorax* 17:329–33

69. Durbin, R. P. 1964. Anion requirements for gastric secretion. *J. Gen. Physiol.* 47:735–48

70. Egan, E. A., Nelson, R. M., Olver, R. E. 1976. Lung inflation and alveolar permeability to non-electrolytes in the adult sheep in vivo. *J. Physiol. London* 260:409–24

71. Egan, E. A., Olver, R. E., Strang, L. B. 1975. Changes in non-electrolyte permeability of alveoli and the absorption of lung liquid at the start of breathing in the lamb. *J. Physiol. London* 244: 161–79

72. Epstein, M. F., Farrell, P. M. 1975. Choline incorporation pathway—primary mechanism for de novo lecithin synthesis in fetal primate lung. *Pediatr. Res.* 9:658–65

73. Fantel, A. G., Shepard, T. H. 1975. Potter Syndrome—nonrenal features induced by oligohydramnios. *Am. J. Dis. Child.* 129:1346–47

74. Farrell, P. M., Avery, M. E. 1975. Hyaline membrane disease. *Am. Rev. Respir. Dis.* 111:657–88

75. Farrell, P. M., Lundgren, D. W., Adams, A. J. 1974. Choline kinase and choline phosphotransferase in developing fetal rat lung. *Biochem. Biophys. Res. Commun.* 57:696–701

76. Farrell, P. M., Zachman, R. D. 1973. Induction of choline phosphotransferase and lecithin synthesis in the fetal lung by corticosteroids. *Science* 179:297

77. Fedrick, J., Butler, N. R. 1972. Hyaline membrane disease. *Lancet* 2:768–69

78. Fisher, J. M., Simnett, J. D. 1973. Morphogenetic and proliferative changes in the regenerating lung of the rat. *Anat. Rec.* 176:389–95

79. Frosolono, M. F., Charms, B. L., Pawlowski, R., Slivka, S. 1970. Isolation characterisation and surface chemistry of a surface active fraction from dog lung. *J. Lipid Res.* 11:439–57

80. Fujiwara, T., Adams, F. H., Sipps, S., El Salawy, A. 1968. Alveolar and whole lung phospholipids of the developing fetal lamb lung. *Am. J. Physiol.* 215:375–82

81. Galdston, M., Shah, D. O., Shinowara, G. Y. 1969. Isolation *and* characterization of a lung lipoprotein surfactant. *J. Colloid Interface Sci.* 29:319–34

82. Gatzy, J. T. 1975. Ion transport across the excised bullfrog lung. *Am. J. Physiol.* 228:1162–71

83. Geelhaar, A., Weibel, E. R. 1971. Morphometric estimation and pulmonary diffusing capacity III. The effect of increased oxygen consumption in Japanese waltzing mice. *Respir. Physiol.* 11:354–66

84. Giannopoulos, G. 1973. Glucocorticoid receptors in lung l. Specific binding of glucocorticoids to cytoplasmic components of rabbit fetal lung. *J. Biol. Chem.* 248:3876–83

85. Gil, J., Reiss, O. K. 1973. Isolation and characterization of lamellar bodies and tubular myelin from rat lung homogenates. *J. Cell Biol.* 58:152–71

86. Gluck, L. E., Chez, R. A., Kulovich, M. V., Hutchinson, D. L., Niemann, W. H. 1974. Comparison of phospholipid indicators of fetal lung maturity in the amniotic fluid of the monkey (Macaca Mulatta) and baboon (papio papio). *Am. J. Obstet. Gynecol.* 120:524–30

87. Gluck, L. E., Kulovich, M. V. 1973. L/S ratios in amniotic fluid in normal and abnormal pregnancies. *Am. J. Obstet. Gynecol.* 115:539–52

88. Gluck, L. E., Kulovich, M. V., Borer, R. C., Brenner, P. H., Anderson, G. G., Spellacy, W. N. 1971. Diagnosis of the respiratory distress syndrome by amniocentesis. *Am. J. Obstet. Gynecol.* 109:440–45

89. Gluck, L. E., Kulovich, M. V., Eidelman, A. I., Cordero, L., Khazin, A. F. 1972. Biochemical development of surface activity in the mammalian lung IV. Pulmonary lecithin synthesis and etiology of the Respiratory Distress Syndrome. *Pediatr. Res.* 6:81–89

90. Gluck, L. E., Motoyama, E. K., Smits, H. L. Kulovich, M. V. 1967. The biochemical development of surface activity in mammalian lung I. *Pediatr. Res.* 1:237–46

91. Goerke, J. 1974. Lung surfactant. *Biophys. Biochim. Acta* 344:241–61

92. Goerke, J., Clements, J. A. 1973. Relative stability of palmitolyl, myristoyl and dipalmitoyl phosphatidyl cholines at 37°C. *Physiologist* 16:323. (Abstr.)

93. Grainger, R. M., Wessells, N. K. 1974. Does RNA pass from mesenchyme to epithelium during an embryonic tissue interaction? *Proc. Natl. Acad. Sci. USA* 71:4747–51

94. Griscom, N. T., Harris, G. B. S., Wohl, M. E. B., Vawter, G. F., Eraklis, A. J. 1969. Fluid filled lung due to airway obstruction in the newborn. *Pediatrics Springfield* 43:383–90

95. Harned, H. S. Jr., Ferreiro, J. 1973. Initiation of breathing by cold stimulation. Effects of change in ambient temperature on respiratory activity of the full-term fetal lamb. *J. Pediatr.* 663–69

96. Harned, H. S. Jr., Griffin, C. A. III, Berryhill, W. S. Jr., MacKinney, L. G.,

Sugioka, K. 1967. Role of carotid chemoreceptors in the initiation of effective breathing of the lamb at term. *Pediatrics* 39:329–36

97. Harned, H. S. Jr., MacKinney, L. G., Berryhill, W. S. Jr., Holmes, C. K. 1966. Effects of hypoxia and acidity on the initiation of breathing in the fetal lamb at term. *Am. J. Dis. Child.* 112:334–42

98. Hathorn, M. K. S. 1975. Analysis of the rhythm of infantile breathing. *Br. Med. Bull.* 31:8–12

99. Hems, D. 1973. Palpable regular jerking movements of the human fetus. A possible respiratory sign of fetal distress. *Biol. Neonat.* 23:223–30

100. Herrington, R. T., Harned, H. S. Jr., Ferreiro, J. I., Griffin, C. A. III. 1971. The role of the central nervous system in perinatal respiration: Studies of chemoregulatory mechanisms in the term lamb. *Pediatrics* 47:857–64

101. Hodson, W. A., Fenner, A., Brumley, G., Chernick, V., Avery, M. E. 1968. Cerebrospinal fluid and blood acid-base relationships in fetal and neonatal lambs and pregnant ewes. *Respir. Physiol.* 4:322–32

102. Homma, H., Kira, S., Takahashi, Y., Imai, H. 1975. A case of alveolar cell carcinoma accompanied by fluid and electrolyte depletion through production of voluminous lung liquid. *Am. Rev. Respir. Dis.* 111:857–62

103. Howie, R. N., Liggins, G. C. 1973. Prevention of Respiratory Distress Syndrome in premature infants by antepartum glucocorticoid treatment. In *Respiratory Distress Syndrome,* ed. C. A. Villee, D. B. Villee, J. Zuckerman, pp. 369–80. New York & London: Academic. 406 pp.

104. Humphreys, P. W., Normand, I. C. S., Reynolds, E. O. R., Strang, L. B. 1967. Pulmonary lymph-flow and the uptake of liquid from the lungs of the lamb at the start of breathing. *J. Physiol. London.* 193:1–29

105. Jansen, A. H., Chernick, V. 1975. Site of central chemosensitivity in fetal sheep. *J. Appl. Physiol.* 39:1–6

106. Johnson, P., Robinson, J. S., Salisbury, D. 1973. The onset and control of breathing after birth. See Ref. 3, pp. 217–21

107. Jones, M. D., Burd, L. I., Bowes, W. A., Battaglia, F. C., Lubchenko, L. O. 1975. Failure of association of premature rupture of membranes with Respir-

atory Distress Syndrome. *New Engl. J. Med.* 292:1253–57

108. Jost, A., Policard, A. 1948. Contribution expérimentale à l'étude du développement prénatal du poumon chez le lapin. *Arch. Anat. Microsc.* 37:323–32

109. Kattwinkel, J., Nearman, H. S., Fanaroff, A. A., Katona, P. G., Klaus, M. H. 1975. Apnea of prematurity: Comparative therapeutic effects of cutaneous stimulation and nasal continuous positive airways pressure. *J. Pediatr.* 86:588–92

110. Kaufman, S. L., Burri, P. H., Weibel, E. R. 1974. The postnatal growth of the rat lung II. Autoradiography. *Anat. Rec.* 180:63–76

111. Kennedy, E. P., Weiss, S. B. 1956. The function of cytidine co-enzymes in the biosynthesis of phospholipids. *J. Biol. Chem.* 222:193–214

112. Keynes, R. D. 1976. Comparative aspects of salt and water transport across the lung. In *Lung Liquids, Ciba Found. Symp.,* ed. M. O'Connor, R. Porter. Amsterdam: North Holland. 330 pp.

113. Keys, A., Willmer, E. N. 1932. "Chloride secreting cells" in the gills of fishes with special reference to the common eel. *J. Physiol. London* 76:368–78

114. Kikkawa, Y., Motoyama, E. K., Cook, C. D. 1965. Ultrastructure of lungs of lambs: The relation of osmiophilic inclusions and alveolar lining layer to fetal maturation and experimentally produced respiratory distress. *Am. J. Pathol.* 47:877–903

115. Kikkawa, Y., Motoyama, E. K., Gluck, L. 1968. Study of the lungs of fetal and newborn rabbits: Morphologic biochemical and surface physical development. *Am. J. Pathol.* 52:177–209

116. King, R. J. 1974. The surfactant system of the lung. *Fed. Proc.* 33:2238–47

117. King, R. J., Clements, J. A. 1972. Surface active materials from dog lung I. Method of isolation. *Am. J. Physiol.* 223:707–14

118. King, R. J., Clements, J. A. 1972. Surface active materials from dog lung II. Composition and physiological correlations. *Am. J. Physiol.* 223:715–26

119. King, R. J., Gikas, E. G., Ruch, J., Clements, J. A. 1974. The radioimmunoassay of pulmonary surface active material in sheep lung. *Am. J. Respir. Dis.* 110:273–81

120. King, R. J., Klass, D. J., Gikas, E. G., Clements, J. A. 1973. Isolation of apoproteins from canine surface active material. *Am. J. Physiol.* 224:788–95

121. King, R. J., Ruch, J., Gikas, E. G., Platzker, A. C., Creasy, R. K. 1975. Appearance of apoproteins of pulmonary surfactant in human amniotic fluid. *J. Appl. Physiol.* 39:735–41

122. Klass, D. J. 1973. Immunochemical studies of the protein fraction of pulmonary surface active material. *Am. Rev. Respir. Dis.* 107:784–89

123. Knill, R., Andrews, W., Bryan, A. C., Bryan, M. H. 1976. Respiratory load compensation in infants. *J. Appl. Physiol.* 40:357–61

124. Knill, R., Bryan, A. C. 1976. An intercostal-phrenic inhibitory reflex. *J. Appl. Physiol.* 40:352–56

125. Kotas, R. V., Le Roy, C. M., Hart, L. K. 1974. Reversible inhibition of lung cell number after glucocorticoid injection into fetal rabbits to enhance surfactant appearance. *Pediatrics Springfield* 53:358–61

126. Landis, E. M. 1964. Heteroporosity of the capillary wall as indicated by cinematographic analysis of the passage of dyes. *Ann. NY Acad. Sci.* 116:765–73

127. Loeschke, H. H. 1974. Central nervous chemoreceptors. In *MTP International Review of Science Physiology Series One: Respiratory Physiology,* Ed. A. C. Guyton, J. G. Widdicombe. 2:167–96. London: Butterworth. 381 pp.

128. Liggins, G. C. 1969. Premature delivery of foetal lambs infused with glucocorticoids. *J. Endocrinol.* 45:515–23

129. Low, F. N., Daniels, C. W. 1952. Electron microscopy of the rat lung. *Anat. Rec.* 113:437–43

130. Maloney, J. E., Adamson, T. M., Brodecky, V., Cranage, S., Lambert, T. F., Ritchie, B. C. 1975. Diaphragmatic activity and lung liquid flow in the unanesthetized fetal sheep. *J. Appl. Physiol.* 39:423–28

131. Marin, L., Dameron, F. 1972. Evolution sur Greffe Hétérochronique de l'ébauche pulmonaire de l'embryon de poulet. Étude ultrastructural des inclusions granulaires et lamellaires. *Z. Anat. Entwicklungsgech.* 138:111–26

132. Marsland, D. W., Callahan, B. J., Shannon, D. C. 1975. The afferent vagus and regulation of breathing in response to inhaled CO_2 in awake newborn lambs. *Biol. Neonat.* 27:102–7

133. Merlet, C., Hoerter, J., Devilleneuve, Ch., Tchobroutsky, C. 1970. Mise en évidence de mouvements respiratoires chez le foetus d'agneau in utero. *J. Physiol. Paris* 62:416–17

134. Merlet, C., Leandri, J., Rey, P., Tchobroutsky, C. 1967. Action du refroidissement localisé dans le déclenchment de la respiration chez l'agneau à la naissance. *J. Physiol. Paris* 59:457–58

135. Motoyama, E. K., Orzalesi, M. M., Kikkawa, Y., Kaibara, M., Wu, B., Zigas, C. J., Cook, C. D. 1971. Effect of cortisol on maturation of the foetal rabbit lung. *Pediatrics Springfield* 48:547–55

136. Motoyama, E. K., Rooney, S. A. 1974. Does the methylation pathway contribute to the biosynthesis of surface active phosphatidyl choline in the lung? *Fed. Proc.* 33:346 (Abstr.)

137. Murphy, B. E. P. 1974. Cortisol and cortisone levels in the cord blood at delivery of infants with and without the Respiratory Distress Syndrome. *Am. J. Obstet. Gynecol.* 19:1112–20

138. Nelson, N. M. 1966. Neonatal pulmonary function. *Pediatric Clinics of North America 1. The Newborn.* 13:769–99

139. Normand, I. C. S., Olver, R. E., Reynolds, E. O. R., Strang, L. B., Welch, K. 1971. Permeability of lung capillaries and alveoli to non-electrolytes in the foetal lamb. *J. Physiol. London* 219:303–30

140. *Nomina Embryologica.* 1974. Int. Anat. Nomenclature Comm: Fed. of Am. Soc. Exp. Biol.

141. Olver, R. E., Davis, B., Marin, M. V., Nadel, J. A. 1975. Active transport of Na^+ and Cl^- across canine tracheal epithelium in vitro. *Am. Rev. Respir. Dis.* 112:811–16

142. Olver, R. E., Reynolds, E. O. R., Strang, L. B. 1973. Foetal lung liquid. See Ref. 3, pp. 186–207

143. Olver, R. E., Strang, L. B. 1974. Ion fluxes across the pulmonary epithelium and the secretion of lung liquid in the foetal lamb. *J. Physiol. London* 241:327–57

144. Olinsky, A., Bryan, M. H., Bryan, A. C. 1974. Influence of lung inflation on respiratory control in neonates. *J. Appl. Physiol.* 36:426–29

145. Oschman, J. L., Berridge, M. J. 1971. The structural basis of fluid secretion. *Fed. Proc.* 30:49–56

146. Overton, E. 1899. The probable origin and physiological significance of cellular osmotic properties. *Pap. Biol. Membr. Struct.*, transl. R. B. Park, ed. D. Branton, R. B. Park. Boston: Little, Brown. 311 pp.

147. Pagtakhan, R. D., Faridy, E. E., Chernick, V. 1971. Interaction between arterial P_{O_2} and P_{CO_2} in the initiation of respiration of foetal sheep. *J. Appl. Physiol.* 30:382–87

148. Petrik, P. 1971. Fine structural identification of peroxisomes in mouse and rat bronchiolar and alveolar epithelium. *J. Histochem. Cytochem.* 19:339–48

149. Platzker, A. C., Kitterman, J. A., Mescher, E. J., Clements, J. A., Tooley, W. H. 1975. Surfactant in the lung & tracheal fluid of the fetal lamb and acceleration of its appearance by dexamethasone. *Pediatrics* 56:554–61

150. Plum, F. 1970. Neurological integration of behavioural and metabolic control of breathing. In *Ciba Found. Symp. The Control of Breathing. Hering-Breuer Centenary Symposium,* ed. R. Porter, pp. 159–75. London: Churchill. 402 pp.

151. Ponte, J., Purves, M. J. 1973. Types of nervous activity which may be measured in the vagus nerve of the sheep fetus. *J. Physiol. London* 229:51–76

152. Potter, E. L. 1961. *Pathology of the Fetus and Infant,* p. 302. Chicago: Yearb. 670 pp.

153. Potter, E. L., Bohlender, G. P. 1941. Intrauterine respiration in relation to development of the fetal lung. *Am. J. Obstet. Gynecol.* 42:14–22

154. Purves, M. J. 1966. Respiratory and circulatory effects of breathing 100% oxygen in the new-born lamb before and after denervation of the carotid chemoreceptors. *J. Physiol. London* 185:42–59

155. Purves, M. J. 1966. The respiratory response of the new-born lamb to inhaled CO_2 with and without accompanying hypoxia. *J. Physiol. London* 185:78–94

156. Reid, L. 1967. The embryology of the lung. In *Ciba Found. Symp.—Development of the Lung,* ed. A. V. S. de Reuck, R. Porter. London: Churchill. 408 pp.

157. Reynolds, E. O. R., Jacobson, H. N., Motoyama, E. K., Kikkawa, Y., Craig, J. M., Orzalesi, M. M., Cook, C. D. 1965. The effect of immaturity and prenatal asphyxia on the lungs and pulmonary function of newborn lambs; the experimental production of respiratory distress. *Pediatrics Springfield* 35:382–92

158. Reynolds, E. O. R., Orzalesi, M. M., Motoyama, E. K., Craig, J. M., Cook, C. D. 1965. Surface properties of saline extracts from lungs of newborn infants. *Acta Pediatr. Scand.* 54:511–18

159. Reynolds, S. R. M., Mackie, J. D. 1961. Development of chemoreceptor re-

sponse sensitivity: Studies in fetuses of lambs and ewes. *Am. J. Physiol.* 201:239–50

160. Rigatto, H., de la Torre Verduzco, R., Cates, D. B. 1975. Effects of O_2 on the ventilatory response to CO_2 in preterm infants. *J. Appl. Physiol.* 39:886–89

161. Rudolph, A. M., Heymann, M. A. 1974. Fetal and neonatal circulation and respiration. *Ann. Rev. Physiol.* 36:187–207

162. Schneeberger, E. E. 1972. Development of peroxisomes in granular pneumocytes during pre- and post-natal growth. *Lab. Invest.* 27:581–89

163. Shelley, S. A., L'Heureux, M. V., Balis, J. U. 1975. Characterization of lung surfactant; factors promoting formation of artifactual lipid-protein complexes. *J. Lipid Res.* 16:224–34

164. Shirai, N., Utida, S. 1970. Development and degeneration of the chloride cell during seawater and freshwater adaptation of the Japanese eel. *Anguilla Japonica. Z. Zellforsch. Mikrosk.* 103:247–64

165. Sjodin, R. A. 1959. Rubidium and cesium fluxes in muscle as related to the membrane potential. *J. Gen. Physiol.* 42:983–1003

166. Sorokin, S. 1961. A study of development in organ cultures of mammalian lungs. *Dev. Biol.* 3:60–83

167. Sorokin, S., Padykula, H. A., Herman, E. 1959. Comparative histochemical patterns in developing mammalian lungs. *Dev. Biol.* 1:125–51

168. Spitzer, H. L., Morrison, K., Norman, J. R. 1968. The incorporation of (L-Me^{14}C) methionine and (Me^{3}H) choline into lung phosphatides. *Biochim. Biophys. Acta* 152:552–58

169. Spooner, B. S., Wessells, N. K. 1970. Mammalian lung development. Interactions in primordium formation and bronchial morphogenesis. *J. Exp. Zool.* 175:445–54

170. Storey, C. F., Knudtson, K. P., Lawrence, B. J. 1953. Bronchiolar ("alveolar cell") carcinoma of the lung. *J. Thorac. Surg.* 26:331–403

171. Thurlbeck, W. M. 1975. Postnatal growth and development of the lung. *Am. Rev. Respir. Dis.* 111:803–44

172. Tierney, D. F. 1974. Lung metabolism and biochemistry. *Ann. Rev. Physiol.* 36:209–231

173. Torrance, R. W. 1976. Arterial chemoreceptors. In *MTP International Review of Science: Physiology. Series 1: Respiratory Physiology,* ed. A. C. Guyton, J. G. Widdicombe, 2:247–71. London & Baltimore: Butterworth. 381 pp.

174. Traderera, J. V. 1967. Control of lung differentiation in vitro. *Dev. Biol.* 16:489–512

175. Wade, J. B., Revel, J. P., Di Scala, V. A. 1973. Effect of osmotic gradients on intracellular function of the toad bladder. *Am. J. Physiol.* 224:407–15

176. Walker, A. M., Alcorn, D. G., Cannata, J. C., Maloney, J. E., Ritchie, B. C. 1975. Effect of ventilation on pulmonary blood volume of the fetal lamb. *J. Appl. Physiol.* 39:969–75

177. Weinhold, P. 1968. Biosynthesis of phosphatidyl choline during prenatal development of the rat lung. *J. Lipid. Res.* 9:262–66

178. Wessells, N. K. 1970. Mammalian lung development. interactions in formation and morphogenesis of tracheal buds. *J. Exp. Zool.* 175:455–66

179. Wessells, N. K., Cohen, J. H. 1968. Effect of collagenase on developing epithelia in vitro. Lung, ureteric bud and pancreas. *Dev. Biol.* 18:294–309

180. West, J. B., Schneider, A. M., Mitchell, M. M. 1975. Recruitment in networks of pulmonary capillaries. *J. Appl. Physiol.* 39:976–84

181. Woodside, G. L., Dalton, A. J. 1958. The ultrastructure of lung tissue from newborn and embryo mice. *J. Ultrastruct. Res.* 2:28–54

182. Wu, B., Kikkawa, Y., Orzalesi, M. M., Motoyama, E. K., Kaibara, M., Zigas, C. J., Cook, C. D. 1973. The effect of thyroxine on the maturation of fetal rabbit lung. *Biol. Neonat.* 22:161–68

183. Zadunaisky, J. A. 1971. Electrophysiology and transparency of the cornea. In *Electrophysiology of Epithelial Cells,* ed. G. Giebisch, pp. 225–55. Stuttgart & New York: Schattauer. 312 pp.

Ann. Rev. Physiol. 39:277–99

CARDIAC DYNAMICS

❖1172

William W. Parmley, John V. Tyberg, and Stanton A. Glantz

Cardiovascular Research Institute, University of California,
San Francisco, California 94143[1]

INTRODUCTION

The possibility of altering the natural course of ischemic heart disease by interventions affecting the mechanical loads on the heart led to important work in three related areas: An analysis of the diastolic pressure-volume relationship of the heart; the importance of afterload as a determinant of ventricular function; and the assessment of regional mechanical performance in the presence of ischemia. Traditional investigations of the left ventricle's diastolic pressure-volume relation concentrated on quantifying the myocardium's elastic properties. New experimental and theoretical evidence suggests that other factors, especially right ventricular pressure changes, play an important role in altering the left ventricular diastolic pressure-volume relationship. Clinical studies demonstrating the beneficial hemodynamic effects of vasodilator drugs led to renewed interest in the concept of afterload as a determinant of ventricular function. Of the several conceptual approaches proposed to define afterload in the intact heart, no one is easily measured or more meaningful than the others. Attempts to preserve ischemic myocardium in people with coronary artery disease motivated work to assess quantitatively regional mechanical performance of the heart during ischemia. Such techniques form the basis for assessing proposed therapeutic interventions. These three topics are closely interrelated in ischemic heart disease, where alterations in the ventricular diastolic pressure-volume relationship and regional function are common, and where changes in afterload can affect function, as well as influencing the viability of jeopardized myocardia.

THE DIASTOLIC PRESSURE-VOLUME RELATIONSHIP

The established view of the left ventricle during diastole assumes it to be an elastic shell—a balloon—that expands as it fills with blood. The pressure inside the ventri-

[1]This work was supported in part by USPHS, NHI Program Project Grant HL 6285. Dr. Glantz is a Senior Fellow of the Bay Area Heart Research Committee.

cle induces balancing stresses in the ventricular muscle, and these stresses distend the muscle in accordance with its exponential stress-strain relationship. Stress equals force per unit cross-sectional area, and strain equals normalized distension. Normalizing distension by muscle length at zero force, results in Lagrangian strain (35); normalizing by instantaneous length produces natural strain (56). The muscle strain (distension) also depends directly on the ventricle's internal volume. Therefore, by manipulating the equations describing the balance between internal pressure and wall stress, the geometric relationship between ventricular volume and wall muscle strain, and the muscle's nonlinear stress-strain relationship, one can derive an equation giving ventricular pressure as a function of ventricular volume in parameters which characterize the passive elasticity of the myocardium. Glantz & Kernoff (35) derived such an equation, then measured left ventricle pressure-volume curves in excised dog hearts and stress-strain curves from the same hearts. They showed that the muscle stiffness computed indirectly from the pressure-volume curves did not differ detectably from the values computed directly from the stress-strain curves.

Even before this work, a number of investigators developed theoretical models along these lines and applied them to clinical data to compute a person's muscle elasticity from his diastolic pressure-volume relationship. They presumed that different diseases change the muscle's passive mechanical properties and that the diastolic pressure-volume curve would reflect these changes. For example, if muscle stiffens with ischemia, a partially ischemic ventricle should have a steeper pressure-volume curve than normal. Since the extent and severity of ischemia play an important role in evaluating people for coronary artery revascularization, considerable attention has been devoted to studying pressure-volume curves in people with ischemia due to coronary artery disease (5, 17, 23, 30, 31, 33, 38, 54, 57). By computing various parameters from the diastolic pressure-volume curve, investigators have hoped to quantify the extent of ischemia. Similar studies have been directed to the manner in which hypertrophy and congestive cardiomopathy affect the pressure-volume curve (39, 57). Mirsky (58) thoroughly reviewed this earlier work, so that we concentrate here on new experimental and theoretical results which provide a new perspective on diastole.

In contrast to the traditional logic about the effects of ischemia on the diastolic pressure-volume curve, Templeton et al (88) showed that regional ischemia has virtually no effect on the ventricle's passive elasticity, and Palacios et al (60) showed that global ischemia did not alter the diastolic pressure-volume curve. Likewise, preliminary theoretical results indicate that it is highly unlikely that muscle stiffness changes produce the large shifts in the pressure-volume curve that have been observed in people during ischemia (65). Another theoretical study (36) demonstrated that one cannot compute reliably any of the proposed compliance indices in the clinical setting. Finally, several clinical investigators (2, 40, 65) have shown that acute hemodynamic interventions which do not affect the myocardium directly shift the diastolic pressure-volume curve. These observations indicate that the prevailing view of the left ventricular pressure-volume curve ignores important effects, among them, probably, the interaction between the right and left ventricle (6, 20, 85).

Templeton el al (88) produced regional ischemia for one hour in isovolumically contracting dog hearts by ligating the proximal left anterior descending coronary artery. To compute the ventricle's elastic and viscous stiffness throughout the cardiac cycle, they first superimposed sinusoidal, high-frequency (22 Hz), small-volume changes ($\Delta V = 0.5$ml) on the ventricle and measured the pressure increment, ΔP, compared with the pressure present in the ventricle without the sinusoidal volume perturbation. They found that the volume stiffness, $\Delta P/\Delta V$, varied linearly with ventricular pressure, P, throughout the entire cycle. This line rotated upward as the ventricle became more and more ischemic following coronary artery ligation. Sodium pentobarbital, another depressant, produced a similar change. Acetylstrophanthidin, an inotropic stimulant, partially reversed the sodium pentobarbital effect. When Templeton et al (88) released the ligation, the $\Delta P/\Delta V$ versus P returned to its control position. By analyzing the relative sizes and phases of the imposed ΔV and resulting ΔP, Templeton et al (88) found that these interventions did not affect the parameter representing the ventricle's passive elasticity, whereas the viscosity parameter increased markedly with ventricular depression. They explained this effect by comparing their results with the depressive effects on the cardiac muscle's force-velocity curve. Viscous stiffness is, by definition, the ratio of a change in force ΔF, to the corresponding change in velocity, ΔU. This ratio, $\Delta F{:}\Delta U$, is similar to the negative reciprocal of the slope of the force-velocity curve. This increase in viscous stiffness with ischemia indicates that the ability of the myocardium to generate velocity at a given force is impaired; i.e. the force-velocity curve is shifted down. Thus ischemia has little direct effect on muscle elasticity, but acts by depressing systolic function. In short, these investigators failed to detect changes in passive muscle elasticity.

Palacios et al (60) reached the same conclusions using a different preparation. They placed dog hearts on right heart bypass and cannulated both left and right main coronary arteries to control total coronary blood flow. They attached two mercury-in-silastic strain gauges to the left ventricle to measure its circumferential and base to apex dimensions. (The circumferential mercury-in-silastic gauge passed through the empty right ventricle adjacent to the septum.) They reduced coronary blood flow to produce global ischemia for periods up to two hours. They found that the end-diastolic pressure versus dimension curves did not change with ischemia or during reflow. Like Templeton et al (88), Palacios et al (60) noted a substantial decrease in systolic performance and also concluded that depressed systolic performance rather than an alteration in the pressure-volume relationship elevated end-diastolic pressure in an otherwise normal left ventricle. They went on to speculate that the shifts that have been observed clinically (5, 17, 54) do not reflect changes in muscle stiffness, but rather the effects of external mechanical constraints, probably the right ventricle.

Parmley et al (65) presented a preliminary theoretical argument that supports these observations; it is quantitatively impossible for changes in muscle elasticity to account for the large shifts observed in the diastolic pressure-volume curve with pacing-induced ischemia. Figure 1A shows beginning and end-diastolic pressures for nine patients in the absence of angina (open points) and during pacing-induced angina (closed points) (5). At a given volume, pressure increased about two and one-half times during angina pectoris. Usually less than half of the ventricle would become ischemic during a typical episode of angina pectoris. As an extreme case, however, assume that the ventricle is a uniform sphere, 50% of which becomes perfectly rigid during angina. The top panel of Figure 1B shows how the normal sphere would expand as pressure increases above zero. Now cut the sphere with a plane through its center and make the lower half perfectly rigid. Furthermore, assume that the plane exerts normal but not tangential forces on the two resulting hemispheres. As pressure increases, the rigid lower hemisphere remains unchanged while the upper hemisphere expands as if the lower half was normal (Figure 1B, bottom panel). Thus, at any given pressure, the volume of the half-rigid ventrile will be half the original volume of the sphere at that pressure (upper hemisphere) plus half the volume with no pressure difference across its walls (lower hemisphere); this calculation yields the solid line in Figure 1B. Note that even with these extreme assumptions, one cannot account for shifts in the pressure-volume curve even half as large as have been observed. While the assumption that the two halves of the

EFFECT OF PACING INDUCED ANGINA ON VENTRICULAR PRESSURE VOLUME RELATIONS

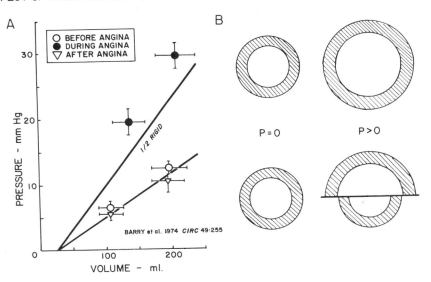

Figure 1   *A* Pacing-induced angina shifts the diastolic pressure-volume curve upwards with pressures increasing by 2½ times. The solid line illustrates the hypothetical pressure-volume curve obtained by assuming that ½ of the ventricle became rigid at the volume corresponding to zero transmural pressure.   *B* Expansion of a normal and half-rigid sphere from a volume corresponding to zero transmural pressure to end diastole. See text for explanation. [Data from Barry et al (5).]

Figure reproduced by permission from Parmley et al (65).

sphere do not remain connected is certainly gross, one can obtain confirming theoretical results from much more realistic theoretical descriptions. S. A. Glantz and R. F. Janz used Janz et al's (47) nonlinear large deformation finite-element model of the left ventricle to show that including stiffness changes, as have been observed in hypoxic isolated papillary muscles, for 40% of the ventricle shifts the pressure-volume curve up less than 25% (unpublished observations). Thus, although hypoxia may slightly alter passive muscle elasticity, these simple changes in muscle stiffness do not explain shifts in the diastolic pressure-volume curve with ischemia.

Other studies showed that hemodynamic interventions shift the diastolic pressure-volume curve as much as ischemia. For example, Alderman & Glantz (2) administered angiotensin and nitroprusside to people without coronary artery disease or segmental wall motion abnormalities. The resulting pressure-volume curves derived from ventriculograms before and after the intervention generally shifted up with angiotensin and down with nitroprusside. If the intact left ventricle behaved as an unconstrained purely elastic shell, all pressure-volume points should fall along the same curve regardless of how one altered filling pressure. Grossman et al (40) reported similar shifts in the pressure volume curve following nitroprusside administeration. Parmley et al (65) found that nitroglycerin also produced downward shifts. Coitart et al (14) reported downward shifts of the pressure-volume curve following propranolol administration in individuals with impaired systolic function. Notice that interventions which shifted the pressure-volume curve up also increased blood pressure, and interventions which dropped the pressure-volume curve also dropped blood pressure. None of these agents are known to affect the passive elasticity of normally oxygenated cardiac muscle (7, 11, 34), yet they changed the diastolic pressure-volume curve. These observations not only raise questions about the validity of using hemodynamic interventions to observe more of the pressure-volume curve, but also underscore the inadequacy of the simple model we have been discussing. By neglecting the effects of the right ventricle and pericardium, we have overlooked their influence in producing important shifts in the ventricle's diastolic pressure-volume relationship.

Before discussing how the right ventricle and pericardium might produce the shifts observed during clinical ischemia and following hemodynamic interventions, we must consider two other potential mechanisms: changes in pleural pressure and in coronary artery perfusion pressure. Alderman & Glantz (2) addressed the first question by measuring the esophageal pressure, which reflects pleural pressure. They found that, while the steady value at end-held inspiration was highly repeatable in a given individual, it varied widely from person to person (−2 to +7 mm Hg). Therefore, it is highly unlikely that changes in pleural pressure could account for a systematic shift in the diastolic pressure-volume curve in the same person with different interventions. On the other hand, the fact that pleural pressure varies over a range of 10 mm Hg makes it difficult to compare one patient's diastolic pressure-volume curve with that of another. Diastolic pressures measured with respect to atmospheric pressure are on the order of 10 mm Hg, as are person-to-person variations in pleural pressure. Therefore the uncertainty in the true baseline for zero transmural pressure across the ventricular wall is as large as the pressure one is measuring. This inability to note the true absolute difference across the ventricular free wall makes it extremely difficult to characterize the pressure-volume curve from clinical measurements in a way that permits interpatient comparison.

Interventions which increase blood pressure shift the diastolic pressure-volume curve up, while those that decrease pressure tend to drop it. Since these pressure changes are reflected in the coronary circulation which passes through the myocardium like a net, Salisbury et al (73) suggested that an increase in coronary perfusion pressure could stiffen the net, and hence the whole ventricle, even without changes in muscle elasticity. Templeton et al (87) investigated this hypothesis using the same preparation previously described and found that increasing coronary perfusion pressure increased systolic pressure and peak dP/dt, but had no effect on the ventricle's $\Delta P/\Delta V$ versus P plot. In short, the ventricle's viscoelastic properties remained constant despite increases in coronary perfusion pressure.

In contrast to changes in pleural pressure or coronary perfusion pressure, changes in right ventricular diastolic pressure probably play an important role in determining the observed shifts in the pressure-volume curve. Taylor et al (85) used exposed dog hearts suspended in a pericardial cradle to show that alterations in right ventricular volume had a substantial effect on left ventricular pressure and volume. They showed that increasing the right ventricular volume from 23–47 ml increased the left ventricular diastolic pressure about 50% at any given volume. Bemis et al (6) used an isolated perfused dog heart with an intact pericardium to show that increases in right ventricular filling pressure increased left ventricular filling pressure and altered its geometry. From a mechanical point of view this result is quite reasonable, since the stress in the septum, which partially defines left ventricular pressure, depends on the pressure gradient across it. Elzinga et al (20) found the same thing in an isolated cat heart. In addition, they showed that removing the pericardium makes the left ventricular pressure less sensitive to right ventricular pressures changes. When the pericardium is intact, interventions which cause substantial volume increases may press the ventricle against the stiff pericardium (44, 69), producing larger pressure increases than one would expect if the unrestricted ventricle expanded (79). External forces acting on the left ventricle, including those that arise from pleural pressure, right ventricular pressure, and the pericardium, must be considered when interpreting left ventricular diastolic pressure and volume, both at rest and during interventions.

This direct mechanical interaction between the two ventricles, amplified by the pericardium's restraining action, suggests that end-diastolic pressure cannot be considered a unique function of end-diastolic volume. Therefore, end-diastolic sarcomere length, which presumably relates directly to end-diastolic volume, cannot be considered a unique function of end-diastolic pressure. That hemodynamic changes do not, in general, simply move the left ventricle along a single diastolic pressure-volume curve indicates that one cannot determine end-diastolic circumferential fiber length from end-diastolic pressure alone. This result brings into question the practice of using end-diastolic pressure interchangeably with end-diastolic fiber length when interpreting clinical data in terms of the Frank-Starling mechanism.

In sum, to better understand diastole, and especially short-term changes in the diastolic pressure-volume relationship, it may be better to assess the interaction between the two ventricles, rather than attempt to define muscle elasticity from pressure-volume data.

There is another compelling theoretical reason for this change in direction: it is almost impossible to reliably compute any of the compliance parameters proposed to date (36). Whereas, in the animal laboratory, one can obtain very accurate data over a wide range of pressures and volumes, one can only obtain relatively noisy data over a nominal range of pressures and volumes in humans. Computer processed frame-by-frame angiograms, catheter tip manometers (2, 23), and echocardiographic methods (33, 39) have increased the fidelity of the data, but the very short segment of the diastolic pressure-volume curve that one can observe clinically does not contain enough information to characterize the entire pressure-volume curve, much less muscle stiffness. To investigate this question, Glantz (36) used pressure-volume curves measured in excised dog left ventricles to compute 15 compliance parameters for two segments of each pressure-volume relation. The lower segment of each curve (3–11 mm Hg) approximated a normal range of diastolic pressures, while the higher range (15–32 mm Hg) approximated the elevated filling pressures of an individual with heart failure. To be suitable for clinical use, a parameter must describe the entire pressure-volume curve from such a short segment. This study examined P_{ed}/V_{ed}, $\Delta P/\Delta V$, $(dp/dV)_{ed}$, $[V(dP/dV)]_{ed}$, $(V/P)(dP/dV)_{ed}$, $\Delta P/\Delta D$, $(\Delta P/\Delta D)/\overline{p}$, single exponentials (30, 31), and more sophisticated derived parameters (23, 35, 56, 57). Unfortunately, all of these parameters changed significantly from one segment of the same pressure-volume curve to the next. In addition, the magnitude of the change differed in different hearts, indicating that there is no simple factor that one can use to correct for the specific curve segment measured in the clinical setting. This fundamental theoretical difficulty precludes computation of a simple parameter which will permit quantitative description of a given person's myocardium by plotting pressure and volume during diastole.

For example, at moderate pressures, the diastolic pressure-volume curve approximates a straight line plotted on semilog graph paper (Figure 2A). This observation led Gaasch and co-workers (30, 31) to fit the pressure-volume curve with an exponential function of the form $P = be^{kV}$, in which b and k are empirical constants. Figure 2B shows that if one uses the two end points of each pressure-volume segment analogous to end diastole, this equation describes the segment quite well, but the two resulting curves differ substantially. The exponential curve which was fit to the lower segment falls below the curve fit to the upper segment at high pressures, and below it at low pressures because even though each pressure-volume curve segment approximates a straight line on semilog paper, neither is a true exponential. The deviations from a true exponential shape, while small over each segment, are large enough to produce significantly different values of the parameters k and b when they are computed in different parts of the same pressure-volume curve. Because of this unavoidable computational artifact, at low pressures the ventricle looks less stiff than it is, and at high pressures it looks stiffer.

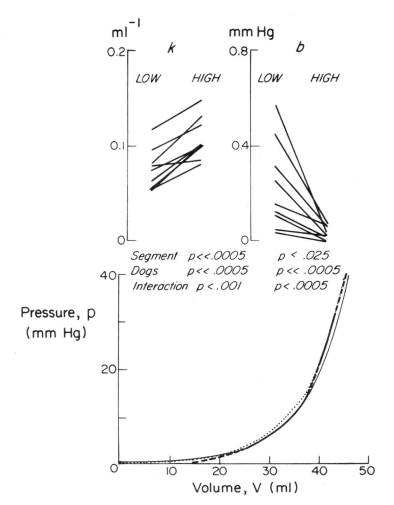

Figure 2 *A* Above pressures of about 2½ mm Hg, the pressure-volume curve for an excised dog heart approximates a straight line on semilogarithmic graph paper. However, the deviations from linearity are sufficient to cause one to obtain significantly different values of exponential parameters fit to the lower and upper segments of the curve. The two segments are shown as solid lines. *B* If one uses beginning and end diastole to evaluate the two parameters b and k in a simple exponential relationship, $p = be^{kV}$, one can obtain close agreement with the measured pressure-volume curve of points included within a given segment, but the exponential diverges from the true pressure-volume curve as one moves away from the segment used to evaluate the parameters k and b. The thin solid line is the exponential fit to the lower segment, and the dotted line is the exponential fitted to the upper segment. The inset shows that both k and b change significantly when one computes their values from different segments of the same curve. Each line represents mean values of six determinations from each dog. In addition, as Fester & Samet (23) indicated, both exponentials intersect the vertical axis at positive pressures, while the true pressure-volume curve must intersect the vertical axis at negative pressures. Reproduced by permission from Glantz (36).

In humans, diastolic pressure, together with the values of compliance indices, tends to increase with heart disease. A tendency toward higher values of the pressure-volume indices in diseased people may reflect the fact that one has obtained points higher on the pressure-volume curve, and not that any change in the mechanical properties of the muscle has occurred. This computational artifact may explain weak, but highly significant, correlations between end-diastolic pressure and compliance indices. This fact—combined with the technical difficulty of measuring pressure-volume curves in man, a variable baseline due to pleural pressure differences from one individual to the next, and the interaction between the two ventricles—probably explains the scatter all investigators report in their data. Simply increasing the fidelity of the measurements will not resolve all these problems. As described above, none of these parameters accurately characterizes the entire diastolic pressure-volume curve from a segment such as one can reasonably expect to obtain in a clinical setting.

In sum, we need to reassess the direction of research on questions related to the diastolic pressure-volume curve. To date, most work has concentrated on developing sophisticated models of the left ventricle with the hope of computing detailed stress distributions or inferring changes in muscle elasticity with disease, especially coronary artery disease. The data cited suggest that the expected changes in passive elasticity are much smaller than had been expected, and are inadequate to explain the clinically observed shifts in the pressure-volume curve. In addition, direct experimental studies in dog hearts, with the effects of the right ventricle minimized, failed to detect changes in elasticity with either segmental or global ischemia. Finally, one cannot obtain enough information in the short segment of the diastolic pressure-volume curve available clinically to compute any of the proposed compliance parameters. On the other hand, strong evidence supports an important role for the interaction between the right and left ventricle in regulating the left ventricular diastolic pressure-volume relationship. This interaction might take the following course, for example, with the administration of a vasodilator drug. These drugs lower both right- and left-sided pressures (13). The reduction in right heart pressures and volume would produce an apparent increase in compliance of the left ventricle (lower end-diastolic pressure at a given volume) (2, 40, 65). Conversely, the administration of a drug that increases pressure would produce an apparent decrease in left ventricular compliance (2). Future work should help us better understand this interaction and help determine whether manipulating the right heart can be used as a therapeutic intervention to treat disorders of the left.

IMPORTANCE OF AFTERLOAD AS A DETERMINANT OF VENTRICULAR FUNCTION

The primary mechanical determinants of each cardiac cycle are preload, afterload, and contractile state (1, 9, 32, 48). Heart rate is of further importance in the description of cardiac performance per unit of time. Previous studies emphasized the importance of heart rate, preload, and contractility, but tended to disregard afterload as an important determinant of ventricular function. As a general definition, afterload can be considered as those forces resisting ejection of ventricular blood into the aorta. Recent clinical studies, however, have documented the ability of vasodilator drugs to improve cardiac performance in people with both acute and chronic heart failure (11–13, 24, 26, 27). By reducing systemic vascular resistance, drugs such as sodium nitroprusside increase cardiac output, reduce left ventricular filling pressure, and reduce myocardial oxygen demand in critically ill patients (13). These studies suggest not only that this "afterload reduction" can improve cardiac performance, but that it may also reduce mortality (11). Vasodilator drugs particularly help individuals with severe mitral regurgitation. These drugs reduce the resistance to ejection at the aortic valve, so forward stroke volume increases by reducing regurgitant volume across the mitral valve. Since end-diastolic volume decreases and total stroke volume remains about the same, ejection fraction increases (12). These important clinical results stimulated renewed interest in afterload as an important determinant of ventricular function.

The terms preload, afterload, and contractile state can be simply defined in isolated cardiac muscle (76, 78). Preload equals the resting stress required to stretch the muscle to a given initial length. Afterload equals the additional stress the muscle develops as it shortens against a contant load. Both shortening velocity and total shortening decrease as the afterload increases (76, 77). The heart's complex geometry and changing fiber direction and the difference between a heart ejecting blood and a muscle lifting a weight make it difficult to apply these concepts to intact the heart. One might approach preloading and afterloading in the intact heart by considering the ventricle a net of one-dimensional muscles that carry a uniaxial stress through the cardiac cyle (32). Such calculations are difficult to make, and become extremely complex when one takes into account the 180° change in fiber direction from epicardium to endocardium (81). In preference to calculated wall stress, one could consider arterial impedance as ventricular afterload. Milnor (55) pointed out the complex relation between wall stress and time during ejection. In fact, the relation between wall stress during ejection and the compliance characteristics of the aorta and great vessels make it difficult to translate pressure or stress into a description of ventricular afterloading. He proposed the term vascular impedance, approximated by the instantaneous ratio of pressure to flow, to describe ventricular afterload. Vascular impedance represents an extension of the old concept of vascular resistance to account for the fact that blood flow is pulsatile (resistance assumes steady flow). By mathematical techniques, pressure and flow can be analyzed as a particular set of sinusoidal waves (harmonics). Each wave is described by its modulus (amplitude), phase angle (position relative to other harmonics), and frequency. The ratio of a pressure harmonic to the flow harmonic at the same frequency is called the impedance at that frequency. Defining afterload as the input of impedance spectra of the ascending aorta appears to be a reasonable description of the external load imposed on the ventricle. It has a conceptual advantage in that, unlike cardiac stress, which is always changing, the impedance spectrum remains constant despite changing pressure and flow through the cardiac cycle. The obvious immediate difficulty in using this definition is its impracticality, since there is no easy way of expressing this information in a manageable form. Nevertheless, the concept of arterial input impedance is important and deserves further investigation as a description of the "afterload" faced by the heart. The clinical importance of expressing afterload as impedance, rather than pressure, is that vasodilator drugs can often increase cardiac output without reducing arterial pressure. Thus, although pressure is unchanged, there is a reduction in the pressure: flow ratio (vascular resistance and impedance), which can be measured to quantitate the beneficial hemodynamic effects of the drug.

Suga and co-workers use the systolic pressure-volume relationship to separate effects of preload, afterload, and contractile state on the heart's performance (82, 83). Studies of isolated heart muscle reveal that, when one plots muscle force against length, the point representing maximum isotonic shortening occurring with any given load falls near the point defined by the total isometric force developed during an isometric contraction at that length (9). Although this relationship is only an approximate one in isolated heart muscle (86), it appears to be more important in describing intact heart performance. In the excised supported canine left ventricle Suga and co-workers (82, 83) showed that the maximum isovolumic pressure that could be developed at different initial volumes fell along a relatively straight line, which they called the isovolumic pressure line. Furthermore, in normally ejecting hearts, the end point of ejection (dicrotic notch of aortic pressure and end-systolic volume) fell along the same isovolumic pressure line. They expressed this concept by defining a function $E(t)=P(t)/V(t)$. This time-varying ratio has a sinusoidal form, the peak of which represents a point on the isovolumic pressure line (83). Thus the height of the peak pressure: volume ratio could be used as an index of contractility relatively independant of preload and afterload. With an increase in cardiac contractile state this line shifted up and to the left; Suga & Sagawa (83) concluded that it defined the heart's contractile state relatively independent of preload or afterload.

The proposed use of the isovolumic pressure line as an index of contractility independent of preload and afterload (82) prompts a brief description of the current status of such indices (16, 50, 63, 64, 66, 96). Indices have been derived to describe the pump function of the heart and the muscle function of the heart during the isovolumic phase and during ejection. In the initial enthusiasm of the search for an ideal index, attempts were focused on defining an index of contractility independent of preload and afterload. Initial studies suggested that V_{max} might be such an index of contractility in isolated heart muscle (76). Under special unloading circumstances, Brutsaert et al demonstrated that the unloaded velocity of shortening is relatively constant over a reasonable preload range (8). As commonly measured, however, V_{max} is somewhat preload dependent, as are other indices of contractility (96). Parmley et al (63) demonstrated in isolated heart muscle that those indices which are the most preload dependent also change the most with contractile state. Similarly, those indices which tended to be preload independent were not as sensitive to changes in contractility. Similar findings have been noted in the intact heart (66, 96). Both Parmley et al (64), in patients with coronary artery disease, and Kreulen et al (50), in patients with other forms of heart disease, demonstrated that V_{max} is no more specific than other indices of contractility in describing the function of the heart. Because of difficulties associated with measuring V_{max}, this index will probably not be as useful as more simply derived indices in describing cardiac function

(61). Peterson et al (67) demonstrated the value of ejection indices of contractility, particularly mean velocity of circumferential fiber shortening (V_{CF}), which has been useful in describing the state of chronic cardiac decompensation both before and after cardiac surgery. It appears that no one index of contractility can describe completely the heart, so it is unwise to continue searching for the ideal index of contractility. It is unlikely that any single index of cardiac performance will provide an overall description of cardiac function; a combination of measurements will always probably be required.

Returning to the pressure-volume loop described by Suga & Sagawa (83), it is interesting to note the alterations in stroke volume produced by changing aortic pressure (afterload). According to this scheme, if one keeps preload and contractility constant, increasing arterial pressure will decrease stroke volume, whereas decreasing arterial pressure will increase stroke volume because of the afterload effect. This pressure-volume relationship accurately describes how a decrease in aortic pressure can increase stroke volume at the same end-diastolic volume and level of contractility. It does not, however, explain convincingly increases in stroke volume without change in arterial pressure. This latter circumstance occurs fairly frequently in heart failure patients receiving vasodilator drugs. Three additional mechanisms could be considered to resolve this dilemma. First, an increase in stroke volume could be produced at a constant end-diastolic volume and arterial pressure if there were an increase in contractile state. In patients receiving vasodilator drugs, however, slowing of the heart rate often occurs, which suggests a reduction in sympathetic tone to the heart. Furthermore, these drugs have no direct inotropic effect on the heart (11). In addition, there tends to be a reduction in end-diastolic volume which would also tend to reduce stroke volume in the pressure-volume relationship described by Suga & Sagawa (83). A second possibility is that a shift in the left ventricular pressure-volume curve produced by lower right-sided pressures could take place (6, 20), increasing left ventricular volume at a given end-diastolic pressure. This effect could explain an increase in stroke volume at a given end-diastolic pressure and arterial pressure, with no change in contractile state. A third possibility exists in patients with segmental ischemia. A reduction in end-diastolic volume may relieve the ischemia of certain segments which could contract more effectively. Under these circumstances there would be an overall increase in the contractility of the heart even though the normal myocardium was unchanged. This possibility seems unlikely since many individuals who have responded favorably to vasodilators did not have coronary artery disease, but had chronic heart failure from other causes (27).

Therefore, although the pressure-volume relationship described by Suga and colleagues (82, 83) appears to be a useful mechanical way of interrelating preload, afterload, and contractile state, under certain circumstances it may not adequately describe the effects of afterload reduction with vasodilator drugs, i.e. when vasodilators improve stroke volume with little or only minor reductions in arterial pressure, and despite a substantial fall in left ventricular filling pressure. It will thus be extremely important to define further the effective afterload faced by the intact heart relative to its expression as wall stress, impedance, arterial pressure, or some other function.

Although there is some difficulty in precisely defining the afterload faced by the heart, particularly in response to vasodilators, the concept has great clinical importance, as recently summarized by Ross (71). His conceptual framework relating afterload, preload, and contractility, emphasizes that an increase in preload can compensate for the decreased stroke volume produced by an acute increase in cardiac loading (Figure 3). He considers aortic pressure as afterload in this scheme. At any given preload there is an inverse relationship between stroke volume and aortic pressure, i.e. stroke volume will fall as aortic pressure increases. With increasing preload, however, these curves shift to the right, so that for the same aortic pressure there is an increase in stroke volume at a higher preload. The dashed lines around point A on Figure 3 indicate the relatively normal ranges of aortic pressure

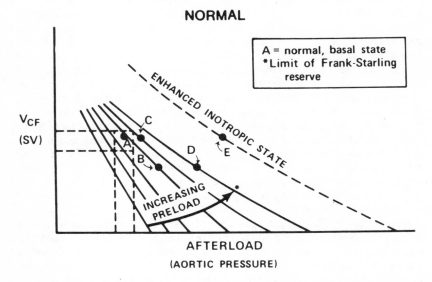

Figure 3 Conceptual diagram of the interrelationship of preload, afterload, and contractile state. The dashed lines which enclose point A indicate the relatively normal range of stroke volume and V_{CF} when plotted against afterload, expressed as aortic pressure. At any given preload, as afterload is increased stroke volume is reduced (A to B). By increasing preload, however, stroke volume can be increased to the lines containing points C and D. As preload reserve is exhausted at increasing afterloads, however, function falls to point D. This afterload mismatch can be corrected by increasing inotropic state which shifts this relationship upward and to the right to point E. This relationship points out how increasing preload can, up to a point, compensate for an increased afterload. Further, an increase in contractile state can additionally compensate for an afterload mismatch and maintain a reasonable stroke volume.

Reproduced by permission from Ross (71).

and stroke volume. As afterload increases, stroke volume falls to point B. An increase in preload, however, may return stroke volume toward normal (point C). At a higher afterload, however, there would be a fall in stroke volume to point D, since the preload reserve (Frank-Starling mechanism) would have been exhausted. Stroke volume could be returned to normal by enhanced inotropic state, which shifts the curves upwards and to the right (point E). Thus an afterload mismatch could be compensated for by either an increase in preload or contractile state. If preload reserve has been used up, however, even an increase in contractile state may not be sufficient to restore stroke volume to normal. This general scheme appears to be conceptually useful in the clinical situation, where the interaction between preload, afterload, and contractility can be manipulated by pharmacologic agents. Certainly recent use of vasodilator drugs (11, 12, 26, 27) emphasizes the importance of reducing afterload as one way of counteracting an afterload mismatch.

The concept of afterload mismatch is also closely related to the concept of the descending limb of the Frank Starling mechanism. In isolated heart muscle it is very difficult to demonstrate a significant descending limb of myocardial function. As one stretches heart muscle to high resting forces, it is difficult to demonstrate much more than a plateau of developed force at lengths longer than L_{max} (78), unless one overstretches the muscle and disrupts fibers to produce irreversible damage. In the intact heart, however, numerous observations have pointed out that there is a descending limb to the ventricular function curve in response to afterloading or further cardiac dilatation. Most likely, this descending limb relates to the increased afterload (52), rather than to a sarcomere descending limb similar to that of skeletal muscle (37). The increased afterload could be imposed both by an increase in arterial pressure, or more commonly, by an increase in wall tension produced as the ventricle increases its size, in accordance with the Laplace relation. Since the distance heart muscle can shorten is inversely related to the afterload, these facts seem sufficient to explain the descending limb noted in ventricular function curves of patients with reduced cardiac reserve (49).

In summary, studies have documented that vasodilator drugs (afterload reduction) can markedly improve hemodynamic performance in patients with heart failure. In attempting to describe the precise afterload faced by the ventricle, however, it is unclear whether wall stress, vascular resistance or impedance, arterial pressure, or some subtle combination of these factors will be the best way to describe the afterload faced by the ventricle. Thus, although the importance of afterload as a determinant of ventricular function is clear, further studies are required to define afterload quantitatively in relation to the other factors affecting ventricular function.

ASSESSMENT OF REGIONAL MECHANICAL PERFORMANCE IN THE PRESENCE OF ISCHEMIA

Ischemic heart disease is regional in its pathology and results in regional changes in contraction. The nature and degree of these changes relate to the force and temporal pattern of contraction of the normal myocardium. Therefore, to understand the mechanical consequences of regional ischemia and to evaluate potentially therapeutic maneuvers, it is necessary to measure the mechanical performance of the particular ischemia segment and the interaction of the ischemic and the normal myocardium. This necessity must be considered when choosing a methodology for the study of regional mechanical performance, particularly in the context of ischemic heart disease.

Methodological Approaches

One approach to the measurement of regional mechanical performance is to measure force directly. The most popular instrument for direct force measurement is the Walton-Brodie strain gauge arch (15, 53, 97), or one of its modifications. Strain gauges are bonded to the surface of a stiff spring metal arch which terminates in two feet sutured to the surface of the ventricle. The early model of the gauge responded only to compressive forces; the movable foot was to be adjusted to stretch the muscle segment so some compressive force was always applied to the arch. Later modifications respond to stretching as well as to compression. Theoretically, such a gauge should measure the net force developed between the segment under the strain gauge arch and the adjacent myocardium. If so, it should be possible to measure the force developed by the ischemic segment and determine how its contraction is affected by the force developed by the normal muscle. However, even in the nonischemic ventricle, the force measured by the strain gauge arch is not always easy to interpret. Robie & Newman (70) showed that contractile force measured by a strain gauge arch declined with increases in preload or afterload. More direct measures of diastolic (41) and systolic wall tension increased, respectively. The authors (70) concluded that the reduction in contractile force recorded by the strain gauge arch was due to ventricular forces tending to pull the feet of the gauge apart. In the case of regional ischemia, this type of problem is compounded by changes in the diastolic pressure-length relationship (19, 51, 95) and the decreasing force of contraction. Hefner et al (41) removed the effects of the muscle under the gauge by deeply incising the epicardial fibers in a direction perpendicular to the long axis of the gauge. With such modification, the gauge measures the force required to prevent the heart wall from cleaving apart along a plane between the feet of the gauge and perpendicular to its long axis. Thus the gauge responds only to the contraction of muscle remote from the gauge. The sensitivity with which the gauge responds to the contraction of a particular remote muscle segment is not readily ascertained. This inability to measure the contraction of a particular muscle segment is an obvious major disadvantage for the study of regional ischemic dysfunction. Another modification isolates the gauge from the surrounding myocardium. Normally, the force of contraction recorded from a segment is attenuated by the stretching affect of the adjacent myocardium (59, 70). To minimize this effect, Schelbert et al (74) placed a rigid frame with pins extending through the wall around the active element of the gauge, which tended to isolate the ischemic area from the normal muscle. Neither approach is satisfactory since the first ignores the mechanical contribution of the region that most conveniently might be made ischemic and the second isolates that segment from any effects of the contraction of normal myocardium.

Dimensional measurements of a ventricular segment have proved very useful in the study of the mechanical effects of regional ischemia. In their classical work describing the effects of coronary artery occlusion on regional contraction, Tennant & Wiggers (89) used an optical myograph to record segment length. Other investigators (68) have observed the surface of the epicardium and recorded the motion of the heart with a high-speed movie camera. The mercury-in-silastic rubber variable resistance gauge (Whitney) (98) has proven to be a very convenient, if somewhat limited, means of recording motion of epicardial segments. Various compliant, spring-caliper gauges have been used to measure segment length (18, 21) and wall thickness (22). Recently, ultrasonic instrumentation, by which distance is computed by measuring the transit time of an ultrasonic wave of known velocity between two piezoelectric crystals, has been developed (10, 28, 72, 80). The frequency response of these systems is flat to high frequency (43); there is obviously no stiffness of the gauge for the heart to overcome; the systems are small and tissue damage is minimal (90); they can be used to measure segment length, ventricular diameter, or wall thickness; and are particularly suitable for the study of chronic, unanesthetized animals (43).

REGIONAL ISCHEMIC DYSFUNCTION

Since Tennant & Wiggers' original observations (89), the results of acute coronary artery occlusion on regional mechanical performance have been described by numerous investigators (4, 42, 45, 68, 75, 84, 90, 91, 92, 95) using a variety of techniques. The earliest changes become apparent within 5–10 sec after occlusion. The contraction appears to be completely normal throughout the period of isovolumic systole and systolic ejection. Only after the aortic valve has closed and pressure and wall stress begin to fall does any abnormality appear. Even though wall stress has declined considerably from peak levels, the ischemic segment apparently becomes unable to maintain even this reduced level of stress and thus is stretched. Over the course of the next several seconds there is a definite beat-to-beat progression of the abnormality of contraction. The passive lengthening and thinning occur earlier and to a greater degree in each succeeding beat. After several beats, systolic shortening is diminished and finally eliminated as the ischemic segment is able to shorten only after ventricular wall stress has fallen to near-diastolic levels (94).

This behavior closely parallels changes seen in the contraction of cat papillary muscles made hypoxic by the substitution of nitrogen for oxygen in the aerating gas (93). Initially, the rate of force development and an index of contractility (V_{max}) were unchanged but force development was diminished due to an abbreviation of contraction. Later, the rate of force development also declined, which aggravated the decrease in force development. Thus it appears that hypoxia and ischemia produce discrete changes in the time course and in the force of contraction. Late systolic bulging of the ventricular segment might be due to only a shortening of the duration of the contraction of the ischemic segment. Failure to shorten during systole implies a diminished capacity to develop force.

The mechanical work done by a segment of muscle in the heart can be calculated by integrating the product of wall stress and the rate of change of segment length. Graphically, this is equivalent to the area of the stress-strain loop (25, 45). [Left ventricular pressure has been used as a first approximation of wall stress (25, 34, 90, 91, 95).] This parameter of segment work approaches zero within the first one or two minutes after coronary artery occlusion (91, 95). Some studies (45, 95) have shown that work becomes negative shortly after occlusion. Negative segment work indicates that some of the work done by normal segments of the ventricle is dissipated in stretching the ischemic segment. Whether or not negative work is measured may depend on the degree of collateral arterial supply available. Also, the studies showing negative segment work have used mercury-in-silastic length gauges (45, 95). These gauges may exaggerate the degree of negative work recorded since the force required to stretch the gauge may be more significant with ischemia (10). Whether or not work is done on the ischemic segment, Hood et al (45) demonstrated by infusing inotropic agents locally and by precipitating ventricular premature contractions that the passively behaving ischemic segment is capable of contraction in the first few minutes after occlusion.

As the segment becomes incapable of shortening during systole, the end-diastolic pressure-length relationship shifts to the right (19, 51, 95). However, Franklin et al (29) reported more recently that no change is seen in the relationship between wall stress (pressure:wall thickness) and segment length, suggesting that ischemia does not really change the stiffness of the passive muscle. Diastolic segment length increases, but this increase produces a reciprocal thinning of the segment wall. This thinning reduces the cross-sectional area of the wall, thus increasing calculated stress in exact relation to the increase in length.

Hood and his co-workers have shown that the stiffness of the ischemic segment increases after more prolonged ischemia. After 6 hr the pressure-length relationship returns to normal (19), and after 3–5 days the curve has moved significantly to the left (46). This stiffening of the aneurysmal segment is of considerable advantage since the distensibility is reduced by sixfold as the acute infarct evolves into a fibrous aneurysm (62).

Estimates of the degree to which mechanical function reverts to normal after reperfusion appear to depend on the experimental preparation and the techniques of measurement and analysis. Banka et al (3) used open-chest anesthetized dogs and measured pre-ejection tension (the force developed between end diastole and the beginning of ejection), ejection tension (peak force minus the force developed when the aortic valve opens), and phasic segment length (peak-to-peak amplitude) using Walton-Brodie strain gauge arches and mercury-in-silastic rubber length gauges, respectively. After a 3-hr period of reperfusion following 30–45 min of occlusion, pre-ejection tension and phasic segment length returned to normal. Ejection tension and total tension (preejection plus ejection tensions) improved but were statistically less than control values (72% and 87% respectively). Thus the force developed by the reperfused segment during systolic ejection remains below the preocclusion value. No attempt was made to measure absolute segment lengths or to relate the phasic pattern of shortening to ventricular pressure development. It remains possible that absolute end-diastolic and end-systolic lengths continued to be larger than during the control period and that a reduced fraction of total segment shortening occurred during ejection when shortening is hemodynamically effective. Tyberg et al (95) also used open-chest anesthetized dogs and measured segment length similarly. Using the area of the pressure-length loop as an index of segment work they showed that segment work improved, but did not approach normal after 1–2 hr of reperfusion following 30 min of coronary occlusion. Diminished segment work indicated that segment shortening during systole was less than normal. Heyndrickx et al (43) recently studied the effects of reperfusion after 5- and 15-min periods of coronary occlusion in awake dogs previously prepared with minature ultrasonic length transducers. Five minute occlusions produced increases in absolute segment length and shortening velocity that persisted for more than 3 hr. Lengths returned to normal in 6 hr. Fifteen minute occlusions produced similar changes of greater absolute magnitude which differed from control after 6 hr and returned to normal only after 24 hr of reperfusion. These mechanical alterations persisted although total coronary artery flow returned to normal after 5–10 min and ST segment elevation disappeared within seconds.

In summary, the mechanical consequences of acute regional ischemia involve characteristic alterations in the time course and force of contraction. Segment work abruptly decreases toward zero. Although the diastolic pressure-length relationship acutely shifts to the right, there is no apparent change in muscle stiffness. Even following coronary occlusions lasting only a few minutes, mechanical performance is measurably depressed for periods of several hours. The clinically relevant question of whether or not coronary artery revascularization can improve function when performed several hours after an ischemic episode remains to be determined. It is clear that such studies should be performed in chronically instrumented, physiologic preparations.

SUMMARY

The studies reported here were selected because of renewed interest in these areas, particularly as they relate to the evaluation and management of patients with coronary artery disease and heart failure. The first section emphasized a new conceptual approach to changes in the diastolic pressure-volume relation of the left ventricle. Although previous studies have concentrated on mathematical models which describe wall stress and stiffness as derived from the pressure-volume relationship, this review emphasizes that hemodynamic factors are very important in acutely altering the pressure-volume relationship of the left ventricle. This is partly due to alterations in right ventricular pressure, which subsequently influence the left ventricular pressure-volume relationship. In addition, recent studies have pointed out that compliance indices measured at low end-diastolic pressures differ from the indices measured at high end-diastolic pressures, so that limited information from one portion of the curve may not be generalized to describe the entire curve.

The section on afterload emphasized the importance of this factor in influencing cardiac function, particularly in the presence of heart failure. In patients with both acute and chronic heart failure, vasodilator drugs which reduce ventricular afterload have produced substantial hemodynamic benefit by reducing the filling pressures of the right and left ventricles and increasing forward cardiac output. This hemodynamic improvement in response to afterload reduction is predictable from the different quantitative descriptions of ventricular afterload. Nevertheless, it is still unclear which method best describes afterload. Although wall stress, impedance, vascular resistance, and aortic pressure have all been utilized as a measure of afterload, each has some shortcomings which may limit its applicability.

The final section reviewed approaches to the measurement of regionally ischemic myocardium. Since current studies have emphasized the importance of identifying and preserving ischemic, but viable, myocardium, this section has reviewed techniques for measuring local mechanical performance. Previous studies with the Walton-Brodie strain gauge and epicardial length gauge did not appear to be as satisfactory as more recent measurements with ultrasonic crystals, which can simultaneously measure wall thickness and segment length. These methods form the basis for ongoing experiments designed to evaluate approaches for preserving ischemic myocardium in the setting of experimental myocardial infarction.

Literature Cited

1. Abbott, B. C., Gordon, D. G. 1975. A commentary on muscle mechanics. *Circ. Res.* 36:1–7
2. Alderman, E., Glantz, S. A. 1976. Acute hemodynamic interventions shift the diastolic pressure-volume curve in man. *Circulation* 54:662–7
3. Banka, V. S., Chadda, K. D., Helfant, R. H. 1974. Limitations of myocardial revascularization in restoration of regional contraction abnormalities produced by coronary occlusion. *Am. J. Cardiol.* 34:164–70
4. Banka, V. S., Helfant, R. H. 1974. Temporal sequence of dynamic contractile characteristics in ischemic and nonischemic myocardium after acute coronary ligation. *Am. J. Cardiol.* 34:158–63
5. Barry, W. H., Brooker, J. V., Alderman, E. L., Harrison, D. C. 1974. Changes in diastolic stiffness and tone of the left ventricle during angina pectoris. *Circulation* 49:255–63
6. Bemis, C. E., Serur, J. R., Borkenhagen, D., Sonnenblick, E. H., Urschel, C. W. 1974. Influence of right ventricular filling pressure on left ventricular pressure and dimension. *Circ. Res.* 34:498–504

7. Brodie, B., Chuck, L., Klausner, S. C., Grossman, W., Parmley, W. W. 1976. Effects of sodium nitroprusside on tension prolongation during recovery from hypoxia. *Am. J. Cardiol.* 37:122
8. Brutsaert, D. L., Claes, V. A., Sonnenblick, E. H. 1971. Velocity of shortening of unloaded heart muscle and the length-tension relation. *Circ. Res.* 29:63–75
9. Brutsaert, D. L., Sonnenblick, E. H. 1973. Cardiac muscle mechanics in the evaluation of myocardial contractility and pump function: Problems, concepts, and directions. *Prog. Cardiovasc. Dis.* 16:337–61
10. Bugge-Asperheim, B., Leraand, S., Kiil, F. 1969. Local dimensional changes of the myocardium measured by ultrasonic technique. *Scand. J. Clin. Lab. Invest.* 24:361–71
11. Chatterjee, K., Parmley, W. W., Ganz, W., Forrester, J. S., Walinsky, P., Crexells, C., Swan, H. J. C. 1973. Hemodynamic and metabolic responses to vasodilator therapy in acute myocardial infarction. *Circulation* 48:1183–93
12. Chatterjee, K., Parmley, W. W., Swan, H. J. C., Berman, G., Forrester, J., Marcus, H. S. 1973. Beneficial effects of

vasodilator agents in severe mitral regurgitation due to dysfunction of subvalvar apparatus. *Circulation* 48:684–90

13. Chatterjee, K., Swan, H. J. C. 1974. Vasodilator therapy in acute myocardial infarction. *Mod. Concepts Cardiovasc. Dis.* 43:119–24

14. Coltart, J., Alderman, E. L., Robison, S. C., Harrison, D. C. 1975. The effects of propranolol on left ventricular function, segmental wall motion and diastolic compliance in man. *Br. Heart J.* 37:357–64

15. Cotten, M. de V., Bay, E. 1956. Direct measurement of changes in cardiac contractile force: Relationship of such measurements to stroke work, isometric pressure gradient and other parameters of cardiac function. *Am. J. Physiol.* 187:122–34

16. Davidson, D. M., Covell, J. W., Malloch, C. J., Ross, J. Jr. 1974. Factors influencing indices on left ventricular contractility in the conscious dog. *Cardiovasc. Res.* 8:299–312

17. Dwyer, E. M. Jr., 1970. Left ventricular pressure-volume alterations and regional disorders of contraction during myocardial ischemia induced by atrial pacing. *Circulation* 42:1111–22

18. Dyke, S. H., Urschel, C. W., Sonnenblick, E. H., Gorlin, R., Cohn, P. F. 1975. Detection of latent function in acutely ischemic myocardium in the dog. *Circ. Res.* 36:490–97

19. Ekong, E. A., Pirzada, F. A., Vokonas, P. S., Hood, W. B. Jr. 1972. Changes in ventricular compliance during experimental myocardial infarction. *Circulation Suppl. 2* 45/46:2–148

20. Elzinga, G., van Grondelle, R., Westerhof, N., van DenBos, G. C. 1974. Ventricular interference. *Am. J. Physiol.* 226:941–47

21. Feigl, E. O., Fry, D. L. 1964. Myocardial mural thickness during the cardiac cycle. *Circ. Res.* 14:541–45

22. Feigl, E. O., Simon, G. A., Fry, D. L. 1967. Auxotonic and isometric cardiac force transducers. *J. Appl. Physiol.* 23:597–600

23. Fester, A., Samet, P. 1974. Passive elasticity of the human left ventricle: The "parallel elastic element." *Circulation* 50:609–18

24. Flaherty, J. T., Reid, P. R., Kelly, D. T., Taylor, D. R., Weisfeldt, M. L., Pitt, B. 1975. Intravenous nitroglycerin in acute myocardial infarction. *Circulation* 51:132–39

25. Forrester, J. S., Tyberg, J. V., Wyatt, H. L., Goldner, S., Parmley, W. W., Swan, H. J. C. 1974. Pressure-length loop: A new method for simultaneous measurement of segmental and total cardiac function. *J. Appl. Physiol.* 37:771–75

26. Franciosa, J. A., Guiha, N. H., Limas, C. J., Rodriguera, E., Cohn, J. N. 1972. Improved left ventricular function during nitroprusside infusion in acute infarction. *Lancet* 1:650–54

27. Franciosa, J. A., Mikulic, E., Cohn, J. N., Jose, E., Fabie, A. 1974. Hemodynamic effects of orally administered isosorbide dinitrate in patients with congestive heart failure. *Circulation* 50:1020–24

28. Franklin, D. L., Kemper, W. S., Patrick, T., McKown, D. 1973. Technique for continuous measurement of regional myocardial segment dimensions in chronic animal preparations. *Fed. Proc.* 32:343 (Abstr.)

29. Franklin, D., Theroux, P., Ross, J. 1974. Diastolic properties and regional relaxation abnormalities of the left ventricle during acute ischemia. *Circulation Suppl. 3* 49/50:2–120 (Abstr.)

30. Gaasch, W. H., Battle, W. E., Oboler, A. A., Banas, J. S., Levine, H. J. 1972. Left ventricular stress and compliance in man: With special reference to normalized ventricular function curves. *Circulation* 45:746–62

31. Gaasch, W. H., Quinones, M. A., Waisser, E., Thiel, H. G., Alexander, J. K. 1975. Diastolic compliance of the left ventricle in man. *Am. J. Cardiol.* 36:193–201

32. Gault, J. H., Ross, J., Braunwald, E. 1968. Contractile state of the left ventricle in man: Instantaneous tension-velocity-length relations in patients with and without diseases of the left ventricular myocardium. *Circ. Res.* 22:451–63

33. Gibson, D. G., Brown, D. J. 1974. Relation between diastolic left ventricular wall stress and strain in man. *Br. Heart J.* 36:1066–77

34. Glantz, S. A. 1975. A three element model describes excised cat papillary muscle elasticity. *Am. J. Physiol.* 228:284–94

35. Glantz, S. A., Kernoff, R. 1975. Muscle stiffness can be determined from diastolic pressure-volume curves. *Circ. Res.* 37:787–94

36. Glantz, S. A. 1976. Ventricular pressure-volume indices change with end diastolic pressure. *Circ. Res.* 39:772–78

37. Gordon, A. M., Huxley, A. F., Julian, F. J. 1966. The variation in isometric tension with sarcomere length in vertebrate muscle fibers. *J. Physiol.* 184:170–92

38. Grossman, W., McLaurin, L. P., Stefadouros, M. A., 1974. Left ventricular stiffness associated with chronic pressure and volume overload. *Circ. Res.* 35:793–800

39. Grossman, W., McLaurin, L. P., Moos, S. P., Stefadouros, M. A., Young, D. T. 1974. Wall thickness and diastolic properties of the left ventricle. *Circulation* 49:129–35

40. Grossman, W., Brodie, B., Mann, T., McLaurin, L. 1975. Effects of sodium nitroprusside on left ventricular diastolic pressure-volume relations. *Circulation* 52:2–35

41. Hefner, L. L., Sheffield, L. T., Cobbs, G. C., Klip, W. 1962. Relation between mural force and pressure in the left ventricle of the dog. *Circ. Res.* 11:654–63

42. Heikkila, J., Tabakin, B. S., Hugenholtz, P. G. 1972. Quantification of function in normal and infarcted regions of the left ventricle. *Cardiovasc. Res.* 6:516–31

43. Heyndrickx, G. R., Millard, R. W., McRitchie, R. J., Maroko, P. R., Vatner, S. F. 1975. Regional myocardial function and electrophysiological alterations after brief coronary artery occlusion in conscious dogs. *J. Clin. Invest.* 56:978–85

44. Holt, J. P. 1970. The normal pericardium. *Am. J. Card.* 26:455–65

45. Hood, W. B., Covelli, V. H., Abelmann, W. H., Norman, J. C. 1969. Persistence of contractile behavior in acutely ischaemic myocardium. *Cardiovasc. Res.* 3:249–60

46. Hood, W. B., Bianco, J. A., Kumar, R. Whiting, R. B. 1970. Experimental myocardial infarction. IV. Reduction of left ventricular compliance in the healing phase. *J. Clin. Invest.* 49:1316–23

47. Janz, R. F., Kubert, B. R., Moriarty, T. F., Grimm, A. F. 1974. Deformation of the diastolic left ventricle: II. Nonlinear geometric effects. *J. Biomech.* 7:509–20

48. Jewell, B. R., Blinks, J. R. 1968. Drugs and the mechanical properties of heart muscle. *Ann. Rev. Pharmacol.* 8:113–30

49. Kivowitz, C., Parmley, W. W., Donoso, R., Marcus, H., Ganz, W., Swan, H. J. C. 1971. Effects of isometric exercise on cardiac performance: The grip test. *Circulation* 44:944–1002

50. Kreulen, T. H., Bove, A. A., McDonough, M. T., Sands, M. J., Spann, J. F., 1975. The evaluation of left ventricular function in man. *Circulation* 51:677–88

51. Lekven, J. 1975. Effect of practolol on left ventricular dimensions during coronary occlusion. *Am. J. Cardiol.* 36:179–84

52. MacGregor, D. C., Covell, J. W., Mahler, F., Ross, J. Jr. 1974. Relations between afterload, stroke volume, and the descending limb of Starling's curve. *Am. J. Physiol.* 227:884–93

53. Mallos, A. J. 1962. Electrical caliper for continuous measurement of relative displacement. *J. Appl. Physiol.* 17:131–34

54. McLaurin, L. P., Rolett, E. L., Grossman, W. 1973. Impaired left ventricular relaxation during pacing-induced ischemia. *Am. J. Cardiol.* 32:751–57

55. Milnor, W. R. 1975. Arterial impedance as ventricular afterload. *Circ. Res.* 36:565–70

56. Mirsky, I., Parmley, W. W. 1973. Assessment of passive elastic stiffness for isolated heart muscle and the intact heart. *Circ. Res.* 33:233–43

57. Mirsky, I., Cohn, P. F., Levine, J. A., Gorlin, R., Herman, M. V., Kreulen, T. H., Sonnenblick, E. H. 1974. Assessment of left ventricular stiffness in primary myocardial disease and coronary artery disease. *Circulation* 50:128–36

58. Mirsky, I. 1976. Assessment of passive elastic stiffness of cardiac muscle: Mathematical concepts, physiological and clinical considerations, directions of future research. *Prog. Cardiovasc. Dis.* 18:277–308

59. Newman, W. H., Walton, R. 1967. Strain-gauge arch recordings from an acutely ischemic area of the left ventricle. *J. Appl. Physiol.* 23:398–400

60. Palacios, I., Johnson, R. A., Newell, J. B., Powell, W. J. Jr. 1976. Left ventricular end-diastolic pressure volume relationships with experimental acute global ischemia. *Circulation* 53:428–35

61. Parmley, W. W., Chuck, L., Sonnenblick, E. H. 1972. Relation of V_{max} to different models of cardiac muscle. *Circ. Res.* 30:34–43

62. Parmley, W. W., Chuck, L., Kivowitz, C., Matloff, J. M., Swan, H. J. C. 1973. In vitro length-tension relations of human ventricular aneurysms: The relationship of stiffness to mechanical disadvantage. *Am. J. Cardiol.* 32:889–94

63. Parmley, W. W., Chuck, L., Yeatman, L. 1975. Comparative evaluation of the specificity and sensitivity of isometric

indices of contractility. *Am. J. Physiol.* 228:506–10

64. Parmley, W. W., Tomoda, H., Diamond, G., Forrester, J. S., Crexells, C. 1975. Dissociation between indices of pump performance and contractility in patients with coronary artery disease and acute myocardial infarction. *Chest* 67:141–46

65. Parmley, W. W., Chuck, L., Chatterjee, K., Swan, H. J. C., Klausner, S. C., Glantz, S. A., Ratshin, R. A. 1976. Acute changes in the diastolic pressure volume relationship of the left ventricle. *Eur. J. Cardiol.* 4(Suppl.):105–20

66. Patterson, R. W., Kent, B. B., Pierce, E. C. II 1972. A comparison of empiric contractile indices in intact dogs. *Cardiology* 57:277–94

67. Peterson, K. L., Skloven, D., Ludbrook, P., Uther, J. B., Ross, J. Jr. 1974. Comparison of isovolumic and ejection phase indices of myocardial performance in man. *Circulation* 49:1088–1101

68. Prinzmetal, M., Schwartz, L. L., Corday, E., Spritzler, R., Bergman, H. C., Kruger, H. E., 1949. Studies on the coronary circulation: VI. Loss of myocardial contractility after coronary artery occlusion. *Ann. Intern. Med.* 31:429–49

69. Rabkin, S. W., Hsu, P. H. 1975. Mathematical and mechanical modeling of the stress-strain relationship of the pericardium. *Am. J. Physiol.* 229:896–900

70. Robie, N. W., Newman, W. H. 1974. Effects of altered ventricular load on the Walton-Brodie strain gauge arch. *J. Appl. Physiol.* 36:20–27

71. Ross, J. Jr. 1976. Afterload mismatch and preload reserve: A conceptual framework for the analysis of ventricular function. *Prog. Cardiovasc. Dis.* 18:255–64

72. Rushmer, R. F., Franklin, D. L., Ellis, R. M. 1956. Left ventricular dimensions recorded by sonocardiometry. *Circ. Res.* 4:684–88

73. Salisbury, P. F., Cross, C. E., Rieben, P. A. 1960. Influence of coronary artery pressure upon myocardial elasticity. *Circ. Res.* 8:794–800

74. Schelbert, H. R., Covell, J. W., Burns, J. W., Maroko, P. R., Ross, J. Jr. 1971. Observations on factors affecting local forces in the left ventricular wall during acute myocardial ischemia. *Circ. Res.* 29:306–16

75. Sedek, G., Lewartowski, B. 1973. Mechanism of changes in left ventricular function after acute experimental coronary occlusion. *Cardiovasc. Res.* 7:313–21

76. Sonnenblick, E. H. 1962. Force-velocity relations in mammalian heart muscle. *Am. J. Physiol.* 202:931–39

77. Sonnenblick, E. H., Downing, S. E. 1963. Afterload as a primary determinant of ventricular performance. *Am. J. Physiol.* 204:604–10

78. Sonnenblick, E. H. 1968. Correlation of myocardial ultrastructure and function. *Circulation* 38:29–44

79. Spotnitz, H. M., Kaiser, G. A. 1971. The effect of the pericardium on pressure-volume relations in the canine left ventricle. *J. Surg. Res.* 11:375–80

80. Stegall, H. F., Kardon, M. B., Stone, H. L., Bishop, V. S. 1967. Portable simple sonocardiometer. *J. Appl. Physiol.* 23:289–93

81. Streeter, D. D., Vaishnav, R. N., Patel, D. J., Spotnitz, H. M., Ross, J., Sonnenblick, E. H. 1970. Stress distribution in the canine left ventricle during diastole and systole. *Biophys. J.* 10:345–63

82. Suga, H., Sagawa, K., Shoukas, A. A. 1973. Load independence of the instantaneous pressure-volume ratio of the canine left ventricle and effects of epinephrine and heart rate on the ratio. *Circ. Res.* 32:314–22

83. Suga, H., Sagawa, K. 1974. Instantaneous pressure-volume relationship and their ratio in the excised, supported canine left ventricle. *Circ. Res.* 35:117–26

84. Tatooles, C. J., Randall, W. C. 1961. Local ventricular bulging after acute coronary occlusion. *Am. J. Physiol.* 201:451–66

85. Taylor, R. R., Covell, J. W., Sonnenblick, E. H., Ross J. Jr. 1967. Dependence of ventricular distensibility on filling of the opposite ventricle. *Am. J. Physiol.* 213:711–18

86. Taylor, R. R. 1970. Active length-tension relations in isometric, afterloaded, and isotonic contractions of cat papillary muscle. *Circ. Res.* 26:279–88

87. Templeton, G. H., Wildenthal, K., Mitchell, J. H. 1972. Influence of coronary blood flow on left ventricular contractility and stiffness. *Am. J. Physiol.* 223:1216–20

88. Templeton, G. H., Wildenthal, K., Willerson, J. T., Mitchell, J. H. 1975. Influence of acute myocardial depression on left ventricular stiffness and its elastic and viscous components. *J. Clin. Invest.* 56:278–85

89. Tennant, R., Wiggers, C. J. 1935. Effect of coronary occlusion on myocardial

contraction. *Am. J. Physiol.* 112:351–61

90. Theroux, P., Franklin, D., Ross, J. Jr., Kemper, W. S. 1974. Regional myocardial function during acute coronary artery occlusion and its modification by pharmacologic agents in the dog. *Circ. Res.* 34:896–908

91. Theroux, P., Ross, J. Jr., Franklin, D., Kemper, W. S., Sasayama, S. 1976. Regional myocardial function in the conscious dog during acute coronary occlusion and responses to morphine, propranolol, nitroglycerin and lidocaine. *Circulation* 53:302–14

92. Tomoda, H., Parmley, W. W., Fujimura, S., Matloff, J. M. 1971. Effects of ischemia and reoxygenation on regional myocardial performance of the dog. *Am. J. Physiol.* 221:1718–21

93. Tyberg, J. V., Yeatman, L. A., Parmley, W. W., Urschel, C. W., Sonnenblick, E. H. 1970. Effect of hypoxia on mechanics of cardiac contraction. *Am. J. Physiol.* 218:1780–88

94. Tyberg, J. V., Forrester, J. S., Parmley, W. W. 1974. Altered segmental function and compliance in acute myocardial ischemia. *Eur. J. Cardiol.* 1:307–17

95. Tyberg, J. V., Forrester, J. S., Wyatt, H. L., Goldner, S. J., Parmley, W. W., Swan, H. J. C. 1974. Analysis of segmental ischemic dysfunction utilizing the pressure-length loop. *Circulation* 44:748–54

96. Van Den Bos, G. C., Elzinga, G., Westerhof, N., Noble, M. I. M. 1973. Problems in the use of indices of myocardial contractility. *Cardiovasc. Res.* 7:83–48

97. Walton, R. P., Hauck, A. L. 1971. *Direct Recordings of Heart Force by Strain Gauge Methods: An Annotated List of References. 1949–1969* Ann Arbor, Michigan: Univ. Microfilm

98. Whitney, R. J. 1953. The measurement of volume changes in human limbs. *J. Physiol.* 121:1–27

Ann. Rev. Physiol. 1977. 39:301–21

LIPIDS AND LIPID METABOLISM

❖1173

E. J. Masoro

Department of Physiology, The University of Texas Health Science Center, San Antonio, Texas 78284

INTRODUCTION

Since this is the first review on lipids to appear in the *Annual Review of Physiology,* it should cover the spectrum of the functional roles of lipids: (*a*) as fuel; (*b*) as membrane components; (*c*) in blood coagulation; (*d*) as components of immune systems; (*e*) as vitamins and hormones; and (*f*) in interfacial phenomena (e.g. in digestive processes and at the gas-liquid interface of lung alveoli).

Space limitations make it impossible to consider all of these areas. Fortunately, the latter four have been the subject of many reviews, not as lipids per se but as components of physiological systems. Therefore this discussion is devoted to two of the functions: as fuel and as membrane components. The following review articles are offered as a guide to the other four areas: blood coagulation (110, 204); immune systems (157); hormones and vitamins (21, 39, 55, 60, 84, 103, 154, 203); interfacial phenomena in digestive processes (15, 16); lung surfactant (91, 127, 195).

LIPIDS AS FUEL

Dietary Lipid As Fuel

DIGESTION   Only the fatty acid and glyceride-glycerol components of dietary lipid are quantitatively significant as sources of fuel (106). Triglycerides supply most of this fuel, but phosphoglycerides, sphingolipids, and the fatty acid esters of both sterols and fat-soluble vitamins also provide small amounts (16).

To be absorbed, these lipids must first be converted to more polar compounds by processes that take place primarily in the lumen of the small intestine (16). The lipids are finely emulsified by the churning action of the intestine plus the detergent action of the bile salts in the intestine. The triglyceride is then converted to the more polar compounds, 2-monoglyceride and free fatty acids (FFA), by a reaction, catalyzed by pancreatic lipase, in which the ester bonds in the 1 and 3 positions of the

301

glyceride-glycerol are hydrolyzed (40). The pancreatic lipase acts at the aqueous-lipid interface of these emulsion particles (170). Although the activity of pancreatic lipase is inhibited by conjugated bile salts above their critical micellar concentration (18), under in vivo conditions this problem is circumvented by co-lipase (18), a protein secreted by the pancreas. Co-lipase binds bile salt micelles (17), which prevents the inhibition of pancreatic lipase. It has been suggested that a ternary complex of co-lipase–bile salts–pancreatic lipase is the enzymatic unit that interacts with the lipid emulsion particle (171).

While pancreatic lipase is the most important enzyme in the digestion of triglycerides, two other enzymes also appear to be involved. Gastric lipase (30), an enzyme secreted by the gastric glands, catalyzes the hydrolysis primarily of triglycerides containing short- and medium-chain length fatty acids (45). Lingual lipase, an enzyme originating in the tongue, soft palate, and anterior and lateral oropharyngeal walls (68), also catalyzes the conversion of triglyceride to FFA and monoglyceride, presumably in the stomach (67). It has been suggested that this reaction, although not quantitatively important, provides the stomach with emulsifying agents (68).

Within the lumen of the intestine, the ester bond at the 2 position of dietary lecithin and possibly other phosphoglycerides is hydrolyzed, yielding FFA and highly polar lysophosphoglycerides (15) in a reaction catalyzed by a phospholipase A of pancreatic origin. The pancreas also secretes cholesterol esterase (sterol ester hydrolase) which catalyzes the hydrolysis of sterol esters to FFA and free sterols (16).

The FFA, monoglyceride, and lysophosphoglyceride, i.e. those digestion products that serve as fuel, diffuse from the lipid phase of the emulsion particle into bile salt:lecithin:cholesterol micelles secreted by the liver and delivered to the intestinal lumen in the bile (15). Since very nonpolar substances cannot, to any great extent, enter these micelles, the digestive enzymes promote this micellarization by yielding products with an increased polarity (138).

ABSORPTION The luminal surface of the intestine is covered by an unstirred water layer about 0.1 mm thick (14). To reach the brush border of the mucosal cells, substances must diffuse through this water layer. In the case of lipids, this diffusion may be the rate-limiting step in their absorption (207). The emulsion particles are too large to diffuse at appreciable rates through the water layer, but the particle size of micelles is small enough to do so. Since the mixed micelles containing FFA, monoglyceride, and lysophosphoglyceride reach high concentrations in the lumen of the intestine during the digestion of a meal, these micelles are the major vehicle in the diffusion of lipid to the brush border of the mucosal cell.

Upon reaching the brush border, the micelle may either enter the cell, or the FFA, monoglycerides, and lysophosphoglycerides may first dissociate from the micelle and then enter the cell; it is not certain which of these occurs or whether both occur (16). It is also not certain if the lipids pass through the plasma membrane by simple diffusion (168) or by a more complex process (137, 145).

Most of the further processing of the absorbed lipid occurs in the endoplasmic reticulum of the mucosal cell, the FFA, 2-monoglycerides, and lysophosphoglycerides having been transported from the plasma membrane to the endoplasmic reticulum most probably by proteins that specifically bind them. A cellular protein that binds FFA as a water soluble complex has been described (144).

In the endoplasmic reticulum, triglyceride and phosphoglycerides are generated from the FFA, monoglyceride, and lysophosphoglycerides; the biochemical pathways involved have been recently reviewed (24). A small amount of the FFA is used to generate cholesterol ester by the acylation of free cholesterol (196), obtained through absorption by processes similar to those described for lipid fuel or by its biosynthesis by the mucosal cell. The endoplasmic reticulum utilizes the triglyceride, phospholipid, cholesterol, and cholesterol ester along with a specific protein called apolipoprotein B (65, 117) to generate a chylomicron, a large spherical structure 0.1 μm or larger in diameter (215). The chylomicron has a large core of material composed primarily of triglyceride (with the cholesterol ester also present) and a surface coat composed of phospholipid and apolipoprotein B (172). Chylomicrons migrate to the Golgi vacuoles (27) and then, through exocytosis, are delivered to the interstitial fluid where they are carried off by the lymph (24).

Short- and medium-chain length fatty acids are not abundant in dietary foodstuffs. They are processed somewhat differently than the long-chain fatty acids, passing as FFA through the mucosal cell and leaving the intestine by way of the portal blood bound to albumin (86).

TRANSPORT   Most of the dietary lipid is delivered in the chylomicron to the venous blood by the lymph flowing through the thoracic duct. The chylomicrons in this lymph are composed by weight of approximately 88% triglyceride, 9% phospholipid, 1.5% cholesterol, 1.5% cholesterol ester, and 1% protein (primarily apolipoprotein B) (44).

Upon entering the blood, the chylomicron adds apolipoprotein C, derived from high-density lipoproteins (HDL), to its coat (43, 72). The chylomicron particle does not remain long in the bloodstream; the half-life of the triglyceride component is less than one hour in man and only a few minutes in rats (44). It is mainly the adipose tissue and the muscle that remove the triglyceride component from the blood, while the cholesterol ester component of the chylomicrons is removed mainly by the liver (188).

Removal of this triglyceride component involves the action of lipoprotein lipase, an enzyme found in adipose tissue, heart, skeletal muscle, lung, and probably other tissues as well (48, 66). This enzyme is located within the major cell type (e.g. cardiac muscle cell of heart, adipocyte of adipose tissue) and on the endothelial surface of the capillaries supplying the tissue (48). The lipoprotein lipase located on the endothelial surface is involved in the removal of the triglyceride from the blood perfusing the tissue (162). The enzyme appears to be biosynthesized within the major cell type of the tissue and transported to its site of function—the endothelial surface of the capillary (13). The lipoprotein lipase activity in a given tissue is modified by nutritional state (38, 48).

The following sequence of events is believed to be involved in the uptake of triglyceride by a tissue. After the chylomicrons attach to the capillary endothelial surface in proper spatial relationship to lipoprotein lipase, they are partially enveloped by the plasma membrane of the endothelial cell (10). The enzyme catalyzes the hydrolysis of the triglyceride; the apolipoprotein C on the coat is required to make the triglyceride an active substrate (44). The products of the hydrolysis are FFA and glycerol. Much of the FFA is taken up by the cells of the tissues where the hydrolysis occurred and some of the FFA and most of the glycerol are released to the blood for utilization elsewhere (44). After extensive hydrolysis of triglyceride, a chylomicron remnant particle (158) is released to the blood from the endothelial surface, along with apolipoprotein C, the latter returning to HDL (43, 72).

This remnant particle is poorer in triglyceride and richer in cholesterol ester per unit mass than is the original chylomicron particle (158). It also contains lipoprotein lipase, removed from the capillary endothelium in the process of detachment (49). The remnant particle is transported in the blood to the liver where it reacts with the plasma membrane of the hepatic parenchymal cell (80). Felts et al have suggested (49) that it is the lipoprotein lipase component of this remnant that is recognized and interacts with a receptor site on the plasma membrane of the hepatocyte. Following this interaction, the remnant appears to fuse with the cell membrane, and the apolipoprotein B (43) and some cholesterol ester (166) are released to the circulation in the form of low-density lipoprotein (LDL). The remaining triglyceride, cholesterol, and cholesterol ester of the remnant particle are hydrolyzed to FFA, glycerol, and cholesterol in reactions catalyzed by a hepatic triglyceridase and cholesterol esterase (11, 97) and are further utilized by liver via a variety of pathways.

CATABOLISM   The fatty acids taken up by the extrahepatic tissues can be stored in the tissues or used as fuel soon after entering; the latter occurs via the β-oxidation and tricarboxylic acid cycle pathways of fatty acid catabolism in heart, skeletal muscle, and other tissues (87). Quantitative information comes from a study of the fate of the fatty acids of chylomicron-triglyceride taken up by perfused hearts, which showed that 50% was catabolized almost immediately as fuel and the rest stored in the heart in the form of triglyceride and phospholipid (98).

Adipose Tissue as a Fuel Reservoir

NATURE AND QUANTITY OF FUEL RESERVE   The average adult man has a total fuel reserve of approximately 166,000 Kcal: about 141,000 as lipid, 24,000 as protein, and 1000 as carbohydrate (26). Lipid, the major fuel reserve of mammals, can be almost fully used without adversely affecting the animal. In contrast, protein has a variety of functional activities and cannot undergo sizeable depletion without adversely affecting the organism.

The lipid fuel reserve is primarily in the form of triglyceride, more than 98% of which is in adipose tissue depots (69).

FUNCTIONAL MORPHOLOGY OF ADIPOSE TISSUE DEPOTS   Although there are many well-known cell types in the adipose tissue depots, it is the adipocytes that function as reservoirs. Spherical or polygonal in shape, they range in diameter from

10 to 120 μm (182). Most of the mass of the adipocyte is in a single droplet of lipid (primarily triglyceride) located in the center of the cell and surrounded by an inconspicuous rim of cytoplasm that contains a flattened nucleus. The cytoplasm is separated from the extracellular fluid by the plasma membrane. A normal adult human is estimated to have about 25 billion adipocytes (83), although this figure may be low since measurements do not take into account the possible presence of preadipocytes (191).

It is generally believed, based on two lines of evidence, that the number of adipocytes in fat depots remains constant during adult life in mammals. First, Hirsch & Han (82) found in rats that the number of adipocytes did not increase between 12 and 26.5 weeks of age in the epididymal depot and between 16 and 26.5 weeks of age in the retroperitoneal depot. Second, factors that acutely alter adipose tissue mass (e.g. fasting, adult-onset obesity) do not change the number of adipocytes in a depot but only alter the size of the cells (1, 82, 179).

However, there is reason to doubt the general validity of this concept (41, 100, 191). Lemonnier (100) found that feeding high-fat diets to adult mice and rats increased the number of adipocytes in certain depots. Also, Stiles et al (191) found that the number of adipocytes increased in the epididymal depot of rats between 26 and 52 weeks of age (i.e. when young adults) and again between 104 and 130 weeks of age (i.e. during old age).

FAT DEPOSITION   When triglyceride is added to the energy reserve of adipose tissue, the process is called fat deposition.

From dietary triglyceride   After a meal containing some fat, the process of fat deposition starts at the endothelial surface of the capillaries supplying the adipose tissue depots where lipoprotein lipase catalyzes the hydrolysis of the triglyceride components of the chylomicrons and, if present, the very low-density lipoproteins (VLDL) to yield FFA and glycerol (129). Much of this FFA is taken up by the adipocyte and, along with L-α-glycerophosphate, is converted by the classical pathway (175) to triglyceride, which is deposited in the lipid vacuole of the adipocyte.

Most of the L-α-glycerophosphate needed for this process is derived from glucose entering the adipocyte from the extracellular fluid (175). However, an unspecified but probably small amount is generated from glycerol by a reaction catalyzed by glycerokinase (152).

Insulin plays an important part in fat deposition. When a meal is eaten, the rate of insulin secretion increases, leading to increased insulin concentration in the body fluids (197), which has several effects. The increased insulin level facilitates the entry of glucose into the adipocytes, thus promoting the generation of the L-α-glycerophosphate needed for triglyceride formation (159), and serves the same purpose by increasing the glycerokinase activity of adipocytes (152). Also, insulin increases the lipoprotein lipase activity in adipose tissue, thus promoting the generation of FFA from chylomicron-triglyceride or VLDL-triglyceride, which in turn increases the rate of entry of FFA into the adipocyte (52).

From dietary carbohydrate   That mammals can convert carbohydrate to fatty acids and deposit them as fat in the adipose tissue depots has been known for more than 100 years. Smith & Abraham (183) recently reviewed the details of the enzymatic steps. However, the following physiologic questions are still under debate: Does fatty acid biosynthesis play a major role in the processing of dietary carbohydrate? What physiological mechanisms control the rate of fatty acid biosynthesis? Where does fatty acid biosynthesis occur?

In 1944, Stetten & Boxer (190) reported that, in rats fed fat-free diets, 30% of the ingested carbohydrate was converted to fatty acids—a finding confirmed in 1949 by Masoro et al (132) with mice. From these studies emerged the general concept that fatty acid biosynthesis is a major pathway in the processing of dietary carbohydrate. Although this concept is still held by many, compelling evidence to the contrary exists in the case of usual dietary circumstances.

In later studies, Masoro and co-workers (130, 151) showed that when rats are fed diets high in carbohydrate but including 10% fat, the conversion of dietary carbohydrate to fatty acid is a minor rather than a major metabolic pathway. Similar results were reported by Lequin & Steyn-Parve (101) and de Freitas & Depocas (37). The conclusion is that when animals eat a diet containing the amount of fat found in usual diets, ingested triglyceride is the primary source of material for fat deposition.

Studies on the regulation of fatty acid biosynthesis support this conclusion. Years ago, it was shown that liver slices from fasted rats and from rats fed diets other than those high in carbohydrate have little ability to convert glucose to fatty acids (131). In 1958, a particularly decisive experiment showed that adding as little as 2.5% fat to a fat-free diet markedly depressed the ability of rat liver slices to carry out fatty acid biosynthesis (81). These basic studies have led to prodigious efforts to uncover the mechanisms involved in the physiologic regulation of fatty acid biosynthesis (2, 125).

Much of the effort has centered on the enzyme acetyl-CoA carboxylase because of data that implicated this enzyme as the rate-limiting step in fatty acid biosynthesis (51, 95, 143), and because the activity of the enzyme can be modified by many factors, e.g. the concentration of citrate (121), divalent cations (174), fatty acyl-CoA (19), and FFA (96). Recently, Guynn et al (62) assessed, under in vivo conditions, the importance of the acetyl-CoA carboxylase reaction as the control point of fatty acid biosynthesis. They concluded that rapid responses, such as loss of fatty acid biosynthetic activity soon after the start of fasting, involve the inhibition of acetyl-CoA carboxylase activity. However, they also concluded that long-term responses, such as the high rate of fatty acid biosynthesis seen in animals fed high-carbohydrate and almost fat-free diets, probably result from increased quantities of the multienzyme complex called fatty acid synthetase.

Other enzymatic steps may also be important in the regulation of fatty acid biosynthesis (187). For example, pyruvate dehydrogenase has been implicated as a site of control (205). Also, cAMP has been shown to inhibit fatty acid biosynthesis (23).

With the report of Masoro et al (132) that fatty acid biosynthesis was not impaired in hepatectomized rats, a vigorous search for extrahepatic sites ensued. On the basis of in vivo studies on mice, Favarger (47) concluded that adipose tissue is the major site of fatty acid biosynthesis. Also, Leveille (104) found that in meal-fed rats, which have high rates of fatty acid biosynthesis, the adipose tissue is the major site of the biosynthesis. However, Patkin & Masoro (151) and de Freitas & Depocas (37) found that in rats fed ad libitum, there was little fatty acid biosynthetic activity in the adipose tissue depots. Moreover, Hems et al (78) found that, in normal mice, the liver is a major site of fatty acid biosynthesis.

In regard to man, much of the data (9, 57, 176), but not all (20), shows that adipose tissue is not a major site of fatty acid biosynthesis. In a recent study, Patel et al (150) concluded that the capacity of human adipose tissue to utilize dietary carbohydrate for fatty acid biosynthesis is extremely low and that the liver plays a major role in this biosynthesis.

When the liver is the major site of fatty acid biosynthesis, the fatty acids so formed must then be transported to the adipose tissue for deposition. The liver generates triglycerides from the fatty acids (and L-α-glycerophosphate), packaging them in VLDL, and secreting the VLDL into the blood (77, 136). The triglycerides in the VLDL are then processed by the adipose tissue much as described above for chylomicrons, with the ultimate deposition of triglyceride in the central vacuole of the adipocyte.

FAT MOBILIZATION   To mobilize the fuel stores of the adipose tissue for use elsewhere, the stored triglyceride must be hydrolyzed to FFA and glycerol (75). The conversion of triglyceride to diglyceride and FFA, the rate-limiting step (192), is catalyzed by an enzyme or enzymes called hormone-sensitive triglyceride lipase or lipases. Hormonal activation of the enzyme is mediated by cAMP, which acts via a protein kinase to convert the inactive lipase to a phosphorylated active form (89, 177). Other lipases complete the conversion to FFA and glycerol.

Since adipocytes contain low glycerokinase activity, most of the glycerol formed by lipolysis is released to the blood (152). However, the FFA can be released or can be re-esterified and redeposited as triglyceride. The extent of re-esterification depends on the amount of L-glycerophosphate made available by its generation from glucose or by glyceroneogenesis (161). The rate of blood flow to the adipose tissue is another factor influencing the rate of release of the lipolysis products (135, 141).

The catecholamines (75) are probably the most important hormonal or humoral factor promoting fat mobilization. They act by binding to a β-receptor on the surface of the adipocyte (102); this leads to increased adenylate cyclase activity (33), which, in turn, increases intracellular cAMP levels and thus stimulates hormone-sensitive triglyceride lipase activity. Other hormones (e.g. glucagon and ACTH) promote fat mobilization by a similar mechanism (75) but they act on different receptors, and their effectiveness depends on the species.

The adrenal medulla is obviously one source of catecholamines. In addition, there is strong evidence that the direct innervation of adipose tissue, by sympathetic postganglionic fibers releasing norepinephrine, plays an important role in regulating fat mobilization (163, 194). The hypothalamus also plays a part in the regulation of fat mobilization (4, 194).

Glucocorticoids can promote fat mobilization (75) in part by inhibiting glucose metabolism by adipocytes (34) and in part by their permissive role in the action of catecholamines (59, 75). Protein synthesis by the adipocyte appears to be involved in both of these actions (34, 59, 75). Growth hormone can also promote fat mobilization. Again, protein synthesis by the adipocyte seems required for this action (75). Hypothyroid animals have little ability to mobilize fat, while hyperthyroid animals show an exaggerated lipolytic response to epinephrine and glucagon. It has been suggested that these responses relate to the control of a specific phosphodiesterase of the adipocyte by thyroid hormones (3).

Insulin is the major antilipolytic hormone involved in regulation of fat mobilization (25). It has been suggested that insulin lowers cAMP levels in the adipocyte (94), presumably by promoting the activity of a membrane-associated phosphodiesterase (120, 184, 216). It has also been reported that insulin inhibits the adenylate cyclase activity of adipocytes (79). However, it must be noted that there is evidence that insulin does not influence fat mobilization by primarily affecting cAMP levels (46).

The rate of fat mobilization begins to rise a few hours after a meal, and gradually increases to the rate observed during prolonged periods of fasting. On the basis of studies with baboons, Koerker et al (93) concluded that during the transition from the fed to fasted state, increased sympathetic nerve activity to the adipose tissue and falling levels of insulin are the major factors promoting fat mobilization. However, once fasting is prolonged, neither mechanism appears important.

Exercise also results in an increased rate of fat mobilization. Increased sympathetic nervous activity to the adipose tissue depots appears to be the major factor (111). Lefebvre (99) believes that glucagon plays a role. Gollnick et al (58) presented evidence that a pituitary hormone is also involved and suggested ACTH as the substance acting directly on the adipocyte. Contracting musculature generates lactate which is released to the blood; rising levels of blood lactate have been found to inhibit fat mobilization induced by the sympathetic nervous system (85).

Mobilized FFA as a Fuel

FFA are rapidly taken up from the blood by a variety of tissues (50), and the rate of uptake increases as the plasma FFA:albumin mole ratio rises (185). The magnitude of this ratio is determined by the rate of fat mobilization. The following discussion focuses on the skeletal muscle and heart because most of the research on the use of FFA as fuel has been done on these tissues.

At rest and during moderate exercise in postabsorptive man, the FFA uptake by skeletal muscle is sufficient to supply all fuel needs (214). Havel et al (70) suggested that some of the FFA entering the muscle cell is directly used for fuel with the remainder going into intracellular lipid pools. Recently, Dagenais et al (35) provided evidence that most if not all the FFA entering the muscle cell goes into a lipid pool and that at the same time an equivalent amount of FFA is derived from this lipid pool for use as fuel.

In the case of vigorously exercising muscle of postabsorptive man, Wahren et al (200) found that FFA was not the sole fuel and, moreover, that the nature of the fuel used varied with the duration of the exercise: after 40 minutes exercise, plasma FFA accounted for 38%, plasma glucose for 27% and the remainder was derived from intracellular stores; after 4 hours exercise, plasma FFA accounted for 61%, plasma glucose for 30%, and the remainder from intracellular stores. The FFA so used was derived from adipose tissue, and the glucose was provided by the liver (164).

On the basis of both in vivo and in vitro studies, it is clear that plasma FFA is a preferred fuel of heart (140). Indeed, the availability of plasma FFA at sufficient concentrations suppresses glucose utilization by heart (139). The rate of FFA uptake for use as fuel by heart increases as plasma FFA concentration increases (139). The rate of utilization of FFA by heart is also influenced by myocardial work and the rate of coronary blood flow (186).

Liver as a Source of Lipid Fuel

GENERATION AND USE OF VLDL-TRIGLYCERIDE The liver secretes triglyceride as a component of VLDL, and this triglyceride is processed by extrahepatic tissues (71) in a manner similar to that described above for chylomicron triglyceride. Sources of the fatty acids of these triglycerides include dietary carbohydrate (via hepatic fatty acid biosynthesis), dietary triglyceride, and FFA derived from a-dipose tissue (173). The rate of FFA uptake by the liver and the rate of secretion of VLDL-triglyceride increase as plasma [FFA] increases. Indeed, in the fasting state, most of the fatty acid of the triglyceride secreted by the liver is derived from FFA mobilized from adipose tissue (5). In studies of postabsorptive man, Kekki & Nikkila (88) found the turnover rate of VLDL-triglyceride averaged 13.2 mg per kg body weight per hour.

GENERATION AND USE OF KETONE BODIES The liver can release into the blood large quantities of ketone bodies (147) which it generates from fatty acids. The enzymatic reactions involved were recently reviewed (108). Although in the fed state little generation of ketone bodies occurs, the liver delivers appreciable quantities of ketone bodies to the circulation soon after fasting commences (114). This increased rate of hepatic ketogenesis is dependent upon the accelerated fat mobilization that occurs in fasting. Also, during fasting, the metabolic pattern of the liver changes and, compared to the fed animal, a greater fraction of FFA entering the liver undergoes β-oxidation and a smaller fraction is used to form triglyceride and phospholipid (114). Hepatic acyl-carnitine transferase activities are low in the fed state and are markedly increased in the fasted state, apparently in part, at least, because of an increase in hepatic carnitine concentration (113). As a result, more FFA can be oxidized to acetoacetate and β-hydroxybutyrate in the fasted state than in the fed state (112). An increase in the glucagon:insulin ratio appears to be involved in the hepatic metabolic response to fasting (114).

Ketone bodies can serve as the principal fuel for many extrahepatic tissues (149), the rate of such use relating to their concentration in the plasma (73, 107, 167). Other factors also affect the rate of ketone body utilization; e.g. the rate of utilization by muscle is reduced in exercise (63) and during prolonged fasting (148). Brain does not use ketone bodies until fasting is prolonged, presumably because plasma ketone body levels are not high enough until then (73). However, it has also been shown that transport of ketone bodies across the blood-brain barrier is induced during prolonged fasting (54).

Intracellular Lipids as Fuel Sources

There has been considerable research on the use by skeletal and cardiac muscle of intracellular lipids as net sources of fuel. On the basis of in vitro studies with skeletal muscle, Neptune et al (142) and Volk et al (199) suggested that fatty acids are made available for β-oxidation by the lipolysis of intramuscular glycerides. Olson & Hoescher (146) found during perfusion of isolated rat hearts without added nutrients that myocardial triglyceride decreased by 70% but there was no change in phospholipid content. With in vivo experiments, Masoro et al (133) found no change in the intracellular lipid levels of skeletal muscle undergoing vigorous exercise. It appears therefore that intracellular lipids do not serve as a net source of fuel for muscle when extracellular fuels are supplied in sufficient quantity. This conclusion is supported by in vivo rat studies (126) showing that there is a net disappearance of triglyceride from skeletal muscle only in extreme circumstances and even then no disappearance of phospholipid occurs.

LIPIDS AND MEMBRANE FUNCTION

Composition and Role of Lipids in Membrane Structure

Lipids and proteins are quantitatively the major components of membranes, but their relative amounts differ in various types of membranes as do the lipid components (109); e.g. the lipid:protein mass ratio reported for rat membranes ranges from 0.202 for liver mitochondria to 1.320 for kidney plasma membranes (213). Lucy (109) generalized that membranes that behave mainly as barriers contain the highest lipid:protein mass ratios.

The amount of cholesterol in a membrane relates to this barrier function; e.g. about 13% of the lipid mass of rat liver plasma membrane is cholesterol (213) while the rat skeletal muscle sarcoplasmic reticulum can be totally free of it (169). The nature of the phospholipid is also a property peculiar to each membrane type. For example, Golgi membranes and plasma membranes are rich in sphingomyelin while mitochondrial membranes contain little (213) and skeletal muscle sarcoplasmic reticulum is free of it (169). The inner mitochondrial membrane is rich in cardiolipin (32) while there are other members that contain little or none (169, 213).

Much of the lipid in biological membranes appears to be in the form of lipid bilayers with the polar regions of the lipid projecting into the aqueous media and the nonpolar regions forming the core of the membrane (22). These bilayers are asymmetric, with some classes of lipids more prevalent in one of the leaflets than in the other (160).

Singer & Nicolson (180) have proposed that much of the membrane lipid is not associated or only weakly associated with membrane proteins although some is tightly associated. Recent work of Yu et al (212) with nonpermeant membrane protein labeling agents showed an increase in labeling when membranes were treated with phospholipase C, which indicates that the protein is shielded from the labeling agent by phospholipid.

It has been theorized that a deterioration of membrane structure plays an important part in the aging processes of animals, but the involvement of lipids in this deterioration has yet to be explored sufficiently (128). In a comprehensive study of rat skeletal muscle sarcoplasmic reticulum membranes, Bertrand et al (7) did show that the membranes of 28-month-old rats were richer in phosphatidylcholine and poorer in phosphatidylethanolamine than the membranes of younger rats. Also, Hegner & Platt (74) found that the plasma membranes of old rats contain less phospholipid and more cholesterol than those of young rats.

The Sources of Membrane Lipids

The endoplasmic reticulum appears to be the major site of phospholipid (178) and cholesterol (29) biosynthesis in cells. The lipids of membranes must originate from either biosynthesis by the cell or from exogenous sources. Since membrane components are constantly turning over (178), considerable intracellular lipid transport must occur. Cells contain soluble proteins involved in the exchange of phospholipids between intracellular membrane structures (36, 76, 208). A net transfer of a particular phospholipid class (e.g. phosphatidylcholine) from a "donor" membrane to a membrane deficient in it has been demonstrated with exchange proteins (42). While similar exchange proteins for cholesterol have not yet been described, there is evidence of an exchange of cholesterol between intracellular membranes which is enhanced by a cytoplasmic substance, probably a protein or lipoprotein (6).

Lipids and Membrane Permeability Characteristics

A major function of membranes is to serve as barriers to the diffusion of substances. The membrane's large areas of lipid bilayers appear to be important in this barrier function. Van Deenan (198) reviewed the factors that could influence the permeability of these bilayer regions and concluded: The nature of the fatty acid moieties of the phospholipids is significant since those rich in unsaturated acids would form bilayers less compact than those rich in saturated acids. The presence of cholesterol in the bilayer reduces permeability by limiting the mobility of the fatty acid moieties of the phospholipids. Since the nature of the polar head groups of the phospholipids influences the net charge on the membrane, the nature of the phospholipid subclasses comprising the membrane should influence ion permeability. Recent experimental work on red blood cells (61) showed that removal of 55% of the plasma membrane cholesterol induced an increased rate of transfer of substances into the cells by nonionic diffusion.

Lipids and Membrane Transport

Much of the transport of materials across membranes involves either facilitated diffusion or active transport, and membrane proteins play key roles in these activities. Nevertheless, abundant evidence exists that lipids are also involved. Space allows only two examples to be discussed—Na^+ and K^+ transport across plasma membranes and Ca^{2+} transport across sarcoplasmic reticulum.

The plasma membranes of most cells contain an ATP-driven transport system in which Na^+ extrusion is coupled to the uptake of K^+ by the cell. A Na^+-K^+-ATPase, which can be isolated from plasma membranes is either the transport system or an important component thereof (181). Although there has been controversy regarding the lipid requirements of this ATPase, the following now seems clear. Delipidation inactivates the Na^+-K^+-ATPase (193). It can be reactivated by relipidation with the acidic phospholipids, phosphatidylserine or phosphatidylglycerol (90, 201), which are more effective when they contain unsaturated fatty acid moieties than saturated ones (201). Cholesterol tends to inhibit this activating action (90) of phospholipids. The molecular mechanism of action of these lipids has been explored but remains unclear (56, 206).

A very limited destruction of the surface phospholipids of isolated renal cortical tubules by phospholipase C decreases the ability of the tubules to transport Rb^+ (Rb^+ can replace K^+ in this transport system) into the cell (118). This same treatment leads to a significant loss of Na^+-K^+-ATPase activity in homogenates prepared from isolated tubules (119). These results indicate that phospholipids are not only needed to promote the activity of the delipidated isolated ATPase but are also involved in the enzyme's function in the transport system of the intact cell.

The sarcoplasmic reticulum of skeletal muscle contains an ATP-driven transport system which transfers Ca^{2+} from the myoplasm into the lumen of the tubular structure (134). That lipids are involved was first indicated by inhibition of Ca^{2+} transport following phospholipase C treatment (123, 210). Recently, it has also been shown that ATP-dependent Ca^{2+} binding by the sarcoplasmic reticulum is inhibited by phospholipase C treatment (189).

MacLennan (115) isolated and purified a lipid-containing protein from these membranes, which he called Ca^{2+}-Mg^{2+}-ATPase. This enzyme can be reacted with phospholipid vesicles to reconstitute the ATP-dependent Ca^{2+} transport process (92, 155), which clearly establishes the enzyme as a component of the sarcoplasmic reticulum transport process. Recently, Racker & Eytan (156) reported that for most effective reconstitution, a coupling factor is also needed; they tentatively identify it as the proteolipid component of sarcoplasmic reticulum (116).

The purified Ca^{2+}-Mg^{2+}-ATPase contains about 40 moles of phospholipid per mole of enzyme. Cellucci et al (28) recently showed the quantitative relationship between phospholipid and enzyme activity. Reduction of phospholipid to 5 moles per mole of enzyme abolishes the ATPase activity while replacement of the phospholipid restores the activity, with marked increments in activity occurring when phospholipid content is increased from 30 to 60 moles per mole of enzyme. By an exchange reaction, Warren et al (202) were able to replace more than 99% of the phospholipid of this purified ATPase with dioleoyl-lecithin without grossly affecting the ATPase activity; they also found that the nature of the polar heads of the phospholipids is less important than the structure of the fatty acid moieties in determining activity.

Martonosi et al (124) have explored the involvement of phospholipid in the ATPase activity and concluded that phosphorylation of the enzyme by ATP (the first step in the ATPase reaction) does not involve phospholipid, but that some aspect leading to dephosphorylation does. Yu et al (211) have established that a histidine residue is involved in the ATPase activity; on the basis of this and other data, Martonosi et al (122) suggested that the principal role of phospholipids in the ATPase activity is to position the catalytic histidine residue so as to promote catalysis of dephosphorylation.

Lipids and Enzymatic Activities

Lucy (109) proposed two criteria for an enzyme to be considered lipid dependent: (a) a loss in activity must follow removal of the lipid, and (b) reactivation of the enzyme must occur on relipidation. Some 26 enzymes, including the Na^+-K^+-ATPase and the Ca^{2+}-Mg^{2+}-ATPase just discussed, meet these criteria (31). Although it is not possible to discuss each of these, it is probably useful to extend our discussion to the complex relationship between phospholipid and adenylate cyclase activity and to consider the role of lipids in β-hydroxybutyrate dehydrogenase activity.

Levy (105) showed that treatment of heart adenylate cyclase with non-ionic detergent resulted in a loss of enzyme response to norepinephrine and glucagon, and that this loss could be rectified by the addition of phosphatidylinositol in the case of norepinephrine and phosphatidylserine in the case of glucagon. Rubalcava & Rodbell (165) found that although treatment of liver membranes with phospholipase C does not influence the basal or F^--stimulated adenylate cyclase activity, it abolishes the stimulatory effect of glucagon on the enzyme. They further concluded that interrelated effects of glucagon and nucleotides on adenylate cyclase require acidic phospholipids. Likewise, in the case of the thyroid, phospholipids do not appear to be involved in the basal or F^--stimulated adenylate cyclase activity, but are needed for the stimulation of the enzyme by thyrotrophin (209). Pfeuffer & Helmreich (153) have reported that activation of membrane-bound adenylate cyclase with GTP analogs results in a stable enzyme which can be stripped of lipids without loss of activity. Birnbaumer (8) concluded that phospholipid intereacts with specific sites on adenylate cyclase and these sites are either part of or intimately related to the mechanism that generates a coupling signal and its transduction into enzyme activation.

Recently, Bock & Fleischer (12) prepared D-β-hydroxybutyrate dehydrogenase as a purified apoenzyme devoid of phospholipid. This lipid-free preparation had no enzymatic activity. Gazzotti et al (53) were able to reactivate the enzyme by adding lecithin or mixtures of phospholipid containing lecithin. The delipidated apoenzyme is incapable of binding the coenzyme NADH, but the relipidated enzyme can do so. It is suggested that the functional role of lecithin relates, at least in part, to this coenzyme binding phenomenon.

In addition to being required for the activity of some enzymes, lipids are also able to restrain activity of certain enzymes (64) but space limits discussion of the latter at this time. The conclusion, however, is clear: by functioning as activators and as restrainers, lipids play an important physiologic role in enzyme regulation.

Literature Cited

1. Abraham, R. R. 1973. Some cellular characteristics of the epididymal adipose tissue in lean and obese-hyperglycaemic mice. *Diabetologia* 9:303–6
2. Abraham, S. 1970. Effect of diet on hepatic fatty acid synthesis. *Am. J. Clin. Nutr.* 23:1120–28
3. Armstrong, K. J., Stouffer, J. E., Van Inwegen, R. G., Thompson, W. J., Robison, G. A. 1974. Effects of thyroid hormone deficiency on cyclic adenosine 3′:5′-monophosphate and control of lipolysis in fat cells. *J. Biol. Chem.* 249:4226–31
4. Barkai, A., Allweis, C. 1975. Transport of plasma FFA in cats; effect of hypothalamic stimulation. *Am. J. Physiol.* 228:1367–75
5. Basso, L. V., Havel, R. J. 1970. Hepatic metabolism of free fatty acids in normal and diabetic dogs. *J. Clin. Invest.* 49:537–47
6. Bell, F. P. 1975. Cholesterol exchange between microsomal, mitochondrial and erythrocyte membranes and its enhancement by cytosol. *Biochim. Biophys. Acta* 398:18–27
7. Bertrand, H. A., Yu, B. P., Masoro, E. J. 1975. The effect of rat age on the composition and functional activities of skeletal muscle sarcoplasmic reticulum membrane preparations. *Mech. Age. Dev.* 4:7–17
8. Birnbaumer, L. 1973. Hormone-sensitive adenyl cyclases as useful models for studying hormone receptor functions in cell-free systems. *Biochim. Biophys. Acta* 306:129–58
9. Björntorp, P., Berchtold, P., Holm, J., Larsson, B. 1971. The glucose uptake of human adipose tissue in obesity. *Eur. J. Clin. Invest.* 1:480–85
10. Blanchette-Mackie, E. J., Scow, R. O. 1973. Effects of lipoprotein lipase on the structure of chylomicrons. *J. Cell Biol.* 58:689–708
11. Boberg, J., Carlson, L. A., Normell, L. 1964. Production of lipolytic activity by the isolated, perfused dog liver in response to heparin. *Life Sci.* 3:1011–19
12. Bock, H., Fleischer, S. 1975. Preparation of a homogeneous soluble D-beta-hydroxybutyrate apodehydrogenase from mitochondria. *J. Biol. Chem.* 250:5774–81
13. Borensztajn, J., Rone, M. S., Sandros, T. 1975. Effects of colchicine and cycloheximide on the functional and nonfunctional lipoprotein lipase fractions of rat heart. *Biochim. Biophys. Acta* 398:394–400
14. Borgström, B. 1953. On the mechanism of the intestinal fat absorption. V. The effect of bile diversion on fat absorption in the rat. *Acta Physiol. Scand.* 28:279–86
15. Borgström, B. 1974. Bile salts—their physiological functions in the gastrointestinal tract. *Acta Med. Scand.* 196:1–10
16. Borgström, B. 1974. Fat digestion and absorption. *Biomembranes* 4B:555–620
17. Borgström, B., Donnér, J. 1975. Binding of bile salts to pancreatic colipase and lipase. *J. Lipid Res.* 16:287–92
18. Borgström, B., Erlanson, C., Sternby, B. 1974. Further characterization of two colipases from porcine pancreas. *Biochem. Biophys. Res. Commun.* 59:902–6
19. Bortz, W. M., Lynen, F. 1963. The inhibition of acetyl CoA carboxylase by long chain acyl CoA derivatives. *Biochem. Z.* 337:505–9
20. Bray, G. A. 1972. Lipogenesis in human adipose tissue: Some effects of nibbling and gorging. *J. Clin. Invest.* 51:537–48
21. Brenner, R. M., West, N. B. 1975. Hormonal regulation of the reproductive tract in female mammals. *Ann. Rev. Physiol.* 37:273–302
22. Bretscher, M. S., Roff, M. C. 1975. Mammalian plasma membranes. *Nature* 258:43–49
23. Bricker, L. A., Marraccini, L. 1975. A phylogenetic study of the role of cyclic AMP in lipid synthesis in vertebrates. *Am. J. Physiol.* 229:211–14
24. Brindley, D. N. 1974. The intracellular phase of fat absorption. *Biomembranes* 4B:621–71
25. Butcher, R. W., Baird, C. E., Sutherland, E. W. 1968. Effects of lipolytic and antilipolytic substances on adenosine 3′,5′-monophosphate levels in isolated fat cells. *J. Biol. Chem.* 243:1705–12
26. Cahill, G. F. Jr. 1970. Starvation in man. *New Engl. J. Med.* 282:668–75
27. Cardell, R. R. Jr., Badenhausen, S., Porter, K. R. 1967. Intestinal triglyceride absorption in the rat. An electron microscopical study. *J. Cell Biol.* 34:123–55
28. Cellucci, M. D., Masoro, E. J., Yu, B. P. 1975. Sensitivity of purified sarcoplasmic reticulum (Ca^{++} + Mg^{++})-

ATPase to phospholipid content. *Physiologist* 18:163

29. Chesterton, C. J. 1968. Distribution of cholesterol precursors and other lipids among rat liver intracellular structures. *J. Biol. Chem.* 243:1147–51

30. Clark, S. B., Brause, B., Holt, P. R. 1969. Lipolysis and absorption of fat in the rat stomach. *Gastroenterology* 56:214–22

31. Coleman, R. 1973. Membrane-bound enzymes and membrane ultrastructure. *Biochim. Biophys. Acta* 300:1–30

32. Comte, J., Maisterrena, B., Gautheron, D. C. 1976. Lipid composition and protein profiles of outer and inner membranes from pig heart mitochondria comparison with microsomes. *Biochim. Biophys. Acta* 419:271–84

33. Cooper, B., Partilla, J. S., Gregerman, R. I. 1975. Adenylate cyclase of human fat cells. Expression of epinephrine sensitive activation revealed by 5'-guanylyl-imidodiphosphate. *J. Clin. Invest.* 56:1350–53

34. Czech, M. P., Fain, J. N. 1971. Dactinomycin inhibition of dexamethasone action on glucose metabolism in white fat cells. *Biochim. Biophys. Acta* 230:185–93

35. Dagenais, G. R., Tancredi, R. G., Zierler, K. L. 1976. Free fatty acid oxidation by forearm muscle at rest, and evidence for an intramuscular lipid pool in the human forearm. *J. Clin. Invest.* 53:421–31

36. Dawson, R. M. C. 1973. The exchange of phospholipids between cell membranes. *Subcell. Biochem.* 2:69–89

37. de Freitas, A. S. W., Depocas, F. 1965. Fatty acid and glyceride glycerol synthesis from glucose during high rates of glucose uptake in the intact rat. *Can. J. Biochem.* 43:437–50

38. Delorme, C. L., Harris, K. L. 1975. Effects of diet on lipoprotein lipase activity in the rat. *J. Nutr.* 105: 447–51

39. De Luca, H. F. 1975. Regulation of vitamin D metabolism. *Life Sci.* 17: 1351–58

40. Desnuelle, P. 1961. Pancreatic lipase. *Adv. Enzymol.* 23:129–61

41. Di Girolamo, M., Mendlinger, S. 1971. Role of fat cell size and number in enlargement of epididymal fat pads in three species. *Am. J. Physiol.* 221: 859–64

42. Ehnholm, C., Zilversmit, D. B. 1973. Exchange of various phospholipids and of cholesterol between liposomes in the presence of highly purified phospholipid exchange protein. *J. Biol. Chem.* 248:1719–24

43. Eisenberg, S., Bilheimer, D. W., Levy, R., Lindgren, F. T. 1973. On the metabolic conversion of human plasma very low density lipoprotein to low density lipoprotein. *Biochim. Biophys. Acta* 326:361–77

44. Eisenberg, S., Levy, R. I. 1975. Lipoprotein metabolism. *Adv. Lipid Res.* 13:1–89

45. Engstrom, J. F., Rybak, J. J., Duber, M. 1968. Evidence for a lipase system in canine gastric juice. *Am. J. Med. Sci.* 256:346–51

46. Fain, J. N. 1975. Insulin as an activator of cyclic AMP accumulation in rat fat cells. *J. Cyclic Nucleotide Res.* 1:359–66

47. Favarger, P. 1955. The synthesis of fats in adipose tissue. *Expos. Ann. Biochim. Med.* 17:57–79

48. Felts, J. M. 1975. Clearance of plasma lipoproteins: Role of lipoprotein lipase, lecithin-cholesterol acyl-transferase, and the effects of drugs. In *International Encyclopedia of Pharmacology and Therapeutics. Pharmacology of Lipid Transport and Atherosclerotic Processes,* ed. E. J. Masoro, Sect. 24, 1:375–402. Oxford: Pergamon

49. Felts, J. M., Itakura, H., Crane, R. T. 1975. The mechanism of assimilation of constituents of chylomicrons, very low density lipoproteins and remnants: A new theory. *Biochem. Biophys. Res. Commun.* 66:1467–75

50. Fredrickson, D. S., Gordon, R. S. Jr. 1958. Transport of fatty acids. *Physiol. Rev.* 38:585–630

51. Ganguly, J. 1960. Studies on the mechanism of fatty acid synthesis. VII. Biosynthesis of fatty acids from malonyl CoA. *Biochim. Biophys. Acta* 40:110–18

52. Garfinkel, A. S., Nilsson-Ehle, P., Schotz, M. C. 1976. Regulation of lipoprotein lipase induction by insulin. *Biochim. Biophys. Acta* 424:264–73

53. Gazzotti, P., Bock, H., Fleischer, S. 1975. Interaction of D-β-hydroxybutyrate apodehydrogenase with phospholipids. *J. Biol. Chem.* 250:5782–90

54. Gjedde, A., Crone, C. 1975. Induction processes in blood-brain transfer of ketone bodies during starvation. *Am. J. Physiol.* 229:1165–73

55. Goldberg, V. J., Ramwell, P. W. 1975. Role of prostaglandins in reproduction. *Physiol. Rev.* 55:325–51

56. Goldman, S. S., Albers, R. W. 1973. Sodium-potassium-activated adenosine

triphosphatase. IX. The role of phospholipids. *J. Biol. Chem.* 248:867–74

57. Goldrick, R. B., Galton, D. J. 1974. Fatty acid synthesis de novo in human adipose tissue. *Clin. Sci. Mol. Med.* 46:469–79

58. Gollnick, P. D., Soule, R. G., Taylor, A. W., Williams, C., Ianuzzo, C. D. 1970. Exercise-induced glycogenolysis and lipolysis in the rat: Hormonal influence. *Am. J. Physiol.* 219:729–33

59. Goodman, H. M. 1970. Permissive effects of hormones on lypolysis. *Endocrinology* 86:1064–74

60. Gorski, J., Gannon, F. 1976. Current models of steroid hormone action: A critique. *Ann. Rev. Physiol.* 38:425–50

61. Grunze, M., Deuticke, B. 1974. Changes of membrane permeability due to extensive cholesterol depletion in mammalian erythrocytes. *Biochim. Biophys. Acta* 356:125–30

62. Guynn, R. W., Veloso, D., Veech, R. L. 1972. The concentration of malonyl-coenzyme A and the control of fatty acid synthesis in vivo. *J. Biol. Chem.* 247:7325–31

63. Hagenfeldt, L., Wahren, J. 1968. Human forearm muscle metabolism during exercise. 3. Uptake, release and oxidation of beta-hydroxybutyrate and observations on the beta-hydroxybutyrate/acetoacetate ratio. *Scand. J. Clin. Lab. Invest.* 21:314–320

64. Hallinan, T. 1974. Lipid effects on enzyme activities: Phospholipid dependence and phospholipid constraint. *Biochem. Soc. Trans.* 2:817–21

65. Hamilton, R. L. 1972. Synthesis and secretion of plasma lipoproteins. *Adv. Exp. Med. Biol.* 26:7–24

66. Hamosh, M., Hamosh, P. 1975. Lipoprotein lipase in rat lung. The effect of fasting. *Biochim. Biophys. Acta* 380:132–40

67. Hamosh, M., Klaeveman, H. L., Wolf, R. O., Scow, R. O. 1975. Pharyngeal lipase and digestion of dietary triglyceride in man. *J. Clin. Invest.* 55:908–13

68. Hamosh, M., Scow, R. O. 1973. Lingual lipase and its role in the digestion of dietary lipid. *J. Clin. Invest.* 52:88–95

69. Havel, R. J. 1972. Caloric homeostasis and disorders of fuel transport. *New Engl. J. Med.* 287:1186–92

70. Havel, R. J., Ekelund, L. G., Holmgren, A. 1967. Kinetic analysis of the oxidation of palmitate 1-^{14}C in man during prolonged heavy muscular exercise. *J. Lipid Res.* 8:366–73

71. Havel, R. J., Kane, J. P. 1975. Quantification of triglyceride transport in blood plasma: A critical analysis. *Fed. Proc.* 34:2250–57

72. Havel, R. J., Kane, J. P., Kashyap, M. L. 1973. Interchange of apolipoproteins between chylomicrons and high density lipoproteins during alimentary lipemia in man. *J. Clin. Invest.* 52:32–38

73. Hawkins, R. A., Williamson, P. H., Krebs, H. A. 1971. Ketone-body utilization by adult and suckling rat brain in vivo. *Biochem. J.* 122:13–18

74. Hegner, D., Platt, D. 1975. Effects of essential phospholipids on the properties of ATPases of isolated rat liver plasma membranes of young and old animals. *Mech. Aging Dev.* 4:191–200

75. Heindel, J. J., Orci, L., Jeanrenaud, B. 1975. Fat mobilization and its regulation by hormones and drugs in white adipose tissue. See Ref. 48, pp. 175–373

76. Helmkamp, G. M. Jr., Nelemans, S. A., Wirtz, K. W. A. 1976. Immunological comparison of phosphatidylinositol and phosphatidyl-choline exchange proteins in bovine brain, liver and heart. *Biochim. Biophys. Acta* 424:168–82

77. Hems, D. A. 1975. Control of hepatic glyceride synthesis. *Proc. Nutr. Soc.* 34:225–31

78. Hems, D. A., Rath, E. A., Verrinder, T. R. 1975. Fatty acid synthesis in liver and adipose tissue of normal and genetically obese (ob/ob) mice during the 24-hour cycle. *Biochem. J.* 150:167–73

79. Hepp, K. D., Renner, R. 1972. Insulin action on the adenyl cyclase system: Antagonism of activation by lipolytic hormone. *FEBS Lett.* 20:191–94

80. Higgins, J. M., Fielding, C. J. 1975. Lipoprotein lipase. Mechanism of formation of triglyceride-rich remnant particles from very low density lipoproteins and chylomicrons. *Biochemistry* 14:2288–93

81. Hill, R., Linazasoro, J. M., Chevallier, F., Chaikoff, I. L. 1958. Regulation of hepatic lipogenesis: The influence of dietary fats. *J. Biol. Chem.* 233:305–10

82. Hirsch, J., Han, P. W. 1969. Cellularity of rat adipose tissue: Effects of growth, starvation, and obesity. *J. Lipid Res.* 10:77–82

83. Hirsch, J., Knittle, J. L. 1970. Cellularity of obese and nonobese human adipose tissue. *Fed. Proc.* 29:1516–21

84. Holick, M. F., De Luca, H. F. 1974. Chemistry and biological activity of vitamin D, its metabolites and analogs.

Adv. Steroid Biochem. Pharmacol. 4: 111–55

85. Issekutz, B. Jr., Shaw, W. A. S., Issekutz, T. B. 1975. Effect of lactate on FFA and glycerol turnover in resting and exercising dogs. *J. Appl. Physiol.* 39:349–53

86. Jackson, M. J. 1974. Transport of short chain fatty acids. *Biomembranes* 4B: 673–709

87. Jones, N. L., Havel, R. J. 1967. Metabolism of free fatty acids and chylomicron triglycerides during exercise in rats. *Am. J. Physiol.* 213:824–28

88. Kekki, M., Nikkila, E. A. 1975. Turnover of plasma total and very low density lipoprotein triglyceride in man. *Scand. J. Clin. Lab. Invest.* 35:171–79

89. Khoo, J. C., Aquino, A. A., Steinberg, D. 1974. The mechanism of activation of hormone-sensitive lipase in human adipose tissue. *J. Clin. Invest.* 53: 1124–31

90. Kimelberg, H. K., Papahadjopoulos, D. 1974. Effects of phospholipid acyl chain fluidity, phase transitions, and cholesterol on ($Na^+ + K^+$)-stimulated adenosine triphosphatase. *J. Biol. Chem.* 249:1071–80

91. King, R. J. 1974. The surfactant system of the lung. *Fed. Proc.* 33:2238–47

92. Knowles, A. F., Racker, E. 1975. Formation of adenosine triphosphate from Pi and adenosine diphosphate by purified Ca^+-adenosine triphosphatase. *J. Biol. Chem.* 250:1949–51

93. Koerker, D. J., Goodner, C. J., Chideckel, E. W., Ensinck, J. W. 1975. Adaptation to fasting in baboon. II. Regulation of lipolysis early and late in fasting. *Am. J. Physiol.* 229:350–54

94. Kono, T., Barham, F. W. 1973. Effects of insulin on the levels of adenosine 3'5'-monophosphate and lipolysis in isolated rat epididymal fat cells. *J. Biol. Chem.* 248:7417–26

95. Korchak, H. M., Masoro, E. J. 1962. Changes in the level of the fatty acid synthesizing enzymes during starvation. *Biochim. Biophys. Acta* 58:354–56

96. Korchak, H., Masoro, E. J. 1964. Free fatty acids as lipogenic inhibitors. *Biochim. Biophys. Acta* 84:750–53

97. Krauss, R. M., Windmueller, H. G., Levy, R. I., Fredrickson, D. S. 1973. Selective measurement of two different triglyceride lipase activities in rat postheparin plasma. *J. Lipid Res.* 14:286–95

98. Kreisberg, R. A. 1966. Effect of diabetes and starvation on myocardial tri-glyceride and free fatty acid utilization. *Am. J. Physiol.* 210:379–84

99. Lefebvre, P. 1975. Glucagon and adipose tissue. *Biochem. Pharmacol.* 24: 1261–66

100. Lemonnier, D. 1972. Effect of age, sex, and site on the cellularity of the adipose tissue in mice and rats rendered obese by a high-fat diet. *J. Clin. Invest.* 51:2907–15

101. Lequin, H. C., Steyn-Parve, E. P. 1962. Some aspects of glucose metabolism in normal and alloxan-diabetic rats. *Biochim. Biophys. Acta* 58:439–48

102. Lesko, L., Marinetti, G. V. 1975. Hormone action at the membrane level. IV. Epinephrine binding to rat liver plasma membranes and rat epididymal fat cells. *Biochim. Biophys. Acta* 382:419–36

103. Leung, K., Munck, A. 1975. Peripheral actions of glucocorticoids. *Ann. Rev. Physiol.* 37:245–72

104. Leveille, G. A. 1967. In vivo fatty acid synthesis in adipose tissue and liver of meal-fed rats. *Proc. Soc. Exp. Biol. Med.* 125:85–88

105. Levy, G. S. 1971. Restoration of norepinephrine responsiveness of solubilized myocardial adenylate cyclase by phosphatidylinositol. *J. Biol. Chem.* 246: 7405–10

106. Lindsay, D. B. 1975. Fatty acids as energy sources. *Proc. Nutr. Soc.* 34: 241–48

107. Little, J. R., Spitzer, J. J. 1971. Uptake of ketone bodies by dog kidney in vivo. *Am. J. Physiol.* 221:679–83

108. Lopes-Cardozo, M., Mulder, I., van Vugt, F., Hermans, P. G. C., van den Bergh, S. G. 1975. Aspects of ketogenesis: Control and mechanism of ketone-body formation in isolated rat-liver mitochondria. *Mol. Cell. Biochem.* 9:155–73

109. Lucy, J. A. 1974. Lipids and membranes. *FEBS Lett.* 40:S105–11

110. Lüscher, E. F. 1975. The effects of lipids and fatty acids on blood coagulation and platelets in relation to thrombosis. *Adv. Exp. Med. Biol.* 60:107–18

111. Luyckx, A. S., Dresse, A., Cession-Fossion, A., Lefebvre, P. J. 1975. Catecholamines and exercise-induced glucagon and fatty acid mobilization in the rat. *Am. J. Physiol.* 229:376–83

112. McGarry, J. D., Foster, D. W. 1974. The metabolism of (–)-octanoylcarnitine in perfused livers from fed and fasted rats. *J. Biol. Chem.* 249:7984–90

113. McGarry, J. D., Rables-Valdes, C., Foster, D. W. 1975. Role of carnitine in

hepatic ketogenesis. *Proc. Natl. Acad. Sci. USA* 72:4385-88

114. McGarry, J. D., Wright, P. H., Foster, D. W. 1975. Hormonal control of ketogenesis. Rapid activation of hepatic ketogenic capacity in fed rats by anti-insulin serum and glucagon. *J. Clin. Invest.* 55:1202-9

115. MacLennan, D. H. 1970. Purification and properties of an adenosine triphosphatase from sarcoplasmic reticulum. *J. Biol. Chem.* 245:4508-18

116. MacLennan, D. H., Yip, C. C., Iles, G. H., Seeman, P. 1973. Isolation of sarcoplasmic reticulum proteins. In *Cold Spring Harbor Symp. Quant. Biol.* 37:469-77

117. Mahley, R. W., Bennett, B. D., Morre, D. J., Gray, M. E., Thistlewaite, W., LeQuire, V. S. 1971. Lipoproteins associated with the Golgi apparatus isolated from epithelial cells of rat small intestine. *Lab. Invest.* 25:435-44

118. Malila, A., DeMartinis, F. D., Masoro, E. J. 1968. Involvement of phospholipids in Rb^+ transport by kidney cortex tubules. *J. Biol. Chem.* 243:6115-22

119. Malila, A., Masoro, E. J. 1970. Inhibition of renal cortical Rb^+ transport by phospholipase C and its relationship to $(Na^+ + K^+)$-adenosine triphosphatase. *Lipids* 5:658-61

120. Manganiello, V., Vaughan, M. 1973. An effect of insulin in cyclic adenosine 3'5' monophosphate phosphodiesterase activity in fat cells. *J. Biol. Chem.* 248:7164-70

120a. Mansbach, C. M. II, Cohen, R. S., Leff, P. B. 1975. Isolation and properties of mixed lipid micelles present in intestinal content during fat digestion. *J. Clin. Invest.* 56:781-91

121. Martin, D. B., Vagelos, P. R. 1962. The mechanism of tricarboxylic acid cycle regulation of fatty acid synthesis. *J. Biol. Chem.* 237:1787-92

122. Martonosi, A., Boland, R., Halpin, R. A. 1973. The biosynthesis of sarcoplasmic reticulum membranes and the mechanism of calcium transport. *Cold Spring Harbor Symp. Quant. Biol.* 37:455-68

123. Martonosi, A., Donley, J., Halpin, R. A. 1968. Sarcoplasmic reticulum. 3. The role of phospholipids in the adenosine triphosphatase activity and Ca^{++} transport. *J. Biol. Chem.* 243:61-70

124. Martonosi, A., Lagwinska, E., Oliver, M. 1974. Elementary processes in the hydrolysis of ATP by sarcoplasmic reticulum membranes. *Ann. NY Acad. Sci.* 227:549-67

125. Masoro, E. J. 1962. Biochemical mechanisms related to the homeostatic regulation of lipogenesis in animals. *J. Lipid Res.* 3:149-64

126. Masoro, E. J. 1966. Skeletal muscle lipids III. Analysis of the functioning of skeletal muscle lipids during fasting. *J. Biol. Chem.* 242:1111-14

127. Masoro, E. J. 1973. Development of the enzymes of lipid biosynthesis in the human fetus. In *Respiratory Distress Syndrome*, ed. C. A. Villee, D. B. Villee, J. Zuckerman, pp. 7-27. New York: Academic

128. Masoro, E. J. 1975. General considerations of membranes. *Adv. Exp. Med. Biol.* 61:81-94

129. Masoro, E. J. 1975. Overview of the process and regulation of lipid transport. See Ref. 48, pp. 1-20

130. Masoro, E. J., Asuncion, C. L., Brown, R. K., Rapport, D. 1956. Lipogenesis from carbohydrate in the negative caloric balance state induced by exposure to cold. *Am. J. Physiol.* 190:177-79

131. Masoro, E. J., Chaikoff, I. L., Chernick, S. S., Felts, J. M. 1950. Previous nutritional state and glucose conversion to fatty acids in liver slices. *J. Biol. Chem.* 185:845-56

132. Masoro, E. J., Chaikoff, I. L., Dauben, W. G. 1949. Lipogenesis from glucose in normal and liverless animals as studied with C^{14}-labelled glucose. *J. Biol. Chem.* 179:1117-25

133. Masoro, E. J., Rowell, L. B., McDonald, R. M., Steiert, B. 1966. Skeletal muscle lipids II. Nonutilization of intracellular lipid esters as an energy source for contractile activity. *J. Biol. Chem.* 241:2626-34

134. Masoro, E. J., Yu, B. P. 1971. Action of drugs on the Ca^{2+} transport system of sarcotubular membranes. *Top. Med. Chem. Absorption Phenomena* 4:97-144

135. Mayerle, J. A., Havel, R. J. 1969. Nutritional effects on blood flow in adipose tissue of unanesthetized rats. *Am. J. Physiol.* 217:1694-98

136. Mayes, P. A. 1975. Hepatic secretion of very low density lipoproteins—Basic mechanisms and the effects of drugs. See Reference 48, pp. 125-74

137. Mishkin, S., Yalovsky, M., Kessler, J. I. 1975. Uptake and compartmental distribution of fatty acid by rat small intestine in vivo. *Am. J. Physiol.* 228:1409-14

138. Deleted in proof.
139. Neely, J. R., Bowman, R. H., Morgan, H. E. 1969. Effects of ventricular pressure development and palmitate on glucose transport. *Am. J. Physiol.* 216: 804–11
140. Neely, J. R., Rovetto, M. J., Oram, J. F. 1972. Myocardial utilization of carbohydrate and lipids. *Prog. Cardiovasc. Res.* 15:289–329
141. Neilsen, S. L., Bitsch, V., Larsen, O. A., Lassen, N. A., Quaade, F. 1969. Blood flow through human adipose tissue during lipolysis. *Scand. J. Clin. Lab. Invest.* 22:124–30
142. Neptune, E. M., Sudduth, H. C., Foreman, D. R., Fash, F. J. 1960. Phospholipid and triglyceride metabolism of excised rat diaphragm and the role of these lipids in fatty acid uptake and oxidation. *J. Lipid Res.* 1:229–35
143. Numa, S., Matsuhashi, M., Lynen, F. 1961. On disorders of fatty acid synthesis in hunger and alloxan diabetes. I. Fatty acid synthesis in the liver of normal and fasting rats. *Biochem. Z.* 334:203–17
144. Ockner, R. K., Manning, J. 1974. Fatty acid-binding protein in small intestine. Identification, isolation, and evidence for its role in cellular fatty acid transport. *J. Clin. Invest.* 54:326–38
145. Ockner, R. K., Pittman, J. P., Yager, J. L. 1972. Differences in the intestinal absorption of saturated and unsaturated long chain fatty acids. *Gastroenterology* 62:981–92
146. Olson, R. E., Hoescher, R. J. 1967. Utilization of endogenous lipids by the isolated perfused rat heart. *Biochem. J.* 103:796–801
147. Owen, O. E., Felig, P., Morgan, A. P., Wahren, J., Cahill, G. F. Jr. 1969. Liver and kidney metabolism during prolonged starvation. *J. Clin. Invest.* 48:574–83
148. Owen, O. E., Reichard, G. A. 1971. Human forearm metabolism during progressive starvation. *J. Clin. Invest.* 50:1536–45
149. Owen, O. E., Reichard, G. A. Jr. 1975. Ketone body metabolism in normal, obese and diabetic subjects. *Isr. J. Med. Sci.* 11:560–70
150. Patel, M. S., Owen, O. E., Goldman, L. I., Hanson, R. W. 1975. Fatty-acid synthesis by human adipose tissue. *Metabolism* 24:161–73
151. Patkin, J. K., Masoro, E. J. 1964. Fatty acid synthesis in normal and cold-acclimated rats. *Can. J. Physiol. Pharmacol.* 42:101–7
152. Persico, P. A., Cerchio, G. M., Jeffay, H. 1975. Glycerokinase in mammalian adipose tissue: Stimulation by lipogenic substances. *Am. J. Physiol.* 228: 1868–74
153. Pfeuffer, T., Helmreich, E. J. M. 1975. Activation of pigeon erythrocyte membrane adenylate cyclase by guanylnucleotide analogues and separation of a nucleotide binding protein. *J. Biol. Chem.* 250:867–76
154. Queener, S., Bell, N. H. 1974. Prostaglandins and endocrinology. In *Year Book of Endocrinology,* ed. T. B. Schwartz, pp. 7–21. Chicago: Year Book Medical
155. Racker, E. 1972. Reconstitution of a calcium pump with phospholipids and a purified Ca^{++}-adenosine triphosphatase from sarcoplasmic reticulum. *J. Biol. Chem.* 247:8198–8200
156. Racker, E., Eytan, E. 1975. A coupling factor from sarcoplasmic reticulum required for the translocation of Ca^{2+} ions in a reconstituted Ca^{++} ATPase pump. *J. Biol. Chem.* 250:7533–34
157. Rapport, M. M., Graf, L. 1969. Immunochemical reactions of lipids. *Prog. Allergy* 13:273–331
158. Redgrave, T. G. 1970. Formation of cholesteryl ester-rich particulate lipid during metabolism of chylomicrons. *J. Clin. Invest.* 49:465–71
159. Renold, A. E. 1965. A brief and fragmentary introduction to some aspects of adipose tissue metabolism, with emphasis on glucose uptake. *Ann. NY Acad. Sci.* 131:7–12
160. Renooij, W., van Golde, L. M. G., Zwaal, R. F. A., Van Deenan, L. L. M. 1976. Topological asymmetry of phospholipid metabolism in rat erythrocyte membranes: Evidence of flip-flop of lecithin. *Eur. J. Biochem.* 61:53–58
161. Reshef, L., Hanson, R. W., Ballard, F. J. 1970. A possible physiological role for glyceroneogenesis in rat adipose tissue. *J. Biol. Chem.* 245:5979–84
162. Robinson, D. S. 1970. Assimilation, distribution and storage. Section C. The function of the plasma triglycerides in fatty acid transport. In *Comprehensive Biochemistry: Lipid Metabolism,* ed. M. Florkin, E. H. Stotz, 18:51–116. Amsterdam: Elsevier
163. Rosell, S., Belfrage, E. 1975. Adrenergic receptors in adipose tissue and their relation to adrenergic innervation. *Nature* 253:738

164. Rowell, L. B., Masoro, E. J., Spencer, M. J. 1965. Splanchnic metabolism in exercising man. *J. Appl. Physiol.* 20:1032–37

165. Rubalcava, B., Rodbell, M. 1973. The role of acidic phospholipids in glucagon action on rat liver adenylate cyclase. *J. Biol. Chem.* 248:3831–37

166. Rudel, L. L., Felts, J. M., Morris, M. D. 1974. Exogenous cholesterol transport in rabbit plasma lipoproteins. *Biochem. J.* 134:531–37

167. Ruderman, N. B., Goodman, M. N. 1973. Regulation of ketone body metabolism in skeletal muscle. *Am. J. Physiol.* 224:1391–97

168. Sallee, V. L., Dietschy, J. M. 1973. Determinants of intestinal mucosal uptake of short- and medium-chain fatty acids and alcohols. *J. Lipid Res.* 14:475–84

169. Sanslone, W. R., Bertrand, H. A., Yu, B. P., Masoro, E. J. 1972. Lipid components of sarcotubular membranes. *J. Cell. Physiol.* 79:97–101

170. Sarda, L., Desnuelle, P. 1958. Action de la lipase pancréatique sur les esters en emulsion. *Biochim. Biophys. Acta* 30:513–21

171. Sari, H., Entressangles, B., Desnuelle, P. 1975. Interactions of colipase with bile salt micelles. 2. Study by dialysis and spectrophotometry. *Eur. J. Biochem.* 58:561–65

172. Schneider, H., Morrod, R. S., Colvin, J. R., Tattrie, N. H. 1973. The lipid core model of lipoproteins. *Chem. Phys. Lipids* 10:328–53

173. Schonfeld, G., Pfleger, B. 1971. Utilization of exogenous free fatty acids for the production of very low density lipoprotein triglyceride by livers of carbohydrate-fed rats. *J. Lipid Res.* 12:614–21

174. Scorpio, R. M., Masoro, E. J. 1970. Differences between manganese and magnesium ions with regard to fatty acid biosynthesis, acetyl-coenzyme A carboxylase activity and malonyl-coenzyme A decarboxylation. *Biochem. J.* 118:391–99

175. Shapiro, B. 1965. Triglyceride metabolism. In *Handb. Physiol. Sect. 5. Adipose Tissue,* ed. A. E. Renold, G. F. Cahill, Jr., pp. 217–23. Wash. DC: Am. Physiol. Soc.

176. Shrago, E., Spennetta, T., Gordon, E. 1969. Fatty acid synthesis in human adipose tissue. *J. Biol. Chem.* 244:2761–66

177. Siddle, K., Halis, C. N. 1975. Hormonal control of adipose tissue lipolysis. *Proc. Nutr. Soc.* 34:233–39

178. Siekevitz, P. 1972. Biological membranes: The dynamics of their organization. *Ann. Rev. Physiol.* 34:117–40

179. Sims, E. A., Goldman, R. F., Gluck, C. M., Horton, E. S., Kelleher, P. C., Rowe, D. W. 1968. Experimental obesity in man. *Trans. Assoc. Am. Physicians* 81:153–70

180. Singer, S. J., Nicolson, G. L. 1972. The fluid mosaic model of the structure of cell membranes. *Science* 175:720–31

181. Skou, J. C. 1965. Enzymatic basis for active transport of Na^+ and K^+ across cell membrane. *Physiol. Rev.* 45:596–617

182. Slavin, B. G. 1972. The cytophysiology of mammalian adipose cells. *Int. Rev. Cytol.* 33:297–334

183. Smith, S., Abraham, S. 1975. Effects of pharmacologic agents on hepatic biosynthesis of fatty acids and cholesterol. See Reference 48, pp. 69–124

184. Soloman, S. S. 1975. Effect of insulin and lipolytic hormones on cyclic AMP phosphodiesterase activity in normal and diabetic rat adipose tissue. *Endocrinology* 96:1366–73

185. Spector, A. A., Steinberg, D., Tanaka, A. 1965. Uptake of free fatty acids by Ehrlich ascites tumor cells. *J. Biol. Chem.* 240:1032–41

186. Spitzer, J. J. 1975. Application of tracers in studying free fatty acid metabolism of various organs in vivo. *Fed. Proc.* 34:2242–45

187. Stansbie, D., Denton, R. M., Bridges, B. J., Pask, H. T., Randle, P. J. 1976. Regulation of pyruvate dehydrogenase and pyruvate dehydrogenase phosphate phosphatase activity in rat epididymal fat-pads. *Biochem. J.* 154:225–36

188. Stein, O., Stein, Y., Fidge, N. H., Goodman, D. S. 1969. The metabolism of chylomicron cholesteryl ester in rat liver, a combined radioautographic-electron microscopic and biochemical study. *J. Cell Biol.* 43:410–31

189. Steinberg, J., Masoro, E. J., Yu, B. P. 1974. Role of sarcoplasmic reticulum phospholipids in calcium ion binding activity. *J. Lipid Res.* 15:537–43

190. Stetten, D. W., Boxer, G. E. 1944. Studies in carbohydrate metabolism; rate of turnover of liver and carcass glycogen, studied with aid of deuterium. *J. Biol. Chem.* 155:231–36

191. Stiles, J. W., Francendese, A. A., Masoro, E. J. 1975. Influence of age on

size and number of fat cells in the epididymal depot. *Am. J. Physiol.* 229:1561–68

192. Strand, O., Vaughan, M., Steinberg, D. 1964. Rat adipose tissue lipases: Hormone-sensitive lipase activity against triglycerides compared with activity against lower glycerides. *J. Lipid Res.* 5:554–62

193. Tanaka, R., Strickland, K. P. 1965. Role of phospholipid in the activation of Na^+, K^+-activated adenosine triphosphatase of beef brain. *Arch. Biochem. Biophys.* 111:583–92

194. Teixeira, V. L., Antunes-Rodrigues, J., Migliorini, R. H. 1973. Evidence for centers in the central nervous system that selectively regulate fat mobilization in the rat. *J. Lipid Res.* 14:672–77

195. Tierney, D. F. 1974. Lung metabolism and biochemistry. *Ann. Rev. Physiol.* 36:209–31

196. Treadwell, C. R., Vahouny, G. V. 1968. Cholesterol absorption. In *Handb. Physiol.: Sect. 6. Alimentary Canal; Vol. III. Intestinal Absorption*, ed. C. F. Code, pp. 1407–38. Wash. DC: Am. Physiol. Soc.

197. Unger, R. H., Eisentraut, A. M. 1969. Entero-insular axis. *Arch. Intern. Med.* 123:261–66

198. Van Deenan, L. L. M. 1972. Permeability and topography of membranes. *Chem. Phys. Lipids* 8:366–73

199. Volk, M. E., Millington, R. H., Weinhouse, S. 1952. Oxidation of endogenous fatty acids of rat tissues in vitro. *J. Biol. Chem.* 195:493–501

200. Wahren, J., Hagenfeldt, L., Felig, P. 1975. Glucose and free fatty acid utilization in exercise. *Isr. J. Med. Sci.* 11:551–59

201. Walker, J. A., Wheeler, K. P. 1975. Polar head-group and acyl sidechain requirements for phospholipid-dependent $(Na^+ + K^+)$-ATPase. *Biochim. Biophys. Acta* 394:135–44

202. Warren, G. B., Toon, P. A., Birdsall, N. J. M., Lee, A. G., Metcalfe, J. C. 1974. Reversible lipid titrations of the activity of pure adenosine triphosphatase-lipid complexes. *Biochemistry* 13:5501–7

203. Wasserman, R. H., Taylor, A. N. 1972. Metabolic roles of fat-soluble vitamins D, E, and K. *Ann. Rev. Biochem.* 41:179–202

204. Weiss, H. J. 1975. Platelet physiology and abnormalities of platelet function. *New Engl. J. Med.* 295:580–88

205. Weiss, L., Loffler, G., Wieland, O. H. 1974. Regulation by insulin of adipose tissue pyruvate dehydrogenase. A mechanism controlling fatty acid synthesis from carbohydrates. *Hoppe-Seyler's Z. Physiol. Chem.* 355:363–77

206. Wheeler, K. P. 1975. Role of phospholipid in the intermediate steps of the sodium-plus-potassium ion-dependent adenosine triphosphatase reaction. *Biochem. J.* 146:729–39

207. Wilson, F. A., Sallee, V. L., Dietschy, J. M. 1971. Unstirred water layers in intestine: Rate determinant of fatty acid absorption from micellar solutions. *Science* 174:1031–33

208. Wirtz, K. W. A. 1974. Transfer of phospholipids between membranes. *Biochim. Biophys. Acta* 344:95–117

209. Yamashita, K., Field, J. B. 1973. The role of phospholipids in TSH stimulation of adenylate cyclase in thyroid plasma membranes. *Biochim. Biophys. Acta* 304:686–92

210. Yu, B. P., DeMartinis, F. D., Masoro, E. J. 1968. Relation of lipid structure of sarcotubular vesicles to Ca^{++} transport activity. *J. Lipid Res.* 9:492–500

211. Yu, B. P., Masoro, E. J., Bertrand, H. A. 1974. The functioning of histidine residues of sarcoplasmic reticulum in Ca^{2+} transport and related activities. *Biochemistry* 13:5083–87

212. Yu, B. P., Masoro, E. J., Morley, T. F. 1976. Analysis of the arrangement of protein components in the sarcoplasmic reticulum of rat skeletal muscle. *J. Biol. Chem.* 251:2037–43

213. Zambrano, F., Fleischer, S., Fleischer, B. 1975. Lipid composition of the Golgi apparatus of rat kidney and liver in comparison with other subcellular organelles. *Biochim. Biophys. Acta* 380:357–69

214. Zierler, K. L., Maseri, A., Klassen, D., Rabinowitz, D., Burgess, J. 1968. Muscle metabolism during exercise in man. *Trans. Assoc. Am. Physicians* 81:266–73

215. Zilversmit, D. B. 1967. Formation and transport of chylomicrons. *Fed. Proc.* 26:1599–1605

216. Zinman, B., Hollenberg, C. H. 1974. Effect of insulin and lipolytic agents on rat adipocyte low Km cyclic adenosine 3':5'-monophosphate phosphodiesterase. *J. Biol. Chem.* 249:2182–87

Ann. Rev. Physiol. 1977. 39:323–47
Copyright © 1977 by Annual Reviews Inc. All rights reserved

MECHANISMS OF HEPATIC BILE FORMATION[1]

❖1174

E. L. Forker

Department of Medicine, University of Iowa College of Medicine, University Hospital, Iowa City, Iowa 52242

INTRODUCTION

Efforts to uncover the physiologic details of bile formation face a number of obstacles which set the liver somewhat apart from other epithelial systems such as the kidney, gallbladder, and intestine in which the mechanisms of solution transport are better understood. In particular, it has so far proved impossible to sample bile at its source. As a result neither the electrical potential difference nor unidirectional solute flux rates are accessible to measurement at the canalicular surface or within the small bile ductules, and the contribution to bile flow at these sites must be determined indirectly. Three other difficulties stand out as especially important. Most of the organic solutes in bile are products of hepatic metabolism, so that the kinetics of solute transport from blood to bile are frequently complicated by changes in chemical configuration. Mixed micelles, which represent the major solid constituent of bile, profoundly alter the colligative properties of bile acid anions and reduce the activities of their inorganic counter-ions. Marked deviations from ideal behavior can occur with other water soluble organic constituents as well. The organic solutes of bile are typically bound to protein in the circulation and within liver cells, with the result that their free or effective concentrations in these compartments are usually unknown.

In view of these technical problems, it is hardly surprising that we still know remarkably little about the fundamental physiology of bile production, even though the last ten years have witnessed a large increase in the number of scientists interested in the problem. Some progress has been made, however, and it is possible to sketch at least the broad outlines of the secretory process and to identify the bases for currently promising speculations. This is the purpose of the present review. The excellent reviews by Wheeler (174, 175) and a later comprehensive summary by

[1]Supported by NIH Grant #AM 09892.

323

Erlinger (46) should be consulted for a detailed review of earlier work.[2] The emphasis here is on recent developments.

BILE FLOW AND INORGANIC ION TRANSPORT

As a digestive secretion, bile comprises mixed micelles of conjugated bile acids, cholesterol, and phospholipid in aqueous solution with the inorganic electrolytes of plasma. With the exception of cholesterol, these components are largely returned to the body by reabsorption from the intestine. As an excretory vehicle, bile serves as a pathway out of the body for a variety of drugs and metabolites, some of which (notably bile pigment and a variety of anionic dyes) for practical purposes have no other excretory route. The bulk of this complex mixture arises from the intralobular or canalicular portion of the biliary tree and is thus a product of parenchymal liver cells, but the final composition of bile is subject to modification in the bile ducts by the addition and/or reabsorption of water and inorganic ions. Like the other secretions which enter the digestive system, bile is always nearly iso-osmotic with plasma, and most of the osmolar load is attributable to inorganic ions. Part of the inorganic ion excretion is associated with the canalicular transport of ionized bile acids which themselves contribute relatively little osmotic activity because the anions aggregate to form micelles. The remainder enters bile independently of bile acids, partly in the canalicular and partly in the extralobular segment of the biliary tree. The clearest example of this latter kind of bile acid–independent secretion is the choleretic action of the intestinal hormone secretin.

Estimation of Canalicular Bile Flow

At present the only way to estimate canalicular bile production quantitatively is to measure the steady-state plasma clearance of a metabolically inert neutral solute such as erythritol. The rationale and limitations of this approach have been discussed in detail by Forker (51–53) and Wheeler (180). Briefly, the method depends on the proposition that a polar uncharged solute, not subject to active transport, enters bile by simple diffusion and convection and that its excretion rate should therefore depend jointly on the permeability of the epithelium and the rate of bile flow at a given locus. In guinea pigs (51, 52) and dogs (180) the excretion of erythritol and mannitol as well as that of several other tests solutes of various molecular radii is consistent with these theoretical considerations. In these experiments the clearances of erythritol and mannitol were strongly correlated with changes in bile flow during bile acid choleresis but unaltered when comparable changes in flow were stimulated by secretin. The most reasonable inferences to be drawn from these observations are that the locus of permeability to erythritol and mannitol is coextensive with the site of bile acid excretion (the canaliculi) and that secretin choleresis arises at an impermeable locus somewhere downstream (i.e. the ducts or ductules). While neither of these conclusions has been confirmed directly,

---

[2]Additional helpful reviews have appeared (26, 29, 44, 45, 127) as well as the proceedings of several international symposia (125, 133, 163, 164).

independent evidence from an analysis of excretory transients and selective arterial injections of secretin (177) is in accord with a ductular site for the action of secretin, and it has been found that hepatocytes are remarkably permeable to erythritol and mannitol (54, 62, 123).

Acceptance of the clearance technique to measure canalicular bile production requires that the selected solute be unable to cross the ductular epithelium and that its permeability in the canaliculi be high enough that diffusion equilibrium is achieved at the highest rates of canalicular flow. Until more direct techniques are available to settle the issue unequivocally, the best criterion for this last requirement is the finding that increments in bile flow produced by bile acid infusion are equivalent to the corresponding increments in clearance over a wide range of bile flows. Acceptable evidence that erythritol meets this requirement has been obtained in dogs (180), hamsters (144), monkeys (160), and man (132). In pigs (43), erythritol fails this test at the highest rates of bile flow although the deviations are small. Mannitol appears to equilibrate in the canaliculi of dogs (180) but not of hamsters (144), rabbits (47), or man (20). In guinea pigs the canalicular membrane presents appreciable restriction to both solutes (51).

The assumption that erythritol is unable to cross the ductular epithelium is less easily tested and has recently been questioned on the basis that dogs may show a small positive slope for the relation between secretin-induced choleresis and erythritol clearance [R. Preisig, personal communication; (8)]. If confirmed, these preliminary data would be equally consistent with a greatly restricted but significant permeability of the ducts to erythritol or a small canalicular contribution to the choleretic effect of secretin. An earlier report (58) that secretin produced a small choleresis and associated increments in erythritol and mannitol clearance in rats is attributable to contamination of the hormone preparation with bile acids. In isolated perfused rat livers (19) and in rabbits (47) the relationship between erythritol clearance and bile flow for a wide range of bile acid excretion rates is linear and extrapolates to the origin, but has a slope slightly greater than one. Since it is unlikely that erythritol is actively secreted, these findings suggest that the ducts or ductules reabsorb erythritol-free fluid at a constant fractional rate of canalicular bile production. Ductular fluid transfer is considered in more detail later, but it bears emphasizing here that ductular secretion of erythritol-free fluid at a constant fractional rate of canalicular bile production cannot be distinguished from failure of erythritol to equilibrate in the canaliculi. By the same token, the appearance of complete canalicular equilibration may be misleading if constant fractional reabsorption of erythritol-free fluid occurs or if ductular epithelium turns out on closer examination to be significantly permeable to erythritol.

Mechanisms of Canalicular Fluid Production

The secretory pressure of bile substantially exceeds sinusoidal blood pressure, and the energy for bile flow must therefore represent the metabolic work of liver cells rather than hydraulic work expended by blood flow. Discounting the active transport of water itself as energetically improbable, we can conclude that the flow of water must be the passive consequence of active solute transport. Theoretical possibilities for the mechanism of coupling between solute transport and water flow include electro-osmosis, exocytosis or vesicular transport, and classical osmosis. There is no evidence that electro-osmosis and vesicular transport are functionally important mechanisms for bulk water flow, and it is therefore assumed that water enters by classical osmosis.

Since bile acids conjugated with glycine or taurine are fully ionized at the pH of bile and account for a large fraction of the total solute content, it is not surprising that bile acid excretion rate is a strong determinant of bile flow. In model systems, bile acids display a critical micellar concentration (CMC) above which spontaneous aggregation of the anions occurs with a marked reduction of the number of particles in solution. One would expect on this basis that the osmotic coefficient of bile acids in the canalicular lumen should depend on their concentration, especially in the region of the CMC. In practice, however, plots of bile acid excretion rate against total flow or canalicular flow (as measured by erythritol clearance) are linear over a wide range of transport rates. To varying degrees, depending on the animal species, such plots display a positive intercept upon extrapolation to the flow axis. Endogenous bile acid synthesis has usually prevented a direct examination of this relationship below the CMC, but in isolated perfused rat livers, where very low bile acid excretion rates can be achieved (19), linearity extends well into the critical range. The intercept actually observed in this case amounts to 60% of normal bile flow and agrees well with the values that would have been obtained by extrapolation. The reason for this unexpected behavior at low bile acid concentrations is not apparent, and it is therefore unwarranted to conclude from the rat data that other species would show a similar linearity near the CMC. Nevertheless the extrapolated value of erythritol clearance at zero bile acid excretion is now widely regarded as defining the bile acid–independent fraction of canalicular flow. Whether this definition is quantitatively correct is uncertain, but it is clear that fluid-generating mechanisms, which cannot be attributed to the active transport of bile acids, are present in the canaliculi.

The best evidence for this conclusion comes from the study of drugs which produce equivalent increments in bile flow and erythritol clearance without changing the rate of bile acid excretion. Since neither the drugs themselves nor their metabolites appear in bile in sufficient concentration to provide the required osmotic drive, the most reasonable inference is that they stimulate the active transport of some other solute or solutes—presumably inorganic electrolytes. Among the best studied of such agents are hydrocortisone (111), the phosphodiesterase inhibitors theophylline and SQ-2009 (9, 10, 48), phenobarbital[3] and several other microsomal enzyme inducers (13, 170, 182), and a bicyclic carboxylic anion, SC-2644 (61, 176).

Theoretically these drugs could produce their choleretic effect in at least two other ways distinct from the active transport of inorganic electrolytes. They might interfere with micelle formation and thus increase the osmotic coefficient of bile acids,

---

[3]Prolonged administration of phenobarbital may in fact augment bile acid synthesis and excretion, but a bile acid–independent effect can be discerned as well (76, 137). Both actions are at least partially attributable to an increase in liver mass.

or they might alter the canalicular membrane or the tight junctions between liver cells, in such a way as to make these structures more permeable to inorganic ions. In either case a given transport rate of bile acids would obligate a greater choleresis. These possibilities have not been rigorously excluded for each of the drugs in question, but the available evidence suggests that neither postulate is very promising. In particular, the slope of the relationship between bile acid excretion and erythritol clearance, which provides an operational index of the osmotic effect of bile acids, is not altered by phenobarbital (13, 182), and no changes in canalicular permeability, as measured by the ratio of sucrose clearance to canalicular flow, are discernible during choleresis induced by SC-2644 (176). It is likely, therefore, that active transport of inorganic ions is the correct explanation, and interest has focused on possible mediators of this effect, especially Na-K-ATPase and cAMP.

Evidence that Na-K-ATPase–mediated sodium transport may be a driving force for canalicular fluid production can be summarized as follows. Ouabain, ethacrynic acid, and amiloride were originally reported to inhibit bile acid–independent erythritol clearance in rabbits (47), and scillaren had the same effect in isolated perfused rat livers (19). Na-K-ATPase has been identified in isolated liver cell membranes and is inhibited in vitro by cardiac glycosides (21). Subsequent efforts to confirm these initial reports have led to somewhat different results, however. Ethacrynic acid has been found to increase bile flow in a number of species including both rabbits and rats (30, 33, 72, 105, 153), and ouabain has produced a choleresis in rats (72, 142). Metabolites of ethacrynic acid and unchanged ouabain are concentrated in bile, and, in the case of ethacrynic acid, at least, a linear relation between drug excretion and erythritol clearance suggests that the choleresis is attributable to an osmotic effect of the drug itself (30). Unfortunately the discrepancy between recent experiments in which this effect was the dominant one and earlier reports of an anticholeretic effect remains unresolved and serves to illustrate the difficulty in interpretation inherent in the study of inhibitors that may have multiple actions. An association between phenobarbital choleresis and enhanced membrane Na-K-ATPase has been both confirmed (154a, 154b) and denied (107; C. Reilly, personal communication).

The recognition that phosphodiesterase inhibitors can stimulate erythritol clearance leads naturally to the suspicion that cAMP may be involved in canalicular electrolyte secretion, and a preliminary report has appeared that dibutyryl cAMP is a choleretic in dogs (114). Most of the investigative effort, however, has focused on the effect of glucagon, a known stimulator of adenylate cyclase. Several reports (10, 42, 93, 98, 103, 109, 143) indicate that glucagon is a moderately effective choleretic in man and dogs, but few directly address the question of whether this flow arises in the canaliculi or the ducts—an issue of special significance in view of the structural similarity between glucagon and secretin and a recent report (109) that secretin increases the biliary excretion of cAMP in man and baboons, though not in dogs. Barnhart (10) found equivalent increases in erythritol clearance and bile flow during glucagon choleresis in anesthetized dogs, but Russell (143), who used conscious dogs could not distinguish the changes in erythritol clearance during glucagon choleresis from those produced by secretin, although the choleresis produced by taurocholate was easily identified on this basis. The data from a third study of this question (103) indicate that glucagon choleresis is associated with a significant increase in bile acid excretion, and that the increment in erythritol clearance actually exceeds the change in bile flow. Prostaglandin E_2, which modulates the production of cAMP in a number of other systems (104) apparently has no effect on bile flow (156). Vasopressin, whose renal action is thought to involve cAMP, is a choleretic in dogs, but produces changes in erythritol clearance and HCO_3^- concentration consistent with stimulation of both canalicular and ductular secretion (135). Bile acid–independent canalicular flow is an especially prominent component of bile production in rats, but neither dibutyryl cAMP nor glucagon is a choleretic (6) in this species, even though glucagon is known to stimulate adenylate cyclase in rat liver membranes (31, 131).

A variety of organic anions other than bile acids are concentrated in bile, and many of these are choleretics. The choleresis may not be entirely accounted for by their osmotic effect, however. A recent study (49) of the biliary contrast agent iodipamide indicates that at least part of its choleretic action may be attributable to direct stimulation of inorganic ion transport. In dogs the biliary excretion of iodipamide is accompanied by the canalicular excretion of three times more water per mole than is taurocholate—a difference substantially greater than that which can be accounted for by the relative changes in vapor pressure or freezing point that occur when these solutes are added to bile. A similar discrepancy between choleretic effect and osmotic activity has been suggested for dehydrocholic acid (158). Actively transported organic anions may also inhibit canalicular bile production. Rose bengal is reported to impair erythritol clearance and canalicular Na-K-ATPase activity (36, 107), and a number of unrelated anions including sulfobromophthalein sodium (BSP) (150), indocyanine green (88), bilirubin (169), and taurocholate (151) may also diminish bile flow when given as large bolus injections or at infusion rates in excess of the liver's capacity to excrete them. Whether these inhibitory effects represent a specific depression of inorganic ion transport, however, is unknown. When organic anions are given at more modest rates, their concentrative transport is typically associated with a linear relation between excretion rate and bile flow (85).

If it is accepted on the evidence reviewed earlier that erythritol achieves diffusion equilibrium in the canaliculi, the same must be true for water. Bile leaving the canaliculi is therefore undoubtedly close to osmotic equilibrium with its surroundings. How and where this occurs, however, is still unclear. The canaliculi are long narrow channels closed at one end, and their surface is expanded by microvilli. These same features are found in the intercellular spaces of the gallbladder and other epithelia involved in isotonic fluid transport. Diamond (37) suggested that active solute transport is confined to a region near the blind end of such structures and that osmotic equilibration occurs as the initially hypertonic fluid flows toward the open end—the so-called standing osmotic gradient hypothesis. In the liver there is no evidence that inorganic ion transport is confined to the central portion of the lobule, and bile acids, which are efficiently removed from sinusoidal blood, would actually be expected to enter the canaliculi predominantly in the periportal region.

It is probable, therefore, that osmotic equilibration is essentially complete at every point along the radius of the liver lobule. Whether the intervillous spaces serve as local osmosis channels and to what extent permeable "tight" junctions between liver cells (54, 66, 113, 148) contribute to rapid osmotic equilibration are open questions. In any case a large hydraulic conductivity would seem to be required for the canalicular apparatus as a whole, which is consistent with its unusual permeability to erythritol and mannitol. Alternative possibilities are that centrilobular hepatocytes are specialized for active solute transport or that osmotic equilibration actually occurs within liver cells, preformed bile entering the canaliculi by exocytosis; but no compelling evidence has appeared for either postulate. It is also possible, of course, that osmotic equilibration occurs at some extralobular site further downstream, but this too seems unlikely because the surface: volume ratio of the biliary tree collapses abruptly at the transition between canaliculi and the portal ductules.

The apparent composition of the bile acid–independent fraction of canalicular flow has been estimated from changes in the flow and composition of common duct bile and the assumption that distal eletrolyte exchange is unimportant (10, 111). An ingenious effort has also been made to estimate the canalicular electrical potential in rats from the distribution of charged and uncharged solutes assumed to have identical permeabilities (25). Unfortunately such data are not sufficient to judge which ion or ions are actively transported and which enter by simple diffusion and convection.

Ductular Modification of Canalicular Bile

Evidence that the choleresis induced by secretin arises somewhere in the ductular system was discussed earlier in connection with the measurement of canalicular bile flow. The changes in flow and composition of bile that occur during secretin choleresis indicate the elaboration of an alkaline electrolyte solution containing HCO_3^- at a concentration 3–5 times the value in plasma. The only direct evidence bearing on the mechanism of this secretion comes from London's measurements of electrical potentials in the hepatic ducts of dogs (110). In these experiments secretin caused an abrupt negativity in the luminal potential indicative of an active transport of anions, presumably HCO_3^-. In rats, where secretin has no effect on bile flow or composition, however, negative potentials in the common duct are associated with bile acid excretion and have been interpreted as reflecting canalicular transport (16), so that London's measurements do not necessarily localize the actual site of the secretin effect.

The calculated ionic composition of the secretin fraction indicates that it would have an osmolality somewhat greater than extracellular fluid. For example Cl^- and HCO_3^- concentrations of 48 and 127 mEq/liter were calculated for isolated perfused pig livers (80). This is probably the explanation for the observation that bile becomes slightly hypertonic during secretin choleresis (134) and also suggests that the locus for secretin activity has a relatively low hydraulic conductivity, which is in keeping with its impermeability to erythritol. It should be remembered, however, that even if the secretin fraction were isotonic, its addition to an isotonic solution of micellar bile acids could lead to hypertonicity in the mixture owing to a reduction in bile acid concentration and a resultant increase in the fraction present as monomers (81).

Other gastrointestinal hormones which may activate or modulate ductular secretion include cholecystokinin (CCK), gastrin, caerulein, and vasoactive intestinal peptide (VIP). The first three of these have an identical sequence of the five C-terminal amino acids and stimulate contraction of the gallbladder. The structure of VIP more nearly resembles secretin and glucagon whose choleretic action was discussed previously. None of these have been studied as carefully as secretin with respect to their effect on erythritol clearance, but because they produce similar increases in HCO_3^- concentration it is assumed that they act in the ducts or ductules. The pure naturally occurring gastrin-like peptides given to dogs with gastric fistulae have relative choleretic potencies in the order caerulein $>$ CCK $>$ gastrin II (94). The synthetic C-terminal octapeptide of CCK is also effective in dogs, although less so than the full molecule (165–167). In monkeys, CCK is much less potent than secretin, but both elicit appreciable increments in bile flow at doses well within the range required for pancreatic stimulation (60). Synthetic pentagastrin alone apparently has no effect on either the flow or composition of dog bile (96). In perfused pig livers, however, both pentagastrin and CCK potentiate the effect of secretin, although they are ineffective (pentagastrin) or minimally effective (CCK) when given alone (91). Secretin is not a choleretic in rabbits nor is CCK or pentagastrin, although all three hormones elicit their usual responses in the stomach and the pancreas (154). In guinea pigs secretin is a weak choleretic and so is CCK (154). VIP is reported to increase bile flow in dogs (136), but its site and mechanism of action are unknown.

There is a hint in these data that eating habits are correlated with hormonal control of bile flow. Thus dogs and primates (including man), which eat intermittently, have well-developed ductular mechanisms for modifying bile flow, whereas in rats, rabbits, and guinea pigs, which eat more or less continuously, the secretin mechanism is weak or absent. It is also of interest that these latter species have high rates of spontaneous bile flow and large bile acid-independent canalicular fractions. In view of the complicated and interrelated actions of the gastrointestinal hormones on gastric acid production, intestinal motility, and gallbladder contraction, changes in the volume and composition of bile during eating and digestion will reflect not only the choleretic effects of the hormones themselves, but changes in the enterohepatic circulation of bile acids as well. Little progress has been made in sorting out the relative importance of these factors to the orderly process of digestion, but a start in this direction has been provided by methods for controlled interruption of the enterohepatic circulation (40) and by experiments such as those recently reported by Strasberg (161), which emphasize the importance of eating to variations in ductular secretion.

In addition to its secretory function, ductular epithelium can also perform electrolyte reabsorption. The most striking examples are seen in dogs with cholinergic blockade (180) and in monkeys with resection of the gastric antrum and small bowel (160)—both procedures designed to suppress hormonally mediated secretory activity of the sort just discussed. At low rates of bile acid transport, bile:plasma ery-thritol concentration ratios are between 2 and 3 in such preparations. Dogs and monkeys are the only animals studied so far in which distal fluid reabsorption appears to be quantitatively important, but as alluded to earlier, erythritol ratios slightly greater than 1 have also been observed in rats and rabbits. Evidence of another kind has been obtained from chronically cholecystectomized dogs (179). The extrahepatic ducts enlarge following this procedure, and after an overnight fast are found to contain several milliliters of bile resembling that from a normal gall-bladder, i.e. the concentration of bile acids is high while [Cl⁻] and [HCO₃⁻] are low. To what extent this adaptive response to cholecystectomy contributes to high steady-state values of the erythritol concentration ratio is uncertain, but it is proba-bly not the whole explanation because bile:plasma erythritol ratios substantially greater than 1 are also observed in acute preparations (61). In both dogs and monkeys distal reabsorption appears to be independent of canalicular bile produc-tion, whereas the relationship between bile flow and erythritol clearance in rats and rabbits suggests that reabsorption is a small constant fraction of erythritol clearance. The reason for this difference is not known.

In general it has been assumed that the bile ducts are not involved to any quantitatively important degree in the transfer of organic constituents except per-haps following acute extrahepatic biliary obstruction when gross leakage of whole bile seems to occur (7). That this generalization will now require reevaluation is indicated by a recent report (77) that the ducts in rats and man may actively reabsorb glucose.

Several efforts have been made to characterize the mechanism of distal fluid transport by perfusing segments of extrahepatic biliary ducts. London's measure-ments of electrical potentials in the hepatic ducts of dogs are consistent with coupled reabsorption of Na^+ and Cl^- by a "neutral" pump, similar perhaps to the system for concentrating bile in the gallbladder, but the actual solute fluxes were not measured (110). Two other studies of common duct segments in dogs (116) and rabbits (28) have revealed small net secretory fluxes of water and inorganic ions, but the quantitative importance of this process to normal bile production cannot be assessed. In dogs the measured fluxes were similar to those associated with secretin stimulation. In the rabbit, as we have seen, the evidence from erythritol clearance data would suggest, if anything, a small net reabsorption for the ductular system as a whole.

Neural Control of Bile Formation

Current interest in the neural control of bile production stems primarily from the observation that insulin and 2-deoxy-D-glucose, which stimulate vagally mediated gastric secretion, are also choleretics (71, 97, 130), even when care is taken to prevent endogenous secretin release by excluding gastric acid from the duodenum. The concentration of HCO₃⁻ rises, though less dramatically than when secretin is given, and the concentration of Cl^- may increase as well—a response previously reported to occur in gastrectomized dogs given histamine (181). The choleresis is bile acid–independent in the sense that bile acid excretion is not enhanced. Evidence on the question of whether these effects are mediated vagally may be summarized as follows. Truncal vagotomy diminishes but does not entirely eliminate the response (71, 97). Bornbeck (130), in discussing unpublished results, reported that selective denervation of the liver, duodenum, small bowel, and stomach completely abolished the effect of 2-deoxy-D-glucose. In dogs with gastric fistulae given a continuous infusion of bile acids to replace the losses incurred by bile collection, direct electrical stimulation of the vagi did not modify bile flow or composition, but small changes similar to those elicited by insulin were observed when the bile acid infusion was omitted (95).

The difficulty in interpreting these observations and the problems involved in designing more critical experiments can be appreciated from the complex neuro-humoral interactions that may occur. For example vagal stimulation releases endogenous gastrin and perhaps CCK (106). Insulin and perhaps 2-deoxy-D-glucose, in addition to producing vagal stimulation, may act directly on the pancreas to release glucagon (87, 168). Unrecognized effects on hepatic blood flow and intestinal motility could be important as well. For all of these reasons it is still unclear whether insulin and 2-deoxy-D-glucose have their effect on the liver directly or by way of neural or humoral mediators, nor has the site of the choleretic effect been identified in the biliary tree.

Adrenergic control mechanisms, if any, are even less well understood then are vagal effects. A bile acid–independent choleresis with associated increases in [HCO_3^-] and [Cl^-] occurred in dogs given dopamine (82), and the changes in bile flow and Cl^- output but not HCO_3^- output, were abolished by simultaneously infusing propranolol. Since catecholamines can stimulate adenylate cyclase in other tissues, this may be the mechanism of their effect on bile formation, but changes in hepatic perfusion and/or release of intestinal hormones have not been excluded.

ORGANIC SOLUTE TRANSPORT

The biliary excretion of inorganic ions, although of great importance to those interested in the mechanism of bile production, is probably of minor importance to body economy. The unique and functionally crucial role of bile is to supply mixed micelles to facilitate the absorption of dietary lipids and to serve as an excretory route for drugs and other metabolites. For survival value, therefore, the organic constituents of bile are the important ones. Recent research has focused, in particular, on the hepatic transport of bile acids and a small group of other organic acids of diagnostic importance, including bilirubin, iodinated X-ray contrast agents, and several dyes. The mechanism of excretion for other drugs, though of obvious pharmacologic importance, has received relatively little attention. Biliary lipid excretion, on the other hand, is beginning to be studied in detail.

Bile Acids and Other Organic Anions

The conjugated bile acids and the other organic acids under consideration here are highly concentrated in bile with respect to their steady-state plasma levels and display more or less well-defined transport maxima. Although the relevant electro-chemical gradients have not been determined, there is little doubt that they are actively transported by parenchymal liver cells. In considering the high bile:plasma concentration ratios as evidence for this conclusion, at least two additional factors should be recalled. To varying degrees these solutes are all bound to protein in the circulation and to intracellular proteins as well. Since bile contains only very low concentrations of protein (38, 39), the effect of this binding is to increase the difference in effective concentration between bile and plasma and between bile and cytoplasm. The tendency for bile acids to aggregate spontaneously as micelles has an opposite effect, and as noted earlier the effective concentration of other anions such as BSP (173), bilirubin (18), and cholecystographic media (49), may also be reduced by association with micelles. Quantitative data with which to evaluate these opposing influences are not available, but it may be noted that the plasma clearance of bile acids nearly equals hepatic plasma flow (121). The gross bile:plasma concentration ratio under these circumstances is approximately the ratio of plasma flow to bile flow or about 2×10^3 for dogs. Correcting this estimate for the critical micellar concentration of taurocholate (approximately 2 mM) indicates a bile:plasma concentration ratio for monomers on the order of 100 for a portal plasma concentration of 20 μM. In dogs perhaps half of this value can be attributed to reabsorption of water from the ducts. The effective canalicular bile:plasma ratio would then be approximately 50, even ignoring the effect of protein binding. Other organic anions generally have lower extraction efficiencies but are probably less extensively associated with micelles.

UPTAKE   The removal or uptake of organic anions from sinusoidal plasma has been studied with particular effectiveness by analyzing first pass indicator dilution curves recorded from hepatic venous blood after an impulse injection of the solute and appropriate reference markers into the portal vein. A trenchant mathematical analysis of this approach has been provided by Goresky (68, 69). The method depends on an idealized model of the sinusoidal circulation which predicts the appearance of material from each sinusoid as a delayed impulse plus a modified Bessel function associated respectively with the transit time in extracellular fluid and the dispersion and loss of material occasioned by its entry into liver cells. In principle this approach can yield the apparent rate constants for bidirectional movement across the sinusoidal face of the cell as well as the rate constant for irreversible removal by metabolism or biliary excretion, but its application to the determination of anion fluxes has so far yielded only the unidirectional uptake constant. The important findings from such studies are that BSP (67), bile acids (63, 138), and indocyanine green (126) all display saturation kinetics at the sinusoidal face of the cell, and that the maximum influx rates are all substantially greater than the respective transport maxima for biliary excretion. Since labeled albumin injected with these anions is fully recovered and appears in the venous outflow with a short transit time, it is also clear that the anions enter liver cells dissociated from their binding proteins in plasma. The bile acid data indicate that taurocholate, cholate, cheno-deoxycholate, and taurochendeoxycholate compete for the same uptake carrier (65, 139), and ion substitution experiments (139) suggest that their transport is at least partially dependent on the presence of Na^+ ions in the perfusate. In one study, taurocholate appeared to competitively inhibit the uptake of BSP (64), and in another (126) indocyanine green increased the apparent K_m for taurocholate by about 12%, although this change was not considered significant.

Uptake of taurocholate has also been studied in vitro by measuring its rate of appearance in isolated rat liver cells (152). Saturation kinetics, competition by another bile acid, and Na^+ dependence were found as well as inhibition by BSP. The uptake of BSP itself was not measured, however, and its inhibition of taurocholate transport was considered noncompetitive.

Estimates of uptake rate can also be obtained from the intact animal by analyzing plasma disappearance curves (140). Using this method Scharschmidt (147) has concluded that bilirubin, BSP, and indocyanine green display saturation kinetics and are mutually competitive in the rat, but could find no evidence of competition for any of these by glycocholate. Vonk (171) reached the same conclusion with respect to indocyanine green and taurocholate. The same experimental approach, however, has led others to conclude that dehydrocholate inhibits the uptake of rose bengal in rabbits (101) and BSP (34) in dogs. At least part of the apparent inconsistency in these data may be attributable to simplifying assumptions implicit in the use of plasma disappearance curves to estimate the uptake rate constants. The lumped compartmental model which this method employs ignores the effect of mixing transients in the peripheral circulation and the translobular concentration profile which develops as the anions traverse the sinusoids. Disregarding these details leads to systematic errors which depend importantly on the uptake rate constant and are therefore different for each solute (56). Even the Goresky model, which avoids these difficulties by eliminating the peripheral circulation and by taking explicit account of the translobular concentration profile, presents difficulties in the quantitative interpretation of competition studies, because in general the concentration ratio of two competing solutes will be different at every point along the sinusoid.

The available data thus indicate that organic anion uptake is mediated by a mechanism of limited capacity which can remove protein-bound materials with remarkable efficiency, but leave unanswered whether there is one carrier or several. It is also not clear whether this process should be regarded as thermodynamically active or passive, but because the intracellular accumulation of organic anions may be accounted for by binding to cytoplasmic proteins, there is no compelling reason to think that their uptake is other than equilibrative. Data consistent with counter-transport of BSP, bilirubin, and indocyanine green (147) support the idea that uptake of these anions occurs by facilitated diffusion, but similar evidence is not available for bile acids.

CONJUGATION AND INTRACELLULAR BINDING   Organic anions destined for biliary excretion are typically, though not invariably, conjugated with polar groups such as glucuronic acid or amino acids as a prerequisite for efficient biliary excretion. Whether in general this reflects a higher affinity of the excretory transport system for the conjugated form or a tendency for the less polar unconjugated form to diffuse out of the biliary tree is not known. In the case of BSP, both conjugated and unconjugated dye are concentrated in bile, and studies with a synthetically prepared conjugate are consistent with the view that both forms compete for the same excretory carrier, for which the conjugated form enjoys the higher affinity (11). Depletion of hepatic taurine in dogs leads to the excretion of unconjugated cholic acid but at a lower clearance rate than when taurocholate is given directly (119).

With the notable exception of bile acids, intracellular binding of organic anions appears largely attributable to two cytosolic proteins, ligandin and Z. Current information about the chemistry of these proteins, their phylogenetic and ontogenetic development, factors which govern their synthesis and degradation, and their distribution in other tissues is contained in two recent reviews by Arias and his colleagues (3,4). Ligandin, which is quantitatively the more important, is identical with glutathione S-transferase B (78), an enzyme which catalyzes the conjugation of BSP as well as a variety of other substrates. The binding affinity of the enzyme is not limited to its substrates, however (100). For example, ligandin also binds bilirubin, indocyanine green, fatty acids, and Evans blue, none of which is conjugated with glutathione. The association constants for these ligands are of the same order of magnitude as for BSP, and in the case of bilirubin even higher.

Apart from its specific catalytic activity, the physiologic role of ligandin remains uncertain. If, as seems likely, the uptake process is bidirectional and equilibrative, one result of intracellular binding would be to increase the steady-state intracellular content over that which would otherwise be present. This could serve to accelerate intracellular diffusion simply by raising the concentration in cytosol. Another possibility is that intracellular binding specifically facilitates the presentation of solutes to their conjugating enzymes or to the canalicular transport system. Ligandin may also play a protective role by excluding potentially toxic materials from sites where they would be harmful. For example, in vitro it protects mitochondrial respiration from the depressant effects of bilirubin (99). This effect is not specific, however, since serum albumin will serve as well. Indeed much of what is known about the ubiquitous binding of materials to ligandin reinforces the idea that its functional role may be to act as a kind of "intracellular albumin." In any event, neither the binding nor the catalytic activity of ligandin is essential for the hepatic transport of BSP, since dogfish and skates concentrate this dye in bile (albeit at a slower rate than in mammals), but their livers contain little or no ligandin (23, 24). Liver homogenates from these elasmobranchs, nevertheless, bind 70–80% of the dye they contain. A similar phenomenon occurs in elasmobranch plasma, which contains no albumin but binds 60–70% of the dye. Whether this non-albumin, nonligandin binding is essential to the transport process is not known, nor is it clear in more advanced species whether the relative affinities of albumin and ligandin favor accumulation in the cell or retention in plasma. Purified ligandin binds bilirubin less well than does albumin (3), but this order is reversed for ligandin in liver supernatant, suggesting that purification of the enzyme is associated with some loss of affinity (102).

A specific intracellular binding protein has not been identified for bile acids, but only about 10% of labeled taurocholate is free in rat liver supernatant subjected to equilibrium dialysis (personal observation).

CANALICULAR EXCRETION   As indicated earlier, transport maxima for unidirectional hepatic uptake exceed the corresponding biliary excretion rates in every case where acceptable measurements are available. Moreover when conjugation is an intermediate step between uptake and excretion, high infusion rates of the unconjugated material are usually followed by the appearance of conjugates in plasma. Plasma disappearance curves, which characteristically display a steep initial slope followed by a more gradual decline, are consistent with the inference to be drawn from these more direct observations that canalicular excretion is normally rate limiting in the sequence of steps between plasma and bile. Since protein binding keeps the effective intracellular concentration low, the canalicular membrane is also the boundary across which the major concentration difference is maintained and, by inference, the membrane is the site for active anion transport.

An apparently complex (and in any case poorly understood) relationship exists between the excretion of bile acids and the canalicular transport of other organic anions. The clearest expression of this is that increasing the rate of bile acid excretion enhances the excretory capacity for BSP (9, 22, 57, 61, 75, 120), bilirubin (35, 70), iopanoic acid (12, 117), and ampicillin (112). For BSP and iopanoic acid this finding is not attributable to the associated bile acid choleresis (9, 12, 61) and is therefore accountable to some direct effect of the bile acids themselves. On the other hand mutant Corriedale sheep with a genetic defect in the canalicular transport of BSP, bilirubin, and iopanoic acid appear to handle taurocholate normally (2)—a finding that has been widely interpreted to mean that bile acids and these other anions have completely separate mechanisms for canalicular excretion. However, while taurocholate produced no discernible change in the small amount of BSP appearing in the bile of mutant sheep, the converse was not examined—a possibly important omission in view of the unexplained choleresis produced by BSP.

The problem of reconciling these observations is complicated still further by reports that under some circumstances BSP and other anions may inhibit the excretion of bile acids, or vice versa (5, 17, 35, 220). In rats the effect of taurocholate on the kinetic relationship between free (i.e. unbound) intracellular BSP and its biliary excretion rate is to increase both the apparent V_{max} and the apparent K_m, suggesting that in addition to its overall acceleration of BSP transport, taurocholate exerts an underlying inhibitory effect as well (57). An early report by Cornelius (32) identified binding of BSP to rat liver membranes which was competitively inhibited by several other organic anions, but not by taurocholate or bilirubin. In a more recent study of cell membranes prepared from the same species, binding of taurocholate was inhibited by BSP but not by indocyanine green or probenecid (1). In neither study is it clear whether the isolated membranes were from the canalicular or the sinusoidal face of the cell or, as seems more likely (27), a mixture of both.

It remains unclear, therefore, whether canalicular excretion is mediated by one discrete transport system for bile acids and another system or systems for other organic anions, or whether these systems are linked in some way. It is possible that the active transport of bile acids provides the driving force for other anions by some sort of co-transport system, or that separate carriers are present and subject to allosteric interactions, but kinetic data of the sort that might refute or confirm these ideas are not available.

However the question of one or multiple carriers is ultimately resolved, it is important to consider one other factor which could contribute to the interaction between bile acids and other anions. The possibility was alluded to earlier that solutes concentrated in bile might be escape by back diffusion. If this were an important feature of organic anion transport, increasing the rate of bile acid excretion could inhibit this tendency by promoting the formation of mixed micelles. BSP, bilirubin, and iodipomide added to bile or bile acid solutions do in fact display changes in their physical properties consistent with an important association with micelles. No direct observations are available of the extent to which back diffusion of these anions occurs in the absence of micelles, however, and it is therefore unknown whether micellar sequestration within the canalicular lumen is of any functional importance in promoting anion excretion. Since substantial reductions in the biliary concentration of BSP produced by bile acid–independent choleretics do not lead to changes in dye excretion (55, 61), it is probable that BSP transport is effectively unidirectional. Final judgment should be reserved, however, until the colligative properties of BSP or some other index of its activity in bile has been measured in relation to its net excretion.

Other Drugs

In view of the rich pharmacologic literature on the biliary excretion of drugs, it is remarkable how little is known about the mechanisms involved. Schanker (145) provided a critical and perceptive review of the problem from a physiologic viewpoint. A more recent comprehensive summary of experimental data is by Smith (155). For the most part interest has centered on hepatic drug metabolism and on correlations between structural configuration and the fraction of a given dose that may be recovered in bile or feces rather than on the mechanisms of hepatocellular transport. Of the factors that determine whether a particular drug will appear predominantly in bile rather than urine, the most important seem to be molecular weight and the configuration of polar groups. In particular, biliary excretion is favored by a high molecular weight and an arrangement of polar groups which make the drug amphipathic (84). The diverse chemical structures of "cholephilic" drugs encourage the speculation that the high molecular weights reflect a correlation with amphipathic behavior rather than a specific requirement for molecular size or shape. Whether the apparent advantage conferred by an amphipathic structure relates to transport across liver cell membranes or to an association with micelles in the canalicular lumen, however, is not clear. Most drugs appearing in bile are glucuronides or other anionic products of intracellular conjugation, but except for the specific anions discussed previously, the relation between bile acid transport and drug excretion appears to have received little attention.

Organic cations are also excreted in bile by a transport system that resembles but is clearly distinct from the one responsbile for the transport of anions. The quaternary ammonium compound, procaine amide ethobromide (PAEB), has been studied extensively as representative of a diverse group of cations that participate in this process (89, 115, 146, 157). More recently a metabolically stable N-acetyl conjugate of PAEB has been synthesized (90), which promises to simplify some of the kinetic problems. In nephrectomized rats, conjugated PAEB is concentrated in bile, and

70–80% of a single dose is excreted by this route in 8 hr. When renal function is unimpaired, however, almost all of the drug appears in urine. Both hepatic uptake (as determined from the accumulation of the drug in liver slices) and biliary excretion are saturable and competitively inhibited by other cations, but not by organic anions such as BSP or probenecid. About 40% of the drug is bound in liver supernatant, but to judge from the experience with other organic cations this is probably not attributable to ligandin or Z.

Some neutral compounds such as ouabain (155) and imipramine (14, 15) are also concentrated in bile. The latter drug is apparently incorporated into bile acid–lecithin micelles, but the mechanism of its hepatic transport is unknown, nor is it clear whether bile acids are essential for its biliary excretion.

Biliary Lipid Excretion

Since bile is a single-phase solution, it is inevitable that the excretion of the water-insoluble lipids, cholesterol and lecithin, will depend upon their incorporation into micelles and that biliary lipid excretion will depend upon bile acid excretion. This qualitative prediction has been amply confirmed, but the actual mechanism of lipid excretion is still undefined. The uncertainties arise partly from complex metabolic relationships between the enterohepatic circulation of bile acids and hepatic synthetic rates of cholesterol and phospholipid, and partly because of difficulties in identifying the origin of the lipids in bile. The complexity of the problem can be appreciated from the following considerations. Increasing the hepatic flux rate of bile acids leads to increased biliary excretion of lecithin, but it is not clear to what extent this reflects an enhancing effect of bile acids on hepatic lecithin synthesis and to what extent it reflects an increased availability of bile acids required for its micellar solubilization. In the case of cholesterol these factors operate in opposite directions. Bile acids inhibit cholesterol synthesis, but enhance its solubility in bile. The kinetic relations are complicated still further by the fact that cholesterol solubility is more importantly related to the bile acid:lecithin concentration ratio than to the concentration of bile acids alone (162).

The biochemistry of hepatic lipid synthesis and the intricacies of the enterohepatic circulation [see (86) for a recent and authoritative summary] are beyond the scope of the present review, but it should be apparent from what has already been said that the transport mechanisms for biliary lipids are not cleanly separable from the synthetic processes that determine their availability, and it is not surprising, therefore, that current interpretations are controversial. Short-term experiments designed to avoid this ambiguity have nevertheless provided some valuable insights. Wheeler (176) examined the lipid composition of dog bile at various rates of bile acid excretion and found that for taurocholate and glycocholate the outputs of lecithin and cholesterol are adequately described by hyperbolic functions of bile acid output. The curves are concave to the bile acid axis so that the individual outputs of these lipids approach limiting rates at high rates of bile acid transport. Dehydrocholate, a synthetic tri-keto bile acid which does not form micelles, did not increase lipid excretion, and SC-2644, a potent canalicular choleretic which does not alter bile acid excretion and therefore reduces the canalicular bile acid concentration, actually depressed the output rates of lecithin and cholesterol. All these findings emphasize the importance of micellar bile acid as a determinant of lipid excretion, and Wheeler has suggested that the experimental curves are consistent with a kinetic model based on simple partitioning of lipids between the canalicular membrane and mixed micelles in the lumen. Curvilinear relationships that are qualitatively similar are reported for rats (79, 141), man (149, 172), sheep (83), and monkeys (41), although there are pronounced species differences in the absolute amounts as well as in the proportions of phospholipid and cholesterol excreted for any given transport rate of bile acids. In general there is a tendency at low rates of bile acid excretion for the concentration of cholesterol to rise in relation to bile acid and phospholipid—a phenomenon which in susceptible species such as man may lead to the formation of unstable micelles and a bile supersaturated with cholesterol.

Unfortunately efforts to identify precursor-product relationships which would help to establish the compartment of origin for biliary lipids have succeeded only in showing that there must be relatively small subpools within the liver, and do not clarify the location at which the flux of bile acids entrain the lecithin and cholesterol (73, 178). A preliminary report (50) has appeared that bile acids incubated with isolated canalicular membranes selectively extract phospholipids with the same fatty acid composition as the lecithin in bile, but it remains to be seen whether the ratio of cholesterol to phospholipid in the solubilized fraction is consistent with the idea that the immediate source for lipids in bile is the canalicular lipid bilayer.

The evidence for the importance of micellar solubilization is not in itself a compelling reason to believe that the process is initiated in the canalicular lumen, and some authors have been attracted by the idea that mixed micelles might be assembled at an interior site, to be later extruded from the cell as a preformed package —presumably by exocytosis. This speculation is encouraged by evidence of a similar mechanism for the export of lipoprotein and albumin from liver cells to the Disse space (108, 122, 124, 159) and by the finding of actin-containing microfilaments attached to the canalicular membrane (59, 118, 128). The proximity of the Golgi apparatus to the biliary pole of hepatocytes and its "compensatory" enlargement in the unobstructed portions of rat livers with segmental bile duct occulsion are also consistent with vesicular transport of biliary lipids (92). Exocytosis itself has not been observed at the canalicular border, however, except in a study by Matter (113) in which horseradish peroxidase was thought to move by vesicular transport from blood to bile and in the reverse direction when the enzyme was introduced by retrograde injection into the common bile duct. Colchicine, which inhibits the export of lipoprotein at the sinusoidal border of hepatocytes, has no effect on biliary lipid excretion (159), but a preliminary report has appeared that another inhibitor of microtubular function, vinblastine, depresses the biliary excretion of bile acids and lecithin, though not of cholesterol (74). Cytochalasin B produces cholestasis and dilatation of the canaliculi in isolated perfused rat livers. These changes are consistent with the idea that contractility of the canalicular microfilaments is essential to normal bile production (129), but the importance, if any, of these structures to a vesicular mechanism for biliary lipid transport is unknown.

SUMMARY

It should be evident from this review of recent investigations that we are still very far from a consistent description of bile formation, much less a satisfactory understanding. Nevertheless certain broad conclusions emerge. Four distinct kinds of active solute transport can be identified, and because bile always has nearly the same osmotic pressure as plasma, each of them is a determinant of bile flow. 1. Concentrative transport of water-soluble organic constituents, of which bile acids are quantitatively most important, occurs in the canaliculi accompanied by the passive flow of water and inorganic electrolytes. Owing to micelle formation the osmotic force for this flow is largely attributable to Na^+ ions that accompany the bile acids anions. 2. The canalicular flow obligated by the excretion of bile acids is supplemented by the entry of additional fluid, the so-called bile acid–independent canalicular fraction. Because no organic component has been identified to account for this phenomenon, the active transport of one or more inorganic ions is probably responsible. The limited evidence available at present suggests that Na^+ ion is the most likely candidate. 3. The extralobular biliary epithelium can modify the flow and composition of bile by the reabsorption of inorganic ions—a process which resembles reabsorption from the gallbladder in the sense that bile in the lumen remains iso-osmotic with plasma while bile acids and the other organic constituents are concentrated. 4. Under the influence of secretin, and to a lesser degree other intestinal hormones, the ducts or ductules can secrete additional fluid in which HCO_3^- is concentrated with respect to plasma. A fifth component of bile is generated by the canalicular excretion of phospholipid and cholesterol, but these are insoluble in water and are incorporated into micelles, and, therefore exert no osmotic force.

The existence of these processes is inferred from studies of many different species, and it should be emphasized that the picture is a composite one. For example, distal fluid reabsorption has been convincingly demonstrated only in dogs and monkeys, and secretin is not a choleretic in rats or rabbits. It should also be clear that the actual mechanisms of solute transport remain poorly defined. Thus the term active transport in the present context should be thought of in its general thermodynamic sense rather than as denoting any particular transport mechanism.

For the future, the most pressing problems are methodologic. To mention only three that seem especially important: ways must be found to sample bile closer to its origin; the proper interpretation of studies with isolated liver cell membranes will require unambiguous methods to certify their source; and descriptions of transport kinetics must somehow be refined to reflect the effective intracellular concentration of solutes as well as their distribution within the liver lobule.

Literature Cited

1. Accatino, L., Simon, F. R. 1976. Identification and characterization of a bile acid receptor in isolated liver surface membranes. *J. Clin. Invest.* 57:496–508
2. Alpert, S., Mosher, M., Shanske, A., Arias, I. M. 1969. Multiplicity of hepatic excretory mechanisms for organic anions. *J. Gen. Physiol.* 53:238–47
3. Arias, I. M., Fleischner, G., Listowsky, I., Kamisaka, K., Mishkin, S., Gatmaitan, Z. 1976. On the structure and function of ligandin and Z protein. In *The Hepatobiliary System*, ed. W. Taylor, pp. 88–104. New York: Plenum
4. Arias, I. M., Fleischner, G., Kirsch, R., Mishkin, S., Gatmaitan, Z. 1976. On the structure, regulation and function of ligandin. In *Glutathione: Metabolism and Function,* ed. I. M. Arias, W. Jacoby, pp. 175–88. New York: Raven
5. Bailey, D. G., Johnson, G. E. 1975. Multiple hepatic excretory mechanisms for organic anions. A study with succinylsulfathiazole and taurocholate in the rat. *Can. J. Physiol. Pharmacol.* 53:97–103
6. Baker, A. L., Kaplan, M. M. 1976. Effects of cholera enterotoxin, glucagon, and dibutyryl cyclic AMP on rat liver alkaline phosphatase, bile flow, and bile composition. *Gastroenterology* 70:577–81
7. Barber-Riley, G. 1963. Rat biliary tree during short periods of obstruction of common duct. *Am. J. Physiol.* 205:1127–31
8. Barnhart, J. L., Combes, B. 1974. A comparison of the biliary clearances of erythritol and mannitol during taurocholate and secretin-induced choleresis in the dog. *Gastroenterology* 67:780 (Abstr.)
9. Barnhart, J. L., Combes, B. 1974. Effect of theophylline on hepatic excretory function. *Am. J. Physiol.* 227:194–99
10. Barnhart, J. L., Combes, B. 1975. Characteristics common to choleretic increments of bile induced by theophylline, glucagon, and SQ-20009 in the dog. *Proc. Soc. Exp. Biol. Med.* 150:591–96
11. Barnhart, J. L., Combes, B. 1977. Biliary excretion of dye in dogs infused with sulfobromophthalein (BSP) or its glutathione conjugate (BSP-GSH). *Am. J. Physiol.* In press
12. Berk, R. N., Goldberger, L. E., Loeb, P. M. 1974. The role of bile salts in the hepatic excretion of iopanoic acid. *Invest. Radiol.* 9:7–15
13. Berthelot, P., Erlinger, S., Dhumeaux, D. P., Preaux, A. 1970. Mechanism of phenobarbital-induced hypercholeresis in the rat. *Am. J. Physiol.* 219:809–13
14. Bickel, M. H., Minder, R. 1970. Metabolism and biliary excretion of the lipophilic drug molecules, imipramine and desmethylimipramine in the rat. I. Experiments *in vivo* and with isolated perfused livers. *Biochem. Pharmacol.* 19:2425–35
15. Bickel, M. H., Minder, R. 1970. Metabolism and biliary excretion of the lipophilic drug molecules, imipramine and desmethylimipramine in the rat. II. Uptake into bile micelles. *Biochem. Pharmacol.* 19:2437–43
16. Binder, H. J., Boyer, J. L. 1973. Bile salts: A determinant of the bile-peritoneal electrical potential difference in the rat. *Gastroenterology* 65:943–48
17. Bloomer, J. R., Boyer, J. L., Klatskin, G. 1973. Inhibition of bilirubin excretion in man during dehydrocholate choleresis. *Gastroenterology* 65:929–35
18. Bouchier, I. A. D., Cooperband, S. R. 1967. Isolation and characterization of a macromolecular aggregate associated with bilirubin. *Clin. Chim. Acta* 15:291–302
19. Boyer, J. L. 1971. Canalicular bile formation in the isolated perfused rat liver. *Am. J. Physiol.* 221:1156–63
20. Boyer, J. L., Bloomer, J. R. 1974. Canalicular bile secretion in man. Studies utilizing the biliary clearance of [¹⁴C] mannitol. *J. Clin. Invest.* 54:773–81
21. Boyer, J. L., Reno D. 1975. Properties of $(Na^+ + K^+)$-activated ATPase in rat liver plasma membranes enriched with bile canaliculi. *Biochim. Biophys. Acta* 401:59–72
22. Boyer, J. L., Scheig, R. L., Klatskin, G. 1970. The effect of sodium taurocholate on the hepatic metabolism of sulfobromophthalein sodium (BSP). The role of bile flow. *J. Clin. Invest.* 49:206–15
23. Boyer, J. L., Schwarz, J., Smith, N. 1976. Biliary secretion in elasmobranchs. I. Bile collection and composition. *Am. J. Physiol.* 230:970–73
24. Boyer, J. L., Schwarz, J., Smith, N., 1976. Biliary secretion in elasmobranchs. II. Hepatic uptake and biliary excretion of organic anions. *Am. J. Physiol.* 230:974–81

25. Bradley, E., Herz, R. 1976. Bioelectric potentials in canalicular bile formation in the rat. In *The Liver. Quantitative Aspects of Structure and Function. 2nd Int. Gstaad Symp.* ed. R. Preisig, J. Bircher, G. Paumgartner, pp. 457–58. Aulendorf: Editio Cantor

26. Brooks, F. P. 1969. The secretion of bile. *Am. J. Dig. Dis.* 14:343–49

27. Chang, K. -J., Bennett, V., Cuatrecasas, P. 1975. Membrane receptors as general markers for plasma membrane isolation procedures. The use of ^{125}I-labeled wheat germ agglutinin, insulin, and cholera toxin. *J. Biol. Chem.* 250:488–500

28. Chenderovitch, J. 1972. Secretory function of the rabbit common bile duct. *Am. J. Physiol.* 223:695–706

29. Chenderovitch, J. 1973. Bile secretion. *Clin. Gastroenterol.* 2:31–47

30. Chenderovitch, J., Raizman, A., Infante, R. 1975. Mechanism of ethacrynic acid-induced choleresis in the rat. *Am. J. Physiol.* 229:1180–87

31. Christoffersen, T., Berg, T. 1974. Glucagon control of cyclic AMP accumulation in isolated intact rat liver parenchymal cells in vitro. *Biochim. Biophys. Acta* 338:408–17

32. Cornelius, C. E., Ben-Ezzer, J., Arias, I. M. 1967. Binding of sulfobromophthalein sodium (BSP) and other organic anions by isolated hepatic cell plasma membranes *in vitro*. *Proc. Soc. Exp. Biol. Med.* 124:665–67

33. Czok, G., Schulze, P. -J. 1973. Die choleretische Wirkung von Ethacrynsäure bei der Ratte. *Arzneim. Forsch.* 23:1712–16

34. Delage, Y. Erlinger, S., Duval, M., Benhamou, J. -P. 1975. Influence of dehydrocholate and taurocholate on bromsulphthalein uptake, storage, and excretion in the dog. *Gut* 16:105–8

35. Dhumeaux, D. P., Berthelot, P., Preaux, A. 1970. A critical study of the concept of maximal biliary transport of sulfobromophthalein in the Wistar rat. *Rev. Eur. Etud. Clin. Biol.* 15:279–86

36. Dhumeaux, D. P., Erlinger, S., Benhamou, J. -P., Fauvert, R. 1970. Effects of rose bengal on bile secretion in the rabbit: Inhibition of a bile salt-independent fraction. *Gut* 11:134–40

37. Diamond, J. M., Bossert, W. H. 1967. Standing-gradient osmotic flow. A mechanism for coupling of water and solute transport in epithelia. *J. Gen. Physiol.* 50:2061–83

38. Dive, C., Heremans, J. F. 1974. Nature and origin of the proteins of bile. I. A comparative analysis of serum and bile proteins in man. *Eur. J. Clin. Invest.* 4:235–39

39. Dive, C., Nadalini, R. A., Vaerman, J. -P., Heremans, J. F. 1974. Origin and nature of the proteins of bile. II. A comparative analysis of serum, hepatic lymph and bile proteins in the dog. *Eur. J. Clin. Invest.* 4:241–46

40. Dowling, R. H., Mack, E., Picott, J., Berger, J., Small, D. M. 1968. Experimental model for the study of the enterohepatic circulation of bile in rhesus monkeys. *J. Lab. Clin. Med.* 72:169–76

41. Dowling, R. H., Mack, E., Small, D. M. 1971. Biliary lipid secretion and bile composition after acute and chronic interruption of the enterohepatic circulation in the Rhesus monkey. IV. Primate biliary physiology. *J. Clin. Invest.* 50:1917–26

42. Dyck, W. P., Janowitz, H. D. 1971. Effect of glucagon on hepatic bile secretion in man. *Gastroenterology* 60:400–4

43. Egger, G., Kutz, K., Strebel, H., Bircher, J., Weber, M., Scholl, E., Preisig, R. 1974. Bile formation in the intact pig. *Am. J. Vet. Res.* 35:1203–8

44. Erlinger, S. 1972. Physiology of bile flow. In *Progress in Liver Diseases*, ed. H. Popper, F. Schaffner, 5:63–82. New York: Grune & Stratton.

45. Erlinger, S. 1974. Influence of drugs on bile flow. *Isr. J. Med. Sci.* 10:354–62

46. Erlinger, S., Dhumeaux, D. P. 1974. Mechanisms and control of secretion of bile water and electrolytes. *Gastroenterology* 66:281–304

47. Erlinger, S., Dhumeaux, D. P., Berthelot, P., Dumont, M. 1970. Effect of inhibitors of sodium transport on bile formation in the rabbit. *Am. J. Physiol.* 219:416–22

48. Erlinger, S., Dumont, M. 1973. Influence of theophylline on bile formation in the dog. *Biomedicine* 19:27–32

49. Feld, G. K., Loeb, P. M., Berk, R. N., Wheeler, H. O. 1975. The choleretic effect of iodipamide. *J. Clin. Invest.* 55:528–35

50. Fisher, M. M., Yousef, I. M. 1975. Bile acid solubilization of bile canalicular membrane phospholipids. *Clin. Res.* 23:621A (Abstr.)

51. Forker, E. L. 1967. Two sites of bile formation as determined by mannitol and erythritol clearance in the guinea pig. *J. Clin. Invest.* 46:1189–95

52. Forker, E. L. 1968. Bile formation in guinea pigs: Analysis with inert solutes of graded molecular radius. *Am. J. Physiol.* 215:56–62

53. Forker, E. L. 1969. The effect of estrogen on bile formation in the rat. *J. Clin. Invest.* 48:654–63

54. Forker, E. L. 1970. Hepatocellular uptake of inulin, sucrose, and mannitol in rats. *Am. J. Physiol.* 219:1568–73

55. Forker, E. L. 1976. Canalicular anion transport—the effect of bile acids and bile acid independent choleretics. In *Chemistry and Physiology of Bile Pigments Fogarty Int. Cent. Proc., No. 35,* ed. P. D. Berk, N. T. Berlin. Wash. DC: US Gov. Print. Office

56. Forker, E. L. 1976. Removal of drugs by the isolated perfused liver–a distributed model for determining the transfer coefficients from the disappearance curve. See Reference 25, pp. 419–21

57. Forker, E. L., Gibson, G. 1973. Interaction between sulfobromophthalein (BSP) and taurocholate. In *The Liver. Quantitative Aspects of Structure and Function. 1st Int. Gstaad Symp.* ed. G. Paumgartner, R. Preisig, pp. 326–36. Basel, Switzerland: Karger

58. Forker, E. L., Hicklin, T., Sornson, H. 1967. The clearance of mannitol and erythritol in rat bile. *Proc. Soc. Exp. Biol. Med.* 126:115–19

59. French, S. W., Davies, P. L. 1975. Ultrastructural localization of actin-like filaments in rat hepatocytes. *Gastroenterology* 68:765–74

60. Gardiner, B. N., Small, D. M. 1976. Simultaneous measurement of the pancreatic and biliary response to CCK and secretin. Primate biliary physiology XIII. *Gastroenterology* 70:403–7

61. Gibson, G. E., Forker, E. L. 1974. Canalicular bile flow and bromosulfophthalein transport maximum: The effect of a bile salt-independent choleretic, SC-2644. *Gastroenterology* 66:1046–53

62. Glasinovic, J. -C., Dumont, M., Duval, M., Erlinger, S. 1975. Hepatocellular uptake of erythritol and mannitol in the dog. *Am. J. Physiol.* 229:1455–60

63. Glasinovic, J. -C., Dumont, M., Duval, M., Erlinger, S. 1975. Hepatocellular uptake of taurocholate in the dog. *J. Clin. Invest.* 55:419–26

64. Glasinovic, J. -C., Dumont, M., Duval, M., Erlinger, S. 1975. Hepatic uptake of taurocholate (TC) and sulfobromophthalein (BSP): Evidence for a common

65. Glasinovic, J. -C., Dumont, M., Erlinger, S. 1974. Hepatocellular uptake of bile acids: Further evidence for a carrier-mediated transport system. *Digestion* 10:323–24 (Abstr.)

66. Goodenough, D. A., Revel, J. P. 1970. A fine structural analysis of intercellular junctions in the mouse liver. *J. Cell. Biol.* 45:272–90

67. Goresky, C. A. 1964. Initial distribution and rate of uptake of sulfobromophthalein in the liver. *Am. J. Physiol.* 207: 13–26

68. Goresky, C. A., Bach, G. G., Nadeau, B. E. 1973. On the uptake of materials by the intact liver. The transport and net removal of galactose. *J. Clin. Invest.* 52:991–1009

69. Goresky, C. A., Bach, G. G., Nadeau, B. E. 1973. On the uptake of materials by the intact liver. Concentrative transport of rubidium-86. *J. Clin. Invest.* 52:975–90

70. Goresky, C. A., Haddad, H. H., Kluger, W. S., Nadeau, B. E., Bach, G. G. 1974. The enhancement of maximal bilirubin excretion with taurocholate-induced increments in bile flow. *Can. J. Physiol. Pharmacol.* 52:389–403

71. Gourlay, S. J., Jones, R. S. 1972. Effect of truncal vagotomy on 2-deoxy-D-glucose and insulin choleresis. *Ann. Surg.* 176:645–48

72. Graf, J., Korn, P., Peterlik, M. 1972. Choleretic effects of ouabain and ethacrynic acid in the isolated perfused rat liver. *Naunyn-Schmiedebergs Arch. Pharmakol.* 272:230–33

73. Gregory, D. H., Vlahcevic, Z. R., Schatzki, P., Swell, L. 1975. Mechanism of secretion of biliary lipids. I. Role of bile canalicular and microsomal membranes in the synthesis and transport of biliary lecithin and cholesterol. *J. Clin. Invest.* 55:105–14

74. Gregory, D. H., Vlahcevic, Z. R., Swell, L. 1976. Role of microtubules in the hepatocellular transport of biliary lipids. *Clin. Res.* 24:45A (Abstr.)

75. Gronwall, R., Cornelius, C. E. 1970. Maximal biliary excretion of sulfobromophthalein sodium in sheep. *Am. J. Dig. Dis.* 15:37–46

76. Gumucio, J. J., Accatino, L., Macho, A. M., Contreras, A. 1973. Effect of phenobarbital on the ethynyl estradiol-induced cholestasis in the rat. *Gastroenterology* 65:651–57

77. Guzelian, P., Boyer, J. L. 1974. Glucose reabsorption from bile. Evidence for a biliohepatic circulation. *J. Clin. Invest.* 53:526–35

78. Habig, W. H., Pabst, M. J., Fleischner, G., Gatmaitan, Z., Arias, I. M., Jakoby, W. B. 1974. The identity of glutathione S-transferase B with ligandin, a major binding protein of liver. *Proc. Natl. Acad. Sci. USA* 71:3879–82

79. Hardison, W. G. M., Apter, J. T. 1972. Micellar theory of biliary cholesterol excretion. *Am. J. Physiol.* 222:61–67

80. Hardison, W. G. M., Norman, J. C. 1968. Electrolyte composition of the secretin fraction of bile from the perfused pig liver. *Am. J. Physiol.* 214:758–63

81. Hardison, W. G. M., Norman, J. C. 1969. Effect of secretin on bile osmolality. *J. Lab. Clin. Med.* 73:34–41

82. Harty, R. F., Rose, R. C., Nahrwold, D. L. 1974. Stimulation of hepatic bile secretion by dopamine. *J. Surg. Res.* 17:359–63

83. Heath, T., Caple, I. W., Redding, P. M. 1970. Effect of the enterohepatic circulation of bile salts on the flow of bile and its content of bile salts and lipids in sheep. *Q. J. Exp. Physiol.* 55:93–103

84. Hirom, P. C., Hughes, R. D., Millburn, P. 1974. The physicochemical factor required for the biliary excretion of organic cations and anions. *Biochem. Soc. Trans.* 2:327–30

85. Hoenig, V., Preisig, R. 1973. Organic-anionic choleresis in the dog: Comparative effects of bromsulfalein, isoglycamide and taurocholate. *Biomedicine* 18:23–30

86. Hofmann, A. F. 1976. The enterohepatic circulation of bile acids in man. *Adv. Intern. Med.* 21:501–34

87. Hokfelt, B., Hultquist, G. 1961. Stimulation of pancreatic islet cells by 2-deoxy-D-glucose. *Proc. Soc. Exp. Biol. Med.* 107:66–68

88. Horak, W., Grabner, G., Paumgartner, G. 1973. Inhibition of bile salt-independent bile formation by indocyanine green. *Gastroenterology* 64:1105–12

89. Hwang, S. W., Reuning, R. H., Schanker, L. S. 1971. The chemical forms in which procaine amide ethobromide is secreted into rat bile. *Xenobiotica* 1:265–72

90. Hwang, S. W., Schanker, L. S. 1973. Hepatic uptake and biliary excretion of N-acetyl procaine amide ethobromide in the rat. *Am. J. Physiol.* 225:1437–43

91. Jablonski, P., Sali, A., Watts, J. McK. 1974. Gastro-intestinal hormones and bile secretion in the perfused pig liver: The effects of secretin, cholecystokinin and pentagastrin. *Aust. N.Z.J. Surg.* 44:173–78

92. Jones, A. L., Schmucker, D. L., Adler, R. D., Ockner, R. K., Mooney, J. S. 1976. A quantitative analysis of hepatic ultrastructure in rats after selective biliary obstruction. See Reference 25, pp. 36–51

93. Jones, R. S., Geist, R. E., Hall, A. D. 1971. The choleretic effects of glucagon and secretin in the dog. *Gastroenterology* 60:64–68

94. Jones, R. S., Grossman, M. I. 1970. Choleretic effects of cholecystokinin, gastrin II, and caerulein in the dog. *Am. J. Physiol.* 219:1014–18

95. Kaminski, D. L., Dorighi, J., Jellinek, M. 1974. Effect of electrical vagal stimulation on canine hepatic bile flow. *Am. J. Physiol.* 227:487–93

96. Kaminski, D. L., Rose, R. C., Nahrwold, D. L. 1973. Effect of pentagastrin on canine bile flow. *Gastroenterology* 64:630–33

97. Kaminski, D. L., Rose, R. C., Nahrwold, D. L. 1973. Effect of truncal vagotomy on insulin choleresis. *Surgery* 74:758–63

98. Kaminski, D. L., Ruwart, M. J., Jellinek, M. 1975. Effect of glucagon on secretin-stimulated bile flow. *Am. J. Physiol.* 229:1480–85

99. Kamisaka, K., Gatmaitan, Z., Moore, C. L., Arias, I. M. 1975. Ligandin reverses bilirubin inhibition of liver mitochondrial respiration *in vitro*. *Pediatr. Res.* 9:903–5

100. Kamisaka, K., Listowsky, I., Gatmaitan, Z., Arias, I. M. 1975. Interactions of bilirubin and other ligands with ligandin. *Biochemistry* 14:2175–80

101. Kelman-Sraer, J., Erlinger, S., Peignoux, M., Benhamou, J. P. 1973. Influence of dehydrocholate on hepatic uptake and biliary excretion of rose bengal in the rabbit. *Biomedicine* 19:415–18

102. Ketterer, B., Tipping, E., Beale, D., Meuwissen, J. A. T. P. 1976. Ligandin, glutathione and carcinogen binding. See Reference 4, pp. 243–57

103. Khedis, A., Dumont, M., Duval, M., Erlinger, S. 1974. Influence of glucagon on canalicular bile production in the dog. *Biomedicine* 21:176–81

104. Kimberg, D. V. 1974. Cyclic nucleotides and their role in gastrointestinal secretion. *Gastroenterology* 67:1023–64

105. Klaassen, C. D., Fitzgerald, T. J. 1974. Metabolism and biliary excretion of ethacrynic acid. *J. Pharmacol. Exp. Ther.* 191:548–56

106. Konturek, S. J., Tasler, J., Obtulowicz, W. 1972. Effect of atropine on pancreatic responses to endogenous and exogenous cholecystokinin. *Am. J. Dig. Dis.* 17:911–17

107. Laperche, Y., Launay, A., Oudea, P., Doulin, A., Baraud, J. 1972. Effects of phenobarbital and rose bengal on the ATPases of plasma membranes of rat and rabbit liver. *Gut* 13:920–25

108. LeMarchand, Y., Patzelt, C., Assimacopoulos-Jeannet, F., Loten, E. G., Jeanrenaud, B. 1974. Evidence for a role of the microtubular system in the secretion of newly synthesized albumin and other proteins by the liver. *J. Clin. Invest.* 53:1512–17

109. Levine, R. A., Hall, R. C. 1976. Cyclic AMP in secretin choleresis. Evidence for a regulatory role in man and baboons but not in dogs. *Gastroenterology* 70:537–44

110. London, C. D., Diamond, J. M., Brooks, F. P. 1968. Electrical potential differences in the biliary tree. *Biochim. Biophys. Acta* 150:509–17

111. Macarol, V., Morris, T. Q., Baker, K. J., Bradley, S. E. 1970. Hydrocortisone cholersis in the dog. *J. Clin. Invest.* 49:1714–23

112. Mandiola, S., Johnson, B. L., Winters, R. E., Longmire, W. P. 1972. Biliary excretion of ampicillin in the anesthetized dog. I. Effect of serum ampicillin concentration, taurocholate infusion rate, biliary secretion pressure, and secretin infusion. *Surgery* 71:664–74

113. Matter, A., Orci, L., Rouiller, C. 1969. A study on the permeability barriers between Disse's space and the bile canaliculus. *J. Ultrastruct. Res. Suppl.* 11:5–71

114. Morris, T. Q. 1972. Choleretic responses to cyclic AMP and theophylline in the dog. *Gastroenterology* 63:187 (Abstr.)

115. Muranishi, S., Schanker, L. S. 1970. Effect of non-nitrogenous onium compounds on biliary excretion of procaine amide ethobromide. *Eur. J. Pharmacol.* 9:116–19

116. Nahrwold, D. L., Shariatzedeh, A. N. 1971. Role of the common bile duct in formation of bile and in gastrin-induced choleresis. *Surgery* 70:147–53

117. Nelson, J. A., Staubus, A. E., Riegelman, S. 1975. Saturation kinetics of iopanoate in the dog. *Invest. Radiol.* 10:371–77

118. Oda, M., Phillips, M. J. 1975. Electron microscopic cytochemical characterization of bile canaliculi and bile ducts *in vitro. Virchows Arch. B* 18:109–18

119. O'Maille, E. R. L., Richards, T. G., Short, A. H. 1965. Acute taurine depletion and maximal rates of hepatic conjugation and secretion of cholic acid in the dog. *J. Physiol. London* 180:67–79

120. O'Maille, E. R. L., Richards, T. G., Short, A. H. 1966. Factors determining the maximal rate of organic anion secretion by the liver and further evidence on the hepatic site of action of the hormone secretin. *J. Physiol. London* 186:424–38

121. O'Maille, E. R. L., Richards, T. G., Short, A. H. 1967. The influence of conjugation of cholic acid on its uptake and secretion: Hepatic extraction of taurocholate and cholate in the dog. *J. Physiol London* 189:337–50

122. Orci, L., LeMarchand, Y., Singh, A., Assimacopoulos-Jeannet, F., Rouiller, Ch., Jeanrenaud, B. 1973. Role of microtubules in lipoprotein secretion by the liver. *Nature* 244:30–32

123. Pardridge, W. M., Jefferson, L. S. 1975. Liver uptake of amino acids and carbohydrates during a single circulatory passage. *Am. J. Physiol.* 228:1155–61

124. Patzelt, C., LeMarchand, Y., Jeanrenaud, B. 1976. Microtubules and secretion processes in the liver: Possible functional models. See Reference 25, pp. 17–31

125. Paumgartner, G., Preisig, R., eds. 1973. *The Liver. Quantitative Aspects of Structure and Function. Proc. 1st Int. Gstaad Symp.* Basel, Switzerland: Karger

126. Paumgartner, G., Reichen, J. 1975. Different pathways for hepatic uptake of taurocholate and indocyanine green. *Experientia* 31:306–7

127. Paumgartner, G., Reichen, J., von Bergmann, K., Preisig, R. 1975. Elaboration of hepatocytic bile. *Bull. NY Acad. Med.* 51:455–71

128. Phillips, M. J., Oda, M., Fisher, M. M., Jeejeebhoy, K. N. 1974. Structure and function of bile canalicular microfilaments. *Am. J. Path.* 78:13a–14a(Abstr.)

129. Phillips, M. J., Oda, M., Mac, E., Steiner, J. W. 1976. Fine structure of the biliary tree. See Reference 3, pp. 245–63

130. Pissidis, A. G., Nyhus, L. M., Bornbeck, C. T. 1973. Neurohumoral control of bile secretion in the cholecystec-

tomized, conscious dog. *Surgery* 74:122–29

131. Pohl, S. L., Birnbaumer, L., Rodbell, M. 1971. The glucagon-sensitive adenyl cyclase system in plasma membranes of rat liver. I. Properties. *J. Biol. Chem.* 246:1849–56

132. Prandi, D., Erlinger, S., Glasinovic, J.-C., Dumont, M. 1975. Canalicular bile production in man. *Eur. J. Clin. Invest.* 5:1–6

133. Preisig, R., Bircher, J., Paumgartner, G., eds. 1976. *The Liver. Quantitative Aspects of Structure and Function. 2nd Int. Gstaad Symp.* Aulendorf: Editio Cantor

134. Preisig, R., Cooper, H. L., Wheeler, H. O. 1962. The relationship between taurocholate secretion rate and bile production in the unanesthetized dog during cholinergic blockade and during secretin administration. *J. Clin. Invest.* 41:1152–62

135. Preisig, R., Strebel, H., Egger, G., Macarol, V. 1972. Effect of vasopressin on hepatocytic and ductal bile formation in the dog. *Experientia* 28:1436–37

136. Rayford, P. L., Miller, T. A., Thompson, J. C. 1976. Secretin, cholecystokinin and newer gastrointestinal hormones. Parts I and II. *N. Engl. J. Med.* 294:1093–1102; 1157–64

137. Redinger, R. N., Small, D. M. 1973. Primate biliary physiology. VIII. The effect of phenobarbital upon bile salt synthesis and pool size, biliary lipid secretion, and bile composition. *J. Clin. Invest.* 52:161–72

138. Reichen, J., Paumgartner, G. 1975. Kinetics of taurocholate uptake by the perfused rat liver. *Gastroenterology* 68:132–36

139. Reichen, J., Paumgartner, G. 1977. Uptake of bile acids by the perfused rat liver. *Am. J. Physiol.* In press

140. Richards, T. G., Tindall, V. R., Young, A. 1959. A modification of the bromsulphthalein liver function test to predict the dye content of the liver and bile. *Clin. Sci.* 18:449–511

141. Robins, S. J., Armstrong, M. J. 1976. Biliary lecithin secretion. II. Effects of dietary choline and biliary lecithin synthesis. *Gastroenterology* 70:397–402

142. Russell, J. Q., Klaassen, C. D. 1973. Biliary excretion of cardiac glycosides. *J. Pharmacol. Exp. Ther.* 186:455–62

143. Russell, T. R., Searle, G. L., Jones, R. S. 1975. The choleretic mechanisms of sodium taurocholate, secretin, and glucagon. *Surgery* 77:498–504

144. Sarfeh, I. J., Beeler, D. A., Treble, D. H., Balint, J. A. 1974. Studies of the hepatic excretory defects in essential fatty acid deficiency. Their possible relationship to the genesis of cholesterol gallstones. *J. Clin. Invest.* 53:423–30

145. Schanker, L. S. 1968. Secretion of organic compounds in bile. In *Handb. Physiol. The Alimentary Canal,* 5:2433–49. Washington DC: Am. Physiol. Soc.

146. Schanker, L. S., Solomon, H. M. 1963. Active transport of quaternary ammonium compounds into bile. *Am. J. Physiol.* 204:829–32

147. Scharschmidt, B. F., Waggoner, J. G., Berk, P. D. 1975. Hepatic organic anion uptake in the rat. *J. Clin. Invest.* 56:1280–92

148. Schatzki, P. F. 1969. Bile canaliculus and space of Disse. Electron microscopic relationships as delineated by lanthanum. *Lab. Invest.* 20:87–93

149. Schersten, T., Lindblad, L., Lundholm, K. 1976. The influence of cholic and chenodeoxycholic acids on the bile flow and the biliary secretion of lecithin and cholesterol in man. See Reference 25, pp. 275–86

150. Schulze, P.-J., Czok, G. 1975. Reduced bile flow in rats during sulfobromophthalein infusion. *Toxicol. Appl. Pharmacol.* 32:213–24

151. Schwarz, H. P., Herz, R., Sauter, K., Paumgartner, G. 1973. Taurocholate induced anticholeresis in the rat. *Eur. J. Clin. Invest.* 3:268 (Abstr.)

152. Schwarz, L. R., Burr, R., Schwenk, M., Pfaff, E., Greim, H. 1975. Uptake of taurocholic acid into isolated rat-liver cells. *Eur. J. Biochem.* 55:617–23

153. Shaw, H. M., Caple, I., Heath, T. J. 1972. Effect of ethacrynic acid on bile formation in sheep, dogs, rats, guinea pigs and rabbits. *J. Pharmacol. Exp. Ther.* 182:27–33

154. Shaw, H. M., Heath, T. J. 1974. Regulation of bile formation in rabbits and guinea pigs. *Q. J. Exp. Physiol.* 59:93–102

154a. Simon, F. R., Sutherland, E. 1975. Effect of phenobarbital and ethinyl estradiol on (Na–K) ATPase and other liver plasma membrane enzymes. *Clin. Res.* 23(3):257A

154b. Simon, F. R., Sutherland, E., Cerzonsky, J., Accatino, L. 1976. Effect of phenobarbital and thyroidectomy on hepatic (Na–K) ATPase activity and bile flow. *Clin. Res.* 24(3):291A

155. Smith, R. L. 1973. *The Excretory Func-*

tion of Bile. London: Chapman & Hall. 283 pp.

156. Sokoloff, J., Berk, R. N. 1973. The effect of prostaglandin E_2 on bile flow and the biliary excretion of iopanoic acid. *Invest. Radiol.* 8:9–12

157. Solomon, H. M., Schanker, L. S. 1963. Hepatic transport of organic cations: Active uptake of a quarternary ammonium compound procaine amide ethobromide by rat liver slices. *Biochem. Pharmacol.* 12:621–26

158. Soloway, R. D., Hofmann, A. F., Thomas, P. J., Schoenfield, L. J., Klein, P. D. 1973. Triketocholanoic (dehydrocholic) acid. Hepatic metabolism and effect on bile flow and biliary lipid secretion in man. *J. Clin. Invest.* 52:715–24

159. Stein, O., Sanger, L., Stein, Y. 1974. Colchicine-induced inhibition of lipoprotein and protein secretion into the serum and lack of interference with secretion of biliary phospholipids and cholesterol by rat liver in vivo. *J. Cell Biol.* 62:90–103

160. Strasberg, S. M., Ilson, R. G., Siminovitch, K. A., Brenner, D., Palaheimo, J. E. 1975. Analysis of the components of bile flow in the rhesus monkey. *Am. J. Physiol.* 228:115–21

161. Strasberg, S. M., Siminovitch, K. A., Ilson, R. G. 1974. Bile production in fasted and fed primates. *Ann. Surg.* 180:356–63

162. Swell, L., Bell, C. C. Jr., Gregory, D. H., Vlahcevic, Z. R. 1974. The cholesterol saturation index of human bile. *Am. J. Dig. Dis.* 19:261–65

163. Taylor, W. 1965. *The Biliary System. Symp. NATO Adv. Study Inst.* Philadelphia: Davis

164. Taylor, W. 1976. *The Hepatobiliary System.* New York: Plenum

165. Thulin, L. 1973. The choleretic effect of pure natural cholecystokinin in dogs. *Acta. Chir. Scand.* 139:635–40

166. Thulin, L. 1973. The choleretic effects in dogs of the synthetic c-terminal octapeptide of cholecystokinin and of two peptide mixtures, G 1 and G 2, derived from upper hog intestine. *Acta Chir. Scand.* 139:641–44

167. Thulin, L. 1973. Effects of gastro-intestinal polypeptides on hepatic bile flow and splanchnic circulation. *Acta Chir. Scand.* 441:(Suppl.)3–31

168. Unger, R. H., Eisentraut, A. M., McCall, M. S., Madison, L. L. 1962. Measurements of endogenous glucagon in plasma and the influence of blood glucose concentration upon its secretion. *J. Clin. Invest.* 41:682–89

169. Upson, D. W., Gronwall, R. R., Cornelius, C. E. 1970. Maximal hepatic excretion of bilirubin in sheep. *Proc. Soc. Exp. Biol. Med.* 134:9–12

170. von Bergmann, K., Schwarz, H. P., Paumgartner, G. 1975. Effect of phenobarbital, spironolactone and pregnenolone-16α-carbonitrile on bile formation in the rat. *Naunyn-Schmiedebergs Arch. Pharmakol.* 287:33–45

171. Vonk, R. J., Veen, H. v. d., Prop. G., Meijer, D. K. F. 1974. The influence of taurocholate and dehydrocholate choleresis on plasma disappearance and biliary excretion of indocyanine green in the rat. *Naunyn-Schmiedebergs Arch. Pharmakol.* 282:401–10

172. Wagner, C. I., Trotman, B. W., Soloway, R. D. 1976. Kinetic analysis of biliary lipid excretion in man and dog. *J. Clin. Invest.* 57:473–77

173. Ware, A. J., Carey, M. C., Combes, B. 1976. Solution properties of sulfobromophthalein sodium (BSP) compound alone and in association with sodium taurocholate (TC). *J. Lab. Clin. Med.* 87:443–56

174. Wheeler, H. O. 1968. Water and electrolytes in bile. See Reference 145, pp. 2409–31

175. Wheeler, H. O. 1972. Secretion of bile acids by the liver and their role in the formation of hepatic bile. *Arch. Intern. Med.* 130:533–41

176. Wheeler, H. O., King, K. K. 1972. Biliary excretion of lecithin and cholesterol in the dog. *J. Clin. Invest.* 51:1337–50

177. Wheeler, H. O., Mancusi-Ungaro, P. L. 1966. Role of bile ducts during secretin choleresis in dogs. *Am. J. Physiol.* 210:1153–59

178. Wheeler, H. O., May, R. J., Loeb, P. M. 1973. Determinants of biliary lipid excretion. See Ref. 57, pp. 368–75

179. Wheeler, H. O., Ramos, O. L. 1960. Determinants of the flow and composition of bile in the unanesthetized dog during constant infusions of sodium taurocholate. *J. Clin. Invest.* 39:161–70

180. Wheeler, H. O., Ross, E. D., Bradley, S. E. 1968. Canalicular bile production in dogs. *Am. J. Physiol.* 214:866–74

181. Zaterka, S., Grossman, M. I. 1966. The effect of gastrin and histamine on secretion of bile. *Gastroenterology* 50:500–5

182. Zsigmond, G., Solymoss, B. 1974. Increased canalicular bile production induced by pregnenole-16α-carbonitrile, spironolactone and cortisol in rats. *Proc. Soc. Exp. Biol. Med.* 145:631–35

Ann. Rev. Physiol. 1977. 39:349–71
Copyright © 1977 by Annual Reviews Inc. All rights reserved

THE THYROID
AND ITS CONTROL[1]

❖1175

Kenneth Sterling and John H. Lazarus[2]

Department of Medicine, Columbia University College of Physicians and Surgeons, and The Protein Research Laboratory, Bronx Veterans Administration Hospital, Bronx, New York, 10468

THYROID HORMONE HOMEOSTASIS

In considering thyroid hormone regulation and homeostasis, it is important to examine some characteristics of this hormone in relation to the others. The hormones may readily be divided into two distinct physicochemical and biological classes. (Table 1). The protein and peptide hormones are water soluble and evidently exist in the plasma without demonstrable interaction with other serum proteins. These hormones have a rapid metabolic turnover with a half-time in minutes. Therefore it is not surprising to observe rather striking fluctuations in concentration in the blood within a few minutes in the case of all these peptide hormones, including parathyroid hormone, thyrocalcitonin, growth hormone, FSH, LH, prolactin, ACTH, MSH, TSH, vasopressin, insulin, secretin, angiotensin II, and glucagon (Table 1). Indeed, the amino acid hormones, epinephrine and norepinephrine, may fluctuate markedly within a few seconds.

In contrast, the "target" hormones—cortisol, progesterone, estradiol, testosterone, and thyroxine—are relatively hydrophobic and exist in aqueous solution in the blood by virtue of their firm binding by one or more serum protein carriers (Table 1). The biologic half-times vary with the magnitude of the "free" or nonprotein-bound moiety. Thus cortisol, which is about 95% protein bound and 5% unbound, has approximately a one-hr half-time, and thyroxine, more than 99.96% protein bound and less than 0.04% unbound, has a biologic half-time of turnover approx-

---

[1]Abbreviations used: T_3, Triiodothyronine; T_4, Thyroxine; TSH, Thyroid Stimulating Hormone; FSH, Follicle Stimulating Hormone; LH, Luteinizing Hormone; ACTH, Adenocorticotropic hormone; MSH, Melanocyte Stimulating Hormone; PTU, Propyl thuouracil; cAMP, cyclic adenosine monophosphate; MIT, Monoiodotyrosine; DIT, Diiodotyrosine; hCG, human Chorionic Gonadotropin; hCT, human Chorionic Thyrotropin; GH, Growth Hormone.

[2]Permanent address: Department of Medicine, University Hospital of Wales, Cardiff, Wales, United Kingdom.

Table 1 Soluble and hydrophobic hormones

Soluble	Hydrophobic
Protein and peptide hormones	Small–molecule "target" hormones
Parathyroid	Cortisol
Thyrocalcitonin	Progesterone
Growth hormone	Estradiol
FSH, LH, prolactin	Testosterone
ACTH, MSH	Thyroxine
TSH	
Vasopressin	
Insulin	
Glucagon	
Secretin	
Angiotensin II	

1 week. The concentration of thyroxine, therefore, ordinarily remains constant for long periods in health and in disease, although it may vary somewhat within a day or two in the postoperative period after major surgery. Cortisol can fluctuate markedly within hours and shows pronounced diurnal variation. Cortisol and thyroxine may be considered the extreme examples within the category of the protein-bound hormones of small molecular size; however, the turnover of even the fastest on the list, cortisol, is sluggish compared to the turnover of the peptide hormones. Aldosterone, which is appreciably less firmly bound than cortisol, has, as expected, a faster turnover than cortisol.

The biologic half-time of turnover of thyroxine (T_4), approximating one week in normal man, is much more prolonged than the biologic half-time of turnover of triiodothyronine (T_3), which is approximately one day. The difference can be largely explained by the much firmer binding of T_4 by the three serum protein carriers. Appropriately, the onset of physiological action of T_3 when given to a myxedematous subject, is more rapid but less sustained than that of T_4. Despite the more rapid effect of T_3 compared to T_4, the effects of thyroid hormone are generally much more sustained than those of the other hormones.

In marked contrast to the emergency functions of the catecholamines and of cortisol, the thyroid hormones generally provide a homeostatic background which is maintained at a constant level for physiological requirements in health.

THYROID AUTOREGULATION

The concept of thyroid autoregulation, whereby levels of certain metabolic activities in the gland are modulated not only by pituitary thyrotropin (TSH) but also by the iodide supply, is apparently unique among the endocrine organs under pituitary control. Experimentally, autoregulatory responses may be examined in hypophysectomized animals either left untreated or given TSH in constant doses. In this situation iodine levels can be made to vary over wide ranges. In vitro experiments using dispersed thyroid cells have also proved valuable. These and other methods have determined that while TSH certainly influences every step in thyroid hormone synthesis and secretion, evidence exists that iodide does so as well (70).

The effect of iodide on the thyroid iodide transport system has been studied in detail ever since the identification of this process which actively transports iodide at the basal membrane of the thyroid cell (5, 158). TSH is the most important factor regulating I^- transport, causing an early increase in thyroid I^- efflux followed by a late increase in unidirectional clearance. The biphasic effect of TSH on I^- transport is mediated by cAMP. The ability of the thyroid to concentrate I^- measured follow-ing hypophysectomy was, as predicted, reduced; but if total thyroidal iodide was then decreased either by iodine restriction or by treatment with PTU, then the iodide concentrating mechanism was stimulated. The striking inverse correlation between glandular content of organic iodine and $T:S[I^-]^3$ ratio (148) led to the postulate that the loss of concentrating ability was mediated by a hypothetical intrathyroidal organic inhibitor of iodide transport (61). This inhibitor has not been isolated. Autoregulatory control remains after hypophysectomy. For example, the $T:S[I^-]$ remained substantial after the operation if it was high before (60). Rats fed a low iodine diet before operation for three generations maintained a high $T:S[I^-]$ after surgery despite thyroid involution (52). When rats maintained on a low or high iodine regimen were hypophysectomized and the thyroids depleted of inorganic I^- in vitro, the $T:M[I^-]^4$ of the iodine-poor glands was higher than that of the iodine-rich glands (82). Further studies have shown that relatively small doses of I^- depressed the $T:S[I^-]$ of hypophysectomized iodine-deficient rats (129). This inhibitory effect could not be correlated with total organic iodine formation or with iodotyrosine or iodothyronine formation, making it hard to accept the view that the inhibitory compound referred to above is an iodotyrosine or thyronine.

Recent extensive studies of changes in thyroid function in response to iodine deficiency in the rat have been carried out by Greer and co-workers (43–45, 54). It is known that the adaptive changes of thyroidal iodine metabolism to iodine defi-ciency, primarily induced by increased pituitary TSH secretion in response to low-ered circulating thyroid hormone levels, include thyroid hypertrophy, high radioiodine uptake, and an increase in intrathyroidal labeled MIT:DIT and $T_3:T_4$ ratios (53, 136). In iodine-deficient infant rats, a high $T_3:T_4$ ratio was not observed until the third month (30), probably because of a coupling deficiency in newborn rats resulting in a proportionately greater formation of iodotyrosines than of iodo-thyronines compared to older animals. The adaptive changes in thyroid hormone levels are largely mediated by an increase in TSH secretion; plasma TSH may be increased as early as the third day of a low iodine diet. Plasma T_4 falls more rapidly than T_3, suggesting that the rise in TSH may be responsive to a fall in the former

---

[3]The ratio $T:S[I^-]$ refers to the concentration gradient of tissue iodide to that of serum iodide.
[4]The ratio $T:M[I^-]$ refers to the concentration gradient of tissue iodide to that of iodide in the medium.

hormone. A major fraction of plasma T_3 in the iodine-deficient state apparently derives from a preferential thyroid secretion rather than from peripheral conversion from T_4. When iodide is administered to iodine-deficient rats, TSH levels fall in proportion to the dose of iodide administered. However, after six weeks of supplementation, radioiodine uptake was inversely correlated with dietary iodine intake despite normal concentrations of TSH, T_4, and T_3. This confirmed the original suggestions that intrathyroidal iodine content is a primary determinant of the iodide concentrating activity of the gland (59, 148). Although thyroid autoregulation is a factor in adapting iodide transport to iodine supply, TSH is still important in the early response to experimental iodine deficiency. Thus autoregulation is a rather sluggish response, indicating perhaps two levels of thyroid control in this situation, a rapid TSH response modulating a slower autoregulatory intrinsic control.

Large doses of iodide will reduce the T:S[I$^-$] acutely due to saturation of the iodide pump by its substrate (158). There is an associated reduction of the unidirectional I$^-$ clearance and an increased exit rate constant (122, 138). Studying these effects on the pump alone is difficult because of the organic binding reactions that occur almost simultaneously with iodide transport. Studies are therefore carried out on glands blocked with thionamides. As the human salivary glands concentrate iodide to many times the plasma level but do not organify it (5), studies of salivary iodide in response to excess iodide loads in human subjects are valuable. For example, one study showed that higher serum concentrations of exogenously administered iodide were required to inhibit the salivary iodide trap in patients with iodide-induced goiter compared to controls (81). This would allow excess iodide to enter the thyroid and cause damage as described by Wolff (159).

The oxidation and subsequent organic binding of thyroidal iodide have been reviewed by Taurog (141). Briefly, in a model system the incubation requirements for iodination include thyroid peroxidase, iodide, acceptor (protein or free tyrosine), and H_2O_2. In such a system, oxidized iodide is able to iodinate tyrosyl residues in thyroglobulin to produce monoiodotyrosine (MIT) and diiodotyrosine (DIT). The subsequent reactions resulting in the production of T_3 and T_4 are influenced by the availability of iodide, best exemplified by the classic investigations of response of thyroid hormone synthesis to acute alterations in the availability of iodide. In rats injected with 10–500 μg^{127}I$^-$ labeled with ^{131}I$^-$, organic binding of injected iodide was decreased so long as plasma iodide remained above 20–35 μg/100 ml (the Wolff-Chaikoff effect) (162). During this decrease in the formation of total organic iodine, qualitative change in the distribution of the organic iodine compounds also occurs, i.e. an increase in the MIT:DIT ratio and a decrease in iodothyronine (T_4 and T_3) formation (160). Increasing doses of iodide administered to rats causes a progressive decrease in ^{131}I uptake, in organification of thyroid iodide, in the proportion of thyroid DIT and iodothyronines among the iodinated amino acids, and in the absolute rate of organic iodinations and iodothyronine synthesis (98). However, the thyroid is apparently able to prevent an acute increase in the formation of active hormones in response to moderate doses of iodide only after a small transient increase of hormone release has depressed TSH secretion (135). The Wolff-Chaikoff effect should probably be defined in terms of the entire phase of iodine metabolism in which iodination decreases in response to increasing doses of iodide rather than in terms of the quantity of organic iodine formed (97). It is apparent that the iodide transport activity and TSH concentrations affect the Wolff-Chaikoff mechanism. For example, increased sensitivity to iodide inhibition observed in rats on a low iodine diet (72) and in rats pretreated with TSH (109) may be explained by the higher T:S[I⁻] established in such conditions. The work of Rosenfeld & Rosenberg (117) has shown when TSH was given to rats prior to administration of large doses of iodide, glandular organification was enhanced compared to rats similarly treated with iodide but without TSH in which organification was severely depressed. The precise mechanism of the acute inhibitory action of excess iodide is not known, but several theories are prevalent: hypoiodous acid, which may be the reactive form of iodine that enters into organic combination in the gland, could be decreased by the addition of excess iodide. Alternatively, the triiodide ion, which is incapable of carrying out iodinations, could be produced from oxidized iodine in the presence of high concentrations of inorganic iodide. The effect of varying concentrations of iodide on the model system described above (139, 140) showed that the rate of I_2 formation appeared to be reciprocally related to the rate of iodination of protein. This suggests that I_2 formation competes with iodination and that the formation of I_2 is favored by a high concentration of I⁻. However, none of these postulated mechanisms has been proved in vivo.

It has been recognized that the Wolff-Chaikoff effect is transient. Attempts to prolong inhibition by maintaining a high serum iodide level either by nephrectomy after a single iodide dose (161) or by repeated injections were unsuccessful beyond 26–40 hr despite continued high serum iodide concentrations (163). The mechanism of "escape" from iodide inhibition was termed an "adaptation" by Braverman & Ingbar (12), who demonstrated that glands that had escaped lost much of their normal ability to concentrate iodide. A pituitary or TSH mechanism for the escape was shown to be unlikely and it was proposed that escape may occur through "intrinsic control mechanisms."

The effects of reduction or increase in the iodine supply on various other parameters of thyroid function have been studied by different methods. Experiments using dispersed thyroid cells in vitro have shown that prior incubation with iodide led to decreased iodide concentrating activity and reduced the stimulation of the pump that could be induced in response to TSH (123). This latter finding indicates that the influence of iodide is also exerted on the cellular mechanisms mediating the response to TSH. For example, excess iodide injection into normal rats significantly decreases thyroidal adenosine triphosphate (ATP) and pyridine nucleotides as early as 5 min after injection (85). Recently, Sherwin & Tong (124) have shown in experiments with dispersed thyroid cells that preincubation with excess iodide led to decreased stimulation of cAMP production, of iodide pump activity, and of iodinating activity in response to added TSH. These investigations suggest therefore that autoregulation of the thyroid gland does include influences of iodide on these processes; however, two other effects of TSH, the stimulation of [¹⁴C] leucine incorporation into protein and of iodide efflux, were not affected by excess iodide and hence were not included in the autoregulatory influence of iodide. Confirmation of the reduced cAMP response to TSH in iodine-enriched compared to iodine-deficient animals had come from a study of hypophysectomized rats on these dietary regimens (110). In the rat, it seems clear that thyroid autoregulation can cope with moderate increases in iodide administration, but excess iodide decreases the release rate of ^{131}I from the labeled thyroid and also decreases the blood hormone concentration more in hyperactive thyroids of rats treated with antithyroid drugs than in untreated rats. TSH levels are not crucial to these changes, which are similar to those described in man (104, 105, 157, 164). Excess iodide blocks thyroid hormone release in patients with Graves' disease (99). The thyroid in this condition, in contrast to the normal gland, is abnormally sensitive to iodide. Recently, iodide-induced hypothyroidism has been observed following inorganic iodide administration to patients rendered euthyroid following treatment for hyperthyroidism (15) and patients with Hashimoto's thyroiditis (14). The occurrence of hyperthyroidism following increased iodide supply in some goitrous subjects (145, 149) could well be due to the failure of one or several of the intrathyroidal control mechanisms which enable the normal thyroid to maintain its hormone secretion within narrow limits in the face of a widely varying iodide supply.

THYROTROPIN (TSH) CONTROL

The introduction of methods for measuring human thyrotropin in serum (65, 89, 103, 106) has made it possible to define further the thyroid pituitary relationships in normal human subjects as well as those with thyroid disorders. Studies of metabolic clearance and production rates of human thyrotropin (115) have demonstrated that changes in the serum concentration of TSH are mainly due to altered pituitary TSH secretion with only a minor contribution from the change in the metabolic clearance rate of the hormone. Like the other glycoprotein hormones (follicle stimulating hormone, luteinizing hormone, and chorionic gonadotropin), TSH possesses two peptide chains designated alpha and beta. The former is practically the same in all four glycoprotein hormones. The development of radioimmunoassays for the two subunits of TSH (7, 79) has shown that normal pituitary glands contain a predominance of free alpha subunit relative to beta TSH in addition to TSH itself. In hypothyroidism secretion of both free subunits occurs. However, this may represent only a quantitative difference from the normal state; the subunits of TSH appear to respond to the same control mechanism as complete TSH (80).

Although general agreement exists that TSH secretion is under negative feedback control by thyroid hormones, the details of thyroid hormone action at the pituitary cell level and the relative importance of T_4 and T_3 in suppressing TSH secretion are unclear. In vitro studies of isolated pituitary preparations have examined the effect of inhibitors of protein synthesis, such as puromycin, cycloheximide, and actinomycin D, on TSH production (9a, 9b). If these compounds were administered before the addition of thyroid hormone, they prevented the inhibition of TSH release normally produced by thyroid hormones. Thus the thyroid hormones may cause the intrapituitary formation of an inhibitory protein or polypeptide that interacts competitively with thyrotropin releasing hormone (TRH, vide infra) in regulating TSH metabolism. The nature of this compound has not been identified.

The relative importance of T_4 and T_3 in feedback inhibition of pituitary TSH release is a very interesting topic, but is far from settled. The finding of high-affinity, low-capacity receptor sites for T_3 in the anterior pituitary (121) gave rise to the concept of T_3 as a primary suppressor of TSH release. However, specific binding sites for T_4 have also been demonstrated in the adenohypophysis, albeit with a lower affinity than T_3 binding sites (130, 137). The possibility of intrapituitary conversion of T_4 to T_3 has been entertained, but was not supported by the findings of a recent study (49).

Studies on the acute effects of T_4, T_3, and iodide on TSH secretion in rats (43) showed that equivalent physiological doses of T_4 and T_3 exerted immediate and indistinguishable effects on suppressing pituitary TSH secretion.

The problem has been approached in human subjects by assessing the diminution in TSH response to TRH produced by T_3 or T_4 administered at various intervals prior to TRH injection. The recent report by Wenzel et al (153) showed a faster and more pronounced inhibition of TSH release by smaller doses of T_3 when compared to T_4. On the other hand, single intravenous injections of T_3 resulting in marked elevation of serum T_3 concentration may fail to alter TSH response to TRH administration for at least several hours (150). Taken altogether, these findings are compatible with the requirement for synthesis of an inhibiting protein or peptide in the adenohypophysis caused by elevated serum hormone concentrations. Pending further information it seems most reasonable at present to consider both T_4 and T_3 as candidates for feedback regulators of TSH production. Recently a new clinical entity of thyrotropin hyperthyroidism caused by selective pituitary resistance to thyroid hormone has been documented (51). The study of this syndrome of inappropriate secretion of TSH may shed further light on the regulation of the hypothalamic pituitary thyroid axis.

The possibility of a direct feedback effect of the thyroid hormones upon the thyroid gland itself must also be considered. Such inhibition of the intrathyroidal enzyme, ornithine decarboxylase, has been shown by T_4 or T_3 pretreatment, which can counteract the stimulatory effect of administered TSH (165). As these effects were more marked in iodine-deficient animals, the role of autoregulation is also suggested. However, work in progress by Ingbar and co-workers (S. H. Ingbar, personal communication) has failed to substantiate this "short-loop feedback" on the thyroid gland.

Sympathetic Regulation

The anatomical and pharmacological studies of Melander and co-workers (91–95) have indicated the importance of the sympathetic adrenergic system in the control of thyroid function. Sympathetic adrenergic nerve fibers are numerous in the human thyroid, and their anatomy suggests an influence of this system on thyroid follicle cells as well as on the thyroid vasculature. Fluorescence histochemistry and electron microscopic autoradiography in mouse thyroids suggest the possibility that the sympathetic innervation may effect prompt short-term alterations in the rate of thyroid hormone secretion (91–95). It appears that aromatic monoamines (norepinephrine and dopamine) can stimulate thyroid hormone synthesis by direct action on alpha-adrenergic receptors in the follicle cells. It also seems probable that the formation of thyroid mast cells, which may participate in the regulation of the synthesis of thyroid hormone, is controlled by TSH. The TSH-regulated activation of the thyroid may be facilitated and partially mediated by amines released from mast cells by TSH. While most of the studies have been done in animals, and species differences have been observed, there is anatomic and biochemical evidence that similar mechanisms may operate in man.

Cold Exposure

Reduction in ambient temperature causes a rise in TSH levels in laboratory and domestic animals. The precise role of changes in thyroid secretion in the homeostatic regulation of metabolism during cold exposure is not clear, although thyroid hormone is essential for survival at lowered environmental temperatures (46). Acute cold exposure in the rat causes a rise in plasma TSH levels within 5–10 min (66, 87). It appears that peripheral thermoreceptors may activate TSH secretion, as hypothalamic core temperatures either show no change or a slight rise in this situation (114). However, that TSH release can also be induced by lowering of core temperature is shown by experiments demonstrating activation of thyroid hormone secretion following hypothalamic cooling in the goat (1), rat (111), and baboon (48). The effect of chronic cold exposure on TSH levels and subsequent thyroid hormone metabolism is less clear. Most experiments performed in many species have failed to show any change in plasma T_4 levels during chronic cold exposure. However, some workers have noted otherwise. Galton & Nisula (50) found that the rat showed an increased fecal excretion of T_4 secondary to enhanced food intake in response to chronic cold exposure. This may result in a decrease in negative feedback at the pituitary level leading to a rise in TSH and thyroid hormone secretion. Another study of rats exposed to cold, which showed no detectable change in plasma TSH but a 50% reduction in plasma T_4, concluded that, although TSH release is stimulated initially during cold exposure by hypothalamic mechanisms, an increased metabolic clearance of the hormone prevents an elevation of plasma levels (42). A peripheral metabolic response to cold is further suggested by recent studies documenting the rise in plasma T_3 levels and kidney T_3 concentration in rats exposed to cold (74, 99). In addition, T_3 binding proteins in parenchymal tissue are increased, as is the T_4 degradation rate (3). However, whether these changes are due to increased thyroidal T_3 secretion, increased peripheral monodeiodination of T_4 to T_3, or reduced plasma, T_3 clearance is unknown. Increased thyroidal T_3 secretion is probably the most reasonable overall explanation.

Acute cold exposure in the rat has been reported by one group (96) to lead to an increase in plasma TRH levels, but this has not been confirmed (31). Increased hypothalamic TRH levels have been reported in rats exposed to cold (113).

Of major interest are the recent findings of Szabo & Frohman (138a) showing depression of the TSH secretory response in cold-exposed rats after administration of antiserum to TSH; this tends to afford support for the hypothalamic mediation of the cold-induced rise in TSH via TRH.

Stress

The study of stress-induced changes in pituitary-thyroid function has produced ambiguous results. Stressful factors may alter pituitary-thyroid function at many levels of control; such factors include altered TRH secretion, changes in responsiveness of the pituitary to TRH, altered metabolism of TSH, altered metabolism of the thyroid hormones in peripheral tissues, and alterations in the physical state of thyroid hormone binding proteins in blood (113). In general, most studies have indicated that TSH secretion is inhibited during exposure to severe stress (55). A few studies have shown that thyroid hormone may be increased after acute stress in the sheep or man or after aversive conditioning in the rhesus monkey (88). In human subjects exposed to subfreezing cold water, an increase in the urinary excretion of immunoassayable TRH has been reported (47), and insulin-induced hypoglycemia has also been reported to cause release of TSH in human subjects with GH deficiency (57) and in normal rats (83).

Hormones

The influence of hormones in modulating TSH secretion has been reviewed by Reichlin and co-workers (113). Acute or chronic exposure to excessively high levels of cortisol will inhibit TSH secretion in man and in the rat (156). The residual pituitary-thyroid activity observed in patients maximally suppressed with exogenous T_3 is further reduced by treatment with high doses of corticoids (100). Corticosteroids appear to reduce the sensitivity of the pituitary to TRH and perhaps also reduce the secretion of TRH. Estrogen effects have been difficult to study because of their known effects on peripheral metabolism of thyroid hormone. The findings that pituitary responsiveness to TRH is greatest in that phase of the menstrual cycle associated with the highest levels of estradiol (late follicular phase) (120) and that the pituitary response to TRH in man is enhanced by prior treatment with estrogens (22) suggest that estrogen sensitization causes the greater TSH secretory response to TRH in women than in men (73). It has recently been reported that the administration of therapeutic amounts of growth hormone to patients with hypopituitarism of hypothalamic origin resulted in a decreased pituitary TSH response to TRH (84, 116). Growth hormone release inhibiting factor (somatostatin), a tetradecapeptide isolated from the hypothalamus, has been reported to inhibit the TSH response to TRH in normal men (58, 125, 151). In addition, somatostatin has been shown to have an inhibitory effect on the high nighttime basal levels of serum TSH (152). These data suggest that somatostatin may have a physiological role in the regulation of TSH secretion. In support of this suggestion is the recent demonstration by Ferland and co-workers (35) that, after injection of sheep antiserum to somatostatin into rats, an increase was noted in basal plasma TSH levels and in TSH secretion in response to cold.

Extremes of Age

Basal TSH levels have been reported to be both normal and slightly increased in the elderly (28, 71). Studies with TRH in elderly men and women, which showed a lesser increase in T_3 concentration after TRH, have not been confirmed and do not indicate a depression of pituitary function (2). Furthermore, since elderly patients can increase their basal serum TSH concentrations strikingly when challenged by frank hypothyroidism, it would follow that the pituitary senses very little, if any, deficiency of thyroid hormone in the normal aging individual (71). Clearly more data are required before the phenomena of aging can be related to the thyroregulatory mechanisms known to exist at present.

There is much current interest in the effect of pregnancy both on the changes in thyroid gland function in the mother and in the fetus. With the development of rapid radioimmunoassay for thyroid hormones in small blood samples, screening for neonatal thyroid disorders is now practical (37).

Some of the changes in maternal thyroid metabolism during pregnancy may be due to the secretion of placental human chorionic thyrotropin (hCT). Although some human placentas may contain as much as 18,500 mU hCT per placenta (67), most placentas contain less than 10 mU hCT. Aborted placentas from 51 to 133 days of gestation show variable but generally low hCT content (68). In addition, purified human chorionic gonadotropin (hCG) has intrinsic thyrotropic activity in the TSH bioassay (101), but it is only 1/4000 as potent as pituitary TSH on a molecular basis. There is difficulty in establishing plasma levels of these hormones during pregnancy because of differences between bioassay and immunoassay. Thus serum bioassayable TSH has been reported to be high early in pregnancy (62); also, hCT by immunoassay has been shown to rise progressively during pregnancy (142). However, Hershman et al (64) found that hCT was low during pregnancy, and TSH only slightly elevated.

It is conceivable that virtually all significant circulating thyrotropic activity in pregnancy plasma may be ascribed exclusively to hCG, which is always elevated in early pregnancy and may rise to astronomical levels in hydatidiform mole and choriocarcinoma (63). Such a view has the virtue of simplicity as well as the bulk of recent supporting evidence.

The fetal pituitary thyroid system has differentiated in the human fetus and appears capable of function (albeit at a low level) by the end of the first trimester of gestation; it also functions independently of maternal control. It would appear that a general maturation of the neural and neuroendocrine systems controlling the secretion of adenohypophyseal hormones occurs at about 20 weeks; hypothalamic activation results in increased hypophyseal TSH synthesis and secretion, followed by increasing thyroid gland activity (36, 38).

At birth, the main physiological event controlling immediate postnatal thyroid function results from a sharp rise in serum TSH due to increased pituitary TSH release during the early minutes and hours of life (39). The cutting of the umbilical cord rather than body cooling is apparently the primary stimulus to this event (119). However, experiments in which TSH was increased when newborn infants were placed in different ambient temperatures suggest that cooling of the newborn in the extrauterine environment also may be an important stimulus (39–41). In response to the postnatal TSH surge, plasma T_4, free T_4, T_3, and free T_3 rise briskly (32), but clinical symptoms of hyperthyroidism do not occur in the newborn because of the transient nature of these rises.

Control of thyroid function during the fetal and neonatal period thus depends on many factors. The development of the hypothalamic-pituitary axis, the stresses experienced by the fetus at delivery, and the developing maturation of fetal enzymes responsible for peripheral metabolism of thyroid hormones are all significant. In addition, the maternal iodine status is clearly important, at least in the rat (vide infra). Other indirect controlling influences on the thyroid at this time, such as potential variation in peripheral tissue sensitivity to thyroid hormones at the cellular level, have yet to be explored.

HYPOTHALAMIC THYROTROPIN RELEASING HORMONE (TRH) CONTROL OF TSH

Ablation of the medial basal hypothalamus of several species has led to diminished TSH secretion and reduced thyroid function (86, 87, 113). In contrast, TSH production may be maintained if a small "hypothalamic island" disconnected from other central nervous system structures is permitted to retain its normal connection with the median eminence and pituitary. Pituitary stalk section or transplantation of the pituitary to a distant site such as the kidney results in diminished TSH production. Conversely, electrical stimulation by carefully placed hypothalamic electrodes produced marked elevation of TSH within ten minutes, a response which was abolished by prior administration of thyroxine to the experimental rat (87).

Such reports along with many others had led to the expectation of the discovery of a "thyrotropin releasing factor" or TRF, a term actually employed by workers prior to the identification of the tripeptide.

The identification of the tripeptide termed "TRF," or "TRH" (thyrotropin releasing hormone) was the outcome of the separate investigations by the laboratories of Guillemin (17–19) and Schally, (10) and must be considered a major advance in neuroendocrinology, since it represents the first proven isolation of a hypothalamic releasing factor. Vast numbers of ovine and porcine hypothalami were extracted, and monumental chemical purification work was required before the tripeptide was isolated and its structure established. Immediately thereafter the tripeptide was synthesized and its biological properties were verified to be the same as the naturally occurring material.

The tripeptide is pyro-Glutamyl-Histidyl-Proline amide (pGlu-His-Pro-NH$_2$). The cyclization of the N-terminal glutamic acid to the pyro-glutamyl structure is essential, as is the amidation of the proline residue of the carboxy terminus, for full activity. Most minor alterations of structure lead to diminished activity, except for methylation of the 3 position of the histidine residue, which increases potency eightfold, probably by enhancing resistance to degradation in plasma. The plasma half-life of the injected tripeptide in human subjects is quite brief, of the order of a few minutes, with apparent half-time components of 3 and 7 minutes. However, amounts of the order of 12-14% of a bolus injection may be recovered in the urine, mainly within the first hour after injection. The material recovered from the urine has shown physiologic potency and immunologic characteristics indistinguishable from the injected tripeptide.

Merely incubating TRH in plasma or serum results in marked degradation, but this does not occur with serum or plasma previously heated at 65°C for 15 minutes (8). These findings suggest degradation by circulating enzymes such as peptidases, with some intact TRH escaping into the urine. These properties are entirely compatible with a releasing factor secreted from the hypothalamus into the hypophyseal portal vessels with immediate action upon arrival in the anterior pituitary, before the occurrence of the appreciable degradation which would occur in the systemic circulation, with the surviving intact TRH excreted by glomerular filtration and appearing in the urine. It must be conceded, however, that some caution should be exercised in drawing conclusions regarding hypothalamic TRH production from measurement of urinary TRH. Even though the concentration of TRH found in the hypothalamus is by far the highest, it has been found widely distributed throughout all areas of the brain, and the extra-hypothalamic areas may account for as much as 80% of the total brain TRH (33). There is even evidence that TRH may have "neurotransmitter" or other nervous system functions quite apart from its presumed role in control of TSH.

The response of normal human subjects to an intravenous injection of 500 μg TRH is a prompt rise in plasma TSH, peaking within 15–30 minutes at a concentration of 16–26 μU/ml in women (slightly lower in men) from a basal mean value of about 6 μU/ml (127, 128). The peak TSH gradually declines to the basal level over the next 150 minutes. The TSH spike usually evokes a definite elevation in serum T_3, but infrequently any elevation of serum T_4.

This response is markedly exaggerated in myxedematous subjects, with a more pronounced rise above the elevated baseline (56a). Thyrotoxic subjects or normals pretreated with T_4 or T_3 show abolition of the TSH rise as well as a suppressed baseline (56a). In some studies (113), inhibition by T_4 or T_3 can be overcome by increased doses of TRH.

Prolactin, as well as TSH, rises on administration of TRH with a similar rapidity, and this response is also suppressed by pretreatment with exogenous thyroid hormones (72a).

The studies of Snyder & Utiger (126), showed that the TSH response to intravenous TRH testing was substantially reduced by administration of small doses of exogenous hormones (15 μg T_3 or 60 μg T_4 daily for 3–4 weeks), which resulted in no detectable increase in the serum values of the administered hormones. The converse study by Vagenakis and co-workers (144) showed increased sensitivity to TRH after minimal lowering of the plasma T_4 by iodide administration. One may interpret these findings to signify the predominating effect of thyroid hormone feedback upon the pituitary, with TRH exerting perhaps a modulating influence, or fine control of the "set-point."

The general picture inferred from all the foregoing is the superimposition of an additional fine control upon the pituitary-thyroid feedback mechanisms, which has been considered to adjust the set-point.

An important illustration of the role of TRH is provided by the disorder called "hypothalamic hypothyroidism" or "tertiary hypothyroidism." It has been found in a number of clinics that hypothyroid subjects without the usual elevation of TSH may indeed have potentially normal pituitary function, as judged by normal or even supranormal TSH rise on administration of TRH. These results led to the inference that the basic defect entailed impaired hypothalamic production of TRH (76, 108).

The mechanism by which TRH stimulates TSH synthesis and release is complex. There is no doubt that TRH is released into the primary capillary tufts of the long portal vessels to arrive at the adenohypophysis. An insight into the control of this mechanism was the observation that, in rats with anterior hypothalamic lesions, much less thyroxine was required to inhibit radioiodine discharge from the thyroid gland than in unlesioned control rats (41a). It would appear that, as the amount of TRH delivered to the pituitary decreases, the sensitivity of the adenohypophysis to feedback inhibition by thyroid hormone is increased. This concept fits with the recent demonstration that chronic exposure of cultured pituitary GH_3 cells to TRH leads to a decrease in the number of TRH receptors (69).

The control of TSH release by TRH is also dependent on intracellular cation concentrations. Calcium ions are necessary for the potassium or TRH-stimulated enhancement of TSH release to occur in vitro (146, 147). However, lysis of TSH storage granules isolated from pituitary tissue was unaffected by calcium or magnesium supplementation (9). TRH stimulated adenohypophyseal cAMP (155, 166), even when calcium was removed from the incubation medium. In this latter case, TSH production was inhibited and it is therefore not precisely clear how the effect of TRH, impinging on the cell surface of a thyrotroph, is translated at the membrane into the production of cAMP, which then stimulates the intracellular synthesis of TSH, its accumulation into storage granules, and finally the lysis of the granules and release of the hormone from the cell.

In contrast to the above data on TRH release, it is not yet known which hypothalamic cell type synthesizes TRH. An elegant study of the biosynthesis of TRH in organ culture of guinea pig median eminence tissue showed that this tissue is capable of TRH synthesis before neuronal degeneration occurs, thus implicating neurons as the synthesizing cells (90). Ependymal cells, in the same site, known to be capable of the uptake of substances related to thyroid function and its control, including TRH, are not the cellular site of synthesis of TRH.

Cold exposure of rats increases the activity of TRH synthetase (114). Norepinephrine also increases the synthesis of TRH, as does dopamine, probably through transformation to norepinephrine (56). There is, therefore, monoaminergic control of the synthesis and, possibly, the secretion of TRH, and TRH has been found to be associated with subcellular hypothalamic particles similar in properties to those of synaptosomes containing norepinephrine and dopamine (4). It has been suggested that thyroid hormones act partially at the level of the brain, possibly to modify the secretion of TRH. Experiments by Knigge & Joseph (75, 78) and work reviewed by Reichlin et al (114) suggest a positive rather than negative feedback effect on the hypothalamus. It is clear that static measurements of TRH in neural tissue may mask dynamics of secretion. A more complete account of the factors determining TRH production awaits future work.

PERIPHERAL METABOLIC REGULATION

Previous reviews (131, 132) discussed in detail the role of the three thyroxine transport proteins of human plasma, namely, thyroxine binding alpha-globulin

(TBG), prealbumin (TBPA, or thyroxine binding prealbumin), and albumin. Almost all circulating T_4 and T_3 is protein bound, and only a minute fraction of a percent is dialyzable or ultrafiltrable in vitro, and presumably, freely diffusible across membranes in vivo, thus able to penetrate cells. This unbound moiety is in equilibrium with the bound fraction of each hormone. Although the circulating concentration of T_4 is more than thirty times as great as that of T_3, the latter is much less firmly bound to all 3 protein carriers, and hence has a relatively greater proportion (about ten times as great) in the unbound diffusible state. This is thought to account for the shorter biological half-time of T_3, about one day in normal human subjects, in contrast to the longer half-time of T_4, which approximates one week.

In comparisons of the amounts of replacement therapy required to maintain euthyroidism in athyreotic human subjects, T_3 is approximately three times as potent as T_4. In many studies in other species, such as the rat, T_3 appears approximately five times as potent as T_4.

There is some minor residual controversy regarding the relative importance of the two hormones in normal metabolism, but it is now clear that T_3 has a very significant, indeed a major, role in normal physiology. Since T_4 may undergo peripheral conversion to T_3 (13, 107, 133, 134), some have argued that all action of T_4 may be due to peripheral conversion to T_3. Nevertheless at the present time it would seem injudicious to conclude that T_4 cannot have any action as such without deiodination to T_3, even though this pathway may be quantitatively the most significant.

Of the circulating T_3, probably one third or less is of thyroidal origin, while the majority or at least two thirds, arises by peripheral deiodination, with the liver and kidneys having an important role in this transformation. From the standpoint of the metabolism of circulating thyroxine, it may be estimated that perhaps 33–40% is monodeiodinated to T_3, perhaps 15–20% is changed to tetraiodothyroacetic acid (TA_4 or "Tetrac") or conjugated and lost in urine or bile, and probably about 50% to so-called reverse T_3 (rT_3), 3', 5',3-triiodo-L-thyronine, which differs from "orthodox T_3" in having an iodine lacking from the A ring rather than the B ring. The degradation of rT_3 is probably 3 times as fast as the rapid rate of T_3 turnover, hence the very low serum concentration of rT_3 (24). As developed below, the partition of T_4 metabolism among these pathways has a significant effect upon circulating T_3 levels. One of these metabolic products, T_3, has physiological activity greater than that of its precursor, T_4. In contrast, TA_4 and rT_3 have been shown to have no significant physiological potency.

With awareness of the importance of T_3 in hormone physiology, the question naturally arose whether conditions exist where T_3 formation from T_4 is diminished. At present, the clinical circumstances where this occurs are quite numerous and are likely to increase.

In view of the important role of the liver and kidney in monodeiodination of T_4 to T_3 (134), it was not unexpected that T_3 formation should be impaired in severe hepatic disease (cirrhosis and hepatitis) (26, 102) as well as in renal insufficiency (34), despite maintenance by hemodialysis. Only successful renal homotransplantation has been shown to reverse the diminished T_3 of advanced renal insufficiency (34).

Studies of cadaver tissues (112) have shown diminution of T_3 in tissues from patients with chronic illnesses as opposed to those who had died after a brief illness. On the other hand, it has been alleged that any major systemic illness, acute or chronic, may lead to diminished T_3 attributable to reduced conversion from T_4 (6).

Advanced old age is characterized by lower T_3 concentrations than are observed in the first six decades of life (118, 127, 128). Even more striking findings are observed in the neonatal state. In the first day of life, the T_3 concentration is negligibly low, but there is a vast excess of rT_3 (25). Immediately on clamping the umbilical cord there is a burst of TSH secretion (see above), which results in thyroidal production of T_3, which begins to rise within hours after birth.

In Cushing's syndrome or in high-dose steroid therapy (27), the T_3 concentration is low, and that of rT_3 elevated; these changes are also noted in a variety of systemic illnesses (154) and the postoperative state (20). Indeed, it is noteworthy that T_3 and rT_3 have been found to vary reciprocally wherever both have been measured (16). Similarly, total starvation for weight reduction results in prompt fall of serum T_3 within 3 days with a reciprocal rise of rT_3 (143). The reduction of serum T_3 has likewise been observed in the chronic food deprivation of anorexia nervosa (11). Recent work related the changes closely to carbohydrate intake, with T_3 falling on low or zero carbohydrate diets, and the reverse changes on restoration of carbohydrates to the diet (29).

A mechanism for the reciprocal relationship between T_3 and rT_3 concentrations has been suggested by the recent findings of Chopra (23). Using a liver homogenate capable of deiodinating T_4 to T_3, Chopra observed that this transformation was markedly retarded by the addition of rT_3 in vitro. This would suggest that elevation of rT_3 may play a causal role in the clinical states in which T_3 formation from T_4 is reduced.

The foregoing conditions with diminished serum T_3 and elevated rT_3 may or may not have "hypometabolism" as a concomitant clinical feature. Since the virtual disappearance of so-called animal calorimetry or oxygen consumption by direct or indirect methods, it becomes difficult to evaluate the status of these patients, from the standpoint of their peripheral tissue performance in terms of calorigenesis or other thyroidal parameters other than serum hormone concentrations. Not only the basal metabolism (BMR), but even the Achilles reflex time is little used in the current era of supersophistication. The present reviewers would be hard put to define the optimal serum T_3 concentration appropriate for someone afflicted with terminal hepatic insufficiency, carcinomatosis, or anorexia nervosa. The term "T_4 euthyroidism" (21) may not be entirely unjustified, regardless of facetious implications that might be drawn from it.

The hormone thyroxine has been known since its crystallization by Edward C. Kendall (77), who found the crystals in his laboratory on Christmas Day of 1916 —six decades ago. The advent of T_3 and the exciting work in the area of T_4 to T_3 transformation have perhaps unduly adumbrated T_4. Finally, it should be reemphasized that T_4 must not be overlooked, and that it can evidently support metabolism in health and disease.

ACKNOWLEDGMENTS

We are grateful to Dr. S. Reichlin for allowing us to examine work in press, and to Dr. Peter O. Milch for help with the bibliographic aspects, as well as for critical and other substantive scholarly contributions. This work was supported in part by US Public Health Service Grant AM10739 and by the Veterans Administration Medical Research Service.

Literature Cited

1. Anderson, M. S., Bowers, C. Y., Kastin, A. J., Schlach, D. S., Schally, A. V., Snyder, P. J., Utiger, R. D., Wilber, J. F., Wise, A. J. 1971. Synthetic thyrotropin-releasing hormone. *N. Engl. J. Med.* 285:1279–83

2. Azizi, F., Vagenakis, A. G. Portnay, G. I., Rapoport, B., Ingbar, S. H., Braverman, L. E. 1975..Pituitary-thyroid responsiveness to intramuscular thyrotropin-releasing hormone based on analysis of serum thyroxine, triiodothyronine and thyrotropin concentrations. *N. Engl. J. Med.* 292:273–77

3. Balsam, A., Leppo, L. E. 1974. Augmentation of the peripheral metabolism of L-triiodothyronine and L-thyronine after acclimation to cold. *J. Clin. Invest.* 53:980–87

4. Barnea, A., Ben-Jonathan, N., Colston, C., Johnston, J. M. Porter, J. C. 1975. Differential sub-cellular compartmentalization of thyrotropin releasing hormone (TRH) and gonadotropin releasing hormone (LRH) in hypothalamic tissue. *Proc. Natl. Acad. Sci. USA* 72:3153–57

5. Bastomsky, C. H. 1974. Thyroid iodide transport. In *Handb. Physiol. Sect. 7,* ed. M. A. Greer, D. H. Solomon, 3: 81–89. Baltimore: Williams & Wilkins. 491 pp.

6. Bermudez, F., Surks, M. I., Oppenheimer, J. H. 1975. High incidence of decreased serum triiodothyronine concentration in patients with nonthyroidal disease. *J. Clin. Endocrinol. Metab.* 41:27–40

7. Binoux, M., Pierce, J. G., Odell, W. D. 1974. Radioimmunological characteristics of human thyrotropin and its subunits: applications for the measurement of human TSH. *J. Clin. Endocrinol. Metab.* 38:674–82

8. Blackwell, R. C., Guillemin, R. 1973. Hypothalamic control of adenohypophyseal secretions. *Ann. Rev. Physiol.* 35:357–90

9. Bowers, C. Y., Lee, K. L. 1967. Stability of thyrotropin granules of rat adenohypophysis: Relation to thyrotropic releasing factor and triiodothyronine action. *Program Am. Endocr. Soc. 49th Meet.* Abstr. No. 122

9a. Bowers, C. Y., Lee, K. L., Schally, A. V. 1968. A study on the interaction of the thyrotropin-releasing factor and L-triiodothyronine; effects of puromycin and cycloheximide. *Endocrinology.* 82:75–82

9b. Bowers, C. Y., Lee, K. L., Schally, A. V. 1968. Effect of actinomycin D on hormones that control the release of thyrotropin from the anterior pituitary glands of mice. *Endocrinology* 82: 303–10

10. Bowers, C. Y., Schally, A. V., Weil, A., Reynolds, G. A., Folkers, K. 1970. Chemical and biological identity of thyrotropin releasing hormones (TRH) of bovine and human origin. *Proc. Int. Thyroid Conf. Vienna, 6th.* 2:1019–40

11. Boyar, R. M., Bradlow, H. L., Fukushima, D. K., O'Connor, J., Zumoff, B., Hellman, L. 1975. "Low triiodothyronine (T_3) syndrome" in anorexia nervosa: "Hypothyroid" effects on steroid metabolism. *Clin. Res.* 23:387 (Abstr.)

12. Braverman, L. E., Ingbar, S. H. 1963. Changes in thyroidal function during adaptation to large doses of iodide. *J. Clin. Invest.* 42:1216–31

13. Braverman, L. E., Ingbar, S. H., Sterling, K. 1970. Conversion of thyroxine (T_4) to triiodothyronine (T_3) in athyreotic human subjects. *J. Clin. Invest.* 49:855–64

14. Braverman, L. E., Ingbar, S. H., Vagenakis, A. G., Adams, L., Maloof, F. 1971. Enhanced susceptibility to iodide myxedema in patients with Hashimoto's disease. *J. Clin. Endocrinol. Metab.* 32:515–21

15. Braverman, L. E., Woeber, K. A., Ingbar, S. H. 1969. Induction of myxedema by iodide in patients euthyroid after radioiodine or surgical treatment of

diffuse toxic goiter. *N. Engl. J. Med.* 281:816–21

16. Burger, A., Nicod, P., Suter, P., Vallotton, M. B., Vagenakis, A., Braverman, L. E. 1976. Reduced active thyroid hormone levels in acute illness. *Lancet* 1:653–55

17. Burgus, R., Dunn, T. F., Desiderio, D., Guillemin, R. 1969. Structure moleculaire du facteur hypothalamique hypophysiotrope TRF d'origine ovine: Evidence par spectrometrie de masse de la sequence PCA-His-PRO-NH₂. *C R Acad. Sci.* 269:1870–73

18. Burgus, R., Dunn, T. F., Desiderio, D., Vale, W., Guillemin, R. 1969. Derivés polypeptidiques de synthèse doues d'activité hypophysiotrope TRF. Nouvelles observations. *C R Acad. Sci.* 269:226–28

19. Burgus, R., Dunn, T. F., Desiderio, D., Ward, D. N., Vale, W., Guillemin, R. 1970. Characterization of the hypothalamic hypophysiotropic TSH-releasing factor (TRF) of ovine origin. *Nature* 226:321–25

20. Burr, W. A., Griffiths, R. S., Black, E. G., Hoffenberg, R., Meinhold, H., Wenzel, K. W. 1975. Serum triiodothyronine and reverse triiodothyronine concentrations after surgical operation. *Lancet* 2:1277–79

21. Burrows, A. W., Shakespear, R. A., Hesch, R. D., Cooper, E., Aickin, C. M., Burke, C. W. 1975. Thyroid hormones in the elderly sick: "T₄ euthyroidism." *Br. Med. J.* 4:437–39

22. Carlson, H. E., Jacobs, L. S., Daughaday, W. H. 1973. Growth hormone, thyrotropin, and prolactin responses to thyrotropin-releasing hormone following diethylstilbestrol pretreatment. *J. Clin. Endocrinol. Metab.* 37:488–90

23. Chopra, I. J. 1976. Extra thyroidal conversion of T₄ to T₃ in vitro: Evidence that reverse T₃ is a potent inhibitor of T₃ production. *Clin. Res.* 24:426 (Abstr.)

24. Chopra, I. J. 1975. Personal communication

25. Chopra, I. J., Sack, J., Fisher, D. A. 1975. Circulating 3, 3', 5'-triiodothyronine (reverse T₃) in the human newborn. *J. Clin. Invest.* 55:1137–41

26. Chopra, I. J., Solomon, D. H., Chopra, U., Young, R. T., Chuateco, G. N. 1974. Alterations in circulating thyroid hormones and thyrotropin in hepatic cirrhosis: Evidence for euthyroidism despite subnormal serum triiodothyro-

nine. *J. Clin. Endocrinol. Metab.* 39:501–11

27. Chopra, I. J., Williams, D. E., Orgiazzi, J., Solomon, D. H. 1975. Opposite effects of dexamethasone on serum concentrations of 3, 3', 5'-triiodothyronine (reverse T₃) and 3, 3', 5-triiodothyronine (T₃). *J. Clin. Endocrinol. Metab.* 41:911–20

28. Cuttelod, S., Lemarchand-Beraud, T., Magnenat, P., Perret, C., Poli, S., Vannotti, A. 1974. Effect of age and kidneys and liver on rate of thyrotropin turnover in man. *Metabolism* 23:101–13

29. Danforth, E., Tyzbir, E. D., Horton, E. S., Sims, E. A. H., Burger, A. G., Braverman, L. E., Vagenakis, A. G., Ingbar, S. H. 1976. Reciprocal changes in serum triiodothyronine (T₃) and reverse T₃ (rT₃) induced by altering the carbohydrate content of the diet. *Clin. Res.* 24:271 (Abstr.)

30. Ekpechi, O. L. V., Van Middlesworth, L. 1973. Iodinated compounds in the thyroids of the offspring of rats maintained on low-iodine diet. *Endocrinology* 92:1376–81

31. Emerson, C. H., Utiger, R. D. 1975. Thyrotropin releasing hormone (TRH) in concentrated extracts of rat plasma. *Program Am. Endocr. Soc. 57th Meet.* Abstr. No. 150

32. Erenberg, A., Phelps, D. L., Lam, R., Oh, W. 1974. Total and free thyroxine and triiodothyronine concentrations in the neonatal period. *Pediatrics* 53:211–16

33. Eskay, R. L., Oliver, C., Grollman, A., Porter, J. C. 1974. Immunoreactive LRH and TRH in the fetal, neonatal and adult rat brain. *Program Am. Endocr. Soc. 56th Meet.* Abstr. No. 55

34. Fang, V. S., Lim, V. S., Refetoff, S. 1974. Triiodothyronine (T₃) hypothyroidism in patients with renal insufficiency. *Proc. 50th Meet. Am. Thyroid Assoc.* (Abstr.)

35. Ferland, L., Labrie, F., Jobin, M., Arimura, A., Schally, A. V. 1975. Physiological role of somatostatin in the control of growth hormone and thyrotrophin secretion. *Biochem. Biophys. Res. Commun.* 68:149–56

36. Fisher, D. A. 1975. Thyroid function in the fetus and newborn. *Med. Clin. N. Am.* 59:1099–1107

37. Fisher, D. A., Burrow, G. N., eds. 1975. *Perinatal Thyroid Physiology and Disease.* New York: Raven. 277 pp.

38. Fisher, D. A., Dussault, J. H. 1974. Development of the mammalian thyroid gland. In *Handb. Physiol. Sect. 7,* ed. M. A. Greer, D. H. Solomon, 3:21–38. Baltimore: William & Wilkins. 491 pp.

39. Fisher, D. A., Odell, W. D. 1969. Acute release of thyrotropin in the newborn. *J. Clin. Invest.* 48:1670–77

40. Fisher, D. A., Oddie, T. H. 1964. Neonatal thyroid hyperactivity: A response to cooling. *Am. J. Dis. Child.* 107:574–81

41. Fisher, D. A., Oddie, T. H., Makoski, E. J. 1966. The influence of environmental temperature on thyroid, adrenal and water metabolism in the new born human infant. *Pediatrics* 37:583–91

41a. Florsheim, W. H. 1958. The effect of anterior hypothalamic lesions on thyroid function and goiter development in the rat. *Endocrinology* 62:783–89

42. Fortier, C., Delgado, A., Ducommun, P., Ducommun, S., Dupont, A., Jobin, M., Kraicer, J., MacIntosh-Hardt, B., Marceau, H., Mialhe, P., Mialhe-Voloss, C., Rerup, C., Van Rees, G. P. 1970. Functional interrelationships between the adenohypophysis, thyroid, adrenal cortex and gonads. *Can. Med. Assoc. J.* 103:864–74

43. Fukuda, H., Yasuda, N., Greer, M. A. 1975. Acute effects of thyroxine, triiodothyronine and iodide on thyrotropin secretion. *Endocrinology* 97:924–31

44. Fukuda, H., Yasuda, N., Greer, M. A. 1975. Changes in plasma thyrotropin, thyroxine, and triiodothyronine after acute or chronic administration of iodide to iodine-deficient rats. *Endocrinology* 97:1196–1204

45. Fukuda, H., Yasuda, N., Greer, M. A., Kutas, M., Greer, S. E. 1975. Changes in plasma thyroxine, triiodothyronine, and TSH during adaptation to iodine deficiency in the rat. *Endocrinology* 97:307–14

46. Gale, C. C. 1973. Neuroendocrine aspects of thermoregulation. *Ann. Rev. Physiol.* 35:391–430

47. Gale, C. C., Hayward, J. S., Green, W. L., Wu, S. Y., Schiller, H., Jackson, I. M. D. 1975. Endocrine response to acute cold in man. *Fed. Proc.* 34:301

48. Gale, C. C., Jobin, M., Proppe, D. W., Notter, D., Fox, H. 1970. Endocrine thermoregulatory responses to local hypothalamic cooling in unanesthetized baboons. *Am. J. Physiol.* 219:193–201

49. Galton, V. A. 1975. The metabolism of thyroid hormones in rat pituitary. *Proc. Int. Thyroid Conf. 7th* Abstr. No. 130;

see also Robbins, J., Braverman, L. E. 1976. *Thyroid Research.* Amsterdam: Excerpta Medica. 251 pp.

50. Galton, V. A., Nisula, B. C. 1969. Thyroxine metabolism and thyroid function in the cold adapted rat. *Endocrinology* 85:79–86

51. Gershengorn, M. C., Weintraub, B. D. 1975. Thyrotropin-induced hyperthyroidism caused by selective pituitary resistance to thyroid hormone. *J. Clin. Invest.* 56:633–42

52. Goldman, M., Rosenberg, L. L., LaRoche, G., Srebnik, H. 1966. Iodine metabolism in intact and hypophysectomized rats of a colony maintained on a low-iodine diet. *Endocrinology* 78:889–92

53. Greer, M. A., Grimm, Y., Studer, H. 1968. Qualitative changes in the secretion of thyroid hormones induced by iodine deficiency. *Endocrinology* 83:1193–98

54. Greer, M. A., Panton, P., Greer, S. E. 1975. The effect of iodine deficiency on thyroid function in the infant rat. *Metabolism* 24:1391–1402

55. Gregerman, R. I. 1971. Intrinsic physiological variables and non thyroidal illness. In *The Thyroid,* ed. S. C. Werner, S. H. Ingbar, pp. 137–52. New York: Harper & Row. 914 pp.

56. Grimm, Y., Reichlin, S. 1973. Thyrotropin-releasing hormone (TRH): Neurotransmitter regulation of secretion by mouse hypothalamic tissue in vitro. *Endocrinology* 93:626–31

56a. Gual, C., Kastin, A. J., Schally, A. V. 1972. Clinical expreience with hypothalamic releasing hormones. Part 1. Thyrotropin-releasing hormone *Rec. Progr. Horm. Res.* 28:173–200

57. Guansing, A., Leung, Y., Ajlouni, K., Hagen, T. C. 1975. Effect of hypoglycemia on TSH release in man. *J. Clin. Endocrinol. Metab.* 40:755–58

58. Hall, R., Besser, G. M., Schally, A. V., Coy, D. H., Evered, D., Goldie, D. J., Kastin, A. J., McNeilly, A. S., Mortimer, C. H., Phenekos, D. Tunbridge, W. M. G., Weightman, D. 1973. Action of growth-hormone release inhibitory hormone in healthy men and acromegaly. *Lancet* 2:581–84

59. Halmi, N. S. 1954. Regulation of rat thyroid in short term iodine deficiency. *Endocrinology* 54:216–24

60. Halmi, N. S. 1964. The accumulation and recirculation of iodide by the thyroid. In *The Thyroid Gland,* ed. R. Pitt-

Rivers, W. R. Trotter. 1:71–86. Washington: Butterworths. 442 pp.
61. Halmi, N. S., Stuelke, R. G. 1956. Problems of thyroidal self-regulation. *Metabolism* 5:646–51
62. Hennen, G., Pierce, J. G., Freychet, P. 1969. Human chorionic thyrotropin: Further characterization and study of its secretion during pregnancy. *J. Clin. Endocrinol. Metab.* 32:52–58
63. Hershman, J. M. 1972. Hyperthyroidism induced by trophoblastic thyrotropin. *Mayo Clin. Proc.* 47:913–18
64. Hershman, J. M., Kenimer, J. G., Higgins, H. P., Patillo, R. A. 1975. Placental thyrotropins. In *Perinatal Thyroid Physiology and Disease,* ed. D. A. Fisher, G. N. Burrow, pp. 11–20. New York: Raven. 277 pp.
65. Hershman, J. M., Pittman, J. A. 1971. Control of thyrotropin secretion in man. *N. Engl. J. Med.* 285:997–1006
66. Hershman, J. M., Read, D. G., Bailey, A. L., Norman, V. D., Gibson, T. B. 1970. Effect of cold exposure on serum thyrotropin. *J. Clin. Endocrinol. Metab.* 30:430–34
67. Hershman, J. M., Starnes, W. R. 1971. Placental content and characterization of human chorionic thyrotropin. *J. Clin. Endocrinol. Metab.* 35:52–58
68. Hershman, J. M., Starnes, W. R., Kenimer, J. G., Patillo, R. A. 1972. Human chorionic thyrotropin. In *Proc. Int. Congr. Endoc. 4th, Wash. DC,* ed. R. O. Scow, pp. 628–87. Amsterdam: Excerpta Medica
69. Hinkle, P. M., Tashjian, A. H. 1975. Decrease in the number of receptors for thyrotropin releasing hormone (TRH in GH₃ pituitary cells after prolonged incubation with TRH. *Program 57th Am. Endocrine Soc.* Abstr. No. 3
70. Ingbar, S. H. 1972. Autoregulation of the thyroid. Response to iodide excess and depletion. *Mayo Clin. Proc.* 47: 814–23
71. Ingbar, S. H. 1976. Aging and thyroid hormone economy. *J. Am. Geriatr. Soc.* 24:49–53
72. Inoue, K., Taurog, A. 1968. Acute and chronic effects of iodide on thyroid radioiodine metabolism in iodine-deficient rats. *Endocrinology* 83:279–90
72a. Jacobs, L. S., Schneider, P. J., Wilber, J. F., Daughaday, W. H., Utiger R. D. 1971. Increased serum prolactin after administration of synthetic thyrotropin releasing hormone (TRH) in man. *J. Clin. Endocrinol. Metab.* 33:996–98
73. Jacobs, L. S., Snyder, P. J., Utiger, R. D., Daughaday, W. H. 1973. Prolactin response to thyrotropin releasing hormone in normal subjects. *J. Clin. Endocrinol. Metabl.* 36:1069–73
74. Jobin, M., Dulac, S., Fortier, C. 1973. Effect of cold exposure on thyroxine (T₄) and triiodothyronine (T₃) secretion in the rat. *Fed. Proc.* 32:110
75. Joseph, S. A., Scott, D. E., Vaala, S. S., Knigge, K. M., Krobisch-Dudley, G. 1973. Localization and content of thyrotropin releasing factor (TRF) in median eminence of the hypothalamus. *Acta Endocrinol Copenhagen* 74:215–25
76. Kaplan, S. L., Grumbach, M. M., Friesen, H. G., Costom, B. H. 1972. Thyrotropin-releasing factor (TRF) effect on secretion of human pituitary prolactin and thyrotropin in children and in idiopathic hypopituitary dwarfism: Further evidence for hypophysiotropic hormone deficiencies. *J. Clin. Endocrinol. Metab.* 35:825–30
77. Kendall, E. C. 1929. Thyroxine. *Am. Chem. Soc. Monogr. Ser. No 47.* New York: Chem. Catalog Co. 265 pp.
78. Knigge, K. M., Joseph, S. A. 1971. Neural regulation of TSH secretion: Sites of thyroxine feedback. *Neuroendocrinology* 8:273–88
79. Kourides, I. A., Weintraub, B. D., Levko, M. A., Maloof, F. 1974. Alpha and beta subunits of human thyrotropin: Purification and development of specific radioimmunoassays. *Endocrinology* 94:1411–21
80. Kourides, I. A., Weintraub, B. D., Ridgway, E. C., Maloof, F. 1975. Pituitary secretion of free alpha and beta subunits of human thyrotropin in patients with thyroid disorders. *J. Clin. Endocrinol. Metab.* 40:872–85
81. Lazarus, J. H. 1974. *The iodide concentrating mechanism.* MD thesis. Univ. Cambridge, England. 153 pp.
82. Lee, G. Y., Ingbar, S. H. 1965. Comparison of the effects of ouabain and of iodine adaptation on the thyroid iodide transport mechanism. *Endocrinology* 77:940–43
83. Leung, Y., Guansing, A. R., Ajlouni, K. A., Hagen, T. C. 1974. Hypoglycemia increases TSH in the rat. *Clin. Res.* 22:559 (Abstr.)
84. Lippe, B. M., Van Herle, A. J., LaFranchi, S. H., Uller, R. P., Lavin, N., Kaplan, S. A. 1975. Reversible hypothyroidism in growth hormone deficient children treated with human growth

hormone. *J. Clin. Endocrinol. Metab.* 40:612–18

85. Maayan, M. L., Ingbar, S. H. 1970. Acute depletion of thyroid ATP and pyridine nucleotides following injection of iodine in the rat. *Endocrinology* 86:83–87

86. Martin, J. B., Boshans, R., Reichlin, S. 1970. Feedback regulation of TSH secretion in rats with hypothalamic lesions. *Endocrinology* 87:1032–40

87. Martin, J. B., Reichlin, S. 1970. Neural regulation of the pituitary thyroid axis. *Proc. 6th Midwest Conf. on the Thyroid,* ed. A. D. Kenny, R. R. Anderson, pp. 1–24. Columbia, New York: Univ. Columbia Press

88. Mason, J. W., Mougey, E. H. 1972. Thyroid (plasma B.E.I.) response to chair restraint in the monkey. *Psychosom. Med.* 34:441–48

89. Mayberry, W. E., Gharib, H., Bilstad, J. M., Sizemore, G. W. 1971. Radioimmunoassay for human thyrotropin: Clinical value in patients with normal and abnormal thyroid function. *Ann. Intern. Med.* 74:471–80

90. McKelvy, J. F., Sheridan, M., Joseph, S., Phelps, C. H., Perrie, S. 1975. Biosynthesis of thyrotropin-releasing hormone in organ cultures of the guinea pig median eminence. *Endocrinology* 97:908–13

91. Melander, A., Ericson, L. E., Sundler, F. 1974. Sympathetic regulation of thyroid hormone secretion. *Life Sci.* 14:237–46

92. Melander, A., Ericson, L. E., Sundler, F., Ingbar, S. H. 1974. Sympathetic innervation of the mouse thyroid and its significance in thyroid hormone secretion. *Endocrinology* 94:959–66

93. Melander, A., Ericson, L. E., Ljunggren, J. G., Norberg, K. A., Persson, B., Sundler, F., Tibblin, S., Westgren, U. 1974. Sympathetic innervation of the normal human thyroid. *J. Clin. Endocrinol. Metab.* 39:713–18

94. Melander, A., Hakanson, R., Westgren, U., Owman, C., Sundler, F. 1973. Significance of thyroid mast cells in the regulation of thyroid activity. *Agents Actions* 3:186

95. Melander, A., Sundler, F., Westgren, U. 1973. Intrathyroidal amines and the synthesis of thyroid hormone. *Endocrinology* 93:193–200

96. Montoya, E., Seibel, M. J., Eilber, J. F. 1975. Thyrotropin releasing hormone secretory physiology: Studies by radioimmunoassay and affinity chromatography. *Endocrinology* 96:1413–18

97. Nagataki, S. 1974. Effect of excess quantities of iodide. In *Handb. of Physiol. Sect. 7,* ed. M. A. Greer, D. H. Solomon, 3:329–44. Baltimore: Williams & Wilkins. 491 pp.

98. Nagataki, S., Ingbar, S. H. 1964. Relation between qualitative and quantitative alterations in thyroid hormone synthesis induced by varying doses of iodide. *Endocrinology* 45:296–304

99. Nejad, I. F., Bollinger, J. A., Mitnick, M., Reichlin, S. 1972. Importance of T_3 (triiodothyronine) secretion in altered states of thyroid function in the rat: Cold exposure, subtotal thyroidectomy and hypophysectomy. *Trans. Assoc. Am. Phys.* 85:295–308

100. Nicoloff, J. S., Fisher, D. A., Appelman, M. D. 1970. A new method for the measurement of thyroidal iodine release in man. *J. Clin. Invest.* 49:1922–29

101. Nisula, B. C., Morgan, F. J., Canfield, R. E. 1974. Evidence that chorionic gonadotropin has intrinsic thyrotropic activity. *Biochem. Biophys. Res. Commun.* 59:86–91

102. Nomura, S. Pittman, C. S. 1974. Hypothyroidism in liver patients due to failure of the peripheral conversion of thyroxine (T_4) to triiodothyronine (T_3). *J. Clin. Invest.* 53:57a (Abstr.)

103. Odell, W. D., Wilber, J. F., Utiger, R. D. 1967. Studies of thyrotropin physiology by means of radioimmunoassay. *Rec. Progr. Horm. Res.* 23:47–85

104. Onaya, T., Halmi, N. S. 1967. Mechanism of the inhibitory effect of iodide on thyroidal ^{131}I release in the rat. *Endocrinology* 81:643–48

105. Onaya, T., Tomizawa, T., Yamada, T., Shichijo, K. 1966. Further studies on inhibitory effect of excess iodide on thyroid hormone release in the rat. *Endocrinology* 79:138–48

106. Patel, Y. C., Burger, H. G., Hudson, B. 1971. Radioimmunoassay of serum thyrotropin: Sensitivity and specificity. *J. Clin. Endocrinol. Metab.* 33:768–74

107. Pittman, C. S., Chambers, J. B., Read, V. H. 1971. The extrathyroidal conversion rate of thyroxine to triiodothyronine in normal man. *J. Clin. Invest.* 50:1187–96

108. Pittman, J. A., Haigler, E. D., Hershman, J. M., Pittman, C. S. 1971. Hypothalamic hypothyroidism. *N. Engl. J. Med.* 285:844–45

109. Raben, M. S. 1949. The paradoxical effects of thiocyanate and of thyrotropin

on the organic binding of iodine by the thyroid in the presence of large amounts of iodide. *Endocrinology* 45:296–304

110. Rapoport, B., West, M. N., Ingbar, S. H. 1975. Inhibitory effect of dietary iodine on the thyroid adenylate cyclase response to thyrotropin in the hypophysectomized rat. *J. Clin. Invest.* 56:516–19

111. Reichlin, S. 1964. Function of the hypothalamus in regulation of pituitary-thyroid activity. In *Brain Thyroid Relationships*, ed. M. P. Cameron, M. O'-Connor, pp. 17–32. London: Churchill

112. Reichlin, S., Bollinger, J., Nejad, I., Sullivan, P. 1973. Tissue thyroid hormone concentration of rat and man determined by radioimmunoassay: Biological significance. *Mt. Sinai J. Med.* 40:502–10

113. Reichlin, S., Martin, J. B., Jackson, I. M. D. 1977. Regulation of thyrotropic hormone (TSH) secretion. In *The Endocrine Hypothalamus*, ed. S. L. Jeffcoate. In press

114. Reichlin, S., Martin, J. B., Mitnick, M. A., Boshans, R. L., Grimm, Y., Bollinger, J., Gordon, J., Malacara, J. 1972. The hypothalamus in pituitary thyroid regulation. *Rec. Prog. Horm. Res.* 28: 229–86

115. Ridgway, E. C., Weintraub, B. D., Maloof, F. 1974. Metabolic clearance and production rate of human thyrotropin. *J. Clin. Invest.* 53:895–903

116. Root, A. W., Snyder, P. J., Rezvani, I., DiGeorge, A. M., Utiger, R. D. 1973. Inhibition of thyrotropin releasing hormone mediated secretion of thyrotropin by human growth hormone. *J. Clin. Endocrinol. Metab.* 36:103–7

117. Rosenfeld, P. S., Rosenberg, I. M. 1966. Early enhancement by thyrotropin of thyroid organification of circulating iodide. *Endocrinology* 78:621–27

118. Rubenstein, H. A., Butler, V. P., Werner, S. C. 1973. Progressive decrease in serum triiodothyronine concentrations with human aging: Radioimmunoassay following extraction of serum. *J. Clin. Endocrinol. Metab.* 37:247–53

119. Sack, J., Beaudry, M., DeLamater, P., Oh, W., Fisher, D. 1974. The mechanism of the T_3 response to parturition *Proc. 50th Meeting Am. Thyroid Assoc.* (Abstr.).

120. Sanchez-Franco, F., Garcia, M. D., Cacicedo, L., Martin-Zurro, A., Escobar del Rey, F. 1973. Influence of the sex phase of the menstrual cycle on thyrotropin (TSH) response to thyrotropin-releasing hormone (TRH). *J. Clin. Endocrinol. Metab.* 37:736–40

121. Schadlow, R. R., Surks, M. I., Schwartz, H. L., Oppenheimer, J. H. 1972. Specific triiodothyronine binding sites in the anterior pituitary of the rat. *Science* 176:1252–54

122. Scranton, J. R., Halmi, N. S. 1965. Thyroidal iodide accumulation and loss in vitro. *Endocrinology* 76:441–53

123. Sherwin, J. R., Tong, W. 1974. The actions of iodide and TSH on thyroid cells showing a dual control system for the iodide pump. *Endocrinology* 94:1465–74

124. Sherwin, J. R., Tong, W. 1975. Thyroidal autoregulation. Iodide-induced suppression of thyrotropin stimulated cyclic AMP production and iodinating activity in thyroid cells. *Biochem. Biophys. Acta* 404:30–39

125. Siler, T. M., Yen, S. S. C., Vale, W., Guillemin, R. 1974. Inhibition by somatostatin on the release of TSH induced in man by thyrotropin-releasing factor. *J. Clin. Endocrinol. Metab.* 38:742–45

126. Snyder, P. J., Utiger, R. D. 1972. Inhibition of thyrotropin response to thyrotropin releasing hormone by small quantities of thyroid hormones. *J. Clin. Invest.* 51:2077–84

127. Snyder, P. J., Utiger, R. D. 1972. Thyrotropin response to thyrotropin releasing hormone in normal females over forty. *J. Clin. Endocrinol. Metab.* 34:1096–98

128. Snyder, P. J., Utiger, R. D. 1972. Response to thyrotropin releasing hormone (TRH) in normal man. *J. Clin. Endocrinol. Metab.* 34:380–85

129. Socolow, E., Dunlap, D., Sobel, R. A., Ingbar, S. H., 1968. A correlative study on the effect of iodide administration in the rat on thyroidal iodide transport and organic iodine content. *Endocrinology* 83:737–43

130. Steinbach, J. J. 1973. Thyroxine and triiodothyronine binding sites in the soluble fraction of the anterior pituitary. *Am. Thyroid Assoc., 50th Meet.* (Abstr.)

131. Sterling, K. 1964. Thyroxine in blood. *Mayo Clin. Proc.* 39:586–608

132. Sterling, K. 1968. Thyroxine binding in serum. In *Radioisotopes in Medicine: In Vitro Studies*, ed. R. L. Hayes, F. A. Goswitz, B. E. P. Murphy, pp. 293–313. Springfield, Virginia: US Atomic Energy Commission, Div. Tech. Info.

133. Sterling, K., Brenner, M. A., Newman, E. S. 1970. Conversion of thyroxine to triiodothyronine in normal human subjects. *Science* 169:1099–1100

134. Sterling, K., Brenner, M. A., Saldanha, V. F. 1973. Conversion of thyroxine to triiodothyronine by cultured human cells. *Science* 179:1000–1

135. Studer, H., Burgi, H., Kohler, H., Garcia, M. C., Morreale de Escobar, G. 1976. A transient rise of hormone secretion: A response of the stimulated rat thyroid gland to small increments of iodide supply. *Acta Endocrinol. Copenhagen* 81:507–15

136. Studer, H., Greer, M. A. 1965. A study of the mechanisms involved in the production of iodine-deficiency goiter. *Acta Endocrinol. Copenhagen* 49:610–28

137. Sufi, S. B., Toccafondi, R. S., Malan, P. G., Ekins, R. P. 1973. Binding of thyroid hormones to a soluble fraction from porcine anterior pituitary. *J. Endocrinol.* 58:41–52

138. Surks, M. I. 1967. Determination of iodide clearance and exit rate constants in incubated thyroid lobes. *Endocrinology* 80:1020–27

138a. Szabo, M., Frohman, L. A. 1976. Suppression of cold stimulated TSH secretion in the rat by anti-TRH serum. *Program. Am. Endocrine Soc. 58th Meet.* No. 265. (Abstr.)

139. Taurog, A. 1970. Thyroid peroxidase-catalyzed iodination of thyroglobulin; inhibition by excess iodide. *Arch. Biochem. Biophys.* 139:212–20

140. Taurog, A. 1970. Thyroid peroxidase and thyroxine biosynthesis. *Rec. Prog. Horm. Res.* 26:189–247

141. Taurog, A. 1974. Biosynthesis of iodoamino acids. In *Handb. Physiol. Sect. 7,* ed. M. A. Greer, D. H. Solomon, 3:101–33. Baltimore: Williams & Wilkins. 491 pp.

142. Tojo, S., Kanazawa, S., Nakamura, A., Kitagachi, S., Mochizuki, M. 1973. Human chorionic TSH (hCTSH, hCT) during normal or molar pregnancy. *Endocrinol. Jpn.* 20:505–16

143. Vagenakis, A. G., Burger, A., Portnay, G. I., Rudolph, M., O'Brien, J. T., Azizi, F., Arky, R. A., Nicod, P., Ingbar, S. H., Braverman, L. E. 1975. Diversion of peripheral thyroxine metabolism from activating to inactivating pathways during complete fasting. *J. Clin. Endocrinol. Metab.* 41:191–94

144. Vagenakis, A. G., Rapoport, B., Azizi, F., Portnay, G. I., Braverman, L. E., Ingbar, S. H. 1974. Hyperresponse to

thyrotropin releasing hormone accompanying small decreases in serum thyroid hormone concentration. *J. Clin. Invest.* 54:913–18

145. Vagenakis, A. G., Wang, C. A., Burger, A., Maloof, F., Braverman, L. E., Ingbar, S. H. 1972. Iodide-induced thyrotoxicosis in Boston. *N. Engl. J. Med.* 287:523–27

146. Vale, W., Burgus, R., Guillemin, R. 1968. On the mechanism of action of TRF: Effects of cycloheximide and actinomycin on the release of TSH stimulated in vitro by TRF and its inhibition by thyroxine. *Neuroendocrinology* 3:34–46

147. Vale, W., Guillemin, R. 1967. Potassium-induced stimulation of thyrotrophin release in vitro. Requirement for presence of calcium and inhibition by thyroxine. *Experientia* 23:855–57

148. Vanderlaan, W. P., Caplan, R. 1954. Observations on a relationship between total thyroid iodine content and the iodide-concentrating mechanism of the thyroid gland of the rat. *Endocrinology* 54:437–47

149. Vidor, G. I., Stewart, J. C., Wall, J. R., Wangel, A., Hetzel, B. S. 1973. Pathogenesis of iodine-induced thyrotoxicosis: Studies in Northern Tasmania. *J. Clin. Endocrinol. Metab.* 37:901–9

150. Wartofsky, L., Dimond, R. C., Noel, G. L., Adler, R. A., Earll, J. M. 1974. Failure of T_3 to block TSH responses (R) to TRH in normal subjects and patients with primary hypothyroidism. *Proc. Am. Thyroid Assoc. 50th Meet.* (Abstr.)

151. Weeke, J., Hansen, A. P., Lundbaek, K. 1974. The inhibition by somatostatin of the thyrotropin response to thyrotropin-releasing hormone in normal subjects. *Scand. J. Clin. Lab. Invest.* 33:101–3

152. Weeke, J., Hansen, A. P., Lundbaek, K. 1975. Inhibition by somatostatin of basal levels of serum thyrotrophin (TSH) in normal men. *J. Clin. Endocrinol. Metab.* 41:168–71

153. Wenzel, K. W., Meinhold, H., Schleusener, H. 1975. Different effects of oral doses of triiodothyronine or thyroxine on the inhibition of thyrotrophin releasing hormone (TRH) mediated thyrotrophin (TSH) response in man. *Acta Endocrinol. Copenhagen* 80:42–48

154. Wenzel, K. W., Meinhold, H. 1975. Triiodothyronine/reverse-triiodothyronine balance and thyroxine metabolism. *Lancet* 2:413

155. Wilber, J. F., Peake, G. T., Utiger, R. D. 1969. Thyrotropin release in vitro: Stimulation by cyclic 3', 5',- adenosine monophosphate. *Endocrinology* 84: 758–60

156. Wilber, J. F. Utiger, R. D. 1969. The effect of glucocorticoids on thyrotropin secretion. *J. Clin. Invest.* 48:2096–2103

157. Wolff, J. 1951. Some factors that influence the release of iodine from the thyroid gland. *Endocrinology* 48:284–97

158. Wolff, J. 1964. Transport of iodide and other anions in the thyroid gland. *Physiol. Rev.* 44:45–90

159. Wolff, J. 1969. Iodide goiter and the pharmacologic effects of excess iodide. *Am. J. Med.* 47:101–24

160. Wolff, J. Chaikoff, I. L. 1948. The inhibitory action of excessive iodide upon the synthesis of diiodotyrosine and of thyroxine in the thyroid gland of the normal rat. *Endocrinology* 43:174–79

161. Wolff, J., Chaikoff, I. L. 1948. Plasma inorganic iodide, a chemical regulator of normal thyroid function. *Endocrinology* 42:468–71

162. Wolff, J., Chaikoff, I. L. 1948. Plasma inorganic iodide as a homeostatic regulator of thyroid function. *J. Biol. Chem.* 174:555–64

163. Wolff, J., Chaikoff, I. L. Goldberg, R. C., Meier, J. R. 1949. The temporary nature of the inhibitory action of excess iodide on organic iodine synthesis in the normal thyroid. *Endocrinology* 45: 504–13

164. Yamada, T., Lewis, A. E. 1968. Studies on the mechanism of the inhibitory action of excess iodide on the release of radioiodine from the rat thyroid gland. *Endocrinology* 82:54–61

165. Yu, S., Friedman, Y. Richman, R., Burke, G. 1976. Altered thyroidal responsitivity to thyrotropin induced by circulating thyroid hormones–Short-loop regulatory mechanism. *J. Clin. Invest.* 57:745–55

166. Zor, U., Kaneko, T., Schneider, H. P. G., McCann, S. M., Field, J. B. 1970. Further studies of stimulation of anterior pituitary cyclic adenosine 3', 5'-monophosphate formation by hypothalamic extracts and prostaglandins. *J. Biol. Chem.* 245:2883–88

Ann. Rev. Physiol. 1977. 39:373-89

THE DIGESTIVE ENZYMES OF THE PANCREAS: A Mixture of Inconstant Proportions

❖1176

S. S. Rothman

Department of Physiology, University of California, San Francisco, California 94143

Although I am fully convinced of the truth of the views given in this volume . . . , I by no means expect to convince experienced naturalists whose minds are stocked with a multitude of facts all viewed, during a long course of years, from a point of view directly opposite to mine.

Charles Darwin, *Origin of the Species*

Our results, I hope, have for ever done away with the crude and barren idea that the alimentary canal is universally responsive to every mechanical, chemical, or thermal agency, regardless of the particular requirements of each phase of digestion. Instead of this hazy conception, we now see delineated an intricate mechanism which, like everything else in nature, is adapted with the utmost delicacy and precision to the work which it has to perform.

Ivan Pavlov, *The Work of the Digestive Glands*

INTRODUCTION

The end products of digestion, the metabolites—amino acids, monosaccharides, fatty acids, and their analogs—are substrates for anabolic and catabolic metabolism. Their utilization by the organism requires a complex series of diverse enzymatic reactions controlled by an equally complex regulatory system. The ultimate fate of a specific metabolite is controlled in large measure, either directly or via the genome, by the variable presence of the substrates and end products of the metabolic reactions themselves. These regulatory processes are thought to have evolved, along with the reactions, to produce a highly ordered reactive system which gives metabolism both specificity and flexibility.

In comparison, digestion, the process which in great part gives rise to the metabolites, is generally thought to have evolved quite differently; while digestive enzymes, like the enzymes of internal metabolism, display admirable enzymatic specificity, digestion has been assumed to lack the regulatory sophistication of metabolism. Neither the contents of the meal (the substrate) nor the end products of its digestion are thought to modulate the rate of specific digestive hydrolyses; that is, the digestion of specific substrates in the intestine is not believed to be regulated. This view is based almost exclusively on the idea that the proportions of different enzymes in the secretions of the glands of the alimentary tract, particularly the pancreas, are constant regardless of the specific hydrolytic needs during the digestion of a meal. Only the amount of enzyme that is secreted can be varied, and not the composition of the mixture.[1] The term *parallel secretion* or *parallel transport* has been applied to this concept since it was first coined by B. P. Babkin (3, 4), and implies that the various enzymes are secreted in parallel or at parallel rates.

Hence, the amount of a specific enzyme secreted would be unrelated to the presence of an appropriate substrate. In fact, its secretion might well occur, and in great quantity, in the complete absence of a satisfactory substrate. In this context, the pancreas—the organ responsible for the secretion of the great majority of digestive enzymes—would secrete its many different digestive hydrolases en masse in response to any and all effective food stimuli, presumably through the action of the parasympathetic transmitter, acetylcholine, and a gastrointestinal hormone, cholecystokinin-pancreozymin. Thus a predominantly starch-containing meal, such as bread or cake, would elicit not only the secretion of pancreatic amylase which digests starch, but equally the secretion of all of the digestive enzymes stored in the pancreas and in the same proportions as in response to a high-protein or high-fat meal.

Proof for the hypothesis of parallel secretion rests on evidence that the pancreas can only transport these secretory products as a mixture of invariant composition. The evidence is both mechanistic (the secretory mechanism requires that the different enzymes be secreted in constant proportions) and phenomenological (the mixture of enzymes in pancreatic juice is observed to be constant).

Phenomenology and mechanism converge in a hypothesis, *exocytosis,* i.e. to cast out of the cell. Exocytosis is a construct proposed for the final step of the secretion

[1]Chronically varying the carbohydrate, protein, or lipid content of the diet can alter the mixture of digestive enzymes found in pancreatic tissue, although it apparently does not always do so in exactly the same way (5, 6, 12, 13, 19, 20, 33, 36, 38, 39). The changes are usually ascribed to long-term alterations in the rate of synthesis of different enzymes produced by specific contents of the diet in an as yet unclear manner. In this view the mixture of digestive enzymes secreted in response to any single meal is stereotyped or preset by its prior synthesis (parallel transport), and the specific contents of a meal undergoing digestion can only alter the mixture of enzymes that will be secreted in the future. Thus, the contents of the current meal is a predictor of the contents of future meals and predetermines the specific mixture of digestive enzymes that will be secreted. While this might be of value when consistent long-term dietary changes occur, it would be useless if, as is often the case, the contents of the next meal cannot be foretold.

process for many organic molecules from a variety of cells, as well as for the secretion of digestive enzymes by the pancreas. It proposes that the contents of intracellular granules containing the secretory products (e.g. the zymogen granule in the pancreas) are released into the extracellular milieu (e.g. the pancreatic duct) as the result of a specialized fusion of cell and granule membrane. This fusion produces a hole in both membranes through which the secretory product can enter the extracellular environment. If, as appears to be the case, each zymogen granule contains roughly the same mix (probably between 10–20 distinct molecular species) of pancreatic digestive enzymes, (27, 34, 53, 59, 67, 70), then exocytosis, as usually conceived, would result in the transport of these molecules in constant proportion to each other unless the content of the granule pool itself changed. This is a mass transport model in that neither the structure nor the concentration of the molecule being moved determines its rate of movement. Rather, the rate of secretion of a particular molecule is determined by the frequency of exocytotic or membrane fusion events. Viewed simply, if such a mechanism existed as the sole secretory process, the parallel secretion of digestive enzyme would in the absence of changes in the enzyme content of the zymogen granules be assured. I say, "viewed simply," because we cannot presently exclude rigorously the possibility that variable secretion might result from regional differences in the enzyme content of pancreatic tissue [such differences have recently been reported (32), although they do not seem large enough to produce substantial variations in the content of secretion (50)] or from the inhomogeneous content of zymogen granules (we cannot say with certainty that no intergranular organization exists). In any event, exocytosis as the sole secretory process is widely believed (21–23, 35) and is consistent with the secretion of a digestive enzyme mixture of invariant composition and, in the absence of convincing evidence for regional or intergranular order, proof for it. However, there is no adequate evidence that exocytosis occurs at all in the pancreas as a normal physiological process, much less as the sole process for enzyme secretion (47, 48). Indeed, a growing body of evidence indicates that a non-exocytotic secretory mechanism may account for enzyme secretion, suggesting that digestive enzyme is secreted by its transport across the apical plasma membrane of the acinar cell from the cytoplasm as the result of equilibrium processes (9–11, 30, 31, 43–45, 47, 48, 50, 51, 54).

The present article puts aside this issue of mechanism and considers the phenomenological evidence for the parallel secretion hypothesis. Are the proportions of various enzymes in pancreatic secretion constant by actual measurement? If so, this would support the exocytosis hypothesis but, perhaps more important, it would suggest that either the regulation of specific digestive hydrolyses does not occur in the intestine or that, if it does, mechanisms are involved that do not require the differential transport of digestive enzymes.

THE ISSUE OF AMOUNTS

On occasion the statement is made that a particular stimulus increases the secretion of digestive enzymes in a parallel fashion when what is actually meant is not that the proportions of the various molecules in secretion remain constant or unchanged when the amount of enzyme in secretion is increased but, rather more generally, that all of the measured molecules responded to the stimulus, although not necessarily to the same quantitative degree. Such a response can be called "parallel," but it must not be confused with the secretion of digestive enzyme as a mixture of constant proportions; it states only that the measured molecules responded to the stimulus. In discussing the nature of secretion we must be careful to restrict the use of the term "parallel secretion" to *the secretion of the digestive enzymes as a mixture of constant proportions.* Thus for a response to a stimulus to be truly parallel, the output or amount of each enzyme secreted per unit time must increase equally— explicitly, by the same percentage of the unstimulated control secretion. Any other use of this term is confusing, since it is not relevant to the question of whether digestive enzymes are secreted as a mixture of constant proportions.

AN INCONSTANT CONSTANCY

The proposition that digestive enzymes are secreted by a single process such as exocytosis, in which the various enzymes are transported in constant proportions to each other, cannot be true only some of the time. It must always be true. Thus a single clear deviation from constancy is all that is required to reject the hypothesis. Put another way, the necessary and sufficient evidence for the proposition of constancy can never come from a specific observation in which the proportions of enzymes are indeed found to be constant, e.g. as a function of time or in response to a stimulus. This is true in a very general sense, because any two linear processes in the universe at their steady-state rates occur in parallel or in constant proportion to each other. More narrowly, if a stimulus or inhibitor changes rates in parallel, then the processes are related in that they are equally altered by the same agent. But related processes need not be linked. Certainly a parallel response would not be surprising for different molecules (digestive enzymes) involved in the same process (digestion) and secreted by the same cells (acinar cells) even if their modes of transport were completely independent. Perhaps we can appreciate this with an example. In the evening when I commute from the University to my home by automobile, I frequently find myself in heavy traffic on the freeway. As I move along at 10 mph, so does the fellow in the fancy sports car in the next lane. As traffic speeds up, we both speed up in parallel; as traffic slows down, we slow down in parallel. Although we may increase or decrease our rates somewhat asynchronously, at the steady state we travel along the highway at roughly the same rate. However, although we are responding equally to the same "stimulus" (congestion) our travel is not linked; far from it, and, as traffic thins out, the sports car rapidly outdistances me.

Thus if we think that a parallel response is due to an obligatorily linked secretion process, such as the exocytosis of zymogen granules of mixed enzyme content, we must seek proof beyond the mere observation of parallel behavior. The process must be parallel under all circumstances to the degree that we can predict the range of these circumstances. For digestive enzyme secretion by such an obligatorily parallel mechanism, we can predict that the proportions of enzymes in secretion must remain unchanged: 1. for all increased (stimulus) and decreased (inhibitor) rates of secretion; 2. for all concentrations of the secretory products, their substrates, or end products in the intestinal lumen, blood, etc; 3. as a function of time in each circumstance; 4. in all steady and unsteady states; and if this is true, then 5. the amount of each product in secretion will be related to every other product in a linear manner (Figure 1); 6. a single or unique linear function will describe the relationship between the secretion of any two products under all conditions and for all rates of secretion (Figure 1); 7. this line will pass through the origin; that is, when one product is not secreted, neither will the other product be secreted; and 8. if we account for measurement error, and the constancy of the precursor or pre-secretory enzyme pool, then the data points will fit the calculated regression line perfectly (with a correlation coefficient of 1.0); that is, there is no variability in the proportions of the various

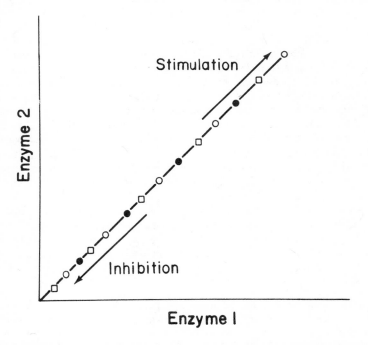

Figure 1   The relationship between the secretion of two enzymes predicted by a model which proposes the obligatorily parallel or linked secretion of different secretory proteins as in the exocytosis of zymogen granules of mixed enzyme content. The open circles, closed circles, and squares show secretion collected in three different unspecified states. In this model the secretion of any two enzymes would always fit the same line regardless of the rate of secretion or other situational factors. The line should intercept at the origin and if precursor pool inconstancy and measurement error had been accounted for, the data points should fit the calculated function with $r = 1$.

products in secretion.[2] Whatever variability is observed should be a constant and unchanging feature of the relationship between two enzymes.

If all of these criteria are fulfilled, then we can accept as reasonable the idea that the products are secreted by a single process which obligatorily links their movement so that a constant mixture is secreted; if we cannot fulfill even one criterion, then we must alter our hypothesis.

THE INCONSTANT MIXTURE

As the title of this review suggests, many requirements of the parallel secretion hypothesis do not, on the basis of the published literature, appear to be fulfilled. Nonparallel secretion has frequently been observed, and the following citations are drawn only from the literature of the past decade or so. Specifically, 1. nonparallel secretion has been observed when the overall rate of protein secretion is increased,[3] unchanged, or decreased (1, 2, 8, 14–17, 26, 40, 41, 43, 45, 46, 50, 51, 54–57, 61, 64, 69); 2. nonparallel secretion has been observed when the concentration of digestive substrate or end product is changed in the intestine or blood (14, 15, 46, 55, 57); 3. nonparallel secretion has been observed as a function of time (57, 60, 61); 4. the relationship between the outputs (secretion) of two enzymes may be nonlinear (46, 50) (Figure 2); 5. the slope of the line relating enzyme outputs can be altered; that is, a single or unique linear function does not account for the relative rates of secretion of different enzymes under all circumstances (Figure 2) (1, 2, 46, 51); 6. intercepts that do not pass through the origin have been observed when the output of one enzyme is plotted against another (Figure 2) (51); 7. the relationship between the outputs of two enzymes is variable beyond mere measurement error and precursor pool inconstancy (1, 2, 29, 46, 51), and the degree to which their secretion covaries can be altered by specific stimuli or conditions (2, 51, 69) (Figure 2).

To account for these observations by a parallel secretory process, we would have to postulate that in each experiment the nonparallel response resulted from an essentially complete turnover in the intracellular enzyme pool due to the secretion of old enzyme and its replacement by a new protein mixture. For most of the specific observations cited above, this could not have been the case based on our knowledge of the time required for such a turnover to take place (25, 28, 48).

---

[2]In an exocytosis construct, r would deviate from 1 as we approach a zero rate of secretion, if we assume that the contents of individual zymogen granules may vary somewhat by chance or otherwise. That is, if secretion rates are so low that secretion can be accounted for by the contents of single granules (or small numbers of granules), then the correlation between the secretion of different enzymes may no longer be perfect.

[3]Cholecystokinin-pancreozymin and its homologues, and acetylcholine and its agonists can produce substantial increases in the secretion of most or all of the various digestive enzymes. While the response often appears to be parallel, numerous nonparallel responses have also been reported (2, 16, 17, 40, 43, 45, 55, 64). Since the secretion of most, if not all of the digestive enzymes is increased by these stimuli, it seems sensible to suppose, in the absence of any special reason to think otherwise, that such nonparallel transport phenomena are "situational—that is, selectivity is merely a kinetic consequence of the secretory mechanism apparently of no physiological importance in the regulation of digestion" (47).

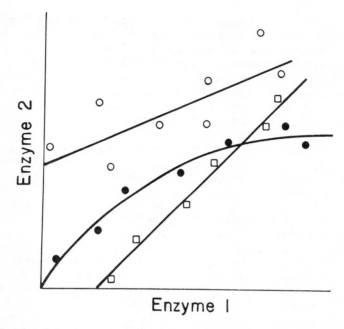

Figure 2 The relationship between the secretion of two enzymes predicted by a model which proposes variable rates of secretion for different secretory proteins. The open circles, closed circles, and squares show secretion collected in three different unspecified states. The relationship between the secretion of two enzymes is shown to vary as the result of changes in the slope of a line or due to a nonlinear relationship between their secretion. The intercept may not be at the origin and goodness of fit to the calculated function may vary in different circumstances (i.e. the covariance of the secretion of different enzymes is not constant) (compare open circles and squares).

THE MEASUREMENT

Thus, to accept the parallel secretion hypothesis, we must conclude that these observations of nonparallel transport were artifactually derived and did not represent true differences in the proportions of the products in secretion. Observations of nonparallel transport have often been countered by the argument that the particular observation is merely the result of an artifact in the enzyme activity assay. Even as Babkin generated the parallel secretion hypothesis, he argued that Pavlov's reports of nonparallel secretion were based on errors in his enzyme measurements (Pavlov did not know that bile salts greatly increase lipase activity because of their ability to act as emulsifiers and did his assays in their absence; nor did he know how to activate proteolytic enzymes effectively) (3, 4, 37, 68). Indeed, a pattern of dispute has followed this question into the present: observation countered by charges of artifact (59, 62, 63, 67).

Unfortunately, criticisms of assays have tended to be "expressions of concern" that a specific observation might have been produced artifactually rather than an account of specific reasons that a particular assay procedure did actually produce an erroneous apparent nonparallel secretion. Such concerns should not be discounted, but for criticism to be more than an expression of discomfort, it must be specific to the exact point at issue. Clearly defined criticism has been notably lacking in this discussion and it is with this need in mind that the following rather simple list of necessary and sufficient criteria for measurements that attempt to compare the secretion (output) of one enzyme to another is proffered:

1. Sensitivity: the assay must be sufficiently sensitive to reliably determine the presence of the enzyme in the quantities found in secretion. Virtually all available assays in current use for a variety of digestive enzymes far exceed this requirement; indeed even Pavlov's insensitive assays were sufficient. Enzyme assays are relatively sensitive instruments for analysis since they are "analytic amplifiers" which permit the detection, by means of their catalytic activities, of small amounts of specific proteins which might not be measurable otherwise.

2. Reproducibility: replications of single samples must give consistent results.

3. Defined substrate specificity: we must know what we are measuring. Ideally, the substrate should be split by one and only one enzyme in the mixture, but this is probably not crucial to the question of parallel transport since distinguishing between the secretion of a group of enzymes which split substrate A vs enzymes which split substrate B might well be sufficient to test the general hypothesis. Actually, relatively specific substrates are available for many of the digestive enzymes, and, as a result of the efforts of three generations of protein chemists, this does not pose a particularly serious problem for today's investigator.

4. The characterization of the relationship between enzyme activity and the size of the sample: criticisms have most often been leveled at assays for not providing optimal activation, activity, or both for an enzyme, as with Pavlov's assays. That is, not all or perhaps any, of the molecules present fully express their hydrolytic proclivities for one reason or another. Despite its frequent invocation, this criticism has no bearing on comparisons between the secretion of different enzymes. It is neither necessary to measure the maximal activity of an enzyme (if we could define it) nor to activate each and every proenzyme (if we could determine the fact), in order to compare their relative outputs. What we must know, if we are to establish a quantitative relationship between the activity that we measure and the secretion of enzyme, is simply how an enzyme's activity relates to its presence or, in other words, how it relates to sample size; we must define or characterize the relationship between activity and the amount of material assayed. For example: Is it linear or nonlinear? Does it intercept at the origin or not? This relationship must be determined in order to calculate quantitatively the presence of an enzyme. The degree of amplification (or "optimization" of the assay), if adequate to the task of measurement, is irrelevant.

Thus, if the sensitivity, reproducibility, and substrate specificity of the assay are adequate, and if the relationship between enzyme activity and the amount of material assayed is known, we can, with some degree of confidence, compare the secretion of two such enzymes based on these measurements.

If these criteria are met, then only the imposed condition itself (time, stimulus, etc) could still confound our interpretation, i.e. a particular experimental treatment might alter the secretion of other substances which might in turn alter the activity or activation of the enzyme. Artifacts of this type have never been described, although they cannot be rigorously excluded on the basis of the published literature. Nevertheless, it does not seem reasonable to expect all nonparallel observations to be explained in such an obscure manner.

Finally, there are reports of nonparallel transport which are not dependent upon enzyme assays (7, 25, 26, 41, 50, 54), for example, the percentage of total labeled protein in secretion accounted for by amylase decreases with time after the addition of radioactive amino acids to rabbit pancreatic tissue (50). The measures in this case were labeled protein and labeled amylase purified by glycogen precipitation. (The data in Figure 3 for the guinea pig show the relative appearance of amylase in zymogen granules to be increasing with time.)

THE OTHER SIDE OF THE ARTIFACT

Although parallel secretory responses certainly occur from time to time, and are perhaps even frequent, we must nevertheless evaluate each report of a parallel response individually. The following are some ways in which the erroneous conclusion can be drawn that the secretion of digestive enzyme is parallel in a given circumstance:

Assay Error

Assay errors of the type just discussed are no less of a concern when the investigator reports that the secretion of digestive enzyme is parallel, than when a nonparallel secretion is reported. Indeed, the same criteria apply explicitly and we do not need to recount them.

In addition to error in activity assays, there can also be problems in analytic assays based on the chemical separation of the different proteins. Protein separation techniques have been used to test the parallel secretion hypothesis with the hope of by-passing potential problems in activity assays (18, 24, 58, 65–67). Usually, in such techniques, enzyme activity is only used to identify the presence of the particular protein, while the amount present is determined by other quantitative techniques, usually the protein content of a particular fraction or fractions. Methods used include column chromatography (18, 24), disc gel electrophoresis (65, 67), and isoelectric focusing (58, 66). Of course, protein separation methodology must fulfill the same criteria as activity assays. Is the method sensitive enough? Does it give reproducible results? What is the relationship between the measure and sample size for the specific material being separated? In addition, there are analytic problems specific to these techniques; in particular, is the separation complete (i.e. is the fraction(s) used routinely free from contamination by other proteins) and is it inclusive (i.e. can all or a constant proportion of the particular protein of interest be routinely recovered)? If these techniques are eventually to be useful as quantitative methods along with activity measurements, these questions must be fully answered. At present, although these chemical separation techniques are elegant and of great potential value, it is not at all clear that they are equal, much less superior, to the relatively simple enzyme activity assay for quantitative analysis.

In experiments designed at least in part to improve the sensitivity and reliability of electrophoretic separations, Tartakoff et al (65, 67) seem to have inadvertently added another complicating variable. They pulse-labeled digestive enzymes with a radioactive amino acid for varying periods of time (usually 5 or 10 min) prior to collecting secretion from tissue in vitro; and used the radioactivity of the separated fractions to indicate the presence of the proteins. This procedure assumes that tracer kinetics apply; i.e. that the secretion rate of a specific newly labeled protein is proportional to the total amount of that protein secreted. Unfortunately, this cannot be assumed since secretion is variably derived from several intracellular enzyme-containing compartments that do not equilibrate with new protein at the same rate

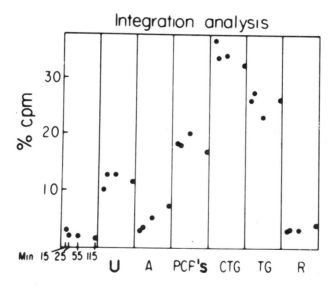

Figure 3   The appearance of labeled protein in zymogen granule fractions extracted from strips of guinea pig pancreas between 15 and 115 min after a 5 min pulse-label with a mixture of ¹⁴C-amino acids. The proteins were separated by SDS gel electrophoresis. The authors concluded that there are no significant differences between the rate of appearance of different proteins (U, unknown; A, amylase; PCP's, procarboxypeptidases; CTG, chymotrypsinogen; TG, trypsinogen; and R, ribonuclease) in zymogen granules. However, note that the ratio of labeled amylase to labeled chymotrypsinogen varies over 3-fold between 15 and 115 min. Other similar differences were seen when discharge into the medium was followed. See the text for further discussion. [Reproduced from Tartakoff et al (67).]

(41, 50, 54). Only when all intracellular digestive enzyme-containing pools are fully equilibrated with labeled protein can we apply tracer kinetics and this requires the prior labeling of tissue for about 5–10 hr in the unstimulated pancreas (25, 28, 48).

The Obscuring of Differences

Real differences between the secretion of different enzymes can be inadvertently obscured in a variety of ways, including:

1. If protein separation or enzyme activity assays are not sufficiently sensitive or reproducible, they may lead to the erroneous conclusion that the relative secretion rate of different enzymes is constant. This can occur if the method cannot adequately distinguish real differences (is insensitive), or obscures real differences within the artifactual variability of the assay (is inadequately reproducible), or both.

2. Differences can be obscured by the natural variability of the secretory system if samples are pooled physically or averaged. We have shown that averaging individual samples, and thereby incorporating the variability of the general level of activity (protein secretion) from gland to gland and time to time into mean values, can obscure large changes in the proportions of various enzymes in the secretory mixture produced by natural stimuli in the resultant large and overlapping variance (think about the effect of averaging values for the three functions shown in Figure 2 on our ability to distinguish differences) (1, 2, 46, 51). Furthermore, physical pooling of samples over a sufficient period of time is bound to obscure differences in the secretion rates of different enzymes that may have occurred in time within the collection period. Indeed, for the boundary condition—when the collection period is of the order of the turnover time of the total intracellular digestive enzyme pool —the proportions of the various enzymes in the collected sample must reflect and necessarily be parallel to their relative rates of synthesis, if, as seems to be the case, intracellular degradation of secretory protein is insubstantial (33, 38, 39). Thus, even if secretory rates were quite disparate over the short run, pooling samples or simply collecting single samples over long intervals, we might produce the false impression that the secretion of different enzymes occurred in constant proportion to their rates of synthesis or by a parallel transport mechanism. This can be a serious problem if the investigator is intent upon collecting relatively large amounts of material for chemical separation (25).

3. Erroneous conclusions can be drawn about the relative rates of secretion of different enzymes if the data are incorrectly normalized. This problem can be seen in the analysis of experiments reported by Scheele & Palade (59). They estimated the presence of several enzymes in secretion augmented by secretagogues in order to test for a parallel response. The amounts of the different enzymes secreted prior to the application of the stimulus were normalized to a common value or a zero response (actually the data were normalized to a value slightly above zero to reflect the spontaneous release of enzyme from tissue strips) (Figure 4). Thus they set the control rates of secretion for the various enzymes equal to each other. The cumulative secretion or total measured response to the secretagogue over the experimental time-course was then set at 100% of the total measured response for each enzyme.

Thus, the total responses for the various enzymes were set equal. This "normalized secretion" as per cent of the total response was then plotted against time after the addition of the stimulant. The data points for each of the four enzymes fit a single linear function quite well, and the investigators concluded that this demonstrated that the secretory response was parallel. However, because of the way in which the data were treated, this plot compared their relative rates of response to the stimulus

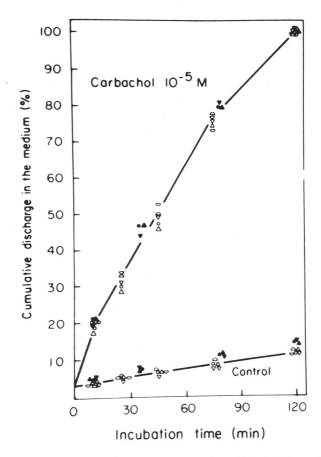

Figure 4 The kinetics of release of seven secretory protein activities into the medium bathing strips of guinea pig pancreas in the presence of 10^{-5} M Carbachol, an acetylcholine agonist, and under control conditions. The authors concluded that these data indicate a parallel response in the secretion of the various enzymes. Note that both zero time secretion rate and cumulative discharge of enzyme into the medium are set at identical values for each of the enzymes. This particular treatment of secretory data is discussed in the text as it relates to problems encountered in the normalization of data. [Reproduced from Scheele & Palade (59).]

instead of the increased output (or amount secreted) of each enzyme. Indeed, these "normalized" data (Figure 4) demonstrate that within the limits of resolution of the particular experiment the response times for the various molecules were roughly equal; but with this particular treatment of the data we cannot distinguish between a parallel response and widely differing quantitative responses.

4. The secretion of different digestive enzymes in any specified steady-state situation is by definition "parallel," although there may be a natural distribution in the relative proportions of different enzymes found in secretion (i.e. r need not equal 1). Thus when an agent, such as a hormone or metabolic end product, is applied to a tissue to change an existent state, the compound must be present at a dose and for a time sufficient to change that state. This problem arose in a recent attempt (62, 63) to repeat an earlier observation (43, 45) which demonstrated that a cholecystokinin-pancreozymin-containing peptide mixture (CCK-PZ) produced a nonparallel response (trypsinogen secretion being favored over chymotrypsinogen secretion) from the rabbit pancreas in organ culture. In the recent study, a more highly purified CCK-PZ was used, but at a dose only minimally effective in increasing protein secretion. Under these circumstances the investigators were unable to repeat the earlier observation. Since the dose of hormone used was only marginally effective, the question remained whether the lack of a differential secretory effect resulted from inadequately altering the control state or whether the original report was either erroneous or influenced by peptides not present in the purer material. We recently repeated these experiments with the pure CCK-PZ polypeptide (purified by Viktor Mutt) and found that at maximal doses a nonparallel response is indeed produced —chymotrypsinogen secretion being only about 25% of that required for a response parallel to trypsinogen (52). On the other hand, a parallel response in the secretion of these two enzymes was observed with maximal cholinergic stimulation (52).

Differences Overlooked

In a sense we have already discussed one aspect of the problem of overlooking differences in secretion rates in the use of the term "parallel response" when the secretion of a group of enzymes is augmented, but not equivalently. In addition, a response is occasionally presumed to be truly parallel, i.e. yielding proportional increments above control values, when this has not actually been proven by applying the null hypothesis to comparisons between control and experimental values (42, 49). Furthermore, differences observed between the rates of secretion of two enzymes may be presumed insignificant for technical reasons, i.e. the analytic or other techniques used are not considered to be sufficiently sensitive or reproducible to distinguish among differences of the magnitude observed. In this way, differences of greater than 100% have been considered to be within measurement error (42, 65, 67) (a recent example is shown in Figure 3).[4] If a technique cannot differentiate between widely divergent values, then to label a response "parallel" under these circumstances is misleading and loses its meaning with respect to the parallel or

---

[4] We have recently estimated the maximum possible random assay error for several activity assays in routine use in our laboratory and found them to be of the order of 2% for amylase, 2% for lipase, 6% for chymotrypsinogen, and 15% for trypsinogen (2, 51).

selective transport of digestive enzymes since it means parallel within a twofold or threefold "nonparallelism." [In Baxter's experiments on pancreatic secretion in rabbits, which Babkin cited as evidence for parallel secretion (4), pilocarpine produced roughly parallel increases in lipase and "trypsin" (protease) secretion, but as the evidence was presented, amylase secretion was increased to a lesser degree and the ratio of amylase to lipase or "trypsin" was altered by about 50%.]

TWO VIEWS OF PARSIMONY

Usually hypotheses that explain phenomena most simply are valued over those requiring more complex explanations. On this basis, it is not surprising that the parallel secretion hypothesis, which proposes an unregulated and nonspecific process, has been the paradigm for the secretion of digestive enzymes by the pancreas for the better part of this century. However, in one important way this simplicity is merely apparent. For while the parallel secretion hypothesis proposes that enzymes are secreted in a nonspecific manner or en masse, it also proposes that they are secreted in constant or fixed proportions. This latter characteristic requires complex models to account for secretion, as the cisternal packaging-exocytosis model of Palade and his colleagues attests (35).

If we consider the secretion of these proteins from another point of view—the perspective of transport processes—then the necessity for such complex models becomes clear. The parsimonious hypothesis for the movement of molecules over short distances assumes in the absence of evidence to the contrary, that molecules move by simple diffusion because simple diffusion is energetically conservative and does not require special (chemical) processes. The flux or, in our case, secretion rate of each type of molecule is determined by its concentration gradient and mobility in the solvent, and is independent of the movement of all other molecular species (at least in dilute solutions). That the criterion of independent movement for different molecular species is not fulfilled by the parallel transport hypothesis (indeed is antithetical to it) makes it a relatively complex hypothesis by this standard.

Of course, while the simplest hypothesis may be best, it is not necessarily, or even usually, correct. Nevertheless, on the basis of current experimental evidence, we cannot dismiss a diffusional paradigm as irrelevant to this process (47). In fact, there is phenomenological evidence that different enzymes may be secreted independently of each other (51).

A FINAL COMMENT

Based on the evidence, the question "does nonparallel transport occur?" can be answered affirmatively; therefore the antithetical assumption that the secretion of digestive enzymes is obligatorily parallel must be rejected.

The issue of parallel vs nonparallel transport is not simply one of characterizing an interesting cellular mechanism for an important process but, in a more general sense, is related to our perception of digestion as a process. Given the existence of nonparallel, or, more to the point, enzyme-selective or enzyme-specific secretion, the next step is understanding its relationship to the digestion of meals.

Literature Cited

1. Adelson, J. W., Rothman, S. S. 1974. Selective pancreatic enzyme secretion due to a new peptide called chymodenin. *Science* 183:1087–89
2. Adelson, J. W., Rothman, S. S. 1975. Chymodenin, a duodenal peptide: Specific stimulation of chymotrypsinogen secretion. *Am. J. Physiol.* 229:1680–86
3. Babkin, B. P. 1906. Einige Grundeigenschaften der Fermente des Pankreassaftes. *Zentralbl. Gestamte Physiol. Pathol. Stoffwechsels* 1:98–108
4. Babkin, B. P. 1950. *Secretory Mechanisms of the Digestive Glands,* pp. 54–58. New York: Hoeber. 1027 pp.
5. Ben Abdeljlil, A., Desnuelle, P. 1964. Sur l'adaptation des enzymes exocrines du pancréas à la composition du regime. *Biochim. Biophys. Acta* 81:136–49
6. Ben Abdeljlil, A., Palla, J. C., Desnuelle, P. 1965. Effect of insulin on pancreatic amylase and chymotrypsinogen. *Biochem. Biophys. Res. Commun.* 18:71–75
7. Christophe, J., Vandermeers, A., Vandermeers-Piret, M. C., Rathé, J., Camus, J. 1973. The relative turnover time *in vivo* of the intracellular transport of five hydrolases in the pancreas of the rat. *Biochim. Biophys. Acta.* 308:285–95
8. Christophe, J., Camus, J., Deschodt-Lanckman, M., Rathé, J., Robberecht, P., Vandermeers-Piret, M. C., Vandermeers, A., 1971. Factors regulating biosynthesis, intracellular transport, and secretion of amylase and lipase in the rat exocrine pancreas. *Hormone Metab. Res.* 3:393–403
9. Dandrifosse, G. 1970. Mechanism of amylase secretion by the pancreas of the pigeon. *Comp. Biochem. Physiol.* 34:229–35
10. Dandrifosse, G. 1972. Existence d'un pool intracellulaire d'amylase soluble dans le pancréas de pigeon. *Comp. Biochem. Physiol. B.* 41:559–72
11. Dandrifosse, G., Simar, L. 1975. Transport of amylase across the apical membrane of the pancreatic exocrine cells. *Pfluegers Arch.* 357:361–68
12. Desnuelle, P. 1963. Quelques exemples d'adaptation enzymatique chez les mammifères. *Rev. Fr. Etud. Clin. Biol.* 8:494–506
13. Desnuelle, P., Reboud, J. P., Ben Abdeljlil, A. 1962. Influence of the composition of the diet on the enzyme content of rat pancreas. In *The Exocrine Pancreas,* ed. A. V. S. De Reuck, M. P. Cameron, pp. 90–114. London: Churchill. 390 pp.
14. Dick, J., Felber, J. P. 1975. Specific hormonal regulation, by food, of the pancreas enzymatic (amylase and trypsin) secretions. *Hormone Metab. Res.* 7:161–66
15. Felber, J. P., Zermatten, A., Dick, J. 1974. Modulation, by food, of hormonal system regulating rat pancreatic secretion. *Lancet* 1974-II:185–87
16. Goldberg, D. M., Sale, J. K., Wormsley, K. G. 1973. Ratio of chymotrypsin to trypsin in human duodenal aspirate. *Digestion* 8:101–9
17. Goldberg, D. M., Wormsley, K. G. 1970. The interrelationships of pancreatic enzymes in human duodenal aspirate. *Gut* 11:859–66
18. Greene, L. J., Hirs, C. H. W., Palade, G. E. 1963. On the protein composition of bovine pancreatic zymogen granules. *J. Biol. Chem.* 238:2054–70
19. Grossman, M. I., Greengard, H., Ivy, A. C. 1942. The effect of dietary composition on pancreatic enzymes. *Am. J. Physiol.* 138:676–82
20. Grossman, M. I., Greengard, H., Ivy, A. C. 1944. On the mechanism of the adaptation of pancreatic enzymes to dietary composition. *Am. J. Physiol.* 141:38–41
21. Jamieson, J. D. 1972. Biology of the secretory process in exocrine cells. In *Salivary Glands and Their Secretions.* ed. N. H. Rowe, pp. 2–7. Ann Arbor: Univ. Mich.
22. Jamieson, J. D. 1973. The secretory process in the pancreatic exocrine cell: Morphologic and biochemical aspects. In *Secretin, Cholecystokinin, Pancreozymin, and Gastrin,* ed. J. E. Jorpes, V. Mutt, pp. 195–217. Berlin: Springer. 376 pp.
23. Jamieson, J. D. 1975. Membranes and secretion. In *Cell Membranes,* ed. G. Weissman, R. Clairborne, pp. 143–52. New York: HP Publishing. 283 pp.
24. Keller, P. J., Cohen, E., Neurath, H. 1958. The proteins of bovine pancreatic juice. *J. Biol. Chem.* 233:344–49
25. Keller, P. J., Cohen, E., Neurath, H. 1959. The proteins of bovine pancreatic juice. II. Rates of synthesis *in vivo* of the cationic proteins. *J. Biol. Chem.* 234:311–15
26. Keller, P. J., Cohen, E., Neurath, H. 1961. The proteins of bovine pancreatic

juice. III. Incorporation in vivo of C^{14}—arginine into trypsinogen, chymotrypsinogen A and ribonuclease. *J. Biol. Chem.* 236:1404–6

27. Kraehenbuhl, J. P., Jamieson, J. D. 1972. Solid-phase conjugation of ferritin to Fab-fragments of immunoglobulin G for use in antigen localization on thin sections. *Proc. Natl. Acad. Sci. USA* 69:1771–75

28. Kramer, M. F., Poort, C. 1972. Unstimulated secretion of protein from rat exocrine pancreas cells. *J. Cell. Biol.* 52:147–58

29. Lagerlöf, H. O., Schütz, H. B., Holmer, S. 1967. A secretin test with high doses of secretin and correction for incomplete recovery of duodenal juice. *Gastroenterology* 52:67–77

30. Liebow, C., Rothman, S. S. 1972. Membrane transport of proteins. *Nature New Biol.* 240:176–78

31. Liebow, C., Rothman, S. S. 1977. Equilibration of pancreatic digestive enzymes across zymogen granule membranes. *Biochem. Biophys. Acta* 455:241–53

32. Malaisse-Lagae, F., Ravazzola, M., Robberecht, P., Vandermeers, A., Malaisse, W. J., Orci, L. 1975. Exocrine pancreas: Evidence for topographic partition of secretory function. *Science* 190:795–97

33. Marchis-Mouren, G., Paséro, L., Desnuelle, P. 1963. Further studies on amylase biosynthesis by pancreas of rats fed on a starch-rich or a casein-rich diet. *Biochem. Biophys. Res. Commun.* 13:262–66

34. Marshall, J. M. Jr. 1954. Distributions of chymotrypsinogen, procarboxypeptidase, desoxyribonuclease, and ribonuclease in bovine pancreas. *Exp. Cell Res.* 6:240–42.

35. Palade, G. E. 1975. Intracellular aspects of the process of protein synthesis. *Science* 189:347–58

36. Palla, J. C., Ben Abdeljlil, A., Desnuelle, P. 1968. Action de l'insuline sur la biosynthèse de l'amylase et de quelques autres enzymes du pancréas de rat. *Biochim. Biophys. Acta* 158:25–35

37. Pavlov, I. P. 1910. *The Work of the Digestive Glands,* pp. 131–48. London: Griffin. 266 pp.

38. Reboud, J. P., Marchis-Mouren, G., Cozzone, A., Desnuelle, P. 1966. Variations in the biosynthesis rate of pancreatic amylase and chymotrypsinogen in response to a starch-rich or a protein-rich diet. *Biochem. Biophys. Res. Commun.* 22:94–99

39. Reboud, J. P., Marchis-Mouren, G., Paséro, L., Cozzone, A., Desnuelle, P. 1966. Adaptation de la vitesse de biosynthèse de l'amylase pancréatique et du chymotrypsinogène à des régimes riches en amidon ou en protéins. *Biochim. Biophys. Acta* 117:351–67

40. Ribet, A., Pascal, J. P., Vaysse, N. 1968. Recherche de la capacité enzymatique maxima du pancréas exocrine humain normal sous perfusion continué de sécrétine et de pancréozymine. *Biol. Gastroenterol.* 2:163–70

41. Robberecht, P., Cremer, M., Christophe, J. 1977. Discharge of newly synthesized proteins in pure juice collected from the human pancreas. Indication of more than one pool of intracellular digestive enzymes. *Gastroenterology* 72: In press

42. Robberecht, P., Cremer, M., Vandermeers, A., Vandermeers-Piret, M., Cotton, P., De Neef, P., Christophe, J. 1975. Pancreatic secretion of total protein and of three hydrolyases collected in healthy subjects via duodenoscopic cannulation. *Gastroenterology* 69:374–79

43. Rothman, S. S. 1967. "Non-parallel transport" of enzyme protein by the pancreas. *Nature* 213:460–62

44. Rothman, S. S. 1969. Transport of protein by pancreatic acinar cells: Random or selective? In *The Exocrine Glands,* ed. S. Y. Botelho, F. P. Brooks, W. B. Shelly, pp. 169–81. Philadelphia: Univ. Penn. Press. 281 pp.

45. Rothman, S. S. 1970. Subcellular distribution of trypsinogen and chymotrypsinogen in rabbit pancreas. *Am. J. Physiol.* 218:372–76

46. Rothman, S. S. 1974. Molecular regulation of digestion: Short-term and bond-specific. *Am. J. Physiol.* 226:77–83

47. Rothman, S. S. 1975. Protein transport by the pancreas. *Science* 190:747–53

48. Rothman, S. S. 1975. Enzyme secretion in the absence of "zymogen granules." *Am. J. Physiol.* 228:1824–34

49. Rothman, S. S. 1976. Does the pancreas secrete digestive enzymes individually or in a group? *Gastroenterology* 70: 635–36

50. Rothman, S. S. 1976. Secretion of new digestive enzyme by the pancreas with minimal transit time. *Am. J. Physiol.* 230:1499–1503

51. Rothman, S. S. 1976. The independent secretion of different digestive enzymes

by the pancreas. *Am. J. Physiol.* 231:1847–51

52. Rothman, S. S. 1977. The non-parallel transport of digestive enzyme produced by cholecystokinin-pancreozymin. To be submitted

53. Rothman, S. S., Burwen, S., Liebow, C. 1974. The zymogen granule: Intragranular organization and its functional significance. In *Advances in Cytopharmacology*, ed. B. Ceccarelli, F. Clementi, J. Meldolesi, 2:341–48. New York: Raven. 388 pp.

54. Rothman, S. S., Isenman, L. D. 1974. Secretion of digestive enzyme derived from two intracellular pools. *Am. J. Physiol.* 226:1082–87

55. Rothman, S. S., Wells, H. 1969. Selective effects of dietary egg white trypsin inhibitor on pancreatic enzyme secretion. *Am. J. Physiol.* 216:504–7

56. Sarles, H., Bauer, J. B., Prezelin, G. 1965. Étude des injections répétées et des perfusions continués de sécrétin chez l'homme. *Arch. Mal. Appar. Dig. Mal. Nutr.* 54:177–94

57. Sarles, H., Figarella, C., Prezelin, G., Souville, C. 1966. Comportment différent de la lipase, de l'amylase et des enzymes protéolytiques pancréatiques après différents modes d'excitation du pancréas humain. *Bull. Soc. Chim. Biol.* 48:951–57

58. Scheele, G. 1975. Two-dimensional gel analysis of soluble proteins. Characterization of guinea pig exocrine pancreatic proteins. *J. Biol. Chem.* 250:5375–85

59. Scheele, G. A., Palade, G. E. 1975. Studies on the guinea pig pancreas. Parallel discharge of exocrine enzyme activities. *J. Biol. Chem.* 250:2660–70

60. Schmidt, H. A., Goebell, H., Johannson, F. 1972. Pancreatic and gastric secretion in rats studied by means of duodenal and gastric perfusion. *Scand. J. Gastroenterol.* 7:47–53

61. Schütz, H. B., Andersson, S., Lagerlöf, H. 1969. Pancreatic exocrine secretion in normal subjects studied by continuous infusion of pancreozymin and secretin. *Scand. J. Gastroenterol.* 4:597–602

62. Glazer, G., Silverman, S., Steer, M. 1976. Parallel secretion of amylase, trypsinogen, and chymotrypsinogen from the *in vitro* rabbit pancreas. *J. Physiol. London* 258:88P–90P

63. Steer, M. L., Glazer, G. 1976. Parallel secretion of digestive enzymes by the *in vitro* rabbit pancreas. *Am. J. Physiol.* 231:1860–65

64. Sullivan, J. F., Burch, R. E., Magee, D. F. 1974. Enzymatic activity and divalent cation content of pancreatic juice. *Am. J. Physiol.* 226:1420–23

65. Tartakoff, A. M., Greene, L. J., Jamieson, J. D., Palade, G. E. 1974. Parallelism in the processing of pancreatic proteins. In *Advances in Cytopharmacology*, ed. B. Ceccarelli, F. Clementi, J. Meldolesi, 2:177–94. New York: Raven. 388 pp.

66. Tartakoff, A., Greene, L. J., Palade, G. E. 1974. Studies on guinea pig pancreas. Fractionation and partial characterization of exocrine proteins. *J. Biol. Chem.* 249:7420–31

67. Tartakoff, A. M., Jamieson, J. D., Scheele, G. A., Palade, G. E. 1975. Studies on the pancreas of the guinea pig. Parallel processing and discharge of exocrine proteins. *J. Biol. Chem.* 250:2671–77

68. Walther, A. A. 1897. *The secretory work of the pancreatic gland.* PhD thesis. St. Petersburg, Russia

69. Wormsley, K. G., Goldberg, D. M. 1972. The interrelationships of the pancreatic enzymes. *Gut* 13:398–412

70. Yasuda, K., Coons, A. H. 1966. Localization by immunofluorescence of amylase, trypsinogen, and chymotrypsinogen in the acinar cells of the pig pancreas. *J. Histochem. Cytochem.* 14:303–13

Ann. Rev. Physiol. 1977. 39:391–415

MICROCIRCULATION

❖1177

Silvio Baez

Departments of Anesthesiology and Physiology, Albert Einstein College of Medicine, Yeshiva University, Bronx, New York 10461

INTRODUCTION

This review covers recent investigations in the field of microcirculatory physiology. Because of the large number of publications and the limited space allocated for the subject, only a portion of the activity in the field is reviewed. Omission of important articles, inclusion of which would have made this a more comprehensive review, was necessary. Fortunately, as a reflection of the veritable explosion of interest in microcirculation, there have been, in addition to an excellent review of microcirculatory physiology and pathophysiology (210), other important reviews of particular aspects of microcirculation, including reviews of local regulatory mechanism (95), of the microcirculatory basis for fluid exchange (92), and of the nervous control of the microcirculation (157). The reader will also be assisted by information offered in the recent review of regional blood flow (116) and the proceedings of a symposium on oxygen transport to tissues (25). The present article covers part of the year 1973, 1974 and 1975, and early 1976, and also cites a few older references required for continuity. The emphasis of the review is on newly incorporated techniques, methodology, and morphology, with comments on transport and exchange aspects of the microcirculation. Selected papers presenting data and ideas of particular interest are discussed in more detail.

METHODOLOGY AND TECHNIQUES

Technological refinements and combined methodological approaches have permitted a broader study of many aspects of microcirculation by intravital microscopy. Increasingly complex configurations of the network are being introduced for a more precise description of hemodynamics in the terminal vascular bed. The successful fabrication of hollow three-dimensional architectural replicas of microvasculature using gallium casting (127) offers fresh opportunity for better analysis of fluid mechanics in the microcirculation. Flow analysis data in idealized models can be compared; the contribution to flow resistance of such factors as distensibility and permeability in vivo, and the effect of endothelial wall on capillary hemodynamic (79), as well, can be assessed in reference to experimental flow data obtained using

391

such semirigid impermeable architectural replicas. Construction of an improved thermal platform device for the maintenance of exposed loops of intestine for small laboratory animals allowed manipulation of supplying macrovessels and nerves and micropressure measurement in the capillary modules of the several layers of the organ (27). Also, improvements in methodology have permitted the introduction of increasing numbers of skeletal (striated) muscles for more precise quantitative geometric assessments of length-diameter-capillary density and measurements of pressure and flow in the tissue microcirculation (10, 34, 45).

Grafting of allogenic femoral marrow within the transparent chamber in subcutaneous tissue of the hamster cheek pouch has allowed follow-up observation of the newly developed microcirculatory pattern of the bone marrow for up to 14 days following implantation (126). The grafted tissue is a practical model for long-term study of bone marrow microcirculation by intravital microscopic methods, provided that infection is controlled. Comparison can be made of microenvironmental conditions suitable for the hematopoiesis in the hamster cheek pouch with those previously described with much difficulty in the bone marrow in situ (31, 33, 123–125, 134). An approach combining vital microscopy, microkymography (46, 47), and microphotoplethysmography (4) was employed for comparative qualitative and quantitative evaluations of several microcirculatory parameters of subcutaneous connective tissues in the human (5), as visualized by the titanium chamber preparation (32). A technique involving no weight change of isolated limbs in the dog has been standardized (30). In a comparative assessment of isogravimetric capillary pressure and transcapillary fluid dynamics, using nonstandardized techniques, the isolation procedures were found to greatly influence the results.

A number of techniques have been used for the quantitative assessment of blood flow velocity in microvessels. High-speed cinemicrophotography was employed for red cell velocity and diameter measurement of arterioles, capillaries, and venules, in a transilluminated subepicardial area of the left ventricle of turtle and dog (184). Red cell velocity was also quantitatively evaluated in human nailfold capillaries using videotape recordings obtained during microscopic observation (29). The rate at which plasma gaps occur between red cells advancing in the televised screen during a frame to frame playback was measured, with a fixed framing rate of 50 per sec. The frame-by-frame method was compared with two densitometric velocity measuring techniques (40). One was implemented by means of a dual channel photometric analyzer interposed between the videotape recorder and the monitor. The instrument measures the average level of illumination in two independent square areas within the televised image and provides analog voltages directly proportional to the average brightness within the windows. Intravascular transit time can be measured directly from the graphic records of the output of the windows placed along the capillary video images. The other method consisted of the direct on-line computation of the speed of the plasma gaps by a specially designed cross-correlator for the speed determination from the densitometer signals of the two windows (185). These modifications based on the dual-slit photometric cross-correlation principle (39, 88, 192), when coupled with videotape recording of the whole image of the capillary bed, allow measurement of red cell velocity and translation of the data to flow volume in any and all vessels in the field of observation (40). When applied to single capillaries of human nailfold, all the methods yielded average values, well within the experimental error of the techniques, which is estimated to be on the order of 0.1 mm/sec (40). The average values of red cell velocity obtained by the frame-by-frame analysis and from densitometer signals were compatible, 1.1 ± 0.36 and 1.1 ± 0.38 mm/sec respectively. A lower 1.02 ± 0.25 mm/sec of the cell velocity was found by the direct on-line cross-correlation method. Velocity in single capillaries has also been measured by the vertical sweep scanning of the vessel using a highly sensitive television camera which produces a scan at 3.3 msec intervals (74). Moving erythrocytes produce two voltage patterns differing from each other in a manner quantitatively related to the velocity of flow. These voltages are passed on-line to a PDP-9 (DEC) computer from which a signal proportional to velocity is directed to an analog chart recorder. Provided that a high-contrast TV picture of the flow RBC is obtained, velocities in the range of 0 to about 1600 μm/sec in capillaries, small arterioles, and venules can be measured with the system. High-speed cinemicrophotographic analysis of dye injection has permitted the simultaneous determination of plasma and cellular velocities in single capillaries (11.6 μm diameter). The information on RBC:plasma ratio can serve to assess other dependent flow and transport variables in the exchange capillary circuitry (179, 180).

Miniaturization of probes (silver/silver chloride) for in situ polarographic measurement of hydrogen in tissue has allowed reliable determination of blood flow in networks of discrete number of capillaries (181) when "microflow" is defined per unit area of tissue. The method allows determination of flow in a volume of several mm^3 of tissue (202). Reexamination of distortion of red cell velocity profiles by the double-slit photometric technique shows that the blunting of red cells has no adverse effect on capillaries where a single cell spans the diameter of the vessel (16). A simple empirical relationship was determined which allows a single double-slit velocity measurement to be used as an on-line volume flow rate reading in arterioles up to 120 μm. However, the study emphasized that the technique does not satisfactorily measure changes in velocity profile as a function of tube diameter because the averaging model parameters also vary with tube size (16). An analog data processor has been devised for the dual-slit method of measuring blood flow velocity (56). Use of monochromatic high-intensity argon ion laser light source for the stimulation of fluorochromes introduced further refinement of fluorescent imaging TV photometry (140–193), permitting not only qualitative assessment of the path of movement of macromolecules from blood across microvessel wall into tissue and the lymphatics, but also the quantitative measurement of the time and spatial course of such movements.

In an effort to correlate structure and function by combining electronmicrography and modern stereological techniques, the number, dimensions, and distribution of endothelial fenestrae were estimated in jejunal villi capillaries of the cat (44). Fenestrae occurred predominantly in the villi tips and to some extent in the crypts, and were more prevalent on the venous side of the microvasculature. Calculation by the Fick and the orifice equations indicates that at the levels of such fenestrated capillaries the endothelium exerts a negligible effect on either capillary filtration or diffusion coefficients. The permeability-surface area product (PS) and the capillary filtration coefficient (CFC) at the fenestrae region of the capillary appear to be entirely controlled or determined by extravascular tissue factors, which confirms the previously proposed concept of "tunnel-capillaries" (175), and the reasoning about their regulation. Estimations of PS and CFC in the zone of fenestrated capillaries suggested the presence of connective tissue channels of about ∼60 nm effective radius and ∼40 nm length, which are possibly oriented toward the capillary vessels. Calculation of the passage of macromolecules through the extravascular tissue gave estimates of 8 mg of albumin min^{-1} 100 g^{-1} of tissue, which agrees with experimental data obtained for cat jejunum (59) as later corrected by others (97). The high calculated rate of passage of macromolecules leaving the jejunum through the extravascular tissue, about 10 times greater than that through the lymph, would appear to indicate that a large extravascular circulation of fluid and macromolecules returns to the circulation via the blood capillary vessels rather than through the lymphatics. The findings, which substantiate the author's previous postulation (43) that the net transfer of macromolecules occurs against increasing concentration gradients of the fenestrated capillary zone, have not gone without criticism (133) and should be taken with some caution. More rigorous analysis of interstitial space physical structure and its effects on the kinetics of molecular forces will be required for analytical description of the nature of osmotic flow. The availability of glucose and other metabolites labeled with ^{11}C, short-life radioactive isotope of carbon (151), or with stable fluorescein thiocarbamoyl dextrans (165), and refinements of the use of fluorescent imaging photometry (140) have proved valuable in the study of many aspects of the microcirculation.

MICROCIRCULATORY CONTROL SYSTEM

To accomplish the primary functions of cell nutrition and bodily fluid balance, the end organ of the circulatory system tends to maintain, under all situations, a radius appropriate for affording steady-state pressure-flow relationships required by the varying and differing demands of cells in tissues and organs. The microcirculation is under constant overall regulatory influences of various forces—nervous, humoral, and biogenic chemicals and mediators. Significant strides have been made toward advancing knowledge concerning the extent of influence of all factors and their interaction. An excellent review on the subject is available (128).

Architectural Aspects of the Microvessel Wall

Sources of information dealing with architectural and dynamic morphology aspects of the microvasculature in vivo are numerous and have been reviewed recently (11, 92, 210). The studies have established that the arterioles and metarterioles are the microvascular structures endowed with distinctly contractile smooth muscle cells, capable of diameter control and involvement in the regulation of blood flow and pressure. These muscular structures constitute the parent microvessel from which endothelial capillaries originate. The smooth muscle is no longer present in the wall of true capillaries, which are thus incapable of active control. Except in the renal glomerulus, the transition from arterial to venous capillaries is assumed to begin at the point where the unidirectional forward flow of blood changes from divergent to convergent. In some organs and tissues the endothelial cells at the arterial end of the capillaries are structurally different from those at the venous end. Whereas the endothelial cells in the arterial end of capillaries in dermis, intestinal villus and connective tissue, and vasa recta of the kidney are of the continuous thick or thin variety, the endothelial cells of corresponding venous capillaries exhibit fenestrations, bridged by a thin membrane (154). The initial postcapillary venules (15–20 μm) empty into collecting venules (30–45 μm). These vessels differ from the large venules (50–1000 μm) by absence of smooth muscle.

Organizational Aspects

The morphological organization of the terminal vascular bed appears to be adapted to the maintenance of the function of the cognate tissues and organs subserved. In most flat practically two-dimensional tissues—mesentery, bat wing, cheek pouch, skin, etc—the capillary network is relatively discrete and appears to have a random distribution (57, 78, 114). A more regular arrangement with uniform intercapillary spacing and cross bridges at regular intervals prevails in skeletal muscle (57), myocardium (18), and external muscle layers of stomach and intestines (8, 81), in all of which the muscle fibers themselves are aligned in parallel. In tissues and organs in which the parenchymal cellular elements have a distinct design, depending on their functional role, the morphology of the capillary network is adapted to maintain the organ's unique functional role. In some tissues the arteriolar vessel terminates by breaking up into an apparently nondescript pattern of capillaries (82). However, in most tissues the majority of capillaries are distributed from lateral muscular offshoots of the terminal arterioles, i.e. the metarterioles or precapillary arterioles (9–16 μm). Studies by both vital microscopy (209) and electronmicroscopy (154) have demonstrated that in the smallest precapillary vessels the smooth muscle cells become progressively less conspicuous and finally absent. The musculo-endothelial metarteriole may terminate either by breaking up into capillaries or, after receiving confluent capillaries which have arisen earlier from it or from neighboring metarterioles, continue its course in the tissue to join a collecting venule. In the latter arrangement the metarteriole, termed "thoroughfare channel" (209), can bypass the major portion of the capillary circulation by virtue of its central location in the network.

PRECAPILLARY SPHINCTER—PRECAPILLARY SPHINCTER AREA   Whether precapillary sphincter function for blood flow distribution in the capillary network is a site or a zone of the terminal microvasculature has been a persistent question, periodically reviewed (11, 92, 210). The pattern of the diminution of smooth muscle cells in the metarteriole or precapillary arteriole varies in different tissues. In the afferent glomerular arteriole of the kidney and the cavernous tissues of the penis, the termination of smooth muscle cells is very abrupt, whereas in organs such as the intestine, lung, and skeletal muscle, a graded decrease in the number of smooth cells occurs (154). In mesentery and facial connective tissue, discrete clusters of 2–3 muscle cells are found at the origin of some arterial capillaries, representing the classical morphological arrangement described in earlier literature (209). Such arrangement is less conspicuous in the intestinal villus (11), gastric muscle (81), and striated muscle—cremaster of rat and mouse (8, 205) and tenuissimus of cat (82) —where a greater number of capillaries arise from the muscular segment of the metarteriole. An interesting recent morphogenetic study (203) showed that arterioles, venules, and capillaries in a number of tissues developed their final shape and arrangement due to the spatial organization of the surrounding parenchymal tissue, the developmental process being (a) the formation of an epiparenchymal vascular plexus transformed into a postcapillary or terminal vascular plexus; (b) the formation of a-v capillaries (thoroughfare channels) arranged in series between terminal arterioles and venules; (c) the development of net capillaries (true capillaries) mostly arising from a-v microvessels, but sometimes from terminal arterioles. Thus most of the true capillaries are arranged in parallel with the centrally located a-v thoroughfare channel.

Functionally the vasomotor activity of muscle cells determining the selective distribution of blood within the capillary network, i.e. the precapillary sphincter, extends over a wide area, from 5 to 100 μm or more, of the terminal vascular bed. Studies show that sphincteric function for blood flow distribution into the capillary bed is usually effected by the most peripherally located smooth muscle cells, where radius instability prevails, even under periods of relative inactivity and conditions of steady systemic pressure and flow. However, the levels of tone and reactivity of the motor cell may shift and prevail higher up in the arteriolar wall, which then becomes the locus of the functional sphincter. Obviously the number of capillaries affected, the intercapillary space and extent of capillary surface area, and attendant functions of transport and exchange will depend on the particular tissue capillary morphology and the level of prevailing activity of the precapillary controlling mechanism in the precapillary microvessels.

Morphologic and morphometric studies have provided additional quantitative information on the geometry of microvessels and on the dimensions, proportions, and disposition of several structural features of the wall.

ENDOTHELIUM   The close membranous contacts of endothelium with smooth muscle cells, myoendothelial junctions (gap-junctions) of 50 μm or less, are found in relatively larger numbers in the precapillary sphincter region (154). However, the functional significance of the endothelium remains elusive. Similar uncertainty prevails over cytoplasmic filaments in microvessel endothelium. Whether such filaments serve as supportive structure of the cell shape or are capable of developing active tension remains unresolved. In a recent quantitative morphologic study (45), by the application of stereology to electron microscopy (55, 187, 197), the geometry of the capillaries in skeletal muscle (gastrocnemius) of dog and the dimensions and proportions of the close and tight junctions were recorded (45). There were ~260 km of capillaries, with a total area of ~2m^2 per 100 g of muscle. The close-junctional length was ~21 km; that of the tight junction was ~430 km. The ratio of close:(close + tight) junction was ∼4.8%. The values adjusted to take account of the random sectioning and other technical features, such as penetration of the section by the stain, showed that there were ∼1.1 × 10^14 free vesicles and 2.5 × 10^14 attached ones per 100 g. The calculated values for mean circumference and axes of capillaries were smaller than those obtained from measurement by in vivo microscopy (171, 195). The difference, attributed to limitation of image resolution by the light microscopy, may also be due to the criteria applied in determining where, topographically, the object of measurement begins and ends, and to the effect of the tissue treatment on electron microscopy as well. The number of capillaries per cm² varies considerably from muscle to muscle and between species (154). Nevertheless, the good correlation with experimental observation (45) of the calculated capillary filtration coefficient (CFC) and the calculated capillary diffusion coefficient (CDC) for a number of molecules attest to the reliability of such an approach.

BASEMENT MEMBRANE The possibility has been reexamined (138) that basement membrane may function not only as a physical barrier for exchange but also as a supportive structure affording apparent rigidity to the capillaries (15, 66). On the basis of the suggested composition and structural organization of proteins present in the membrane (106), a given 0.1 μm thickness, and Young's modulus of tubular membrane of 0.7 – 1.0 × 10^8 dyn cm^{-2} (198), the distensibility of the capillary basement membrane was calculated to be 3.0 × 10^{-3} μm/mm Hg; hence the membrane is capable of sustaining considerable transmural pressure change with minimal modification in microvessel radius (138). With the obtained values of distensibility it was calculated that a rise in transmural pressure of 10 mm Hg would increase capillary basement membrane radius by less than 1.0%, or 0.03 μm, and change capillary diameter by about only 0.6 μm over a pressure range of – 100 mm Hg (138). Thus attention has been shifted from ground substance of surrounding tissue to the capillary wall proper as the structure that apparently gives mechanical support for the rigidity of the blood capillaries.

The capillary basement membrane was calculated to be ∼2.5 m²/100 g of striated muscle and ∼50 nm deep (45). Using 0.01 ml min^{-1} (mm Hg)^{-1} for CFC in muscle, the hydraulic conductivity of the capillaries was calculated to be ∼10^{-7} ml cm (sec dyne 100 g)^{-1} of tissue, a conductivity ∼10^7 times that of the capillaries for the whole basement membrane. While the basement membrane would be an important barrier for macromolecules, it is unlikely to be so for small molecules (45).

Two morphometric methods for the quantitative evaluation of basement membrane thickness were compared using retinal capillaries of rat (20). One was that of Siperstein et al (170), in which sites for measuring the membrane are chosen at random; the other, is that of Williamson et al (201), in which two carefully chosen minimal measurements per capillary are made. A comparative statistical analysis of the data showed that the second method (201) is simpler, less time consuming, and more precise (20).

ENDOCAPILLARY SURFACE Studies dealing with the nature and the possible rheological function of the material occupying the endothelium-plasma interface have been reviewed recently (50). The thin, 50–60 Å material noted to be heavily stained by the PAS procedure (169) may be something other than hyaluronic acid, as it was stained with ruthenium red (168). Ruthenium red was also found to stain fibrinogen and fibrin (52), substances which, on the basis of viscous resistance and viscoelasticity behavior, have been proposed as the materials lining endocapillary surface.

A small number of short microvilli project from the luminal surface, as revealed by both scanning (172) and transmission (154) electron microscope. The significance and permanence of these endothelial features remain controversial. Whether they are normally present in the intact microvasculature or formed under stress of the procedures remains unresolved. Recent demonstration by scanning electron microscopy of the formation of microvilli in the mesentery of living animals by mere exposure to a number of physiological fluids (61, 149) suggests that such structures may be the result of transient adaptation of the living cell retained by fixation procedures.

PERICYTES   Recent studies have demonstrated the existence of pericytes in lung alveolar capillaries of the rat, guinea pig, dog, and human (194). The pericytes were fewer in this organ than in capillaries of myocardium, striated muscle, and pancreas. The pericyte was characterized by a close association with the capillary basement membrane, which ensheathes it by the formation of branched cytoplasmic processes approaching the endothelium in its finest ramifications, by a predominant occurrence of pinocytosis along the outer cell membrane, and by the presence of a web of cytoplasmic filaments along the membrane close to the endothelium. The strategic distribution of the filamentous web toward the inner surface of the cytoplasm, together with the reported observation that isolated strips of pulmonary septa tissue exhibit contractility (102), has prompted the cautious suggestion that the pericyte might be involved in microvessel radius regulation in the prevalent low blood pressure system of the lesser circulation, and hence of the ventilation:perfusion ratio (102). However, although such filaments, also present in endothelium (118) and fibroblasts (86, 102, 118, 154), exhibit strategic distribution and structural alignments in the cytoplasms, their contractile capability has yet to be demonstrated. Their presence in the pericytes in the alveolar septa of the lung might be related to the special sheath of connective tissue described as "posts" (160), which would serve as a supportive structure for the alveolus-capillary circuitry on which the hypothesis of the "sheat-flow" concept has been propounded (174, 175).

Electron optical techniques and X-ray diffraction (3, 156, 176) have aided in defining the organization and intimate characteristics of contractile protein in vascular smooth muscle. The studies indicate that the ability of vascular smooth muscle to develop tension, in spite of the relatively low (16:1) ratio of thin to thick filaments when compared to striated muscle, may be due to the greater length (2.2 μm) and the parallel arrangement of the myosin filaments (176). A lateral ordering of the myosin filaments into lattice, 600–800 Å, and an apparent organization into contractile units, groups of 3–5 filaments, are some of the characteristics of contractile protein in anterior portal vein smooth muscle of rabbit (156). Such electron probe analysis may eventually permit the distinction of the nature and intrinsic organization of filaments in cells sustaining little or no active tension, such as immature muscle cells, endothelial cells, pericytes, and others (86). Predominance of the single-unit type of smooth muscle "pacemaker cells" (6, 65), such as occur in portal vein (93) and bat wing (196), may depend on the organizational pattern and dimensions of the myofilament lattice and of the grouping of the filaments into a given set of contractile units. Lateral ordering and grouping of the myofilaments are not readily evident in smooth muscle of large arteries (156), where action potential is primarily triggered by nervous discharge (105).

NEUROGENIC INFLUENCE   Descriptions of the neurogenic participation in microcirculatory control have been based by and large on observation of whole organs. However, information is accruing from direct microscopic studies permitting description of responses of single vessels or vessel units in an increasing number of tissues. The use of the fluorescent histochemistry methods of Falk et al (58) has allowed description of the extent of distribution and relative density of adrenergic innervation in mesentery of rat (67, 69) and of adipose tissue—subcutis, mesentry, and omentum—in dog (17). A rich adrenergic innervation accompanies arteries and arterioles in these tissues. The network of varicose fibers runs along terminal arterioles in rat mesentery (67), but no direct innervation was seen in precapillary arterioles. Stimulation of the parivascular nerve strands in rat mesentery resulted in constriction of the arteries and terminal arterioles, but not of the precapillary arterioles, i.e. metarterioles (17, 68, 69). The magnitude of in vitro neurogenic contractile response of isolated veins obtained from various parts of the vascular tree of rabbit was also found to be greater in veins with a greater density of adrenergic innervation (22). Myelinated nerves and denuded terminal axons with granular and agranular vesicles occur in the vicinity (5–1000 Å) of smooth muscle cells in precapillary sphincter area (154), and recent studies showed that all microvessels in precapillary sphincter in mesoappendix and cremaster muscle can respond with active constriction to topical electrical stimulation of vasoactive sites in the central nervous system (12, 175). Systematic stimulation disclosed that in the microvessels of these tissues, responsiveness increased toward the most peripheral vascular units and the sphincters (12).

The vascular nerves are by and large adrenergic. However, acetylcholinesterase-containing neurons have recently been detected in the wall of arterioles of chronically denervated gracilis muscle (132); their activation is believed to be responsible for the prompt vasodilatation in the early phase of postcontraction vasodilatation (84). The exact location of adrenergic receptors in the vessel wall has also been the subject of much concern. Further evidence for a sympathetic β-adrenergic dilator effect was noted in studies of skeletal muscle in cat (186). The dilator response seen upon neural stimulation appeared to be confined to small-diameter resistance vessels and to precapillary sphincters (114, 115). In adipose tissue microvasculature, electrical stimulation of the supplying adrenergic nerves invariably causes vasoconstriction, whereas intravenous norepinephrine induced vasodilatation (158). The study suggests that the α-receptor is located in the medio-adventitial region of the vessel wall, close to the adrenergic nerve terminals, and the β-receptor further inward in the wall and primarily affected by catecholamines (158). Such selective spatial distribution of receptors restricted to the smallest single smooth muscle-layered microvessels in the precapillary region (114, 115) would account for the fivefold greater constrictor response to topical than to intra-arterial norepinephrine recently reported in the cremaster muscle of the mouse (206). It may also be the basis of the disparity seen in the flow velocity response to splenic nerve stimulation in omental adipose tissue microvasculature (159).

A more precise description of the extent of the nervous influence on microcirculation will require further rigorous exploration of the exact termination of the vascular nerve fibers and the type of receptor influence, both in the vessel wall and in the surrounding parenchymal cells of the cognate tissue. Detailed morphological and physiological information is also lacking concerning sensory nerves distributed with microvessels. Whether they are only sensors of pain to sudden stretch and pressure of the microvessels or, perhaps, also sensors of chemical and/or flow velocity variations remains to be clarified.

NERVOUS-HORMONE INTERACTION

As discussed in a previous excellent review of the subject (130), a number of potent naturally occurring vasoactive substances can participate either directly or by interaction, synergistic or antagonistic, in modulating microcirculatory blood flow. Recent studies show that prostaglandins (PGs) E_1, E_2, and A_2 inhibit vasoconstrictor responses to sympathetic nerve stimulation in isolated rabbit kidney (119). However, all three PGs were found to enhance the constrictor response to the nerve stimulation in rat kidney (119). The modulatory action of the PGs can be species dependent. The observed (120) potentiations by angiotensin of vasoconstrictor response to nerve stimulation in isolated rat mesentery arteries is believed to be due to increased release of the transmitter and to inhibition of neuronal reuptake (85). Arteriolar vasoconstriction by electrical stimulation of the CNS in rat can be completely abolished by nonvasodilating doses of histamine and bradykinin (13). The capability of PGs E_1 and E_2 of modulating microvascular responses has also been observed by the use of their specific inhibitors in the intact animal (131).

Bradykinin appears to exert strong influence on coronary resistance either by a direct action on coronary resistance microvessels and/or by inducing prostaglandin E (PGE) release (141). Prostaglandin E biosynthesis occurs in the effluent of perfused isolated rabbit's heart (135, 142, 199). Locally synthesized PGE may affect the coronary vasculature not only directly but also by influencing afferent and efferent neural activity affecting vasomotor tone (101, 143). Such observations suggest that this potent vasodilator substance can also participate in local regulation of the myocardial microcirculation. Angiotensin, one of the most potent direct-acting coronary vasoconstrictor materials known, can influence myocardial perfusion indirectly by enhancing postsynaptic norepinephrine release from stimulated sympathetic adrenergic nerves (166) and by augmenting myocardial contractility and oxygen requirement.

PHYSICAL-MECHANICAL PROPERTIES

Periodicity of Blood Pressure

The persistence of pulsation into the terminal vascular bed has prompted investigations of the effect of such periodicity of both pressure and flow upon a number of microcirculatory parameters and their variables. A study of cyclically superimposed pulsation on the same pressure gradients showed little or no nonlinearity in the steady-state flow rate of Newtonian fluids perfused through long and short rigid tubes (109). Results of the theoretical and experimental study suggested that a pulsatile effect seen in the vascular tree must be due to intrinsic wall features and flow characteristics, such as wall distensibility, vascular smooth muscle reactivity, and non-Newtonian flow behavior (109).

Analysis of the effects of static and dynamic passive stretch and shortening on the electrical activity and active force in isolated portal vein of the rat (94) has provided further evidence supporting the myogenic nature of vascular tone and of the response to stretch observed in autoregulating vasculatures. Increase in electrical and mechanical activity in response to passive stretch and inhibitory effects in response to passive shortening, greater in the dynamic phases of passive lengthening or shortening of the muscle than in the steady-state situation, supports observations that skeletal muscle vascular resistance increases significantly during pulsatile pressure perfusion (110, 129). The myogenic response, unmodified after blockade of α- and β-receptors, was ascribed to deformation of a "sensing structure" in the vessel wall (94). The nature of such a structure and of the primary stimulus initiating the response, i.e. change in length (dL/dt) or in passive forces (dP/dt), remains undetermined. Earlier observations (9, 99), showing autoregulation in mesenteric arterioles in the absence of periodic flow, raise the question of whether periodicity constitutes an essential feature for a more efficient response of vascular smooth muscle in general or whether it is a peculiarity restricted to selected vasculatures.

Evaluation of longitudinal spread of induced activity of isolated rabbit arteries and portal vein shows that different sections of the vascular tree display individuality in their ability to support propagation (23). The calculated distance of propagation of the activity was found to be greatest in the portal vein, less in the artery, and absent in the aortic strip; this is in harmony with observations of cell-to-cell conduction of impulses, which is also more pronounced in portal mesenteric vein (93, 113) but insignificant in most large arteries (24, 38). Such individual differences of vascular smooth muscles in developing tension as a response to cyclic stretch and in sustaining propagation of induced activity may be due to, among other factors, differences in the lateral ordering of the contractile units of the myosin filaments, as demonstrated by electron optical and X-ray diffraction techniques for portal vein and arteries in rabbit (3, 156, 176).

Pulsatile effects were also described in the microvasculature by a "pressure diffusion" equation, where the diffusion coefficient was determined in light of the dimensions and known mechanical properties of the microvessels at each branching order (80). Pressure and red cell velocity were measured throughout the microvasculature of the rabbit omentum and data analysis made in terms of a homologue network model. Measurable pressure and velocity pulsatile effects persist through this microvascular bed. The observed decay of pressure and flow amplitude and a corresponding phase increase were interpreted as indicating that the microcirculatory network behaves as a relatively compliant system. The results of data analysis by the pressure diffusion equation indicated that effects in semipermeable microvessels could be accounted for by compliance due to exchange, as well as by compliance due to elasticity (80).

The way in which steady and oscillatory components interact to establish the pressure-flow relationship has also been examined by analyzing elastic storage and dissipation of energy in a viscoelastic material such as blood (183). Because of the intercellular forces involved in erythrocyte aggregation (104, 163) and the time required for the formation of the cell aggregates in a tube (173, 182), steady flow will occur through slippage either at the boundary or between the aggregates in the bulk, or by both simultaneously. In view of the fact that in small tubes, in which at moderate flow slippage occurs in the bulk (37, 72), the pressure-flow relationship alone may not reveal how slippage is apportioned between the surface and the bulk, experimental and theoretical methods were employed to explore the roles of the steady and oscillatory pressure components in determining blood flow. For steady flow, the pressure was linearly related to the volume flow, but followed a nonlinear relation at higher stress levels. For oscillatory flow, the pressure was resolved into an energy dissipative component and a recoverable energy component (quadrature component). With glycerol solutions both pressure components were linearly proportional to the flow volume amplitude, the quadrature component being inertial-like. With blood both components exhibited nonlinear effects and at small amplitude the quadrature component was elastic, i.e. springlike (183). As predicted earlier (51, 85), at higher shear rates the loss of elastic structure permits the inertial effects to become more dominant. If the shearing stress is large enough the aggregates will break and flow will become augmented.

MICROPRESSURE AND FLOW

Interest in the transport phenomena associated with blood-tissue exchange has led to an intensified examination of pressure and flow distribution in the microcirculation. The use of either idealized networks or the network configuration of a well-defined capillary bed has provided useful quantitative information for a more precise analytical description of hemodynamics in the terminal vasculature. In a modular network configuration of the cat mesentery microvasculature, the intravascular pressure, pressure gradient, and wall shear stress were computed on the basis of Poiseullian dynamic behavior and presented as functions of vessel diameter (112). While the computed and in vivo intravascular pressures showed a disparity on the arterial side of the true capillaries, fair agreement was found on the venous side. The attendant distribution of vessel wall shear stress showed a value corresponding to about half that previously obtained for a hypothetical network analysis (162). The difference between computed and measured intravascular pressure gradients on the arterial side of the true capillaries was attributed to the effects of precapillary sphincter action and non-Newtonian rheological behavior, not accounted for in the Poiseuillian flow analysis. A distinct hydraulic pressure drop at the entrance of the capillary vessels has been predicted by an idealized analysis of hemodynamics at such branching sites (189) and comprehensively quantitated in studies by vital microscopy (211, 212).

A recent analysis of RBC velocity profiles derived from in vivo measurements (164) showed a higher RBC velocity in the outermost edge of the blood stream than would be the case for a Poiseuillian profile. This permitted prediction of a much higher shear rate at the vessel wall than rates reported on the basis of hemodynamic analysis in vitro. The rheological properties of the blood were obtained by plotting the velocity of individual erythrocytes as a function of the midstream velocity and the radius of microvessels ranging from 16 to 54 μm. In consonance with previous in vitro flow data (35, 36, 73), profiles were found to be asymmetric and the RBC velocity quite unsteady both in pre- and postcapillary microvascular segments. The profiles are blunter than Newtonian fluid profiles in laminar flow, and the blunting becomes more pronounced as the vessel diameter decreases. The degree to which the profiles are blunted greatly depends on the diameter of the vessels. In vessels smaller than 16 μm all RBC move with the same velocity, forming a single flat front. The study indicates that the flow of red cells is not directly proportional to that of plasma. In capillaries the RBC flow exceeded the plasma flow, which is in agreement with recent results by others using a different approach for the simultaneous determination of plasma and cellular velocities (179, 180).

Analysis of pressure-flow relationship was also made in a topological model based on the wing capillary bed of the little brown bat (121). An ensemble of calculated resistance functions of each vessel of the model was used for an evaluation of the resistance of the bed, and of the pressure and velocity distribution throughout the microvasculature. Evaluation of the relationship between changes in vessel diameter and their effects on the input resistance of the total bed shows comparatively larger influence on the input resistance of changes in the larger diameter vessels than in the smaller diameter vessels. Also, a bimodal characteristic was noted in the effects of diameter changes of a single branching order with respect to pressure within a distal branching order, e.g. dilation of second-order branches will reduce the pressure loss through second-order branches; it tends to increase pressure in distal branches and to reduce input resistance in the first-order arteriole. The analysis of the model and integration of effects of both macro- and microvascular components indicates that the fourth order of vessel modulation is by itself a powerful controller of capillary hemodynamics, which is likely due to the precapillary sphincter action and non-Newtonian rheological behavior noted above. These studies emphasize the view that more rigorous analysis of blood flow in arterioles and venules will require a more exact knowledge of the pressure and flow distribution at branching sites in more models of terminal vascular networks in the body, coupled with a more precise description of the motion of individual blood cells and plasma. The interpretation of measurements of localized microvascular hemodynamics should be made in the context of the overall "microvascular-macrovascular" topology and dependent parameters and variables.

Application of the modified Wiederhielm electronic servo-null system (60, 87, 90, 91, 200) for the analysis by direct biomicroscopy of hydraulic pressure distribution in microvasculatures in an increasing number of tissues and organs has led to diverse views concerning physiological regulation of the capillary pressure, previously suggested by more indirect approaches (59, 96). Systematic analysis (96) of hydraulic pressure distribution at several branching sites in the mesenteric microvasculature of the cat (211, 212) and evaluation of precapillary and postcapillary resistance (63) have directly demonstrated the tendency toward maintenance of constancy of the pressure in the capillary module of this tissue. Pressure in endothelial capillaries remained constant ($+3$ mm Hg) in spite of the much greater pressure fluctuation simultaneously determined in precapillary and postcapillary vessels. Pressure in selected capillaries changed only as little as 6 mm Hg in the vascular bed of this tissue (63, 76, 212) when arterial pressure was varied through a range of as much as 190 mm Hg, starting at 40–150 mm Hg. Resistance was found to be 68% in the precapillary segment, 20.5% in the postcapillary segment, and 11.5% in intervening capillaries, when arteriolar inflow and venular outflow pressures were analyzed in an isolated autoperfused loop of the cat intestine at normal perfusion pressure (63). Two response characteristics were noted when perfusion pressure was lowered from 100 to 20 mm Hg. In some instances the precapillary resistance fell, while postcapillary resistance remained invariant. This type of response corresponds to the local regulatory adjustment based on myogenic and/or metabolic mechanism (98, 139). However, no simple explanation can be found for others in which the response to the decrease in perfusion pressure was dominated by a disproportionately greater increase in venular resistance. Arteriovenous response, possibly quantitatively greater in the non-autoregulating vasculatures (83, 96), or passive recoil of the thin-walled tube (98) were considered as possible important factors in the response. Evaluation of the greater increase in postcapillary resistance in apparently non-autoregulating vascular bed is further complicated by lack of information about the geometry of the thin-walled venules and small veins. A clearer picture will emerge regarding such response characteristics when quantitative information becomes available concerning other participating factors in postcapillary segments, for example, consideration of rheologic modification that might be occurring in blood flowing in flat venules and veins, elipsoidal-shaped in cross section (14, 70, 145). Also, pertinent information on flow in tapered tubes (7) and on wall tension in bent blood vessels (191) is missing in data analysis in the in situ and in idealized models of the microvasculature.

Extension of the analysis of pressure distribution to the more complex capillary module of the intestinal mural microcirculation disclosed different values of pressure at different locations of the same splanchnic circulation (28, 76, 77). The capillary pressure in the mesentery averaged 30–33 mm Hg, in the intestinal muscle layers 22–24 mm Hg, and in mucosal villi only 13–15 mm Hg. The latter values are much lower than previously reported for villi capillaries (108), and more in keeping with the notion of the absorptive kinetics of the mucosal capillary module of the organ. The observation that pressure in capillaries of the muscular layer changes in direct proportion to fluctuation in arterial pressure has led to the conclusion that capillary pressure in the intestinal muscle coat is not regulated and, by inference, that the relative constancy of capillary pressure in the mesenteric vasculature of the cat might be a phenomenon unique to the tissue microvascular module (77), i.e. merely a reflection of vascular changes associated with flow regulation and closely linked to the nature of vascular architecture.

Systematic pressure and diameter measurements were also made in microvasculature of the skeletal tenuissimus muscle in the anesthetized cat (64). Pressure in arterioles of 70 μm or larger was proportional to systemic arterial pressure, while in the capillary bed proper there was a pressure drop of about 15% of systemic pressure. Pressure in the small, 8–15 μm, postcapillary venules averaged 24 mm Hg, close to capillary blood pressure. The main source of arteriolar resistance regulating downstream micropressure was arterioles with diameter ranging from 35 to 20 μm. In the study, papaverine decreased pressure in arterioles larger than 20 μm in diameter but the micropressure increased in the smaller arterioles, resulting in an increase in capillary pressure and promoting filtration. Administration of iso-proterenol decreased both arteriolar and venular pressure, and hence the capillary pressure, thus enhancing absorption (64). The different responses of consecutive segments of precapillary vessels to the smooth muscle relaxants emphasize the need for more precise quantitative information concerning "venular-arteriolar" response. The critical transmural pressure eliciting the venular-arteriolar response appears to be different in different vascular beds (14, 21).

TRANSPORT-EXCHANGE

Whether transport of water and solutes across the capillary wall is by cytopensis or by interendothelial gaps is a perennial question. Electron microscopic studies show a few areas of extremely attenuated cytoplasm of endothelium—fenestrae—in capillaries of oral mucosa in rabbit. Such areas predominate in the capillary bed of parotid and submaxillary glands (136). The fenestrated areas are bridged by a thin diaphragm, occasionally missing. Injected ferritin and thorotrast markers were present in pinocytic vesicles, rarely in the intercellular junctions in the tissue. The ferritin and thorotrast were in both dense bodies and multivesicular bodies, the latter thought to be formed by the fusion of small vesicles (49) and to play a role in the mechanism of endothelial transport of large and small molecules of various substances (49, 137). Combined intravital fluorescence microscopy and electron microscopy using fluorescent isothiocyanate-ferritin conjugate tracer (155) showed that the so-called leaky spots (179) present along venous capillaries and post-capillary venules represent slightly widened spaces between apposed endothelial cells. Although the ferritin micelles appeared at the same interendothelial junctional sites previously described when peroxidase was used as tracer (103), some uncertainty remained that the intercellular route of transport does represent a physiological route. The mesentery in the animals studied (rat, cat) is a delicate structure, easily damaged on handling, and intercellular gaps might have resulted from the action of released histamine or serotonin (117). Interendothelial gaps in mammals appear to be found predominantly in organs or tissues (153, 154) where such permeability-promoting substance also abounds and absorptive function prevails. However, such large-size interendothelial junctions have also been recently described in electron microscopic studies of a predominantly nonabsorptive organ capillary bed, i.e. that of the myocardium. Significantly larger interendothelial junction distances were measured for subendocardial capillaries than for subepicardial capillaries (2, 71). Variety in the size and configuration of endothelial junctional complexes appears to be related to diversity of normal tissue functions and metabolic demands (62). Sarcomere resting lengths, extent of shortening during systole, and tension generated are greater in the deeper than in the superficial layers (177, 178) of the myocardium, requiring a relatively higher energy availability in the subendocardial layers (204). The presence of larger interendothelial gaps in subendocardial capillaries in mammals, coupled with greater blood flow (207) in this region, would facilitate transport and exchange of energy-rich substrates necessary for effective subendocardial sarcomere contraction. The concept of the role of intercellular cement and ground substance in transport of solutes across the capillary wall (48) remains operative. However, physiological and morphological data concerning the transport of different substances across the capillary wall do not yet support a single conclusive hypothesis accounting for all known facts.

Whether water and inert solutes use the same pathway to cross the capillary barrier has been further examined using a relatively simple idealized model of the membrane (41). Taking into account factors such as energy barrier (54, 121, 150) and direct interaction of solute with membrane, a new description of the magnitude of the osmotic reflection coefficient (J) was derived (41). When the newly obtained J was employed to reexamine previously interpreted data (146, 188), using Durbin's relation (54), compatible pore radius reflection coefficients of 20 Å and 1000 Å respectively were realized. Analysis of another model (148) indicated that the proportion of water flux passing via the cells increases with increasing size of the solute. Several studies (1, 19, 41, 190) emphasize the importance of appropriate measurement of the forces involved in the osmotic reflection coefficient (i.e. the proportionality factor between "net" driving pressure and rate at which fluid moves through the capillary wall) as basic to the problem of capillary permeability analysis when even such relatively simple hydrodynamic models are used.

The translation of the exchange phenomena from a two-dimensional geometry into a three-dimensional system, by analysis of Starling's hypothesis in terms of the properties of the endothelial barrier and the surrounding tissue, brought forth additional new mechanisms for consideration (89). Two types of exchange capillaries were defined: tube capillaries, where the rate of fluid exchange between intra- and extravascular space is determined by the capillary filtration coefficient; and tunnel capillaries, where the rate of exchange is determined by the hydraulic properties of the interstitium. The studies indicated that in three-dimensional tissue the permeability appears to be also determined by capillary spacing and the properties and state of the pericapillary space, i.e. the intercellular cement and ground substance of the connective tissue (89, 92). Such a view was further substantiated in a recent study of fluid movement across the capillary wall (161). The mathematical analysis also showed that the motion of fluid in interstitium obeys a nonlinear form of Darsy's law, in which the porosity and hydrodynamic conductivity of the tissues vary with the interstitial fluid pressure. Further information on the basis of fluid exchange in the microcirculation can be found in a recent incisive discussion (92).

The mechanism of a nonhydraulic pathway for large molecules has been examined by the selective action of histamine and bradykinin on the blood-lymph barrier in the capillary bed of the dog paw (42, 100, 152). Histamine and bradykinin, but not 5-HT and other vasodilators used, increased the capillary permeability surface area for protein up to 10 times and, for Dextran-110, up to 30 times, the normal limit of variation. The data could not be fitted to theoretical predictions for an increase of the size or number of large pores, but could be accounted for by an increase in size and volume turnover of endothelial vesicles (42, 100, 152). Similar conclusions have been reached in a recent reevaluation of factors influencing vesicular transit times (ts), such as boundary conditions and outcome probability of vesicle-plasma membrane collision (45). The theoretical and experimental study using values for endothelial cell width of striated muscle obtained by application of stereology to electron microscopy showed that although the values of ts can be greatly influenced by cell width, they are not influenced by viscosity. Thus a greater turnover of large vesicles, with a PS value of $\sim 5 \times 10^{-3}$, joining and leaving the luminal surface per unit time is possible. The studies also indicate that for small molecules, whose PS values are $\sim 10^3$ times greater, some other transport system, such as close intercellular junctions, may be necessary and sufficient (45).

A multiple indicator diffusion technique was used to further characterize the carriers across the capillary wall (167, 208). No evidence was found for a basic amino acid carrier in the dog brain capillary bed, but a carrier for long-chain neutral amino acids appeared to be present. Use of labelled ouabain indicated the absence of a Na-K pump at the interface where glucose and amino acid carriers are presumably located (53, 208). And the instantaneous reduction of glucose extraction by the analog phlorizin (mol wt 436) suggested that the inhibitory action must be on the luminal aspect of the endothelium and not at the tight intercellular junction (147, 208). The cross inhibition and rapid sampling techniques using glucose and other metabolites labeled (107) with ^{11}C, a short-life radioactive isotope of carbon, may also permit characterization of the specificity of the metabolite carrier system and its anatomical location in the brain capillary bed in humans (111).

ACKNOWLEDGMENT

The author's work has been supported by Grant HL-06736 from the US Public Health Service.

Literature Cited

1. Anderson, J. L., Quinn, J. A. 1974. Restricted transport in small pores. A model for steric exclusion and hindered particle motion. *Biochem. J.* 14:130–50
2. Anversa, P., Giacomelli, F., Wiener, J. 1973. Regional variation in capillary permeability of ventricular myocardium. *Microvasc. Res.* 6:273–85
3. Ashton, F. T., Somlyo, A. V., Somlyo, A. P. 1975. The contractile apparatus of vascular smooth muscle: Intermediate high voltage stereo electron microscopy. *J. Mol. Biol.* 98:17–29
4. Assano, M., Yoshida, K., Tatai, K. 1965. Microphotoelectric phethysmography using a rabbit ear chamber. *J. Appl. Physiol.* 20:1056–62
5. Assano, M., Brånemark, P. I., Castenholz, A. 1973. A comparative study of continuous qualitative and quantitative analysis of microcirculation in man. *Advances in Microcirculation.* Basel: Karger. 5:31 pp.
6. Axelsson, J., Phil, D., Wahlström, B., Johansson, B., Jonsson, O. 1967. Influence of the ionic environment on spontaneous electrical and mechanical activity of the rat portal vein. *Circ. Res.* 21:609–18
7. Azuma, T., Oka, S. 1974. Circumferential tension in the wall of bent blood vessels. *Microvasc. Res.* 7:10–18
8. Baez, S. 1959. *Microcirculation in the Intramural Vessels of the Small Intestine in the Rat,* ed. S. R. M. Reynolds, B. W. Zweifach, pp. 114–29. Urbana, Illinois: Univ. Press
9. Baez, S. 1968. Bayliss response in the microcirculation. *Fed. Proc.* 27: 1410–15
10. Baez, S. 1973. An open cremaster muscle preparation for the study of blood vessels by in vivo microscopy. *Microvasc. Res.* 5:384–94
11. Baez, S. 1977. Microvascular morphology. *Microcirculation,* ed. G. Kaley, B. M. Altura. Baltimore, Maryland: Univ. Park. In press
12. Baez, S., Feldman, S. M., Gootman, P. M. 1977. Central neural influence upon precapillary microvessels and sphincters in mesentery and striated muscle. *J. Physiol.* In press
13. Baez, S., Gootman, P. M., Feldman, S. M., Orkin, L. R. 1973. Betahistine HCl antagonism upon neural influence on microcirculation. *Bibli. Anat.* 12: 437–42
14. Baez, S., Laidlaw, Z., Orkin, L. R. 1974. Localization and measurement of microvascular responses to venous pressure elevation in the rat. *Blood Vessels* 11:260–76
15. Baez, S., Lamport, H., Baez, A. 1960. Pressure effects in living microscopic vessels. *Flow Properties of Blood,* ed. A. L. Copley, G. Stainsby, pp. 122–36. London: Pergamon
16. Baker, M., Wayland H. 1974. On-line volume flow rate and velocity profile measurement for blood in microvessels. *Microvasc. Res.* 7:131–43
17. Ballard, K., Malmfors, T., Rosell, S. 1974. Adrenergic innervation and vascular patterns in canine adipose tissue. *Microvasc. Res.* 8:164–71
18. Bassingthwaighte, J. B., Yipintsoi, T., Harvey, R. B. 1974. Microvasculature of the dog left ventricular myocardium. *Microvasc. Res.* 7:229–49
19. Bean, C. P. 1972. The physics of porous membrane. *Membranes,* ed. G. Eisenman, 1:1–54. New York: Dekker
20. Beauchemin, M. L., Antille, G., Leuenberger, P. M. 1975. Capillary basement membrane thickness: A comparison of two morphometric methods for its estimation. *Microvasc. Res.* 10:76–82
21. Benitez, D., Baez, S. 1976. Venous-arteriolar response in striated cremaster muscle in the rat. *Proc. 24th Meet. Microcirc. Microvasc. Res.,* p. 115
22. Bevan, J. A., Hosmer, D. W., Ljung, B., Pegram, B. L., Su, C. 1974. Innervation pattern and neurogenic response of rabbit veins. *Blood Vessels* 11:172–82
23. Bevan, J. A., Ljung, B. 1974. Longitudinal propagation of myogenic activity in rabbit arteries and in the rat portal vein. *Acta Physiol. Scand.* 90:703–15
24. Bevan, J. A., Nedergaard, O. A., Osher, J. V., Su, C., Torok, J., Verity, M. A. 1970. On the mechanism of neuromuscular transmission in blood vessels. *Proc. 4th Int. Congr. Pharmacol.* 2:7–23. Basel, Switzerland: Schwabe
25. Bircher, H. I. 1974. Symposium: The oxygen transport to tissue. *Microvasc. Res.* 3:275–76
26. Block, A. J., Poole, S., Vane, J. R. 1974. Modification of basal release of prostaglandins from rabbit isolated hearts. *Prostaglandins* 7:473–86
27. Bohlen, H. G., Gore, R. W. 1976. Preparation of rat intestinal muscle and mucosa for quantitative microcirculatory studies. *Microvasc. Res.* 11:103–10
28. Bohlen, H. G., Gore, R. W. 1974. Mi-

crovascular pressures in innervated intestinal muscle. *Fed. Proc.* 33:393

29. Bollinger, A., Butti, P., Barras, J. P., Trachsler, H., Siegenthaler, W. 1974. Red blood cell velocity in nailfold capillaries of man measured by a television microscopy technique. *Microvasc. Res.* 7:61–72

30. Brace, R. A., Guyton, A. C. 1976. Effect of hindlimb isolation procedure on isogravimetric capillary pressure and transcapillary fluid dynamics in dogs. *Circ. Res.* 38:192–95

31. Brånemark, P. I. 1959. Vital microscopy of bone marrow in rabbit. *Scand. J. Clin. Invest.* 11 (Suppl. 38):1–82

32. Brånemark, P. I. 1971. *Intravascular anatomy of blood cells in man.* Monograph. Basel, Switzerland: Karger

33. Brånemark, P. I., Breine, U., Johansson, B., Roylance, P. J., Rockert, H., Yoffey, J. M. 1964. Regeneration of bone marrow. *Acta Anat.* 59:1–46

34. Brånemark, P. I., Eriksson, E. 1971. Method for studying qualitative and quantitative changes of blood flow in skeletal muscle. *Acta Physiol. Scand.* 84:284–88

35. Bugliarello, G., Hayden, F. W. 1963. Detailed characteristics of the flow of blood in vitro. *Trans. Soc. Rheol.* 7:209–30

36. Bugliarello, G., Kapeer, C., Hsiao, G. C. C. 1964. The profile viscosity and other characteristics of blood flow in a non-uniform shear field. *Proc. 4th Int. Rheol. Conf.* 14:351–70. New York: Wiley

37. Bugliarello, G., Sevilla, J. 1970. Velocity distribution and other characteristics of steady and pulsatile blood flow in fine glass tubes. *Biorheology* 7:85–107

38. Burnstock, G., Prosser, C. L. 1969. Conduction in smooth muscles: Comparative electrical properties. *Am. J. Physiol.* 199:376–82

39. Burton, K. S., Johnson, P. C. 1972. Reactive hyperemia in individual capillaries of skeletal muscle. *Am. J. Physiol.* 223:517–24

40. Butti, P., Intaglietta, M., Reimann, H., Hollinger, C., Bollinger, A., Anliker, M. 1975. Capillary red cell blood velocity measurements in human nailfold by videodensitometric methods. *Microvasc. Res.* 10:220–27

41. Carry, F. E. 1974. A hydrodynamic description of the osmotic reflection coefficient with application to pore theory of transcapillary exchange. *Microvasc. Res.* 8:236–52

42. Carter, R. D., Joyner, W. L., Renkin, E. M. 1974. Effects of histamine and some other substances on molecular selectivity of the capillary wall to plasma protein and dextran. *Microvasc. Res.* 7:31–48

43. Casley-Smith, J. R. 1971. Endothelial fenestrae in intestinal villi: Difference between the arterial and venous end of capillaries. *Microvasc. Res.* 3:49–68

44. Casley-Smith, J. R., O'Donoghue, P. J., Crocker, K. W. 1975. The quantitative relationship between fenestrae in jejunal capillaries and connective tissue channels: Proof of "tunnel-capillaries." *Microvasc. Res.* 9:78–100

45. Casley-Smith, J. R., Green, H. S., Harris, J. L., Wadey, P. J. 1975. The quantitative morphology of skeletal muscle capillaries in relation to permeability. *Microvasc. Res.* 10:43–64

46. Castenholz, A. 1967. "Mikrokymographie"—ein Verfahren zur Registrierung von Bewegungsvorgängen im mikroskopischen Bereich. *Z. Wiss Mikrosk.* 68:193–207

47. Castenholz, A. 1969. Microkymography and its applications in microcirculatory investigations. *Adv. Microcirc.* 2:24–36

48. Chambers, R., Zweifach, B. W. 1940. Capillary endothelia cement in relation to permeability. *J. Cell. Comp. Physiol.* 52:255–72

49. Chernukh, A. M., Alekseev, O. V. 1969. Vesiculatory process in endothelium of blood capillaries under normal and pathological conditions. *Bibl. Anat.* 10:256–60

50. Copley, A. L. 1974. Hemorheological aspects of the endothelium plasma interface. *Microvasc. Res.* 8:192–212

51. Copley, A. L., Huang, C. R., King, R. G. 1973. Rheogoniometric studies of whole human blood at shear rates from 1000 to 0.009 sec^{-1}. Part 1. Experimental findings. *Biorheology* 10:17–22

52. Copley, A. L., Scheinthal, B. M. 1970. Nature of the endothelial layer as demonstrated by ruthenium red. *Exp. Cell Res.* 59:491–92

53. Durán, W. N., Yudilevich, D. L. 1974. Capillary and cellular barriers to ouabain transport in the heart. *Microvasc. Res.* 7:84–88

54. Durbin, R. P. 1960. Osmotic flow of water across cellulose membranes. *J. Gen. Physiol.* 44:315–26

55. Elias, H. A., Henning, A., Schwartz, D. E. 1971. Stereology: Application to

biomedical research. *Physiol. Res.* 51:158–200

56. Elmore, M. D. 1975. An analog data processor for the dual-slit method of measuring blood flow velocity. *Microvasc. Res.* 9:136–40

57. Eriksson, E., Myrhage, R. 1972. Microvascular blood flow in skeletal muscle. *Acta Physiol. Scand.* 86:211–22

58. Falck, B., Hillarp, N. A., Thieme, G., Thorp, A. 1962. Fluorescence of monoamines by a fluoresence method. *Acta Physiol. Scand.* 56 (Suppl. 197): 1–26

59. Folkow, B., Lundgren, O., Wallentin, I. 1963. Studies of the relationship between flow resistance capillary filtration coefficient and regional blood volume in the intestine of the cat. *Acta Physiol. Scand.* 57:270–83

60. Fox, J. R., Wiederhielm, C. A. 1973. Characteristics of the servocontrolled micropipet pressure system. *Microvasc. Res.* 5:324–25

61. Frasher, W. G., Oshima, K., Unruh, C. 1976. Scanning electron microscopy of superfused mesentery. *24th Annual Meet. Microcirc. Soc.* p. 118 (Abstr.)

62. Friend, D. S., Gilula, M. B. 1972. Variation in tight and gap junctions in mammalian tissue. *J. Cell. Biol.* 53:758–76

63. Fronek, K., Zweifach, B. W. 1964. Pre- and postcapillary resistance in cat mesentery. *Microvasc. Res.* 7:351–61

64. Fronek, K., Zweifach, B. W. 1975. Microvascular pressure distribution in skeletal muscle and the effect of vasodilation. *Am. J. Physiol.* 228(3):791–98

65. Funaki, S., Bohr, D. F. 1964. Electrical and mechanical activity of isolated vascular smooth muscle of the rat. *Nature* 203:192–94

66. Fung, Y. C., Zweifach, B. W., Intaglietta, M. 1966. Elastic environment of the capillary bed. *Circ. Res.* 19:441–61

67. Furness, J. B. 1973. Arrangement of blood vessels and their relation with adrenergic nerves in the rat mesentery. *J. Anat.* 115:347–64

68. Furness, J. B., Marshall, J. M. 1973. Constrictor responses and flow changes in the rat mesenteric microvasculature resulting from the stimulation of paravascular nerves. *Bibl. Anat.* 12:404–9

69. Furness, J. B., Marshall, J. M. 1974. Correlation of the directly observed responses of mesenteric vessels of the rat to nerve stimulation and noradrenaline with the distribution of adrenergic nerves. *J. Physiol.* 239:75–88

70. Gaehtgens, P., Uekerman, U. 1971. The distensibility of mesenteric venous microvessels. *Pfluegers Arch. Gesamte Physiol. Menschen Tiere.* 330:206–16

71. Gaehtgens, P., Wayland, H., Meiselman, H. J. 1971. Velocity profile measurements in living microvessels in the cat. *Microvasc. Res.* 2:151–62

72. Giacomelli, F., Anversa, P., Wiener, J. 1975. Interendothelial gap size of subendocardial vs. subepicardial capillaries. *Microvasc. Res.* 10:38–42

73. Goldsmith, H. L. 1972. The flow of model particles and blood cells, and its relation to thrombosis. *Progress in Hemostasis*, Vol. 1, Chap. 4, pp. 97–140

74. Goodman, A. H., Guyton, A. C., Drake, R., Laflin, J. H. 1974. A television method for measuring capillary red cell velocities. *J. Appl. Physiol.* 37: 126–30

75. Gootman, P. M., Baez, S., Feldman, S. M. 1973. Microvascular responses to central neural stimulation in the rat. *Am. J. Physiol.* 225:1375–83

76. Gore, R. W. 1974. Pressures in cat mesenteric arterioles and capillaries during changes in systemic arterial blood pressure. *Circ. Res.* 34:581–91

77. Gore, R. W., Bohlen, H. G. 1975. Pressure regulation in the microcirculation. *Fed. Proc.* 34:2031–37

78. Grafflin, A. L., Bagley, E. H. 1953. Studies of peripheral blood vascular beds. *Bull. Johns Hopkins Hosp.* 92:47–73

79. Gross, J. F., Aroesty, J. 1972. Mathematical models of capillary flow: A critical review. *Biorheology* 9:225–64

80. Gross, J. F., Intaglietta, M., Zweifach, B. W. 1974. Network model of pulsatile hemodynamics in the microcirculation of the rabbit omentum. *Am. J. Physiol.* 226:1117–23

81. Guth, P. H., Rosenberg, A. 1972. In vivo microscopy of the gastric microcirculation. *J. Digest. Dis.* 17:391–98

82. Hammersen, F. 1968. The pattern of the terminal vascular bed and the ultrastructure of capillaries in skeletal muscle. *Oxygen Transport in Blood and Tissue*, ed. D. W. Lübbers, U. C. Luft, G. Thews, E. Witzleb, pp. 184–261. Stuttgart: Thieme

83. Hanson, K. M., Johnson, P. C. 1962. Evidence for local arteriovenous reflex in intestine. *J. Appl. Physiol.* 17:509–13

84. Honig, C. R., Frierson, J. L. 1976. Neurons intrinsic to arterioles initiate post-contraction vasodilation. *Am. J. Physiol.* 230:493–507

85. Huang, C. R., King, R. G., Copley, A. L. 1973. Rheogoniometric studies of whole human blood at shear rates down to 0.0009 sec⁻¹. Part II. Mathematical interpretation. *Biorheology* 10:23–28

86. Hung, K. S., Hertweck, M. S., Hardy, J. D., Loosli, G. G. 1972. Filamentation fibroblast in pulmonary alveolar wall., *30th Ann. Proc. Electron Microsc. Soc. Am.*, ed. C. T. Arceneaux, pp. 248–49

87. Intaglietta, M. 1973. Pressure measurement in the microcirculation with active and passive transducers. *Microvasc. Res.* 5:317–23

88. Intaglietta, M., Silverman, N. R., Tompkins, W. R. 1975. Capillary flow velocity measurements in vivo and in situ by television methods. *Microvasc. Res.* 10:165–79

89. Intaglietta, M., de Plomb, E. P. 1973. Fluid exchange in tunnel and tube capillaries. *Microvasc. Res.* 6:153–68

90. Intaglietta, M., Pawula, R. F., Tompkins, W. R. 1970. Pressure measurements in the mammalian microcirculation. *Microvasc. Res.* 2:212–20

91. Intaglietta, M., Tompkins, W. R. 1971. Micropressure measurement with 1 micron and smaller cannulas. *Microvasc. Res.* 3:211–14

92. Intaglietta, M., Zweifach, B. W. 1974. Microcirculatory basis of fluid exchange. *Adv. Biol. Med. Phys.* 15:111–59

93. Johansson, B., Ljung, B. 1967. Spread of excitation in the smooth muscle of the rat portal vein. *Acta Physiol. Scand.* 70:312–22

94. Johansson, B., Mellander, S. 1975. Static and dynamic components in the vascular myogenic response to passive changes in length as revealed by electrical and mechanical recordings from the rat portal vein. *Circ. Res.* 36:76–83

95. Johnson, P. C. 1975. Local regulatory mechanism in the microcirculation. *Symp. Fed. Proc.* 34:2005–37

96. Johnson, P. C., Hanson, K. M. 1963. Effect of arterial pressure on arterial and venous resistance of the intestine. *J. Appl. Physiol.* 17:503–8

97. Johnson, P. C., Hanson, K. M. 1966. Capillary filtration in the small intestine of the dog. *Circ. Res.* 19:766–72

98. Johnson, P. C. 1960. Autoregulation of intestinal blood flow. *Am. J. Physiol.* 199:311–18

99. Johnson, P. C., Wayland, H. 1967. Regulation of blood flow in single capillaries. *Am. J. Physiol.* 212:1405–15

100. Joyner, W. L., Carter, R. D., Raizes, G. S., Renkin, E. M. 1974. Influence of histamine and some other substances on blood-lymph transport of plasma protein and dextran in the dog paw. *Microvasc. Res.* 7:19–30

101. Junstad, M., Wennmalm, A. 1973. Prostaglandin mediated inhibition of noradrenaline release at different nerve impulse frequencies. *Acta Physiol. Scand.* 89:544–49

102. Kapanci, Y., Assimacopoulos, A., Zwahlen, A., Irle, C., Gabbiani, G. 1974. Contractile interstitial cells in pulmonari alveolar septa A possible regulator of ventilation perfusion ratio. *J. Cell. Biol.* 60:375–92

103. Karnovsky, M. J. 1967. The ultrastructural basis of capillary permeability. Studies with peroxidase as a tracer. *J. Cell. Biol.* 35:213–36

104. Katchalsky, A. 1964. Polyelectrolytes and their biological interactions. *Biophysics* 4:9–41

105. Keating, W. R. 1966. Electrical and mechanical response of arteries to stimulation of sympathetic nerve. *J. Physiol.* 185:701–15

106. Kefalides, N. A. 1973. Structure and biosynthesis of basement membranes. *Int. Rev. Connect. Tissue Res.* 6:33

107. Kleinzeller, A., McAvoy, E. M. 1973. Sugar transport across the peritubular face of renal cells of the flounder. *J. Gen. Physiol.* 62:169–84

108. Koniges, H. G., Otto, M. 1937. Studies on the filtration mechanisms of the intestinal lymph and on the action of acetylcholine on it and on the circulation of the intestinal villi. *Q. J. Exp. Physiol. Cogn. Med. Sci.* 26:319–29

109. Krishnakumar, C. K., Rovick, A. A., Lavan, Z. 1976. The pressure effect of pulsations on time mean flow rate. *Microvasc. Res.* 11:41–49

110. La Lone, B. J. 1975. *Local regulation of skeletal muscle blood vessels: Influence of pulse pressure and vasomotor tone.* PhD thesis. Michigan State Univ., Ann Arbor, Mich.

111. Lassen, N. A., Trap-Jensen, J., Alexander, S. C., Olesen, J., Paulson, O. B. 1971. Blood-brain barrier studies in man using double indicator method. *Am. J. Physiol.* 200:1627–33

112. Lipowsky, H. H., Zweifach, B. W. 1974. Network analysis of microcirculation of cat mesentery. *Microvasc. Res.* 7:73–83

113. Ljung, B., Stage, L. 1970. Adrenergic excitatory influences on initiation of conduction of electrical activity in the

rat portal vein. *Acta Physiol. Scand.* 80:131–41

114. Lundvall, J., Järhult, J. 1974. Beta adrenergic micro-vascular dilatation evoked by sympathetic stimulation. *Acta Physiol. Scand.* 92:572–74

115. Lundvall, J., Järhult, J. 1976. Beta adrenergic dilator component of the sympathetic vascular response in skeletal muscle. *Acta Physiol. Scand.* 96:180–92

116. Lundgren, O., Jodal, M. 1975. Regional blood flow. *Ann. Rev. Physiol.* 37:395–414

117. Majno, G., Palade, G. E. 1961. Studies on inflammation. I. The effect of histamine and serotonin on vascular permeability: An electron microscopic study. *J. Biophys. Biochem. Cytol.* 11:571–605

118. Majno, G., Shea, M. S., Leventhal, M. 1969. Endothelial contraction induced by histamine-like mediators. *J. Cell. Biol.* 42:647–72

119. Malick, K. U., McGiff, J. C. 1975. Modulation by prostaglandins of adrenergic transmission in the isolated perfused rabbit and rat kidney. *Circ. Res.* 36:599–609

120. Malick, K. U., Nasiletti, A. 1976. Facilitation of adrenergic transmission by locally generated angiotensin II in rat mesenteric arteries. *Circ. Res.* 38:26–29

121. Manning, G. S. 1968. Binary diffusion and bulk flow through a potential-energy profile: A kinetic basis for the thermodynamic equations of flow through membranes. *J. Chem. Phys.* 49:2668–75

122. Mayrovitz, H. N., Wiedeman, M. P., Noodergraaf, A. 1975. Microvascular hemodynamic variations accompanying microvessel dimensional changes. *Microvasc. Res.* 10:322–39

123. McClugage, S. G., McCuskey, R. S., Meineke, H. A. 1971. Microscopy of living bone marrow in situ. II. Influence of the microenvironment on hemopoiesis. *Blood* 38:96–107

124. McClugage, S. G., McCuskey, R. S. 1973. Relationship of the microvascular system to bone resorption and growth in situ. *Microvasc. Res.* 6:132–34

125. McCuskey, R. S., McClugage, S. G., Younker, W. J. 1971. Microscopy of living bone marrow in situ. *Blood* 38:87–95

126. McCuskey, P. A., McCuskey, R. S., Meineke, H. A. 1975. Studies of the hemopoitic microenvironment. IV. In vivo and histochemical study of allo-grafts of bone marrow in the hamster cheek pouch chamber. *Exp. Hematol.* 3:297–308

127. Meiselman, H. J., Cokelet, G. R. 1975. Fabrication of hollow vascular replicas using a gallium injection technique. *Microvasc. Res.* 9:182–89

128. Mellander, S. 1970. Systemic circulation: Local control. *Ann. Rev. Physiol.* 32:313–44

129. Mellander, S., Arvidsson, S. 1974. Possible "dynamic" component in the myogenic vascular response related to pulse pressure distension. *Acta Physiol. Scand.* 90:283–85

130. Mellander, S., Johansson, B. 1968. Control of resistance, exchange, and capacitance functions in the peripheral circulation. *Pharmacol. Rev.* 20:117–96

131. Messina, E. J., Weiner, R., Kaley, G. 1975. Inhibition of bradykinin vasodilation and potentiation of norepinephrine and angiotensin vasoconstriction by inhibitors of prostaglandin synthesis in skeletal muscle of the rat. *Circ. Res.* 37:430–37

132. Meyers, H. A., Shenk, E. A., Honig, C. R. 1975. Ganglion cells in arterioles of skeletal muscle: Role in sympathetic vasodilation. *Am. J. Physiol.* 229:126–38

133. Michel, C. C. 1974. The transport of solute by osmotic flow with particular reference to transport of protein across the venous fenestrae of visceral capillaries. *Microvasc. Res.* 8:122–24

134. Miller, M. L., McCuskey, R. S. 1973. Innervation of bone marrow in rabbit. *Scand. J. Hemat.* 10:17–23

135. Minkes, M. S., Douglas, J. R. Jr., Needleman, P. 1973. Prostaglandin released by the isolated perfused rabbit heart. *Prostaglandins* 3:438–45

136. Mohamed, A. H. 1975. Ultrastructural permeability studies in capillaries of rabbit oral mucosa and salivary glands. *Microvasc. Res.* 9:287–303

137. Mohamed, A. H., Waterhouse, J. P., Friederici, H. H. R. 1974. The microvasculature of the rabbit gingiva as affected by progesterone an ultrastructural study. *J. Periodontol.* 45:50–60

138. Murphy, M. E., Johnson, P. C. 1975. Possible contribution of basement membrane to the structural rigidity of blood capillaries. *Microvasc. Res.* 9:242–45

139. Nagle, F. J., Scott, J. B., Swindale, B. T., Haddy, F. J. 1968. Venous resistances in skeletal muscle and skin during local blood flow regulation. *Am. J. Physiol.* 214:885–91

140. Nakamura, Y., Wayland, H. 1975. Macromolecular transport in the cat mesentery. *Microvasc. Res.* 9:1–21
141. Needleman, P., Key, S. L., Denny, S. E., Isakson, P. C., Marshall, G. R. 1975. Mechanisms and modification of bradykinin-induced coronary vasodilation. *Proc. Natl. Acad. Sci. USA* 72:2060–63
142. Needleman, P., Key, S. L., Isakson, P. C., Kulkarni, P. S. 1975. Relationship between oxygen tension, coronary vasodilation and prostaglandin biosynthesis in the isolated rabbit heart. *Prostaglandins* 9:123–34
143. Neto, F. R., Brasil, J. C. F., Antonio, A. 1974. Bradykinin-induced coronary chemoreflex in the dog. *Arch. Pharmacol.* 283:135–42
144. Nicoll, P. A., Webb, R. L. 1946. Blood circulation in the subcutaneous tissue of the living bat's wing. *Ann. NY Acad. Sci.* 46:697–709
145. Öberg, B. 1967. The relationship between active constriction and passive recoil of veins at various distending pressures. *Acta Physiol. Scand.* 71:233–47
146. Pappenheimer, J. R., Renkin, E. M., Borrero, L. M. 1951. Filtration, diffusion and molecular sieving through peripheral capillary membranes. *Am. J. Physiol.* 167:13–46
147. Pardridge, W. M., Oldendorf, W. H. 1975. Kinetics of blood-brain barrier transport of hexoses. *Biochem. Biophys. Acta* 382:377–92
148. Perl, W. 1971. Modified filtration-permeability model of transcapillary transport—a solution of the Pappenheimer pore puzzle? *Microvasc. Res.* 3:233–51
149. Peine, C. J., Low, F. N. 1975. Scanning electron microscopy of superfused mesentery. *24th Ann. Meet. Microcirc. Soc.,* p. 118 (Abstr.)
150. Perl, W. 1973. A friction coefficient, series-parallel channel model for transcapillary flux of non-electrolytes and water. *Microvasc. Res.* 6:169–93
151. Raichle, M. E., Larson, K. B., Phelps, M. E., Grubb, R. L., Welch, M. J., Ter-Pogosian, M. M. 1975. In vivo measurement of brain glucose transport and metabolism employing glucose-^{11}C. *Am. J. Physiol.* 228:1936–48
152. Renkin, E. M., Carter, R. D., Joyner, W. L. 1974. Mechanism of the sustained action of histamine and bradykinin on transport of large molecules across capillary walls in the dog paw. *Microvasc. Res.* 7:49–60
153. Revel, J. P., Karnovsky, M. J. 1967. Hexagonal subunits in intercellular junctions of the mouse heart and liver. *J. Cell. Biol.* 33:C7–12
154. Rhodin, J. A. G. 1974. *Histology,* pp. 346–68. New York: Univ. Press
155. Rhodin, J. A. G., Wayland, H., Nakamura, Y. 1974. Combined intravital fluorescence microscopy and electronmicroscopy for studying vascular permeability. *Proc. VIII Eur. Conf. Microcirc:Symp. "Modern Methods in Microvascular Research," Le Touquet, France, June*
156. Rice, R. V., McManus, G. M., Devine, C. E., Somlyo, A. P. 1971. A regular organization of thick filaments in mammalian smooth muscle. *Nature New Biol.* 231:242–43
157. Rosell, S. 1977. Nervous control of the microcirculation. *Microcirculation,* ed. G. Kaley, B. M. Altura. New York: Plenum In press
158. Rosell, S., Belfrage, E. 1975. Adrenergic receptors in adipose tissue and their relation to adrenergic innervation. *Nature* 253:738–39
159. Rosell, S., Intaglietta, M., Tuma, R., Arfors, K. E. 1974. Microvascular flow velocity in cat omental adipose tissue as affected by sympathetic nerve stimulation. *Acta Physiol. Scand.* 92:399–403
160. Rosenquist, T. H., Bernick, S., Sobin, S. S., Fung, Y. C. 1973. The structure of the pulmonary alveolar sheet. *Microvasc. Res.* 5:199–212
161. Salathe, E. P., An, K. N. 1976. A mathematical analysis of fluid movement across capillary wall. *Microvasc. Res.* 11:1–23
162. Schmid-Schoenbein, H. 1972. Blood rheology in the microcirculation. *Pfluegers Arch.* 336 (Suppl.) 84–87
163. Schmid-Schoenbein, H., Wells, R. 1971. Red cell aggregation and red cell deformation: Their influence on blood rheology in health and disease. *Theoretical and Clinical Hemorheology,* ed. H. Hartert, A. L. Copley, pp. 348–55. New York: Springer
164. Schmid-Schoenbein, H., Gosen, J. V., Heinich, L., Volger, E. 1973. A counter rotating "rheoscope chamber" for the study of the microrheology of blood cell aggregation by microscopic observation and microphotometry. *Microvasc. Res.* 6:366–76
165. Schmid-Schoenbein, G. W., Zweifach, B. W. 1975. RBC velocity profiles in arterioles and venules of the rabbit omentum. *Microvasc. Res.* 10:153–64

166. Schröder, U., Arfors, K. E., Tangen, O. 1976. Stability of fluorescein labeled dextrans in vivo and in vitro. *Microvasc. Res.* 11:33–39

167. Schumann, H. J., Starke, K., Werner, U. 1975. Interactions of inhibitors of noradrenaline uptake and angiotensin on the sympathetic nerves of the isolated rabbit heart. *Br. J. Pharmacol.* 39:390–97

168. Sepulveda, F. V., Yudilevich, D. L. 1975. The specificity of glucose and amino acid carriers in the capillary of the dog brain. *J. Physiol.* 250:21–23

169. Shea, S. M. 1971. Lanthanum staining of the surface coat of cells. *J. Cell. Biol.* 51:611–20

170. Shirahama, T., Cohen, A. S. 1972. The role of mucopolysacharides in vesicle architecture and endothelial transport. An electron microscope study of myocardial blood vessels. *J. Cell. Biol.* 52:198–206

171. Siperstein, M. D., Unger, R. H., Madison, L. L. 1968. Studies of muscle capillary basement membranes in normal subjects, diabetic and prediabetic patients. *J. Clin. Invest.* 47:1937–99

172. Smaje, L. H., Zweifach, B. W., Intaglietta, M. 1970. Micropressure and capillary filtration coefficients in single vessels of the cremaster muscle of the rat. *Microvasc. Res.* 2:96–110

173. Smith, V., Ryan, J. W., Michie, D. D., Smith, D. S. 1971. Endothelial projections as revealed by scanning electron microscopy. *Science* 173:925–27

174. Sobin, S. S., Fung, Y. C., Tremer, H. M., Rosenquist, T. H. 1972. Elasticity of the pulmonary alveolar microvascular sheet in the cat. *Circ. Res.* 30:440–50

175. Sobin, S. S., Tremer, H. M., Fung, Y. C. 1970. Morphometric basis of the sheetflow concept of the pulmonary alveolar microcirculation in the cat. *Circ. Res.* 26:397–417

176. Somlyo, A. P., Somlyo, A. V. 1976. Ultrastructural aspects of activation of contraction of vascular smooth muscle. *Fed. Proc.* 35:1289–94

177. Sonnenblick, E. H. 1967. *Discussion. Coronary Circulation and Energetics of the Myocardium,* ed. G. Marchetti, B. Toscardi. Basel, Switzerland: Karger. 52 pp.

178. Spotnitz, H. M., Sonnenblick, E. H., Spiro, D. 1966. Relation of ultrastructure to function in the intact heart: Sarcomere structure relative to pressure volume curves of intact left ventricles of dog and cat. *Circ. Res.* 18:49–66

179. Starr, M. C., Frasher, W. G. Jr. 1975. A method for the simultaneous determination of plasma and cellular velocities in the microvasculature. *Microcirc. Res.* 10:95–101

180. Starr, M. C., Frasher, W. G. Jr. 1975. In vivo cellular and plasma velocities in microvessels of the cat mesentery. *Microvasc. Res.* 10:102–6

181. Stosseck, K., Lübbers, D. W., Cottin, N. 1974. Determination of local blood flow (microflow) by electrochemically generated hydrogen. *Pfluegers Arch.* 348:225–38

182. Thorsen, G. B., Hint, H. 1950. Aggregation, sedimentation and intravascular sludging of erythrocytes. *Acta Chir. Scand.* 154:3–50

183. Thurston, G. B. 1975. Elastic effects in pulsatile flow. *Microvasc. Res.* 9:145–57

184. Tillmanns, H., Ikeda, S., Hansen, H., Sarma, J. S. M., Fauvel, J., Bing, R. J. 1975. Microcirculation in the left ventricle of the dog and turtle. *Circ. Res.* 34:561–69

185. Tompkins, W. R., Monti, R., Intaglietta, M. 1974. Velocity measurement by self-tracking correlator. *Rev. Sci. Instrum.* 45:647–49

186. Tuttle, R. S., Moe, G. K. 1973. Reflex beta-adrenergic vasodilation in the cat. *Am. J. Physiol.* 225:402–7

187. Underwood, E. E. 1970. *Quantitative Stereology.* Reading, Mass: Addison-Wesley

188. Vargas, F., Johnson, J. A. 1964. An estimate of reflection coefficient from rabbit heart capillaries. *J. Gen. Physiol.* 47:667–77

189. Vawter, D., Fung, Y. C., Zweifach, B. W. 1974. Distribution of blood flow and blood pressure from microvessel into a branch. *Microvasc. Res.* 8:44–52

190. Verniory, A., Du Bois, R., Decoodt, P., Gassee, J. P., Lambert, P. P., 1973. Measurement of the permeability of biological membranes. Application to the glomerular wall. *J. Gen. Physiol.* 62:489–507

191. Walawender, W. P., Chen, Y. T. 1975. Blood flow in tapered tubes. *Microvasc. Res.* 9:190–205

192. Wayland, H., Johnson, P. C. 1967. Erythrocyte velocity measurement in microvessels by a two-slit photometric method. *J. Appl. Physiol.* 22:333–37

193. Wayland, H., Fox, J. R., Elmore, M. D. 1974. *Proc. Symp. Mod. Methods Microvasc. Res. VIII Europ. Conf. Microcirc. Le Touquet, France*

194. Weibel, E. R. 1974. On pericytes, particularly their existence on lung capillaries. *Microvasc. Res.* 8:218–35
195. Wiedeman, M. P. 1963. Dimensions of blood vessels from distributing artery to collecting vein. *Circ. Res.* 12:375–78
196. Wiedeman, M. P. 1966. Contractile activity of arterioles in the bat wing during intraluminal pressure changes. *Circ. Res.* 19:559–63
197. Weikel, E. R. 1969. Stereological principles for morphometry in electron microscopic cytology. *Int. Rev. Cytol.* 26:235–302
198. Welling, L. W., Grantham, J. J. 1973. Physical properties of isolated perfused renal tubules and tubular basement membranes. *J. Clin. Invest.* 51:1063–75
199. Wennmalm, A., Pham Huu Chan, Junstad, M. 1974. Hypoxia causes prostaglandin release from perfused rabbit hearts. *Acta Physiol. Scand.* 91:133–35
200. Wiederhielm, C. A., Woodbury, J. W., Kirk, S., Rushmer, R. F. 1964. Pulsatile pressures in the microcirculation of frog's mesentery. *Am. J. Physiol.* 207:173–76
201. Williamson, J. R., Vogler, N. J., Kilo, C. 1969. Estimation of vascular basement membrane thickness. Theoretical and practical considerations. *Diabetes* 18:567–78
202. Wodick, R., Lübbers, D. W., Grunewald, W. 1969. Auswertverfahren zur Bestimmung der Organdurchblutung nach Atmung von Wasserstoffgemischen. *Pfluegers Arch.* 307:R51
203. Wolff, J. R., Goerz, C. Bär, T. H., Güldner, F. H. 1975. Common morphogenetic aspects of various organotropic microvascular pattern. *Microvasc. Res.* 10:373–95
204. Wong, A. Y. K., Rautaharju, P. M. 1968. Stress distribution within the left ventricular wall approximated as a thick elipsoidal shell. *Am. Heart J.* 75:649–62
205. Yamaki, T., Baez, S., Orkin, L. R. 1977. Microvasculature in cremaster muscle of the mice. *Proc. 1st Int. Cong. Microcirc. Toronto, Canada, June 1975* In press
206. Yamaki, T., Baez, S., Orkin, L. R. 1976. Cremasteric arteriolar response to drugs by topical and intraarterial route of administration in the mouse. *Microvasc. Res.* 11:130 (Abstr.)
207. Yipintsoi, T., Scanlon, P. D., Knopp, T. J., Bassingthwaighte, J. B. 1973. Regional distribution of diffusible tracers and carbonized microspheres in the left ventricle of the isolated dog heart. *Circ. Res.* 33:573–87
208. Yudilevich, D. L., Sepulveda, F. V. 1976. The specificity of amino acid and sugar carriers in the capillary of the dog brain studied in vivo by rapid indicator dilution. *Proc. Microcirc. Soc. Neurochem. Satellite Symp. on "Transport Phenomena in the Nervous System, Italy, 1975,* ed. G. Levi, L. Batistin, A. Lajtha
209. Zweifach, B. W. 1969. Small blood vessel dynamics. *Dynamics of Thrombus Formation and Dissolution,* ed. S. A. Johnson, M. M. Guest, p. 45. Philadelphia, Pennsylvania: Lippincott. 376 pp.
210. Zweifach, B. W. 1973. Microcirculation. *Ann. Rev. Physiol.* 35:117–50
211. Zweifach, B. W. 1974. Quantitative studies of microcirculatory structure and function. I. Analysis of pressure distributions in the terminal bed in cat mesentery. *Circ. Res.* 34:843–57
212. Zweifach, B. W. 1974. Quantitative studies of microcirculatory structure and function. II. Direct measurement of capillary pressure in splanchnic mesenteric vessels. *Circ. Res.* 34:858–66

Ann. Rev. Physiol. 1977. 39:417–48

NEURAL GENERATION OF THE BREATHING RHYTHM

❖1178

Robert J. Wyman

Department of Biology, Yale University, New Haven, Connecticut 06520

INTRODUCTION

The model of breathing rhythm generation which until recently has been almost universally accepted is based on reciprocal inhibitory connections between an inspiratory and an expiratory population of respiratory neurons. This hypothesis has taken many forms in the past (21, 29, 31, 82, 84, 100). Earlier versions usually claimed that the inspiratory population is tonically active and must be periodically inhibited by the expiratory population. More modern versions hypothesize that the inspiratory and expiratory populations are similar to each other and that each inhibits the other.

This hypothesis is now in severe difficulty. The medulla alone is able to produce rhythmic breathing. In the eupneic (normal) breathing seen in deep anesthesia, expiratory muscles are not activated; expiration is passive. The only medullary interneurons known to be active in expiration (deep anesthesia) are those of the nucleus retroambigualis (90) which do not make synaptic connections with medullary inspiratory cells (90, 92). Thus any theory of respiratory rhythmicity requiring reciprocal inhibition between inspiratory and expiratory populations of neurons seems to be ruled out.

This review presents recent and old evidence which this author believes can lead to a new concept of the mechanism of breathing rhythm generation. The conclusions drawn and models presented do not in any way represent a consensus of the views of respiration researchers. Since no such consensus exists, the review is necessarily a selection of that material which this author finds most compelling. The focus of the review is the generation of the basic breathing rhythm rather than the control of that rhythm by homeostatic and sensory inputs. Other aspects of breathing research are discussed in recent reviews and symposia (29, 31, 33a, 69, 90, 93, 102, 105, 132, 138). This review is aimed primarily at the nonspecialist, but it is hoped that some of the theoretical and experimental suggestions may interest researchers in the field.

Overview

Neural circuits in the medulla are capable of generating the rhythmic output which drives the diaphragm. This output has three phases: an augmenting inspiratory discharge, a rapid turnoff of the discharge, and a pause during expiration. These three phases can be generated with or without phasic sensory inputs. Of the three phases, the termination of inspiration seems to be the key timing event which sets the rhythmic parameters of breathing. Much of the review focuses on new information on the neurophysiology of the inspiration terminating off switch. Evidence is reviewed showing that the effects of lung expansion, CO_2, temperature, and the pneumotaxic center can be explained by their effect on the off switch.

Much less is known about the other two phases of breathing, but evidence is presented here about the role of various brain nuclei and reflexes in these phases. Much is still unknown about the generation of rhythmic breathing; among other unknowns, the review discusses the possibility that some of the component cells are autorhythmic.

CENTRAL PATTERN GENERATORS

Much of the advance in recent years in understanding the generation of motor output patterns has centered around the topics of central pattern generators, coupled oscillators, and neuronal autorhythmicity. If the central nervous system (CNS) is capable of generating a reasonably normal motor output pattern in the absence of timing cues from sense receptors, the neural circuit generating the output is called a central pattern generator (CPG). The existence of a CPG is demonstrated by deafferentation or paralysis which eliminates phasic sensory input. In a few cases, the deafferented CNS can produce a normal motor pattern, e.g. the cardiac ganglion in lobsters (59). In most cases, elimination of sensory input results in a quiescent animal with no motor output. The missing factor may be timing information in the input, or it may just be the total amount of input. The pattern-generating neurons may need phased bursts of input or they may just need a sufficient level of background synaptic activity to be able to function normally. The former case is that of a reflex pattern generator, the latter of a central generator. The two cases may be distinguished by replacing the normal sensory input with input which is random, or tonic, or otherwise temporally unrelated to the output motions. If a near normal output is now produced, the pattern generator is termed "central."

Even though a central pattern generator may not require phasic inputs, they may nonetheless be present. These sensory inputs may be used to "fine tune" the pattern, or they may even override and drive the central pattern generator. These points are all illustrated in the classic case of locust flight (134). The wing stretch receptors which fire a burst at the top of every wing stroke (135) give strong phasic sensory input to the pattern generator (22). If the sensory input is eliminated, the CNS is quiescent and produces no motor output. However, if, in the deafferented animal, the wing nerves or the nerve cord itself is stimulated with a random or a tonic pattern, then normal flight motor output may be produced (136). Thus the locust is said to have a central pattern generator for flight. The sensory input increases the output frequency (135, 136) and makes fine tuning adjustments to flight control parameters (52). In some situations the central pattern generator may be overridden by phasic sensory input. Thus, if the wing is experimentally moved at a frequency close to that of the central pattern generator, the central pattern generator will be driven by sensation from the wing and take up the frequency of the wing (128).

In many animals there is more than one central pattern generator for the same movement. Thus in the crayfish abdomen each segment has a central pattern generator for swimmeret beating (67). In this case the most posterior generator drives the others. If the most posterior ganglion is cut off, the next most anterior will become the driver (67). In the scyphozoan jelly fish each of the eight marginal ganglia can drive rhythmic beating of the bell. Each oscillator is excitatorily coupled to the others. The fastest oscillator imposes its rhythm upon and drives the others (65). The slower, driven oscillators can send excitation back to the driver oscillator, and this feedback may influence the rhythm (81).

Breathing Has a Central Pattern Generator

For cat breathing, the existence of a central pattern generator is easily demonstrated. The animal is paralyzed and the phrenic motor nerve to the diaphragm is recorded from while the animal is artificially respirated. If the respirator is now switched off for a few breaths, the animal is motionless and there is no possibility of any proprioceptor being stimulated at respiratory frequency. Under these conditions the phrenic nerve maintains a rhythmic discharge very similar to that found in normal breathing (83). This proves unequivocally that there is a central pattern generator capable of driving ventilation.

MEDULLARY PATTERN GENERATOR   The medulla, and possibly the spinal cord, have central pattern generators for breathing. Although the pons and higher centers have great influence on breathing, they are not necessary for the generation of periodic breathing. Hoff & Breckenridge (19, 63) were the first to show that when the brain stem is sectioned between the pons and the medulla breathing "is often indistinguishable from the breathing of the mid-collicular" decerebrated animal. Wang, Ngai & Frumin (126) confirmed that, in the best cases, after vagotomy and section in the rostral medulla "respiratory movement appeared entirely normal." In fact rhythmic breathing persists when the medulla and cervical cord are totally isolated by sectioning above them (between medulla and pons), below them (at the sixth cervical segment, which leaves the phrenic outflow intact), and around them (by section of the cranial nerves and cervical dorsal roots) (126).

Other experiments have eliminated spinal cord input to the medulla by sectioning at C1 (39, 115), but these have left the pons attached. The brain stem (medulla plus pons) does not require spinal cord input, and each bilateral half of the brain stem is capable of oscillation by itself. Salmoiraghi & Burns (115) found units firing with a presumably respiratory rhythm in an isolated brain stem piece bordered by midcollicular decerebration, midline sagittal section, hemisection at C1, and section of the cranial nerves.

SPINAL CORD PATTERN GENERATOR   It is not definitely known whether the spinal cord has the capability of respiratory pattern generation. Older research supported the claim from a variety of experiments on rabbits, cats, and dogs that the spinal cord, after isolation from the brain stem, could generate rhythmic respiratory movements (78, 130). This was especially easy to demonstrate in newborn animals, but also could be shown for older animals and adults (9, 79, 130). Not all modern researchers accept the claim that the rhythmic thoracic movements seen were of a respiratory nature. This work has been extensively reviewed by Cordier & Heymans (33).

The adult spinal cord, separated from the medulla, produces no respiratory output. A 4 mm midline section centered at the obex is sufficient to halt respiratory movements (115). It is presumed that medullary efferents decussate here and descend to drive the spinal motoneurons. It is not known whether the necessary descending input is phasic, or whether tonic descending input could also excite a spinal oscillator. This last possibility is suggested by an old experiment in which strychnine (which would change tonic activity levels) restores respiratory movements in an animal with an isolated spinal cord (131). Although preliminary recordings from phrenic motoneurons (8) seemed to show that these cells have autorhythmic properties, more extensive studies (54, 55) have not confirmed these findings. Nothing is known of any possible autorhythmic properties of the spinal interneurons which drive intercostal motoneurons (4).

The Pattern of Breathing

The pattern of phrenic activity driven by the central generator, as seen in phrenic motoneurons, is a long inspiratory discharge whose intensity rises rather linearly and has an abrupt cessation followed by a silent period (Solid line in Figure 1B). In the quiet breathing of awake or anesthetized animals, expiration is passive; there is virtually no activity in expiratory muscles. Thus this review focuses on the patterning of the inspiratory discharge. The problem could be considered essentially solved if we knew the answer to three questions: 1. How does the inspiratory discharge rise at the rate it does; 2. How does it turn off when it does; and 3. How does it turn on again after a period of silence? We of course also want to know the effect of sensory inputs on these three mechanisms. In recent years there has been a large advance toward answering question 2. The answers to questions 1 and 3 are still very speculative.

THE TERMINATION OF INSPIRATION

Inspiration is Normally Terminated by a Reflex Mechanism

When phasic sensory input has been eliminated, a rising inspiratory discharge is generated and terminated by the central pattern generator. The inspiratory duration is longer than that seen in the intact animal. Sensory input from normal filling of the lungs can change the centrally generated inspiration in only one way: the inspiration may be terminated prematurely by lung inflation. If the inflation is insufficient to terminate inspiration it does not affect the pattern of the phrenic discharge. If the inflation is sufficient to act, it has no effect on phrenic discharge other than to abruptly terminate the inspiration prematurely (Figure 1). Thus the inflation reflex serves only as a trigger to terminate inspiration. Although the net effect of inflation may be termed "inhibitory to inflation," impulses generated by inflation do not continuously subtract from the inspiratory output; if they did, the level of phrenic discharge would be lower at all points when inflation is allowed than when inflation is not allowed. This is not the case (Figure 1). Inflation generates only an all-or-none off trigger to terminate an otherwise normal inspiration (14). Lung volume manipulations during expiration, although they may alter the expiratory pause, do not influence the following inspiration (73). These sensory effects, termed *Hering-Breuer reflexes* (62), are mediated by impulses traveling in the vagus nerves. All the effects of lung volume disappear when the vagi are sectioned; when this happens, the pattern of phrenic discharge becomes identical to that identified as originating from the central pattern generator, i.e. that characteristic of the paralyzed, motionless animal (solid line Figure 1*B*).

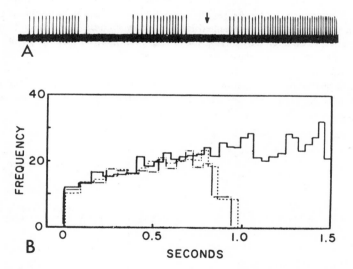

Figure 1   A   Record of discharge of a single phrenic motoneuron in an animal breathing naturally. At the arrow lungs were made motionless (by opening pneumothorax cannulae). Without lung-volume feedback, the next inspiratory discharge was much prolonged.   *B*   Plot of the frequency of discharge from a phrenic motoneuron in a sudden-pneumothorax experiment similar to that of *A*. The broken lines show the frequency during the last two normal inspirations before the pneumothorax, and the solid line shows the frequency of the first discharge during the pneumothorax. The ordinate of each horizontal segment represents the frequency calculated from the interval between two successive impulses. The plot shows that the first 0.7 sec of discharge was the same whether the lungs became distended or not.

[Figure 1 from Larrabee & Knowlton (80).]

The lung volume needed to terminate an inspiration is not constant during a breath. By means of a "servo-respirator" a paralyzed animal may be respirated in phase with its own phrenic discharge. The electrical activity of the phrenic is amplified and used to control the respirator (25). If the respirator is turned off for one cycle, the phrenic will nevertheless discharge with the centrally generated pattern. If a sufficiently large puff of air is introduced into the lungs during this inspiration, the phrenic discharge may be terminated. A large puff is needed to terminate inspiration early, a progressively smaller puff is needed to terminate inspiration later. There is little effect of the rate of inflation; lung volume attained is the important variable [but see (47)]. The lung volume necessary to terminate an inspiration falls with the characteristic shown in Figure 2A. The right end of the curve, when no puff is delivered, is exactly the inspiratory duration found in vagotomized or paralyzed animals, i.e. that set by the central pattern generator (58).

The curve of Figure 2A also holds when the lungs are expanded by diaphragm activity. In a normal breath, lung volume will increase until it reaches termination threshold, at which point expiration will ensue (Figure 2B). At high CO_2 levels the diaphragm contracts more rapidly and the volume threshold is reached more rapidly and at a high volume. At low CO_2 phrenic activity is weak, the lungs inflate slowly, and the volume threshold is reached later at a low volume (25). The volume of a breath can also be altered by having the animal breathe from a closed jar of limited volume. This acts as an elastic load; for a given diaphragmatic force, the lungs expand less. In this manner slow breaths can be achieved. Altered CO_2 and elastic loads can be combined to achieve breaths of any volume (up to a maximum). The termination of inspiration always occurs when the breath crosses the volume-threshold curve (Figure 2B) (58).

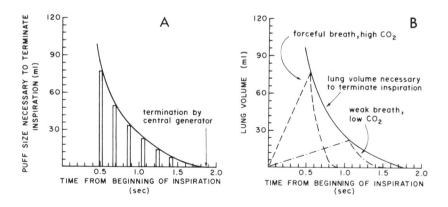

Figure 2   A   Plot of puff size necessary to terminate inspiration, as a function of the time during inspiration when the puff is delivered.   *B*   The same curve with breaths superimposed. Dashed line is the time course of a rapid breath, as under conditions of high CO_2. Dot-dash line is the time course of a slow breath, as under conditions of low CO_2 or elastic load. [Figure 2 adapted from Clark & von Euler (25).]

In humans only deep breaths are sufficiently large to trigger the Hering-Breuer reflex (25). Low-volume eupneic breaths are terminated at the maximum duration by the central pattern generator. It may be that, in man, the lung volume sense receptors have a threshold not reached in shallow breaths.

THE TERMINATION OF INSPIRATION IS THE KEY EVENT IN TIMING THE RESPIRATORY CYCLE   The turn-off characteristic for inflation determines inspiratory duration and end-tidal volume for each breath. Since the force of inspiration increases all during a breath, this turn-off point also determines maximum inspiratory force. The reflex termination of inspiration also resets the whole respiratory cycle. Expiratory duration is proportional to the duration of the preceding inspiration (25, 58), but inspiratory duration is not dependent on preceding expiratory duration (73) or other parameters of the preceding breath. Thus the inspiratory cut-off point determines inspiratory and expiratory duration independently for each breath. The sum of these determines total respiratory period and frequency. Hence the Hering-Breuer trigger seems to be the master control in setting the rhythmic parameters of breathing.

Neurophysiology of the Hering-Breuer Reflex

The lung volume information causing the Hering-Breuer reflex is known to originate in the slowly adapting stretch receptors of the bronchi, whose axons travel in the vagus nerves (1, 72, 132). The group of slowly adapting stretch receptors fire at a rate closely proportional to the square root of lung volume (25). If the curve of Figure 2A is redrawn to show the rate of firing in the slowly adapting stretch receptors necessary to terminate an inspiration, then the hyperbolic shape will be flattened out somewhat by the square root transformation of the ordinate scale. In this flattened curve the threshold for termination of inspiration by vagal firing would seem to fall with a roughly linear time course.

From the characteristics of the Hering-Breuer reflex described, it can be concluded that somewhere in the brain there is a group of cells which generates an inspiration-terminating trigger signal when it receives sufficient vagal input. The threshold for generating this trigger signal must fall continuously (and very approximately linearly) from the beginning of each inspiration. The neurophysiological problem is thus to find these cells and to describe their connections and mode of action.

NUCLEUS OF THE SOLITARY TRACT   The vagal afferents have their first synapses in the nucleus of the solitary tract. von Euler et al (35) recorded from a large number of respiratory cells in this region. They found that virtually all the cells had their period of firing during inspiration. The inspiratory cells recorded from were injected, through the recording electrode, with the intracellular dye procion-yellow. The position and morphology of the cells were reconstructed from postmortem serial sections. Stereotaxic coordinates were only accepted for tracks in which the position of a procion-yellow cell could confirm the absolute location. By using this precise anatomical technique, von Euler et al (35) showed that the cells sat in a very restricted anatomical locus, the ventrolateral nucleus of the solitary tract, a nucleus with a radius in any cross section of about 300 μm.

The pattern of firing of these inspiratory cells was very similar to that of phrenic motoneurons: a roughly linearly augmenting discharge, with a steep cessation. These inspiratory cells retained their pattern of firing even when the animal was paralyzed and the respirator switched off for a few breaths (Figure 3*A* and 4*A*). Thus the pattern of inspiratory firing in these cells is not due to sensory input from the expanding lungs, but is due to the central pattern generator. These cells either receive, or generate themselves, a proper inspiratory pattern of firing. [A discussion of the still unsolved question of whether these cells generate or receive the pattern

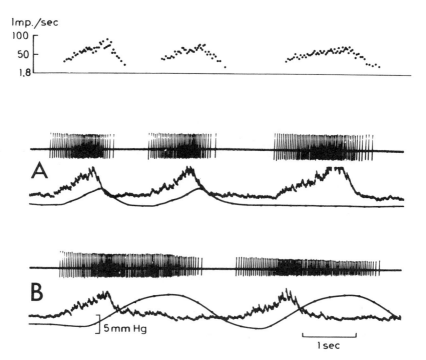

Figure 3   Inspiratory neuron of the ventrolateral nucleus of the solitary tract which responds to vagal input (IV cell).   *A*   From above: Plot of reciprocal of interspike intervals of a medullary neuron spike train, the neuron spike train, "integrated" phrenic record, intratracheal pressure. During the first two inspirations the respirator was driven by the "integrated" phrenic activity (with some time lag). During the last inspiration the respirator was switched off to eliminate proprioceptive feedback. The neuron and phrenic nerve continued to fire in a respiratory pattern, but the inspiration was prolonged. The postulated input causing this is called *central inspiratory excitation* (CIE).   *B*   In the middle of the first inspiration, the respirator was turned on and driven by a sine wave generator. The firing of the phrenic was not disturbed, but the firing pattern of the neuron appeared to be the sum of CIE input and feedback from lung stretch receptors.

[Figure 3 from von Euler et al (35) and unpublished data.]

is deferred until later. For the purpose of exposition, it is assumed that the cells receive centrally patterned inspiratory excitation (CIE).]

INSPIRATORY-VAGAL (IV) CELLS   In addition to receiving CIE, approximately half of the above-designated cells also receive vagal input from the lung stretch receptors (6, 35). This can be demonstrated by inflating the lungs or by shocking the vagus nerve at an intensity appropriate to stimulate the lung volume fibers (Figure 3B). Thus this subgroup, here termed *inspiratory-vagal* (IV) cells, receives two inputs, both of which increase during the course of an inspiration and are silent during expiration: the CIE and lung stretch receptor input. The remaining cells not receiving vagal input are termed *inspiratory-spinal* (IS) cells.

All the IV cells can be driven by single shocks to the vagus with a one-to-one response up to high frequencies. The latencies of response of some cells certainly indicate monosynaptic connections. Whether the longer latency of others is due to slow conduction in thin afferent branches, or to more intercalated synapses, is not known.

The threshold for driving the IV cells from the vagus decreases roughly linearly during the course of an inflation (35). It takes a stronger shock to the vagus, exciting

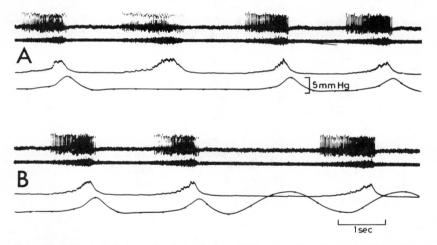

Figure 4   Spike train from an inspiratory neuron of the ventrolateral nucleus of the solitary tract with no vagal input, but with a descending spinal axon (IS cell). In *A* and *B:* top trace is neuron spike train, second trace is phrenic activity, third trace is "integrated" phrenic activity, bottom trace is intratracheal pressure.   *A*   In the first and last two inspirations the respirator was driven by "integrated" phrenic activity. During the second discharge, the respirator was off, revealing CIE drive.   *B*   The first two inspirations were with a phrenic-driven respirator. The respirator was then switched to sine wave generator. The cell and phrenic fired in the pattern driven by the central generator, even though the inspiratory discharge occurred at the trough of tracheal pressure. The two larger than normal lung inflations caused no activity in the cell.

[Figure 4 from von Euler et al (35) and unpublished data.]

more stretch receptor axons, to drive the IV cells early in inspiration than late in inspiration. These cells are clearly summing their CIE input with their vagal input. Since the CIE input rises roughly linearly during the course of an inspiration, the extra vagal input required to drive the cell should decrease roughly linearly. This should explain the falling threshold of these cells to vagal input. Thus these cells have the proper threshold characteristics to mediate the Hering-Breuer reflex.

In normal breathing these cells receive a rising CIE input and in parallel a rising vagal input. Their firing rate should reflect the sum of these two inputs (Figure 3 A, impulses/sec plot for the first two inspirations). With the respirator off, the IV cells do not receive a rising vagal input, but only the CIE input. As a result the IV discharge has a slower rate of rise (Figure 3A, impulses/sec plot for last inspiration). However, because the CIE lasts longer and increases steadily, so also does the IV discharge. The final firing rate reached by the IV cells is similar whether the lungs fill or not (Figure 3A, impulses/sec plot). This suggests that the inspiration off trigger occurs at a fixed level of firing of the IV cells whether they have vagal input or not. It is tempting to believe that the IV cell output may itself be the inspiration off trigger and that it directly inhibits the CIE generator (Figure 5A). Under this supposition the IV cells are responsible for the termination of inspiration whether this happens at the central pattern generator duration or at the shorter duration seen in the reflex override. The off switch would function as shown in Figure 6A when artificial inflations are delivered, and as in Figure 6B when normal vagal feedback is allowed.

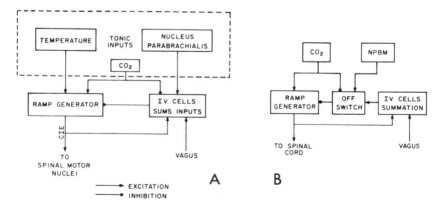

Figure 5   A   Simplest network to explain Hering-Breuer reflex. CIE ramp activity sums in the IV cells with impulses from the slowly adapting lung stretch receptors travelling in the vagus nerve. At a certain value of the sum, the IC cells send an inspiration terminating off trigger to the ramp generator. Tonic inputs are described in the text; they contribute a tonic drive or inhibition to the ramp generator and/or the IV cells.   *B*   Alternative model for the off switch. This model interposes a separate group of off-switch neurons between the IV cells and the ramp generator. In this model, CO_2 and NPBM input play on the off-switch cells instead of the IV cells. Similar to model of Bradley et al (18).

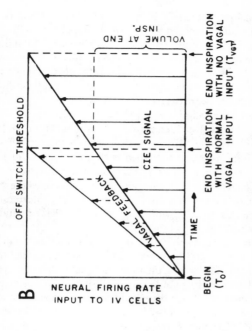

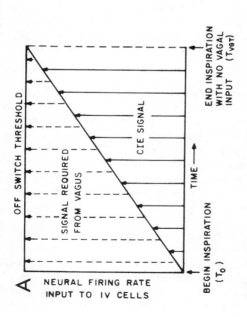

Figure 6 Operation of the inspiratory off switch. Diagram shows the inputs to the IV cells. The threshold at which the IV cells generate the off switch is shown as constant during a breath. *A* The CIE signal increases continuously. It alone will eventually cause the IV cells to reach off-switch threshold. Inspiration then terminates at the CPG duration, as seen after vagotomy, T_{vGT}. At any time earlier than this a sufficient lung inflation signal can sum with the CIE and cause the IV cells to reach off threshold early. The volume feedback required to reach the off-switch threshold decreases with time from beginning of inspiration. *B* With the vagi intact the lung volume feedback signal sums with the CIE and the off threshold is reached earlier. The volume of the lungs at any time is roughly proportional to the CIE signal. The lung volume attained at inspiratory cut off with normal vagal input is marked at the right of the graph. The volume attained without vagal feedback would be proportional to the full length of the vertical axis.

A key prediction of the model presented here is that the off trigger should occur at a fixed level of firing of the IV cells no matter when termination occurs. Although the figures of von Euler et al (35), including Figure 3 of this paper, would indicate that this might be the case, the prediction has not been given a direct experimental test. This test should be very high on the priority list for future experimentation.

We have shown that the IV cells have the requisite properties to mediate the off switch, but this does not prove that they are the responsible cells. In all the published studies of units in the nucleus of the solitary tract (NST) (6, 12, 13, 35, 36, 45) it has been found that virtually all the cells which receive direct input from the lung volume receptors also receive CIE input. If this is true, then in the first afferent nucleus all the lung volume information is combined with CIE input in just the proper way to perform the Hering-Breuer reflex. In that case it seems unlikely that the lung volume information is later separated out again and used in some other way to perform the Hering-Breuer reflex. On this basis it can be strongly inferred that cells in the solitary tract which sum the CIE with lung volume feedback do indeed mediate the Hering-Breuer reflex.

A possible objection to this conclusion involves the small cells that sit in the medial part of the NST. E. G. Merrill (personal communication) reported that these cells fire during inspiration, are excited by lung inflation, and can be driven by vagal stimulation at monosynaptic latencies. It is not known if all these cells receive both CIE and vagal input. Due to their small size they could not be adequately studied by Merrill and may conceivably have been missed in other microelectrode studies of the NST (6, 12, 13, 35, 36, 45). There are two published reports (35, 75) of authors finding rare respiratory cells that exhibited no rhythmic firing when respiratory movements were stopped. In one case (75), these cells were from the medial part of the NST. It is possible that these cells received vagal input but not CIE input, or they may have been IV neurons with a large vagal input and only a relatively small CIE input. A. J. Berger (unpublished) reports 32 NST cells firing with lung volume but not with the phrenic.

AN INTERPOSED OFF-SWITCH POPULATION? PHASE-SPANNING CELLS   In Figure 5A the off trigger is shown as coming from the IV cells and directly inhibiting the ramp generating population of the central pattern generator. Some authors (18, 29, 31) think it more likely that a separate "off-switch" population is interposed between the IV cells and the ramp generator (Figure 5B). There is currently no strong evidence, one way or the other, to distinguish between the two models. It seems just as likely that IV cells directly turn off the ramp generating cells at a specific threshold, as that the IV cells turn on a switch population at a specific threshold. The problems in conceptualizing a population acting as a trigger switch are the same in both models.

If there is a separate off-trigger population, then they should fire around the time of the inspiration (I) to expiration (E) transition. Rhythmic cells firing at this time have been found in the brain stem and have been termed "phase-spanning" I-E cells (27, 28, 32). I-E cells are rarely found in the NST region (45); they are found mostly in the rostral pons (32, 77), a region which is not necessary for rhythmic breathing. There is not even evidence that these cells form a distinct population. Waldron (125) recorded respiratory units all over the medulla and pons and plotted for each unit the phase in the respiratory cycle when the unit commenced firing, and the phase when the unit stopped firing. She found two "natural clusters" that correspond to I and E populations. There was no evidence for a separate phase-spanning population, although at the edges of the natural clusters there were some units that fired late enough in inspiration or early enough in expiration to fit the description of phase-spanning neurons.

This work has been greatly extended recently with similar results. Vibert et al (123, 124) made a histogram of the phase of peak firing frequency of 5000 respiratory units sampled anatomically at random from the pons and medulla. They again observed two main populations, an inspiratory and an expiratory. Troughs were observed in the histogram at the transition from I to E and E to I, arguing against special large phase-spanning populations. Taking into account the location of the units, by dividing the recording area into cubes 0.7 mm on a side, did not change this conclusion.

Nevertheless there are some cells which do fire at the IE transition. A small but important population of these could easily get lost in the type of macroanatomy described by Waldron (125) and Vibert et al (123, 124).

THE EFFECT OF CO_2 ON INSPIRATION

This section presents evidence that the effect of CO_2 on breathing can be explained as an effect on the CIE generator and an effect on the off switch. There are three basic facts regarding the effect of CO_2 on inspiration:

1. Increased CO_2 levels cause more intense firing during inspiration in all the motor-related neurons (e.g. phrenic, IV, and IS cells). Because of the increased phrenic activity, the lungs expand more rapidly at high CO_2 than at low.

2. The volume-termination curve (Figure 2A) is approximately the same when measured at any level of CO_2 (25, 57, 58). 1. and 2. together determine that at high CO_2 breathing is both more rapid and deeper than at low CO_2, as can be seen in Figure 2B.

3. After vagotomy CO_2 increases the depth of breathing, but has little or no effect on the duration of inspiration (16, 17, 37, 57, 58). The duration is that set by the central pattern generator.

This section attempts to fit these facts into the model being developed (Figures 5 and 6).

CO_2 as a Tonic Drive Adding to the CIE

The location of chemosensory cells and their afferent pathways is still a matter for argument. Nevertheless, compared to the rhythm of breathing, blood chemical levels change slowly and thus constitute tonic variables. Tonic excitation from chemoreceptors could feed directly into the central pattern generating cells. At the beginning of inspiration, the CIE, as manifested in the spike frequencies of phrenic motorneurons (Figure 1) and the solitary tract cells (Figure 3 and 4), commences at a moderately high level. Thereafter there is a ramp-like increase in the frequencies. It is tempting to separate the firing pattern into two components, a baseline firing rate due to tonic drives on the respiratory system, and an increasing portion due to a ramp generator. The model of Figure 6A, amended to include this component, would appear as Figure 7A. If increased CO_2 drive (and any other tonic drives) simply add to the CIE, then the firing pattern with increased drive should have an increased baseline component but no change in the slope of the ramp (Figure 6B). The model of Bradley et al (18) is basically of this form.

At high CO_2 the CIE signal is more intense. One would expect that after vagotomy the off threshold would be reached proportionately earlier in a breath. This is not the case. CO_2 has very little or no effect on the duration of a breath after vagotomy (16, 17, 36, 58). A very simple explanation for this phenomenon would have the tonic signal from the CO_2 receptors inhibit the IV cells as much as they increase the CIE (Figure 5A). The total level of excitation of the IV cells would then be independent of the level of CO_2 drive, and the off-switch parameters would remain constant. In the model of Bradley et al (18) (Figure 5B), the tonic CO_2 signal is excitatory to the inspiratory ramp generator and inhibitory to the separate off-trigger population. Figures 7A and 7B show how the off switch is independent of CO_2 levels in their model.

Both models (Figures 5A and 5B) account for the fact that the volume-termination curve is independent of CO_2 level (25, 58). The CIE discharge is higher at high CO_2. However, since the termination threshold is raised equally, either by inhibition of the IV cells, or inhibition of the off switch cells, the added vagal feedback necessary to reach threshold remains unchanged. As can be seen from Figures 7A and 7B this is true at any time during inspiration.

One method of distinguishing between the models of Figures 5A and 5B is the following. The model of Figure 5A predicts that the rate of firing of the IV cells at the time of inspiratory termination should be independent of CO_2 levels. The model of Figure 5B predicts that the rate of firing of the IV cells at the time of inspiratory termination should increase with increasing CO_2 levels. Recording from IV cells at different levels of CO_2 will give a straightforward test of these predictions. This test should receive high priority for future experimentation.

The constancy of the volume-threshold curve in Figure 7 depends on the assumption that CO_2 adds a tonic increment to the CIE and the off threshold. However, CO_2 may act to increase the rate of rise of the CIE ramp while having tonic effects on the off-switch cells. In this case neither of the Figure 5 models will preserve the constancy of the volume-threshold curve. Figure 8 shows how in this case inspiratory duration after vagotomy, T_{VGT}, may remain constant with CO_2 changes, but then the volume-threshold curve is changed, larger inflations being required early in a breath at higher CO_2 levels. An effect of this nature is seen with pontine stimulation (see below). There is scattered inadequate evidence [e.g. Figures 6 and 7 in (27)] that both the baseline and the rate of rise of the ramp of the CIE are increased with increased CO_2 drive. Further documentation of this is one of the simple and important experiments that needs to be done. Neurophysiological understanding will be more difficult if the tonic and phasic components of the CIE are not separable.

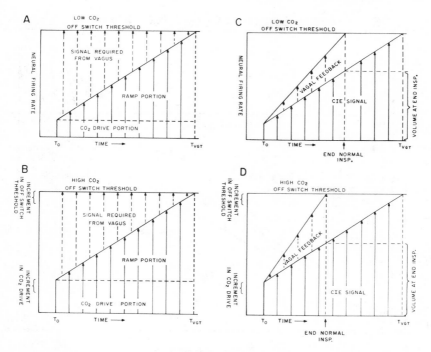

Figure 7 Effect of CO_2 in the model of Figure 5*B*.   *A* CO_2 is considered to add a tonic baseline component to the CIE activity. The total CIE, then, is the firing rate indicated by solid arrows as the sum of the CO_2 drive portion and the ramp generator portion. The IV cells receive this CIE as input.   *B*   At higher CO_2 levels the baseline CO_2 activity is increased. The ramp component is unchanged by CO_2. In addition, the off-switch cells are inhibited tonically by CO_2, thus at high CO_2 the off-switch threshold is higher. However since the CIE and the off-switch threshold are raised equally, the difference between the two is unchanged and is independent of CO_2 level. Thus, as seen in 7*A* and 7*B*, the signal required from the vagus to terminate inspiration (volume-threshold curve) is independent of CO_2 level. Duration of inspiration after vagotomy (T_{VGT}) is also independent of CO_2 level.   *C* and *D*   The vagal feedback at low and high CO_2 is shown in these diagrams. Since the lungs expand more rapidly at high CO_2 (7*D*), the vagal feedback also increases more rapidly than at low CO_2 (7*C*). The CIE and vagal feedback sum to reach the off threshold earlier at high CO_2 (7*D*) than at low CO_2 (7*C*). Thus with vagal feedback intact, CO_2 produces faster and deeper breaths.

Exceptions to the CO_2 Independence of the Volume-Threshold Curve

In some experimental situations inspiratory duration shortens with increasing CO_2 even after vagotomy. This has been attributed to factors which disrupt the equality of the augmenting effects of CO_2 on the CIE and the off-threshold (16–18). Barbituate anesthesia has been suggested as one of these factors (15–17), but even in unanesthetized cats Gill (53) reports a strong decrease in inspiratory duration

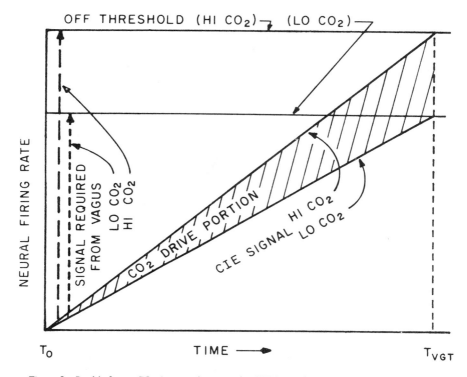

Figure 8   In this figure CO_2 does not increase the CIE by adding a tonic baseline component, but by increasing the slope of the CIE ramp. In this model the signal required from the vagus to terminate inspiration is not independent of CO_2 levels. The figure shows the off threshold raised by just the right amount to make T_{VGT} independent of CO_2. Other assumptions about how the off threshold changes with CO_2 lead to different changes in the volume-threshold curve with CO_2 changes. This is true whether the off threshold is raised by inhibition of the IV cells (Figure 5*A*) or by inhibition of a separate off-switch population (Figure 5*B*).

Stimulation of the NPBM may be used instead of vagus stimulation to reach off threshold. This figure predicts that a greater NPBM shock would be required early in inspiration at high CO_2 than at low CO_2. This has been demonstrated experimentally (40, 42).

with increased CO_2. Gill's preparation was decerebrate, deafferented (section of cranial nerves IX, X, XI, XII) and spinalized at C7-C8. This result should be reexamined.

Bradley et al (16) found a transient shift in the volume-termination curve when they administered step changes in CO_2. After vagotomy there was initial prolongation of inspiration with a concomitant higher tidal volume, followed by a shortening of inspiratory duration to its previous value without a concomitant fall in tidal volume. The authors explained this as due to different rates of response of the two CO_2 effects to changes in chemical drive; the off-threshold rise was more rapid than the CIE increase (18).

This explanation requires that the initial response to a CO_2 increase should be a prolongation of the inspiratory burst, with the same rate of rise of activity to a higher final frequency at inspiratory termination. Following this the rate of rise of activity should increase, reaching the same final frequency at a shorter inspiratory duration. This prediction can and should be tested in a single-unit electrophysiological study.

Function of the Hering-Breuer Reflex

Superficially it may seem obvious that the function of the Hering-Breuer reflex is to compensate for occluded airways. When the lungs do not fill normally in a breath, the inspiration continues longer until the diaphragm reaches a more complete state of contraction. But the Hering-Breuer reflex probably does not operate in cases of occluded airways. In the cat, *normal* breaths are terminated by the Hering-Breuer reflex. Occluded airways would result in a slow lung filling and termination of inspiration by the central pattern generator; the Hering-Breuer reflex would not be called into operation. In humans, the Hering-Breuer threshold curve is such that the termination of inspiration by this reflex occurs only in the deepest breaths with rapidly filling lungs (25); that normal breathing or occluded airway breathing would not call the reflex into operation. There must, then, be another function for the Hering-Breuer reflex.

Under conditions of high CO_2, the central pattern generator, after vagotomy, does not change its frequency but only the rate and maximum degree of contraction of the diaphragm. Respiratory volume can increase only by the difference between normal and maximal tidal volume. With an operating Hering-Breuer reflex, however, the more rapidly inflating lungs will reach the Hering-Breuer off-trigger volume earlier in inspiration and at a larger than normal volume (Figures 2*B*, 7*C*, and 7*D*). Inspiration will terminate earlier, the expiratory pause will be proportionately smaller, and the whole cycle will repeat at a higher frequency. Hence with the Hering-Breuer reflex not only does the tidal volume increase, but the rate also increases. The ventilation rate increases by the product of the two factors. Thus the Hering-Breuer reflex converts a central pattern generator mechanism, which is only capable of adjusting tidal volume, into a combined central and reflex pattern generator capable of adjusting both volume and frequency.

THE PONS

As stated earlier, the pons is not necessary for rhythmic breathing (19, 63, 126), but neurons in the pons have a strong effect on respiration. Lesions in certain parts of the pons or transections in the pons cause apneusis (arrest of respiratory activity in deep inspiration), at least temporarily. Because of this the pons was thought to contain a center that promoted expiration, the pneumotaxic center. In reciprocal inhibition theories of breathing rhythm generation, the pneumotaxic center is usually identified as the expiratory center. This has led to much work on the role of the pons in respiration. Several authors have found (and some have not, see below) neurons firing with a respiratory rhythm in the pons. However, after isolation from the medulla, the pons does not show units with respiratory periodicity (26, 66).

Rostral Pons: Nucleus Parabrachialis Medialis (NPBM)

The so-called pneumotaxic center has been identified as corresponding to the nucleus parabrachialis medialis and the Kölliker-Fuse nucleus of the rostral pons (10, 30). This region is of unknown function.

It was a mystery why some authors (10, 11, 32) found many respiratory units in the pons, while others (23, 114, 137) were unable to find any such units until Feldman et al (44, 45) discovered that the two results depend on whether or not the vagi were sectioned. When the vagi were intact "strikingly few respiratory modulated units were seen in the pons" (44). When inflation of the lungs was prevented, however, cells that were previously firing tonically changed to a respiratory modulated pattern. Sensory input from lung inflation, via the vagus, prevented respiratory modulation of the pontine cells. These results were obtained from recording mainly in the NPBM region. It now appears that during normal (vagus intact) breathing, the cells of the NPBM fire tonically. It is obviously important to know if this result holds for the rest of the pons.

The prevention of respiratory modulation is not due to direct inhibition or excitation of the NPBM cells by vagal input, since neither electrical shocks to the vagus (10) nor increases in lung inflation (44, 45) affect the firing pattern of NPBM cells. Feldman et al (44, 45) concluded that the pulmonary afferents inhibit a pathway presynaptic to the NPBM cells. This conclusion is, of course, speculative. Anesthesia also suppresses the respiratory modulation of the NPBM (11). Since rhythmic breathing is similar in both anesthetized and unanesthetized cats, this is another reason to conclude that cyclic activity in NPBM neurons can not be essential to the genesis of rhythmic breathing (38).

These results completely invalidate virtually all previous speculations concerning the action of the "pneumotaxic center" (PC) since they all required cells that fire with a respiratory rhythm (29, 43, 46, 108).

The tonic output of the NPBM feeds into the inspiratory off switch. Stimulation in the NPBM can prematurely terminate an inspiration (10, 30). When the NPBM is lesioned, inspirations are prolonged; it appears that the off-switch threshold is raised (38, 47) by being deprived of its NPBM input. Lesions in the NPBM which greatly raise the off-switch threshold do not affect the rate of rise of inspiratory activity or its responsiveness to changes in CO_2 levels (38). [Lesions in nearby regions can reduce sensitivity to CO_2 (38, 49, 110–112), but this is a clearly separable effect (38).]

The NPBM output seems to directly sum with the CIE and the vagal feedback to achieve the off-switch threshold. The strength of NPBM stimulation needed to terminate inspiration falls during the course of inspiration (30, 40, 42). When vagal feedback is interrupted, the NPBM stimulation necessary falls with a time course directly proportional to the increase in the CIE signal as measured by the phrenic activity (40, 42). When vagal feedback is intact, the NPBM stimulation required to terminate inspiration is less at all times. The difference between NPBM stimulation needed with vagal feedback and without vagal feedback increases during the course of a breath with a time course comparable to the increase in vagal feedback; i.e.

NPBM stimulation can substitute for an equivalent amount of vagal input to reach off threshold (42).

The conclusion from these experiments is that the NPBM output feeds into the same off-switch mechanism as the CIE and the vagal feedback. The simplest realization of this would be to have the NPBM output directly feed into the IV cells of the NST (Figure 5*A*). Alternatively they could feed into the postulated off-switch cells (Figure 5*B*).

Apneusis

If both the NPBM input and the vagal input to the off switch are eliminated, then off-switch threshold is never reached and "apneusis" results (10, 82, 84, 100, 126). In an apneustic breath an inspiration starts normally but inspiratory activity keeps increasing beyond the normal cutoff. Inspiratory activity rises to a very high rate of firing which can be maintained for many minutes. Apneusis may be reversibly induced by NPBM lesions and manipulation of lung volume (38, 120). When the pump is switched off in expiration, the next inspiration starts normally, but without vagal input, the off threshold is not reached and an apneustic breath results. If the lungs are now inflated the off threshold is reached and rhythmic breathing resumes (38, 120).

The rate of rise of the apneustic breath is the same as for normal breaths at all CO_2 levels. The final level reached by apneustic breaths and rhythmic breaths increases along parallel curves when CO_2 is raised (38). The rise in the tonic level of apneustic activity with rise in CO_2 supports the hypothesis that CO_2 adds a tonic increment to the CIE.

Apneustic inspirations do eventually terminate. The duration of the inspiration can be many seconds or minutes. The mechanism of termination at these long times is unknown. If the animal is kept in good physiological condition by artificial respiration, the duration of the apneustic breaths gradually become shorter, and eventually a fairly regular rhythm of breathing returns (19, 38, 63). In the case of partial NPBM lesion this sometimes takes about 3–5 hrs. Further NPBM lesions can then reinstate apneusis (38). However, recovery is also seen after complete section between the NPBM and the medulla (19, 63). The conclusion is that the NPBM normally has an input to the inspiratory off switch, but after lesion the excitability of the off switch cells can readjust to function without that input. This is not surprising; there are many other examples of the gradual recovery of normal excitability by a neuronal group after ablation of an area projecting to it (e.g. 109). The NPBM input is not necessary for rhythmic respiration.

Effects of Temperature

Keeping other variables constant, a rise in temperature leads to an increase in the rate of rise of inspiratory activity (16, 38, 56, 57). However it seems that the off threshold is unchanged by temperature. The off threshold may be tested by NPBM stimulation at the beginning of a breath when the CIE and vagal feedback contribution to the off trigger are low. The intensity of stimulation in the NPBM required to terminate inspiration very early in a breath is independent of temperature (42). With an increase in the rate of rise of CIE [and, if intact, the concomitant vagal feedback (56, 116)] and no change in off threshold, inspiration is terminated earlier at high temperatures. Expiratory duration is proportionately shortened; the proportionality is unaffected by variations in body temperature (58). As a result, total respiratory frequency increases. These affects may be modeled simply, as in Figure 5A, by a temperature-sensitive input to the CIE generator.

PROBLEMS WITH THE THEORY

The theory developed in this review (see also 18, 138) is that inspiratory activity (CIE) can be thought of as the sum of a tonic drive (including explicitly CO_2 drive) and a ramp generator. The slope of the ramp does not change much in response to the variables studied. Inspiration is terminated when the sum of two phasic and at least two tonic variables reaches a fixed threshold. The two phasic variables are the CIE ramp and the vagal feedback from bronchial stretch receptors; the tonic variables discussed are an NPBM input and an inhibitory component from CO_2 receptors. This simple theory predicts the volume threshold curve (Figure 2), and its independence of CO_2 levels (Figure 7). It also predicts the effects of experimental manipulations of lung volume, vagal section and stimulation, NPBM stimulation and lesion, altered CO_2 levels, and temperature changes. The theory seems easily expandable to include the effects of other (mostly tonic) inputs.

The role of CO_2 is probably not adequately accounted for in the theory. Two problems have already been discussed: 1. CO_2 does not seem to act only as a tonic variable but probably also increases the rate of rise of the CIE ramp generator; 2. the volume-threshold curve is not always found to be constant after changes in CO_2 levels.

The hypothesis that CO_2 adds equally to the CIE and the off threshold during both normal and apneustic breathing is contradicted by two experiments. In the first experiment apneusis was induced by anterior pontine section and immobilization of the lungs in expiratory position. The lungs were then inflated; apneusis was interrupted and rhythmic respiration recurred (120). Apparently the tonic vagal input from the inflated lungs was sufficient, when summed with the CIE, to reach off threshold. The amount of tonic vagal input needed to reach off threshold should be constant with changes in CO_2, but it was found that a greater lung volume was needed at higher CO_2 levels to interrupt apneusis (139). Thus it seems that CO_2 increases the off switch threshold more than the CIE.

The above result might be explained by assuming that pontine section interrupts the circuits mediating the CIE responses to CO_2, but a similar result was found with apneusis induced by a small NPBM lesion which did not reduce CIE responsiveness to CO_2 (40, 42). It was found that the amount of NPBM stimulation required to terminate inspiration early in a breath, when the vagal feedback was small enough to be ignored, increased as CO_2 level increased. This also contradicts the theory.

This last experiment can be explained by assuming that the effect of CO_2 on the CIE is to increase the slope of the ramp rather than to add a tonic amount (42)

(Figure 8). However, in this form of the theory the volume-threshold curve is no longer independent of CO_2.

There are three augmenting signals: the CIE, the vagal feedback, and the NPBM activity after vagotomy. These three signals may all be considered to be the sum of a tonic portion and a superimposed ramp. The effect of CO_2 can be neither a pure increase in the tonic portion, nor a pure increase in the ramp slope. The former is ruled out by the data on NPBM stimulation at different CO_2 levels; the latter is ruled out by the constancy of the volume-threshold curve at different CO_2 levels (Figure 8). If the volume-threshold curve is not precisely constant with changes in CO_2, especially early in inspiration, then the theory may explain the data by assuming that CO_2 affects both the tonic portion and the ramp slope of the CIE (cf 18). We need more data on the precise shape of the volume-threshold curve, the CIE discharge, the vagal feedback, and the pontine discharge at different CO_2 levels.

INSPIRATION AND EXPIRATION

So far this review has discussed primarily the timing of the off switch and some tonic variables affecting the inspiratory activity. We must now turn to the other two aspects of breathing rhythm generation which require explanation: 1. How is the rise in inspiratory activity generated; and 2. What determines the timing of the expiratory pause. Much less is known about these two topics than about the off switch. Hence, on these topics, there is great room for speculation.

Inspiration

THE GREAT MYSTERY: WHERE IS THE CIE GENERATOR?   There are three known populations of respiratory neurons in the medulla: the nucleus ambiguus (NA), the nucleus retroambigualis (NRA), and the nucleus of the solitary tract (NST). If one of these groups is the CIE generator, then it must drive, or entrain, the other groups.

The nucleus ambiguus cells are the motoneurons to the pharyngeal and laryngeal accessory respiratory muscles. In deep barbiturate anesthesia, while breathing is eupneic, these accessory respiratory muscles are "almost completely silent" (89, 90). This eliminates the NA motoneurons as candidates for the central pattern generation (CPG).

Cells of the NRA and the NST both have firing patterns very similar to the final motor output (35, 90), and both groups of cells have axons descending to the spinal cord (36, 90). The NST cells have extensively ramifying axons in the NRA region, but the NRA cells do not send axons to the NST (90, 92). Thus, if one nucleus drives the other directly, it must be the NST cells that drive the NRA.

We conclude that the NST is the most likely site of the CIE generator. Unfortunately the evidence is contradictory on whether ablation of the NST stops breathing. Oberholzer & Tofani (97) reported that bilateral destruction of the NST area "causes only slight changes in the respiration of animals" with prior bilateral vagotomy. Koepchen et al (76) reported that "the pattern is severely altered." Brodie & Borison (20) reported that gross destruction of the rostrodorsal medulla, including the NST, resulted in "gasping," while E. G. Merrill (personal communication) reported that even minor lesions in the NST could result in drastic disruptions. We must admit that at this stage we are not sure if the CIE generator resides in the NST.

SOLITARY TRACT CELLS WITHOUT VAGAL INPUT   As discussed earlier, virtually all the inspiratory cells of the solitary tract retain their firing pattern when phasic sensory feedback from proprioceptors is eliminated. Thus they all receive or generate CIE. All the inspiratory NST cells also have spinal axons (12, 96). About half of the cells, the IV cells, receive vagal input from lung stretch receptors (Figure 3). The other half of the NST inspiratory cells, do not receive input from the vagus (Figure 4) (6, 35). Termed *inspiratory-spinal* (IS) cells, the IS cells are anatomically intermingled with the IV cells in the ventrolateral nucleus of the solitary tract[(35), see also Figure 3 of (13)]. Their spinal axons descend in the ventrolateral columns (96), at least to C4 (36), and some are known to descend as far as C8 (12). Since the output pattern of these cells is very similar to the pattern of firing of the phrenic motoneurons (35) it is likely that these cells are premotor neurons which drive the phrenic motoneurons. The IS cells are one candidate for the central pattern ramp generator.

HOW IS THE RISE IN INSPIRATORY ACTIVITY GENERATED?   Although we do not know which cells generate the rising CIE, there has been much speculation on how the augmenting activity could be produced. Most hypotheses rely on reciprocal excitation among members of the inspiratory population. Once activity in the population is initiated, the mutual excitation would gradually increase the firing rate. It has been reported several times that the inspiratory respiratory cells are interconnected by excitatory axon collaterals. Burns & Salmoiraghi (21) argued that "if all the neurones in a self-reexciting system could be excited simultaneously by a strong stimulus, self-reexcitation should stop abruptly because all individuals in the system would pass simultaneously into the absolute refractory phase." Upon stimulating in the medulla, they found that a shock, delivered late in inspiration, would indeed stop the discharge. A stronger shock was needed to have the same effect earlier in inspiration. In retrospect it is most likely that they were stimulating vagal afferents in the medulla and triggering a Hering-Breuer off-reflex. Thus their experiment provides no evidence for self-reexcitation.

Other evidence for mutual excitation (7, 36) is equally weak. It is based on the fact that antidromic activation of respiratory cells via their spinal axons requires a higher stimulus voltage during the cell's natural period of quiet than during its discharging period. This result may mean that the extra fibers recruited by the larger stimulus assist the antidromic invasion by some spatially summating (synaptic) pathway. This assisting pathway could be collaterals of the descending respiratory axons, but it could also be due to synaptic excitation from other ascending or descending neurons. The technique of stimulating in spinal tracts does not allow accurate identification of the stimulated fibers.

Nucleus retroambigualis cells may be antidromically activated from their spinal axons and show the lowering of activation threshold during their period of natural firing (91). Nevertheless E. G. Merrill (91, personal communication) showed that these cells are not crosslinked by excitatory collaterals: 1. antidromic activation of other NRA cells does not increase a cell's excitability; 2. cross correlation of NRA spike trains shows no evidence of cross linking; and 3. the varying susceptibility to antidromic invasion is due to a varying threshold of the axon itself during the respiratory cycle.

We conclude that there is no definitive evidence of excitatory interconnections within a population of respiratory cells.

The Alternation of Respiratory Phases

Most theories of respiratory rhythm generation invoke reciprocally inhibiting inspiratory and expiratory populations of neurons (21, 29, 31, 82, 84, 100). In these theories each population is activated by tonic drives and perhaps by reciprocal excitatory connections within each population. These theories require that each population "fatigues" near the end of its active period (21). If it did not fatigue, a population, once it started firing, would fire forever due to its tonic inputs and reciprocal excitation; the other population would be inhibited forever. If the neurons fatigued, however, they would eventually reduce their firing rate. This would reduce the inhibition of the reciprocal population, which by some mechanism of inhibitory rebound would then turn on and completely suppress the activity of the first population. These theories are no longer tenable because 1. respiratory neurons do not fatigue and 2. there is no known expiratory population with the requisite connections.

FATIGUE   An early intracellular study (113) seemed to show that the firing level for threshold depolarization progressively increased during the burst discharge of individual respiratory neurons. This rise of the firing level was thought to eventually terminate a neuron's firing and was thus thought of as "fatigue." A recent intracellular study (104) of respiratory neurons refutes this. Firing level correlates with discharge frequency. When discharge frequency increases through most of the burst, so does firing level. However, when discharge frequency decreases near the end of the burst, firing level recovers to its original value. Thus, at termination, firing level is the same as at onset and hence cannot be invoked as the cause of termination. Intracellular injection of currents also shows that these neurons have neither pronounced accommodation nor adaptation (104). The lack of fatigue is readily seen during apneusis. In apneusis the inspiratory neurons fire at a rate much higher than is seen in normal breaths for periods as long as one-half hour.

EXPIRATORY CELLS   Expiratory populations may reside in the pons or the medulla. The pons is not necessary for rhythmic breathing (19, 63, 126) and in any case in the normal vagus-intact animal may not have cells firing with a respiratory rhythm (44, 45). In the medulla of a deeply anesthetized cat with eupneic breathing, the only active expiratory neurons are those of the NRA (90), which do not make synaptic connections with medullary (or pontine) inspiratory cells (68, 92). Thus any theory of respiratory rhythmicity requiring reciprocal inhibition by two alternately active populations of nerve cells seems to be ruled out. Reciprocal inhibition may exist between inspiratory and expiratory populations, and may play a role in forceful breathing when many expiratory cells are active, but it cannot be necessary for the eupneic breathing seen in deeply anesthetized cats.

It seems necesssary that inspiratory cells themselves must be capable of generating the rhythm of breathing. We have already seen how an inspiratory population (the IV cells) is responsible for the termination of inspiration. The possibility that a single group of respiratory neurons could generate repetitive bursts has been discussed before (51) but has suffered from a lack of real neurophysiological examples.

THE POSSIBILITY OF AUTORHYTHMICITY   There are in the invertebrates, however, small groups of neurons, or even single neurons, which can generate repetitive bursts without interaction with an antagonist population. Many of the individual cells of these ganglia are autorhythmic, that is, without synaptic input they continue to fire single spikes at a regular frequency, or fire bursts of spikes alternating with periods of silence.

Invertebrate neurons which show spontaneously rhythmic depolarizations include pacemaking and bursting cells in the cardiac ganglia of lobsters (60, 98), crabs (121), and mantis shrimps (127), in the stomatogastric ganglion of lobsters (87), in *Aplysia* (3, 24, 48, 119), and other mollusks (70, 133). In other cases the cells which show spontaneous rhythms do not generate spikes, but only slow waves. They drive spiking neurons however, possibly by continuously modulated transmitter release as in nonspiking vertebrate retina cells (129). Included in this category are neurons driving cockroach walking (99) and gill ventilation control neurons in lobsters and hermit crabs (88). The best-studied system is the ganglion which drives the heart of the lobster (61, 85, 86, 98). This 9-cell ganglion produces rhythmic bursts even when it is totally isolated in vitro from the rest of the animal. The frequency, amplitude, and duration of the bursts (normally about 1 per 2.5 sec) can be influenced by both tonic input and phased proprioceptive input. All the cells fire in only one phase of the cycle—contraction. It is similar to what would be required to generate the rhythmic bursting of breathing in mammals.

The type of autorhythmic properties that have been well demonstrated in invertebrates have not usually been looked for in vertebrate systems. There are currently no methods applicable to cells deep within a brain that could be used to identify autorhythmic cells. We can hope that further study of invertebrate autorhythmic cells will provide diagnostic tools that can be used in vertebrates. If there are nonspiking cells involved in pattern generation, as in some invertebrates, they would not even be noticed in the course of microelectrode penetration within the brain. The respiratory system of lampreys (64, 106, 107) may provide a simple enough experimental preparation to answer some of these questions.

Thus it is still not known whether the component cells of the respiratory generator are spontaneous pacemakers, even though it was a "generally held" idea in Adrian's time (2). Intracellular records from medullary respiratory neurons (e.g. 113) show slow potentials very much like those seen in invertebrate pacemaking and spontaneous bursting cells. Sears (117) recorded intracellular slow potentials in intercostal motoneurons and Mitchell & Herbert (94, 95) recorded intracellular slow depolarizing and slow hyperpolizing potentials in NA and NRA cells. It is crucial to know whether these slow potentials are synaptically driven or are autorhythmic. In some of these cases, the slow waves have been shown to be due to membrane permeability changes (95, 103, 117). The hyperpolarizing waves in the intercostals (117) and the expiratory cells of the ambiguus-retroambigualis complex (95) are due to chloride permeability changes. Mitchell & Herbert (95) injected current into two inspiratory cells of the medulla and found a reversal potential for the slow depolarizing potentials of −10 mV. These results do not answer the question of whether the permeability changes are synaptically driven or are autorhythmic.

Expiration

Although we do not know the mechanism by which expiration alternates with inspiration, we do know some of the factors which influence expiratory duration.

The basic fact about expiratory duration is that in normal circumstances it is proportional to the preceding inspiratory duration (75). The proportionality is not changed by chemical drives, body temperature, elastic loading, or vagotomy (58). Expiratory duration is not timed solely by feedback from lung deflation; the proportionality holds in paralyzed cats without lung movements (25). During apneustic breathing expiratory duration is proportional only to the duration of the rising phase of inspiratory activity; it does not increase further as the inspiratory plateau phase lengthens in duration (38).

INFLATION REFLEX   Lung-volume manipulations can affect expiratory duration (73). These effects are carried by the vagus since all effects are abolished by vagotomy. An inflation pulse delivered in the first 70% of expiration will prolong expiration. Even short inflation pulses delivered early in expiration prolong expiratory duration; the effect of the inflation is only seen long after the inflation pulse is over. The prolongation is proportional to the volume of the inflation pulse. Within the 70% sensitive period the time of delivery of a pulse or the time of onset of an inflation step has little effect on expiratory duration.

Inflations delivered during the last 30% of expiration have no effect, even if they are as large as 3 times the eupneic tidal volume. The fraction of the expiratory duration in which volume changes are no longer effective is constant and independent of changes in total expiratory duration or preceding inspiratory duration (41, 73).

DEFLATION REFLEX   A deflation step initiated in the first 85% of expiration will shorten expiration. Steps initiated after that have no effect. The last 15% of expiration is termed the *deflation-insensitive period*. With deflations larger than a certain volume threshold, the deflation-insensitive period is immediately initiated and inspiration occurs 0.15 of a control expiration later. This termination threshold falls linearly with time from the beginning of expiration to the beginning of the insensitive period. Deflations below the threshold have graded effects.

It is clear that lung volume has a much more complicated effect on expiration than it does on inspiration. The neurophysiology of these effects is completely unknown.

NPBM EFFECT   Stimulation in the dorsomedial part of the NPBM can terminate expiration immediately (10, 30). The intensity of NPBM stimulation necessary to terminate expiration falls during expiration (30). This is very similar to the fall of threshold for the inspiration off switch. Bilateral lesion of the NPBM increases the magnitude of effects of inflation seen in expiration, but does not qualitatively change these effects (74).

In short, the control of expiratory duration remains obscure. The duration of expiration is certainly dependent on the maximum level of activity reached by the previous inspiration and on lung volume inputs during expiration. Several authors (11, 18, 30, 50) suggested that the inhibitory activity of the inspiration off-switch neurons continues to act in a slowly decaying manner to keep inspiration inhibited for the expiratory period (41). During the reflex-sensitive part of this time, these cells are open to modulating influences from volume receptors and other inputs. This model requires that the inhibitory cells fire all during expiration, so this is a form of the reciprocal inhibition model of breathing. Difficulties in finding an expiratory population of neurons to perform this function have been discussed.

An alternative model is suggested from invertebrate rhythmic burst generators. The inspiratory neurons may, in their silent period, undergo some recovery processes whose duration depends on the maximum intensity of their previous firing period. Sensory inputs could affect the rate of recovery.

OVERALL ORGANIZATION OF THE RESPIRATORY SYSTEM

We are now in a position to suggest an overall outline of the organization of the cat respiratory system. There is a central pattern generator in the medulla. The current "best guess" is that the cells of the nucleus of the solitary tract are the pattern generator. This pattern generator sets the basic rhythm of inspiration. The inspiratory-vagal cells of the NST integrates the CIE, the pulmonary stretch receptor feedback, and tonic variables (CO_2 drive, NPBM output) to produce the off trigger which normally terminates inspiration.

More rostral to this nucleus are various nuclei (e.g. NPBM) which can affect breathing. The output of these nuclei may be tonic or phasic, but they probably act only to modulate the central pattern generator rather than to change its basic mode of rhythm generation (e.g. 10). When these upper centers fire with a respiratory rhythm, this may be due to input from the central pattern generator which drives them. The phase of their firing (29) with respect to this input could be changed by local circuits. The function of these nuclei is unknown, but some of them must incorporate homeostatic variables (blood gas tensions, body temperature, etc), and cortical inputs into the adjustment of the breathing system.

The so-called inspiratory apneustic center of Pitts, Magoun & Ranson (101), stimulation of which causes tonic inspiratory muscle contraction, is now known to reside in the cells of the nucleus reticularis gigantocellularis and the rostral part of the nucleus reticularis ventralis (5, 118). Microelectrode recordings show that this area is devoid of units firing with a respiratory rhythm (5). This alone is sufficient to refute the theories of respiratory rhythmicity of Pitts (100) and Pitts et al (101), which require that the apneustic center be periodically silenced in expiration. These cells fire tonically and have axons descending to the spinal cord (122) where they play on spinal circuits that excite inspiratory neurons and inhibit expiratory neurons (5, 118).

Lateral to the nucleus of the solitary tract, and probably driven by it (92), is the nucleus retroambigualis. Mitchell & Herbert (94) concluded that the cells of this nucleus are not the medullary chemoreceptors and do not participate in the generation of normal respiratory rhythm. This nucleus, which is driven by the central pattern generator, is possibly responsible for further shaping of the motor output pattern. Aside from the "linearly" rising inspiratory activity to the diaphragm, the motor command for the inspiratory-expiratory pattern of the external and internal intercostals must be patterned, as well as the various phasic patterns fed to the accessory throat respiratory muscles (125) whose motoneuron cell bodies lie in the nucleus ambiguus. Merrill (90) recently published an excellent review of his work on the nucleus retroambigualis and its connectivity. The NRA has axons which descend and ramify in the spinal segments (90) and indeed some of them monosynaptically excite thoracic respiratory motoneurones (71).

The spinal cord has rich segmental mechanisms of its own, as demonstrated by von Euler [see (34) for references] and Sears [see (4) for references]. This is the only part of the respiratory system which has been conclusively shown to have reciprocal inhibitory connections between an expiratory and an inspiratory population (4, 5).

PROSPECT

Breathing is one of the few areas of brain activity where a function is anywhere near to being understood on the basis of the unit activity of nerve cells. This is very exciting. At the current moment, functional theory (i.e. the interrelationship of breathing parameters: inspiratory duration, inspiratory strength, CO_2 levels, temperature) has proceeded ahead of electrophysiological single-unit analysis. Some straightforward and diagnostic single-unit experiments can now be done. This review has mentioned a few; specialists are aware of others. As these experiments are done we can expect further significant progress in the understanding of the neural generation of rhythmic breathing movements.

Literature Cited

1. Adrian, E. D. 1933. Afferent impulses in the vagus and their effect on respiration. *J. Physiol. London* 79:332–58
2. Adrian, E. D., Buytendijk, F. J. 1931. Potential changes in the isolated brain stem of the goldfish. *J. Physiol.* 71:121–35
3. Alving, B. O. 1968. Spontaneous activity in isolated somata of *Aplysia* pacemaker neurons. *J. Gen. Physiol.* 51: 29–45
4. Aminoff, M. J., Sears, T. A. 1971. Spinal integration of segmental, cortical and breathing inputs to thoracic respiratory motoneurones. *J. Physiol.* 215: 557–75
5. Andersen, P., Sears, T. A. 1970. Medullary activation of intercostal fusimotor and alpha motoneurones. *J. Physiol.* 209:739–55
6. von Baumgarten, R., Kanzow, E. 1958. The interaction of two types of inspiratory neurons in the region of the tractus solitarius of the cat. *Arch. Ital. Biol.* 96:361–73
7. von Baumgarten, R., Nakayama, S. 1964. Spontane und reizbedingte Anderungen der antidromen Erregbarkeit von bulbären respiratorischen Nervenzellen der Katze. *Pfluegers Arch. Gesamte Physiol. Menschen Tiere* 281: 245–58
8. von Baumgarten, R., Schmiedt, H., Dodich, N. 1963. Microelectrode studies of phrenic motoneurons. *Ann. NY Acad. Sci.* 109:536–46
9. Beccari, E. 1936. Le problème des centres respiratoires médullaires. *Arch. Intern. Physiol.* 43:90–103
10. Bertrand, F., Hugelin, A. 1971. Respiratory synchronizing function of nucleus parabrachialis medialis: Pneumotaxic mechanisms. *J. Neurophysiol.* 34:189–207
11. Bertrand, F., Hugelin, A., Vibert, J. F. 1974. A stereologic model of pneumotaxic oscillator based on spatial and temporal distributions of neuronal bursts. *J. Neurophysiol.* 37:91–107
12. Bianchi, A. L. 1971. Localisation et étude des neurones respiratoires bulbaires. Mise en jeu antidrômique par stimulation spinale ou vagale. *J. Physiol. Paris* 63:5–40
13. Bianchi, A. L., Barillot, J. C. 1975. Activity of medullary respiratory neurons during reflexes from the lungs in cats. *Respir. Physiol.* 25:335–52
14. Boyd, T. E., Maaske, C. A. 1939. Vagal inhibition of inspiration and accompa-

nying changes of respiratory rhythm. *J. Neurophysiol.* 2:533–42
15. Bradley, G. W. 1976. The effect of CO_2, body temperature and anaesthesia on the response to vagal stimulation. See Reference 33a
16. Bradley, G. W., von Euler, C., Marttila, I., Roos, B. 1974. Transient and steady state effects of CO_2 on mechanisms determining rate and depth of breathing. *Acta Physiol. Scand.* 92:341–50
17. Bradley, G. W., von Euler, C., Marttila, I., Roos, B. 1974. Steady state effects of CO_2 and temperature on the relationship between lung volume and inspiratory duration (Hering-Breuer threshold curve). *Acta Physiol. Scand.* 92:351–63
18. Bradley, G. W., von Euler, C., Marttila, I., Roos, B. 1975. A model of the central and reflex inhibition of inspiration in the cat. *Biol. Cybernetics* 19:105–16
19. Breckenridge, C. G., Hoff, H. E. 1950. Pontine and medullary regulation of respiration in the cat. *Am. J. Physiol.* 160:385–94
20. Brodie, D. A., Borison, H. L. 1957. Evidence for a medullary inspiratory pacemaker. Functional concept of central regulation of respiration. *Am. J. Physiol.* 188:347–54
21. Burns, B. D., Salmoiraghi, G. C. 1960. Repetitive firing of respiratory neurones during their burst activity. *J. Neurophysiol.* 23:27–46
22. Burrows, M. 1975. Monosynaptic connections between wing stretch receptors and flight motoneurones of the locust. *J. Exp. Biol.* 62:189–219
23. Carregal, E. J. A., Williams, B., Birzis, L. 1967. Respiratory centers in the dog and squirrel monkey: A comparative study. *Respir. Physiol.* 3:333–48
24. Chew, C. F., von Baumgarten, R., Takeda, R. 1971. Pacemaker properties of completely isolated neurons in *Aplysia californica*. *Nature New Biol.* 233:32–29
25. Clark, F. J., von Euler, C. 1972. On the regulation of depth and rate of breathing. *J. Physiol. London* 222:267–95
26. Cohen, M. I. 1958. Intrinsic periodicity of the pontile pneumotaxic mechanism. *Am. J. Physiol.* 195:23–27
27. Cohen, M. I. 1968. Discharge patterns of brain-stem respiratory neurons in relation to carbon dioxide tension. *J. Neurophysiol.* 31:142–65
28. Cohen, M. I. 1969. Discharge patterns of brain-stem respiratory neurons dur-

ing Hering-Breuer reflex evoked by lung inflation. *J. Neurophysiol.* 32:356–74

29. Cohen, M. I. 1970. How respiratory rhythm originates: Evidence from discharge patterns of brainstem respiratory neurones. See Reference 102, pp. 125–57

30. Cohen, M. I. 1971. Switching of the respiratory phases and evoked phrenic responses produced by rostral pontine electrical stimulation. *J. Physiol.* 217: 133–58

31. Cohen, M. I. 1974. The genesis of respiratory rhythmicity. In *Central Rhythms and Regulation,* ed. W. Umbach, H. Koepchen, pp. 15–35. Stuttgart: Hippokrates

32. Cohen, M. I., Wang, S. C. 1959. Respiratory neuronal activity in pons of cat. *J. Neurophysiol.* 22:33–50

33. Cordier, D., Heymans, C. 1935. Le centre respiratoire. *Ann. Physiol. Physicochim. Biol.* 11:535–771

33a. Duron, B., ed. 1976. Respiratory centers and afferent systems. *Coll. Inst. Natl. Santé Rech. Med., Amiens, France*

34. von Euler, C. 1970. Fusimotor activity in spindle control of natural movements with special reference to respiration. In *Excitatory Synaptic Mechanisms,* ed. P. Andersen, J. K. S. Jansen, pp. 341–49. Oslo: Universitetsforlaget

35. von Euler, C., Hayward, J. N., Marttila, I., Wyman, R. J. 1973. Respiratory neurones of the ventrolateral nucleus of the solitary tract of cat: Vagal input, spinal connections and morphological identification. *Brain Res.* 61:1–22

36. von Euler, C., Hayward, J. N., Marttila, I., Wyman, R. J. 1973. The spinal connections of the inspiratory neurones of the ventrolateral nucleus of the tractus solitarius of cat. *Brain Res.* 61:23–33

37. von Euler, C., Herrero, F., Wexler, I. 1970. Control mechanisms determining rate and depth of respiratory movements. *Respir. Physiol.* 10:93–108

38. von Euler, C., Marttila, I., Remmers, J. E., Trippenbach, T. 1976. Effects of lesions in the parabrachial nucleus on the mechanisms for central and reflex termination of inspiration in the cat. *Acta Physiol. Scand.* 96:324–37

39. von Euler, C., Soderberg, U. 1952. Medullary chemosensitive receptors. *J. Physiol.* 118:545–54

40. von Euler, C., Trippenbach, T. 1975. Cyclic excitability changes of the inspiratory 'off-switch' mechanisms. *Acta Physiol. Scand.* 93:560–62

41. von Euler, C., Trippenbach, T. 1976. Temperature effects on the inflation reflex during expiratory time in the cat. *Acta Physiol. Scand.* 96:338–50

42. von Euler, C., Trippenbach, T. 1976. Excitability changes of the inspiratory 'off-switch' mechanism tested by electrical stimulation in nucleus parabrachialis in the cat. *Acta Physiol. Scand.* 97:175–88

43. Feldman, J. L. 1976. A network model for control of inspiratory cutoff by the pneumotaxic center with supportive experimental data in cats. *Biol. Cybernetics* 21:131–38

44. Feldman, J. L., Cohen, M. I., Wolotsky, P. 1976. Powerful inhibition of pontine respiratory neurons by pulmonary afferent activity. *Brain Res.* 104:341–46

45. Feldman, J. L., Cohen, M. I., Wolotsky, P. 1976. Phasic pulmonary afferent activity drastically alters the respiratory modulation of neurons in the rostral pontine pneumotaxic center. See Reference 33a

46. Feldman, J. L., Cowan, J. D. 1975. Large scale activity in neural nets. II. A model for the brainstem respiratory oscillator. *Biol. Cybernetics* 17:39–51

47. Feldman, J. L., Gautier, H. 1976. The interaction of pulmonary afferents and pneumotaxic center in control of respiratory pattern in cats. *J. Neurophysiol.* 39:31–44

48. Frazier, W. T., Kandel, E. R., Kupfermann, I., Waziri, R., Coggeshall, R. E. 1967. Morphological and functional properties of identified neurons in the abdominal ganglion of *Aplysia californica. J. Neurophysiol.* 30:1288–1351

49. Gautier, H., Bertrand, F. 1975. Respiratory effects of pneumotaxic center lesions and subsequent vagotomy in chronic cats. *Respir. Physiol.* 23:71–85

50. Gautier, H., Remmers, J. E., Bartlett, D. 1973. Control of the duration of expiration. *Respir. Physiol.* 18:205–21

51. Gessell, R. 1940. A neurophysiological interpretation of the respiratory act. *Ergeb. Physiol.* 43:477–639

52. Gettrup, E., Wilson, D. M. 1964. The lift-control reaction of flying locusts. *J. Exp. Biol.* 41:183–90

53. Gill, P. K. 1963. The effects of end-tidal CO_2 on the discharge of individual phrenic motoneurones. *J. Physiol.* 168:239–57

54. Gill, P. K., Kuno, M. 1963. Properties of phrenic motoneurones. *J. Physiol.* 168:258–73

55. Gill, P. K., Kuno, M. 1963. Excitatory and inhibitory actions on phrenic motoneurones. *J. Physiol.* 168:174–289

56. Grunstein, M. M., Fisk, W. M., Leiter, L. A., Milic-Emili, J. 1973. Effect of body temperature on respiratory frequency in anesthetized cats. *J. Appl. Physiol.* 34:154–59

57. Grunstein, M. M., Milic-Emili, J. 1977. Interactions between central and vagal respiratory control mechanisms in cats. In press

58. Grunstein, M. M., Younes, M., Milic-Emili, J. 1973. Control of tidal volume and respiratory frequency in anesthetized cats. *J. Appl. Physiol.* 35:463–76

59. Hagiwara, S. 1961. Nervous activities of the heart in Crustacea. *Ergeb. Biol.* 24:287–311

60. Hagiwara, S., Bullock, T. H. 1957. Intracellular potentials in pacemaker and integrative neurons of the lobster cardiac ganglion. *J. Cell Comp. Physiol.* 50:25–47

61. Hartline, D. K. 1967. Integrative physiology of the lobster cardiac ganglion. PhD thesis. Harvard University, Cambridge, Massachusetts

62. Hering, E., Breuer, J. 1868. Self-steering of respiration through *Nervus vagus. Sitzungsber. Akad. Wiss. Wien. Math. Naturwiss. Kl. Abt. 2* 57:672–77 [Translated in (102, pp. 359–94)]

63. Hoff, H. E., Breckenridge, C. G. 1949. The medullary origin of respiratory periodicity in the dog. *Am. J. Physiol.* 158:157–72

64. Homma, S. 1975. Velar motoneurons of lamprey larvae. *J. Comp. Physiol.* A104:175–83

65. Horridge, G. A. 1959. The nerves and muscles of medusae. VI. The rhythm. *J. Exp. Biol.* 36:72–92

66. Hukuhara, T. 1973. Neuronal organization of the central respiratory mechanisms in the brain stem of the cat. *Acta Neurobiol. Exp. Warsaw* 33:219–44

67. Ikeda, K., Wiersma, C. A. G. 1964. Autogenic rhythmicity in the abdominal ganglia of the crayfish: The control of swimmeret movements. *Comp. Biochem. Physiol.* 12:107–15

68. Kalia, M. 1976. Direct projection of neurons in the "dorsal respiratory group" (NTS) to the pneumotaxic center (NPBM) in the cat. *Fed. Proc.* 35:634

69. Karczewski, W. A., Widdicombe, J. G., eds. 1973. *Neural Control of Breathing. Int. Symp. Acta Neurobiol. Exp. Warsaw* 33:1–432

70. Kater, S. B., Kaneko, C. R. S. 1972. An endogenously bursting neuron in the gastropod mollusc, *Helisoma trivolvis:* Characterization in vivo. *J. Comp. Physiol.* 79:1–14

71. Kirkwood, P. A., Sears, T. A. 1973. Monosynaptic excitation of thoracic expiratory motoneurones from lateral respiratory neurones in the medulla of the cat. *J. Physiol.* 234:87P–89P

72. Knowlton, G. C., Larrabee, M. G. 1946. A unitary analysis of pulmonary volume receptors. *Am. J. Physiol.* 147:100–14

73. Knox, C. K. 1973. Characteristics of the inflation and deflation reflexes during expiration in the cat. *J. Neurophysiol.* 36:284–95

74. Knox, C. K., King, G. W. 1976. Changes in the Breuer-Hering reflexes following rostral pontine lesion. *Respir. Physiol.* 28:189–206

75. Koepchen, H. P., Langhorst, P., Seller, H., Polster, J., Wagner, P. H. 1967. Neuronale Aktivität im unteren Hirnstamm mit Beziehung zum Kreislauf. *Pfluegers Arch. Gesamte Physiol. Menschen Tiere* 294:40–64

76. Koepchen, H. P., Lazar, H., Borchert, J. 1974. On the role of nucleus infrasolitarius in the determination of respiratory periodicity. *Proc. XXVI Int. Cong. Physiol. Sci. New Delhi,* p. 81

77. Kumagai, H., Sakai, F., Sakuma, A., Hukuhara, T. 1966. Relationship between activity of respiratory center and EEG. *Progr. Brain Res.* 21A:98–111

78. Langendorff, O., Nitschmann, R. 1880. Studien uber die Innervation der Athembewegungen. I. Ueber die spinalen Centren der Athmung. *Arch. Physiol.* pp. 518–49

79. Langendorff, O. 1881. Studien uber die Innervation der Athembewegungen. V. Ueber reizung der verlangerten markes. *Arch. Anat. Physiol. Physiol. Abt.* pp. 519–37

80. Larrabee, M. G., Knowlton, G. C. 1946. Excitation and inhibition of phrenic motoneurones by inflation of the lungs. *Am. J. Physiol.* 147:90–99

81. Lerner, J., Mellen, S. A., Waldron, I., Factor, R. M. 1971. Neural redundancy and regularity of swimming beats in scyphozoan medusae. *J. Exp. Biol.* 55:177–84

82. Lumsden, T. L. 1923. Observations on the respiratory centres in the cat. *J. Physiol. London* 57:153–60

83. MacDonald, J. S., Reid, E. W. 1898. Electromotive changes in phrenic

nerve. A method of investigating the action of the respiratory center. *J. Physiol.* 23:100–11

84. Marckwald, M. 1887. Die Athembewegungen und deren Innervation beim Kaninchen. *Z. Biol.* 23:149–283

85. Mayeri, E. 1973. Functional organization of the cardiac ganglion of the lobster, *Homarus americanus. J. Gen. Physiol.* 62:448–72

86. Maynard, D. M. 1955. Activity in a crustacean ganglion. II. Pattern and interaction in burst formation. *Biol. Bull. Woods Hole, Mass.* 109:420–36

87. Maynard, D. M. 1972. Simpler networks. *Ann. NY Acad. Sci.* 193:59–72

88. Mendelson, M. 1971. Oscillator neurons in crustacean ganglia. *Science* 171:1170–73

89. Merrill, E. G. 1970. The lateral respiratory neurones of the medulla: Their associations with nucleus ambiguus, nucleus retroambigualis, the spinal accessory nucleus and the spinal cord. *Brain Res.* 24:11–28

90. Merrill, E. G. 1974. Finding a respiratory function for the medullary respiratory neurons. In *Essays on the Nervous System,* ed. R. Bellairs, E. G. Gray, pp. 451–86. Oxford: Clarendon

91. Merrill, E. G. 1974. Antidromic activation of lateral respiratory neurones during their silent periods. *J. Physiol.* 241:118–19P

92. Merrill, E. G. 1975. Preliminary studies on nucleus retroambiguus-nucleus of the solitary tract interactions. *J. Physiol.* 244:54P–55P

93. Mitchell, R. A., Berger, A. J. 1975. Neural regulation of respiration. *Am. Rev. Respir. Dis.* 111:206–24

94. Mitchell, R. A., Herbert, D. A. 1974. The effect of carbon dioxide on the membrane potential of medullary respiratory neurons. *Brain Res.* 75:345–49

95. Mitchell, R. A., Herbert, D. A. 1974. Synchronized high frequency synaptic potentials in medullary respiratory neurons. *Brain Res.* 75:350–55

96. Nakayama, S., von Baumgarten, R. 1964. Lokalisierung absteigender Atmungsbahnen im Ruckenmark der Katze mittels antidromer Reizung. *Pfluegers Arch. Gesamte Physiol. Menschen Tiere* 281:231–44

97. Oberholzer, R. J. H., Tofani, W. O. 1960. The neural control of respiration. In *Handb. Physiol. Sect. I, Vol. II, Neurophysiology,* pp. 1111–29. Wash. DC: *Am. Physiol. Soc.*

98. Otani, T., Bullock, T. H. 1959. Effects of presetting the membrane potential of the soma of spontaneous and integrating ganglion cells. *Physiol. Zool.* 32:104–14

99. Pearson, K. G., Fourtner, C. R., Wong, R. K. 1973. Nervous control of walking in the cockroach. *Adv. Behav. Biol.* 7:495–514

100. Pitts, R. F. 1946. Organization of the respiratory center. *Physiol. Rev.* 26:609–30

101. Pitts, R. F., Magoun, H. W., Ranson, S. W. 1939. Localization of the medullary respiratory centers in the cat. *Am. J. Physiol.* 126:673–88

102. Porter, R., ed. 1970. *Breathing: Hering-Breuer Centenary Symp. Ciba Found.* London: Churchill. 402 pp.

103. Richter, D. W., Heyde, F., Gabriel, M. 1975. Intracellular recordings from different types of medullary respiratory neurons of the cat. *J. Neurophysiol.* 38:1162–71

104. Richter, D. W., Heyde, F. 1975. Accomodative reactions of medullary respiratory neurons of the cat. *J. Neurophysiol.* 38:1172–80

105. Roberts, J., ed. 1976. *Symp. Neural Control Respir. Fed. Proc.* 35:1965–2023

106. Rovainen, C. M. 1974. Respiratory motoneurons in lampreys. *J. Comp. Physiol.* 94:57–68

107. Rovainen, C. M., Schieber, M. H. 1976. Ventilation of larval lampreys. *J. Comp. Physiol. A* 104:185–203

108. Rubio, J. E. 1972. A new mathematical model of the respiratory center. *Bull. Math. Biophys.* 34:467–83

109. Ruch, T. C. 1965. Transection of the human spinal cord. In *Physiology and Biophysics,* ed. T. C. Ruch, H. D. Patton. Philadelphia: Saunders, 1242 pp. 19th ed.

110. St. John, W. M. 1972. Respiratory tidal volume responses of cats with chronic pneumotaxic center lesions. *Respir. Physiol.* 16:92–108

111. St. John, W. M. 1973. Characterization of the tidal volume regulating function of the pneumotaxic center. *Respir. Physiol.* 18:64–79

112. St. John, W. M. 1975. Differing responses to hypercapnia and hypoxia following pneumotaxic center ablation. *Respir. Physiol.* 23:1–9

113. Salmoiraghi, G. C., von Baumgarten, R. 1961. Intracellular potentials from respiratory neurones in brain-stem of

cat and mechanism of rhythmic respiration. *J. Neurophysiol.* 24:203–18

114. Salmoiraghi, G. C., Burns, B. D. 1960. Localization and patterns of discharge of respiratory neurones in brain-stem of cat. *J. Neurophysiol.* 23:2–13

115. Salmoiraghi, G. C., Burns, B. D. 1960. Notes on mechanism of rhythmic respiration. *J. Neurophysiol.* 23:14–26

116. Schoener, E. P., Frankel, H. M. 1972. Effect of hyperthermia and Pa_{CO_2} on the slowly adapting pulmonary stretch receptor. *Am. J. Physiol.* 222:68–72

117. Sears, T. A. 1964. The slow potentials of thoracic respiratory motoneurons and their relation to breathing. *J. Physiol.* 175:404–24

118. Sears, T. A. 1966. Pathways of supraspinal origin regulating the activity of respiratory motoneurons. In *Muscular Afferents and Motor Control. Nobel Symp. 1,* ed. R. Granit, pp. 187–96. Stockholm: Almqvist & Wiksell

119. Strumwasser, F. 1968. Membrane and intracellular mechanisms governing endogenous activity in neurons. In *Physiological and Biochemical Aspects of Nervous Integration,* ed. F. Carlson. Englewood Cliffs, New Jersey: Prentice-Hall

120. Tang, P. C., Young, A. C. 1956. Interrelations of CO_2, O_2 and vagal influences on respiratory centers. *Fed. Proc.* 15:184

121. Tazaki, K. 1971. The effects of tetrodotoxin on the slow potential and spikes in the cardiac ganglion of the crab, *Eriocheir japonicus. Jpn. J. Physiol.* 21:529–36

122. Torvik, A., Brodal, A. 1957. The origin of reticulospinal fibers in the cat. *Anat. Rec.* 128:113–37

123. Vibert, J. F., Bertrand, F., Denavit-Saubie, M., Hugelin, A. 1976. Discharge patterns of bulbo-pontine respiratory unit populations in cat. *Brain Res.* 114:211–25

124. Vibert, J. F., Bertrand, F., Denavit-Saubie, M., Hugelin, A. 1976. Three dimensional representation of bulbo-pontine respiratory networks architecture from unit density maps. *Brain Res.* 114:227–44

125. Waldron, I. 1970. Activity patterns in respiratory muscles and in respiratory neurones of the rostral medulla of the cat. *J. Physiol.* 208:373–83

126. Wang, S. C., Ngai, S. H., Frumin, M. J. 1957. Organization of central respiratory mechanisms in the brain stem of the cat: Genesis of normal respiratory rhythmicity. *Am. J. Physiol.* 190:333–42

127. Watanabe, A., Obara, S., Akiyama, T. 1967. Pacemaker potentials for the periodic burst discharge in the heart ganglion of a Stomatopod, *Squilla oratoria. J. Gen. Physiol.* 50:839–62

128. Wendler, G. 1974. The influence of proprioceptive feedback on locust flight coordination. *J. Comp. Physiol.* 88:173–200

129. Werblin, F. S., Dowling, J. E. 1969. Organization of the retina of the mudpuppy *Necturus maculosus.* II. Intracellular recording. *J. Neurophysiol.* 32:339–55

130. Wertheimer, E. 1886. Sur les centres respiratoires de la moelle epiniere. *CR Soc. Biol.* 38:34–36

131. Wertheimer, M. E. 1905. Sur les modifications de la respiration produites par les injections intraveineuses de soude chez les animaux à moelle cervicale sectionnée. *CR Soc. Biol.* 59:668–69

132. Widdicombe, J. G. 1974. Reflexes from the lungs in the control of breathing. *Recent Adv. Physiol.* 9:239–78

133. Willows, A. O. D., Getting, P. A., Thompson, S. 1973. Bursting mechanisms in molluskan locomotion. *Adv. Behav. Biol.* 7:457–75

134. Wilson, D. M. 1961. The central nervous control of flight in a locust. *J. Exp. Biol.* 38:471–90

135. Wilson, D. M., Gettrup, E. 1963. A stretch reflex controlling wingbeat frequency in grasshoppers. *J. Exp. Biol.* 40:171–85

136. Wilson, D. M., Wyman, R. J. 1965. Motor output patterns during random and rhythmic stimulation of locust thoracic ganglia. *Biophys. J.* 5:121–43

137. Woldring, S., Dirken, M. N. J. 1951. Site and extension of bulbar respiratory center. *J. Neurophysiol.* 14:227–41

138. Wyman, R. J. 1976. Neurophysiology of the motor output pattern generator for breathing. *Fed. Proc.* 35:2013–23

139. Young, A. C. 1974. Neural control of respiration. In *Physiology and Biophysics,* Vol. II, ed. T. C. Ruch, H. D. Patton. Saunders: Philadelphia. 558 pp. 20th ed.

Ann. Rev. Physiol. 1977. 39:449–71

OSMOREGULATION IN AMPHIBIANS AND REPTILES

♦1179

Vaughan H. Shoemaker

Department of Biology, University of California, Riverside, California 92502

Kenneth A. Nagy

Department of Biology and Laboratory of Nuclear Medicine and Radiation Biology, University of California, Los Angeles, California 90024

INTRODUCTION

Osmoregulation can have various meanings depending on the organism in question and the viewpoint of the investigator. Strictly speaking, the term implies maintenance of the osmotic pressure of the body fluids, irrespective of their solute composition or volume. In this review "osmoregulation" signifies the processes by which the amounts of water and specific solutes within the body of an organism are maintained constant or within tolerable limits. We examine the various avenues of in- and output in the hope of clarifying their relative significance in the water, electrolyte, and nitrogen budgets of amphibians and reptiles.

The environment is a major factor in determining the nature of the osmoregulatory challenge facing any organism, and amphibians and reptiles are represented in a wide variety of habitats. Terrestrial forms range from deserts to rain forests, and aquatic forms range from fresh water to the seas. Reptiles as a group are more broadly distributed across this spectrum of habitat types, being generally less dependent on the availability of fresh water and humid environments than amphibians. Nevertheless, some amphibians can withstand the potentially dehydrating conditions imposed by arid or hypersaline environments, and these provide interesting examples of physiological adaptation. Both groups are large and phyletically diverse, and relatively few examples of each have been studied in detail. This makes generalization both difficult and hazardous. Fortunately, investigators have tended to select species for study with an eye toward phylogeny and habitat, so that patterns of adaptation can be broadly sketched.

There are a number of reviews bearing on this topic: Bentley (4, 5, 8, 9), Bradshaw (15, 16), Cloudsley-Thompson (24), Dantzler (27, 28), Dantzler & Holmes (29), Deyrup (33), Dunson (46, 47), Peaker & Linzell (101), Scheer et al (111), Shoemaker (116), and Templeton (123). Each has its own particular emphasis and will provide

449

the reader with many details not included here. We hope that our focus on the budgetary components of the osmoregulatory process will lead to a better understanding of their importance to the welfare of the animal in its natural environment.

INPUT

Potential avenues of water and salt uptake include drinking, feeding, and uptake across the skin or mucous membranes, whereas nitrogen is generally gained only via food. Water produced in oxidative metabolism is also an avenue of input to the animal.

Drinking

Amphibians apparently do not rely on drinking to gain water in most natural situations. For amphibians in fresh water, drinking would compound the problem of water excess imposed by the high rates of osmotic influx of water across the skin (see below.) Scheer et al (111) reported that *Rana pipiens* "drinks" in fresh water (0.5 mM NaCl), but the rate (0.4 ml kg^{-1} hr^{-1}) is insignificant compared to osmotic influx. Bentley (7) found even lower rates of oral water intake in two urodeles (0.1 ml kg^{-1} hr^{-1} in *Siren* and none in *Amphiuma*). More surprising is that terrestrial amphibians have not been observed to drink even when dehydrated, but changes in skin permeability may nevertheless allow very rapid water uptake. Frogs placed in hypersaline media do drink appreciable quantities (13, 73), but they are generally unable to survive. The few species of adult amphibians that are known to adapt to high salinities (e.g. *Rana cancrivora, Bufo viridis, Xenopus laevis, Batrachoseps relictus*) do so by accumulating sufficient solutes so that the osmotic movement of water is inward and drinking is unnecessary (59, 60, 75, 106). However, drinking may play a role in the initial stages of saline adaptation in *B. viridis*. There is also circumstantial evidence that toads (*Bufo bufo*) drink when maintained in 150 mM NaCl (54). The euryhaline tadpoles of *R. cancrivora* remain hypo-osmotic to their environment at high salinities, implying that they drink to replace cutaneous and urinary water losses. This has not been directly confirmed (61).

Little is known about drinking in most reptiles in the field, and intake rates have not been measured in those that are known to drink. Most terrestrial reptiles will drink in captivity, especially when water is sprayed on cage sides or foliage to form droplets. Seawater drinking is generally absent in captive marine reptiles, such as sea snakes (48), estuarine turtles (44), and littoral lizards (42, 45), although several of these animals may drink when given fresh water. An estuarine subspecies of the snake *Natrix sipedon* does not drink seawater, but a freshwater subspecies does drink when placed in seawater and dies as a result (102). Reptiles normally living in freshwater situations, including crocodiles (35) and freshwater turtles (12), generally drink in captivity. Krakauer et al (72) suggested that small burrowing snakes and amphisbaenians drink water contained in moist soil. In the Australian desert lizard *Moloch horridus*, water that contacts the skin is channeled to the mouth via capillary grooves, absorbed by hygroscopic mucus secreted near the lips, and swallowed (10). But *Phrynosoma m'calli*, a lizard occupying a similar niche in American deserts, does not show this phenomenon (81). A snake (*Bitis peringueyi*) living in the Namib Desert may drink water that condenses on its skin during the desert's periodic advective fogs (79). Laboratory measurements of water balance in several lizards indicate that the desert species can maintain balance without drinking, but more mesic species cannot (31, 95).

In the field, an Australian lizard (*Amphibolurus ornatus)* drinks rainwater in summer and uses it to excrete dietary electrolytes stored in the body during dry periods (17). Free-living desert lizards (*Dipsosaurus dorsalis* and *Uma scoparia*) labeled with tritiated water, show increased water turnover during a summer rain, indicating the animals either drank or exchanged water across the skin (92, 93). In contrast, tritium-labeled chuckwallas (*Sauromalus obesus*) showed no evidence of drinking rainwater that was available in summer (96).

Food

In most amphibians and in freshwater reptiles, where water influx is usually large, the food may account for only a small fraction of total input. However, for many terrestrial and nondrinking marine reptiles, preformed water in the diet may be the major avenue of water gain. Moreover, nearly all input of salts and nitrogen-containing compounds occurs through feeding, although cutaneous uptake of salts from water can occur in amphibians (see below). Thus the relative amounts of water, salts, and nitrogen in various diets are important considerations. Assuming that rates of food consumption are proportional to energy requirements, the available water, nitrogen, and electrolyte contents per unit assimilable energy are calculated for several foods and diets (Table 1). Several points emerge from this analysis: 1. nitrogen imposes a potentially greater osmotic stress than electrolytes, especially for carnivores, insectivores, and granivores; 2. herbivores must excrete potassium at comparatively high rates but vegetation is generally more succulent than other diets; and 3. sodium is a relatively unimportant osmolyte in these examples.

Table 1 Nitrogen, electrolyte, and water input from various foods and diets: values are given relative to digestible energy to permit physiologically meaningful comparison between diets

Food (Animal)	Nitrogen	Sodium	Potassium	Calcium	Chloride	Water
	μmol kcal^{-1}					ml kcal^{-1}
Beef steak (raw) (Human)[a]	423	7	23	0.5	—	0.12
Millet seed (Human)[a]	346	0.3	34	. 1.5	—	0.04
Cabbage (raw) (Human)[a]	619	36	249	51	—	3.85
Mixed desert plants (Lizard, *Sauromalus*)[b]	803	14	268	—	127	0.62
Mealworms (*Tenebrio*) (Lizard, *Uta*)[c]	877	4	34	—	19	0.34
(Frog, *Phyllomedusa*)[d]	920	8	29	—	18	0.27

Calculated from: [a]Watt & Merrill (129); [b]Nagy (96) and Nagy & Shoemaker (99); [c]Nagy (unpublished); [d]Shoemaker & McClanahan (118).

Adult amphibians are carnivorous (usually insectivorous), and their diet is thus especially high in nitrogen and relatively low in electrolytes. Urinary excretion of dietary nitrogen as ammonia or urea requires amounts of water vastly in excess of inputs from the diet and oxidative metabolism (118). Thus feeding amphibians generally depend heavily on other water sources, even if they are able to minimize evaporative water by either behavioral or physiological means. A few species of anuran amphibians excrete nitrogen primarily as insoluble uric acid or urate salts and have low rates of evaporative water loss (39, 80, 117, 118). Fluxes of water, electrolytes, and nitrogen in one of these (*Phyllomedusa sauvagei*) maintained in the laboratory on a diet of insects as the only water source are similar to those of desert reptiles (Tables 2 and 3). Unfortunately, osmoregulatory studies of amphibians are almost always conducted on fasting animals, thus the role of diet is presently difficult to assess.

Input rates of water, electrolytes, and nitrogen via the diet are known for only a few reptiles, all desert dwellers (Tables 2 and 3). In these animals, the food provides from 60 to 90% of total water input and all of the salt and nitrogen input.

Metabolic Water

From Table 2 it is clear that rates of oxidation water production are low in comparison to water losses even in xerophylic reptiles and amphibians. In no case does

Table 2 Itemized water budgets in various desert reptiles and two species of arboreal frogs; food and metabolism are the only sources of water provided in these examples

| Species | Water fluxes (ml kg^{-1} day^{-1}) | | | | | | | | Conditions |
| | Input | | | Output | | | | | |
	food	metabolism	total	evaporation	feces	urine	salt gland	total	diet (references)
Desert iguana *Dipsosaurus dorsalis*	26.9	3.6	30.5	8.6	18.6	0.8	2.5	30.5	field, summer; desert vegetation (90)
Mojave Fringe-toed Lizard *Uma scoparia*	7.1	4.7	11.8	11.0	3.3	0.2	1.5	16.0	field, summer; desert arthropods and vegetation (93)
Colorado Fringe-toed Lizard *Uma notata*	9.2	2.1	11.3	8.1	2.3[a]	—	0.9	11.3	estimated field, summer; insects (*Tenebrio* larvae) (31)
Chuckwalla *Sauromalus obesus*	21.1	3.4	24.5	12.3	7.6	1.9	2.7	24.5	field, spring; desert vegetation (96)
Grooved Tortoise *Testudo sulcata*	23.9	3.7	27.6	7.4	3.7	18.3	—	29.4	outdoors, summer; green vegetation (23)
Desert snake *Spalerosophis cliffordi*	15.3	1.4	16.7	12.4	1.2	0.1	—	14.5	laboratory, 30° C; mice (38)
Argentine tree frog *Phyllomedusa sauvagei*	6.1	2.5	8.6	17.1	0.5	3.8	—	21.4	laboratory, 26° C; insects (*Tenebrio* larvae) (117, 118)
Mexican tree frog *Pachymedusa dacnicolor*	6.1	2.5	8.6	250	1	1.6	—	258	laboratory, 26° C; insects (*Tenebrio* larvae) (118)

[a]Includes urinary losses.

Table 3 Itemized nitrogen and electrolyte budgets for desert lizards (*Sauromalus obesus* and *Uma scoparia*) and tree frogs (*Phyllomedusa sauvagei* and *Pachymedusa dacnicolor*)[a]; food and metabolism were the only sources of water in these studies.

Species	Nitrogen and electrolyte fluxes (mmol kg^{-1} day^{-1})				
	Input	Output			
	food	urine	salt gland	feces	total
NITROGEN					
Sauromalus	19.3	13.5	—	5.8	19.3
Phyllomedusa	23.8	17.6	—	1.4	19.0
Pachymedusa	23.8	1.1	—	3.5	4.6
POTASSIUM					
Sauromalus	6.6	2.9	3.0	0.5	6.4
Uma	1.7	0.9	1.0	0.2	2.1
Phyllomedusa	0.72	0.32	—	0.03	0.35
Pachymedusa	0.72	0.21	—	0.09	0.30
SODIUM					
Sauromalus	0.51	0.13	0.16	0.2	0.49
Uma	0.81	0.17	0.97	0.07	1.21
Phyllomedusa	0.22	0.33	—	0.03	0.36
Pachymedusa	0.22	0.01	—	0.09	0.10
CHLORIDE					
Sauromalus	3.1	0.04	2.1	0.2	2.3
Uma	0.6	0.01	0.6	0.1	0.7
Phyllomedusa	0.5	0.3	—	0.1	0.4
Pachymedusa	0.5	0.004	—	0.1	0.1

[a]Conditions and references as in Table 2.

metabolic water match evaporation, indicating that normally active desert reptiles cannot remain in water balance without either drinking or eating succulent food. However, when a reptile uses a humid burrow, evaporation may be reduced to the point where oxidation water input balances losses. Reptiles living continuously in very moist soil, such as the small fossorial snakes and amphisbaenians in tropical regions, may exemplify this situation.

Skin

Water moves readily by osmosis across the skin of amphibians, and for steady-state animals maintained in fresh water this results in a very large net water influx. Although the magnitude of this influx varies with body size, species, and temperature, it is typically on the order of 500 ml kg^{-1} day^{-1}, with the more terrestrial species tending to have higher cutaneous permeabilities (5, 94). Aquatic urodeles apparently have lower rates of osmotic influx ($\sim$ 100 ml kg^{-1} day^{-1}) (7). Dicker & Elliott (34) placed freshwater-adapted *Rana cancrivora* into various concentrations of

NaCl, urea, and sucrose. Initial net water fluxes observed were directly proportional to the osmotic gradient, regardless of the nature or concentration of the solute. Thus an amphibian entering a hyperosmotic environment will initially lose water across the skin. However, euryhaline species adapted to high salinities maintain the solute concentration of their body fluids slightly above that of the medium and thus still obtain water by osmosis, albeit at lower rates than animals in fresh water.

Amphibians may incur substantial water deficits during periods spent out of water. In many species of anurans (but apparently not in most urodeles), loss of body water elicits an increase in the hydraulic conductivity of the skin, which enables the animal to rehydrate very rapidly either in water or from a wet surface. However, there are large interspecific differences such that some species show almost no change in the permeability of the skin, and others increase rates of water uptake by about an order of magnitude. The spadefoot toad (*Scaphiopus couchi*) rehydrates rapidly only in the first day or two following emergence from its overwintering burrow (66). At least part of this interspecific difference is caused by differences in the responsiveness of the skin to arginine vasotocin (5, 67). In some cases the ventral pelvic skin appears to be primarily responsible for this rapid water uptake, and the animals rehydrate almost as rapidly in a shallow layer of water as when totally immersed (2, 85). Hypervascularization of the pelvic skin may also enhance water uptake (21, 107). Also, in species (e.g. *Bufo*) with extensive "sculpturing" of the outer skin surface, water moves in capillary channels over most of the body from the ventral surface that is in contact with water (21, 76).

Soil moisture appears to be a major source of water for some amphibian species. Passive cutaneous uptake of water from soil is theoretically possible if the free energy of water in the animal (an inverse function of the concentration of the body fluids) is less than the free energy of water in the soil (determined by the forces binding water to soil particles.) In some cases the direction of water movement follows this simple prediction (84), but other species require wetter soil than would be predicted on this basis. Fossorial frogs can apparently absorb water from dryer soil than species that do not normally burrow (128), and the urodeles tested all require very wet soil for water uptake to occur (119). Intimate contact between the skin and the soil-capillary channels is required for water transfer, and interspecific differences may be due to differences in skin surface structure affecting this contact (68). As soil dries and its water potential falls, the soil-body gradient may shift to favor a net efflux of water. One factor operating in the animal's favor in this situation is that dryer soil has a lower hydraulic conductivity. Also, some species isolate themselves from the drying soil by forming cocoons from multiple layers of dead epithelium and possibly other materials (86, 104, 114). In the spadefoot toad an impervious cocoon is not formed, but the burrowed animals accumulate high concentrations of urea in the body fluids and thereby maintain a more favorable gradient with soil water (84, 86).

The skin of adult anurans and urodeles is capable of net transport of sodium and chloride inward, even when the animals are exposed to environmental concentrations less than those usually found in fresh water ($\sim$ 0.2–1 mM). The net rate of cutaneous influx of Na in unfed animals in Na balance can be approximated from the rate of urinary excretion of this ion. For *Rana pipiens* and *Bufo marinus* in "fresh water" this is between 0.1 and 1 meq kg^{-1} day^{-1} (57, 111), and values for two aquatic urodeles calculated from Bentley's data (7) also fall within this range. Estimates made using isotopic sodium (63, 64, 94) tend to be somewhat higher ($\sim$ 1–3 meq kg^{-1} day^{-1}). Sodium uptake via the skin probably exceeds dietary gains (Table 3) in amphibians that spend most of their time in water. Active sodium uptake shows saturation kinetics and is concentration dependent within the range of sodium concentrations found in fresh water. K_s typically falls between 0.1 and 0.5 mM, with the more aquatic species having the higher affinities (64, 94). Sodium depletion of the animal increases the rate of cutaneous uptake, but not K_s. Aldosterone increases sodium uptake across frog skin in vivo and in vitro, and this is thought to be the primary means by which anurans regulate sodium gains by this route (5). Neurohypophyseal hormones also increase active sodium transport across amphibian skin, but the stimuli for their release (dehydration or solute loading) are opposite to those for aldosterone and do not coincide with situations in which increased sodium uptake would be physiologically important.

Amphibians are exceptional in their ability to conserve sodium while producing urine at high rates, and the necessity of cutaneous uptake for the maintenance of sodium balance has recently been called into question. Frogs are not demonstrably sodium depleted when kept in running deionized water for up to 60 days (82), or in tap water containing amelioride, which blocks the sodium pump (6). Thus cutaneous sodium uptake is probably essential in aquatic amphibians fasting for long periods, but available evidence indicates that dietary sodium intake is usually more than adequate to balance losses. It is conceivable that amphibians could obtain sodium from moist soil, but no information is available on this. Interestingly, in vitro measurements of short circuit current and transepithelial potentials indicate that *R. cancrivora* continues to actively transport sodium inward even in a hypersaline environment (60, 62). However, urinary sodium concentrations remain very low (5–20 mM) when these frogs are adapted to hypersaline media (60), suggesting that sodium influxes are not particularly large.

In larval amphibians the gills rather than the skin provide the site of active sodium and chloride uptake, and the skin's acquisition of transport function occurs abruptly at metamorphosis (36).

Water permeability of reptilian skin in contact with aqueous solutions has been demonstrated by measuring the movement of tritiated water between the animal and its bathing medium (56, 105, 125). However, gross influxes and effluxes measured in this way are so large (because of exchange diffusion) that net cutaneous water flux is difficult to determine. Using gravimetric methods, Cloudsley-Thompson (22) found no cutaneous water gain from damp sand or a water bath in *Crocodilus niloticus*, even by dehydrated animals. Similar results were obtained by Diefenbach (35) in *C. niloticus* and *Caiman crocodilus*, and by Krakauer et al (72) in several small snakes and amphisbaenians immersed in moist sand. Evidence that *Caiman sclerops* and the freshwater turtles *Pseudemys scripta* and *Trionyx spinifer* gain water across their skin (11, 12), has been questioned on methodological grounds

(35). To date, no reptile has been convincingly shown to take up or lose significant quantities of water by osmosis across the skin, in marked contrast to amphibians. Moreover, Robinson & Dunson (105) have shown that the skin of the euryhaline turtle *Malaclemys terrapin* is essentially impermeable to sodium.

Cloaca and Pharynx

It is not known whether water or salts enter amphibians from the aquatic environment across epithelia other than the skin. Some arboreal forms are reported to fill their bladders via the anus for use in wetting egg masses deposited in trees (103).

Freshwater turtles (*Trionyx spinifer, Pseudemys scripta, Chelydra serpentina, Chrysemys picta*) take up sodium from dilute solutions (41, 127). The uptake sites appear to be the mucous membranes of the pharynx, cloaca, and cloacal bursae, all of which display active sodium transport in vitro (41). Some chloride follows the sodium, but most of the anion influx involves some other substance, possibly bicarbonate. These membranes apparently do not transport potassium. The euryhaline marine turtle *Caretta caretta* does not take up sodium or potassium from dilute solutions (53). Although the cloaca is known to reabsorb urinary water in many terrestrial reptiles, cloacal uptake of environmental water has not been demonstrated in aquatic forms. *Caiman crocodilus* showed no weight gain when its cloaca was irrigated with distilled water or physiological saline (35).

OUTPUT

Amphibians and reptiles lose water, salts, and nitrogen in feces and urine, and solute-free water by evaporation from skin and respiratory tract. Some terrestrial and marine reptiles also lose salts and water via salt glands. For animals living in freshwater, fossorial, or damp tropical habitats, water may be so abundant that the problem is how to excrete the excess while conserving salts that may be in short supply. On the other hand, marine and terrestrial forms may be required to excrete or store excess nitrogen and salts while conserving water.

Evaporation

The integument of most amphibians offers little if any resistance to water evaporation. Rates of evaporative loss are thus highly dependent on humidity, temperature, and wind velocity. Tracy (126) estimated that evaporative loss rates for *Rana pipiens* in Michigan could vary from 30 to 1600 ml kg^{-1} day^{-1}. Numerous measurements under a variety of environmental conditions have failed to show physiologically significant interspecific variations in evaporation rates related to the appearance or "wetness" of the skin or the animal's habitat preference. Such differences as have been observed in both anurans and salamanders probably reflect differences in size and shape as well as postural and other behavioral differences (5, 114, 121). For the vast majority of amphibians, body size is the major intrinsic factor determining the rate of evaporative water loss (114, 121). Large amphibians lose much less water per unit of surface than smaller ones, probably because the unstirred boundary layer increases with body size, and this is the major determinant of water flux when the skin itself is highly permeable (100). The secretion of mucus apparently does not affect the rate of water loss, but may play a role in basking species by preventing skin damage due to desiccation when evaporation rates are very high (77).

A few species of frogs do not depend on a humid environment to prevent rapid dehydration away from water. Two African tree frogs of the genus *Chiromantis* (39, 80) and several members of the South American genus *Phyllomedusa* (118) exhibit rates of evaporative loss similar to those of desert lizards under comparable conditions and only about 5% of those typical of anurans. The *Phyllomedusa* possess specialized glands in the skin which secrete a waxy substance onto the skin surface (14). The *Chiromantis* apparently lack lipid glands, and the mechanism by which its skin is rendered impermeable remains to be determined. Histologically the skin of *Chiromantis petersi* appears indistinguishable from that of other anurans, except there are multiple layers of iridophores in the dermis of dorsal skin (39). It has been postulated that the typically low resistance to cutaneous evaporation in amphibians is a necessary consequence of the use of this organ for water uptake and gas exchange. Cutaneous respiration has not been measured in either *Chiromantis* or *Phyllomedusa,* but both can take up water rapidly through the skin (39, 118).

The formation of a cocoon, mentioned previously in connection with water exchange with the soil, can also greatly reduce evaporative water losses in air (86). However, the cocoon renders the frog immobile and forms slowly, and would thus be of little use to the animal in exposed situations. Also, species of frogs which have poorly vascularized skin co-ossified with the cranium show reduced rates of water loss in this region (113), but the benefits of this in the water economy of the frog have not been evaluated.

Water losses due to pulmonary ventilation have not been measured in amphibians, but cutaneous permeability is so high in most cases that respiratory losses are negligible by comparison. Judging from the situation in reptiles (see below), pulmonary losses probably are a significant component in *Chiromantis* and *Phyllomedusa.*

Bentley (5, 9), Cloudsley-Thompson (24), and Templeton (123) discussed several generalizations about evaporation from reptiles. In dry air at 23° C rates of total evaporation in different species range from 3 to about 2000 ml kg^{-1} day^{-1}. The highest rates occur in small ($\sim$ 1 g) burrowing snakes (72), and are like those seen in small amphibians. Evaporation rates are strongly correlated with habitat aridity: diurnal desert lizards have the lowest rates and subtropical fossorial snakes and amphisbaenians show the highest. This correlation obscures any potential relationships between evaporation and body mass, surface:volume ratio (although this occurs within a given species), or taxonomic group. However, even in desert reptiles, which have the lowest rates of water loss per unit area of skin, cutaneous evaporation still accounts for about 50% or more of total evaporation at 23° C. Evaporation from the skin increases with decreasing humidity and increasing temperature. However, pulmonary water loss increases more as temperature increases, so that cutaneous evaporation becomes a smaller fraction of the total. Pulmonary evaporation rates are surprisingly variable in reptiles and do not necessarily reflect metabolic rate: ratios of pulmonary evaporation (mg) to oxygen consumption (ml) vary from

0.5 to 4.9, the higher values generally found in aquatic reptiles. Explanations for this may involve difference in 1. oxygen extraction abilities, and 2. extent of any nasal heat exchanger. Oxygen extraction values vary from about 1 to 4 ml O_2 removed per 100 ml air ventilated. Pulmonary evaporation can be reduced by exhaling through a cool nasal passage, which cools the air and causes some of its water vapor to condense mucous membranes. The nose is cooled during inhalation by conduction and evaporation. One lizard (*Dipsosaurus*) has been shown to exhale air that is cooler than its body.

Since the above reviews were written, several studies bearing on evaporation in reptiles have been published. Licht & Bennett (74) and Bennett & Licht (3) measured evaporation rates in several mutant snakes (*Pituophis* and *Natrix*) having few or no scales, no superficial dermal layer, and a much thinner keratin layer than normal members of their species. Evaporative water losses in the scaleless snakes were not higher than in normal snakes, indicating that scales and a thick keratin layer may not account for low rates of cutaneous evaporation in snakes. Working with fourteen species of snakes, Cohen (26) reached several conclusions regarding evaporation: water loss increases with wind velocity and temperature, cutaneous evaporation increases twofold or more during the shedding cycle, coiled snakes have less exposed surface area and lose less water as a result, cutaneous water loss accounts for about 75% of total evaporation in mesic as well as xeric snakes, and total evaporation correlates well with habitat aridity. The correlation between evaporation rates and habitat aridity has been questioned by Dmi'el (37), who found that two species of colubrid snakes lost water three times faster than two species of vipers, even though one viper lives in a mediterranean climate, and one colubrid occurs in a desert. Similarly, Duvdevani & Borut (49) found that evaporation rates in four species of *Acanthodactylus* lizards from arid portions of Israel were up to five times higher than other desert lizards, but a habitat correlation exists within the genus. In the snakes Dmi'el (37) studied, evaporation increased during activity, but cutaneous losses remained unchanged, indicating that movement and bending of the skin during activity does not increase cutaneous water loss. Elick & Sealander (51) found that cutaneous evaporation rates in juvenile snakes (*Diadophis punctatus* and *Carphophis vermis*) are much higher than in adults of the same species when expressed in terms of surface area.

Important problems remaining to be investigated include the nature of the barrier to cutaneous evaporation, the occurrence and function of nasal heat exchangers in various species, and the mechanisms for regulating cutaneous and pulmonary evaporation within a species.

Salt Glands

There is no evidence that any amphibian possesses salt glands. Several excellent reviews of salt glands in reptiles are available (29, 43, 46, 47, 101) which cover the literature through about 1974. The following brief account of salt glands stems from these reviews. Salt-secreting glands are located in the eye orbit (lachrymal gland) in marine euryhaline turtles, near the base of the tongue (posterior sublingual gland) in sea snakes, and in the nasal region (lateral or external nasal gland) in lizards. Freshwater and terrestrial turtles, terrestrial snakes, and many lizard species apparently do not have functional salt glands. The organization of reptile salt glands is generally similar to that in birds: many blind-ending branched tubules anastomose to form the short excretory duct. The tubules contain three types of cells: the principal (salt-secreting) cells, which touch the basement membrane surrounding each tubule and join at their apices via junctional complexes to form the narrow central lumen; mucous cells located primarily in the blind end of the tubule; and small basal cells of unknown function. Principal cell ultrastructure in reptiles is generally similar to birds, including abundant lateral and basal mitochondria, Golgi bodies, sparse apical microvilli, and extensive lateral (but not basal as in birds) folding and interdigitating of plasma membranes.

The composition and maximum rates of secretion of salt gland fluid are related to habitat and diet. Marine turtles and sea snakes produce secretions containing primarily sodium (400–900 mM) and chloride (600–1000 mM) but little potassium (20–30 mM). Potassium concentrations in fluid from marine iguanas (*Amblyrhynchus cristatus*) are higher (235 mM), but NaCl is still the primary solute (up to 1400 mM). In terrestrial lizards, potassium concentrations are much higher (200–1400 mM), and potassium is the predominant cation in herbivorous species. Some terrestrial lizards show remarkable plasticity regarding composition of salt gland secretions, with sodium: potassium and chloride: bicarbonate ratios changing greatly in an appropriate response to different salt loads. However, these adjustments may require several days. Maximum secretion rates are highest in the marine iguana and sea snakes (2.0–2.5 mmol NaCl kg^{-1} hr^{-1}), but are about one-tenth this in terrestrial lizards (secreting primarily potassium chloride). The salt glands in desert lizards are very important in osmoregulation, eliminating about half of the dietary potassium and most of the sodium (Table 2).

The mechanism of secretion in reptiles is not known [however, see discussion of mechanism in birds in Peaker & Linzell (101)]. The presence of folds and channels in principal cell membranes suggests that a "standing osmotic gradient" may be operating, but this would not account for formation of an hyperosmotic secretion into the lumen from each cell. Recent evidence indicates that salt gland Na-K-ATPase activities were similar in a lizard (*Dipsosaurus dorsalis*), a sea snake (*Pelamis platurus*), and an euryhaline turtle (*Malaclemys terrapin)* [the Na-K-ATPase activity increased in the turtle with an increased plasma Na concentration (40)]. K-dependent ATPase is located primarily in the lateral membrane folds of principal cells in *D. dorsalis* glands (52). In nasal glands from the lizard *Lacerta muralis* and the amphisbaenian *Trogonophis wiegmanni,* the light microscope revealed striations (which correspond to lateral membrane folds), suggesting that these reptiles may have functional salt glands (109) however, salt secretions have not yet been found in these species.

Aldosterone reduces sodium but not potassium excretion by lizard salt glands (101). Several other adrenal hormones may influence salt gland function, but results to date are inconclusive.

Digestive Tract

The role of the digestive tract in osmoregulation by amphibians and reptiles has been virtually ignored until recently. Although the water and salt content of several foods have been examined [summarized by Bentley (9)], assimilation of these dietary substances has received little attention. In *Phyllomedusa sauvagei* feeding on insects (*Tenebrio* larvae), fecal water loss amounts to about 10% of dietary intake, not because the feces are especially dry ($\sim$ 60% water), but because the food is highly digestible (118). Fecal cation losses relative to intake in this species were 4% of potassium and 14% of sodium. Comparable values for *Hyla pulchella* were 37% of potassium and 46% of sodium, and the other five species of anurans used in this study fell within this range. All species examined lost about 17% of dietary chloride via the feces. The relative role of absorption and secretion of ions by the gut in determining fecal output are unknown, but there is indication that the colon plays a part in regulation of fecal sodium losses in toads (*Bufo*) (25, 54, 55).

In the few reptiles studied, estimated fecal water losses range from 8 to 70% of food water inputs (Table 2). Reptiles feeding on plant matter have high rates of fecal water loss, apparently because vegetation is relatively indigestible compared to other diets. Generally, less than 20% of the potassium and chloride in the food is lost in the feces, but herbivorous lizards lose 30–40% of the ingested sodium via this route (Table 3). In an herbivorous lizard (*Sauromalus obesus*), assimilation percentages for some substances not shown in Table 2 are organic matter 87%, ash 5%, magnesium 49%, and calcium 68% (98). The rate of calcium assimilation is relatively high in these lizards ($\sim$ 0.5 mmol kg^{-1} day^{-1}), but the means by which excess calcium is excreted remain unknown. Calcium is excreted by the kidneys in water snakes, but apparently not in alligators, where fecal excretion occurs instead (29). Templeton et al (124) suggested that the gut or cloaca may regulate the flux of sodium and potassium between feces and body fluids.

Kidneys

Amphibian and reptilian nephrons have proximal and distal segments which are usually connected by a short intermediate segment. There are no loops of Henle, and no amphibian or reptile kidney is known to produce hyperosmotic urine. In amphibians, ciliated nephrostomes open to the coelomic cavity. Coelomic fluid can enter the renal tubules by this route in urodeles and may add to the glomerular filtrate. Nephrostomes of anurans connect to the renal veins, and they may play a role in water resorption from the bladder (114). Peritubular circulation in both amphibians and reptiles is derived from the efferent glomerular arterioles and from renal portal veins.

The amphibian kidney is admirably suited for life in fresh water and, so far as is known, all amphibians can produce dilute urine at very high rates ($\sim$ 10–25 ml kg^{-1} hr^{-1}) when maintained in fresh water. Glomerular filtration rates (GFR) are high ($\sim$ 20–50 ml kg^{-1} hr^{-1}) in this situation, and can be considerably higher in experimentally water-loaded animals. In anurans, only about half of the filtered water is resorbed in the tubules, but resorption of sodium and chloride may be nearly complete ($\sim$ 99%), see e.g. (57). In larval salamanders, GFR tends to be lower

($\sim$ 8–16 ml kg^{-1} hr^{-1}), but only 10–30% of the filtered water and 90–95% of the filtered sodium are resorbed when the animals are in fresh water (71, 122). When the concentration of the environmental medium is increased, GFR is drastically reduced and fractional water resorption increases markedly. Urinary sodium concentrations in adult anurans and urodeles in fresh water are commonly about 1 mM (7, 57, 94).

Amphibians deprived of water also quickly reduce urine output, again by reducing GFR and increasing fractional water resorption, and the concentration of the urine approaches that of the plasma. Although they are unable to produce hyperosmotic urine, renal water conservation is well developed in amphibians because they can become completely anuric after loss of only a few percent of the body water. It is usually assumed that glomerular filtration ceases altogether, but analysis of kidney function is difficult when no urine is produced.

Arginine vasotocin (AVT) and, frequently, mammalian neurohypophyseal peptides have strong antidiuretic action in most amphibians tested. In many cases this results from a combination of glomerular and tubular effects resembling those seen during water deprivation. Dehydration causes the release of AVT in amphibians, and it is generally supposed that antidiuresis and the other components of the "water-balance response" to dehydration (increased water uptake via the skin and bladder) are controlled by this hormone (8). However, a recent attempt to correlate circulating AVT levels with rates of urine production in the bullfrog gave inconsistent results, suggesting that other factors are also involved (110). Corticosteroids, especially aldosterone, may be involved in control of renal sodium excretion, but in vivo evidence is scanty (20).

Most amphibians excrete nitrogen primarily as urea and ammonia. Aquatic forms are generally ammonotelic when in fresh water. Some forms, such as *Xenopus laevis*, which is primarily aquatic but sometimes forced to aestivate in soil, switch readily from ammonia to urea formation. Energetically, ammonia is the most economical vehicle for nitrogen excretion, but its toxicity precludes its use when water turnover is low. It has been suggested that the main advantages of excretion of ammonia by aquatic amphibians are in cation conservation and pH regulation (70), but evidence is scanty.

In semiterrestrial species, ureotelism appears to be the rule, but these animals often excrete appreciable amounts of ammonia while in water and become completely ureotelic when water influx is low. Reduction or cessation of urine production has been shown to lead to the accumulation of urea in a variety of anurans, and has recently been reported in a salamander (*Ambystoma tigrinum*) (32). Plasma urea levels of several hundred mM appear to be without deleterious effect, and may in fact place the animal in a more favorable situation for obtaining water from soil or saline solutions. There is some evidence for increased rates of urea synthesis in these situations, but the mechanisms governing this are unknown. Accumulated urea is rapidly eliminated by the kidneys when the animals return to water. For some species there is evidence for active tubular secretion of urea, but when plasma levels of urea are appreciable, urinary urea concentrations usually approximate those in the plasma. This is true even in the crab-eating frog (*Rana cancrivora*) adapted to saline conditions where active tubular resorption of urea would be beneficial (112).

In this situation urine flow rates are greatly reduced (matching osmotic influx) by reducing GFR to one-fourth "normal" and resorbing more than 90% of the filtrate.

Several representatives of the genus *Phyllomedusa* excrete a significant fraction of their nitrogen wastes as urate, ranging from 80% in *P. sauvagei* to 20% in *P. hypochondrialis* (118). About 5% of the excreted nitrogen is ammonium, with the balance made up of urea. In these species the partitioning of nitrogen among the various products is independent of water turnover, and most of the ammonium excreted is in the form of precipitated urate salts. When uricotelic frogs are maintained out of water and fed, precipitated urate accumulates in the bladder, indicating continued renal function during water deprivation in these species. In *P. sauvagei*, urate excretion prevents the rapid build up of urea in the body fluids and also aids in electrolyte excretion (45% of the sodium input and 22% of the potassium input were excreted in precipitated form). *Chiromantis xerampelina* and *C. petersi* also excrete large amounts of urate, and these species presumably reap similar benefits (39, 80). Uricotelism combined with low rates of evaporative water loss place these arboreal amphibians in a position similar to that of insectivorous lizards in terms of their ability to osmoregulate without access to fresh water. The extent to which kidney function in these species differs from the typical amphibian pattern remains to be elucidated.

In normally hydrated reptiles, GFR ranges from 0.5 to 16 ml kg^{-1} hr^{-1} (28). Although terrestrial species tend to have lower GFR than freshwater and marine species, this is not always true. GFR usually doubles or triples in water-loaded animals, but some species show decreases and others increases of more than tenfold. In salt-loaded or dehydrated reptiles, GFR usually decreases, but again there are exceptions. In several species of turtles, ureteral urine flow stops when plasma osmotic pressures increase sufficiently, apparently because filtration ceases. Urine flow stops in the desert tortoise (*Gopherus agassizii*), when plasma osmolality has increased 100 mosM above normal. In the freshwater turtle (*Pseudemys scripta*), this occurs with only a 20 mosM increase (30). Changes in GFR within an individual reptile apparently result primarily from differences in the number of functioning glomeruli.

Tubular resorption of filtered water in reptiles ranges from about 40 to 90% in normally hydrated or water-loaded animals to as high as 98% in dehydrated or salt-loaded animals, which are close to producing no ureteral urine at all (28). Sodium resorption ranges from 55 to 98% in normally hydrated animals to as high as 99.5% in dehydrated turtles (*Pseudemys scripta*). Changes in sodium resorption with water and salt loads in various species are inconsistent and generally not large. For potassium the few results available indicate that tubular reabsorption can approach 100%, but under different conditions, tubular secretion of potassium occurs, and net potassium excretion can exceed filtration more than twofold (28). The osmotic concentration of ureteral urine varies from about 30 to 100% of plasma osmotic concentration. Although there are hints of some correlations between habitat and renal parameters in reptiles, the small number of species examined to date does not warrant generalizations. In the few reptiles examined, AVT decreases GFR and increases tubular resorption of water and sodium, and may decrease secretion of potassium (28). Aldosterone apparently has little effect on renal function (16).

Nitrogenous excretory products in reptiles are primarily urea and uric acid (or "urate"), although aquatic reptiles such as freshwater turtles and crocodiles can excrete up to about 40% of total nitrogen output as ammonia. Urea is important in most turtles, regardless of habitat, but snakes and lizards eliminate more than 90% of their waste nitrogen as urate. In aquatic reptiles, most urinary ammonia is apparently synthesized and secreted directly into the filtrate by the kidney tubules. Urea generally enters kidney tubules by filtration, although there is some evidence for active secretion and resorption (28). Most of the urate appearing in the urine of terrestrial reptiles is actively secreted by the tubules. Relatively large volumes of water accompany excretion of ammonia and urea because both are very soluble, and high concentrations of ammonia are toxic. However, urate precipitates easily, thus removing its contribution to urine osmotic pressure. Moreover, much of the urinary cation load may be bound to the precipitate, thereby reducing urine osmotic concentration even further and facilitating water resorption. Although precipitated urate has been found in ureteral urine, it is not known whether precipitation occurs in the kidney at a site where tubule function may be affected. Tubular transport of urate in snakes is dependent on potassium but not sodium. Rates of ammonia excretion via ureteral urine have been measured in only three reptiles, and range from 0.5 to about 1.7 mmol kg^{-1} day^{-1}. Little is known about rates of renal output of urea or urate.

The formation and excretion of urinary precipitates in lizards have been investigated recently. In three desert lizards eating natural diets, about 40% of total potassium output, and 14% of total sodium output, was in the form of urinary precipitates (90, 93, 96). The rate of bound potassium excretion in *S. obesus* increases with increasing potassium intake, and at a given potassium-intake rate, precipitated potassium output is independent of dietary nitrogen levels (97). Apparently, this is accomplished by recruiting body nitrogen to produce urate when nitrogen intake is low, as well as by packing more potassium onto each urate molecule (molar ratios of potassium: urate range from 0.01 to 3.17). Minnich (91) presented evidence that cations are chemically bound to urate in reptiles, but McNabb et al (88), McNabb & McNabb (87), and Lonsdale & Sutor (78) suggested that precipitated cations may be physically bound or trapped in bird urinary solids. The relative roles of the kidney and cloaca in precipitate formation are not clearly defined.

Cloaca and Bladder

The bladder of amphibians is a distensible outpouching of the cloaca and, except in highly aquatic forms, is usually quite capacious. Semiterrestrial anurans are commonly observed to retain urine equivalent to 20–50% of the bladder empty weight. Bladder capacity in urodeles in generally much less than in anurans (1, 120). The anuran bladder resembles the skin in that its permeability to water is generally variable and under the control of antidiuretic hormone (AVT). The responsiveness of the bladder to antidiuretic hormones diminishes markedly with water loading, and this may also play a role in regulation of resorption from the bladder (50). Moreover, the amphibian bladder is capable of actively resorbing sodium from the bladder contents. The rate of sodium transport by anuran bladders in vitro is usually increased by neurohypophyseal peptides, aldosterone, insulin, and epinephrine, and a variety of synergistic effects have been reported. The bladders of most urodeles studied appear unresponsive to AVT and also perhaps to aldosterone (5, 8).

The potential osmoregulatory utility of dilute urine stored in the bladder has long been recognized. Bufonid toads subjected to dehydration in air have been found to maintain the concentration of the body fluids remarkably constant until bladder reserves are exhausted (108, 115). A similar phenomenon has recently been reported in a salamander (*Ambystoma tigrinum*) (1). In dehydrating spadefoot toads (*Scaphiopus couchi*), bladder water is also resorbed, but the plasma solute concentrations fluctuate unpredictably before water losses exceed stored reserves (83). It thus appears likely that a major function of the amphibian bladder is to provide a water source to compensate losses in amphibians foraging on land. The bladder probably plays a similar role in fossorial forms, allowing the animal to store water when soil moisture is high for use in the event that the soil dries (84).

The bladder could also serve to decrease urinary sodium losses from amphibians in fresh water; bladder urine from sodium-depleted toads (*Bufo marinus*) in distilled water has a lower sodium concentration (approximately 0.2 mM) than ureteral urine (1–2 mM) (89). However, bladders tend to be small in aquatic amphibians, and ureteral urine can be as dilute as urine from the bladder, see e.g. (54, 57). In saline-adapted *Bufo* the sodium and osmotic concentrations of bladder urine tend to be higher than in ureteral urine (54), but these differences are neither large nor consistent. Thus there is little evidence that post-renal modification of the urine by the amphibian bladder plays an important osmoregulatory role when the animals are in fresh or saline water, but may be significant in situations leading to sodium depletion.

Uricotelic frogs (*Phyllomedusa* and *Chiromantis*) accumulate large amounts of urate in the bladder when they are fed and deprived of additional water. It seems likely that water resorption and urate precipitation occur in the bladders of these animals, but this awaits definitive study.

Sections on cloaca and bladder function in reptiles can be found in reviews by Dantzler & Holmes (29), Bradshaw (16), and Bentley (9). Ureteral urine enters the cloaca, and may enter the urinary bladder in reptiles that have one (turtles and many lizards, but not snakes or crocodilians). There is some indication that urine may also enter the colon or large intestine, as occurs in birds. Much circumstantial evidence suggests that these organs can modify ureteral urine before it is voided. Cloacal and bladder membranes actively resorb sodium from urine, and are permeable to water in varying degrees. Water resorption may occur in conjunction with ion transport, or simply in response to plasma colloid osmotic pressure (9). There is some evidence that the cloaca may resorb bicarbonate and secrete potassium. From values for GFR and tubular water resorption in normally hydrated reptiles given above, we estimate that ureteral urine flow ranges from 30 to 220 ml kg^{-1} day^{-1}. When compared to rates of water loss via voided urine (0.1 to 18 ml kg^{-1} day^{-1}; see Table 2), it is evident that post-renal water resorption can be very important in water balance in some species. In fact, the abilities of reptilian kidneys to vary urine composition are rather unimpressive when compared to those of mammalian kidneys. However, urine that is finally voided can be quite different from that produced by the kidneys, again suggesting that the cloaca, bladder, and intestine play major roles in reptilian osmoregulation. Recently, Bradshaw (16) has shown that the cloaca of a lizard (*Amphibolurus ornatus*) can resorb up to 450 ml H_2O kg^{-1} day^{-1}, 24 mmol sodium kg^{-1} day^{-1} and 5.5 mmol potassium kg^{-1} day^{-1} when these animals are water loaded. These resorption rates are much higher than total input rates estimated for several lizards (Tables 2 and 3). Braysher (18) reported that cloacal, but not ureteral, urine of a related species (*Amphibolurus maculosus*) can be hyperosmotic to plasma. In the lizard *Varanus gouldii*, AVT doubled the rates of water and sodium resorption by increasing sodium transport and cloacal permeability to water (19). However, in a freshwater turtle (*Chrysemys picta*) hypophysectomy had no effect on urine plasma electrolyte concentrations (127). Aldosterone injections have little effect on the composition of voided urine in lizards, but turtle bladders respond by conserving sodium. There is some evidence that corticosterone promotes sodium excretion in lizards (15).

BALANCE AND STORAGE

Fully hydrated amphibians typically have a high water content ($\sim$ 800 ml kg^{-1}) and low concentrations of plasma sodium (100–120 mM) and total solutes (200–250 mosM) compared to other vertebrates. This may aid in maintenance of water and salt balance in fresh water and is probably part of the basis for the tolerance of many amphibians to large losses of water via evaporation. Many semiterrestrial species of anurans can withstand the loss of about half of their body water (400 ml kg^{-1}) and the attendant doubling of body fluid concentrations, and some species have even greater tolerances. Urodeles are generally more aquatic and less tolerant of desiccation, but *Ambystoma tigrinum* survives the loss of 450 ml kg^{-1} (1).

Dehydration tolerance coupled with the ability to store large volumes of water in the bladder presumably allow amphibians to exploit terrestrial environments where water efflux by evaporation exceeds influx from feeding. Reduction or cessation of urine production and storage of urea also aid in this, as does the rapid rate of rehydration through the skin of anurans when water is available. Thus most of the more terrestrial amphibians appear adapted to let their water balance swing through wide oscillations, the period of which is dependent on environmental conditions determining the rate of evaporative water loss. These oscillations are avoided or greatly damped in those xerophylic arboreal species that have greatly reduced evaporative losses and are uricotelic.

Amphibians adapted to saline media store solutes and remain at least slightly hyperosmotic to their environment. Studies in which exposure is relatively brief (a week or less) generally show that storage of electrolytes is the primary factor in raising the osmotic concentration of the plasma (59, 69, 71), whereas long-term acclimation usually results in the accumulation of considerable concentrations of urea (65, 106) or some other non-electrolyte (75), and in increased salinity tolerance. The exceptional ability of *Rana cancrivora* to survive in saline media is probably related to the exceptionally high rates of urea production exhibited in this species. Experimentation with unfed amphibians may lead to underestimation of salinity tolerance, because these fasting animals must deaminate a significant fraction of their protein to produce and maintain high concentrations of urea (106).

The composition and volumes of body fluids in reptiles as a whole are generally similar to those for birds and mammals, although reptiles show wider variation. Fluid volumes, in ml per kg body mass range from 650–760 for total water, 360–580 for intracellular fluid, 150–350 for extracellular fluid, and 33–70 for plasma volume (9). Similarly, plasma electrolyte concentrations in reptiles are not unusual, with sodium concentrations ranging from about 112 to 140 mM in normally hydrated freshwater species, and from 150 to 180 in steady-state terrestrial forms. The marine iguana has 178 mM sodium, but the plasma of a sea snake (*Pelamis platurus*) contains 264 mM sodium. By appropriate utilization of the various avenues of output, reptiles are apparently able to remain in balance, although the details of this are known for only a few species (Tables 2 and 3). However, in some reptiles under certain conditions, balance is not achieved, and net storage or depletion of water, salts, or nitrogen occurs.

There are no documented cases of reptiles storing water in anticipation of dehydrating conditions, although this may occur in the desert tortoise *Gopherus agassizii* (30), and the desert lizard *Aporosaura anchietae* (79). But storage of electrolytes occurs in at least one lizard: during droughts, *Amphibolurus ornatus* continues to eat sodium-rich ants, thereby maintaining normal fluid volumes but tolerating an increase in plasma sodium concentration up to 300 mM (17). High-plasma sodium concentrations have been found in other lizards, but these apparently resulted from water loss rather than salt storage. During winter hibernation in fresh water, plasma-sodium concentration in the turtle *Trionyx spinifer* can drop as low as 81 mM. The euryhaline turtle *Malaclemys centrata* stores urea in body fluids in adjusting to a seawater environment (58). Among terrestrial lizards, tolerance to dehydration appears to be correlated with habitat, with desert species surviving up to 50% body mass loss (95). Reptiles in general are able to tolerate much wider variations in body water content and electrolyte concentrations than can birds or mammals. As in amphibians, this enhances survivorship in stressful situations.

CONCLUDING STATEMENT

Reptiles, because of low skin permeability, uricotelism, and salt glands, are well adapted to remain in water and solute balance with moderate to low rates of water turnover. Dietary and metabolic water inputs are frequently sufficient to offset losses attendant upon excretion, elimination, and gas exchange, as well as cutaneous losses. Amphibians generally have very high rates of water turnover unless, like fossorial forms, they exploit environmental situations where water fluxes across their highly permeable skins are low. Many amphibians have remarkable tolerances (shared to a considerable degree by reptiles) to osmotic imbalances, and are able to rectify these rapidly when water becomes available. Striking exceptions to these generalizations are found in both amphibians and reptiles, and these departures from the usual pattern provide insights into the physiological adaptability of these diverse and interesting groups of vertebrates.

Literature Cited

1. Alvarado, R. H. 1972. The effects of dehydration on water and electrolytes in *Ambystoma tigrinum*. *Physiol. Zool.* 45:43–53
2. Baldwin, R. A. 1974. The water balance response of the pelvic "patch" of *Bufo punctatus* and *Bufo boreas*. *Comp. Biochem. Physiol. A* 47:1285–95
3. Bennett, A. F., Licht, P. 1975. Evaporative water loss in scaleless snakes. *Comp. Biochem. Physiol. A* 52:213–15
4. Bentley, P. J. 1966. Adaptations of amphibia to arid environments. *Science* 152:619–23
5. Bentley, P. J. 1971. *Endocrines and Osmoregulation*, pp. 135–97. New York: Springer. 300 pp.
6. Bentley, P. J. 1973. Role of the skin in amphibian sodium metabolism. *Science* 181:686–87
7. Bentley, P. J. 1973. Osmoregulation in the aquatic urodeles *Amphiuma means* (the Congo eel) and *Siren lacertina* (the mud eel). Effects of vasotocin. *Gen. Comp. Endocrinol.* 20:386–91
8. Bentley, P. J. 1974. Actions of neurohypophyseal peptides in amphibians, reptiles, and birds. *Handb. Physiol. Sect. 8, Endocrinology,* Chap. 20, pp. 545–63
9. Bentley, P. J. 1976. Osmoregulation in reptiles. In *Biology of the Reptilia,* ed. C. Gans, W. R. Dawson. 5A:365–412. New York: Academic. 556 pp.
10. Bentley, P. J., Blumer, W. F. C. 1962. Uptake of water by the lizard, *Moloch horridus*. *Nature* 194:699–700
11. Bentley, P. J., Schmidt-Nielsen, K. 1965. Permeability to water and sodium of the crocodilian *Caiman sclerops*. *J. Cell. Comp. Physiol.* 66:303–9
12. Bentley, P. J., Schmidt-Nielsen, K. 1970. Comparison of water exchange in two aquatic turtles, *Trionyx spinifer* and *Pseudemys scripta*. *Comp. Biochem. Physiol.* 32:363–65
13. Bentley, P. J., Schmidt-Nielsen, K. 1971. Acute effects of sea water on frogs (Rana pipiens). *Comp. Biochem. Physiol. A* 40:547–48
14. Blaylock, L. A., Ruibal, R., Platt-Aloia, K. 1976. Skin structure and wiping behavior of phyllomedusine frogs. *Copeia* 1976:283–95
15. Bradshaw, S. D. 1972. The endocrine control of water and electrolyte metabolism in desert reptiles. *Gen. Comp. Endocrinol. Suppl.* 3:360–73
16. Bradshaw, S. D. 1975. Osmoregulation and pituitary-adrenal function in desert reptiles. *Gen. Comp. Endocrinol.* 25:230–48
17. Bradshaw, S. D., Shoemaker, V. H. 1967. Aspects of water and electrolyte changes in a field population of *Amphibolurus* lizards. *Comp. Biochem. Physiol.* 20:855–65
18. Braysher, M. L. 1976. The excretion of hyperosmotic urine and other aspects of the electrolyte balance of the lizard *Amphibolurus maculosus*. *Comp. Biochem. Physiol. A* 54:341–45
19. Braysher, M. L., Green, B. 1970. Absorption of water and electrolytes from the cloaca of an Australian lizard, *Varanus gouldii* (Gray). *Comp. Biochem. Physiol.* 35:607–14
20. Chester Jones, I., Bellamy, D., Chan, D. K. O., Follett, B. K., Henderson, I. W., Phillips, J. G., Snart, R. S. 1972. Biological actions of steroid hormones in nonmammalian vertebrates. In *Steroids in Nonmammalian Vertebrates,* ed. D. R. Idler, pp. 414–80. New York: Academic
21. Christensen, C. 1974. Adaptations in the water economy of some anuran amphibia. *Comp. Biochem. Physiol. A* 47:1035–49
22. Cloudsley-Thompson, J. L. 1969. Water-relations of the young nile crocodile. *Br. J. Herpetol.* 4:107–12
23. Cloudsley-Thompson, J. L. 1970. On the biology of the desert tortoise *Testudo sulcata* in Sudan. *J. Zool. London* 160:17–33
24. Cloudsley-Thompson, J. L. 1971. *The Temperature and Water Relations of Reptiles.* England: Merrow. 159 pp.
25. Cofré, G., Crabbé, J. 1967. Active sodium transport by the colon of *Bufo marinus:* Stimulation by aldosterone and antidiuretic hormone. *J. Physiol. London* 188:177–90
26. Cohen, A. C. 1975. Some factors affecting water economy in snakes. *Comp. Biochem. Physiol. A* 51:361–68
27. Dantzler, W. H. 1970. Kidney function in desert vertebrates. *Mem. Soc. Endocrinol.* 18:157–90
28. Dantzler, W. H. 1976. Renal function (with special emphasis on nitrogen excretion). See Reference 9, 5A:447–503
29. Dantzler, W. H., Holmes, W. N. 1974. Water and mineral metabolism in reptilia. In *Chemical Zoology, Amphibia and Reptilia,* ed. M. Florkin, B. T. Scheer, 9:277–336. New York: Academic

30. Dantzler, W. H., Schmidt-Nielsen, B. 1966. Excretion in fresh-water turtle (*Pseudemys scripta*) and desert tortoise (*Gopherus agassizii*). *Am. J. Physiol.* 210:198–210

31. Deavers, D. R. 1972. Water and electrolyte metabolism in the arenicolous lizard *Uma notata notata. Copeia* 1972:109–22

32. Delson, J., Whitford, W. G. 1973. Adaptation of the tiger salamander, *Ambystoma tigrinum*, to arid habitats. *Comp. Biochem. Physiol. A* 46:631–38

33. Deyrup, I. J. 1964. Water balance and kidney. In *Physiology of the Amphibia,* ed. J. A. Moore, pp. 251–328. New York: Academic

34. Dicker, S. E., Elliott, A. B. 1970. Water uptake by the crab-eating frog *Rana cancrivora,* as affected by osmotic gradients and neurohypophyseal hormones. *J. Physiol. London* 207:119–32

35. Diefenbach, C. O. daC. 1973. Integumentary permeability to water in *Caiman crocodilus* and *Crocodylus niloticus.* (Crocodilia: Reptilia). *Physiol. Zool.* 46:72–78

36. Dietz, T. H., Alvarado, R. H. 1974. Na and Cl transport across gill chamber epithelium of *Rana catesbeiana* tadpoles. *Am. J. Physiol.* 226:764–70

37. Dmi'el, R. 1972. Effect of activity and temperature on metabolism and water loss in snakes. *Am. J. Physiol.* 223:510–16

38. Dmi'el, R., Zilber, B. 1971. Water balance in a desert snake. *Copeia* 1971:754–55

39. Drewes, R. C., Hillman, S. S., Putnam, R. W., Sokol, O. M. 1977. Water, ion and nitrogen balance in the treefrog, *Chiromantis petersi,* with comments on the structure of the integument. *J. Comp. Physiol.* In press

40. Dunson, M. K., Dunson, W. A. 1975. The relation between plasma Na$^+$ concentration and salt gland Na-K ATPase content in the diamond back terrapin and the yellow-bellied sea snake. *J. Comp. Physiol.* 101:89–97

41. Dunson, W. A. 1967. Sodium fluxes in fresh-water turtles. *J. Exp. Zool.* 165:171–82

42. Dunson, W. A. 1969. Electrolyte excretion by the salt gland of the Galapagos marine iguana. *Am. J. Physiol.* 216:995–1002

43. Dunson, W. A. 1969. Reptilian salt glands. In *Exocrine Glands,* ed. S. Y. Botelho, F. P. Brooks, W. B. Shelley,

pp. 83–101. Philadephia: Univ. Penn. Press

44. Dunson, W. A. 1970. Some aspects of electrolyte and water balance in three estuarine reptiles, the diamond back terrapin, American and "salt water" crocodiles. *Comp. Biochem. Physiol.* 32:161–74

45. Dunson, W. A. 1974. Salt gland secretion in a mangrove monitor lizard. *Comp. Biochem. Physiol. A* 47:1245–55

46. Dunson, W. A. 1975. Salt and water balance in sea snakes. In *The Biology of Sea Snakes,* ed. W. A. Dunson, pp. 329–53. Baltimore: Univ. Park. 530 pp.

47. Dunson, W. A. 1976. Salt glands in reptiles. See Reference 9, 5A:413–45

48. Dunson, W. A., Dunson, M. K. 1974. Interspecific differences in fluid concentration and secretion rate of sea snake salt glands. *Am. J. Physiol.* 227:430–38

49. Duvdevani, I., Borut, A. 1974. Oxygen consumption and evaporative water loss in four species of *Acanthodactylus* (Lacertidae). *Copeia* 1974:155–64

50. Eggena, P. 1972. Osmotic regulation of toad bladder responsiveness to neurohypophyseal hormones. *J. Gen. Physiol.* 60:665–78

51. Elick, G. E., Sealander, J. A. 1972. Comparative water loss in relation to habitat selection in small colubrid snakes. *Am. Midl. Nat.* 88:429–39

52. Ellis, R. A., Goertemiller, C. C. Jr. 1974. Cytological effects of salt stress and localization of transport ATPase in the lateral nasal glands of the desert iguana, *Dipsosaurus dorsalis. Anat. Rec.* 285–97

53. Evans, D. H. 1973. The sodium balance of the euryhaline marine loggerhead turtle *Caretta caretta. J. Comp. Physiol.* 83:179–85

54. Ferreira, H. G., Jesus, C. H. 1973. Salt adaptation in *Bufo bufo. J. Physiol. London* 228:583–600

55. Ferreira, H. G., Smith, M. W. 1968. Effect of a saline environment on sodium transport by the toad colon. *J. Physiol. London* 198:329–43

56. Gans, C., Krakauer, T., Paganelli, C. V. 1968. Water loss in snakes: Interspecific and intraspecific variability. *Comp. Biochem. Physiol.* 27:747–61

57. Garland, H. O., Henderson, I. W. 1975. Influence of environmental salinity on renal and adrenocortical function in the toad, *Bufo marinus. Gen. Comp. Endocrinol.* 27:136–43

58. Gilles-Baillien, M. 1970. Urea and osmoregulation in the diamondback terra-

pin *Malaclemys centrata centrata* (Latreille). *J. Exp. Biol.* 52:691–97

59. Gordon, M. S. 1962. Osmotic regulation in the green toad (*Bufo viridis*). *J. Exp. Biol.* 39:261–70

60. Gordon, M. S., Schmidt-Nielsen, K., Kelly, H. M. 1961. Osmotic regulation in the crab-eating frog (*Rana cancrivora*). *J. Exp. Biol.* 38:659–78

61. Gordon, M. S., Tucker, V. A. 1965. Osmotic regulation in the tadpoles of the crab-eating frog (*Rana cancrivora*). *J. Exp. Biol.* 42:437–45

62. Gordon, M. S., Tucker, V. A. 1968. Further observations on the physiology of salinity adaptation in the crab-eating frog (*Rana cancrivora*). *J. Exp. Biol.* 49:185–93

63. Greenwald, L. 1971. Sodium balance in the leopard frog (*Rana pipiens*). *Physiol. Zool.* 44:149–61

64. Greenwald, L. 1972. Sodium balance in amphibians from different habitats. *Physiol. Zool.* 45:229–37

65. Harpur, R. P. 1968. Osmorégulation et métabolisme de l'urée: Comparison entre *Bufo viridis* et *Rana temporaria*. *Can. J. Zool.* 46:295–301

66. Hillyard, S. D. 1975. The role of antidiuretic hormones in the water economy of the spadefoot toad, *Scaphiopus couchi. Physiol. Zool.* 48:242–51

67. Hillyard, S. D. 1976. Variation in the effects of antidiuretic hormone on the isolated skin of the toad, *Scaphiopus couchi. J. Exp. Zool.* 195:199–206

68. Hillyard, S. D. 1976. The movement of soil water across the isolated amphibian skin. *Copeia* 1976:314–20

69. Ireland, M. P. 1973. Studies on the adaptation of *Xenopus laevis* to hyperosmotic media. *Comp. Biochem. Physiol. A* 46:469–76

70. Jungreis, A. M. 1976. Minireview: Partition of excretory nitrogen in amphibia. *Comp. Biochem. Physiol. A* 53:133–41

71. Kirschner, L. B., Kerstetter, T., Porter, D., Alvarado, R. H. 1971. Adaptation of larval *Ambystoma tigrinum* to concentrated environments. *Am. J. Physiol.* 220:1814–19

72. Krakauer, T., Gans, C., Paganelli, C. V. 1968. Ecological correlation of water loss in burrowing reptiles. *Nature* 218:659–60

73. Krogh, A. 1939. *Osmotic Regulation in Aquatic Animals.* London: Cambridge Univ. Press. 242 pp.

74. Licht, P., Bennett, A. F. 1972. A scaleless snake: Tests of the role of reptilian scales in water loss and heat transfer. *Copeia* 1972:702–7

75. Licht, P., Feder, M. E., Bledsoe, S. 1975. Salinity tolerance and osmoregulation in the salamander *Batrachoseps. J. Comp. Physiol.* 102:123–34

76. Lillywhite, H. B., Licht, P. 1974. Movement of water over toad skin: Functional role of epidermal sculpturing. *Copeia* 1974:165–71

77. Lillywhite, H. B., Licht, P. 1975. A comparative study of integumentary mucous secretions in amphibians. *Comp. Biochem. Physiol. A* 51:937–41

78. Lonsdale, K., Sutor, D. J. 1971. Uric acid dihydrate in bird urine. *Science* 172:958–59

79. Louw, G. N. 1972. The role of advective fog in the water economy of certain Namib Desert animals. *Symp. Zool. Soc. London* 31:297–314

80. Loveridge, J. P. 1970. Observations on nitrogenous excretion and water relations of *Chiromantis xerampelina* (Amphibia, Anura). *Arnoldia Rhodesia* 5:1–6

81. Mayhew, W. W., Wright, S. J. 1971. Water impermeable skin of the lizard *Phrynosoma m'calli. Herpetologica* 27:8–11

82. McAfee, R. D. 1972. Survival of *Rana pipiens* in deionized water. *Science* 178:183–85

83. McClanahan, L. L. Jr. 1967. Adaptations of the spadefoot toad, *Scaphiopus couchi,* to desert environments. *Comp. Biochem. Physiol.* 20:73–99

84. McClanahan, L. L. Jr. 1972. Changes in body fluids of burrowed spadefoot toads as a function of water potential. *Copeia* 1972:209–16

85. McClanahan, L. L. Jr., Baldwin, R. 1969. Rate of water uptake through the integument of the desert toad, *Bufo punctatus. Comp. Biochem. Physiol.* 28:381–89

86. McClanahan, L. L. Jr., Shoemaker, V. H., Ruibal, R. 1976. Structure and function of the cocoon of a ceratophryd frog. *Copeia* 1976:179–85

87. McNabb, R. A., McNabb, F. M. A. 1975. Minireview: Urate excretion by the avian kidney. *Comp. Biochem. Physiol. A* 51:253–58

88. McNabb, R. A., McNabb, F. M. A., Hinton, A. P. 1973. The excretion of urate and cationic electrolytes by the kidney of the male domestic fowl (*Gallus domesticus*). *J. Comp. Physiol.* 82:47–57

89. Middler, S. A., Kleeman, C. R., Edwards, E. 1968. The role of the urinary bladder in salt and water metabolism of the toad, *Bufo marinus*. *Comp. Biochem. Physiol.* 26:57–68

90. Minnich, J. E. 1970. Water and electrolyte balance of the desert iguana, *Dipsosaurus dorsalis*, in its natural habitat. *Comp. Biochem. Physiol.* 35:921–33

91. Minnich, J. E. 1972. Excretion of urate salts by reptiles. *Comp. Biochem. Physiol. A* 41:535–49

92. Minnich, J. E., Shoemaker, V. H. 1970. Diet, behavior and water turnover in the desert iguana, *Dipsosaurus dorsalis*. *Am. Midl. Nat.* 84:496–505

93. Minnich, J. E., Shoemaker, V. H. 1972. Water and electrolyte turnover in a field population of the lizard, *Uma scoparia*. *Copeia* 1972:650–59

94. Mullen, T. L., Alvarado, R. H. 1976. Osmotic and ionic regulation in amphibians. *Physiol. Zool.* 49:11–23

95. Munsey, L. D. 1972. Water loss in five species of lizards. *Comp. Biochem. Physiol. A* 43:781–94

96. Nagy, K. A. 1972. Water and electrolyte budgets of a free-living desert lizard, *Sauromalus obesus*. *J. Comp. Physiol.* 79:39–62

97. Nagy, K. A. 1975. Nitrogen requirement and its relation to dietary water and potassium content in the lizard *Sauromalus obesus*. *J. Comp. Physiol.* 104:49–58

98. Nagy, K. A. 1977. Cellulose digestion and nutrient assimilation in *Sauromalus obesus*, a plant-eating lizard. *Copeia* In press

99. Nagy, K. A., Shoemaker, V. H. 1975. Energy and nitrogen budgets of the free-living desert lizard *Sauromalus obesus*. *Physiol. Zool.* 48:252–62

100. Nobel, P. S. 1974. Boundary layers of air adjacent to cylinders. *Plant Physiol.* 54:177–81

101. Peaker, M., Linzell, J. L. 1975. *Salt Glands in Birds and Reptiles*. London: Cambridge Univ. Press. 307 pp.

102. Pettus, D. 1958. Water relationships in *Natrix sipedon*. *Copeia* 1958:207–11

103. Pyburn, W. F. 1970. Breeding behavior of *Phyllomedusa callidryas* and *Phyllomedusa dacnicolor* in Mexico. *Copeia* 1970:209–18

104. Reno, H. W., Gehlbach, F. R., Turner, R. A. 1972. Skin and aestivational cocoon of the aquatic amphibian, *Siren intermedia* Le Conte. *Copeia* 1972:625–31

105. Robinson, G. D., Dunson, W. A. 1976. Water and sodium balance in the estuarine diamondback terrapin (*Malaclemys*). *J. Comp. Physiol.* 105:129–52

106. Romspert, A. P. 1976. Osmoregulation in the African clawed frog, *Xenopus laevis*, in hypersaline media. *Comp. Biochem. Physiol. A* 54:207–10

107. Roth, J. J. 1973. Vascular supply to the ventral pelvic region of anurans as related to water balance. *J. Morphol.* 140:443–60

108. Ruibal, R. 1962. The adaptive value of bladder water in the toad, *Bufo cognatus*. *Physiol. Zool.* 35:218–23

109. Saint Girons, H., Joly, J. 1975. Histologie et ultrastructure de la gland nasal externe du lacertilien *Lacerta muralis* et de l'Amphisbénien *Trogonophis wiegmanni* (Reptilia, Lacertidae et Trogonophidae). *Arch. Biol.* 86:97–126

110. Sawyer, W. H., Pang, P. K. T. 1975. Endocrine adaptation to osmotic requirements of the environment: Endocrine factors in osmoregulation by lungfishes and amphibians. *Gen. Comp. Endocrinol.* 25:224–29.

111. Scheer, B. T., Mumbach, M. W., Thompson, A. R. 1974. Salt balance and osmoregulation in salientian amphibians. See Reference 29, pp. 51–65

112. Schmidt-Nielsen, K., Lee, P. 1962. Kidney function in the crab-eating frog (*Rana cancrivora*). *J. Exp. Biol.* 39:167–77

113. Seibert, E., Lillywhite, H. B., Wassersug, R. J. 1974. Cranial coossification in frogs: Relationship to rate of evaporative water loss. *Physiol. Zool.* 47:261–65

114. Seymour, R. S., Lee, A. K. 1974. Physiological adaptations of anuran amphibians to aridity: Australian prospects. *Aust. Zool.* 18:53–65

115. Shoemaker, V. H. 1964. The effects of dehydration on electrolyte concentrations in a toad, *Bufo marinus*. *Comp. Biochem. Physiol.* 13:261–71

116. Shoemaker, V. H. 1975. Adaptations to aridity in amphibians and reptiles. In *Physiological Adaptation to the Environment*, ed. F. J. Vernberg, pp. 143–54. New York: Intext Educational

117. Shoemaker, V. H., Balding, D., Ruibal, R., McClanahan, L. L. Jr. 1972. Uricotelism and low evaporative water loss in a South American frog. *Science* 175:1018–20

118. Shoemaker, V. H., McClanahan, L. L. Jr. 1975. Evaporative water loss, nitrogen excretion and osmoregulation in

phyllomedusine frogs. *J. Comp. Physiol.* 100:331–45

119. Spight, T. M. 1967. The water economy of salamanders: Exchange of water with the soil. *Biol. Bull. Woods Hole Mass.* 132:126–32

120. Spight, T. M. 1967. The water economy of salamanders: Water uptake after dehydration. *Comp. Biochem. Physiol.* 20:767–71

121. Spight, T. M. 1968. The water economy of salamanders: Evaporative water loss. *Physiol. Zool.* 41:195–203

122. Stiffler, D. F., Alvarado, R. H. 1974. Renal function in response to reduced osmotic load in larval salamanders. *Am. J. Physiol.* 266:1243–49

123. Templeton, J. R. 1972. Salt and water balance in desert lizards. *Symp. Zool. Soc. London* 31:61–77

124. Templeton, J. R., Murrish, D. E., Randall, E. M., Mugaas, J. N. 1972. Salt and water balance in the desert iguana *Dipsosaurus dorsalis.* 1. Effect of dehydration, rehydration and full hydration. *Z. Vergl. Physiol.* 76:245–54

125. Tercafs, P. R., Schoffeniels, E. 1965. Phénomènes de permeabilité au niveau de la peau des reptiles *Ann. R. Soc. Zool. Belge* 96:9–22

126. Tracy, C. R. 1975. Water and energy relations of terrestrial amphibians: Insights from mechanistic modeling. In *Perspectives in Biophysical Ecology,* ed. D. M. Gates, R. B. Schmerl, pp. 325–46. New York: Springer

127. Trobec, T. N., Stanley, J. G. 1971. Uptake of ions and water by the painted turtle, *Chrysemys picta. Copeia* 1971:537–42

128. Walker, R. F., Whitford, W. G. 1970. Soil water absorption capabilities in selected species of anurans. *Herpetologica* 26:411–18

129. Watt, B. K., Merrill, A. L. 1963. *Composition of Foods. US Dep. Agric. Handb. No. 8.* Wash. DC: US Gov. Printing Office. 190 pp.

Ann. Rev. Physiol. 1977. 39:473–527

REGULATORY PEPTIDES OF THE HYPOTHALAMUS

❖1180

Wylie Vale, Catherine Rivier, and Marvin Brown

Laboratories for Neuroendocrinology, The Salk Institute of Biological Studies, La Jolla, California 92037

INTRODUCTION

The peptides that are the principal subject of this review were originally detected in extracts of the hypothalamus as a result of their effects on the secretory functions of the anterior pituitary gland. According to the portal-vessel chemotransmitter hypothesis (155, 192), neurosecretory cells in the hypothalamus produce factors or hormones which reach the adenohypophysis by way of the hypothalamic-hypophyseal portal system. These neural factors act in concert with other blood-borne signals from the periphery to regulate the functions of the various anterior pituitary cells. To date, three peptides have been purified and characterized, and furthermore shown to have unequivocal hypophysiotropic activities by numerous investigators. These are TRF, LRF, and somatostatin (SS) whose alternative names, sequences, and principal actions on the anterior pituitary are shown in Table 1.

All three of these peptides have biological actions on the central nervous system (CNS) in addition to their effects on the anterior pituitary. Furthermore, TRF, LRF, and somatostatin are widely distributed throughout the brain, and somatostatin is found in and can influence the function of the pancreas and gastrointestinal tract as well. In general, the hypothalamic regulatory peptides (HRP) appear to act as local extracellular signals or messengers, as cells containing (producing) the HRP are found in, are adjacent to, or have restrictive vascular or possibly cerebral spinal-fluid links to cells that can respond to these peptides. Peptides with such local actions have been termed members of the paracrine rather than the endocrine system (152).

The observations indicating that these peptides are exclusively neither hypothalamic nor hypophysiotropic present problems of classification as well as nomenclature to neuroendocrinologists. In the interest of historical continuity, we continue to refer to these peptides as hypothalamic and maintain the original "releasing-factor" terminology until such time as IUPAC-IUB-approved trivial names gain acceptance. Analyses for the purpose of categorizing the HRP as hormones, neurotransmitters, or a separate class of extracellular messengers reveal the

Table 1   Sequences and principal actions of TRF, LRF, and SS on the anterior pituitary

Name	Date characterized	Sequence	Principal hypophysiotropic actions	
TRF, TRH (thyroliberine)	1968	pGlu-His-Pro-NH$_2$	TSH↑	PRL↑
LRF, LRH, GnRH (gonadoliberine)	1971	pGlu-His-Trp-Ser-Tyr-Gly-Leu-Arg-Pro-Gly-NH$_2$	LH↑	FSH↑
Somatostatin	1972	H-Ala-Gly-Cys-Lys-Asn-Phe-Phe-Trp | | Ho-Cys-Ser-Thr-Phe-Thr-Lys	GH↓	TSH↓

arbitrary nature of such distinctions. It is most important that the full spectra of activities, distributions, and physiological and pathological significances be carefully defined for each substance.

In addition to TRF, LRF, and somatostatin, we discuss some of the physiological and chemical evidences for the existence of the following putative hypothalamic adenohypophysiotropic factors: a GH releasing factor, GRF; an ACTH releasing factor, CRF; a PRL release-inhibiting factor, PIF; a PRL releasing factor, PRF; and possibly two substances that modify the secretion of MSH, an MIF (MSH release-inhibiting factor), and a MRF (MSH-releasing factor). There is also a possibility that the neurohypophyseal peptides vasopressin and oxytocin, putative neurotransmitters like dopamine, or other substances known to be present in the CNS such as prostaglandins might reach the adenohypophysis in biologically effective concentrations.

The hypothalamic hormones were reviewed last year in this series by Reichlin and colleagues (401), who extensively described many aspects of this field. We therefore do not cover in detail topics such as the mechanisms of HRP biosynthesis and the neurotransmitter regulation of hypothalamic regulatory peptides (HRP) secretion and instead discuss subjects such as the mechanism of action of the HRP and biological activities of HRP analogs. Finally, we describe several other peptides found in the hypothalamus which, in addition to their biological activities for which they were characterized, have indirect hypophysiotropic or CNS actions.

CHARACTERISTICS AND MECHANISM OF ACTION OF HYPOTHALAMIC REGULATORY PEPTIDES

The initial secretory responses by cells sensitive to the HRP are very prompt in onset and are immediately reversed when the peptides are removed from the in vivo or in vitro system. There are effective means for the rapid removal of exogenous and presumably endogenous HRP, including renal clearance and tissue or blood enzyme degradation as reflected in the short half lives of the exogenous HRP in vivo (187, 232, 398). In addition, endogenous HRP can be effectively removed by dilution by peripheral blood or extracellular fluid.

The characterized HRP, TRF, LRF, and somatostatin exert in vitro effects at concentrations ≥30–100 pM with the half-maximal responses observed from 0.5 to

2 nM (489, 495). The initial step in the mechanism of action of these peptides probably involves interaction with plasma-membrane receptors. Binding sites to TRF (149, 184, 212, 275) and LRF (189, 454) have been reported in pituitary cells and membrane fractions. Somatostatin- and TRF-binding sites have been found in brain membrane preparations (69, 351). The biological relevance of the pituitary binding sites has been supported by the good agreement between the biological activities and relative binding affinities of a large number of analogs of TRF (188, 212, 494). The greater than tenfold differences observed between the apparent HRP-receptor affinities determined from in vitro secretion experiments and the binding studies have been suggested to reflect an excess of receptors, whereby only a fraction of receptors needs to be occupied to result in a maximal secretory response, thus shifting the secretory-response curve to the left of the binding curve (418, 494).

The demonstration of binding sites of two different affinities and the observation that the presence of unlabeled TRF can alter the rate of dissociation of previously bound tritiated TRF from its receptor may be interpreted to suggest that the K_d of the TRF-receptor interaction can be lowered by occupation of other (vicinal) TRF receptors (184, 498). Such negative cooperation between hormone receptors had originally been proposed for insulin (121).

Not only might the presence of TRF alter the affinity of its own receptors, but there are reports (213, 476) that incubation of TRF-responsive cells with TRF results in a decrease in the number of TRF binding sites. Either estrogen or goitrogen treatment of rats, which increases the PRL and TSH response to TRF (127, 492, 496), has been reported to increase the number of TRF binding sites (277) without affecting receptor affinity for TRF. Thus there may be several regulatory mechanisms operative at the receptor level that serve to modulate the responses to the HRP.

The intracellular mechanisms that are proposed to transduce the initial signal generated by HRP-receptor interaction are similar to those mediating secretory responses in a variety of other endocrine and neural cells. The HRP stimulation of pituitary hormone secretion is an energy-requiring process that possibly involves changes in membrane permeability, in the distribution of calcium, and in cyclic nucleotide levels (38, 279).

Imae et al (227) demonstrated quenching of intrinsic tryptophan fluorescence of membranes of GH_3 cells following addition of TRF. These results may reflect a change in membrane conformation associated with TRF-receptor occupation. Observations that elevated medium potassium concentrations increase the secretion rate of all pituitary hormones in vitro led to the hypothesis that changes in membrane potentials or permeability characteristics might be associated with hormonal secretion (269, 425, 486, 516). Secretagogues such as cAMP derivatives (see below), high $[K^+]$, and hypothalamic extracts modify adenohypophyseal membrane potentials (17, 532). Kidokoro (259) has shown that TRF increases the rate of spontaneous depolarization of GH_3/PRL-secreting rat-tumor cells. TRF has furthermore been found to depolarize or hyperpolarize neurons in a variety of CNS regions (138, 339, 402).

The stimulated secretion of pituitary hormones is dependent on extracellular calcium (259, 315, 425, 480, 485). Furthermore, ionophores such as A23187, which increase the permeability of biological membranes to divalent cations, particularly calcium, are effective stimulators of pituitary hormone secretion (502). Several observations of pharmacological interactions of somatostatin with calcium iono- phores or elevated calcium levels on the secretion of insulin have been interpreted to suggest a direct effect of somatostatin on β-cell calcium distribution (114, 159, 467). A direct effect of several pituitary secretagogues on calcium fluxes has been found, including high-potassium or hypothalamic extracts (329, 364) and synthetic TRF (502). The TRF-mediated increase in Ca^{2+}efflux from GH_3 cells might reflect a redistribution of intracellular calcium, resulting in higher concentrations of un- bound cytoplasmic calcium, which readily equilibrates with the extracellular fluid. Therefore, an increase in calcium activity derived from extracellular and/or in- tracellular sources could play a role in the secretory process, which is consistent with the concept of stimulus-secretion coupling proposed by Douglas and colleagues for secretory processes in general (126).

Cyclic AMP and its derivatives, or agents that increase adenohypophyseal in- tracellular AMP such as prostaglandins, cholera toxin, or cyclic nucleotide phos- phodiesterase inhibitors, stimulate the secretion of pituitary hormones and often potentiate the responses to various other secretagogues including the HRP (115, 164, 203, 383a). Furthermore, direct effects of synthetic HRP on intracellular cyclic nucleotide levels have been reported. Several groups find LRF to increase intracellu- lar cyclic AMP in incubated anterior pituitary glands (35, 238). A series of LRF agonists were found to have similar potencies to release LH and to elevate AMP (242), while LRF analogs that are competitive antagonists of LRF inhibit LRF- mediated increases both in secretion of LH and in intracellular cyclic AMP levels (279).

TRF has been reported to marginally increase cAMP concentrations in incubated anterior pituitary glands (277) and GH_3 cells (115). Somatostatin, which inhibits the secretion of GH and TSH, rapidly lowers resting and stimulated cAMP levels in several in vitro pituitary preparations (37, 38, 208, 241). Paradoxically, somatostatin (SS) blocks the release of GH due to exogenous cAMP derivatives, suggesting that SS acts distally to adenyl cyclase. Among the possible explanations (278, 495) for these phenomena is that SS might inhibit both the synthesis and expression of cAMP (495). Cyclic AMP levels in brain slices have been reported to be either lowered or elevated, depending upon the region of the brain studied and the length of time of SS exposure (143, 204). Kaneko et al (241) found a concomitant increase in pituitary cGMP concentrations. It is tempting to suggest that cGMP, which has effects opposite to cAMP in some but not all tissues (177), might in part mediate the inhibition of pituitary hormone secretion. However, cGMP and its derivatives are weak stimulators of the secretion of pituitary hormones (364) and phorbol myristate acetate (PMA), a co-carcinogen that elevates the cGMP in several tissues (146), is a highly potent releaser of GH, TSH, LH, FSH, PRL, and ACTH (503 and unpub- lished results).

The initial secretory response of the anterior pituitary involves the exocytotic release of previously synthesized hormones. Inhibitors of protein and mRNA synthesis have little or no short-term effect on the amounts of pituitary hormones released by HRP, indicating that continuous de novo synthesis of the appropriate pituitary hormone or any other putative peptide or protein mediator is not required for the acute response to the HRP (41, 276, 487).

There is accumulating evidence that the HRP can influence the rates of pituitary hormone synthesis. Chronic treatment of cultured pituitary cells with TRF, LRF, or purified CRF preparation increases the total hormone (cell and fluid) levels of TSH (489), LH (276, 489), or ACTH (503). SS, on the other hand, decreases the total amount of GH and TSH in pituitary-cell cultures after prolonged exposure (490, 496) and inhibits the synthesis of insulin by cultured rat pancreas cells (163a). TRF stimulates the synthesis of PRL and inhibits GH synthesis in GH_3 cells (211, 470, 498). Several groups (18, 147, 328) have been able to demonstrate the cell-free translation of poly A–rich RNA from GH_3 cells by wheat germ of mouse ascite ribosomes into GH or PRL. Evans & Rosenfeld (147) have shown that TRF treatment of GH_3 cells increases the amount of translation product of PRL mRNA, suggesting that the TRF-induced increased rate of PRL synthesis is transcriptionally mediated.

Since other secretagogues such as cAMP derivatives (211, 276, 309, 503) or PMA (503) also increase the rate of pituitary hormone synthesis, it is unlikely that the HRP themselves act directly at the genomic level. Furthermore, the argument that hormone depletion is the only signal for an increased rate of synthesis is not supported by the observation that both intra- and extracellular levels of PRL are elevated by TRF in GH_3 cells (211, 498). Either an intracellular mediator such as cAMP or some other factor sensitive to the increase in secretory rate may be responsible for possible transcriptional changes leading to increased pituitary hormone synthesis.

LUTEINIZING HORMONE RELEASING FACTOR

Hypophysiotropic Actions

Luteinizing hormone releasing factor (LRF) was isolated from porcine and subsequently ovine hypothalamic extracts and characterized as a decapeptide pGlu-His-Trp-Ser-Tyr-Gly-Leu-Arg-Pro-Gly-NH$_2$ (68, 326). This peptide has been shown to stimulate the secretion of both LH and FSH, induce ovulation, and increase sperm counts and the production of gonadal steroids (30, 401) in a variety of species including humans. Active immunization of rabbits with LRF results in infertility and gonadal atrophy in both males and females (9, 462). Furthermore, the administration of anti-LRF serum to either normal or castrated rats lowers both LH and FSH levels, presumably by neutralizing endogenous LRF, thereby revealing a key role of the decapeptide in maintaining the secretion of both gonadotropins (10, 256, 262). Since there are clinical and experimental circumstances during which the secretion of LH and FSH can be dissociated (72, 165, 416, 455), other substances that would selectively influence one of the two gonadotropins have been proposed.

Since the characterization of LRF, some investigators have reported the evidence for a distinct hypothalamic FSH releasing factor (42, 446) while other groups have been unable to demonstrate a zone of FSH-releasing activity other than LRF (67, 435). Another possibility to explain the dissociation of LH and FSH secretion is that LRF is the sole hypothalamic stimulator of LH as well as FSH secretion and that peripheral (in particular, gonadal) factors might have differential effects on the secretion of LH and FSH. One such factor, an aqueous testicular extract, termed "inhibin" (314) has been reported to selectively block spontaneous and LRF-induced secretion of FSH, but not LH (154, 255, 302, 441). We have partially purified an enzyme from testicular extracts that rapidly degrades LRF (499). When these extracts are given with LRF in vivo or in vitro, the response to LRF is, as expected, reduced or abolished. These types of studies in the absence of proper controls could be misinterpreted as evidence for a gonadotropin release inhibiting factor.

The most likely mechanism by which dissociation of LH and FSH secretion might occur would involve differential feedback by sex steroids. This feedback represents a complex mechanism, since not only is it exerted both at the pituitary and hypo-thalamic level, but the pituitary's responsiveness to LRF varies with endocrine status (e.g. stage of the cycle and pregnancy) and the age of the animal (1, 2, 109, 141, 182, 214, 324, 325, 354, 444, 506, 518). Furthermore, exposure of intact animals or cultured pituitaries to steroids prior to LRF stimulation can either inhibit or stimulate the pituitary's responsiveness to LRF depending on the dose, route of administration, and time lapse following steroid treatments (190, 258, 325, 386, 434, 506, 511, 531). However, the nature and the ratio of various steroids influence LH and FSH responses to LRF differently (1, 244, 292, 468, 531). FSH release due to LRF appears to be more susceptible to the inhibitory effect of 17 β-estradiol than LH release, but testosterone and especially dihydrotestosterone, which is not con-verted to estrogens, exerts a stronger inhibitory action on LH. Progesterone alone inhibits stimulation of both LH and FSH in response to LRF, and the combination of progestational steroids with 17 β-estradiol suppresses the stimulation of LH more effectively than progesterone or estradiol alone (1, 386, 456, 468, 506, 531).

There is immunocytochemical evidence that the two gonadotropins can appear in the same pituitary cell and therefore might be secreted by the same cell type (206a). The experimental and clinical conditions modifying the ratio of LH to FSH secreted are in general chronic, and could reflect changes in the amounts of readily releasable LH or FSH rather than specific acute effects on the release of a particular gonadotropin.

Distribution of Luteinizing Hormone Releasing Factor

The highest concentration of radioimmunoassayable LRF in the rat hypothalamus is found in the median eminence with lower concentrations in the arcuate and ventromedial nuclei (359). Immunocytochemical studies have shown LRF in gran-ules with axon terminals in the zona externa near portal capillaries in the median eminence (178, 370). It has been proposed that the arcuate nucleus and possibly the preoptic area contain the cell bodies of these fibers, which reach the median eminence via the tubero infundibular tract (23, 338). There is, however, no general agreement on the localization of LRF in perikarya (see 537 for review). LRF has been detected in the preoptic region localized in the organum vasculosum of the lamina terminalis by immunocytochemistry (536), radioimmunoassay (239), and bioassay (522).

The existence of LRF in nerve fibers in the para-olfactory cortex, the amygdala, and other extrahypothalamic regions has also been reported (25, 217). Recent behavioral (340, 374) and electrophysiological (138, 339) studies have supported a possible direct action of LRF on the central nervous system that could modulate sexual behavior independently of sex steroid or pituitary gonadotropin status. The delivery of LRF to appropriate neural cells mediating this response could occur by either the direct projections of LRF fibers or transport through the cerebrospinal fluid.

Both bioassayable and immunoassayable LRF-like activity have been reported to be present in hypothalamo-hypophyseal portal (75, 144) as well as peripheral blood (232, 442). However, there are considerable discrepancies in the results of different investigators. The findings of Jeffcoate et al (231), de la Cruz et al (119), and Jonas et al (234) have suggested that unextracted serum of various species contains multiple immunoreactive LRF-like substances that are different from the decapeptide. The very high (>50 pg/ml) levels reported by several investigators on nonextracted plasma of various species are possibly artifactual and should be considered very cautiously (12). Using alcoholic extractions to eliminate non-LRF immunoreactive substances, two of these groups detected the decapeptide in blood. Arimura et al (11) found 1–17 pg/ml of LRF-like immunoreactivity in acid ethanol–extracted plasma of women at midcycle, while Jonas et al (234) found less than 1.2 pg of immunoreactive LRF/ml in methanol-extracted women's plasma at any stage of the cycle. Keys et al (257) could not detect LRF-immunoreactivity in methanol-extracted sheep plasma throughout the cycle using a method which could have detected as little as 12 pg/ml.

Biological Activities of LRF Analogs

LRF and other hypothalamic hypophysiotropic peptides have already been applied to the diagnosis of a number of suspected human endocrinopathies. However, the therapeutic application of these peptides is limited by factors such as short duration of action, activity when given orally, and lack of complete specificity of effects. Several laboratories have synthesized hundreds of analogs of these peptides in a search for substances that would possess useful biological properties such as higher potency, a longer duration of action, different specificity patterns, or antagonist behavior. These analogs also provide useful tools for structure/function relationship studies in which various determinants of biological activities can be investigated. The biological activity of an analog relative to the native hormone can reflect variations in distribution, metabolism, receptor affinity, or intrinsic activity (ability to generate a signal following receptor interaction). Observations of analogs that differ in one or more ways from the parent compound can contribute to an appreciation of the physiological significance of these determinants.

Analogs with modifications to each residue in LRF have been synthesized and tested in vivo and in vitro for agonist and antagonist activity (333, 412, 498, 500). These studies have provided insight into structural requirements for high potency and intrinsic activity (see below). Although a complete discussion of these studies is beyond the scope of this review, the activities of the most biologically interesting peptides will be described.

More potent LRF agonists have been obtained with the modification of three amino acids in LRF: Gly^6, Leu^7, and Gly^{10}-NH_2. We reported earlier that substitution of glycine in the sixth position of LRF by D-alanine increased in vitro LH-releasing potency fourfold, while [L-Ala^6]-LRF was only 0.01 times as potent (335). Subsequently, replacements of Gly^6 by other aliphatic and basic D-amino acids were also found to enhance activity to about the same extent. Peptides with aromatic D-amino acids in the sixth position are even more potent (108, 411, 499, 500): [D-Phe^6]-LRF or [D-Tyr^6]-LRF = 15; [D-Trp^6]-LRF = 36 in our hands. Analogs with C-terminal modifications such as des-Gly^{10}-[Pro^9-N-Et]-LRF first reported by Fujino et al (160) and des-Gly^{10}-[Pro^9-N-CH_2CF_3]-LRF (108) are four and nine times more potent than LRF. Replacement of Leu in the seventh position by N^αMe-Leu (293, 500) or several other residues such as t-But-Cys (266) have also been found to increase the potency of LRF or some of its analogs.

In many cases the potencies of analogs modified at several residues approximate the products of the potencies of the singly modified analogs. For example, des-Gly^{10}-[D-Ala^6, Pro^9-N-Et]-LRF (104, 499) is 15 times and des-Gly^{10}-[D-Trp^6, Pro^9-N-Et]-LRF is 144 times as potent as LRF in vitro in our studies (500). In contrast, Coy et al (107) reported that analogs combining D-aromatic amino acids in the sixth position and the C-terminal modification of Fujino are much less potent, with des-Gly^{10}-[D-Trp^6,Pro^9-N-Et]-LRF being considerably less active than [D-Trp^6]-LRF. The reason for the discrepancy between the results of these groups could relate to either differences in the peptide preparations or in biological testing. $N\alpha$ methylation of Leu^7 increases the potency of some LRF analogs with D-Ala^6: [D-Ala^6, N^αMe-Leu]-LRF = 7 times and des-Gly^{10}-[D-Ala^6, N^αMe-Leu^7, Pro^9-N-Et]-LRF = 30 times the potency of LRF in vitro (293, 500).

The high potencies of LRF agonists modified at the sixth, seventh, and tenth position have been related to: (a) higher receptor affinity secondary to changes in overall conformation, hydrophobicity, localized shape, or charge characteristics and (b) relative resistance of the peptide to degradation in the various biological test systems used.

While LRF is only slowly degraded by plasma or serum (232, 263), a variety of tissue extracts including testis, anterior pituitary, and brain rapidly inactivates both its biological and immunological properties (194, 263, 499, 500). Koch showed that the Gly^6-Leu^7 bond in LRF was cleaved by brain extracts (263). Marks & Stern (319) found that both the Gly^6-Leu^7 and the Pro-Gly^{10}-NH_2 peptide bonds were hydrolyzed, and furthermore that LRF analogs with D-Ala^6 and Pro^9-N-Et modifications were resistant to cleavage. The results of Marks & Stern, carried out at peptide concentrations of 250 μM, could have been due to low-K_m enzymes. We have made similar observations at much lower peptide concentrations (300 nM) and found (500) that the relative rates of destruction of the biological activity of several analogs during incubation with brain extracts were in the following order: LRF $>$ [D-Ala^6]-LRF $>$ [D-Ala^6, N$^\alpha$Me-Leu^7]-LRF $>$ des-Gly^{10}-[D-Ala^6, N$^\alpha$Me-Leu^7, Pro^9-N-Et]LRF. This latter analog, with three modifications, was completely stable during a 1-hour incubation in a brain extract. The possible participation of such enzymes in the degradation of endogenous and exogenous LRF and its analogs is suggested by the high activity of resistant peptides.

All of the more potent agonists also exhibit prolonged activity in vivo (104, 404, 500, 512). Intravenous or subcutaneous injection of peptides such as [D-Trp^6]-LRF, des-Gly^{10}-[D-Trp^6, Pro^9-N-Et]-LRF (500) or des-Gly^{10}-[D-Leu^6, Pro^9-N-Et]–LRF (512) results in greater integrated plasma gonadotropin levels than observed in response to even much higher doses of LRF. For example, the injection of 10 ng of [D-Trp^6]-LRF causes twofold higher plasma LH and FSH concentrations integrated over 5 hr than does 10 μg of LRF. Such highly potent analogs of LRF are already being applied to the treatment of human infertility (31) and additionally will be valuable in regulating animal fertility.

Some modifications involving the His^2 or Trp^3 residues in LRF have resulted in analogs with reduced intrinsic activities (as reflected in lower response maxima). The first reported (491) competitive antagonist was des-His^2-LRF, which decreased in vitro LRF-mediated LH secretory rate by 50% at a dose ratio (IDR$_{50}$) of 2000:1 (antagonist:LRF). Des-His^2-LRF, [Gly^2]-LRF, [Ala^2]-LRF, and [D-Ala^2]-LRF have $<$5, 30, 50, and $<$5% intrinsic activity, respectively (412), showing the role of the peptide backbone in its proper configuration in partially fulfilling the requirements for intrinsic activity. While a hydrophobic residue in position two, such as isoleucine, gives an analog with full intrinsic activity, but with only 0.5% of LRF's potency, aromatic amino acids such as Phe, Try, Trp, or His are required for higher potency: [Phe^2]-LRF = 4%, [Try^2]-LRF = 15, [Trp^2]-LRF = 60% (411, 494). We found [D-Ala^2]-LRF to be a low-potency antagonist (336), and subsequently Rees et al (400) reported that [D-Phe^2]-LRF was a competitive inhibitor of LRF that had a higher antagonist potency (IDR$_{50}$ = 700:1) than des-His^2-LRF.

As is the case with LRF agonists, D-amino acids in place of the original Gly^6 enhance antagonist potency: des-His^2-[D-Ala^6]-LRF, IDR$_{50}$ $\simeq$ 300:1 (335, 500). The C-terminal modification of Fujino however, does not increase the in vitro potency of antagonists (des-His^2, Gly^{10}-[Pro^9-N-Et], LRF, IDR$_{50}$ = 300:1) (279, 498). Replacement of Leu by N$^\alpha$Me-Leu^7 in some antagonists increases potency; the most potent in vitro antagonist reported thus far is [D-Phe^2, D-Trp^6, N$^\alpha$Me-Leu^7]-LRF, IDR$_{50}$ $\simeq$ 9:1 (412, 502). Therefore the antagonists' low potencies, which result from the alterations necessary to reduce intrinsic activity, can be in part compensated for by other modifications that enhance potency.

Antagonists of LRF have been found to inhibit the release of LH and FSH in vivo (10, 106, 500, 512) in response to LRF, although somewhat higher dose ratios are required. The more potent antagonists have prolonged inhibitory activity in vivo (106, 500); for example $\leq$200 μg [D-Phe^2, D-Trp^6-N$^\alpha$Me-Leu^7]-LRF blocks the response to 30 ng LRF administered 6 hr later (Vale and Rivier, unpublished results). Several LRF antagonists have been found to inhibit ovulation in experimental animals (25, 100, 117, 118, 512). Since these antagonists presumably act specifically by inhibiting the interaction of LRF with its receptors (498), these results provide additional support for a role of LRF in gonadotropin secretion and reproductive physiology. These antagonists, which bind to LRF receptors but lack the ability to initiate the events leading to stimulation of secretion, are also useful tools for the investigation of the mechanisms coupling binding with the generation of intracellular signals. In addition, the possible use of these antagonists as fertility-control agents is under investigation.

THYROTROPIN RELEASING FACTOR

Adenohypophyseal and CNS Actions of Thyrotropin Releasing Factor

Thyrotropin releasing factor (TRF) was purified from hypothalamic extracts based on its ability to stimulate the secretion of TSH in the rat and mouse. The sequence of ovine (66) and porcine (344) TRF has been determined to be pGlu-His-Pro-NH_2. The synthetic tripeptide has been shown to stimulate TSH secretion in vitro at concentrations $\geq 10^{-10} M$ and in vivo at doses from 50 to 500 ng/kg body weight in all mammalians studied, including humans (30). Subsequently TRF was found to stimulate TSH as well as PRL secretion in humans and other mammalians (see below). In addition, TRF stimulates the secretion of GH in cattle, rats under specific conditions (74, 97, 252, 406, 498), and humans with acromegaly (148) or chronic renal insufficiency (33). In the GH_3 PRL/GH-secreting cell line, TRF inhibits GH secretion under some conditions (470, 502) and stimulates GH release under others (278). High doses (≥ 100 μg/kg body weight) will inhibit morphine- or pentobarbital-stimulated GH secretion in the rat, most likely through a CNS-mediated mechanism (see below) (55, 89).

Improvement of depressive symptoms in humans by TRF, which could not be attributed to the effects of this peptide on TSH or thyroid hormone secretion, was one of the first indications that TRF might have direct CNS actions (245, 249, 390, 393). Although considerable controversy exists over these studies in humans (99, 341), Prange and co-workers and others have provided evidence that TRF does produce significant antidepressant activity in animal models independent of the pituitary-thyroid axis (249, 334, 384, 393). Other neuropharmacological studies have demonstrated TRF to reverse duration of anesthesia and hypothermia induced by barbiturates, ethanol, chloral hydrate, chlorpromazine, and diazepam (51, 52, 391, 393); to lower the LD_{50} for strychnine (55); elevate the LD_{50} for barbiturates (55); and to potentiate behavioral changes following 5-hydroxytryptamine accumulation in rats (191). TRF also potentiates the anticonvulsant activity of phenobarbital (346). Wei et al (520) demonstrated motor activity similar to that observed in the morphine-abstinence syndrome following TRF microinjection into morphine-sensitive brain areas of rats addicted to morphine. We have also recently demonstrated the onset of rapid tail vibration in morphinized rats administered TRF (54).

Abundant neuropharmacologic data recently thoroughly reviewed by Prange et al demonstrate an interaction of TRF with other CNS-acting drugs (393).

TRF alone, given intracerebroventricularly, increases spontaneous motor activity of free-moving rats (439), alters the sleep-awake pattern and rapid-eye-movement sleep in cats (260), and, given intraperitoneally, produces anorexia in rats (21). de Wied has reported inhibition of conditioned avoidance responses following TRF administration (123).

Studies in which TRF was iontophoresed into selected populations of neurons throughout the CNS resulted in an overall suppression of the rate of discharge and of single-unit activity (138, 402). TRF is released from synaptosomial structures after electrical stimulation and dopamine treatment, while 5-hydroxytryptamine (5-HT) inhibits this release (26). An interaction of TRF with brain monoamines was first suggested by the effect of TRF to potentiate DOPA in parygline-treated mice (379). Recent studies have demonstrated that TRF increases brain norepinephrine turnover (253), releases ^{3}H-norepinephrine and ^{3}H-dopamine (222) from isolated synaptosomes, and enhances disappearance of norepinephrine from nerve terminals as determined by amine fluorescence (98). Generally, no increase in brain norepinephrine, dopamine, or 5-HT content has been observed following TRF administration (393). However, TRF does increase brain dopamine following DOPA-parygline treatment. Although TRF does not alter the activity of brain tyrosine hydroxylase, it inhibits the conversion of dopamine to norepinephrine (456). A role for the dopaminergic system in the CNS action of TRF is suggested by the two following observations: 1. Cohn et al (94) reported head-to-tail rotation in rats given TRF intracerebroventricularly, a behavior pattern linked to alterations in central dopaminergic activity. 2. α-methyl-p-tyrosine has been reported to reduce the activity of TRF in the dopamine potentiation test, suggesting a dopamine-mediated mechanism.

As is the case with SS, LRF, neurotensin (NT), and substance P (SP), TRF appears to be one member of a growing list of brain oligopeptides that may be important neurotrophic or neurotransmitter substances. The degree to which these peptides are involved in cell-to-cell communication in determining metabolism, mood and behavior, or information processing remains to be determined.

Anatomic and Phylogenetic Distribution of Thyrotropin Releasing Factor

The presence of TRF in the hypothalamus has been established with chemical, biological, and immunological procedures (67, 315, 344). The greatest hypothalamic concentrations of immunoreactive TRF are found in the median eminence, followed by the medial part of the ventromedial, the paraventricular, the dorsomedial, and arcuate nuclei (63). The preoptic and septal region and all other hypothalamic nuclei had significant, although lower, concentrations of TRF. Krulich et al reported the presence of bioassayable TRF in the median eminence, dorsomedial hypothalamus, and preoptic area (272).

Immunoreactive TRF has been found throughout the extrahypothalamic brain of rats, although at much lower levels than in the hypothalamus (337, 355, 524).

However, >80% of total brain TRF is found outside of the hypothalamus by virtue of the greater mass of the extrahypothalamic regions. TRF has been reported in the hypothalamus and/or extrahypothalamic brain of several vertebrate species, including human, rat, chicken, snake, frog, salmon, lamprey, and *Amphioxus* as well as the circumesophageal organs of gastropods (197, 228).

The distribution of TRF in extrahypothalamic brain areas suggests that this peptide might play some role as a neurotropic substance independent of its effects on pituitary secretion. The presence of TRF in species lacking a pituitary gland (197) suggests that the presence and possible actions of TRF phylogenetically antedated its hypophysiotropic effects. In addition, the distribution of TRF throughout the CNS correlates well with the location of high-affinity TRF-binding sites (69) and regional distribution of TRF-degradative enzymes (195).

Immunoreactive TRF has been reported to be present in peripheral and portal blood, urine, and cerebrospinal fluid of rats and/or man and sometimes to vary under several experimental circumstances (12, 144, 230).

The measurement of TRF by radioimmunoassay techniques in peripheral blood is complicated by the presence of enzymes (397, 488) or other factors (484) that degrade TRF or that interfere in the radioimmunoassay. Methods designed to prevent inactivation and concentrate the samples have been applied. Using affinity chromatography of peripheral blood, Emerson & Utiger (142) and Montoya et al (337) estimated 7–30 pg/ml blood in the rat. Neither group found chronic thyroxine treatment (which inhibits TSH secretion) to modify blood or plasma TRF levels; Montoya et al reported cold exposure (which stimulates TSH secretion) to elevate peripheral TRF levels, while Emerson & Utiger found no effect. Eskay et al (145) extracted rat trunk blood in methanol and detected 8–11 pg/ml TRF; this level was slightly increased by cold exposure. Peptidase inhibitor–treated adult human plasma extracted by methanol or by charcoal was reported to contain ≤19 pg/ml (422) by one group and a mean of 19.8 pg/ml (356) by another. The increase in plasma TSH levels in rats following cold exposure can be prevented by prior administration of anti-TRF serum, thus supporting a role of endogenous TRF in mediating that response (459).

The validity of TRF radioimmunoassays on unextracted or on alcohol- or charcoal-extracted urine has been challenged (288, 484) on the lack of bioassay agreement, differences in labilities to serum degradation, and the demonstration that substances in urine such as urea, creatinine, and phosphate interact in the TRF radioimmunoassays. Recently Leppäluoto et al (289) described an ion-exchange method for purifying TRF from urine that shows rat urine concentrations of 2–20 pg/ml, a value severalfold lower than those reported with other extraction methods.

TRF Structure-Activity Relationships

The numerous structural analogs (450, 494, 498) of TRF have led to several conclusions. The structural requirements for high potency are stringent, as subtle changes to any amino acid in TRF usually result in considerable loss of biological potency. The abilities of most analogs to compete with ^{3}H-TRF for binding to pituitary cells can be related to their relative potencies to stimulate TSH or PRL secretion (212,

494), indicating that changes in receptor affinities determine the differences in potency. Even drastic changes to only one residue, such as its replacement by alanine, while decreasing potency to less than 1/1000 that of TRF, results in analogs with full intrinsic activity. [$^\tau$Me-His^2]-TRF is eight times more potent than TRF, while its isomer [$^\pi$Me-His^2]-TRF has <0.1% of TRF's potency. Recently Coy et al reported [β Pyrazolyl (1) Ala^2]-TRF to be 1.5 times more potent than TRF (105).

TRF has been shown (397, 488) to be rapidly degraded during incubation in serum. We have reported that a number of TRF analogs with modifications to the His^2 or Pro-NH$_2^3$ (488) positions are similarly inactivated by serum. However, several analogs such as [Pro^1]-TRF, [N-CH$_3$-pGlu^1]-TRF and [N-formyl-Pro^1]-TRF with modifications to the first amino acid are resistant to serum inactivation (500). Of these, [N-formyl-Pro^1], [$^\tau$Me-His^2]-TRF is the most active with approximately 40% TRF potency (412, 500). It is possible that the pGlu residue is involved in the binding of TRF to the "enzyme(s)" that inactivate this molecule.

Based on earlier observations that various C-terminal secondary amides of TRF had about 15% potency (494), we prepared analogs that would be suitable for coupling to other molecules with retention of biological activity. pGlu-$^\tau$Me-His-Pro-NH-(CH$_2$)$_6$-NH$_2$ with 45% potency has been tethered to dextran (500), yielding a biologically active high molecular weight complex.

Two groups (211, 406) tested the effects of TRF analogs on the secretion of PRL and tentatively concluded that the TRF receptors involved in the stimulation of TSH and PRL by TRF are similar in terms of the specificities.

Lybeck et al (304) have reported that cyclopentylcarbonyl-histidine-pyrrolidineamide (cpc-His-pyr) is an antagonist of TRF in vivo. While these observations have not been confirmed by others (451), Sievertsson et al (451) recently reported that the related compound, cpc-β-(2-thienyl)-ala-pyr, is a very low-potency antagonist of TRF requiring a dose ratio of 10,000: 1 (analog: TRF) to demonstrate partial inhibitory effects on the TRF-mediated secretion of TSH in vitro.

There may be differences, however, between the specificities of pituitary vs CNS TRF receptors, as several analogs are reported to differ in potencies in assays based on hypophysiotropic compared to neurotropic activities (392). These differences, however, have not been apparent using some neurotropic assay systems (54), although there are differences between the abilities of some analogs to compete with TRF for binding to brain compared to adenohypophyseal membrane preparations (69).

PROLACTIN RELEASE INHIBITING FACTOR

The concept that PRL secretion is mainly under inhibitory control evolved from studies showing that hypothalamic lesions, stalk section, and transplantation of the pituitary outside the sella turcica result in increased PRL secretion, and that pituitary cells maintained in culture release large amounts of PRL (8, 243, 273, 311).

Of all the substances exhibiting prolactin release inhibiting factor (PIF) activity, dopamine, and other dopaminergic agonists (apomorphine, ergot derivatives) are the most effective inhibitors of PRL secretion in vivo and in vitro. Dopamine antagonists such as haloperidol, pimozide, and perphenazine have no effect on in vitro pituitary cells when given alone, but will reverse the inhibition of PRL secretion due to dopamine agonists. Observations that dopamine antagonists are potent stimulators of PRL secretion have been interpreted to suggest reversal of the effects of dopamine either reaching the pituitary via the portal blood or at the hypothalamic level, resulting in a decrease in the delivery of a PIF to the pituitary. The question of whether dopamine has a physiological regulatory function at the pituitary level as a PIF has not been resolved (92, 96, 124, 161, 280, 281, 310, 312, 313, 334, 352, 443, 452, 502).

In addition, several other known substances are reported to inhibit the secretion of PRL in vitro. Cholinergic agents such as carbachol, acetylcholine, or oxitremorine also inhibit the release of PRL both in vitro (502) and in vivo (183, 291, 316, 457). The in vitro inhibition induced by carbachol is reversed by very low concentrations of atropine and much higher levels of D-tubocurarine, indicating that the cholinergic receptors involved in this response are probably of a muscarinic type (502).

Recently, γ-amino butyric acid (GABA) has been reported to inhibit PRL secretion in vitro (437); we find, however, no effect of GABA on PRL secretion by cultured pituitary cells in vitro (408). GABA, administered intraventricularly, by itself slightly stimulates PRL secretion (331, 408), but inhibits the PRL release due to morphine (408). When given intravenously, GABA inhibits the secretion of PRL induced by a variety of substances including morphine (408). Somatostatin has a slight inhibitory effect on PRL secretion in some in vitro systems, but has generally little effect on PRL levels in vivo (see below). Finally, La Bella et al have found some metallic ions, nickel, zinc, copper, and others, to inhibit PRL secretion in vitro (274). Thus there are a variety of known substances that may be present in brain extracts and that could contribute to any observed PRL release inhibiting activity.

Hypothalamic (133, 193, 265, 431, 460, 478) and extrahypothalamic (497) brain extracts inhibit the secretion of PRL in a variety of in vitro and in vivo assay systems. Some investigators have reported that all the PRL release inhibiting activity of their purified PIF preparations was related to the presence of catecholamines (460), but others have provided physicochemical evidence in various chromatography systems that there is a PIF activity distinguishable from that attributed to catecholamines (193). It has also been demonstrated that various extracts inhibit PRL secretion in the presence of dopaminergic antagonists, whereas, as mentioned above, dopamine-induced inhibition of PRL is blocked by these antagonists (394, 497, 502). PIF also appears to be distinct from SS (193, 502), since the content of SS in hypothalamic or cortical extracts as assessed by biological and immunological assays is not sufficient for inhibition of PRL secretion and the dose-response curves to SS and brain extracts differ. The existence of a brain peptide with PRL release inhibiting activity is favored by experiments showing that proteolytic enzyme digestion of some partially purified PIF preparations results in loss of biological activity (193, 502).

PROLACTIN RELEASING FACTOR

Several physiological and experimental circumstances are associated with rapid elevations in plasma prolactin releasing factors (PRL) levels (311). Since the pituitary spontaneously secretes PRL at a high rate following removal of hypothalamic inputs, these responses may reflect the inhibition of endogenous PIF release. Alternatively, the release of PRL under some conditions may be in part mediated by a PRL releasing factor.

TRF is a potent stimulator of PRL secretion in most mammalians including humans (116, 150, 207, 230, 254, 395). While having only minor effects on PRL release by the normal rat pituitary in vivo and in vitro (209, 298, 406, 492), TRF consistently releases PRL from rat GH_3 tumor cells (470) or pituitary cells from hypothyroid rats in culture (492), lactating and pregnant or diestrus female rats (32), and estrogen-pretreated male rats (342, 406).

Several groups have reported that hypothalamic extracts can stimulate PRL secretion in some assay systems (91, 133, 265, 268, 330, 406, 469, 475). Because TRF is a known releaser of PRL in most mammalian species, the possibility of TRF being wholly or partially responsible for this PRL releasing activity has been examined by several experimental approaches.

Several in vivo studies have demonstrated that estrogens not only stimulate PRL secretion per se (2), but can allow TRF to exhibit PRL releasing activity in male rats (406). Using such a preparation, the relative PRL and TSH releasing potencies of structural TRF analogs are comparable (406), indicating that the functional TRF receptors in the two cell types are similar. In vitro experiments have also indicated that the TRF receptors characterized by competitive binding of ^3H-TRF to PRL/GH-secreting GH_3 cells are closely related to those on TSH-secreting tumor cells (188, 212), in that similar specificities and dissociation constants for TRF on the two cell types were observed (494).

Crude methanol or acid hypothalamic extracts release PRL in male rats (8, 209, 406). Some investigators have observed this releasing activity also to be dependent upon steroid pretreatment of the test animal (209, 406), whereas others found hypothalamic extracts to release PRL as effectively in normal male rats (120, 330, 342). We have reported (406) that there is sufficient TSH releasing activity (although not necessarily all due to TRF) to account for the PRL releasing activity of pig and rat hypothalamic fragments extracted by one method (2N HOAc followed by methanol-2N HOAc, 9:1, and defatting with ether-hexane). Other workers have reported the presence of more PRL releasing activity in hypothalamic extracts than could be explained by the TRF content and further that the chromatographic behavior and liability to plasma inactivation of the PRL releasing activity differed from that of TRF (156). The basis for the above discrepancies probably lies in the differences between extraction procedures as well as the methods used to quantitate PRL- and TSH-releasing activities (24, 229, 406).

It is now known that a variety of identified substances present in hypothalamic extracts such as biogenic amines and peptides in addition to TRF (see below) can modify PRL secretion by acting indirectly initially through extrapituitary mechanisms. In addition, we have found (337) that hypothalamic fragments contain a lipoidal substance (209) soluble in both 90% methanol and hexane that is a powerful stimulator of PRL and GH secretion in non-pretreated male rats in vivo. Any claim for the existance of a peptidic PRL releasing factor other than TRF must be substantiated by the appropriate chemical evidence as well as by the demonstration that this substance acts directly at the level of the anterior pituitary gland.

PRL and TSH secretions in the rat are dissociated in a variety of physiological circumstances, such as stress, nursing, etc (32, 311, 343). Since dopaminergic agonists have been shown to lower or prevent the TRF-induced secretion of PRL without affecting the TSH secretion (87, 209, 210, 349) and since SS inhibits the secretion of TSH while having little influence on PRL secretion (496), no conclusion as to an identity of PRF and TRF can be derived from noncoincident PRL and TSH secretion rates.

Several amines also have stimulatory effects on PRL secretion in vivo but not in vitro, suggesting CNS sites of action. α-Adrenergic agonists such as phenylephrine and clonidine elevate plasma PRL, effects that are prevented by the α-adrenergic antagonists phentolamine and dibenzyline (281, 407). Dopaminergic pathways may also be involved in the rise in plasma PRL levels observed after administration of clonidine, since activation of noradrenergic receptors by this agent has been reported to decrease the activity of the tubero infundibular dopaminergic system (334). There is also evidence for the involvement of serotonergic mechanisms in control of prolactin secretion (267, 281, 299) as both serotonergic agonists and antagonists release PRL in vivo. Administration of histamine results in a rapid increase in plasma PRL levels, which is abolished by concomitant injection of the H_1-histamine receptor blocker diphenhydramine (Rivier, Brown, and Vale, unpublished results).

A variety of peptides found in the pituitary or hypothalamus also influence in vivo but not in vitro PRL secretion. The hypotensive peptides neurotensin (NT) and substance P (SP) are potent releasers of PRL in vivo (407). Since changes in blood pressure have been reported to alter the secretion of pituitary hormones (294), the possibility exists that the influence of NT and SP on PRL secretion is exerted through such a mechanism. This hypothesis, however, seems improbable since another vasoactive peptide, bradykinin, does not release PRL in vivo (Rivier, Brown, and Vale, unpublished results). The fact that NT-induced stimulation of PRL secretion is partially reversed by diphenhydramine suggests the possibility that histamine pathways are involved in the modulation of PRL secretion by NT as well as in its action on blood pressure, and insulin and glucagon secretion (see below). Naloxone does not interact with NT or SP, indicating that their effects are probably not mediated through activation of opiate receptors. A dramatic release of PRL in vivo is observed after injection of morphine (313, 353) an effect blocked by the opiate antagonist naloxone (407). α- and β-MSH and, to a lesser degree, $ACTH_{1-39}$, $ACTH_{4-10}$, and $ACTH_{18-39}$ also interfere with the PRL-releasing effect of morphine (407), while not affecting the response to TRF. It is of interest that the opiate-like peptides (see below) related to the C-terminal region of β-LPH also have a morphinomimetic effect on the secretion of PRL in vivo following intracerebroventricular injection (413a).

SOMATOSTATIN

The tetradecapeptide somatostatin (SS) was isolated (49) from hypothalamic extracts by following the peptide's ability to inhibit the spontaneous release of GH from enzymatically dispersed rat anterior pituitary cells in vitro (490). SS was found also to inhibit the in vitro secretion of GH mediated by a number of secretagogues such as cAMP derivatives, prostaglandins, theophylline, and hypothalamic extracts (with GH-releasing activity) (490, 495).

With the availability of synthetic material, numerous reports have confirmed this inhibitory action on GH secretion in vitro and in vivo in several species [for review see (495)].

In some species including dogs, rats, sheep, baboons, and humans, SS inhibits elevations of plasma GH induced by L-dopa (296), arginine (65, 338, 373, 447), insulin (201, 373), exercise (202), sleep (360), suckling (86), protein-calorie malnutrition (376), meals (29, 171), chlorpromazine (250, 251, 427), morphine, NT, SP (50, 54, 322, 407), pentobarbital (49, 54), prostaglandin E_2 (54, 458), hypothalamic extracts (458), electrical stimulation (321), and catecholamines (251, 417). In man and animals, inhibition of GH secretion by SS is followed by a postinhibitory rebound (201, 296, 321, 417). That this rebound does not occur in animals with lesions of the hypothalamic ventromedial nucleus suggests that this increase in GH may be dependent on some hypothalamic influence, possibly a GRF (323).

Although SS does have a direct pituitary effect on the inhibition of GH, an additional brain site of action cannot be excluded (53). It has recently been demonstrated that while TRF does not inhibit the spontaneous secretion of GH in vitro, it reverses the stimulatory effect of morphine or pentobarbital in vivo under a variety of circumstances (54, 89, 95). Since SS does have a wide CNS distribution (discussed below) and affects several behavioral parameters (discussed below), this peptide might also alter GH secretion via some suprapituitary mechanism.

SS lowers plasma GH levels in acromegaly (28, 29, 176, 338, 373, 530). Acromegaly may arise from hypothalamic SS insufficiency leading to prolonged unopposed secretion of GH and adenoma formation (28), although at present there is no supporting evidence for this hypothesis. Also lacking direct supporting evidence is the suggestion that the elevated levels of GH in Huntington's chorea may be secondary to decreased brain SS content (287). The release of GH by TRF and LRF in acromegaly is the only stimulus not inhibited by SS (175). A role for the use of SS in treatment of acromegaly has been preempted by ergot alkaloids, which are more effective and may be administered orally and less frequently.

Sustained inhibition of GH secretion for extended periods of time to assess the effects on growth or microangiopathy of diabetes mellitus has thus far been impossible due to the rapid plasma half-time of SS. Although early reports suggested the existence of analogs of SS with extended durations of action, these observations were probably artifacts of the bioassay systems used (53).

The physiological importance of SS as a regulator of GH secretion has recently been demonstrated in passive immunization studies. Administration of anti-SS to rats increases basal GH levels and prevents the inhibition of GH secretion following stress (16, 151, 473).

SS affects the secretion of other pituitary hormones as well. Results of acute and chronic administration of SS to cultured rat pituitary cells indicate that it inhibits both the synthesis and the release of TSH (496). In humans, SS lowers basal TSH secretion during the onset of REM sleep (519) and in hypothyroid patients (300). SS also decreases in vitro PRL secretion in some systems (496) and lowers PRL levels in some but not all acromegalic subjects (530).

TRF-induced secretion of TSH is blocked by SS in a dose-related manner, while PRL secretion is unaffected (496). This phenomenon, which has been observed in man and experimental animals (76, 127, 448, 483, 496), is rapid in onset and rapidly reversed. Studies of the kinetics of this inhibition indicate that it does not result from a competition between SS and TRF for binding to cellular TRF receptors; furthermore, SS interferes with other stimuli of TSH secretion such as high potassium and theophylline (496).

Thyroid hormones act at the pituitary level to inhibit the secretion of TSH due to TRF and other stimuli. Unlike SS, thyroid hormones have a long latent period, but a prolonged period of action and can be blocked by inhibitors of protein synthesis. Since SS and thyroid hormones act in concert to inhibit TSH secretion in vitro and in vivo (496), we proposed that the secretion of TSH is under acute positive control by TRF, whereas its negative control is exerted chronically by thyroid hormones and acutely by SS. All three elements modulate TSH secretion in a concentration- and time-dependent manner (496). In addition, sex steroids might also play a role, as the TSH response to TRF is diminished by castration and enhanced by estrogen or estrogen-plus-progesterone administration (496). Drouin et al subsequently reported antagonism of the thyroid hormone inhibition of TSH release by estrogen administration (127).

A physiologic inhibitory role of SS in the regulation of TSH has been supported by passive-immunization studies showing that administration of anti-SS serum to rats enhances the release of TSH due to cold (15, 151) or exogenous TRF, and inhibits the ether-stress–induced fall in TSH secretion (16).

Both hypothalamic and extrahypothalamic brain extracts have been shown to inhibit TRF-mediated TSH secretion in vitro in a manner parallel to that caused by SS (495). Whether all of the TSH release inhibiting activity in these extracts is due to SS has not been determined.

Pancreas and Gut Actions

Since the observations of Ruch et al (417) and Koerker et al (264) and those of Yen et al (529) and Mortimer et al (338) that SS administration lowered plasma insulin and glucagon levels in baboons and humans, numerous in vitro and in vivo studies have confirmed these results. In vitro SS inhibits the basal secretion of insulin and glucagon (157, 233, 477), as well as the rise of insulin and glucagon stimulated by arginine (217, 233), theophylline (158, 172, 477), and isoproterenol (172), increases of insulin stimulated by glucose (112, 157, 158, 477), glucagon (449), calcium (113, 158), tolbutamide (158), cytochalasin B (158), and dibutyryl cAMP, and increase of glucagon stimulated by epinephrine (477, 521) from isolated islets, enzymatically dispersed cultured neonatal rat pancreatic cells, or the perfused rat pancreas.

In humans (5, 122, 166, 169, 338, 373, 517), baboons (88, 264), dogs (423), and rats (58) SS inhibits the basal secretion of insulin and glucagon. In some of these species SS also inhibits the secretion of insulin induced by meals (30), i.v. or oral glucose (29, 60, 88, 139, 166, 284, 445), arginine (60, 167, 373), glucagon (168, 423), gastric inhibitory polypeptide (368), secretin (88), tolbutamide (88, 168), and iso-proterenol (88), and prevents the secretion of glucagon stimulated by meals (125, 166, 171), arginine (60, 88, 167), insulin-induced hypoglycemia (88), epinephrine, and insulin deprivation (174). SS differs from all other known pancreatic se-cretagogues in that it inhibits the secretion of insulin and glucagon induced by virtually all known stimuli for each respective hormone release (173). The physi-ologic significance of this dual action of SS on inhibition of both insulin and gluca-gon remains to be determined. The distribution of SS anatomically between the α and β cells of the islets strongly suggests that this peptide may indeed somehow be involved in physiologic control of insulin and glucagon secretion (see below). SS may act as a transmitter of information from D cells to α or β cells (i.e. paracrine action) in the pancreatic islets.

Use of SS in the study and experimental treatment of diabetes mellitus has been instrumental in defining the possibly important role of glucagon as a diabetogenic hormone in insulinopenic circumstances (71, 125, 166, 170, 181, 199, 424, 481). SS decreases fasting and postprandial hyperglycemia in juvenile-type diabetes up to 50% in the absence of insulin (166, 170, 199). The mechanism for this reduction of plasma glucose is suggested to be by lowering plasma glucagon concentrations, which are inappropriately elevated for the level of plasma glucose in most juvenile-type diabetics (125, 166, 170, 199, 424, 481). SS in combination with small doses of insulin may be advantageous over insulin alone in treatment of insulin-dependent diabetics (199). SS also prevents the development of diabetic ketoacidosis after the acute withdrawal of insulin from patients with insulin-dependent diabetes mellitus (170). However, the use of SS in combination with insulin in treatment of manifest diabetic ketoacidosis offers no advantage over insulin alone (303). Recently some controversy has arisen over the importance of hyperglucagonemia in the controlled insulin-dependent diabetic (445). The SS-induced improvement of glucose tolerance following a standard diabetic meal may not be secondary to a reduction of glucagon secretion and reduced hepatic glucose production, but instead may be related to decreased gastrointestinal absorption of glucose (515). This possibility is based on the observations of Wahren & Felig, who have shown SS to reduce splanchnic blood flow by as much as 40%.

Gut actions of SS are not surprising, since SS-like activity is present in discrete cells of the gastrointestinal tract (see below). SS has been reported to inhibit gastrin secretion both in vitro (205) and in vivo (33) and to inhibit the secretion of the following substances in vivo: gastric acid (22, 180), secretin (34), pepsin (180), gastric inhibitory polypeptide (368), vasoactive intestinal polypeptide (30), and motilin (30). SS also stimulates and inhibits pancreatic exocrine secretion at low and high doses, respectively (414). At low doses SS acts as a partial agonist and at higher doses as an antagonist of pancreatic exocrine secretion induced by secretin.

SS has been used successfully in short-term studies to inhibit the secretion of a gastrinoma (33), an insulinoma (90, 295), a pancreatic islet-cell carcinoma producing insulin and gastrin (110), and a vasoactive intestinal polypeptide–secreting tumor (S.R. Bloom, personal communication). SS may be of use in the diagnosis of insulinomas, since it does not inhibit the secretion of insulin induced by tolbutamide in patients with this tumor but does inhibit tolbutamide-induced insulin secretion in normal individuals (295).

SS has been reported to elevate plasma cortisol in cats after intracerebroventricular infusion (332). There are no reports of SS increasing ACTH or adrenal steroid production when given by any other route. Moreover, SS inhibits the secretion of ACTH in Nelson's syndrome (479).

Neurotropic Actions of Somatostatin

The wide distribution of SS throughout the brain and spinal cord supports its possible role as a neurotropic substance. The first evidence that SS might have some neurotropic action was the observation of a tranquilizing effect of large doses of peptide administered to monkeys (529). Subsequently Segal & Mandell demonstrated that intracerebroventricular injection of SS into rats resulted in a decrease in spontaneous motor activity (439). SS has also been demonstrated to decrease the LD_{50} and lengthen the anesthesia time of barbiturates (55, 391), increase the LD_{50} of strychnine (55), induce "barrel rotation," sedation and hypothermia (94a), potentiate the L-dopa paragyline test (381), reduce slow wave sleep (403), abolish REM sleep (403), and increase appetite (403). The induction of barrel rotation was reversed by pretreatment of animals with atropine (93), thus suggesting the involvement of cholinergic mechanisms in this behavioral activity.

SS has been demonstrated to increase brain levels of cAMP both in vivo and in vitro (143, 204). Havlicek et al (204) recently reported an increase in brain cAMP in animals exhibiting "barrel rotation" following intracerebroventricular somatostatin administration. Pretreatment of these animals with a β-adrenergic blocking drug prevented the SS associated rise in cAMP but did not prevent the onset of barrel rotation, suggesting that the changes in cyclic nucleotide concentration were not related to the behavioral activity. Renaud recently reported a decrease in the spontaneous firing of neurons in the hypothalamus, brain stem, cerebellum, and cerebral cortex after iontophoresis of SS (402).

Distribution of Somatostatin

SS-like activity (SLA) has been identified by several immunological and biological assay methods to be distributed in the central nervous system, gastrointestinal tract, and pancreas. Although the chromatographic and solubility (14, 501) characteristics of the SLA in crude extracts of tissues differ from that of SS, the close agreement between radioimmunoassays using three different antisera (each recognizing different parts of the SS molecule) and a bioassay suggests considerable homology between the molecules responsible for SLA and SS (501). The bulk of the biological and immunological SLA in tissues may well be due to a larger form of SS. Whether this would be a pro-SS or a physiologic form of SS remains to be determined. SS was isolated and characterized from ovine (48), and subsequently porcine (436), hypothalamic extracts, leaving little doubt that at least some portion of hypothalamic SLA is due to the tetradecapeptide. However, since the fraction of the ovine hypothalamic extract purified contained less than 1% of the total SLA in the starting material, the possibility of other forms of SS was raised in our early reports (48, 495). Recently we obtained immunological evidence for an N-terminally extended big SS in one side fraction of these extracts (501).

Both biological (271, 497) and immunological techniques (3, 12, 64, 128, 215, 369) have shown the SLA to be concentrated in the median eminence. Using electronmicroscopic immunological methods, Pelletier (370) and Dubois (130) reported granules in numerous nerve endings on portal capillaries in the zona externa of the rat suggestive of a neurosecretory mechanism for the delivery of this peptide to the adenohypophysis.

Other hypothalamic regions that have relatively high immunoreactive SS concentrations are the arcuate, ventromedial, ventral premammilary, periventricular, and medial preoptic nuclei (3, 64, 371). Of these, only the ventromedial was devoid of SLA biological activity (495), possibly due to the presence of GRF in that area (271).

SS-like activity was first identified in the extrahypothalamic brain by bioassay (495, 497); this observation was confirmed by radioimmunoassay. Over ten times more SLA is found in the extrahypothalamic brain than in the hypothalamus (64, 501, Table 2). SLA is distributed generally throughout the CNS, with high concentrations found in the preoptic region, amygdala, and circumventricular organs (4, 64, 128, 260a, 371, Table 3). Consistent with this finding of SS in circumventricular organs we can detect significant amounts of SLA in the CSF of rats (501), and Patel et al (362) reported SLA in the spinal fluid of human subjects. SLA has also been found in the spinal cord (495). Hokfelt et al (216) identified SLA by immunocytochemistry in the substantia gelatinosa of the dorsal horn and in the adjacent parts of the lateral funiculus as well as a few spinal ganglion cell bodies.

SS-like activity has been demonstrated in the pancreas by immunocytochemistry (129, 131, 215, 301), radioimmunoassay (14, 363, 501), and bioassay (501, 502).

Table 2 Phylogenetic and anatomic distribution of immunoreactive somatostatin (IRSS)

	N	ng IRSS/mg wt wt tissue (ng IRRS/organ)			
		Brain	Hypothalalamus	Pancreas	GI
Rat	6	0.38 ng SS/mg (609) ng SS/org	2.49 (49)	0.34 (205)	0.33 (2815)
Pigeon	4	1.6 (2486)	2.18 (50)	49.5 (48,474)	0.40 (7338)
Frog	4	1.3 (226)	— —	18.6 (2164)	0.70 (4961)
Catfish	4	0.2 (117)	— —	44.8 (3519)	0.084 (2133)
Hagfish	3	0.92 (48)	— —	1.22 (16)	<0.02 —

Table 3 Brain distribution of neurotensin- and somatostatin-like activities[a]

Tissue	Neurotensin ng/mg protein	Somatostatin ng/mg protein
Pineal	<0.02	0.3 ± 0.1
Cervical cord	0.14 ± 0.07	2.4 ± 0.2
Medulla	0.18 ± 0.07	2.4 ± 0.3
Olfactory tubercle	0.07 ± 0.04	0.5 ± 0.1
N. accumbens	1.37 ± 0.26	2.4 ± 0.5
Septal area	0.66 ± 0.09	1.9 ± 0.5
Caudate-putamen	0.03 ± 0.01	0.6 ± 0.2
Preoptic area	1.69 ± 0.42	4.3 ± 1.0
Cingulate cortex	<0.02	0.7 ± 0.2
Anterior hypothalamus	0.36 ± 0.15	2.7 ± 0.5
Medial basal hypothalamus	0.91 ± 0.12	73.1 ± 26.6
Posterior	0.33 ± 0.16	2.5 ± 0.4
Thalamus	0.08 ± 0.04	0.5 ± 0.1
Dorsal hippocampus	<0.02	0.5 ± 0.1
Amygdala	0.65 ± 0.06	3.7 ± 0.4
Central grey mesencephalon	0.74 ± 0.08	1.4 ± 0.3
Substantia nigra	0.29 ± 0.09	0.3 ± 0.1
Interpenduncular N.	0.85 ± 0.14	0.4 ± 0.1
Entorhinal cortex	0.05 ± 0.02	1.6 ± 0.3
Midbrain	0.14 ± 0.08	1.2 ± 0.3
Pons	0.09 ± 0.05	0.9 ± 0.2
Cerebellum	<0.02	0.4 ± 0.1

[a] Data from M. Brown, R. Kobayashi, and W. Vale (56).

Subsequent to the initial report of Dubois, several groups (179, 215, 357, 372, 385) localized SLA in a cell type whose function had previously been unknown, the D cell. In view of the close association of the D cells with the A_2 (glucagon-secreting) and B (insulin-secreting) cells and of the effects of SS on the secretion of insulin and glucagon, a possible physiological role of somatostatin in the regulation of glucagon and/or insulin has been suggested (129, 495). Consistently there are reported changes in SLA concentrations in the rat endocrine pancreas in experimental diabetes mellitus (357). Prior to the discovery of SS, Hellman & Lernmark demonstrated inhibition of insulin secretion by an extract of D cells (206) from pigeon pancreas.

The gastrointestinal tract also contains substantial SLA (14, 501, Table 2, 363). Arimura reported that highest concentrations are found in the fundus and pyloric antrum of the stomach with detectable amounts in the duodenum and jejunum. SLA has been identified in nerve fibers as well as other cells similar to D cells throughout the gastrointestinal mucosa usually in the midzone of the glands but occasionally in the basal region or tips of the villi (215, 385). It is possible that such SS-containing cells exert localized effects on the function of a variety of gastrointestinal secretory contractable cells.

SLA has been found in a variety of vertebrate species (130, Table 2, 501). Using immunocytochemical procedures, Dubois found SLA in the median eminence of several mammalians, a bird, amphibian, and a teleost fish (130). In the trout, fibers containing SLA were observed to directly innervate the adenohypophysis, suggesting a direct neural control of adenohypophyseal hormone secretion in that species (130). We have found SLA immunological activity in the brain and pancreas of the rat, pigeon, frog, catfish, torpedo (elasmobranch), and hagfish (501). SLA was detectable in the gastrointestinal tract of all of the above species except for the hagfish. In the mammalians, highest concentrations of SLA occur in the hypothalamus (2.5 ng/mg); the greatest total amounts of SLA are found in the gastrointestinal tract. By contrast with mammalians the highest concentrations of SLA in all of the lower species are found in the pancreas with the pigeon and the catfish having pancreatic concentrations of approximately 50 and 45 ng SLA/mg respectively. These concentrations are consistent with the high numbers of D cells in the pancreas of these species (415).

In summary, SS or closely related substances are ancient molecules whose anatomic distribution is as widespread as their actions.

Biological Activities of Somatostatin Analogs

Analogs of SS have been synthesized and biologically tested for effects on the secretion of pituitary GH and TSH, pancreatic glucagon, and insulin and gastric acid as well as several behavior parameters. In addition to the goals outlined in the section on LRF analogs, peptides with different spectra of biological activities are particularly sought (see below).

SS was characterized in 1972 (48) as the tetradecapeptide

H-Ala-Gly-Cys-Lys-Asn-Phe-Phe-Trp-Lys-Thr-Phe-Thr-Ser-Cys-OH .

    1   2   3   4   5   6   7   8   9   10   11   12   13   14

The native hormone was isolated in the oxidized or cyclized form; however, synthetic reduced or oxidized SS has the same activities in a variety of biological assays (495). Based on the low (but distinct) potencies of a variety of SS analogs which are unable to form a covalent bond between the residues in positions 3 and 14 such as [S-Me-Cys^{3,14}]-SS or [Ala^{3,14}]-SS, we suggested that the linear reduced form of SS is oxidized under the conditions of the bioassays (409, 490, 500). Our stated reservation (493) that the low potencies of the noncyclizable analogs might reflect a requirement for either of the Cys residues independent of their contribution to the secondary structure of the molecule has been satisfied by the observation of Veber and colleagues (509), who found that non-Cys containing SS analogs with carbon-carbon bonds between residues 3 and 14 had high biological activity. The observation that [S-Me-Cys^{3,4}]-SS has 4% potency and full intrinsic activity suggests that intramolecular associations other than the disulfide bond maintain the molecule in a conformation recognizable by SS receptors (409, 493). In contrast to somatostatin itself, the reduced forms of several analogs have much lower biological activities than their corresponding oxidized forms, reflecting perhaps the role of other residues in determining the formation of the disulfide bond (412, 500).

Several series of analogs have been synthesized and tested; these involve: 1. progressive shortening or extending of the peptide from the N or C terminal; 2. systematic deletion of single residues; 3. replacement of residues by alanine; 4. replacement of each residue by its corresponding D–amino acid; 5. replacement of residues by other amino acids. Interpretation of the activities of these series has allowed a nascent appreciation of the role of the backbone and its configuration and the various functional groups in determining biological activity.

SS analogs which involve deletion or modification of the Ala^1-Gly^2 side chain have high potency (409). Thus [Tyr^1]-SS was synthesized for the purpose of obtaining an iodinatable molecule which could be used as a tracer in radioimmunoassays and have high activity for radio-receptor studies (413, 493). Indeed, [^{125}I-Tyr^1]-SS has been used in several radioimmunoassays (13, 362, 501) and has been shown to exhibit specific binding to membrane fractions of the rat brain (L. H. Lazarus and W. Vale, unpublished results). The high activity of N- or C-terminally extended SS analogs [$(Gly)_3$-Ala^1]-SS = 100%; [Cys^{14}-NH_2]-SS = 50% are consistent with the possibility that the higher molecular weight substances with somatostatin-like biological and immunological activity could be either C- or N-terminally extended SS (501).

The series in which alanine replaces single residues in somatostatin is particularly useful in giving an appreciation of the role of various functional groups in the presence of an intact backbone (60, 412, 495). The following residues can be replaced by alanine with retention of > 50% SS potency, Lys^4, Asn^5, Thr^{10}, Thr^{12}, Ser^{13}, suggesting that the associated functional groups of those residues do not contribute significantly to high potency or intrinsic activity.

In contrast, replacement of Phe^6, Phe^7, Trp^8, Lys^9, or Phe^{11} by alanine reduces potency to less than 4%. None of these analogs is completely inactive nor are they antagonists. At high doses they behave as full agonists but with low receptor affinity. Whether the altered affinities of the analogs are secondary to differences between their conformations and that of SS or whether they reflect the involvement of the particular functional groups in receptor binding has not been determined.

Tyrosine can replace either Phe^7 or Phe^{11} but not Phe^6 with retention of full potency (413). We have suggested that Phe^6 might play a different role in SS from Phe^7 or Phe^{11} in that the former could be involved in receptor binding whereas the other two phenylalanines, in agreement with the model of Puett & Holladay (221), might contribute to the building of a hydrophobic region through the stacking of their aromatic rings (412).

Analogs involving modifications to Trp^8 in SS have low potency, including [Ala^8]-SS and [Gly^8]-SS except for [D-Trp^8]-SS, which is eight times more potent than SS on inhibition of GH, insulin, and glucagon (60, 410, 500). Analogs with D–amino acids other than Trp at the eighth position such as [D-Tyr^8]-SS or [D-Ala^8]-SS have low potency (412). The high potency of [D-Trp^8]-SS might reflect the stabilization of a turn in that region of the molecule, as suggested by the results of Puett & Holladay (221), or could result from a greater resistance of this peptide to degradation in biological assays. Marks & Stern reported that brain extracts degrade high concentrations of somatostatin by cleavages between residues Phe^6-Phe^7, Trp^8-Lys^9, and Thr^{10}-Phe^{11} (320). However, [D-Trp^8]-SS is also more potent in vitro under assay conditions where we have found complete recovery of exogenous somatostatin. Furthermore, this peptide does not exhibit prolonged activity in vivo, thus suggesting that its enhanced biological activity is secondary to factors other than resistance to enzymic degradation.

The receptor requirements for Lys^9 in SS are also quite stringent since other basic amino acids such as Arg or Orn cannot substitute for Lys^9 with maintenance of high potency (412).

In summary, high biological potency is related to strict requirements for Phe^6, Trp^8, and Lys^9 while other aromatic groups can replace Phe^7 and Phe^{11}. The remaining amino acids contribute primarily to the integrity of the ring, an important role as exemplified by the less than 15% potency to inhibit GH secretion of all analogs involving deletion of an amino acid in the SS ring (412).

As discussed above, SS inhibits the secretion of growth hormone, insulin, glucagon, and several gastrointestinal hormones. Current clinical interest in the use of SS to inhibit glucagon secretion in human diabetes mellitus has prompted us to search for analogs of SS with monospecific activities on inhibition of selected hormones. Most of the analogs of SS have similar potencies to inhibit growth hormone, insulin, and glucagon (60, 410, 500). However, des-Asn^5-SS was reported by Sarantakis et al (426) to inhibit the secretion of insulin and not of glucagon. We have confirmed this observation and have prepared des-Asn^5-[D-Trp^8]-SS which has greater potency while still retaining the dissociated activity (57, 59). Des-Asn^5-[D-Trp^8]-SS has 60, < 1 and 12% of SS's potency to inhibit insulin, glucagon, and growth hormone (57, 59). Administration of des-Asn^5-SS to rats also produces a prompt rise in plasma glucose. This hyperglycemia is preceded temporally by a lowering of plasma insulin and elevation of plasma glucagon (57, 59). Subsequently we have found [D-Cys^3]-SS and [D-Ser^{13}]-SS to also selectively inhibit the secretion of insulin (59). Of greater potential clinical significance has been our finding that [D-Cys^{14}]-SS has a higher glucagon- than insulin-inhibiting potency (59). Relative to SS, [D-Cys^{14}]-SS has 240, 10, and 100% potency to block GH, insulin, and glucagon secretion. These results suggest that there are exploitable differences between the somatostatin receptors of the three cell types involved, regarding their structural requirements for ligand recognition.

GROWTH HORMONE RELEASING FACTOR

The existence of growth hormone releasing factor (GRF) is supported by the following observations: 1. Interruption of hypothalamic-pituitary continuity results in a decrease in GH secretion (323). If somatostatin was the sole regulator of GH secretion one would expect a rise in GH under these circumstances. 2. Stimulation of certain brain areas results in a rapid increase in GH secretion which cannot be accounted for on the basis of post-SS inhibitory rebound (323). 3. Hypothalamic ventro-medial nucleus lesions abolish post-SS inhibitory rebound, thus suggesting the importance of another factor, GRF, in producing this rebound in normal animals (323). 4. Passive immunization with anti-SS antisera elevates GH levels, but the pulsatile spikes of GH continue, further suggesting a GRF (151, 473).

Several laboratories have reported the presence of releasing activity in hypothalamic extracts (17, 111, 317, 318, 348, 523). A peptide isolated from porcine hypothalamic extracts based on a complex and probably invalid bioassay was characterized to be H-Val-His-Leu-Ser-Ala-Glu-Glu-Lys-Glu-Ala-OH (432). This decapeptide, termed "GH-RH," was found to be inactive in modifying the secretion of immunoreactive GH in vivo and in vitro (433) in a variety of species including man (246), and was subsequently revealed by Veber et al (508) to be related to the amino terminal sequence of the β chain of hemoglobin. Other investigators have reported that crude or partially purified hypothalamic extracts or CSF (19) can stimulate the secretion of radioimmunoassayable GH (111, 317, 318, 348, 458, 523). We have found two substances in hypothalamic extracts with GRF-like activity: one which is similar to myelin basic protein (513) and releases GH and other pituitary hormones in vitro from cultured pituitary cells or incubated hemipituitaries. This highly basic material, which is inactive in vivo has no physiological significance. The other is probably nonpeptidic and can be extracted with hexane from alcoholic extracts of brain tissue. The hexane-soluble material might be related to the E-series prostaglandins, which are highly potent stimulators of GH and other pituitary hormones in vivo and in vitro (407). Prostaglandins may reach the anterior pituitary through the portal system and play a role in the regulation of GH secretion.

CORTICOTROPIN RELEASING FACTOR

The role of the hypothalamus in the regulation of ACTH secretion has been supported by a variety of experimental observations showing that electrical stimulation of the hypothalamus elevates ACTH and corticosterone levels (39, 135, 528) and that lesions of this area reduce pituitary adrenal function (136). Direct evidence for the existence of a hypothalamic corticotropin releasing factor was provided in 1955 by the results of Guillemin & Rosenberg (198) and Saffran & Schally (419). Two substances with ACTH releasing activity were later purified from neurohypophyseal extracts, one related to α-MSH and the other to vasopressin; however, neither was fully characterized (430). Progress toward the isolation of hypothalamic CRF has been hampered by the lack of reliable, sensitive, and simple bioassays. Radioimmunoassays (327, 399, 405) and improved bioassays (428) for rat ACTH and in vitro systems using dispersed (297, 365, 387) or cultured (463, 502, 503) pituitary cells and improved in vivo CRF assays (306, 405) are being profitably applied to the study of the hypothalamic regulation of ACTH secretion and to the purification of CRF.

The in vivo administration of either crude or partially purified hypothalamic extracts to rats prepared in a variety of ways to decrease effects mediated by endogenous CRF, elevates plasma ACTH levels monitored either directly or as reflected through increases in corticosterone production. [For review, see (510)].

Similar hypothalamic extracts stimulate the secretion of ACTH by pituitary cells or glands in vitro. (297, 387, 503). Vasopressin stimulates ACTH secretion in vivo and in vitro at low concentrations (388, 405, 503, 526).

Early suggestions that vasopressin might be the physiologic CRF have been refuted by observations that Battleborough rats, which do not synthesize vasopressin, have essentially normal ACTH secretory patterns in all but a few circumstances (6, 528). Furthermore, the dose-response curves and maximal ACTH secretory rates observed with vasopressin and partially purified hypothalamic extracts (HE) are different; hypothalamic extracts have far greater effects on ACTH secretion than does vasopressin (388, 503, 526).

Several groups have investigated the possible interactions between vasopressin and CRF. Yates et al reported that low doses of vasopressin potentiate the ACTH release induced by hypothalamic extract (527), whereas Portanova & Sayers, having observed that the amounts of ACTH secreted in response to vasopressin and crude hypothalamic extracts are less than with the extract alone, proposed that neurohypophyseal polypeptides are partial agonists of ACTH secretion (388). Other investigators find only minor or no pharmacological interaction between arginine- or lysine-vasopressin and crude hypothalamic extracts (503, 526).

Recently, Pearlmutter et al reported that G-25 Sephadex chromatography of a rat hypothalamic extract yielded two separable zones with no activity when assayed separately but with high ACTH releasing activity when administered together (366).

Jones et al (236, 237) and our group (503) reported that ion-exchange chromatography can be used to separate either hypothalamic incubates or extracts into two zones, both with ACTH releasing activity. In our experience, the two fractions exhibit qualitatively distinguishable activities: one exhibits high intrinsic activity, increasing the cultured pituitary cells' ACTH secretion rate 5–20 fold, while the other increases ACTH secretion only from 1.5–3 fold over control levels. We have seen that several peptides such as β-MSH, $ACTH_{18-139}$, and β-LPH, as well as vasopressin, have similar moderate effects on ACTH secretion in vitro while α-MSH, $ACTH_{4-10}$, substance P, neurotensin, TRF, LRF, and somatostatin have no effect (503).

The α-adrenergic agonists, such as norepinephrine, phenylephrine, and clonidine also can stimulate ACTH secretion slightly by cultured anterior pituitary cells (503), an effect which can be blocked by phentolamine or dibenzaline but not propranolol. Generally α-adrenergic agonists inhibit the in vivo secretion of ACTH (505), an effect probably mediated by the CNS, as Jones and colleagues found norepinephrine to inhibit the ACh or serotonin-mediated release of CRF from hypothalamic fragments incubated in vitro (235). Thus it is possible that in vivo a direct pituitary effect of α-adrenergic substances on pituitary corticotrophs is obscured by the consequences of their CNS actions.

In view of the documented extrahypothalamic distributions of TRF, LRF, and SS (see above), the ACTH-releasing activity extracts of the extrahypothalamic rat brain were tested in vitro and found indeed to contain a CRF-like activity, which is destroyed by acid hydrolysis and partially inhibited by prior administration of steroids (503). Lymangrover & Brodish reported the existence of an extrahypothalamic CRF, which they called "tissue-CRF" (304, 307). They proposed that tissue-CRF might represent an extra source of CRF released under conditions where hypothalamic CRF is secreted in inadequate amounts. This would explain several puzzling physiological studies which showed that debrained animals possess a "stress" response (140).

Whether these extrahypothalamic CRFs are related to the interaction between the hypothalamic and other brain structures has not yet been determined.

Modulation of the ACTH secretory role by glucocorticoids is well documented and has been proposed to act primarily at either the hypothalamic or pituitary level (122a, 137, 153, 261, 453, 525, 528, 534). Whereas the ACTH regulatory effects of glucocorticoids on the brain are controversial [see (528) for review], there is no question that they can act directly on the appropriate pituitary cells to inhibit the secretion of ACTH. Since the first report (153) that glucocorticoids could inhibit the vasopressin-mediated release of ACTH by incubated hemi-pituitary glands, several groups have shown that a variety of glucocorticoids could inhibit the in vitro secretion of ACTH mediated by hypothalamic extracts, cAMP derivatives, phosphodiesterase inhibitors, elevated medium $[K^+]$, and other substances (153, 269, 503). In our studies, 2–200 nM dexamethasone and 10–1000 nM corticosterone inhibit basal and hypothalamic extract stimulated ACTH secretion by cultured pituitary cells in a dose- and time-dependent manner (503, 525). Similar results with higher steroid concentrations were obtained by Sayers & Portanova (429). The glucocorticoid inhibition of ACTH secretion is reversed by inhibitors of protein synthesis (503) and prevented by inhibitors of DNA-directed RNA synthesis (7, 503).

NEURAL FACTORS REGULATING MELANOCYTE STIMULATING HORMONE (MSH) SECRETION

Convincing evidence now exists that α-MSH is a hormone whose biological activities and regulation are different from those of ACTH (134, 247, 482). The release of α-MSH from the pars intermedia is primarily under the inhibitory control of the hypothalamus, as evidenced by increased MSH secretion in cultured pituitary cells (40) or after hypothalamic lesions (80, 474). There is evidence that catecholamines might exhibit direct as well as CNS-mediated inhibitory effects on pituitary MSH secretion (40, 465). Spontaneous release of MSH by rat pituitary cells is inhibited by dopamine and α-adrenergic agonists such as norepinephrine and phenylephrine. In addition, isoproterenol, a β-adrenergic agonist, stimulates in vitro release of MSH (40). Both α- and β-adrenergic effects in vivo and in vitro are blocked, respectively, by dibenamine and propranolol (40, 465).

Hypothalamic peptides have also been claimed to modify MSH secretion. A tripeptide identical to the N-terminus portion (H-Pro-Leu-Gly-NH$_2$) of oxytocin has been proposed as MIF-I (81, 83, 221, 345), which may be cleaved from oxytocin by a hypothalamic enzyme. Another peptide, MIF-II, has been characterized as H-Pro-His-Phe-Arg-Gly-NH$_2$, but it is reported to have only one thousandth of the activity of H-Pro-Leu-Gly-NH$_2$ (345). Hypothalamic extracts are reported to contain MSH-releasing activity (464). The penta-peptide H-Cys-Tyr-Ile-Gln-Asn-OH has been reported to represent MRF (223), also possibly cleaved from oxytocin by an enzyme present in the hypothalamus (82). Although studies on the site of action, distribution, and excretion of H-Pro-Leu-Gly-NH$_2$ have appeared (248), several groups have found MIF-II and MRF to be completely inactive (185, 475) in mammalians.

Following the report by Cotzias et al (101) that MSH aggravates the symptoms of Parkinson's disease, H-Pro-Leu-Gly-NH$_2$ was tested in animal models to assess its therapeutic usefulness in treating this neurologic disorder. H-Pro-Leu-Gly-NH$_2$ antagonizes oxotremorine-induced tremors in normal and hypophysectomized mice, thus suggesting its efficacy in treatment of Parkinson's disease (378, 380); it was further found to potentiate the excitation caused by L-dopa-parygline treatment in normal and hypophysectomized mice (226, 382). These results suggested a direct CNS action of H-Pro-Leu-Gly-NH$_2$ independent of MSH secretion. MIF-I is reported to activate the EEG and to possess weak analgesic properties (383). Possible involvement of H-Pro-Leu-Gly-NH$_2$ in CNS dopaminergic mechanisms is suggested by the observation of increased mounting behavior in rats and stereotypes in cats following administration of the peptide (350, 383).

CNS ACTIONS OF PEPTIDES RELATED TO ACTH AND β-LPH

A variety of behavioral and other neurotropic effects have been ascribed to ACTH and related peptides such as α-MSH or β-MSH, which contain the sequence H-Met-Glu-His-Phe-Arg-Trp-Gly-OH (ACTH$_{4-10}$, α-MSH$_{4-10}$ or β-MSH$_{45-51}$) (123, 393). These peptides as well as many analogs related to ACTH$_{4-10}$ will delay the extinction of approach behavior in intact rats and reverse the disturbances in the acquisition of conditioned avoidance behavior in hypophysectomized rats (123, 393). In addition, they have other effects such as antagonizing the action of morphine or pentobarbital in several circumstances (393, 407, 471, 472, 535). Acting through the CNS, ACTH, α-MSH, and β-MSH inhibit the secretion of PRL and GH stimulated by morphine (407).

ACTH contains the sequences of α-MSH (Ac-ACTH$_{1-13}$-NH$_2$) and CLIP (ACTH$_{18-39}$) (438). We have recently found CLIP also to have inhibitory effects on the morphine-mediated secretion of GH and PRL by rats when administered intracerebroventricularly and in addition to cause piloerection, decreased motor, and decreased exploratory activity (W. Vale, C. Rivier, M. Brown, unpublished observation.)

β-Lipotropin (β-LPH), a 91 amino acid peptide originally isolated and characterized from ovine pituitary glands based on its ability to release free fatty acids from fat pads, includes the sequence of β-MSH (β-LPH$_{41-58}$) and a C-terminal region β-LPH$_{61-91}$, which is identical to the largest of several novel characterized peptides with opiate-like activity. In 1975, Hughes et al (224) isolated a pentapeptide called methionine-enkephalin from porcine brain based on its ability to mimic morphine in several assay systems. Such peptidic opiate ligands, termed *endorphins* or *enkephalins*, had been proposed earlier based on a variety of pharmacological studies (102, 225, 361). The sequence of methionine-enkephalin is related to β-LPH$_{61-65}$, as is another opiate-like peptide isolated and characterized from porcine posterior pituitary and hypothalamic extracts by Guillemin and co-workers (200, 283), β-LPH$_{61-76}$ (α-endorphin). The entire C-terminal fragment, β-LPH$_{61-91}$ (C fragment or β-endorphin), identified by Bradbury et al (43, 44) in porcine pituitary extracts and by Li & Chung (290) from camel pituitary extracts, is also morphinomimetic. Biochemical studies (46, 283) have raised the possibility that β-LPH might be a precursor for the opiate-like peptides. Methionine enkephalin and α- and β-endorphin have been demonstrated to exhibit specific binding to opiate receptors in brain synaptosomal preparations and to inhibit the electrically induced contractions of guinea pig ileum and mouse vas deferens (45, 46, 103, 283, 290). These activities are inhibited by the opiate antagonist naloxone. Furthermore, β-endorphin has been reported to produce analgesia in the cat (45) and methionine enkephalin has been reported to induce analgesia in mice (70) and to affect the firing rate of single neurons in the rat brain stem (47).

SUBSTANCE P

Substance P (SP) was first described by von Euler & Gaddum as a substance isolated from equine gut and brain which produced hypotension in vivo and intestinal contraction in vitro (514). Subsequently, Leeman and associates isolated and characterized an undecapeptide from bovine hypothalamus by following the ability of this peptide to produce salivation in rats (85). The co-identity of equine gut SP and bovine "sialogen" has been established, and this peptide is now termed substance P (285). The role of SP as a peptide neurotransmitter was first suggested by Lembeck (286) and is supported by several observations. SP is present in the central and peripheral nervous system in presynaptic structures as determined by immunohistochemistry and subcellular fractionation methods (132, 218, 219, 220, 358, 461). SP causes spinal motoneuron and Betz cell depolarization (270, 358, 375), which is specifically inhibited by β-(4-chlorophenyl)-γ-aminobutyric acid, an agent that suppresses monosynaptic and polysynaptic reflexes without affecting the electrical properties of spinal motoneurons (421). Furthermore, a brain enzyme capable of rapidly inactivating SP has been described (27).

SP has been reported to abolish abstinence syndrome in morphinized rats (285). It has also been reported to stimulate LH and FSH secretion in vitro (152a). Similar to neurotensin, SP administration to rats produces hyperglycemia, which is most likely secondary to elevation of plasma glucagon levels and decrease of plasma insulin levels (61). Similar effects of SP have been observed on insulin and glucagon secretion from the perfused dog pancreas in vitro (S. Patton, W. Vale, M. Brown, unpublished observations).

SP is present in equine, bovine, and rat brain, spinal cord, and gut (219, 220, 358, 367, 461, 533). SP has been demonstrated to be present in high concentrations in the dorsal roots of the spinal cord (358), and is also present in the intrinsic nerve plexuses of the gut and in the intestinal wall. In human brain the highest concentrations of SP have been found in the substantia nigra and hypothalamus and the lowest concentrations in the spinal cord, medulla, and frontal cortex (389). Recent immunohistofluorescence studies demonstrate cell bodies positive for SP only in the medial habenula and a rather wide brain distribution of SP-positive nerve fibers (218).

NEUROTENSIN

Neurotensin (NT), a tridecapeptide isolated and characterized from bovine hypothalamus by Leeman and co-workers (78, 79), has been reported to increase vascular permeability, decrease blood pressure, increase hematocrit, and stimulate gut contraction. NT has also been reported to release LH and FSH in vitro (79) and GH and prolactin in vivo (407). The in vivo effect of NT to increase plasma levels of GH and prolactin is probably secondary to a CNS locus of action (407). NT also produces a rapid hyperglycemia when administered to rats (61, 77). This hyperglycemia following NT administration (61) is preceded by an elevation of plasma levels of glucagon and a decrease of plasma levels of insulin. Similar effects of NT have been observed on insulin and glucagon secretion from the perfused dog pancreas in vitro (G. Patton, W. Vale, M. Brown, unpublished observations). The possibility that NT may exert its actions via histamine release from mast cells or histamine-containing nerve terminals is suggested by the observations that its actions on blood pressure, vascular permeability, blood glucose and GH, prolactin, insulin and glucagon secretion are reversed by the H_1-histamine receptor blocker diphenhydramine (62, 407).

A CNS action of NT is supported by its wide CNS distribution (56) (Table 3), and its ability to enhance the depressant effects of phenobarbital (347). Additionally, NT binds to rat synaptosomal preparations in vitro, and the binding affinities of NT to these synaptosomal preparations correlate well with the CNS distribution of NT (282).

Following the development of a sensitive radioimmunoassay, NT immunoactivity has been demonstrated in the rat brain as shown in Table 3 with highest concentrations in the preoptic area, nucleus accumbens, and medial basal hypothalamus (56). As is the case with TRF, SP, and SS, NT is widely distributed throughout the brain and spinal cord and is virtually absent in the cerebellum. NT has also recently been found to be present in porcine and rat gut by radioimmunoassay (56) and in canine gut by immunofluorescence (357a).

MISCELLANEOUS PEPTIDES

Recently, immunoactive gastrin (507) and vasoactive intestinal polypeptide (VIP) (420) have been reported to be present in human and canine brain respectively. The gastrin-like activity was found in highest concentrations in the cerebral cortex and lower concentrations throughout other brain areas including the hypothalamus. VIP-like activity is also present in high concentrations in the cerebral cortex and is found in the hypothalamus. VIP has been observed to produce EEG changes and exert an analeptic effect on barbiturate anesthesia in dogs. (S. Said, personal communication). The effects of these hormones on neuronal and pituitary function remain to be described, but they appear to be two more members of the growing list of brain-gastrointestinal peptides.

The observation of direct effects of angiotensin II on drinking behavior (152b), vasopressin secretion, CNS pressor activity (20, 393), and the presence of renin (163) and angiotensin-forming enzyme (162) in brain areas including the hypothalamus is yet another example of a possibly important brain hormone regulating CNS and pituitary function. Angiotensin II also has been reported to potentiate the effects of dopa-parygline in mice (226).

In summary, the HRP exhibit a wide range of biological activities affecting the function of not only the anterior pituitary gland but also the CNS, pancreas and gastrointestinal tract. In addition, these peptides have broad anatomic distributions which can generally be correlated with the distribution of HRP-responsive cells. Such coincidences suggest, but do not demonstrate, physiological roles for the HRP in regulating the functions of these diverse cells. Passive immunization studies with anti-LRF, SS, and TRF sera, and experiments with competitive LRF antagonists, affirm the physiological hypophysiotropic significance of each of these peptides. A future appreciation of the importance of the HRP in the CNS, pancreas, gastrointestinal tract, and other sites yet to be discovered will provide new understanding of the physiology and perhaps pathology of those systems.

The synthesis and biological analysis of the activities of analogs of the characterized HRP will provide not only insight into the structural determinants for biological activity, but useful tools for the study and treatment of pituitary, pancreatic, and gastrointestinal endocrinopathies as well as disorders of the central nervous system.

Acknowledgments

Research support for the Laboratories for Neuroendocrinology at the Salk Institute of Biological Studies, was provided by NIH grants AM 18811–01, AM 16707, The National Foundation (grant 1–411), and The Rockefeller Foundation (RF 69078). The authors wish to express their gratitude to Lisa Worrells, Paulette Manning, Lana Chan, Alice Wolfe, and Dr. Marilyn Perrin for their timely assistance in preparing this manuscript.

Literature Cited

1. Aiyer, M. S., Fink, G. 1974. The role of sex steroid hormones in modulating the responsiveness of the anterior pituitary gland to luteinizing hormone releasing factor in the female rat. *J. Endocrinol.* 62:553–72

2. Ajika, K., Krulich, L., Fawcett, C. P., McCann, S. M. 1972. Effects of estrogen on plasma and pituitary gonadotropins and prolactin, and on hypothalamic releasing and inhibiting factors. *Neuroendocrinology* 9:304–15

3. Alpert, L. C., Brawer, J. R., Jackson, I. M. D., Patel, Y. 1975. Somatostatin and LRH: Immunohistochemical evidence for distinct hypothalamic distribution. *Endocrinology* 95:239A

4. Alpert, L. C., Brawer, J. R., Patel, Y. C., Reichlin, S. 1976. Somatostatinergic neurons in anterior hypothalamus: Immunohistochemical localization. *Endocrinology* 98:255–58

5. Alberti, K. G. M. M., Christensen, N. J., Christensen, S. E., Hansen, A. P., Iversen, J., Lundbaek, K., Seyer-Hansen, K., Orskov, H. 1973. Inhibition of insulin secretion by somatostatin. *Lancet* 2:1299–1301

6. Arimura, A., Saito, T., Bowers, C. Y., Schally, A. V. 1967. Pituitary adrenal

activation in rats with hereditary hypothalamic diabetes insipidus. *Acta Endocrinol.* 54:155–65

7. Arimura, A., Bowers, C. Y., Schally, A. V., Saito, M., Miller, M. C. III. 1969. Effect of corticotropin-releasing factor, dexamethasone and actinomycin D on the release of ACTH from rat pituitaries in vivo and in vitro. *Endocrinology* 85:300–11

8. Arimura, A., Dunn, J. D., Schally, A. V. 1972. Effect of infusion of hypothalamic extracts on serum prolactin levels in rats treated with nembutal, CNS depressants, or bearing hypothalamic lesions. *Endocrinology* 90: 378–83

9. Arimura, A., Sato, H., Kumasaka, T., Worobec, R. B., Debeljuk, L., Dunn, J., Schally, A. V. 1973. Production of antiserum to LH-releasing hormone (LH-RH) associated with gonadoal atrophy in rabbits: Development of radioimmunoassays for LH-RH. *Endocrinology* 93:1092–1103

10. Arimura, A., Debeljuk, L., Schally, A. V. 1974. Blockade of the preovulatory surge of LH and FSH and of ovulation by anti-LH-RH serum in rats. *Endocrinology* 95:323–25

11. Arimura, A., Kastin, A. J., Schally, A. V. 1974. Immunoreactive LH-releasing hormone in plasma: Midcycle elevation in women. *J. Clin. Endocrinol. Metab.* 38:510–13

12. Arimura, A., Schally, A. V. 1975. Immunological studies on hypothalamic hormones. In *Hypothalamic Hormones: Chemistry, Physiology, Pharmacology and Clinical Uses,* ed. M. Motta, P. G. Crosignani, L. Martini, pp. 27–42. New York: Academic

13. Arimura, A., Sato, H., Coy, D. H., Schally, A. V. 1975. Radioimmunoassay for GH-release inhibiting hormone. *Proc. Soc. Exp. Biol. Med.* 148:784–89

14. Arimura, A., Sato, H., Dupont, A., Nishi, N., Schally, A. V. 1975. Somatostatin: Abundance of immunoreactive hormone in rat stomach and pancreas. *Science* 189:1007–9

15. Arimura, A., Schally, A. V. 1976. Increase in basal and thyrotropin-releasing hormone (TRH)-stimulated secretion of thyrotropin (TSH) by passive immunization with antiserum to somatostatin in rats. *Endocrinology* 98: 1069–72

16. Arimura, A., Smith, W. D., Schally, A. V. 1976. Blockade of the stress-induced decrease in blood GH by anti-somato-statin serum in rats. *Endocrinology* 98:540–43

17. Ashworth, R., Wakabayashi, K., McGovern, W., Dhariwal, A. P. S., McCann, S. M. 1968. The possible relationship between membrane depolarization and the action of the hypothalamic releasing factors on the pituitary cell. *Proc. 24th Int. Cong. Physiol. Sci.* 2:19

18. Bancroft, F. C., Wu, G-J, Zubay, G. 1973. Cell-free synthesis of rat growth hormone. *Proc. Natl. Acad. Sci.* 70 No. 12:3646–49

19. Barbato, T., Lawrence, A. M., Kirsteins, L. 1974. Cerebrospinal fluid stimulation of pituitary protein synthesis and growth-hormone release in vitro. *Lancet* April:599–600

20. Barker, J. L. 1976. Peptides: Roles in neuronal excitability. *Physiol. Rev.* 56:435–52

21. Barlow, T. S., Cooper, B. R., Breese, G. R., Prange, A. J. Jr., Lipton, M. A. 1975. Effects of thyrotropin releasing hormone (TRH) on behavior: Evidence for an anorexic-like action. *Abstr. Neurosci.* 1:519

22. Barros, D'Sa, A. A. J., Bloom, S. R., Baron, J. H. 1975. Direct inhibition of gastric acid by growth-hormone release-inhibiting hormone in dogs. *Lancet* 4:886–87

23. Barry, J., Dubois, M., Carette, B. 1974. Immunofluorescence study of the pre-optico infundibular LRF neurosecretory pathway in the normal castrated or testosterone treated male guinea pig. *Endocrinology* 95:1416–23

24. Bassiri, R. M., Utiger, R. D. 1974. Thyrotropin-releasing hormone in the hypothalamus of the rat. *Endocrinology* 94:188–94

25. Beattie, C. W., Corbin, A., Foell, T. J., Garsky, V., McKinley, W. A., Rees, R. W. A., Sarantakis, D., Yardley, J. P. 1974. Luteinizing hormone-releasing hormone. Antiovulatory activity of analogs substituted in positions 2 and 6. *J. Med. Chem.* 17:1016

26. Bennett, G. W., Edwardson, J. A., Holland, D., Jeffcoate, S. L., White, N. 1975. Release of immunoreactive luteinizing hormone-releasing hormone and thyrotrophin-releasing hormone from hypothalamic synaptosomes. *Nature* 257:323–24

27. Benuck, M., Marks, N. 1975. Enzymatic inactivation of substance P by a partially purified enzyme from rat brain. *Biochem. Biophys. Res. Commun.* 65:153–60

28. Besser, G. M. et al 1974. Growth hormone release inhibiting hormone in acromegaly. *Br. Med. J.* 1:352–55

29. Besser, G. M. et al 1974. Long-term infusion of growth hormone release inhibiting hormone in acromegaly: Effects on pituitary and pancreatic hormones. *Br. Med. J.* 4:622–27

30. Besser, G. M., Mortimer, C. H. 1976. Clinical neuroendocrinology. In *Frontiers in Neuroendocrinology*, ed. L. Martini, W. F. Ganong, pp. 227–54. New York: Raven

31. Besser, G. M. 1976. Clinical implications of growth hormone release-inhibiting hormone. In *Hypothalamus and Endocrine Functions*, ed. F. Labrie, J. Meites, G. Pelletier, pp. 127–143. New York: Raven

32. Blake, C. A. 1974. Stimulation of pituitary prolactin and TSH release in lactating and proestrous rats. *Endocrinology* 94:503–8

33. Bloom, S. R. et al 1974. Inhibition of gastrin and gastric-acid secretion by growth-hormone release-inhibiting hormone. *Lancet* 11:1106–9

34. Boden, G., Sivitz, M. C., Owen, O. E. 1975. Somatostatin suppresses secretin and pancreatic exocrine secretion. *Science* 190:163–64

35. Borgeat, P., Chavancy, G., Dupont, A., Labrie, F., Arimura, A., Schally, A. V. 1972. Stimulation of adenosine 3',5'-cyclic monophosphate accumulation in anterior pituitary gland *in vitro* by luteinizing hormone-releasing hormone. *Proc. Natl. Acad. Sci.* 69:2677–81

36. Borgeat, P., Labrie, F., Côte, J., Ruel, F., Schally, A. V., Coy, D. H., Coy, E. J., Yanaihara, N. 1974. Parallel stimulation of cyclic AMP accumulation and LH and FSH release by analogs of LH-RH in vitro. *J. Mol. Cell. Endocrinol.* 1:7–20

37. Borgeat, P., Labrie, F., Drouin, J., Belanger, A. 1974. Inhibition of adenosine 3',5'-monophosphate accumulation in anterior pituitary gland in vitro by growth hormone-release inhibiting hormone. *Biochem. Biophys. Res. Commun.* 56, No. 4:1052–59

38. Boss, B., Vale, W., Grant, G. 1975. Hypothalamic hormones. In *Biochemical Actions of Hormones*, ed. G. Litwack, pp. 87–117. New York: Academic

39. Bouille, C., Bayle, J. D. 1973. Effects of hypothalamic stimulation on pituitary-adrenocortical activity in conscious unrestrained pigeons. *Neuroendocrinology* 12:284–94

40. Bower, A., Hadley, M. E., Hruby, V. J. 1974. Biogenic amines and control of melanophore stimulating hormone release. *Science* 184:70–72

41. Bowers, C. Y., Lee, K. L., Schally, A. V. 1968. Effect of actinomycin D on hormones that control the release of thyrotropin from the anterior pituitary glands of mice. *Endocrinology* 82:303–10

42. Bowers, C. Y., Currie, B. L., Johansson, K. N. G., Folkers, K. 1973. Biological evidence that separate hypothalamic hormones release the follicle stimulating and luteinizing hormones. *Biochem. Biophys. Res. Commun.* 50:20–26

43. Bradbury, A. F., Smyth, D. G., Snell, C. R. 1975. Biosynthesis of β-MSH and ACTH. In *Peptides: Chemistry, Structure, Biology*, ed. R. Walter, J. Meienhofer, pp. 609–15. Ann Arbor, Mich: Ann Arbor Sci.

44. Bradbury, A. F., Smyth, D. G., Snell, C. R. 1975. Prohormones of β melanotropin (β MSH) and corticotropin (ACTH) structure and activation. In *Polypeptide Hormones: Molecular and Cellular Aspects*, pp. 61–69. New York: Excerpta Medica

45. Bradbury, A. F. et al 1976. C fragment of lipotropin has a high affinity for brain opiate receptors. *Nature* 260:793–95

46. Bradbury, A. F., Smyth, D. G., Snell, C. R. 1976. Prohormones of β melanotropin (β-melanocyte-stimulating hormone, β-MSH) and corticotropin (adrenocorticotropic hormone, ACTH): Structure and activation. In *Polypeptide Hormones: Molecular and Cellular Aspects* (CIBA Found. Symp. 41 in honor of Sir Frank Young), pp. 61–75. North Holland: Elsevier

47. Bradley, P. B., Briggs, I., Gayton, R. J., Lambert, L. A. 1976. Effects of microiontophoretically applied methionine-enkephaline on single neurones in rat brain stem. *Nature* 261:425–26

48. Brazeau, P. et al 1973. Hypothalamic polypeptide that inhibits the secretion of immunoreactive pituitary growth hormone. *Science* 179:77–79

49. Brazeau, P., Rivier, J., Vale, W., Guillemin, R. 1974. Inhibition of growth hormone secretion in the rat by synthetic somatostatin. *Endocrinology* 94:184–87

50. Brazeau, P., Vale, W., Guillemin, R. 1974. Trans-hypothalamic effects of drugs of abuse on the secretion of pituitary hormones. In *Narcotics and the*

Hypothalamus, ed. E. Zimmerman, R. George, pp. 109–19. New York: Raven

51. Breese, G. R., Cott, J. M., Cooper, B. R., Prange, A. J. Jr., Lipton, M. A. 1974. Antagonism of ethanol narcosis by thyrotropin releasing hormone. *Life Sci.* 14:1053–63

52. Breese, G. R. et al 1974. Effects of thyrotropin-releasing hormone (TRH) on the actions of pentobarbital and other centrally acting drugs. *J. Pharmacol. Exp. Ther.* 193:11–22

53. Brown, M., Rivier, J., Vale, W., Guillemin, R. 1975. Variability of the duration of inhibition of growth hormone release by N$^\alpha$-Acylated-des-[Ala^1-Gly^2]-H$_2$ somatostatin analogs. *Biochem. Biophys. Res. Commun.* 65: 752–56

54. Brown, M., Vale, W. 1975. Growth hormone release in the rat: Effects of somatostatin and thyrotropin-releasing factor. *Endocrinology* 97:1151–56

55. Brown, M., Vale, W. 1975. Central nervous system effects of hypothalamic peptides. *Endocrinology* 96:1333–36

56. Brown, M., Kobayashi, R., Vale, W. 1977. Brain distribution of neurotensin and somatostatin. *Endocrinology.* Submitted for publication

57. Brown, M., Rivier, J., Vale, W. 1976. Somatostatin analogs with dissociated biological activities. *Fed. Proc.* 35: A3171

58. Brown, M., Rivier, J., Vale, W. 1976. Pancreatotrophic effects of somatostatin (SS) and SS-analogs. *Abstr. V Int. Congr. Endocrinol., Hamburg, Germany,* p. 178

59. Brown, M., Rivier, J., Vale, W. 1976. Somatostatin analogs with selected biological activities. *Metabolism.* 25:Suppl. 1, pp. 1501–3

60. Brown, M., Rivier, J., Vale, W. 1976. Biological activity of somatostatin and somatostatin analogs on inhibition of arginine-induced insulin and glucagon release in the rat. *Endocrinology* 98: 336–43

61. Brown, M., Vale, W. 1976. Glucoregulatory effects of neurotensin and substance P. *Endocrinology* 98:819–22

62. Brown, M., Villarreal, J., Vale, W. 1976. Neurotensin and substance P: Effects on plasma insulin and glucagon levels. *Metabolism.* 25:Suppl. 1, pp. 1459–61

63. Brownstein, M. J., Palkovits, M., Saavedra, J. M., Bassiri, R., Utiger, R. D. 1974. Thyrotropin-releasing hormone in specific nuclei of rat brain. *Science* 185:267–69

64. Brownstein, M., Arimura, A., Sato, H., Schally, A. V. Kizer, J. S. 1975. The regional distribution of somatostatin in the rat brain. *Endocrinology* 96: 1456–61

65. Bryce, D., Yeh, M., Funderburk, C., Todd, H., Hertelendy, F. 1975. Studies on growth hormone secretion VII. Effects of somatostatin on plasma GH, insulin, and glucagon in sheep. *Diabetes* 24:842–50

66. Burgus, R., Dunn, T. F., Desiderio, D., Ward, D. N., Vale, W., Guillemin, R. 1970. Characterization of the hypothalamic hypophysiotropic TSH-releasing factor (TRF) of ovine origin. *Nature* 226:321–25

67. Burgus, R. et al 1976. Isolation and characterization of hypothalamic peptide hormones. In *Hypothalamus and Endocrine Functions,* ed. F. Labrie, J. Meites, G. Pelletier, pp. 355–72. New York: Raven

68. Burgus, R., Butcher, M., Amoss, M., Ling, N., Monahan, M., Rivier, J., Fellows, R., Blackwell, R., Vale, W., Guillemin, R. 1972. Primary structure of the hypothalamic luteinizing hormone-releasing factor (LRF) of ovine origin. *Proc. Natl. Acad. Sci.* 69:278–82

69. Burt, D. R., Snyder, S. H. 1975. Thyrotropin releasing hormone (TRH): Apparent receptor binding in rat brain membranes. *Brain Res.* 93:309–28

70. Buscher, H. H. et al 1976. Evidence for an analgesic activity of enkephalin in the mouse. *Nature* 261:423–25

71. Cahill, G. F., Soeldner, J. S. 1974. Diabetes, glucagon and growth hormone. *N. Engl. J. Med.* 291:577–79

72. Cargille, C. M., Ross, G. T., Yoshini, T. 1969. Daily variations in plasma follicle stimulating hormone, luteinizing hormone and progesterone in the normal menstrual cycle. *J. Clin. Endocrinol.* 29:12–19

73. Carlson, H. E., Jacobs, L. S., Daughaday, W. H. 1973. Growth hormone, thyrotropin and prolactin responses to thyrotropin-releasing hormone following diethylstilbestrol pretreatment. *J. Clin. Endocrinol. Metab.* 37:488–90

74. Carlson, H., Mariz, I. 1973. TRH: A releasing factor for GH in perfused rat pituitaries. *Endocrinology* 93:A-141

75. Carmel, P. C., Araki, S., Ferin, M. 1975. Prolonged stalk blood collection in rhesus monkeys. Pulsatile release of

gonadotropin-releasing hormone (Gn RH). *Endocrinology* 96:104A

76. Carr, D. et al. 1975. Growth hormone release inhibiting hormone: Actions on thyrotropin and prolactin secretion after thyrotrophin-releasing hormone. *Br. Med. J.* 3:67–69

77. Carraway, R., Demers, L., Leeman, S. 1973. Hyperglycemic effect of a hypothalamic peptide. *Fed. Proc.* 32:1

78. Carraway, R., Leeman, S. E. 1973. The isolation of a new hypotensive peptide, neurotensin, from bovine hypothalami. *J. Biol. Chem.* 248:6854–61

79. Carraway, R., Leeman, S. E. 1975. The amino acid sequence of a hypothalamic peptide, neurotensin. *J. Biol. Chem.* 250:1907–11

80. Carrillo, A. J., Kastin, A. J., Dunn, J. D., Schally, A. V. 1973. MSH activity in plasma and pituitaries of rats with large hypothalamic lesions. *Neuroendocrinology* 12:120–28

81. Celis, M. E., Taleisnik, S., Walter, R. 1971. Regulation of formation and proposed structure of the factor inhibiting the release of melanocyte-stimulating hormone. *Proc. Natl. Acad. Sci. USA* 68:1428–33

82. Celis, M. E., Taleisnik, S. 1974. Estrogen influence on the hypothalamic enzymes involved in the formation of melanocyte-stimulating hormone release-inhibiting factor (MSH-R-IF). *Proc. Soc. Exp. Biol. Med.* 145:142–44

83. Celis, M. E., Taleisnik, S., Walter, R. 1971. Release of pituitary melanocyte-stimulating hormone by the oxytocin fragment, H-Cys-Tyr-Ile-Gln-Asn-OH. *Biochem. Biophys. Res. Commun.* 45:564–69

84. Deleted in proof

85. Chang, M. M., Leeman, S. E. 1970. Isolation of a sialogogic peptide from bovine hypothalamic tissue and its characterization as substance P. *J. Biol. Chem.* 245:4784–90

86. Chen, H. J., Mueller, G. P., Meites, J. 1974. Effects of L-dopa and somatostatin on suckling-induced release of prolactin and GH. *Endocrine Res. Commun.* 1(3):283–91

87. Chen, H. J., Meites, J. 1975. Effects of biogenic amines and TRH on release of prolactin and TSH in the rat. *Endocrinology* 96:10–14

88. Chideckel, E. W. 1975. Somatostatin blockade of acute and chronic stimuli of the endocrine pancreas and the consequences of this blockade on glucose homeostasis. *J. Clin. Invest.* 55:754–62

89. Chihara, K., Kato, Y., Ohgo, S., Iwasaki, Y., Abe, H., Maeda, K., Imura, H. 1976. Stimulating and inhibiting effects of thyrotropin-releasing hormone on growth hormone release in rats. *Endocrinology* 98:1047–53

89a. Chiodini, P. G. et al 1975. Stable reduction of plasma growth hormone (hGH) levels during chronic administration of 2-Br-α-ergocryptine (CB-154) in acromegalic patients. *J. Clin. Endocrinol. Metab.* 40:705–8

90. Christensen, S. E., Hansen, A. P., Lundbaek, K., Orskov, H., Seyer-Hansen, K. 1975. Somatostatin and insulinoma. *Lancet* 1:1426

91. Clemens, J. A., Shaar, C. J., Tandy, W. A., Roush, M. E. 1971. Effects of hypothalamic stimulation on prolactin secretion in steroid treated rats. *Endocrinology* 89:1317–20

92. Clemens, J. A., Shaar, C. J., Smalstig, E. B., Bach, N. J., Kornfeld, E. C. 1974. Inhibition of prolactin secretion by ergolines. *Endocrinology* 94:1171–76

93. Cohn, M. L., Cohn, M. 1975. "Barrel rotation" induced by somatostatin in the non-lesioned rat. *Brain Res.* 96:138–41

94. Cohn, M. L., Cohn, M., Taylor, F. H. 1975. Thyrotropin releasing factor (TRF) regulation of rotation in the non-lesioned rat. *Brain Res.* 96:134–37

94a. Cohn, M. L. 1975. Cyclic AMP, thyrotropin releasing factor and somatostatin: key factors in the regulation of the duration of narcosis. In *Molecular Mechanism of Anesthesia*, ed. B. R. Fink, pp. 485–500. New York: Raven

95. Collu, R., Clermont, M. J., Letarte, J., Leboeuf, G., Ducharme, J. R. 1975. Inhibition of pentobarbital-induced release by thyrotropin releasing hormone. *Endocr. Res. Commun.* 2:123–35

96. Collu, R., Jéquier, J.-C., Leboeuf, G., Letarte, J., Ducharme, J. R. 1975. Endocrine effects of pimozide, a specific dopaminergic blocker. *J. Endocrinol. Metab.* 41:981–84

97. Convey, E. M., Tucker, H. A., Smith, V. G., Zolman, J. 1973. Bovine prolactin, growth hormone, thyroxine and corticoid response to thyrotropin-releasing hormone. *Endocrinology* 92:471–76

98. Constantinidis, J., Geissbuehler, F., Gaillard, J. M., Bovaguimian, T., Tissot, R., 1974. Enhancement of cerebral noradrenaline turnover by thyrotropin-releasing hormone: Evidence by fluores-

cence histochemistry. *Experientia* 30: 1182

99. Coppen, A. et al. 1974. Thyrotrophin-releasing hormone in the treatment of depression. *Lancet* 8:433–35

100. Corbin, A., Beattie, C. W. 1975. Inhibition of the pre-ovulatory proestrous gonadotropin surge, ovulation and pregnancy with a peptide analogue of luteinizing hormone releasing hormone. *Endocrine Res. Commun.* 2:1–23

101. Cotzias, G. C., Von Woert, M. H., Schiffer, L. M. 1967. Aromatic amino acids and modification of Parkinsonism. *N. Engl. J. Med.* 276:374–79

102. Cox, B. M., Opheim, K. E., Teschemacher, H., Goldstein, A. 1975. A peptide-like substance from pituitary that acts like morphine 2. purification and properties. *Life Sci.* 16:1777–82

103. Cox, B. M., Goldstein, A., Li, C. H. 1976. Opioid activity of a peptide β-LPH-(61–91), Derived from β-Lipotropin. *Proc. Natl. Acad. Sci.* 73:1821–23

104. Coy, D., Coy, E., Schally, A. V., Vilchez-Martinez, J., Hirotsu, Y., Arimura, A. 1974. Synthesis and biological properties of [D-Ala-6, Des-Gly-NH$_2$-10]-LH-RH ethylamide, a peptide with greatly enhanced LH- and FSH-releasing activity. *Biochem. Biophys. Res. Commun.* 57:335–40

105. Coy, D. H., Hirotsu, Y., Redding, T. W., Coy, E. J., Schally, A. V. 1975. Synthesis and biological properties of the 2-L-β-(pyrazolyl-1) alanine analogs of luteinizing hormone-releasing hormone and thyrotropin-releasing hormone. *J. Med. Chem.* 18, No. 9:948

106. Coy, D. H., Schally, A. V., Vilchez-Martinez, J. A., Coy, E. J., Arimura, A. 1975. Stimulatory and inhibitory analogs of LH-RH. See Reference 12, pp. 1–12

107. Coy, D. H., Vilchez-Martinez, J. A., Coy, E. J., Nishi, N., Arimura, A., Schally, A. V. 1975. Polyfluoroalkylamine derivatives of luteinizing hormone-releasing hormone. *Biochemistry* 14(9):1848

108. Coy, D., Labrie, F., Savary, M., Coy, E., Schally, A. V. 1976. LH releasing activity of potent LH-RH analogs *in vitro*. *Biochem. Biophys. Res. Commun.* 67:576–82

109. Cumming, I. A., Buckmaster, J. M., Cerini, J. C., Cerini, M. E., Chamley, W. A., Findlay, J., Goding, J. R. 1972. Effect of progesterone on the release of luteinizing hormone induced by a synthetic gonadotrophin-releasing factor in the ewe. *Neuroendocrinology* 10:338–48

110. Curnow, R. T., Carey, R. M., Taylor, A., Johanson, A., Murad, F. 1975. Somatostatin inhibition of insulin and gastrin hypersecretion in pancreatic islet-cell carcinoma. *N. Engl. J. Med.* 292:1385–86

111. Currie, B. L., Johansson, K. N. G., Greibrokk, T., Folkers, K., Bowers, C. Y. 1974. Identification and purification of factor A-GHRH from hypothalami which releases growth hormone. *Biochem. Biophys. Res. Commun.* 60(2): 605–9

112. Curry, D. L., Bennett, L. L., Li, C. H. 1974. Direct inhibition of insulin secretion by synthetic somatostatin. *Biochem. Biophys. Res. Commun.* 58: 885–89

113. Curry, D. L., Bennett, L. L. 1974. Reversal of somatostatin inhibition of insulin secretion by calcium. *Biochem. Biophys. Res. Commun.* 60:1015-19

114. Curry, D. L., Bennett, L. L. 1976. Does somatostatin inhibition of insulin secretion involve two mechanisms of action? *Proc. Natl. Acad. Sci.* 73(1):248–51

115. Dannies, P. S., Gautvik, K. M., Tashjian, A. H. Jr. 1976. A possible role of cyclic AMP in mediating the effects of thyrotropin-releasing hormone on prolactin release and on prolactin and growth hormone synthesis in pituitary cells in culture. *Endocrinology* 98(5): 1147–59

116. Debeljuk, L., Arimura, A., Redding, T., Schally, A. V. 1972. Effect of TRH and triiodothyronine on prolactin release in sheep. *Proc. Soc. Exp. Biol. Med.* 142:421–23

117. De la Cruz, A., Coy, D. H., Schally, A. V., Coy, E. J., De la Cruz, K. G., Arimura, A. 1975. Blockade of the pre-ovulatory LH surge in hamsters by an inhibitory analog of LH-RH[1] (38855). *Proc. Soc. Exp. Biol. Med.* 149:576–79

118. De la Cruz, A., Coy, D. H., Vilchez-Martinez, J. A., Arimura, A., Schally, A. V. 1976. Blockade of ovulation in rats by inhibitory analogs of luteinizing hormone-releasing hormone. *Science* 191:195–96

119. De la Cruz, K., Arimura, A. 1974. Evidence for the presence of immunoreactive plasma LH-RH which is unrelated to LH-RH decapeptide. *Endocrinology* 95:103A

120. Deis, R. P., Alonso, N. 1975. Effect of synthetic thyrotrophin releasing factor on prolactin and luteinizing hormone

510   VALE ET AL

secretion in male and female rats during various reproductive states. *J. Endocrinol.* 67:425–30

121. DeMeyts, P., Roth, J., Neville, D. M., Gavin, J. R., Lesniak, M. A. 1973. Insulin interactions with its receptor: Experimental evidence for negative cooperativity. *Biochem. Biophys. Res. Commun.* 55:154–61

122. DeVane, G. W., Siler, T. M., Yen, S. S. C. 1974. Acute suppression of insulin and glucose levels by synthetic somatostatin in normal human subjects. *J. Clin. Endocrinol. Metab.* 38:913–15

122a. de Wied, D. 1964. The site of the blocking action of dexamethasone on stress-induced pituitary ACTH release. *J. Endocrinol.* 29:29–37

123. de Wied, D., Witter, A., Greven, H. M. 1975. Behaviorally active ACTH analogues. *Biochem. Pharmacol.* 24:1463–68

124. Dickerman, S., Kledzik, G., Belato, M., Chen, H. J., Meites, J. 1974. Effects of haloperidol on serum and pituitary prolactin, LH and FSH, and hypothalamic PIF and LRF. *Neuroendocrinology* 15:10–20

125. Dobbs, R. et al 1975. Glucagon: Role in hyperglycemia of diabetes mellitus. *Science* 187:544–47

126. Douglas, W. W., Kanno, T., Sampson, S. R. 1967. Influence of the ionic environment on the membrane potential of adrenal chromaffin cells and on the depolarizing effect of acetylcholine. *J. Physiol.* 191:107–21

127. Drouin, J., DeLéan, A., Rainville, D., Lachance, R., Labrie, F. 1976. Characteristics of the interaction between thyrotropin-releasing hormone and somatostatin for thyrotropin and prolactin release. *Endocrinology* 98:514–21

128. Dubé, D., Leclerc, R., Pelletier, G., Arimura, A., Schally, A. V. 1975. Immunohistochemical detection of growth hormone release inhibiting hormone (somatostatin) in the guinea-pig brain. *Cell Tissue Res.* 161:385–92

129. Dubois, M. P. 1975. Immunoreactive somatostatin is present in discrete cells of the endocrine pancreas. *Proc. Natl. Acad. Sci. USA* 72:1340–43

130. Dubois, M. P., Barry, J., Leonardelli, J. 1974. Mise en évidence par immunofluorescence et répartition de la somatostatine (SRIF) dans l'éminence médiane des Vertébrés (Mammifères, Oiseaux, Amphibiens, Poissons). *C. R. Acad. Sci. Tome Ser. D* 279:1899–1902

131. Dubois, P. M., Paulin, C., Assan, R., Dubois, M. P. 1975. Evidence for immunoreactive somatostatin in the endocrine cells of human foetal pancreas. *Nature* 256:731–32

132. Duffy, M. J., Mulhall, D., Powell, D. 1975. Subcellular distribution of substance P in bovine hypothalamus and substantia nigra. *J. Neurochem.* 25:305–7

133. Dular, R., LaBella, F., Vivian, S., Eddie, L. 1974. Purification of prolactin-releasing and inhibiting factors from beef. *Endocrinology* 94:563–67

134. Dunn, J. D., Kastin, A. J., Carrillo, A. J., Schally, A. V. 1972. Additional evidence for dissociation of melanocyte-stimulating hormone and corticotrophin release. *J. Endocrinol.* 55:463–64

135. Dunn, J. D., Critchlow, V. 1973. Electrically stimulated ACTH release in pharmacologically blocked rats. *Endocrinology* 93:835–42

136. Dunn, J. D., Critchlow, V. 1973. Pituitary-adrenal function following ablation of medial basal hypothalamus. *Proc. Soc. Exp. Biol. Med.* 142:749–54

137. Dupouy, J. P. 1975. Sites of the negative feedback action of corticosteroids on the hypothalamo-hypophysial system of the rat fetus. *Neuroendocrinology* 16:148–55

138. Dyer, R. G., Dyball, R. E. J. 1974. Evidence for a direct effect of LRF and TRF on single unit activity in the rostral hypothalamus. *Nature* 252:486–88

139. Efendic, S., Luft, R. 1975. Studies on the mechanism of somatostatin action on insulin release in man. *Acta Endocrinol.* 78:516–23

140. Egdahl, R. H. 1960. The effect of brain removal, decortication and mid brain transection on adrenal cortical function in dogs. *Acta Endocrinol.* 51:49–50

141. Eldridge, J. C., McPherson, J. C. III, Mahesh, V. B. 1974. Maturation of the negative feedback control of gonadotropin secretion in the female rat. *Endocrinology* 94:1536–40

142. Emerson, C. H., Utiger, R. D. 1975. Plasma thyrotropin-releasing hormone concentrations in the rat. *J. Clin. Invest.* 56:1564–70

143. Enock, D., Cohn, M. L. 1975. Somatostatin (SRIF) effects *in vivo* and *in vitro* on cyclic AMP concentrations in rat brain. *Neuroscience* 1:451 (Abstr.)

144. Eskay, R. L., Oliver, C., Ben-Jonathan, N., Porter, J. C. 1975. Hypothalamic hormones in portal and systemic blood. See Reference 12, pp. 125–37

145. Eskay, R. L., Oliver, C., Warberg, J., Porter, J. C. 1976. Inhibition of degradation and measurement of immunoreactive thyrotropin-releasing hormone in rat blood and plasma. *Endocrinology* 98:269

146. Estensen, R. D., Hill, H. R., Quie, P. G., Hogan, N., Goldberg, N. D. 1973. Cyclic GMP and cell movement. *Nature* 245:458–60

147. Evans, G. A., Rosenfeld, M. G. 1976. Cell-free synthesis of a prolactin precursor directed by mRNA from cultured rat pituitary cells. *J. Biol. Chem.* 251(9):2842–47

148. Faglia, G., Beck-Peccoz, P., Ferrari, C., Ambrose, B., Spada, A., Travaglini, P. 1973. Plasma growth hormone response to thyrotropin-releasing hormone in acromegaly. *J. Clin. Endocrinol. Metab.* 36:1259–62

149. Faivre-Bauman, A., Gourdji, D., Grouselle, D., Tixier-Vidal, A. 1975. Binding of thyrotropin releasing hormone and prolactin release by synchronized GH3 rat pituitary cell line. *Biochem. Biophys. Res. Commun.* 67(1):50–57

150. Fell, L. R., Findlay, J. K., Cumming, I. A., Goding, J. R. 1973. Effect of synthetic TRF on prolactin release in sheep. *Endocrinology* 93:487–91

151. Ferland, L., Labrie, F., Jobin, M., Arimura, A., Schally, A. V. 1976. Physiological role of somatostatin in the control of growth hormone and thyrotropin secretion. *Biochem. Biophys. Res. Commun.* 68:149–56

152. Feyrter, F. 1953. *Über die Peripheren Endokrinen (Parakrinen) Drüsen des Menschen,* P. 2. Vienna & Dusseldörf: Maudrich

152a. Fisher, G., Humphries, J., Folkers, K. 1974. Synthesis and some biological activities of substance P. *J. Med. Chem.* 17:843–46

152b. Fitzsimons, J. T. 1972. Thirst. *Physiol. Rev.* 52:458–561

153. Fleischer, N., Vale, W. 1968. Inhibition of vasopressin-induced ACTH release from the pituitary by glucocorticoids in vitro. *Endocrinology* 83:1232–36

154. Franchimont, P., Chari, S., Hagelstein, M. T., Duraiswami, S. 1975. Existence of a follicle-stimulating hormone inhibiting factor 'inhibin' in bull seminal plasma. *Nature* 257:402–4

155. Friedgood, H. B. 1936. (Personal communication to J. Porter): See Porter, J. C., Goldman, B. D., Wilber, J. F. 1970. Hypophysiotropic hormones in portal vessel blood. In *Hypophysiotropic Hormones of the Hypothalamus: Assay and Chemistry,* ed. J. Meites, pp. 282–97. Baltimore, Md: Williams & Wilkins

156. Frohman, L. A., Azabo, M. 1975. Evidence for the existence of prolactin releasing activity distinct from TRH in porcine hypothalamic extracts. *Endocrinology* 96:A86

157. Fujimoto, W. Y., Ensinck, J. W., Williams, R. H. 1974. Somatostatin inhibits insulin and glucagon release by monolayer cell cultures of rat endocrine pancreas. *Life Sci.* 15:1999–2004

158. Fujimoto, W. Y. 1975. Somatostatin inhibition of glucose-, tolbutamide-, theophylline-, cytochalasin B-, and calcium-stimulated insulin release in monolayer cultures of rat endocrine pancreas. *Endocrinology* 97:1494–1500

159. Fujimoto, W. Y., Ensinck, J. W. 1976. Somatostatin inhibition of insulin and glucagon secretion in rat islet culture: Reversal by ionophore A23187. *Endocrinology* 98:259–62

160. Fujino, M., Yamazaki, I., Kobayashi, S., Fukuda, T., Shinagawa, S., Nakayama, R. 1974. Some analogs of luteinizing hormone releasing hormone (LH-RH) having intense ovulation-inducing activity. *Biochem. Biophys. Res. Commun.* 57:1248–56

160a. Fuxe, K., Hokfelt, T. 1970. Central monoaminergic systems and hypothalamic function. In *The Hypothalamus,* ed. L. Martini, M. Motta, F. Fraschini, pp. 123–38. New York: Plenum

161. Gala, R. R., Boss, B. 1975. Serum prolactin levels of rats under continuous estrogen stimulation and 2 Br-α-Ergocryptine (CB-154) injection (38800). *Proc. Soc. Exp. Biol. Med.* 149:330–32

162. Ganten, D. et al 1971. Angiotensinforming enzyme in brain tissue. *Science* 173:64–65

163. Ganten, D. et al 1971. Renin in dog brain. *Am. J. Physiol.* 221:1733–37

163a. Garcia, S. D., Jarrousse, C., Rosselin, G. 1976. Interaction of glucose, cyclic amp, somatostatin, and sulfonylureas on the [³H] leucine incorporation into immunoreactive insulin. *J. Clin. Invest.* 57:260–343

164. Gautvik, K. M. 1976. Effects of prostaglandins on prolactin and growth hormone synthesis and secretion in cultured rat pituitary cells. *Endocrinology* 98:352–58

165. Gay, V. L., Sheth, N. A. 1972. Evidence for a periodic release of LH in castrated

male and female rats. *Endocrinology* 90:158–62

166. Gerich, J. E. et al 1974. Effects of somatostatin on plasma glucose and glucagon levels in human diabetes mellitus. *N. Engl. J. Med.* 291:544–47

167. Gerich, J. E. et al 1974. Inhibition of pancreatic glucagon responses to arginine by somatostatin in normal man and in insulin-dependent diabetics. *Diabetes* 23:876–80

168. Gerich, J. E., Lorenzi, M., Schneider, V., Forsham, P. H. 1974. Effect of somatostatin on plasma glucose and insulin responses to glucagon and tolbutamide in man. *J. Clin. Endocrinol. Metab.* 39:1057–60

169. Gerich, J. E. et al 1975. Evidence for a physiologic role of pancreatic glucagon in human glucose homeostasis: Studies with somatostatin. *Metabolism* 24:175–82

170. Gerich, J. E. et al 1975. Prevention of human diabetic ketoacidosis by somatostatin. Evidence for an essential role of glucagon. *N. Engl. J. Med.* 292:985–89

171. Gerich, J. E., Lorenzi, M., Karam, J. H., Schneider, V., Forsham, P. H. 1975. Abnormal pancreatic glucagon secretion and postprandial hyperglycemia in diabetes mellitus. *J. Am. Med. Assoc.* 234:159–65

172. Gerich, J. E., Lovinger, R., Grodsky, G. M. 1975. Inhibition by somatostatin of glucagon and insulin release from the perfused rat pancreas in response to arginine, isoproterenol and theophylline: Evidence for a preferential effect on glucagon secretion. *Endocrinology* 96:749–54

173. Gerich, J. E., Charles, M. A., Grodsky, G. M. 1976. Regulation of pancreatic insulin and glucagon secretion. *Ann. Rev. Physiol.* 38:353–88

174. Gerich, J. E., Lorenzi, M., Tsalikian, E., Karam, J. H. 1976. Studies on the mechanism of epinephrine-induced hyperglycemia in man. *Diabetes* 25:65–71

175. Giustina, G. et al 1974. Failure of somatostatin to suppress thyrotropin releasing factor and luteinizing hormone releasing factor-induced growth hormone release in acromegaly. *J. Clin. Endocrinol. Metab.* 38:906–9

176. Giustina, G., Peracchi, M., Reschini, E., Panerai, A. E., Pinto, M. 1975. Dose-response study of the inhibiting effect of somatostatin on growth hormone and insulin secretion in normal subjects and acromegalic patients. *Metabolism* 24:807–15

177. Goldberg, N., O'Dea, R. F., Haddox, M. K. 1974. Cyclic GMP. In *Recent Advances in Cyclic Nucleotide Research,* ed. P. Greengard, G. Robison. New York: Raven

178. Goldsmith, P. C., Ganong, W. F. 1975. Ultrastructural localization of luteinizing hormone releasing hormone in the median eminence of the rat. *Brain Res.* 97:181–93

179. Goldsmith, P. C., Rose, J. C., Arimura, A., Ganong, W. F. 1975. Ultrastructural localization of somatostatin in pancreatic islets of the rat. *Endocrinology* 97:1901–94

180. Gomez-Pan, A. et al 1975. Direct inhibition of gastric acid and pepsin secretion by growth-hormone release-inhibiting hormone in cats. *Lancet* 4:888–90

181. Goodner, C. J. 1975. Somatostatin leads to glucagon's renaissance. *N. Engl. J. Med.* 292:1022–23

182. Gordon, J. H., Reichlin, S. 1974. Changes in pituitary responsiveness to luteinizing hormone-releasing factor during the rat estrous cycle. *Endocrinology* 94:974–78

183. Grandison, L., Gelato, M., Meites, J. 1974. Inhibition of prolactin secretion by cholinergic drugs. *Proc. Soc. Exp. Biol. Med.* 145:1236–39

184. Grant, G., Vale, W., Guillemin, R. 1972. Interaction of thyrotropin releasing factor with membrane receptors of pituitary cells. *Biochem. Biophys. Res. Commun.* 46:38–36

185. Grant, H., Clark, E., Rosanoff, I. 1973. Evidence that Pro-Leu-Gly-NH_2 tocinoic acid, and Des-Cys-tocinoic acid do not affect secretion of melanocyte stimulating hormone. *Biochem. Biophys. Res. Commun.* 51:100–6

186. Deleted in proof

187. Grant, G., Vale, W. 1973. Hypothalamic control of anterior pituitary hormone secretion—characterized hypothalamic hypophysiotropic peptides. In *Current Topics in Experimental Endocrinology,* ed. V. H. T. James, pp. 37–72. New York: Academic

188. Grant, G., Vale, W., Guillemin, R. 1973. Characteristics of the pituitary receptor for thyrotropin releasing factor. *Endocrinology* 92:1629

189. Grant, G., Vale, W., Rivier, J. 1973. Pituitary binding sites for [^{3}H]-labelled luteinizing hormone releasing factor (LRF). *Biochem. Biophys. Res. Commun.* 50:771–78

190. Greeley, G. H. Jr., Allen, M. B. Jr., Mahesh, V. B. 1975. Potentiation of luteinizing hormone release by estradiol at the level of the pituitary. *Neuroendocrinology* 18:233–41

191. Green, A. R., Grahame-Smith, D. G. 1974. TRH potentiates behavioural changes following increased brain 5-hydroxytryptamine accumulation in rats. *Nature* 251:524–26

192. Green, J., Harris, G. W. 1947. The neurovascular link between the neurohypophysis and adenohypophysis. *J. Endocrinol.* 5:136–46

193. Greibrokk, T., Hansen, J., Knudsen, R., Lam, Y., Folkers, K., Bowers, C. Y. 1975. On the isolation of a prolactin inhibiting factor (hormone). *Biochem. Biophys. Res. Commun.* 67:338–44

194. Griffiths, E. C., Hooper, K. C., Jeffcoate, S. L., Holland, D. T. 1973. Possible control of luteinizing hormone releasing hormone by enzymatic degradation. *Lancet* 2:862

195. Griffiths, E. C., Hooper, K. C., Jeffcoate, S. L., White, N. 1976. Inactivation of thyrotrophin releasing hormone (TRH) by peptidases in different areas of the rabbit brain. *Brain Res.* 105:376–80

196. Deleted in proof

197. Grimm-Jorgensen, Y., McKelvy, J. F., Jackson, I. M. D. 1975. Immunoreactive thyrotrophin releasing factor in gastropod circumoesophageal ganglia. *Nature* 254:620

198. Guillemin, R., Rosenberg, B. 1955. Humoral hypothalamic control of anterior pituitary. A study with combined tissue cultures. *Endocrinology* 57:599–607

199. Guillemin, R., Gerich, J. E. 1976. Somatostatin: Physiological and clinical significance. *Ann. Rev. Med.* 27:379–88

200. Guillemin, R., Ling, N., Burgus, R. 1976. Endorphines, peptides d'origine hypothalamique et neurohypophysaire à activité morphinomimetique. Isolement et structure moleculaire d' α-endorphin, *C. R. Acad. Sci. Ser. D,* 282:783–85

201. Hall, R. 1973. Action of growth-hormone-release inhibitory hormone in healthy men and in acromegaly. *Lancet* 2:581–84

202. Hansen, A. P. Orskov, H., Seyer-Hansen, K., Lundbaek, K. 1973. Some actions of growth hormone release inhibiting factor. *Br. Med. J.* 3:523–24

203. Harms, P. G., Ojeda, S. R., McCann, S. M. 1973. Prostaglandin involvement in hypothalamic control of gonadotropin and prolactin release. *Science* 141:760–61

204. Havlicek, V. et al 1976. Somatostatin (SRIF) action on cyclic AMP in rat brain; role of central adrenergic mechanisms. *Fed. Proc.* 35:A3175

205. Hayes, J. R., Johnson, D. G., Koerker, D., Williams, R. H. 1975. Inhibition of gastrin release by somatostatin in vitro. *Endocrinology* 96:1374–76

206. Hellman, B., Lernmark, A. 1969. Inhibition of the in vitro secretion of insulin by an extract of pancreatic αl cells. *Endocrinology* 84:1484–88

206a. Herbert, D. 1976. Immunocytochemical evidence that luteinizing hormone (LH) and follicle stimulating hormone (FSH) are present in the same cell type in the rhesus monkey pituitary gland. *Endocrinology* 98:1554–57

207. Hershman, J. M., Kojima, A., Friesen, H. G. 1973. Effect of thyrotropin-releasing hormone on human pituitary thyrotropin, prolactin, placental lactogen, and chorionic thyrotropin. *J. Clin. Endocrinol. Metab.* 36:497–501

208. Hertelendy, F., Todd, H., Yeh, M. 1974. Inhibition by somatostatin of prostaglandin stimulated growth hormone release and cyclic AMP accumulation in rat pituitary glands. *Int. Res. Commun. Syst.* 2:1216

209. Hill-Samli, M., MacLeod, R. M. 1974. Interaction of thyrotropin-releasing hormone and dopamine on the release of prolactin from the rat anterior pituitary in vitro. *Endocrinology* 95:1189–92

210. Hill-Samli, M., MacLeod, R. M. 1975. Thyrotropin-releasing hormone blockade of the ergocryptine and apomorphine inhibition of prolactin release in vitro (38839). *Proc. Soc. Exp. Biol. Med.* 149:511–14

211. Hinkle, P. M., Tashjian, A. H. 1974. Interaction of the thyrotropin releasing hormone with pituitary cells in culture. In *Hormones and Cancer,* ed. Mcterns, pp. 203–27. New York: Academic

212. Hinkle, P. M., Woroch, E. L., Tashjian, A. H. Jr. 1974. Receptor-binding affinities and biological activities of analogs of thyrotropin-releasing hormone in prolactin-producing pituitary cells in culture. *J. Biol. Chem.* 249:3085–90

213. Hinkle, P. M., Tashjian, A. H. 1975. Thyrotropin releasing hormone regulates the number of its own receptors in the GH$_3$ strain of pituitary cells in culture. *Biochemistry* 14:3845–51

214. Hobson, W., Hansel, W. 1974. Increased *in vitro* pituitary response to

LH-RH after *in vivo* estrogen treatment. *Proc. Soc. Exp. Biol. Med.* 146:470–74

215. Hokfelt, T. et al 1975. Cellular localization of somatostatin in endocrine-like cells and neurons of the rat with special references to the A₁-cells of the pancreatic islets and to the hypothalamus. *Acta Endocrinol.* 80 (suppl. 200):5–41

216. Hokfelt, T., Elde, R., Johansson, O., Luft, R., Arimura, A. 1975. Immunohistochemical evidence for the presence of somatostatin, a powerful inhibitory peptide, in some primary sensory neurons. *Neurosci. Lett.* 1:231–35

217. Hokfelt, T., Fuxe, K., Goldstein, M., Johansson, O., Fraser, H., Jeffcoate, S. L. 1976. Immunofluorescence mapping of central monoamine and releasing hormone (LRH) systems. In *Anatomical Neuroendocrinology,* ed. W. E. Stumpf, L. D. Grant. Basel, Switzerland: Karger. In press

218. Hokfelt, T., Kellerth, J. O., Nilsson, G., Pernow, B. 1975. Substance P: localization in the central nervous system and in some primary sensory neurons. *Science* 190:889–90

219. Hokfelt, T., Kellerth, J. O., Nilsson, G., Pernow, B. 1975. Experimental immunohistochemical studies on the localization and distribution of substance P in cat primary sensory neurons. *Brain Res.* 100:235–52

220. Hokfelt, T., Meyerson, B., Nilsson, G., Pernow, B., Sachs, C. 1976. Immunohistochemical evidence for substance P-containing nerve endings in the human cortex. *Brain Res.* 104:181–206

221. Holladay, L. A., Puett, D. 1975. Physicochemical characteristics and proposed conformation of somatostatin. In *Peptides: Chemistry, Structure and Biology,* ed. R. Walter, J. Meienhoffer, pp. 175–79. Ann Arbor, Michigan: Ann Arbor Sci. Publ.

222. Horst, W. D., Spirt, N. 1974. A possible mechanism for the antidepressant activity of thyrotropin releasing hormone. *Life Sci.* 15:1073–82

223. Hruby, V. J., Smith, C. W., Bower, A., Hadley, M. E. 1972. Melanophore stimulating hormone: Release inhibition by ring structures of neurohypophysial hormones. *Science* 176:1331–32

224. Hughes, J. et al 1975. Identification of two related pentapeptides from the brain with potent opiate agonist activity. *Nature* 258:577–79

225. Hughes, J., Smith, T., Morgan, B., Fothergill, L. 1975. Purification and properties of enkephalin—the possible endogenous ligand for the morphine receptor. *Life Sci.* 16:1753–58

226. Huidobro-Toro, J. P., Scotti de Carolis, A., Longo, V. G. 1974. Action of two hypothalamic factors (TRH, MIF) and of angiotensin II on the behavioral effects of L-DOPA and 5-hydroxytryptophan in mice. *Pharmacol. Biochem. Behav.* 2:105–9

227. Imae, T., Fasman, G., Hinkle, P., Tashjian, A. 1975. Intrinsic tryptophan fluorescence of membranes of GH₃ pituitary cells: Quenching by thyrotropin releasing hormone. *Biochem. Biophys. Res. Commun.* 62:923

228. Jackson, I. M. D., Reichlin, S. 1974. Thyrotropin-releasing hormone (TRH): Distribution in hypothalamic and extrahypothalamic brain tissues of mammalian and submammalian chordates. *Endocrinology* 95:854–61

229. Jackson, I. M. D., Reichlin, S. 1974. Thyrotropin releasing hormone (TRH): Distribution in the brain, blood and urine of the rat. *Life Sci.* 14:2253–66

230. Jacobs, L. S., Snyder, P. J., Wilber, J. F., Utiger, R. D., Daughaday, W. H. 1971. Increased serum prolactin after administration of synthetic thyrotropin-releasing hormone (TRF) in man. *J. Clin. Endocrinol.* 33:996–98

231. Jeffcoate, S. L., Holland, D. T. 1974. Chromatographic heterogeneity of immunoreactive luteinizing hormone releasing hormone in blood from the rabbit, sheep and rat. *J. Endocrinol.* 62:333–40

232. Jeffcoate, S. L., Holland, D. T., White, N., Fraser, H. M., Gunn, A., Crighton, D. B., Foster, J. P., Griffiths, E. C., Hooper, K. C., Sharp, P. J. 1975. The radioimmunoassay of hypothalamic hormones (TRH and LHRH) and related peptides in biological fluids. See Reference 12, pp. 279–98

232a. Johansson, K. N. G., Currie, B. L., Folkers, K. 1974. Identification and purification of factor B-GHRH from hypothalami which releases growth hormone. *Biochem. Biophys. Res. Commun.* 60(2):610–15

233. Johnson, D. G., Ensinck, J. W., Koerker, D., Palmer, J., Goodner, C. J. 1975. Inhibition of glucagon and insulin secretion by somatostatin in the rat pancreas perfused in situ. *Endocrinology* 96:370–74

234. Jonas, H. A., Burger, H. G., Cumming, I. A., Findlay, J. K., de Kretser, D. M. 1975. Radioimmunoassay for luteinizing hormone-releasing hormone (LHRH): Its application to the measurement of LHRH in ovine and human plasma. *Endocrinology* 96:384–93

235. Jones, M. T., Hillhouse, E., Burden, J. 1976. Secretion of corticotropin releasing hormone in vitro. See Reference 30, pp. 195–226

236. Jones, M. T., Hillhouse, E., Burden, J. 1976. Chemistry of CRF. See Reference 30, pp. 195–226

237. Jones, M. T. et al 1977. Chemistry of CRF. *Fed. Proc.* In press

238. Jutisz, M., Kerdelhue, B., Berault, A., Paloma de la Llosa, M. 1972. On the mechanism of action of the hypothalamic gonadotropin releasing factors. In *Gonadotropins,* ed. B. B. Saxena, C. G. Beling, H. M. Gandy, pp. 64–71. New York: Wiley Interscience

239. Deleted in proof

240. Kamberi, I. A., McCann, S. M. 1972. Effects of implants of testosterone in the median eminence and pituitary on FSH secretion. *Neuroendocrinology* 9:20–29

241. Kaneko, T., Oka, H., Saito, S., Munemura, M., Musa, K., Oda, T., Yanaihara, N., Yanaihara, C. 1973. *Endocrinol. Jpn.* 20:535

242. Kaneko, T., Saito, S., Oka, H., Oda, T., Yanaihara, N. 1973. Effects of synthetic LH-RH and its analogs on rat anterior pituitary cyclic AMP and LH and FSH release. *Metabolism* 22:77–78

243. Kanematsu, S., Sawyer, C. H. 1973. Elevation of plasma prolactin after hypophysial stalk section in the rat. *Endocrinology* 93:238–41

244. Kao, L. W. L., Weisz, J. 1975. Direct effect of testosterone and its 5 α reduced metabolites on pituitary LH and FSH release *in vitro:* Change in pituitary responsiveness to hypothalamic extract. *Endocrinology* 96:253–60

245. Kastin, A. J., Ehrensing, R. H., Schalch, D. S., Anderson, M. S. 1972. Improvement in mental depression with decreased thyrotropin response after administration of thyrotropin-releasing hormone. *Lancet* 10:740–42

246. Kastin, A. J., Schally, A. V., Gual, C., Glick, S., Arimura, A. 1972. Clinical evaluation in men of a substance with growth hormone-releasing activity in rats. *J. Clin. Endocrinol. Metab.* 35:326–29

247. Kastin, A. J., Beach, G. D., Hawley, W. D., Kendall, J. W. Jr., Edwards, M. S., Schally, A. V. 1973. Dissociation of MSH and ACTH release in man. *J. Clin. Endocrinol. Metab.* 36:770–72

248. Kastin, A. J., Viosca, S., Schally, A. V. 1974. Regulation of melanocyte-stimulating hormone release. *Handb. Physiol.* Sect. 7, Vol. 4 (Part 2):551–62

249. Kastin, A. J., Plotnikoff, N. P., Hall, R., Schally, A. V. 1975. Hypothalamic hormones and the central nervous system. See Reference 12, pp. 261–68

250. Kato, Y., Chihara, K., Ohgo, S., Imura, H. 1974. Effects of hypothalamic surgery and somatostatin on chlorpromazine-induced growth hormone release in rats. *Endocrinology* 95:1608–13

251. Kato, Y., Chihara, K., Ohgo, S., Imura, H. 1974. Inhibiting effect of somatostatin on growth hormone release induced by isoprenaline or chlorpromazine in rats. *J. Endocrinol.* 62:687–88

252. Kato, Y. et al 1975. Plasma growth hormone responses to thyrotropin-releasing hormone in the urethane-anesthetized rat. *Endocrinology* 96:1114–18

253. Keller, H. H., Bartholini, G., Pletscher, A. 1974. Enhancement of cerebral noradrenaline turnover by thyrotropin-releasing hormone. *Nature* 248:528–29

254. Kelly, P. A., Bedirian, K. N., Baker, R. D., Friesen, H. G. 1973. Effect of synthetic TRH on serum prolactin, TSH and milk production in the cow. *Endocrinology* 92:1289–93

255. Keogh, E. J. et al 1976. Selective suppression of FSH by testicular extracts. *Endocrinology* 98:997–1004

256. Kerdelhue, B., Catin, S., Jutisz, M. 1975. Short and long term effects of anti LH-RH serum administration on gonadotropic regulation of the female rat. See Reference 12, pp. 43–56

257. Keyes, W. R., Kelch, R. P., Niswender, G. D., Jaffe, R. B. 1973. Quantitation of endogenous and exogenous gonadotropin releasing hormone by radioimmunoassay. *J. Clin. Endocrinol. Metab.* 36:1263–67

258. Keyes, W. R. Jr., Jaffe, R. B. 1975. Strength-duration characteristics of estrogen effects on gonadotropin response to gonadotropin-releasing hormone in women. I. Effects of varying duration of estradiol administration. *J. Clin. Endocrinol. Metab.* 41:1003–8

259. Kidokoro, Y. 1975. Spontaneous calcium action potentials in a clonal pituitary cell line and their relationship to prolactin secretion. *Nature* 258:741–42

260. King, C. D. 1975. Inhibition of slow wave sleep and rapid eye movement

sleep by thyrotropin releasing hormone in cats. *Pharmacologist* 17:211

260a. Kizer, J. S., Palkovits, M., Brownstein, M. 1976. Releasing factors in the circumventricular organs of the brain. *Endocrinology* 98:311–16

260b. Kizer, J. S., Palkovits, M., Zivin, J. Jr., Brownstein, M., Saavedra, J. M., Kopin, I. J. 1974. The effect of endocrinological manipulations on tyrosine hydroxylase and dopamine-β-hydroxylase in individual hypothalamic nuclei of the adult male rat. *Endocrinology* 95:799–812

261. Kloet, E. R., Van Der Vies, J., de Wied, D. 1974. The site of the suppressive action of dexamethasone on pituitary-adrenal activity. *Endocrinology* 94:61–73

262. Koch, Y., Chobsieng, P., Zor, U., Fridkin, M., Lindner, H. R. 1973. Suppression of gonadotropin secretion and prevention of ovulation in the rat by antiserum to synthetic gonadotropin-releasing hormone. *Biochem. Biophys. Res. Commun.* 55:623–29

263. Koch, Y., Baram, T., Chobsieng, P., Fridkin, M. 1974. Enzymatic degradation of luteinizing hormone-releasing hormone (LH-RH) by hypothalamic tissue. *Biochem. Biophys. Res. Commun.* 61:95–103

264. Koerker, D. J. et al 1974. Somatostatin: Hypothalamic inhibitor of the endocrine pancreas *Science* 184:482–84

265. Kokubu, T., Sawano, S., Shiraki, M., Yamasaki, M., Ishizuka, Y. 1975. Extraction and partial purification of prolactin-release stimulating factor in bovine hypothalami. *Endocrinol. Jpn.* 22:213–17

266. König, W., Sandow, J., Greiger, R. 1975. Structure-function relationships of LH-RH/FSH-RH. See Reference 221, pp. 883–88

267. Kordon, C., Blake, C. A., Terkel, J., Sawyer, C. H. 1973/1974. Participation of serotonin-containing neurons in the suckling-induced rise of plasma prolactin levels in lactating rats. *Neuroendocrinology* 13:213–23

268. Kragt, C. L., Meites, J. 1965. Stimulation of pigeon pituitary prolactin release by pigeon hypothalamic extract in vitro. *Endocrinology* 76:1169–73

269. Kraicer, J. J., Milligan, J. V., Gosbee, J. L., Conrad, R. G., Branson, C. M. 1969. In vitro release of ACTH: Effects of potassium, calcium and corticosterone. *Endocrinology* 85:1144–53

270. Krnjevic, K., Morris, M. E. 1974. An excitatory action of substance P on cuneate neurones. *Can. J. Physiol. Pharmacol.* 52:736–44

271. Krulich, L., Illner, P., Fawcett, C. P., Quijada, M., McCann, S. M. 1972. Dual hypothalamic regulation of growth hormone secretion. In *Growth and Growth Hormone,* ed. A. Pecile, E. E. Muller, pp. 306–16. Amsterdam: Excerpta Medica

272. Krulich, L., Quijada, M., Hefco, E., Sundberg, D. K. 1974. Localization of thyrotropin releasing factor (TRF) in the hypothalamus of the rat. *Endocrinology* 95:9–17

273. Krulich, L., Hefco, E., Aschenbrenner, J. E. 1975. Mechanism of the effects of hypothalamic deafferentiation on prolactin secretion in the rat. *Endocrinology* 96:107–18

274. LaBella, F., Dular, R., Vivian, S., Queen, G. 1973. Pituitary hormones releasing or inhibiting activity of metal ions present in hypothalamic extracts. *Biochem. Biophys. Res. Commun.* 52:786–91

275. Labrie, F., Borden, N., Poirier, G., Delean, A. 1972. Binding of TRF to plasma membranes of bovine anterior pituitary gland. *Proc. Soc. Natl. Acad. Sci.* 69:283

276. Labrie, F. et al 1973. Control of protein synthesis in anterior pituitary gland. In *Karolinska Symp. Res. Methods in Reproductive Endocrinology,* ed. E. Diczfalusy, pp. 301–40. Stockholm: Karolinska Inst.

277. Labrie, F. et al 1975. Mechanism of action and modulation of activity of hypothalamic hypophysiotropic hormones. See Reference 12, pp. 109–24

278. Labrie, F. et al 1976. New aspects of the mechanism of action of hypothalamic regulatory hormones. In *Hypothalamus and Endocrine Functions,* ed. F. Labrie, J. Meites, G. Pelletier, pp. 147–169. New York: Raven

279. Labrie, F., Pelletier, G., Borgeat, P., Drouin, J., Ferland, L., Belanger, A. 1976. Mode of action of hypothalamic regulatory hormones in the adenohypophysis. See Reference 30, pp. 63–93

280. Lal, S., De la Vega, C. E., Sourkes, T. L., Friesen, H. G. 1973. Effect of apomorphine on growth hormone, prolactin, luteinizing hormone and follicle-stimulating hormone levels in human serum. *J. Clin. Endocrinol. Metab.* 37:719–24

281. Lawson, D. M., Gala, R. R. 1975. The influence of adrenergic, dopaminergic, cholinergic and serotoninergic drugs on plasma prolactin levels in ovariectomized, estrogen-treated rats. *Endocrinology* 96:313–18

282. Lazarus, L. H., Brown, M. 1977. Specific binding of neurotensin to rat synaptosomal preparations *in vitro. Life Sci.* Submitted for publication

283. Lazarus, L. H., Ling, N., Guillemin, R. 1976. β-Lipotropin as a prohormone for the morphinomimetic peptides, endorphins and enkephalins. *Proc. Natl. Acad. Sci.* 73:2156–59

284. LeBlanc, H., Anderson, J. R., Sigel, M. B., Yen, S. S. C. 1975. Inhibitory action of somatostatin on pancreatic α and β cell function. *J. Clin. Endocrinol. Metab.* 40:568–72

285. Leeman, S. E., Mroz, E. A. 1975. Substance P. *Life Sci.* 15:2033–44

286. Lembeck, F. 1953. Zur frage der zentralen übertragung afferenter impulse. III. Mitteihung. Das vorkommen und die bedeutung der substanz P in den dorsalen wurzeln des ruckenmarks. *Naunyn-Schmiedebergs' Arch. Exp. Pathol. Pharmakol.* 219:197–213

287. Leopold, N. A., Podolsky, S. 1975. Exaggerated growth hormone response to arginine infusion in Huntington's Disease. *J. Clin. Endocrinol. Metab.* 41:160–63

288. Leppäluoto, J. 1975. Binding of TRF analogs to TRF antiserum. *VII Int. Thyroid Conf. Boston, Mass. June 9–13.* Int. Congr. Ser. No. 361 (Abstr.) Amsterdam: Excerpta Medica

289. Leppäluoto, J., Ling, N., Vale, W. 1976. Purification and measurement of urinary TRF. *V Int. Congr. of Endocrinology, Hamburg Fed. Rep. Germany, July 18–24,* p. 333. (Abstr.)

290. Li, C. H., Chung, C. 1976. Isolation and structure of an untriakontapeptide with opiate activity from camel pituitary glands. *Proc. Natl. Acad. Sci.* 73:1145–48

291. Libertun, C., McCann, S. M. 1974. Further evidence for cholinergic control of gonadotropin and prolactin secretion (38374). *Proc. Soc. Exp. Biol. Med.* 147:498–504

292. Libertun, C., Cooper, K. J., Fawcett, C. P., McCann, S. M. 1974. Effects of ovariectomy and steroid treatment on hypophyseal sensitivity to purified LH-releasing factor (LRF). *Endocrinology* 94:518–25

293. Ling, N., Vale, W. 1975. Analogs of luteinizing hormone releasing factor (LRF). Synthesis and biological activity of [Nα-Me)Leu⁷]LRF. *Biophys. Biochem. Res. Commun.* 63:801–6

294. Lorenzen, L. C., Ganong, W. F. 1976. Effect of drugs related to alpha-ethyltryptamine on stress-induced ACTH secretion in the dog. *Endocrinology* 80:889–92

295. Lorenzi, M., Gerich, J. E., Karam, J. H., Forsham, P. H. 1975. Failure of somatostatin to inhibit tolbutamide-induced insulin secretion in patients with insulinomas: A possible diagnostic tool. *J. Clin. Endocrinol. Metab.* 40:1121–24

296. Loveinger, R. et al 1974. Effect of synthetic somatotropin release inhibiting factor on the increase in plasma growth hormone elicited by L-dopa in the dog. *Endocrinology* 95:943–46

297. Lowry, P. J. 1974. A sensitive method for the detection of corticotrophin releasing factor using a perfused pituitary cell column. *J. Endocrinol.* 62:163–64

298. Lu, K., Shaar, C. J., Kortright, K. H., Meites, J. 1972. Effects of synthetic TRH on in vitro and in vivo prolactin release in the rat. *Endocrinology* 91:1540–45

299. Lu, K., Meites, J. 1973. Effects of serotonin precursors and melatonin on serum prolactin release in rats. *Endocrinology* 93:152–55

300. Lucke, C., Hoffken, B., von zur Muhlen, A. 1975. The effect of somatostatin on TSH levels in patients with primary hypothyroidism. *J. Clin. Endocrinol. Metab.* 41:1082–84

301. Luft, R., Efendic, S., Hokfelt, T., Johansson, O., Arimura, A. 1974. Immunohistochemical evidence for the localization of somatostatin-like immunoreactivity in a cell population of the pancreatic islets. *Med. Biol.* 52:428–30

302. Lugaro, G., Casellato, M. M., Mazzola, G., Fachini, G., Carrea, G. 1974. Evidence for the existence in spermatozoa of a factor inhibiting the follicle stimulating hormone releasing synthesis. *Neuroendocrinology* 15:62–68

303. Lundbaek, K. et al 1976. Failure of somatostatin to correct manifest diabetic ketoacidosis. *Lancet* 1:215–18

304. Lybeck, H., Leppäluoto, J., Virkkunen, P., Schafer, D., Carlsson, L., Mulder, J. 1973. *Neuroendocrinology* 12:366–70

305. Lymangrover, J. R., Brodish, A. 1973/74. Physiological regulation of

tissue-CRF. *Neuroendocrinology* 13:234–45

306. Lymangrover, J. R., Brodish, A. 1973. Time-course of response to hypothalamic extract and multiple use of lesioned rats for CRF assay. *Neuroendocrinology* 12:98–109

307. Lymangrover, J. R., Brodish, A. 1973. Tissue CRF: An extrahypothalamic corticotrophin releasing factor (CRF) in the peripheral blood of stressed rats. *Neuroendocrinology* 12:225–35

308. MacLeod, R., Fontham, E. 1970. Influence of ionic environment on the *in vitro* synthesis and release of pituitary hormones. *Endocrinology* 86:863–69

309. MacLeod, R. M., Lehmeyer, J. E. 1970. Release of pituitary growth hormone by prostaglandins and dibutyryl adenosine cyclic 3', 5'-mono-phosphate in the absence of protein synthesis. *Proc. Natl. Acad. Sci.* 67:1172–79

310. MacLeod, R. M., Lehmeyer, J. E. 1974. Studies on the mechanism of the dopamine-mediated inhibition of prolactin secretion. *Endocrinology* 94:1077–85

311. MacLeod, R. M. 1976. Regulation of prolactin secretion. See Reference 30, pp. 169–94

312. McCann, S. M. et al 1972. The role of monoamines in the control of gonadotropin and prolactin secretion. In *Brain Endocrine Interaction,* ed. K. Knigge, D. Scott, A. Weindl, pp. 224–44. Basel: Karger

313. McCann, S. M., Ojeda, S. R., Libertun, C., Harms, P. G., Krulich, L. 1974. Drug-induced alterations in gonadotropin and prolactin release in the rat. In *Narcotics and the Hypothalamus,* ed. E. Zimmerman, H. Hecht, pp. 121–36. New York: Raven

314. McCullough, D. R. 1932. Dual endocrine activity of testis. *Science* 76:19–23

315. McKelvy, J. F., Grimm-Jorgensen, Y. 1975. Studies on the biosynthesis of thyrotropin releasing hormone. See Reference 12, pp. 13–25

316. McLean, B. K., Nikitovitch-Winer, M. B. 1975. Cholinergic control of the nocturnal prolactin surge in the pseudopregnant rat. *Endocrinology* 97:763–70

317. Machlin, L. J., Jacobs, L. S., Cirulis, N., Kimes, R., Miller, R. 1974. An assay for growth hormone and prolactin-releasing activities using a bovine pituitary cell culture system. *Endocrinology* 95:1350–58

318. Malacara, J. M., Valverde-R., C., Reichlin, S., Bollinger, J. 1972. Elevation of plasma radioimmunoassayable growth hormone in the rat induced by porcine hypothalamic extract. *Endocrinology* 91(5):1189–98

319. Marks, N., Stern, F. 1974. Enzymatic mechanisms for the inactivation of luteinizing hormone-releasing hormone (LH-RH). *Biochem. Biophys. Res. Commun.* 1458–63

320. Marks, N., Stern, F. 1975. Inactivation of somatostatin (GH-RIH) and its analogs by crude and partially purified rat brain extracts. *FEBS Lett.* 55:220–24

321. Martin, J. B. 1974. Inhibitory effect of somatostatin (SRIF) on the release of growth hormone (GH) induced in the rat by electrical stimulation. *Endocrinology* 94:497–502

322. Martin, J. B., Audet, J., Saunders, A. 1975. Effects of somatostatin and hypothalamic ventromedial lesions on GH release induced by morphine. *Endocrinology* 96:836–47

323. Martin, J. B. 1976. Brain regulation of growth hormone secretion. See Reference 30, pp. 129–68

324. Martin, J. E., Tyrey, L., Everett, J. W., Fellows, R. E. 1974. Variation in responsiveness to synthetic LH-releasing factor (LRF) in proestrous and diestrous-3 rats. *Endocrinology* 94:556–62

325. Martin, J. E., Tyrey, L., Everett, J. W., Fellows, R. E. 1974. Estrogen and progesterone modulation of the pituitary response to LRF in the cyclic rat. *Endocrinology* 95:1664–73

326. Matsuo, H., Baba, Y., Nair, R. M. G., Arimura, A., Schally, A. V. 1971. Structure of the porcine LH- and FSH-releasing hormone. I. Proposed amino acid sequence. *Biochem. Biophys. Res. Commun.* 43:1374–1439

327. Matsuyama, H., Ruhmann-Wennhold, A., Nelson, D. H. 1970. Biologic and immunologic similarities between rat and human adrenocorticotropin (ACTH). *Endocrinology* 87:756–63

328. Maurer, R. A., Stone, R., Gorski, J. 1976. Cell-free synthesis of a large translation product of prolactin messenger RNA *J. Biol. Chem.* 251(9)2801–7

329. Milligan, J., Kraicer, J. 1971. Ca uptake during the in vitro release of hormones from the rat adenohypophysis. *Endocrinology* 89:766–73

330. Milmore, J. E., Reece, R. P. 1975. Effects of porcine hypothalamic extract on prolactin release in the rat. *Endocrinology* 96:732–38

331. Mioduszewski, R., Grandison, L., Meites, J. 1976. Stimulation of prolactin

release in rats by GABA (39139). *Proc. Soc. Exp. Biol. Med.* 151:44–46

332. Moldow, R. 1975. Effect of intracranial somatostatin (SRIF) implantation on ACTH release. *Endocrinology* 96:A146

333. Momany, F. A. 1976. Conformational energy analysis of the molecule luteinizing hormone releasing hormone. 2. Tetrapeptide and decapeptide analogues. *J. Am. Chem. Soc.* 98:2996–3000

334. Monachon, M-A., Burkard, W. P., Jalfre, M., Haefely, W. 1972. *Arch. Pharmakol.* 274:192

335. Monahan, M., Amoss, M., Anderson, H., Vale, W. 1973. Synthetic analogs of the hypothalamic luteinizing hormone releasing factor with increased agonist or antagonist properties. *Biochemistry* 12:4616–20

336. Monahan, M., Vale, W., Rivier, C., Grant, G., Guillemin, R. 1973. Analogues of LRF with inhibitory action or greater potency than the natural decapeptide hormone. *Endocrinology* 93:194A

337. Montoya, E., Seibel, M. J., Wilber, J. F. 1975. Thyrotropin-releasing hormone secretory physiology: Studies in radioimmunoassay and affinity chromatography. *Endocrinology* 96:1413–18

338. Mortimer, C. H. et al 1974. Effects of growth-hormone release-inhibiting hormone on circulating glucagon, insulin, and growth hormone in normal, diabetic, acromegalic, and hypo-pituitary patients. *Lancet* 2:697–701

339. Moss, R. L. 1976. Unit responses in preoptic and arcuate neurons related to anterior pituitary function. See Reference 30, pp. 95–128

340. Moss, R. L., McCann, S. M. 1973. Induction of mating behavior in rats by luteinizing hormone-releasing factor. *Science* 181:177–79

341. Mountjoy, C. Q., Price, J. S., Weller, M., Hunter, P., Hall, R., Dewar, J. H. 1974. A double-blind crossover sequential trial of oral thyrotropin-releasing hormone in depression. *Lancet* 5:958–60

342. Mueller, G. P., Chen, H. J., Meites, J. 1973. In vivo stimulation of prolactin release in the rat by synthetic TRH (37645). *Proc. Soc. Exp. Biol. Med.* 144:613–15

343. Mueller, G. P., Chen, H. T., Dibbet, J. A., Chen, H. J., Meites, J. 1974. Effects of warm and cold temperatures on release of TSH, GH, and prolactin in rats. *Proc. Soc. Exp. Biol. Med.* 147:698–700

344. Nair, R. M. G., Barrett, J. F., Bowers, C. Y., Schally, A. V. 1970. Structure of porcine thyrotropin releasing hormone. *Biochemistry* 9:1103–6

345. Nair, R. M. G., Kastin, A. J., Schally, A. V. 1971. Isolation and structure of a hypothalamic MSH release-inhibiting hormone. *Biophys. Biochem. Res. Commun.* 43:1376–81

346. Nemeroff, C. B., Prange, A. J. Jr., Bissette, G., Breese, G. R., Lipton, M. A. 1975. Thyrotropin-releasing hormone (TRH) and its β-alanine analogue: Potentiation of the anticonvulsant potency of phenobarbital in mice. *Psychopharmacol. Commun.* 1:305–17

347. Nemeroff, C. B., Bissette, G., Prange, A. J. Jr., Loosen, P. T., Lipton, M. A. 1976. Centrally administered neurotensin potentiates the depressant actions of pentobarbital. *Proc. 58th Endocrine Soc. Meet.,* p. 312. (Abstr.)

348. Deleted in proof

349. Noel, G. L., Suh, H. K., Frantz, A. G. 1973. L-Dopa suppression of TRH-stimulated prolactin release in man. *J. Clin. Endocrinol. Metab.* 36:1255–58

350. North, R. B., Harik, S. I., Snyder, S. H. 1973. l-prolyl-l-leucyl-glycinamide (PLG): Influences on locomotor and stereotyped behavior of cats. *Brain Res.* 63:435–39

351. Ogawa, N., Friesen, H., Martin, J., Brazeau, P. 1976. Radio-receptor assay for somatostatin. *Endocrinology* 98:A154

352. Ojeda, S. R., Harms, P. G., McCann, S. M. 1974. Effect of blockade of dopaminergic receptors on prolactin and LH release: Median eminence and pituitary sites of action. *Endocrinology* 94:1650–57

353. Ojeda, S. R., Harms, P. G., McCann, S. M. 1974. Possible role of cyclic AMP and prostaglandin E_1 in the dopaminergic control of prolactin release. *Endocrinology* 95:1694–1703

354. Ojeda, S. R., Kalra, P. S., McCann, S. M. 1975. Further studies on the maturation of the estrogen negative feedback on gonadotropin release in the female rat. *Neuroendocrinology* 18:242–55

355. Oliver, C., Charvet, J. P., Codaccioni, J-L., Vague, J. 1974. Radioimmunoassay of thyrotropin-releasing hormone (TRH) in human plasma and urine. *J. Clin. Endocrinol. Metab.* 39:406–9

356. Oliver, C., Eskay, R. L., Ben-Jonathan, N., Porter, J. C. 1974. Distribution and concentration of TRH in the rat brain. *Endocrinology* 548:46

357. Orci, L. et al 1975. Reactivité de la cellule a somatostatin de l'ilot de Langerhans dans le diabete experimental. *C. R. Acad. Sci.* 281:1883–85

357a. Orci, L., Baetens, D., Rufener, C., Brown, M., Vale, W., Guillemin, R. 1976. Neurotensin evidence for immunoreactive mucosa. *Life Sci.* 19: 559–62

358. Otsuka, M., Konishi, S., Takahashi, T. 1975. Hypothalamic substance P as a candidate for transmitter of primary afferent neurons. *Fed. Proc.* 34:1922–28

359. Palkovits, M., Arimura, A., Brownstein, M., Saavedra, J. M. 1974. Luteinizing hormone releasing hormone (LH-RH) content of the hypothalamic nuclei in the rat. *Endocrinology* 95:554–58

360. Parker, D. C. et al 1974. Inhibition of the sleep-related peak in physiologic human growth hormone release by somatostatin. *J. Clin. Endocrinol. Metab.* 38:496–99

361. Pasternak, G. W., Goodman, R., Snyder, S. H. 1975. An endogenous morphine-like factor in mammalian brain. *Life Sci.* 16:1765–69

362. Patel, Y. C., Weir, G. C., Reichlin, S. 1975. Anatomic distribution of somatostatin (SRIF) in brain and pancreatic islets as studied by radioimmunoassay. *Endocrinology* 96:A154

363. Patel, Y. C., Weir, G. C., Reichlin, S. 1976. Immunoreactive somatostatin in gut and pancreatic islets of rat. Submitted for publication

364. Peake, G. T. 1973. The role of cyclic nucleotides in the secretion of pituitary growth hormone. In *Frontiers in Neuroendocrinology,* ed. W. F. Ganong, L. Martini, pp. 173–208. New York: Oxford Univ. Press

365. Pearlmutter, A., Rapino, E., Saffran, M. 1974. A semi-automated in vitro assay for CRF: Activities of peptides related to oxytocin and vasopressin. *Neuroendocrinology* 15:106–19

366. Pearlmutter, A., Rapino, E., Saffran, M. 1975. The ACTH releasing hormone of the hypothalamus requires a co-factor. *Endocrinology* 97:1336–39

367. Pearse, A. G. E., Polak, J. M. 1975. Immunocytochemical localization of substance P in mammalian intestine. *Histochemistry* 41:373–75

368. Pederson, R. A., Dryburgh, J. R., Brown, J. C. 1975. The effect of somatostatin on release and insulinotropic action of gastric inhibitory polypeptide. *Can. J. Physiol. Pharmacol.* 53:1200–5

369. Pelletier, G., Labrie, F., Arimura, A., Schally, A. V. 1974. Electron microscopic immunohistochemical localization of growth hormone-release inhibiting hormone (somatostatin) in the rat median eminence. *Am. J. Anat.* 140: 445–50

370. Pelletier, G., Labrie, F., Puviani, R., Arimura, A., Schally, A. V. 1974. Electron, microscopic localization of luteinizing hormone releasing hormone in the rat median eminence. *Endocrinology* 95:314–15

371. Pelletier, G. et al 1975. Localization of growth hormone-release-inhibiting hormone (somatostatin) in the rat brain. *Am. J. Anat.* 142:397–401

372. Pelletier, G., Leclerc, R., Arimura, A., Schally, A. V. 1975. Immunohistochemical localization of somatostatin in the rat pancreas. *J. Histochem. Cytochem.* 21:699–701

373. Peracchi, M. et al 1974. Effect of somatostatin on blood glucose, plasma growth hormone, insulin, and free fatty acids in normal subjects and acromegalic patients. *Metabolism* 23:1009–15

374. Pfaff, D. W. 1973. Luteinizing hormone-releasing factor potentiates lordosis behavior in hypophysectomized ovariectomized female rats. *Science* 178:417–18

375. Phillis, J. W., Limacher, J. J. 1974. Substance P excitation of cerebral cortical Betz cells. *Brain Res.* 69:158–63

376. Pimstone, B. L., Becker, D., Kronheim, S. 1975. Disappearance of plasma growth hormone in acromegaly and protein-calorie malnutrition after somatostatin. *J. Clin. Endocrinol. Metab.* 40:168–71

377. Plotnikoff, N. P., Kastin, A. J., Anderson, M. S., Schally, A. V. 1971. DOPA potentiation by a hypothalamic factor, MSH release-inhibiting hormone (MIF). *Life Sci.* 10:1279–83

378. Plotnikoff, N. P., Kastin, A. J., Anderson, M. S., Schally, A. V. 1972. Oxotremorine antagonism by a hypothalamic hormone, melanocyte-stimulating hormone release-inhibiting factor (MIF) (36558). *Proc. Exp. Biol. Med.* 140:811–14

379. Plotnikoff, N. P., Prange, A. J. Jr., Breese, G. R., Anderson, M. S., Wilson, I. C. 1972. Thyrotropin releasing hormone: Enhancement of Dopa activity by a hypothalamic hormone. *Science* 178:417–18

380. Plotnikoff, N. P., Kastin, A. J. 1974. Oxotremorine antagonism by Prolyl-

leucyl-glycine-amide administered by different routes with several anticholinergics. *Pharmacol. Biochem. Behav.* 2:417–19

381. Plotnikoff, N. P., Kastin, A. J., Schally, A. V. 1974. Growth hormone release inhibiting hormone: Neuropharmacological studies. *Pharmac. Biochem. Behav.* 2:693–96

382. Plotnikoff, N. P., Minard, F. N., Kastin, A. J., 1974. DOPA potentiation in ablated animals and brain levels of biogenic amines in intact animals after prolyl-leucyl-glycinamide. *Neuroendocrinology* 14:271–79

383. Plotnikoff, N. P., Prange, A. J. Jr., Breese, G. R., Anderson, M. S., Wilson, I. C. 1974. The effects of thyrotropin-releasing hormone on DOPA response in normal, hypophysectomized and thyroidectomized animals. In *The Thyroid Axis, Drugs and Behavior,* ed. A. J. Prange, pp. 103–14. New York: Raven

383a. Plotnikoff, N. P., Breese, G. R., Prange, A. J. Jr. 1975. Thyrotropin releasing hormone (TRH): DOPA potentiation and biogenic amine studies. *Pharmacol. Biochem. Behav.* 3:665–70

384. Plotnikoff, N. P., Prange, A. J. Jr. 1975. Thyrotropin releasing hormone: Enhancement of Dopa activity in thyroidectomized rats. *Life Sci.* 14:1271–78

385. Polak, J. M., Pearse, A. G. E., Grimelius, L., Bloom, S. R., Arimura, A. 1975. Growth-hormone release-inhibiting hormone in gastrointestinal and pancreatic D cells. *Lancet* 5:1220–22

386. Pomerantz, D. K., Foxcroft, G. R., Nalbandov, A. V. 1975. Acute and chronic estradiol-17β inhibition of LH release in prepubertal female pigs: Time course and site of action. *Endocrinology* 96:558–63

387. Portanova, R., Sayers, G. 1973. An in vitro assay for corticotropin releasing factor(s) using suspensions of isolated pituitary cells. *Neuroendocrinology* 12:236–48

388. Portanova, R., Sayers, G. 1973. Isolated pituitary cells: CRF-like activity of neurohypophysial and related polypeptides. *Proc. Soc. Exp. Med. Biol.* 143:661–66

389. Powell, D., Leeman, G. W., Niall, H. D., Potts, J. T. Jr. 1973. Radioimmunoassay for substance P. *Nature New Biol.* 241:252–54

390. Prange, A. J. Jr., Wilson, I. C., Lara, P. P., Alltop, L. B., Breese, G. R. 1972. Effects of thyrotropin-releasing hormone in depression. *Lancet* 11:999–1002

391. Prange, A. J. Jr. et al 1974. Thyrotropin releasing hormone: Antagonism of pentobarbital in rodents. *Life Sci.* 14:447–55

392. Prange, A. J. et al 1975. Modification of pentobarbital effects by natural and synthetic polypeptides: Dissociation of brain and pituitary effects. *Life Sci.* 16:1907–14

393. Prange, A. J. Jr., Nemeroff, C. B., Lipton, M. A., Breese, G. R., Wilson, I. C. 1977. In *Handbook of Psychopharmacology,* ed. L. L. Iversen, S. D. Iversen, S. H. Snyder. New York: Plenum. In press

394. Quijada, M., Illner, P., Krulich, L., McCann, S. M. 1973/1974. The effect of catecholamines on hormone release from anterior pituitaries and ventral hypothalami incubated in vitro. *Neuroendocrinology* 13:151–63

395. Rakoff, J. S., Siler, T. M., Sinha, Y. N., Yen, S. S. C. 1973. Prolactin and growth hormone release in response to sequential stimulation by arginine and synthetic TRF. *J. Clin. Endocrinol. Metab.* 37:641–44

396. Rappaport, R. S., Grant, N. H. 1974. Growth hormone releasing factor of microbial origin. *Nature* 248:73–75

397. Redding, T. W., Schally, A. V. 1967. Studies on the inactivation of thyrotropin-releasing hormone (TRH) *Proc. Soc. Exp. Biol. Med.* 131:415–20

398. Redding, T. W., Coy, E. J. 1974. The disappearance, distribution, and excretion of ^{125}I-labeled tyrosine-l-growth hormone release-inhibiting factor (^{125}I-Tyr-l-GIF) in mice, rats and man. *Endocrinology* 94:A198

399. Rees, L. H., Cook, D. M., Kendall, J. W., Allen, C. F., Dramer, R. M., Ratcliffe, J. G., Knight, R. A. 1971. A radioimmunoassay for rat plasma ACTH. *Endocrinology* 89:254–60

400. Rees, R., Foell, T., Chai, S., Grant, N. 1974. Synthesis and biological activities of analogs of the luteinizing hormone-releasing hormone (LH-RH) modified in position 2. *J. Med. Chem.* 17:1016–19

401. Reichlin, S., Saperstein, R., Jackson, I. M. D., Boyd, A. E. III, Patel, Y. 1976. Hypothalamic hormones. *Ann. Rev. Physiol.* 38:389–424

402. Renaud, L. P., Martin, J. B., Brazeau, P. 1975. Depressant action of TRH, LH-RH and somatostatin on activity of central neurones. *Nature* 255:233–35

403. Rezek, M., Havlicek, V., Hughes, K. R., Friesen, H. 1975. Central action of somatostatin: Role of hippocampus. *Neurosci. Abstr.* 1:253

404. Rippel, R., Johnson, E., White, W., Fujino, M., Yamazaki, I., Nakayama, R. 1973. Ovulating and LH-releasing activity of a highly potent analog of synthetic gonadotropin-releasing hormone. *Endocrinology* 93:1449

405. Rivier, C., Vale, W., Guillemin, R. 1973. An *in vivo* corticotropin-releasing factor (CRF) assay based on plasma levels of radioimmunoassayable ACTH. *Proc. Soc. Exp. Biol. Med.* 142:842–45

406. Rivier, C., Vale, W. 1974. In vivo stimulation of prolactin secretion in the rat by thyrotropin releasing factor and related peptides and hypothalamic extracts. *Endocrinology* 95:978–83

407. Rivier, C., Brown, M., Vale, W. 1976. Substances modifying PRL and GH secretion *in vivo*. *Proc. 58th Endocrine Soc. Meet,.* p. 119. (Abstr.)

408. Rivier, C., Vale, W. Unpublished results.

409. Rivier, J., Brazeau, P., Vale, W., Guillemin, R. 1975. Somatostatin analogs. Relative importance of the disulfide bridge and of the Ala-Gly side chain for biological activity. *J. Med. Chem.* 18:123–26

410. Rivier, J., Brown, M., Vale, W. 1975. D-Trp^8-somatostatin more potent than the native molecule. *Biochem. Biophys. Res. Commun.* 65:746–51

411. Rivier, J., Ling, N., Monahan, M., Rivier, C., Brown, M., Vale, W. 1975. Luteinizing hormone releasing factor and somatostatin analogs. See Reference 43, pp. 863–70

412. Rivier, J., Brown, M., Rivier, C., Ling, N., Vale, W. 1977. Hypothalamic hypophysiotropic hormones: Review on the design of synthetic analogs. *14th Eur. Peptide Symp., Wepion, Belgium.* In press

413. Rivier, J., Brown, M., Vale, W. 1976. Tyrosylated analogs of somatostatin. *J. Med. Chem.* 19:1010–13

413a. Rivier, C., Vale, W., Ling, N., Brown, M., Guillemin, R. 1977. Stimulation *in vivo* of the secretion of prolactin and growth hormone by β-endorphin. *Endocrinology.* In press

414. Robberecht, P., Deschodt-Lanckman, M., De Neef, P., Christophe, J. 1975. Effects of somatostatin on pancreatic exocrine function. *Biochem. Biophys. Res. Commun.* 67:315–23

415. Roth, A. 1968. Quantitative studies on the islets of Langerhans in the pigeon. *Acta. Anat.* 69:609–22

416. Rubin, R. P., Kales, A., Adler, R., Fagan, T., Odell, W. 1971. Gonadotropin secretion during sleep in normal adult men. *Science* 175:196–98

417. Ruch, W. et al 1973. Studies on somatostatin (somatostatin release inhibiting factor) in conscious baboons. In *Advances in Human Growth Hormone Research*, ed. S. Raiti, pp. 271–89. Wash. DC: US Gov. Printing Office

418. Rudinger, J., Pliska, V., Krejci, I. 1972. Oxytocin analogs in the analysis of some phases of hormone action. In *Recent Progress in Hormone Research*, ed. E. B. Astwood, pp. 447–91. New York & London: Academic

419. Saffran, M., Schally, A. V. 1955. The release of corticotropin by anterior pituitary tissue in vitro. *Can. J. Biochem. Physiol.* 33:408–15

420. Said, S. I., Rosenberg, R. N. 1976. Vasoactive intestinal polypeptide: Abundant immunoreactivity in neural cell lines and normal nervous tissue. *Science* 192:907–8

421. Saito, K., Konishi, S., Otsuka, M. 1975. Antagonism between Lioresal and substance P in rat spinal cord. *Brain Res.* 97:177–80

422. Saito, S., Musa, K., Yamamoto, S., Oshima, I., Funato, T. 1975. Radioimmunoassay of thyrotropin releasing hormone in plasma and urine. *Endocrinol. Jpn.* 22(4):303–9

423. Sakurai, H., Dobbs, R., Unger, R. H. 1974. Somatostatin-induced changes in insulin and glucagon secretion in normal and diabetic dogs. *J. Clin. Invest.* 54:1395–1402

424. Sakurai, H., Dobbs, R. E., Unger, R. H. 1975. The role of glucagon in the pathogenesis of the endogenous hyperglycemia of diabetes mellitus. *Metabolism* 24:1287–97

425. Samli, M. H., Geschwind, I. I. 1968. Some effects of energy-transfer inhibitors and of Ca^{++}-free and of K^+-enhanced media on the release of luteinizing hormone from the rat pituitary gland in vitro. *Endocrinology* 82:225–31

426. Sarantakis, D., McKinley, W. A., Jaunakais, I., Clark, D., Grant, N. H. 1976. Structure activity studies on somatostatin. *Clin. Endocrinol.* 5:275s–78s

427. Sawano, S., Baba, Y., Kokubu, T., Ishizuka, Y. 1974. Effect of synthetic

growth hormone-release inhibiting factor on the secretion of growth hormone and prolactin in rats. *Endocrinology Jpn.* 21:333–405

428. Sayers, G., Swallow, R., Giordano, D. 1971. An improved technique for the preparation of isolated rat adrenal cells: A sensitive, accurate and specific method for the assay of ACTH. *Endocrinology* 88:1063–68

429. Sayers, G., Portanova, R. 1974. Secretion of ACTH by isolated anterior pituitary cells: Kinetics of stimulation by corticotropin-releasing factor and of inhibition by corticosterone. *Endocrinology* 94:1723–30

430. Schally, A. V., Andersen, R. N., Lipscomb, H. S., Long, J. M., Guillemin, R. 1964. Evidence for the existence of two corticotropin releasing factors, α -CRF and β-CRF. *Nature* 188:1192–93

431. Schally, A. V., Kuroshima, A., Ishido, U., Redding, I., Bowers, C. Y. 1965. The presence of prolactin inhibiting factor (PIF) in extracts of beef, sheep and pig hypothalami. *Proc. Soc. Exp. Biol. Med.* 118:350–52

432. Schally, A. V., Baba, Y., Nair, R. M. G., Bennett, C. D. 1971. The amino acid sequence of a peptide with growth hormone-releasing activity isolated from porcine hypothalamus. *J. Biol. Chem.* 246:6647–50

433. Schally, A. V., Arimura, A., Kastin, A. J. 1973. Hypothalamic regulatory hormones. *Science* 179:341–50

434. Schally, A. V., Redding, T. W., Arimura, A. 1973. Effect of sex steroids on pituitary responses to LH- and FSH-releasing hormone *in vitro. Endocrinology* 93:893–902

435. Schally, A. V. et al 1976. Reexamination of porcine and bovine hypothalamic fractions for additional luteinizing hormone and follicle stimulating hormone-releasing activities. *Endocrinology* 98:380–91

436. Schally, A. V., Dupont, A., Arimura, A., Redding, T. W., Nishi, N., Linthicum, G., Schlesinger, D. H. 1976. Isolation and structure of somatostatin from porcine hypothalami. *Biochemistry* 15:509–14

437. Schally, A. V., Redding, T. W., Linthicum, G. L. 1976. Inhibition of prolactin release in vivo and in vitro by natural hypothalamic and synthetic gamma-aminobutyric acid. *Endocrinology* 98:A216

438. Scott, A. P., Lowry, P. J., Bennett, H. P. J., McMartin, C., Ratcliffe, J. G.

1974. Purification and characterization of porcine corticotropin-like intermediate lobe peptide. *J. Endocrinol.* 61: 639–80

439. Segal, D. S., Mandell, A. J. 1974. Differential behavioral effects of hypothalamic polypeptides. In *The Thyroid Axis Drugs, and Behavior.* ed. A. J. Prange, Jr., pp. 129–33. New York: Raven

440. Sétalo, G., Vigh, S., Schally, A. V., Arimura, A., Flerko, B. 1975. LH-RH containing neural elements in the rat hypothalamus. *Endocrinology* 96: 135–42

441. Setchell, B. P., Jacks, F. 1974. Inhibin-like activity in rat testes fluid. *J. Endocrinol.* 62:675–76

442. Seyler, L. E. Jr., Reichlin, S. 1974. Feedback regulation of circulating LRF concentrations in men. *J. Clin. Endocrinol. Metab.* 39:906–12

443. Shaar, C. J., Clemens, J. A. 1974. The role of catecholamines in the release of anterior pituitary prolactin in vitro. *Endocrinology* 95:1202–12

444. Shaar, C. J., Euker, J. S., Riegle, G. D., Meites, J. 1975. Effects of castration and gonadal steroids on serum luteinizing hormone and prolactin in old and young rats. *J. Endocrinol.* 66:45–51

445. Sherwin, R. S., Fisher, M., Hendler, R., Felig, P. 1976. Hyperglucagonemia and blood glucose regulation in normal, obese and diabetic subjects. *N. Engl. J. Med.* 294:456–61

446. Shin, S. H., Kraicer, J. 1974. LH-RH radioimmunoassay and its applications: Evidence of antigenically distinct FSH-RH and a diurnal study of LH-RH and gonadotropins. *Life Sci.* 14:281–88

447. Siler, T., Vandenberg, G., Yen, S. S. C. 1973. Inhibition of growth hormone release in humans by somatostatin. *J. Clin. Endocrinol. Metab.* 37:632–34

448. Siler, T. M., Yen, S. S. C., Vale, W., Guillemin, R. 1973. Inhibition by somatostatin on the release of TSH induced in man by thyrotropin-releasing factor. *J. Clin. Endocrinol. Metab.* 38:742–45

449. Sieradzki, J., Schatz, H., Nierle, C., Pfeiffer, E. F. 1975. Somatostatin-induced inhibition of insulin secretion from isolated islets of rat pancreas in presence of glucagon. *Horm. Metab. Res.* 7:284–87

450. Sievertsson, H., Chang, J. K., Folkers, K., Bowers, C. Y. 1972. Synthisis of di- and tri-peptides and assay in vivo for activity in the thyrotropin releasing

hormone and luteinizing releasing hormone systems. *J. Med. Chem.* 15:3–11

451. Sievertsson, H., Castensson, S., Andersson, K., Bjorkman, S. 1975. Thyrotropin and prolactin inhibitory studies by compounds related to the thyrotropin releasing hormone. *Biochem. Biophys. Res. Commun.* 66:1401–7

452. Smalstig, E. B., Sawyer, B. D., Clemens, J. A. 1974. Inhibition of rat prolactin release by apomorphine in vivo and in vitro. *Endocrinology* 95:123–29

453. Smelik, P. G., Papaikonomou, E. 1973. Steroid feedback mechanisms in pituitary-adrenal function. *Prog. Brain Res.* 39:99–109

454. Spona, J. 1973. LH-RH stimulated gonadotropin release mediated by two distinct pituitary receptors. *FEBS Lett.* 35:59–62

455. Stevens, V. C. 1969. Comparison of FSH and LH patterns in plasma urine and urinary extracts during the menstrual cycle. *J. Clin. Endocrinol. Metab.* 29:904–10

456. Stolk, J. M., Nisula, B. C. 1975. Interaction of the tripeptide pyroglutamyl histidyl-proline amide (thyrotropin releasing factor) with brain norepinephrine metabolism: Evidence for an extrahypophyseal action of TRH on central nervous system function. In *Hormones, Homeostasis and the Brain,* ed. W. H. Gropen, T. B. Van Wimersma Greidanus, B. Bohus, D. de Wied, pp. 47–56. Amsterdam: Elsevier

457. Subramanian, M. G., Gala, R. R. 1976. The influence of cholinergic, adrenergic, and serotonergic drugs on the afternoon surge of plasma prolactin in overiectomized, estrogen-treated rats. *Endocrinology* 98:842–48

458. Szabo, M., Frohman, L. A. 1975. Effects of porcine stalk medium eminence and prostaglandin E_2 on rat growth hormone secretion in vivo and their inhibition by somatostatin. *Endocrinology* 96:955–61

459. Szabo, M., Frohman, L. 1976. Suppression of cold-stimulated TSH secretion in the rat by anti-TRH serum. *Endocrinology* 98:A189

460. Takahara, J., Arimura, A., Schally, A. V. 1974. Suppression of prolactin release by a purified porcine PIF preparation and catecholamines infused into a rat hypophysial portal vessel. *Endocrinology* 95:462–65

461. Takahashi, T., Konishi, S., Powell, D., Leeman, S. E., Otsuka, M. 1974. Identification of the motoneuron-depolarizing peptide in bovine dorsal root as hypothalamic substance P. *Brain Res.* 73:59–69

462. Takahashi, M., Yoshinaga, K. 1974. Active immunization of rats with luteinizing hormone releasing hormone. *Endocrinology* 94:A80

463. Takebe, K., Yasuda, N., Greer, M. 1975. A sensitive and simple in vitro assay for corticotropin-releasing substances utilizing ACTH release from cultured anterior pituitary cells. *Endocrinology* 97:1248–55

464. Taleisnik, S., Orias, R. 1965. A melanocyte-stimulating hormone-releasing factor in hypothalamic extracts. *Am. J. Physiol.* 208:213–18

465. Taleisnik, S., Tomatis, E. 1972. Role of catecholamines in the control of melanocyte-stimulating hormone secretion in rats. *Neuroendocrinology* 10: 235–45

467. Taminato, T., Seino, Y., Goto, Y., Imura, H. 1975. Interaction of somatostatin and calcium in regulating insulin release from isolated pancreatic islets of rats. *Biochem. Biophys. Res. Commun.* 66(3):928–34

468. Tang, L. K. L., Spies, H. G. 1975. Effects of gonadal steroids on the basal and LRF-induced gonadotropin secretion by cultures of rat pituitary. *Endocrinology* 96:349–55

469. Tang, L. K. L., Spies, H. G. 1976. Effects of hypothalamic-releasing hormone on LH, FSH and prolactin in pituitary monolayer cultures (39171). *Proc. Soc. Exp. Biol. Med.* 151:189–92

470. Tashjian, A. H., Barowsky, N. J., Jensen, D. K. 1971. Thyrotropin releasing hormone: Direct evidence for stimulation of prolactin by pituitary cells in culture. *Biochem. Biophys. Res. Commun.* 43:516–23

471. Terenius, L. 1975. Effect of peptides and amino acids on dihydromorphine binding to the opiate receptor. *J. Pharm. Pharmacol.* 27:450–52

472. Terenius, L., Gispen, W. H., de Wied, D. 1975. ACTH-like peptides and opiate receptors in the rat brain: Structure-activity studies. *Eur. J. Pharmacol.* 33:395–99

473. Terry, L. C., Martin, J. B., Willoughby, J. O., Brazeau, P. 1976. Antiserum to somatostatin prevents stress-induced inhibition of growth hormone (GH) in the rat. *Abstr. Fed. Proc.* 35:A3173

474. Thody, A. J. 1974. Plasma and pituitary MSH levels in the rat after lesions of

hypothalamus. *Neuroendocrinology* 16:
323–31
475. Thody, A. J. et al 1974. The lack of
effect of MSH release inhibiting factor
(MIF) on the secretion of β-MSH in
normal men. *J. Clin. Endocrinol.
Metab.* 38:491–93
476. Tixier-Vidal, A., Gourdji, D., Pradelles,
P., Morgat, J. L., Promageot, P., Kerdelhue, B. 1975. A cell culture approach
to the study of TRH receptors. In *Hypothalamic Hormones: Chemistry, Physiology, Pharmacology and Clinical Uses,*
ed. M. Motta, P. G. Crosignani, L.
Martini, pp. 89–108. New York: Academic
477. Turcot-Lemay, L., Lemay, A., Lacy, P.
E. 1975. Somatostatin inhibition of insulin release from freshly isolated and
organ cultured rat islets of Langerhans
in vitro. *Biochem. Biophys. Res. Commun.* 63:1130–38
478. Turpen, C., Arimura, A., Dunn, J.
1973. Effect of hypothalamic extract on
serum prolactin levels 24 hr. following
forebrain removal. *Proc. Soc. Exp. Biol.
Med.* 144:651–53
479. Tyrrell, J. B., Lorenzi, M., Gerich, J. E.,
Forsham, P. H. 1975. Inhibition by
somatostatin of ACTH secretion in Nelson's syndrome. *J. Clin. Endocrinol.
Metab.* 40:1125–27
480. Udeschini, G., Cocchi, D., Panerai, A.
E., Gil-Ad, I., Rossi, G., Chiodini, P.
G., Liuzzi, A., Muller, E. E. 1976.
Stimulation of growth hormone release
by thyrotropin-releasing hormone in
the hypophysectomized rat bearing an
ectopic pituitary. *Endocrinology* 98:
807–13
481. Unger, R. H. 1975. Diabetes and the
alpha cell. *Diabetes* 25:136–51
482. Usategui, R. et al 1976. Immunoreactive α-MSH and ACTH levels in rat
plasma and pituitary. *Endocrinology*
98:189–96
483. Utsumi, M., Makimura, H., Yamada,
A., Tateiwa, M., Mori, H., Kusaka, T.,
Sakoda, M., Baba, S. 1974. Effect of
somatostatin (growth hormone inhibiting factor: GIF) on TRH-induced TSH
release in rats. *Endocrinology Jpn.*
21:449–52
484. Vagenakis, A. G., Roti, E., Mannix, J.,
Braverman, L. E. 1975. Problems in the
measurement of urinary TRH. *J. Clin.
Endocrinol. Metab.* 41:801–4
485. Vale, W., Burgus, R., Guillemin, R.
1967. Presence of calcium ions as a requisite for the in vitro stimulation of TSH

release by hypothalamic TRF. *Experientia* 23:853–55
486. Vale, W., Guillemin, R. 1967. Potassium induced stimulation of thyrotropin release in vitro: Requirement for
presence of calcium and inhibition by
thyroxine. *Experientia* 23:855–57
487. Vale, W., Burgus, R., Guillemin, R.
1968. On the mechanism of action of
TRF: Effects of cycloheximide and actinomycin on the release of TSH stimulated in vitro by TRF and its inhibition
by thyroxine. *Neuroendocrinology* 3:
34–46
488. Vale, W., Burgus, R., Dunn, T. F.,
Guillemin, R. 1971. In vitro plasma inactivation of thyrotropin releasing factor (TRF) and related peptides: Its inhibition by various means and by the
synthetic dipeptide PCA-His-OMe.
Hormones 2:193–203
489. Vale, W., Grant, G., Amoss, M., Blackwell, R., Guillemin, R. 1972. Culture of
enzymatically dispersed anterior pituitary cells: Functional validation of a
method. *Endocrinology* 91:562–72
490. Vale, W., Brazeau, P., Grant, G., Nus-
sey, A., Burgus, R., Rivier, J., Ling, N.,
Guillemin, R. 1972. Premières observations sur le mode d'action de la somatostatine un facteur hypothalamique qui
inhibe la sécrétion de l'hormone de
croissance. *C. R. Acad. Sci. Paris*
275:2913
491. Vale, W., Grant, G., Rivier, J., Monahan, M., Amoss, M., Blackwell, R.,
Burgus, R., Guillemin, R. 1972. Synthetic polypeptide antagonists of the
hypothalamic luteinizing hormone releasing factor. *Science* 176:933–34
492. Vale, W., Blackwell, R., Grant, G.,
Guillemin, R. 1973. TRF and thyroid
hormones on prolactin secretion by rat
anterior pituitary cells *In vitro. Endocrinology* 93:26–33
493. Vale, W., Brazeau, P., Rivier, C.,
Rivier, J., Guillemin, R. 1973. Biological studies with somatostatin. In *Advances in Growth Hormone Research,*
pp. 159–82. Wash. D.C.: Natl. Inst.
Health
494. Vale, W., Grant, G., Guillemin, R.
1973. Chemistry of the hypothalamic
releasing factors—studies on structure-
function relationships. In *Frontiers in
Neuroendocrinology,* ed. L. Martini, W.
F. Ganong, pp. 375–413. New York:
Oxford Univ. Press
495. Vale, W., Brazeau, P., Rivier, C.,
Brown, M., Boss, B., Rivier, J., Burgus,
R., Ling, N., Guillemin, R. 1975.

Somatostatin. *Rec. Prog. Hormone Res.* 31:365–97

496. Vale, W., Rivier, C., Brazeau, P., Guillemin, R. 1974. Effects of somatostatin on the secretion of thyrotropin and prolactin. *Endocrinology* 95: 968–77

497. Vale, W., Rivier, C., Palkovits, M., Saavedra, J. M., Brownstein, M. 1974. Ubiquitous brain distribution of inhibitors of adenohypophysial secretion. *Endocrinology* 94:A–78

498. Vale, W., Rivier, C. 1975. Hypothalamic hypophysiotropic hormones. In *Handbook of Psychopharmacology*, ed. L. L. Iverson, S. D. Iverson, S. H. Snyder, pp. 195–238. New York: Plenum

499. Vale, W., Rivier, C., Rivier, J., Ling, N., Monahan, M., Guillemin, R. 1975. Synthetic and native substances modifying secretion of gonadotropins. *Endocrinology* 96:A99

500. Vale, W., Rivier, C., Brown, M., Leppäluoto, J., Ling, N., Monahan, M., Rivier, J. 1976. Pharmacology of hypothalamic regulatory peptides. *Clin. Endocrinol. 5(Suppl.):261s–273s*

501. Vale, W., Ling, N., Rivier, C., Rivier, J., Villarreal, J., Brown, M. 1976. Anatomic and phylogenetic distribution of somatostatin. *Metabolism.* 25:1491–94

502. Vale, W. et al 1976. Application of adenohypophyseal cell cultures to neuroendocrine studies. In *Hypothalamus and Endocrine Functions*, ed. F. Labrie, J. Meites, G. Pelletier, pp. 397–429. New York: Plenum

503. Vale, W., Rivier, C. 1976 Regulation of ACTH secretion by anterior pituitary cells in culture. *Fed. Proc.* 35: In press

504. Valverde-R, C., Chieffo, V., Reichlin, S. 1972. Prolactin-releasing factor in porcine and rat hypothalamic tissue. *Endocrinology* 91:982–93

505. Van Loon, G. R., Scapagnini, U., Moberg, G. P., Ganong, W. F. 1971. Evidence for central adrenergic neural inhibition of ACTH secretion in the rat. *Endocrinology* 89:1464–69

506. Vandenberg, G., DeVane, G., Yen, S. S. C. 1974. Effects of exogenous estrogen and progestin on pituitary responsiveness to synthetic hormone-releasing factor. *J. Clin. Invest.* 53:1750–54

507. Vanderhaeghen, J. J., Signeau, J. C., Gepts, W. 1975. New peptide in the vertebrate CNS reacting with antigastrin antibodies. *Nature* 257:604–5

508. Veber, D. F., Bennett, C. D., Milkowski, J. D., Gal, G., Denkewalter, R. G.,

Hirschmann, R. 1971. Synthesis of a proposed growth hormone releasing factor. *Biochem. Biophys. Res. Commun.* 45:235–39

509. Veber, D. F. et al 1976. Nonreducible cyclic analogues of somatostatin. *J. Am. Chem. Soc.* 98:2367–69

510. Vernikos-Danellis, J., Marks, B. H. 1969. Hypophysiotropic hormones of the hypothalamus. In *Assay and Chemistry*, ed. J. Meites. Baltimore: Williams & Wilkins

511. Vilchez-Martinez, J. A., Arimura, A., Debeljuk, L., Schally, A. V. 1974. Biphasic effect of estradiol benzoate on the pituitary responsiveness to LH-RH. *Endocrinology* 94:1300–3

512. Vilchez-Martinez, J., Coy, D., Coy, E., De la Cruz, A., Nishi, N., Schally, A. V. 1975. Prolonged inhibition of gonadotropin release and suppression of ovulation by synthetic antagonists of LH-RH. *Endocrinology* 96:354A

513. Villarreal, J. A., Vale, W., Brown, M., Butcher, M., Brazeau, P., Rivier, C., Burgus, R. 1976. Myelin basic protein: A substance that releases immunoreactive growth hormone in vitro. *Biochem. Biophys. Res. Commun.* 70(2):551–58

514. von Euler, U. S., Gaddum, J. H. 1931. An unidentified depressor substance in certain tissue extracts. *J. Physiol.* 72:74–87

515. Wahren, J., Felig, P. 1976. Somatostatin (SRIF) and glucagon in diabetes: Failure of glucagon suppression to improve i.v. glucose tolerance and evidence of an effect of SRIF on glucose absorption. *Clin. Res.* 24:461A

516. Wakabayashi, K., Kamberi, I. A., McCann, S. M. 1969. In vitro response of the rat pituitary to gonadotropin-releasing factors and to ions. *Endocrinology* 85:1046–56

517. Ward, F. R., LeBlanc, H., Yen, S. S. C. 1975. The inhibitory effect of somatostatin on growth hormone, insulin and glucagon secretion in diabetes mellitus. *J. Clin. Endocrinol. Metab. 41:527–32*

518. Watkins, B. E., Meites, J., Riegle, G. D. 1975. Age-related changes in pituitary responsiveness to LHRH in the female rat. *Endocrinology* 97:543–48

519. Weeke, J., Hansen, A. P., Lundbaek, K. 1975. Inhibition by somatostatin of basal levels of serum thyrotropin (TSH) in normal men. *J. Clin. Endocrinol. Metab.* 41:168–71

520. Wei, E., Sigel, S., Loh, H., Way, E. L. 1975. Thyrotropin-releasing hormone

and shaking behaviour in rat. *Nature* 253:739–40

521. Weir, G. C., Knowlton, S. D., Martin, D. B. 1974. Somatostatin inhibition of epinephrine-induced glucagon secretion. *Endocrinology* 95:1744–46

522. Wheaton, J. E., Krulich, L., McCann, S. M. 1975. Localization of luteinizing hormone releasing hormone LRH in the preoptic area and hypothalamus of the rat using radioimmunoassay. *Endocrinology* 97:30–38

523. Wilson, M. C., Steiner, A. L., Dhariwal, A. P., Peake, G. T. 1974. Purified ovine growth hormone releasing factor: Effects on growth hormone secretion and pituitary cyclic nucleotide accumulation. *Neuroendocrinology* 15:313–27

524. Winokur, A., Utiger, R. D. 1974. Thyrotropin releasing hormone: Regional distribution in rat brain. *Science* 185:265–67

525. Yasuda, N., Takebe, K., Greer, M. A. 1976. Studies on ACTH dynamics in cultured adenohypophyseal cells: Effect of adrenalectomy or dexamethasone *in vivo*. *Endocrinology* 98:1717

526. Yasuda, N., Greer, M. A. 1976. Studies on the corticotropin-releasing activity of vasopressin, using ACTH secretion by cultured rat adenohypophyseal cells. *Endocrinology* 98:936–42

527. Yates, F. E., Russell, S. M., Dallman, M. F., Hedge, G. A., McCann, S. M., Dhariwal, A. P. 1971. Potentiation by vasopressin corticotropin release induced by corticotropin-releasing factor. *Endocrinology* 88:3–15

528. Yates, F. E., Maran, J. W. 1974. Stimulation and inhibition of adrenocorticotropin release. *Handb. Physiol. Volume 4* Sect. 7:367–404

529. Yen, S. S. C. et al 1973. Effects of somatostatin on GH, TSH and insulin secretion in human subjects. In *Advances in Human Growth Hormone Research*, ed. J. R. Geiger, S. Raiti, pp. 609–34. Wash. DC: US Gov. Print. Office

530. Yen, S. S. C., Siler, T. M., DeVane, G. W. 1974. Effect of somatostatin in patients with acromegaly. *N. Engl. J. Med.* 290:935–38

531. Yen, S. S. C., Vandenberg, G., Siler, T. M. 1974. Modulation of pituitary responsiveness to LRF by estrogen. *J. Clin. Endocrinol. Metab.* 39:170–77

532. York, D. H., Baker, F. L., Kraicer, J. 1973. Electrical changes induced in rat adenohypophysial cells, *in vivo*, with hypothalamic extract. *Neuroendocrinology* 11:212–28

533. Zetler, G. 1970. Biologically active peptides (substance P). In *Handbook of Neurochemistry*, ed. A. Lajtha, pp. 135–48. New York: Plenum

534. Zimmermann, E., Smyrl, R., Critchlow, V. 1972. Suppression of pituitary-adrenal response to stress with physiological plasma levels of corticosterone in the female rat. *Neuroendocrinology* 10:246–56

535. Zimmermann, E., Krivoy, W. 1973. Antagonism between morphine and the polypeptides ACTH, ACTH$_{1-24}$ and β-MSH in the nervous system. In *Drug Effects on Neuroendocrine Regulation, Prog. Brain Res.*, 39:383–92

536. Zimmerman, E. A., Hsu, K. C., Ferin, M., Kozlowski, G. P. 1974. Localization of gonadotropin-releasing hormone (Gn-RH) in the hypothalamus of the mouse by immunoperoxidase technique. *Endocrinology* 95:1–8

537. Zimmerman, E. A. 1976. Localization of hypothalamic hormones by immunocytochemical techniques. See Reference 30, pp. 25–62

Ann. Rev. Physiol. 1977. 39:529–57
Copyright © 1977 by Annual Reviews Inc. All rights reserved

PEPTIDE HORMONE RECEPTORS

K. J. Catt and M. L. Dufau

Reproduction Research Branch, National Institute of Child Health
and Human Development, Bethesda, Maryland 20014

INTRODUCTION

There is now abundant evidence that peptide hormones and transmitter molecules such as catecholamines and acetylcholine exert their primary actions on target cells by binding to specific high-affinity receptor sites in the plasma membrane. The existence of such receptors, previously implied in theories of drug and hormone action, has recently been demonstrated in numerous target cells for peptide hormones and transmitters by direct binding studies with radioactive ligands. In several tissues, occupancy of specific binding sites by labeled hormone has been correlated with activation of characteristic target cell responses, confirming that such sites are biologically significant hormone receptors. In other tissues, peptide receptors have been provisionally identified by their high affinity and specificity for biologically active forms of the corresponding hormone. When applicable, the use of competitive antagonists to block both hormone binding and the consequent target cell response has provided additional validation of putative hormone receptors. Certain receptor sites, such as those for acetylcholine and catecholamines, have been most effectively characterized by the use of labeled antagonists (12, 123, 176). The relatively low affinity of the acetylcholine receptor for cholinergic ligands (52) and the low concentration of β-adrenergic receptors in target cells (106) caused difficulty in the characterization of these receptors by studies employing labeled agonists.

The cell membrane as a site of action of peptide hormones was proposed by Sutherland and colleagues (74, 167) based upon observations which included the finding that interaction of catecholamines with the plasma membrane of pigeon erythrocytes led to activation of adenylate cyclase. Since then, the majority of peptide hormones have been shown to bind to plasma membrane receptors and to influence membrane-associated activities such as adenylate cyclase and ion transport. Further evidence for the surface location of peptide hormone receptors was provided by the finding that brief exposure of target tissue to hormone was followed by a prolonged biochemical response, attributable to bound hormone, and that addition of specific antiserum would rapidly terminate the action of peptide hormones in vitro (134). Furthermore, hormonal stimulation of adenylate cyclase was widely observed in plasma membranes from broken cells, and enzymes modifying membrane proteins and lipids were found to abolish the hormonal responsiveness of adenylate cyclase (138). The surface location of peptide hormone receptors has also been indicated by demonstrations that peptide hormones retain biological activity when coupled to macromolecular carriers which are presumably unable to enter the cell (27), though the reliability of this approach has been questioned (88). However, the most compelling evidence for the location of peptide hormone receptors in the plasma membrane has been derived by direct binding studies with membrane preparations or intact cells and radioactive, biologically active hormones. Such studies permit accurate determination of the binding characteristics and hormonal specificity of the cellular receptor sites, and their functional relationship to target-cell responses. This approach is particularly useful when applied to intact cell preparations in which both binding and activation studies are performed under identical conditions of incubation (92, 93, 120).

Since the general scheme of peptide hormone action upon membrane receptors and adenylate cyclase was proposed on the basis of studies with catecholamines, vasopressin, glucagon, and ACTH[1] (167), many peptide hormones have been shown to cause activation of adenylate cyclase and elevation of intracellular cAMP levels (145). Although cAMP appears to act as the second messenger in the action of numerous peptide hormones, there are now well-recognized dissociations between cAMP formation and target cell responses during hormone action (6, 17, 21, 120, 175). Also, for certain hormones, such as insulin and growth hormone, the mechanism of target cell activation has not been clarified. Even in tissues for which cAMP is accepted as a second messenger of peptide hormone action, it is not known how such a single effector system is translated into a number of individual target cell responses. This question is complicated by the dual nature of many peptide and protein hormones, which function as trophic factors with long-term effects on cell growth and differentiation, and also as acute regulators of cell responses such as steroidogenesis and hormone secretion. The relationship between these two aspects of peptide hormone action is not well understood, and most of our knowledge about cellular responses to hormone-receptor interaction is based on studies of the acute actions of peptide hormones upon their target cells.

Direct measurements of the properties and concentration of peptide hormone receptors were initiated by studies on the binding of radioiodinated ACTH (96) and angiotensin II (108) to receptors in adrenal tissue. Since then, numerous peptide hormones have been shown to bind to membrane receptors in target cells with high specificity and affinity, and peptide hormone receptors have been extensively studied

---

[1]Abbreviations used in this review: ACTH, adrenocorticotrophic hormone; AIB, α-amino isobutyric acid; cAMP, cyclic 3', 5'-adenosine monophosphate; FSH, follicle stimulating hormone; Gpp(NH)p, 5'-guanylylimidodiphosphate; GTP, guanosine triphosphate; hCG, human chorionic gonadotropin; LH, luteinizing hormone; NSILA-s, nonsuppressible insulin-like activity, soluble in acid ethanol; TSH, thyroid stimulating hormone.

in tissue homogenates, dispersed cells, membrane preparations, and solubilized cell fractions (82, 149). Many of the properties of individual receptor sites, such as those for insulin, gonadotropins, and other peptide hormones, have been recently reviewed in detail (19, 21–23, 31–33, 50, 83, 87, 140). Rather than to extend the catalogue of such receptors, this review concentrates upon the general properties of peptide hormone receptors, and those aspects of receptor function relevant to the regulation of target cell responses under physiological conditions.

ANALYSIS OF HORMONE-RECEPTOR INTERACTIONS

Early studies on hormone binding to target tissues employed measurements of the disappearance of unlabeled hormone from incubation medium (26, 164), or of its uptake by the target cells, by procedures such as radioimmunoassay. The use of radioactive hormones for in vitro binding studies (165) was initially complicated by the uncertain biological activity and binding specificity of radioiodinated hormones. However, in vivo studies with radioiodinated hormones clearly demonstrated selective and specific uptake of tracer hormone by recognized target cells. Thus, specific uptake of ^{125}I-labeled luteinizing hormone was observed in the Leydig cells of the testis (34). The introduction of methods for labeling peptide hormones to high specific radioactivity, with retention of biological activity, permitted in vitro demonstration of hormone receptor sites (149). Direct measurement of hormone binding to specific receptor sites has been performed in a large number of target tissues, and binding of virtually all known peptide hormones and ligands to specific receptors has been demonstrated by the use of radioiodinated or tritiated derivatives. The majority of such binding studies were initially performed in cell homogenates and/or partially purified membrane fractions. However, the increasing use of cell cultures and enzyme-dispersed target tissues has led to the utilization of intact cells for studies on hormone-receptor interactions, with several attendant advantages.

When appropriately prepared, intact target cells display the same high specificity and affinity for peptide hormones (61, 93, 102, 120) and catecholamines (13) as broken cell preparations. Furthermore, the use of dispersed cells permits correlations between hormone binding and biological responses which depend upon the metabolic activities of the intact cells. Hormone binding to intact cell preparations is studied under conditions of medium composition and temperature which are more commensurate with those which pertain in vivo, and the processes of hormone and receptor degradation are frequently less marked than in cell homogenates and membrane preparations. Also, the use of intact and viable cells facilitates the study of regulatory actions of extracellular hormone concentrations upon specific receptors, a process which has been recently observed to occur in vitro as well as in vivo (83). Such analyses of hormone-receptor interactions and the consequent metabolic responses are most appropriately performed in homogeneous cell populations. Cell dispersions prepared from endocrine target tissues and circulating cells are usually heterogeneous, and require additional purification before use in studies of hormonal stimulus-response coupling. The use of cultured cells facilitates the preparation of target cell suspensions and offers potentially greater homogeneity when cloned cells are employed. However, it should be noted that the frequently neoplastic or transformed nature of cultured cells may alter the nature and properties of the surface receptors.

The majority of peptide hormone receptors studied in cells or particulate fractions by direct binding methods with labeled hormones have shown relatively simple saturation properties, consistent with the presence of one or more sets of binding sites with relatively high affinity for the hormonal ligand. Several peptide hormone receptors, including those for luteinizing hormone (16), growth hormone (101), and prolactin (158), interact with the respective hormone in accordance with binding isotherms for a single set of homogeneous non-interacting sites. For such receptors, the direct binding curve can be fitted by models based upon the Langmuir and Michaelis-Menten equations for a single binding site; Scatchard plots are linear over a wide range of hormone concentrations, and Hill plots give a slope of unity. However, certain other receptors, including those for ACTH (98), insulin (37, 38), angiotensin II (65), and catecholamines (107), show more complex binding curves and concave Scatchard plots. Such findings indicate the presence of two or more sets of binding sites, or of site-site interactions which lead to negative cooperativity during the binding process. The latter mechanism has been shown to occur during binding of insulin by specific receptors in many target tissues (35), and leads to progressive reduction of binding affinity during increasing occupancy of receptor sites. The occurrence of negative cooperativity during hormone-receptor interaction cannot be distinguished from the effects of multiple sets of binding sites by equilibrium data alone. Recognition of negative cooperativity requires the demonstration of an increase in the dissociation rate constant with increasing degrees of receptor occupancy (38). This mechanism has been proposed to serve as a buffer against the biological effects of elevated hormone concentrations, while preserving high sensitivity to changes within the physiological range of circulating hormone concentration (35, 38).

The occurrence and biological implications of negative cooperativity have been most clearly and extensively demonstrated for the insulin receptor; cooperative binding by other hormonal ligands has been less extensively validated. Although objections to the interpretation of insulin binding data as the result of negative cooperativity have been raised (33), the studies of De Meyts and others have provided evidence that negatively cooperative interactions occur not only among insulin receptors, but also with receptors for nerve growth factor, epidermal growth factor, thyrotropin, and catecholamines (35).

THE NATURE OF PEPTIDE HORMONE RECEPTORS

Current attitudes about hormone receptors are still based upon the notion of a "receptive substance" that mediates hormone action, an idea introduced by Langley in 1905 to express his view that combination with a component of the target tissue is a necessary part of drug action (see 166). The term "receptor" was subsequently employed to express this concept, and has been extensively utilized in pharmacological studies in which drug antagonists were employed to analyze the properties of receptor sites for various neurotransmitters and neurohormones. The use of labeled agonist and antagonist molecules for direct analysis of receptor sites was made possible by the use of radioactive hormones of high specific activity, a technique which had been extensively developed for the radioimmunoassay of circulating concentrations of peptide hormones in plasma (89, 149).

Quantitative binding studies with isotopically labeled hormones which retain biological activity have defined a series of characteristics that apply to the majority of peptide hormone receptors. The universal feature of receptors is their ability to recognize and bind the respective chemical messenger or hormone in the presence of a vast excess of other molecular species. This property is most readily demonstrable with labeled hormone, as a selective high-affinity binding reaction which leads to the formation of a specific hormone-receptor complex. Such interactions have been observed in a multitude of hormone-responsive tissues during the last six years (149). In many studies, the presence of specific binding sites in appropriate target tissues has been accepted as evidence for the presence of hormone receptors. Also, specific binding sites have been described in cells which are not currently recognized as target tissues, e.g. insulin and growth hormone receptors in lymphocytes (61, 102), and prolactin receptors in liver and adrenal (140). Although the conventional view of receptors embodies a response as well as a recognition component, the over-rigid use of such a definition would exclude such receptors for which the functional response is as yet undetermined, and those which are isolated, solubilized, or situated upon an unresponsive cellular component (150). The biological validity of receptor sites which are solely characterized by hormone binding studies has been most persuasively developed during investigation of receptors for which the response function is relatively poorly defined.

The more comprehensive view of a hormone receptor embodies the dual functional properties of recognition plus translation of the hormone-receptor interaction into a specific biological response. Whether such a response is peptide secretion, steroidogenesis, contraction, or ion transport, the usual mechanism which mediates hormone action is stimulation of adenylate cyclase and formation of cAMP.

In many target tissues, a reasonable correspondence between hormone binding and subsequent biochemical responses has been observed in membrane fractions or intact cells. Correlations between receptor occupancy and adenylate cyclase activity have been extensively demonstrated in membrane fractions e.g. of the adrenal with ACTH (96), the liver with glucagon (8), the kidney with vasopressin (11), the avian erythrocyte with catecholamine (13), the testis tubule with FSH (117), and the ovary with LH (121). In intact tissue and isolated target cells, hormone binding has also been correlated with the synthesis and release of cAMP (17, 24, 115, 120). In certain tissues which exhibit relatively small adenylate cyclase responses to hormonal stimulation after homogenization, quite marked increases in cAMP formation can be observed in the intact cell, and are closely correlated with hormone binding to tissue receptor sites (120). Correlation of hormone binding with more distal responses has been observed less frequently, with insulin and glucose oxidation in fat cells (64, 93) or AIB transport in thymocytes (68), catecholamines and sodium transport in erythrocytes (4), LH with testicular androgen production (17, 19, 120), and angiotensin II with aldosterone production by the zona glomerulosa cell (40).

It has been proposed that the definition of hormone receptors should be restricted to tissue binding sites which can be equated with a defined biochemical response, and the potential error of equating all hormone binding sites with receptors has been stressed (9, 32). However, specific binding of labeled ligands has been shown to provide a valuable indication of hormone receptor sites when appropriate requirements of the binding technique are observed. These include the use of labeled hormone of demonstrated biological activity (frequently attainable by monoiodination and tritiation), the accurate determination of nonspecific binding, and the exclusion of binding to degradative or other enzymic activities in tissue fractions. The majority of peptide hormone receptors exhibit high specificity for biologically active hormones and their derivatives, high binding affinity with equilibrium association constants of 10^9-10^{11} M^{-1}, and saturability at relatively low hormone concentrations. The latter properties reflect the relatively low concentration of hormone receptors in target tissues, usually of the order of a few thousand sites per cell. The binding reaction is always temperature dependent and fairly rapid, and is frequently reversible in broken-cell preparations. Unfortunately, the exact determination of binding constants and thermodynamic properties of receptors is complicated by the occurrence of hormone and receptor degradation during in vitro binding studies at physiologic temperatures. Although such degradative processes can be measured and corrected by appropriate techniques (91), there is a paucity of data about the kinetic and equilibrium binding properties of hormone receptors under conditions which pertain in vivo. In particular, the rates of hormone association and dissociation are markedly influenced by temperature, and the turnover of hormone molecules at the receptor sites during in vivo conditions of temperature and perfusion has not been adequately studied by direct binding techiques.

PHYSICO-CHEMICAL PROPERTIES OF PEPTIDE HORMONE RECEPTORS

The protein nature of plasma membrane receptors for polypeptide hormones has been clearly indicated by their susceptibility to digestion by a variety of proteolytic enzymes and peptidases. In addition, several such receptors have been influenced by exposure to phospholipase, suggesting that they contain a significant phospholipid component, or that binding activity is influenced by association with the phospholipid membrane structure (28, 43, 104). Several receptors (for insulin, LH, and TSH) have been reported to contain carbohydrate moieties, and the LH receptor has been shown to depend upon disulfide groups for maintenance of the biologically active conformation (46).

The role of gangliosides in ligand-receptor interactions has recently been indicated by the finding that cholera toxin activates adenylate cyclase in many eukaryotic cells after binding to a specific monosialoganglioside (G_{M1}) in the plasma membrane (77). In the gut mucosa, the biological effect of the toxin has been correlated with the G_{M1} ganglioside concentration and with the number of toxin binding sites (78). Also, adipocytes incubated with G_{M1} ganglioside show increased toxin binding and enhanced lipolytic responses to the toxin (30). Recently, transformed fibroblasts which lacked G_{M1} and were unresponsive to choleragen were shown to bind the ganglioside and to exhibit adenylate cyclase responses to choleragen after incubation with radioactive G_{M1} (53). These and other data have led to the conclusion that the G_{M1} ganglioside is the surface membrane receptor for choleragen.

Exposure of cells to choleragen is followed by a marked and prolonged increase in adenylate cyclase activity, after an initial lag which may reflect rearrangement of the toxin-ganglioside complex within the membrane (33), or an intermediate step such as membrane phosphorylation. The toxin-activated enzyme in erythrocyte membranes is further enhanced by guanyl nucleotides and catecholamines (33). The similarity between the choleragen-ganglioside interaction and many hormone-receptor interactions is obvious, and suggests that analysis of the mechanism of toxin action should assist in understanding of the process by which hormone-receptor interaction causes activation of adenylate cyclase in the plasma membrane of target cells. Also, it has been proposed that a ganglioside forms part of the thyroid cell receptor for thyrotropin, a hormone which shares certain sequence homologies with cholera toxin (130).

Physico-chemical characterization of peptide hormone receptors has been complicated by their relatively insoluble nature, a characteristic shared by many membrane proteins. This has led to the use of various detergents to extract receptors from membrane fractions prior to analysis of the solubilized preparation by gel filtration and density gradient centrifugation. In a few tissues, receptors have been released from particles and cells by limited enzyme digestion (168), or by incubation of cells under conditions which favor shedding of surface receptors (61, 114). However, the most useful forms of soluble hormone receptors for physico-chemical analysis have been prepared by extraction of membrane fractions and homogenates with non-ionic detergents such as Triton X-100 and Lubrol. Dissolution of plasma membranes by detergents usually leads to loss of the functional coupling between hormone binding sites and membrane-associated activities such as adenylate cyclase. However, partial restoration of hormone-stimulated adenylate cyclase activity has been observed after removal of detergent (132). Rarely, hormone-responsiveness of solubilized adenylate cyclase has been retained after extraction from tissue fractions with non-ionic detergents (51, 142, 151).

Although spontaneous solubilization of insulin and growth hormone receptors has been demonstrated during incubation of cultured lymphocytes in detergent-free aqueous medium (87, 114), the yield from spontaneous release of receptor sites is very low. Also, this method of extraction has not yet been followed by complete characterization of the soluble receptor sites. By contrast, extraction of hormone-responsive tissues with non-ionic detergents (29, 43, 45, 47, 116, 158), organic solvents (39), ionic detergents (50), and proteolytic enzymes (168) has provided soluble receptors which retain the binding properties of the original particulate receptors, and which are amenable to physical characterization. Specific receptor sites which have been extracted from cell membranes include those for acetylcholine (39, 52, 122), insulin (29), glucagon (63, 104), LH-hCG (43, 45), FSH (23), prolactin (158), and growth hormone (116). The definition of a soluble receptor is somewhat arbitrary, but receptors which are completely solubilized should not be sedimented by centrifugation at 360,000 X g for 3 hr, and are retarded during gel filtration on 6% agarose. Most detergent-solubilized receptors retain high binding affinity and specificity in the presence of detergents, and also after removal of detergent by dialysis (25). In certain receptors, removal of detergent has caused denaturation with irreversible loss of binding properties (29).

The preformed hormone-receptor complexes produced by saturation of target tissues with labeled hormone in vitro or in vivo can be readily extracted as a soluble species by treatment with nonionic detergent (25, 48). Such soluble hormone-receptor complexes are usually more stable than the free or uncharged soluble receptors, and have certain advantages for physical characterization. In the ovary, LH receptors prelabeled in vivo by injection of ^{125}I-hCG were shown to have identical physical characteristics with the hormone-receptor complexes formed by labeling particulate fractions in vitro prior to solubilization (48). A number of free receptors and hormone-receptor complexes have been analyzed by gel filtration and density gradient centrifugation, yielding approximate molecular weights ranging from 1.5 to 4.0×10^5. An exception to this finding has been the TSH receptors of molecular weight about 25,000 which were recently reported to be thyroid membranes by trypsin treatment (168). This relatively small binding site appeared to have lost hormonal specificity, and exhibited binding characteristics for TSH consistent with the presence of negative cooperativity. Since the presence of negative cooperativity implies the existence of clusters of receptors, or of a polymeric molecule, such a binding peptide with molecular weight of 25,000 merits further analysis.

Most detergent-solubilized receptors have behaved as asymmetric proteins during physical analysis, with relatively large hydrodynamic radii (60–70 Å) in relation to their sedimentation constants of 6.5–9.0 S (29, 43, 158). This behavior is largely a consequence of the glycoprotein nature and marked asymmetry of the receptor molecule (95), but could also be partly attributable to binding of detergent by the solubilized protein. The effect of detergent binding upon derivation of molecular weight has been most thoroughly studied in the case of the acetylcholine receptor. Here, the molecular weight of the soluble nicotinic receptors after corrections for detergent binding was about 275,000, a value 15–20% smaller than the apparent molecular weight derived from uncorrected hydrodynamic measurements (122). Purification of detergent-solubilized hormone receptors has been performed by conventional fractionation procedures, and also by affinity chromatography upon gel-ligand complexes. Such purifications have usually been performed on a relatively small scale, the major exception being the cholinergic receptor protein from the electric tissue of certain fish (123). Purification by affinity chromatography has also been applied to the isolation of receptors for insulin (29), LH-hCG (49), and prolactin (158). Although derived in relatively small yield, the purified receptors exhibit quite marked stability, and retain full affinity and binding specificity for the hormonal ligand. In the case of LH-hCG receptors from the rat testis, a purification factor of approximately 15,000-fold from the original material was attained. This degree of purification is equivalent to 50% homogeneity of the receptors, based upon the approximate molecular weight of 200,000. The most highly purified receptor preparation migrated as a single component during SDS-gel electrophoresis, with an approximate molecular weight of 90,000, suggesting that the detergent-extracted free receptor could consist of a dimer composed of two 94,000 mol wt subunits (49). Prolactin receptors from mammary tissue have also been purified by affinity chromatography, and antibodies raised to the purified material have been reported to inhibit the biological actions of prolactin upon receptors in target tissues (159). It is clear that application of affinity chromatography procedures to the purification of larger quantities of receptor sites from target tissues has considerable potential for studies on the structural and immunological properties of the receptors, and the functional relationships between hormone binding and activation of membrane-associated enzyme systems.

RELATIONSHIP OF HORMONE RECEPTORS TO MEMBRANE COMPONENTS

Although "receptor" is a convenient operational term for the membrane surface components with which hormones interact, its use implies a lack of knowledge of the specific chemical structures involved in the binding reaction (33). Once the locus of a drug or ligand is known, it is more appropriately described by its chemical nature than as a "receptor." As noted above, receptors can be defined in terms of their specific recognition and binding functions, or defined more broadly to include the changes which lead to the specific biological response. The structural arrangement of hormone receptors within the cell membrane is not yet known. Several possibilities have been suggested to relate the properties of receptors to current knowledge of the structure of the plasma membrane, and to explain the mechanisms by which receptor occupancy leads to modification of specific membrane-associated enzymes. The original view that hormone receptors were structurally coupled to adenylate cyclase and served as regulatory subunits of the enzyme (144) has been replaced by other models (33, 83, 136) more consistent with the fluid nature of cell membranes (160). The need for alternative models was also emphasized by observations suggesting that multiple hormone receptors could activate a single adenylate cyclase system in dispersed fat cells (33).

The mobile receptor hypothesis, which has been proposed as a mechanism for modulation of adenylate cyclase within the cell membrane by hormone-receptor interaction, is based upon the assumption that receptor and enzyme molecules are normally discrete and separate structures (33, 136). Occupancy of receptor sites by hormone is proposed to increase the affinity of the receptor for other membrane structures such as adenylate cyclase. Such a two-step model of hormone-receptor interaction with adenylate cyclase is consistent with the possibility that lateral diffusion of receptors and enzyme molecules occurs within the fluid matrix of the plasma membrane (160). It has also been proposed to provide explanations for multiple hormonal activation of protein kinase in a single cell type, as noted above, and for the potential modulation of two separate and independent membrane processes by a single hormone receptor if the complex exhibits affinity for more than one regulatory macromolecule. This model could explain certain discrepancies between hormone binding and enzyme activation in broken cell preparations, and is compatible with the actions of guanyl nucleotides upon hormone-stimulated adenylate cyclase activity in many eukaryotic cell membranes (33). Mobility of hormone receptors within a fluid membrane matrix could also be relevant to activation of adenylate cyclase in epithelial cells which exhibit morphological polarity, as in intestine, kidney, liver, and bladder. Finally, competitive antagonists of peptide hormones are visualized to retain binding affinity for the receptor molecule, while unable to produce the necessary alteration of receptor conformation and affinity which leads to the second step of combination with adenylate cyclase (33). This would be consistent with observations that the effects of guanyl nucleotides upon ligand dissociation from receptors are less marked with antagonists than with agonists (100), and that β-adrenergic antagonists which occupy receptor sites and exhibit negative cooperativity do not induce desensitization of the receptor sites (99).

Although hormone receptor sites appear to be physically distinct from adenylate cyclase, the two molecules obviously possess an intimate functional connection consistent with earlier proposals that the receptor acts as a regulatory site of the adenylate cyclase complex. In certain tissues, the correspondence between hormone receptor concentration and adenylate cyclase activity is so close as to retain a place for the unitary nature of the receptor-cyclase complex as a transmembrane entity. Such a close connection does not require that the two entities reside in the same molecule, but suggests that a tightly associated receptor-cyclase complex exists in the membranes of certain target cells. The dependence of hormonal activation of adenylate cyclase in certain membranes and solubilized preparations upon phospholipids has indicated that a coupling component of lipid nature is necessary for the association of the two activities (104). Also, certain studies have demonstrated hormonal activation of adenylate cyclase in detergent-solubilized systems (51, 142, 151), and that receptor binding activity and adenylate cyclase co-elute during physical fractionation of solubilized membranes (51). Studies on the relationship between specific hormone receptors and adenylate cyclase activity under a variety of developmental and physiological conditions have also shown a close correlation between the two activities. Thus, the appearance of gonadotropin receptors in the fetal rabbit testis is closely associated with the acquisition of cAMP responses to LH stimulation and with the ability to synthesize testosterone (20). Furthermore, the desensitization phenomena described elsewhere in this chapter have shown a close correlation between loss of hormone-sensitive adenylate cyclase and hormone receptors. Certain of the studies on desensitization have shown a decrease in the total quantity of available adenylate cyclase (89), suggesting that a significant proportion of the adenylate cyclase may be inactivated during desensitization of the hormone receptor sites. The possibility of a close physical association between peptide receptor sites and adenylate cyclase within the cell membrane should not be excluded, particularly in target cells which display marked temporal and quantitative correlations between the two activities. The existence of proteins which span the lipid bilayer has been most clearly demonstrated for glycophorin, which penetrates the red cell membrane and possesses terminal polar regions and a central apolar domain. The outer carbohydrate portion of this molecule has been recently shown to function as a "receptor" for influenza virus (111). Whether the penetration of a segment of the glycophorin polypeptide chain into the cell cytoplasm serves to transmit signals initiated by bound ligands on the external surface has yet to be determined. However, the potential significance of such a mechanism for hormone receptor interactions is obvious.

In other models, attempts have been made to account for the functional complexity of the adenylate cyclase system, which contains at least three sites at which individual ligands react to modify the activity of the enzyme (148). These include the hormone receptor site, the catalytic site which reacts with ATP chelated to magnesium, and a nucleotide regulatory site which reacts preferentially with guanyl nucleotides. From kinetic studies of the effect of guanyl nucleotides on the activation of hepatic adenylate cyclase by glucagon, it has been proposed that the adenylate cyclase complex can exist in different forms, or conformations, which can be interconverted by the concordant actions of the hormone and guanyl nucleotide. This model envisages that the different conformations have different reactivities (affinities) for the substrate, resulting in differing degrees of activation depending on the particular combination of hormone and nucleotide present. Such effects of GTP have also been observed in a number of other hormone-responsive tissues. Synthetic analogs of GTP resistant to enzymic hydrolysis have also been shown to activate several adenylate cyclase systems, suggesting that guanyl nucleotides do not function as phosphate donors but as allosteric activators of adenylate cyclase (109). One such analog, Gpp(NH)p, activates the hepatic enzyme in the absence of glucagon through the same nucleotide site as GTP. Binding of labeled Gpp(NH)p to cell membranes has been demonstrated in turkey erythrocytes (4), and has been correlated in hepatic membranes with the degree of activation of adenylate cyclase (148). In addition, the combination of hormone treatment and Gpp(NH)p has been shown to produce extremely prolonged activation states of the adenylate cyclase of erythrocyte membranes (4, 155). Gpp(NH)p has also been shown to enhance the basal as well as the hormone-stimulated activated activity of adenylate cyclase in a wide variety of animal tissues (109). Such effects of GTP and analogs suggest that regulation of nucleotide interaction with the catalytic unit of adenylate cyclase may constitute a general feature of peptide hormone action. Recently, guanine nucleotide regulation of β-adrenergic-dependent adenylate cyclase activity in avian erythrocyte membranes has been demonstrated (13), and the presence of the nucleotides has been shown to be necessary for correlations between receptor binding and adenylate cyclase activation by β-adrenergic agonists.

The effects of guanyl nucleotides upon adenylate cyclase are accompanied in certain tissues by an action upon the binding affinity of the corresponding hormone receptor sites. Both GTP and Gpp(NH)p have been shown to reduce the affinity of hepatic receptors for glucagon (148) and adrenal receptors for angiotensin II (66). In each case, the change in affinity is caused by an increase in the dissociation rate constant of the hormone-receptor complex (18, 148). The relationship of the change in receptor affinity to the actions of guanyl nucleotides on enzyme activity is not clear, but the effect upon hormone binding could represent a separate action with less widespread significance than the activation of adenylate cyclase.

THE NATURE OF HORMONE-RECEPTOR INTERACTION

Until recently, methods for measuring the reaction between hormones and receptors provided largely indirect evidence about the physico-chemical interactions involved in hormone binding. The importance of phospholipids for hormone binding to receptors (5, 28, 43) and the effects of temperature and agents such as urea upon the binding process suggest that hydrophobic interactions are important for binding of peptide hormones to their receptor sites (138). In other peptides, such as ACTH and angiotensin II, electrostatic interactions are also involved in the interaction. A basic region of the ACTH molecule is important for binding to adrenal receptors (75, 76), and binding of angiotensin II to adrenal receptors is markedly influenced by the basicity of the N-terminal residue (153). The activation processes which result from hormone binding can also be influenced by electrostatic effects. Thus, low concentrations of polylysine stimulate adenylate cyclase and steroidogenesis in adrenal and Leydig cells (177), apparently via electrostatic interaction with anionic groups on the plasma membrane.

Significant insights about the role of hydrophobic interactions in receptor binding have been provided by the recent studies of Blundell and colleagues upon the three-dimensional structures of insulin (10, 141, 178) and glucagon (154). In the insulin molecule, the relatively constant surface region which determines biological activity includes many hydrophobic residues. Binding of insulin to its receptor has been proposed to occur by a process analogous to dimerization, and to depend upon the additive effects of hydrophobic interactions and hydrogen bonds (141, 178). Other important findings were that effects of modification of specific amino acid residues upon biological activity and receptor binding could be correlated with changes in the conformation of the insulin molecule, and that interaction of several insulin residues with the receptor was necessary for full receptor binding (141).

In contrast to the relatively rigid structure of insulin, which appears necessary to achieve the specific three-dimensional arrangement of amino acids necessary for receptor binding, the glucagon molecule has an elongated and fairly flexible structure (154). Like insulin, glucagon molecules readily aggregate by hydrophobic bonding, in this case to a trimeric structure. At the low concentrations present in the circulation, glucagon probably circulates as a monomer with random conformations. It is suggested that the biologically active conformation is a helical structure which interacts with the receptor through two hydrophobic regions at each end of the helix, and that the extended N-terminal part of the molecule is important for activation of adenylate cyclase (146, 154).

These observations indicate that both insulin and glucagon molecules associate via their hydrophobic regions during storage as granules, and also bind to receptor sites by predominantly hydrophobic interactions. The presence of two hydrophobic regions, first observed in the glucagon monomer, has also been noted in secretin and vasoactive intestinal peptide. Certain smaller molecules such as thyrotropin-releasing hormone, luteinizing hormone-releasing hormone, angiotensin II, and bradykinin also exhibit twofold symmetry. This has led to the suggestion that symmetrical features of peptide sequences are reflected in the receptor structure, and that such peptides bind to two similar or identical subunits in the receptor (C. R. Beddell, P. J. Goodford, G. C. Sheppey, and T. L. Blundell, submitted for publication). As noted above, the presence of two subunits in a solubilized receptor preparation has been recently suggested by studies in the isolated LH receptor (49), and the acetylcholine receptor contains several subunits (52). The extent to which subunit structure occurs in hormone receptors is not known, but its presence in receptors for acetylcholine and LH could reflect a general property relevant to the evolution of symmetry and internal homologies in peptide hormones, as well as to the occurrence of cooperative interactions during receptor binding.

The nature of the processes which terminate hormone-receptor interaction in vivo has not been defined. It would appear that mechanisms in addition to the normal process of dissociation according to the law of mass action must operate to terminate the binding of hormone molecules to receptor sites. The role of a degradative mechanism for hormone release has been considered, but the majority of hormone degradation observed during in vitro binding studies occurs independently of the interaction with receptors (56). As might be expected, the hormone which is specifically bound to receptors is fully active biologically when examined by rebinding analysis and bioassay following elution from the target tissue (42, 90). This feature can be used to advantage for the purification of labeled peptide hormone to be used in receptor binding analysis, since a form of affinity chromatography upon particulate receptor sites can be employed to select the biologically active molecules from the labeled hormone preparation (42).

RADIOLIGAND-RECEPTOR ASSAYS

The development of radioligand-receptor assays to measure and characterize hormones was preceded by almost a decade of development in techniques of radioimmunoassay and other forms of saturation analysis which employed plasma binding proteins to measure steroids and thyroid hormones. Following the use of uterine estradiol receptors for measurement of plasma estrogens (95), comparable radioligand-receptor assays were developed for numerous peptide hormones including ACTH (97), gonadotropins (14, 15), insulin (58, 72), angiotensin II (65, 152), growth hormone (71, 72, 101, 172), and prolactin (157). The major advantage of radioligand-receptor assays is the ability of receptors to recognize the molecular conformations responsible for the biological activity of peptide hormones. This property differs from that of radioimmunoassays, which use antibodies that are more likely to recognize conformations other than those responsible for biological activity. In addition to their application to the measurement of bioactive hormones in tissue extracts and body fluids, radioligand-receptor assays are of considerable value for studies on the structure-function properties of native hormones and derivatives or analogs. For many hormone derivatives, a close correlation has been found between biological activity and affinity for specific receptor sites, suggesting that binding and activation properties are conferred by the same site on the hormone. In certain peptides, such as ACTH (75, 76) and glucagon (146), it has been possible to distinguish between regions responsible for receptor binding and activation of adenylate cyclase. In the case of glycoprotein hormones, it is likely that carbohydrate residues have an important influence upon binding and activation properties. Thus a dissociation between receptor binding and activation of cell responses is apparent during successive removal of carbohydrate residues from human chorionic gonadotropin. Removal of sialic acid and galactose residues causes considerable loss of in vitro bioactivity, with retention of binding activity (41, 170, 171). More extensive removal of carbohydrate residues causes loss of both receptor binding and biological activity (126). The asialo- and asialo-agalacto-derivatives of chorionic gonadotropin can act as competitive inhibitors of gonadotropin action when appropriate concentrations of the modified and native hormones are employed (126). However, due to their extremely rapid plasma clearance in vivo, such modified glycoprotein hormones are only effective as competitive antagonists under in vitro conditions.

The most effective antagonists of hormonal ligands have been produced by modification of relatively small peptides, such as angiotensin II. Competitive antagonists of angiotensin II, formed by replacement of C-terminal phenylalanine by aliphatic residues, and agonist analogs and fragments of angiotensin II, exhibit binding affinity for particulate adrenal cortex receptors in direct proportion to their biological activities upon aldosterone production in the adrenal cortex (152). The use of radioligand-receptor assays for analysis of agonist and antagonist peptide derivatives provides a valuable screening method for evaluation of the receptor binding properties of peptide analogs. Obviously, the complete characterization of an antagonist derivative requires measurement of inhibitory potency upon a characteristic cellular response, as well as the estimate of relative binding affinity that is provided by radioligand-receptor assay. The use of radioligand-receptor assays for catecholamines, employing radioactive antagonists to identify the specific β-adrenergic receptor sites (12, 127), has also been employed for extensive comparisons of the biological activities and binding affinities of agonists and antagonists (13, 99).

Radioligand-receptor assays have been of considerable value for the measurement of peptide hormones for which no radioimmunoassay has been developed. This method has been used to identify hepatic receptors which have high affinity for NSILA-s and low affinity for insulin (119). The radioligand-receptor assay for NSILA-s has been used to demonstrate high circulating concentrations of NSILA-s in certain patients with hypoglycemia associated with non-islet cell tumors (118, 150). A radioligand-receptor assay has also been developed for the measurement of plasma concentrations of somatomedin, a peptide which is presumed to mediate the actions of growth hormone (173).

RECEPTOR OCCUPANCY AND ACTIVATION OF TARGET CELL RESPONSES

The majority of studies on the biological consequences of hormone-receptor interactions have indicated that activation of adenylate cyclase and target cell responses are elicted as functions of receptor occupancy. However, in many tissues, the binding affinity of the receptor site is less than the hormone concentration required for a half-maximum biological response, and the complete biological response is evoked by occupancy of a small proportion of the available receptors. Even when increasing receptor occupancy is accompanied by increasing responses over a wide range of hormone binding, the response is usually not directly proportional to the number of receptors occupied. Also, it is well recognized that many hormones can stimulate the production of much more cAMP than is necessary to evoke a maximum biological response in the target cell (6, 17, 44, 73, 117, 120, 125). Such observations have led to the recognition that many hormone-responsive tissues are characterized by the presence of "spare" receptors or "receptor reserve" analogous with the situation recognized by Stephenson during studies on drug-responsive tissues (166). The term "spare receptors" has been widely employed to acknowledge the contribution of Stephenson, but has never been used in the literal sense to suggest that such receptors are devoid of biological function. Indeed, the original paper of Stephenson (166), which also introduced the concept of nonlinear coupling in drug responses, as well as the properties of "affinity" and "efficacy" in drugs, clearly stated that occupancy of spare receptors by agonist will produce a full response, as in the presence of a surmountable blockade by antagonists.

Virtually all subsequent reports on the existence of "spare" receptors in hormone-responsive tissue have also attributed a functional role to such receptors, most commonly that of increasing the sensitivity of the target cell to activation by a low level of hormone in the extracellular fluid (17, 93, 94). It has also been well recognized that the term "spare" is used in a purely relative sense, since the degree of receptor excess may differ according to the biological response which is measured. For example, receptors are rarely "spare" for adenylate cyclase, as exemplified by correlations between binding and adenylate cyclase activity (70, 174), although nonlinear coupling between receptor occupancy and the enzyme response is sometimes observed (11, 147). Likewise, hormone binding to intact target cells is usually accompanied by serial increases in cAMP production, and there does not appear to be a true excess of receptors which are not coupled to adenylate cyclase. However, measurement of more distal responses, such as muscle contraction (166), steroidogenesis (6, 17, 115, 120), glucose oxidation or inhibition of lipolysis (59, 93, 94), and ion transport (60), often shows that the maximum biological response is evoked by occupancy of only a small fraction of the receptor population. The activation of a small number of receptors needed to reach the threshold required to elicit a cellular response would clearly be facilitated by the presence of a relatively large pool of total receptors. In this way, the presence of a large number of receptors could be essential for occupancy of the much smaller number required for cell activation, and the term "spare" could then be regarded as inappropriate in the literal sense. However, preoccupation with the use of the term "spare receptors" is largely a semantic issue, since it has not been claimed that such receptors have no biological importance.

Although the occurrence of spare receptors in drug- and hormone-responsive tissues was originally noted by analysis of dose-response curves, and by the use of antagonists (166), the presence of receptor excess has been most clearly established by direct binding studies with labeled hormones in intact cell preparations (59, 93, 115, 120). This effect is particularly marked in the interstitial cells of the testis, where occupancy of only 1% of the total receptor population will produce complete activation of steroidogenesis and testosterone production (17, 120). However, in the same cells, binding of labeled gonadotropin is accompanied by a progressive increase in the production and release of cAMP. This finding indicates that most or all of the binding sites identified with radioactive hormone can be regarded as functionally active receptors, with the capacity to stimulate adenylate cyclase activity and cAMP formation. The close correspondence between receptor occupancy and adenylate cyclase activation is relevant to the suggestion made above that there may be a close physical and functional connection between the two activities within the cell membrane. Extensive studies on the binding properties of receptors in testicular Leydig cells have not revealed a detectable difference between the small number of receptors required for a full steroidogenic response and the remaining 99% of the receptors. It appears that activation of any 1% of the total receptor population is sufficient to evoke the full target-cell response.

In certain tissues, hormone binding and the consequent biological response can be closely correlated over the entire range of receptor occupancy (40, 68). Occupancy of the angiotensin II receptors of the adrenal glomerulosa cell is correlated with increasing steroidogenesis and aldosterone production over the whole range of hormone binding, indicating that there are no spare receptors for steroidogenesis in this cell type (40). A similarly close correlation between insulin binding and stimulation of amino acid transport has been observed in isolated thymocytes (68). It is possible that a wide range of relationships between receptor occupancy and specific cellular responses will be observed in various target tissues. This could range from the extreme case of the interstitial cells of the testis, with full activation by minimal receptor occupancy, to the almost continuous relationship between occupancy and response observed in the glomerulosa cell and the thymocyte. Within a single cell type, such as the fat cell during exposure to insulin, increasing degrees of receptor occupancy elicit sequential biological responses. Here, inhibition of lipolysis is caused by very low receptor occupancy, stimulation of glucose metabolism is maximum when 2–3% of the receptors are occupied, and stimulation of amino acid transport and protein synthesis occurs at higher degrees of receptor occupancy (68, 93, 94).

ROLE OF ADENYLATE CYCLASE AND PROTEIN KINASE IN PEPTIDE HORMONE ACTION

Following the original description of the cAMP-dependent mechanism by which epinephrine stimulates hepatic glycogenolysis (167), numerous observations in hormone-response target tissues have supported the role of cAMP as an intracellular mediator of peptide hormone action (145). Early studies in the adrenal gland demonstrated correlations between cAMP and steroidogenesis during ACTH stimulation (73). Such studies also showed that cAMP levels continued to rise with hormone concentrations that were supramaximal for steroidogenesis, with a 25-fold higher concentration of ACTH required for maximum cAMP production than for maximum steroid production. Despite the extensive evidence that many hormone-responsive activities of target cells are mediated by the production of cAMP, an increasing number of disparities between cAMP production and acute metabolic responses has been observed in target tissues exposed to low hormone concentrations (21, 113). Such observations have usually been made during experiments with enzyme-dispersed target cells which are highly sensitive to hormonal stimulation in vitro. Dispersed cell preparations frequently exhibit a maximum hormonal response, such as steroidogenesis, in the absence of a detectable stimulation of cAMP production (6, 17, 120, 125, 131). Such dissociations have raised the possibility that low concentrations of trophic hormone might act upon steroidogenesis by an extra-cyclic AMP pathway (120). Alternatively, cAMP could still function as the intracellular messenger, by translocation within an extremely small intracellular pool which is not detectable against the total cell content of cAMP.

The exact nature of the activation pathway which operates during target-cell stimulation by low hormone concentrations has not yet been resolved. However, it cannot be excluded that cAMP has a mediating function exerted by turnover or translocation of the nucleotide, rather than by a gross increase in intracellular concentration. At higher concentrations of trophic hormone, quite marked increases in intracellular and extracellular cAMP concentrations are observed in vitro (120, 137). Because trophic hormones produce a multiplicity of metabolic responses in their target cells, it could be expected that increasing degrees of receptor occupancy might be associated with the production of discrete biological responses. Since the major function of steroidogenic target tissues is to maintain the secretion of their respective hormones, it is also not surprising that activation of steroidogenesis should be one of the most sensitive metabolic responses in the cell. The relationship between higher concentrations of cAMP, stimulated by exposure to elevated concentrations of circulating hormones, and other aspects of cell metabolism and differentiation has yet to be established. In certain tissues, attempts to correlate activation of protein kinase with stimulation of steroidogenesis by low hormone concentrations have been unsuccessful (137). This finding again suggests the existence of an alternative pathway which does not involve cAMP, or that extremely minute changes in both cAMP and protein kinase activity are adequate for full stimulation of steroidogenic responses.

The resolution of these questions will depend upon the use of highly purified target cell preparations, combined with precursor incorporation studies on the biosynthesis of cAMP, and the identification of specific substrates for phosphorylation by protein kinase during hormonal stimulation. Since the protein kinases present in various target tissues appear to be relatively similar in terms of physical properties, substrate specificities, and affinities for cAMP, it is not easy to see how a single enzyme can provide the common pathway between hormonal activation of adenylate cyclase and the initiation of multiple responses to receptor occupancy. However, localization of protein kinase in specific intracellular organelles or compartments could facilitate the role of the enzyme as a mediator of multiple target cell responses. In particular, the presence of a membrane-associated protein kinase, which is activated by cAMP translocation following receptor occupancy at low hormone concentrations, could explain the dissociation observed between cAMP on steroidogenesis during hormone stimulation. Recent studies in the interstitial cells of the testis have revealed the presence of two forms of protein kinase, with sedimentation constants of 4S and 6.5S, respectively (137). Additional studies have indicated that the 4S form of the enzyme predominates in particulate fractions of the interstitial cell, and that both forms are present in the cytosol. If closely associated with adenylate cyclase in the plasma membrane, the particulate form of the enzyme could be amenable to selective activation during hormonal stimulation of target cells in vitro. The presence of multiple forms of protein kinase, with selective localization within hormone-responsive target cells, could help to explain the ability of peptide hormones to elicit a wide variety of metabolic responses from target tissues, with mediation via a single coupled enzyme system consisting of adenylate cyclase and protein kinase.

REGULATION OF RECEPTOR CONCENTRATION AND AFFINITY

Prolonged exposure of target tissues to high circulatory concentrations of hormones and drugs is frequently followed by loss of sensitivity to the biological effects of the regulatory molecule. Such effects have been particularly well described for insulin (3, 85, 86) and catecholamines (128), and appear to result from loss or inactivation of a proportion of the receptor population of the target cell. In addition to the in vivo effects of high insulin levels upon the concentration of insulin receptors in target tissues, prolonged exposure of cultured cells to insulin in vitro has also been shown to decrease insulin receptors (62). Such receptor modulation has also been observed with human growth hormone and insulin receptors in cultured human lymphocytes (103). The effect of each hormone was specific for its own receptor, and did not diminish the concentration of receptors for the other hormone.

The "desensitization" of adenylate cyclase in certain target tissues by catecholamines has been shown to be accompanied by a decrease in the number of β-adrenergic receptor sites in the desensitized cells (55, 143). Exposure of frog erythrocytes to β-adrenergic catecholamines for several hours in vivo (128) and in vitro (99, 124) produced selective desensitization of adenylate cyclase to catecholamines and a commensurate loss of β-adrenergic receptor sites. Similar changes have been observed in the rat pineal gland, where desensitization of catecholamine responsiveness was also accompanied by loss of specific catecholamine receptors (89). Such mechanisms may account for the initial rapid physiologic response generated by catecholamines, and the subsequent desensitization accompanied by decreasing cAMP levels and reduced physiologic responses. An interesting and important observation was the inability of β-adrenergic antagonists to produce desensitization, and their ability to block the action of agonists upon desensitization (99).

Although drug- and hormone-induced desensitization cannot be solely attributed to changes in receptor function, there is now good evidence that prolonged occupancy of receptors by certain agonists leads to selective inactivation of receptor sites, with desensitization of adenylate cyclase and more distal target cell responses to hormonal stimulation. A further example of this process has been observed during the action of LH and chorionic gonadotropin upon the gonads, with initial stimulation followed by a prolonged period of desensitization (79). These changes have been shown to result from loss of specific receptor sites following occupancy by administered hormone, with consequent losses of adenylate cyclase activity, cAMP production, and steroidogenesis, and are related to the hormonal desensitization of adenylate cyclase in the ovary of rabbit and rat, recently described by Hunzicker-Dunn & Birnbaumer (80).

This phenomenon is likely to be of generalized nature, and could account for the frequent occurrence of hormone resistance in states characterized by high circulating levels of hormones and other regulatory ligands. The extent to which receptor occupancy and receptor inactivation occur in individual target tissues has yet to be determined. However, it is likely that desensitization will include a complex group of processes including occupancy, degradation or processing of hormone-receptor complexes, and temporary inactivation of receptor sites and adenylate cyclase following occupancy. The converse form of regulation by peptide hormone, leading to an increase in specific receptors, has been observed in the prolactin receptors of the liver (139, 140) and may occur during action of trophic hormones upon their target cells. Also, receptor induction by other hormones has been observed during estrogen stimulation of hepatic prolactin receptors (139), and during the action of FSH upon LH receptors in the granulosa cells of the ovary (179).

The modulation of receptor function in target tissues is most commonly achieved by alteration in receptor concentration, as in the examples described above. Modulation of receptor affinity appears to be a less frequent mechanism for changing target cell sensitivity, with one important exception. This is the occurrence of negative cooperativity during certain hormone-receptor interactions, a mechanism which was first noted by De Meyts during studies on the insulin receptor (35). In a wide variety of tissue receptors for insulin, as well as receptors for TSH, growth factors, and catecholamines (36, 169), the finding of concave Scatchard plots during analysis of binding data has been attributed to negative cooperativity. The distinction between negatively cooperative site-site interactions and site heterogeneity has been made by direct kinetic analysis of dissociation data (38). The occurrence of negative cooperativity in certain hormone receptors is relevant to several aspects of hormone action. Such cooperativity provides high sensitivity to low hormone concentrations, while minimizing the effects of acute increases in circulating hormone concentrations. This mechanism seems particularly appropriate for receptor sites of hormones and transmitters that are active at very low concentrations, and which produce acute and potentially harmful effects at higher concentrations, i. e. insulin and catecholamines.

A structural consequence of the occurrence of negative cooperativity during hormone binding is the requirement for receptor clusters or oligomers that can undergo hormone-induced conformational changes (36). In both insulin and catecholamine receptors, quite low fractional occupancy of the total receptor sites causes marked negative cooperativity during binding studies. This implies that such receptors occur as relatively large clusters with moderate site-site interaction, or as smaller groups with strong site-site interactions. Recent ultrastructural studies on the localization of insulin-ferritin complexes in fat cells (81) and liver membranes (133) have shown good correlations between binding data with labeled insulin and direct uptake of ferritin-insulin complexes to the cell surface. Binding of the complexes was observed to the outer surface of the plasma membrane in each tissue, and occurred both as clusters and in a diffuse pattern. In fat cells, ferritin-insulin complexes were also observed in "surface connected vesicles," which consist of multibranched invaginations of the plasma membrane into the cytoplasm (81). The presence of clusters of morphologically defined receptors upon the surface of target cells is clearly relevant to the proposed models of De Meyts et al (38) and Levitzki (105) for negative cooperativity in the insulin receptor.

The mechanism of negative cooperativity is clearly separable from the process of "down regulation" or desensitization of receptors by homologous hormone. Both events are related to occupancy of the receptors, but not all hormone analogs which cause negative cooperativity also produce desensitization. This is particularly apparent in the case of the β-adrenergic receptor, where both agonists and antagonists induce negatively cooperative interactions in proportion to their affinities for the receptor (99). However, competitive antagonists, which occupy the receptor site without activating adenylate cyclase, produce negative cooperativity but do not cause desensitization of receptor sites. Thus, occupancy is sufficient for cooperativity, whereas both occupancy and the ability to activate cell responses appear to be necessary for negative regulation and desensitization (37).

RECEPTOR STUDIES IN DISEASE STATES

The alterations in hormonal sensitivity which occur in many endocrine disorders could be partly related to changes at the receptor level, with a consequent change in target cell sensitivity. It is well recognized that many syndromes characterized by hormone excess are accompanied by decreased sensitivity to the respective hormones, and conversely that syndromes of hormone deficiency are frequently accompanied by increased sensitivity to the missing hormone. Although such changes in sensitivity are partially attributable to the effects of changes in occupancy by the endogenous hormone, several recent studies have demonstrated that exposure to elevated hormone concentrations leads to a decrease in the concentration of target cell receptors. Conversely, certain forms of hormone deficiency have been shown to be accompanied by increased concentrations of receptors in the respective target tissues. Obviously, such changes in specific receptor concentration could be an important factor in the regulation of hormonal sensitivity of the target cells.

The most extensive observations upon the regulation of specific receptors by circulating hormones have been performed by Roth and colleagues during studies on the insulin resistance associated with obesity in animal models and in man. Such studies have shown that obesity of any kind, and in all species studied, is accompanied by a significant decrease in the concentration of insulin receptors in liver (85, 163), fat cells (57), thymic lymphocytes (162), and mononuclear leukocytes (156). Such changes were observed in the insulin receptors of leukocytes and adipose tissue of obese humans (3, 86). In addition, dietary treatment was shown to improve insulin tolerance, and cause partial recovery of the receptor deficiency. Detailed studies on the liver membranes of obese hypoglycemic mice have shown that the insulin receptors are decreased in number, but possess normal affinity, binding kinetics, temperature dependence, and biological specificity (85). As in other forms of obesity, the insulin resistance in this species is attributable to a reduction in the number of specific insulin receptors per cell. Such a reduction in insulin binding in thymic lymphocytes of obese mice is accompanied by a decreased effect of insulin on amino acid transport, suggesting that the reduced receptor concentration influences the metabolic action of insulin in such cells (163). Furthermore, another form of obese mouse (db/db), and normal mice that became obese after gold thioglucose treatment, also exhibited decreased insulin receptor concentration in liver plasma membranes (150).

The various models studied have shown a consistent relationship between the degree of hyperinsulinemia and the extent of insulin receptor loss, suggesting that plasma insulin concentration has an important regulatory action upon the concentration of insulin receptors in target cells. Such observations have important implications for a variety of hormone-resistant endocrine disorders in which deficient end-organ function in the presence of elevated circulating hormone concentrations has been traditionally ascribed to a primary defect in the target cell (150). It is now clear that chronic hypersecretion of peptide hormones can in some circumstances lead to a marked decrease in sensitivity at the target cell level, due to hormone-induced receptor deficiency. For this reason, it has become necessary to reexamine previous concepts about hormone resistance and end-organ failure, and to consider the possibility that elevation of hormone concentration might be responsible for moderate to severe loss of target cell sensitivity (150). However, it should be noted that not all forms of hormone resistance are attributable to changes in tissue receptors, as exemplified by the presence of normal insulin binding during the decreasing insulin sensitivity of thymic lymphocytes as endogenous insulin levels increase during aging in the rat (69).

The extent to which hormonal regulation of tissue receptor concentration is responsible for alterations in hormone sensitivity during human endocrine disorders has not been determined. However, the conclusions concerning insulin resistance and receptor deficiency have been adequately supported by experimental evidence and clinical studies, including the observation that adipose tissue from obese subjects exhibits decreased insulin binding (112). Whether similar changes are responsible for the reduced tissue sensitivity which accompanies chronic elevations of circulating growth hormone, chorionic gonadotropin, calcitonin, and angiotensin II has yet to be elucidated. However, regulation of receptors by the prevailing hormone concentration appears likely to operate under these circumstances, and may also account for enhanced sensitivity of target organs during trophic hormone deficiency. Although there will obviously be exceptions to this regulatory mechanism, it is clear that receptor modulation by circulating hormone concentrations will be an important physiological process in vivo.

Alterations in hormone binding to specific receptor sites have also been shown to result from changes in the pH and composition of extracellular fluid. Thus insulin binding to plasma membrane and intact cells is markedly reduced by a decrease in pH, an event which could contribute to the insulin resistance associated with diabetic ketoacidosis (150). Changes in ionic composition have been shown to produce quite marked effects upon hormone interaction with receptors in cell fractions in vitro. Binding of ACTH to adrenal receptors was markedly reduced by increasing calcium concentration (96), and binding of angiotensin II to adrenal glomerulosa receptors was shown to increase with rising sodium concentrations (67). Such changes have not yet been shown to be significant in vivo, but raise the possibility that altered target cell sensitivity in vivo during electrolyte imbalance, such as the diabetes insipidus which accompanies hypokalemia and hypercalcemia, could be partially caused by reduced affinity of receptors for hormone (150).

A more dramatic form of receptor disorder has been recently recognized to result from the development of circulating antibodies to certain tissue receptors. In patients with myasthenia gravis, humoral antibodies which block acetylcholine receptors at the neuromuscular junction have been demonstrated (1, 2, 7). Also, rabbits immunized with purified acetylcholine receptors exhibit a syndrome similar to myasthenia gravis in the human (135). Patients with Graves disease have been shown to have circulating immunoglobulins which bind to thyrotropin receptors in the thyroid gland (129, 161). Such antibodies block the thyroid hormone secretion (110). More recently, a defect in insulin-receptor interaction in certain patients with acanthosis nigricans has been attributed to the presence of circulating antibodies directed against the insulin receptor (54). In other patients with this condition, markedly reduced insulin binding to receptors of circulating monocytes was demonstrated, suggesting a primary receptor defect (84, 86). The occurrence of these three recognized antibodies to target cell receptors suggests that this phenomenon might prove to be a general, although probably uncommon etiologic factor in endocrine disease.

Literature Cited

1. Aharonov, A., Abramsky, O., Tarrab-Hazdai, R., Fuchs, S. 1975. Humoral antibodies to acetylcholine receptor in patients with myasthenia gravis. *Lancet* 2:340–42
2. Almon, R. R., Andrew, C. G., Appel, S. H. 1974. Serum globulin in myasthenia gravis: Inhibition of α-bungarotoxia binding to acteylcholine receptors. *Science* 186:55–56
3. Archer, J. A., Gorden, P., Gavin, J. R., Lesniak, M. A., Roth, J. 1973. Insulin receptors in human circulating lymphocytes: Application to the study of insulin resistance in man. *J. Clin. Endocrinol. Metab.* 36:627–33
4. Aurbach, G. D., Spiegel, A. M., Gardner, J. D. 1975. β-Adrenergic receptors, cyclic AMP and ion transport in the avian erythrocyte. *Adv. Cyclic Nucleotide Res.* 5:117–32
5. Barden, N., Labrie, F. 1973. Receptor for thyrotropin-releasing hormone in plasma membranes of bovine anterior pituitary gland: Role of lipids. *J. Biol. Chem.* 248:7601–6
6. Beall, R. J., Sayers, G. 1972. Isolated adrenal cells: Steroidogenesis and cyclic AMP accumulation in response to ACTH. *Arch. Biochem. Biophys.* 148:70–76
7. Bender, A. N., Ringel, S. P., Engel, W. K., Daniels, M. P., Vogel, Z. 1975. Myasthenia gravis: A serum factor blocking acetylcholine receptors of the human neuromuscular junction. *Lancet* 1:606–9
8. Birnbaumer, L., Pohl, S. L. 1973. Relation of glucagon-specific binding sites to glucagon-dependent stimulation of adenylyl cyclase activity in plasma mem-

branes of rat liver. *J. Biol. Chem.* 248:2056–61

9. Birnbaumer, L., Pohl, S. L., Kaumann, A. J. 1974. Receptors and acceptors: A necessary distinction in hormone binding studies. *Adv. Cyclic Nucleotide Res.* 4:239–81

10. Blundell, T., Dodson, G., Hodgkin, D., Mercola, D. 1972. Insulin: The structure in the crystal and its reflection in chemistry and biology. *Adv. Protein Chem.* 26:279–402

11. Bockaert, J., Roy, C., Rajerison, R., Butler, D., Jard, S. 1976. In *Cell Membrane Receptors for Viruses, Antigens and Antibodies, Polypeptide Hormones, and Small Molecules,* ed. R. F. Beers, E. G. Bassett, pp. 365–77. New York: Raven. 540 pp.

12. Brown, E. M., Aurbach, G. D., Hauser, D., Troxler, F. 1976. β-Adrenergic receptor interactions. Characterization of iodohydroxybenzylpindolal as a specific ligand. *J. Biol. Chem.* 251:1232–38

13. Brown, E. M., Fedak, S. A., Woodard, C. J., Aurbach, G. D., Rodbard, D. 1976. β-Adrenergic receptor interactions. Direct comparison of receptor interaction and biological activity. *J. Biol. Chem.* 251:1239–46

14. Catt, K. J., Dufau, M. L., Tsuruhara, T. 1971. Studies on a radioligand-receptor assay system for luteinizing hormone and chorionic gonadotropin. *J. Clin. Endocrinol. Metab.* 32:860–63

15. Catt, K. J., Dufau, M. L., Tsuruhara, T. 1972. Radioligand-receptor assay of luteinizing hormone and chorionic gonadotropin. *J. Clin. Endocrinol. Metab.* 34:123–32

16. Catt, K. J., Dufau, M. L., Tsuruhara, T. 1972. Gonadotrophin binding sites of the rat testis. *Biochim. Biophys. Acta* 279:194–201

17. Catt, K. J., Dufau, M. L. 1973. Spare gonadotropin receptors in rat testis. *Nature New Biology* 244:219–21

18. Catt, K. J., Baukal, A., Ketelslegers, J.-M., Douglas, J., Saltman, S., Fredlund, P., Glossmann, H. 1974. Angiotensin II receptors of the adrenal gland. Location and modulation by cations and guanyl nucleotides. *Acta Physiol. Lat. Am.* 24:515–19

19. Catt, K. J., Tsuruhara, T., Mendelson, C., Ketelslegers, J.-M., Dufau, M. L. 1974. In *Hormone Binding and Target Cell Activation in the Testis,* ed. M. L. Dufau, A. R. Means, pp. 1–30. New York: Plenum, 371 pp.

20. Catt, K. J., Dufau, M. L., Neaves, W. B., Walsh, P. C., Wilson, J. D. 1975. LH-hCG receptors and testosterone content during differentiation of the testis in the rabbit embryo. *Endocrinology* 97:1157–65

21. Catt, K. J., Dufau, M. L. 1976. Basic concepts of the mechanism of action of peptide hormones. *Biol. Reprod.* 14:1–15

22. Catt, K. J., Ketelslegers, J-M., Dufau, M. L. 1976. In *Methods in Receptor Research.* Part I, ed. M. Blecher, pp. 175–250. New York: Dekker. 383 pp.

23. Catt, K. J., Dufau, M. L. 1977. In *Isolation of Hormone Receptors,* ed. G. S. Levey, pp. 171–200. New York: Dekker

24. Channing, C. P., Kammerman, S. 1974. Binding of gonadotropin to ovarian cells. *Biol. Reprod.* 10:179–98

25. Charreau, H. E., Dufau, M. L., Catt, K. J. 1974. Multiple forms of solubilized gonadotropin receptors from the rat testis. *J. Biol. Chem.* 294:4189–95

26. Crofford, O. B. 1968. The uptake and inactivation of native insulin by isolated fat cells. *J. Biol. Chem.* 243:362–69

27. Cuatrecasas, P. 1969. Interaction of insulin with the cell membrane: The primary action of insulin. *Proc. Natl. Acad. Sci. USA* 63:450–68

28. Cuatrecasas, P. 1971. Unmasking of insulin receptors in fat cells and fat cell membranes. *J. Biol. Chem.* 246:6532–42

29. Cuatrecasas, P. 1972. Properties of the insulin receptor isolated from liver and fat cell membranes. *J. Biol. Chem.* 247:1980–91

30. Cuatrecasas, P. 1973. Cholera toxin-fat cell interaction and the mechanism of activation of the lipolytic response. *Biochemistry* 12:3567–76

31. Cuatrecasas, P. 1974. Membrane receptors. *Ann. Rev. Biochem.* 43:169–214

32. Cuatrecasas, P. 1975. Hormone receptors—their function in cell membranes and some problems related to methodology. *Adv. Cyclic Nucleotide Res.* 5:79–104

33. Cuatrecasas, P., Hollenberg. M. D., Chang, K-J., Bennett, V. 1975. Hormone-receptor complexes and their modulation of membrane function. *Rec. Prog. Horm. Res.* 31:37–84

34. DeKretser, D. M., Catt, K. J., Burger, H. G., Smith, G. C. 1969. Radioautographic studies on the localization of ^{125}I-labeled human luteinizing and growth hormone in immature male rats. *J. Endocrinol.* 43:105–11

35. De Meyts, P., Roth, J., Neville, D. M., Gavin, J. R., Lesniak, M. A. 1973. Insulin interactions with its receptors: Experimental evidence for negative cooperativity. *Biochem. Biophys. Res. Commun.* 55:154–61

36. De Meyts, P. 1976. Cooperative properties of hormone receptors in cell membranes. *J. Supramol. Struct.* 4:241–58

37. De Meyts, P. 1976. See Reference 11, p. 68

38. De Meyts, P., Bianco, A. R., Roth, J. 1976. Site-site interactions among insulin receptors. Characterization of the negative cooperativity. *J. Biol. Chem.* 251:1877–88

39. De Robertis, E. 1971. Molecular biology of synaptic receptors. *Science* 171:963–71

40. Douglas, J., Saltman, S., Fredlund, P., Kondo, T., Catt, K. J. 1976. Receptor binding of angiotensin II and antagonists: Correlation with aldosterone production by isolated adrenal glomerulosa cells. *Circ. Res.* 24 (Suppl. 2): 108–12

41. Dufau, M. L., Catt, K. J., Tsuruhara, T. 1971. Retention of in vitro biological activities by desialylated hormone luteinizing hormone and chorionic gonadotropin. *Biochem. Biophys. Res. Commun.* 41:1022–29

42. Dufau, M. L., Catt, K. J., Tsuruhara, T. 1972. Biological activity of human chorionic gonadotropin released from testis binding sites. *Proc. Natl. Acad. Sci. USA* 69:2414–16

43. Dufau, M. L., Charreau, E. H., Catt, K. J. 1973. Characteristics of a soluble gonadotropin receptor from the rat testis. *J. Biol. Chem.* 248:6973–82

44. Dufau, M. L., Watanabe, K., Catt, K. J. 1973. Stimulation of cyclic AMP production by the rat testis during incubation with hCG in vitro. *Endocrinology* 92:6–11

45. Dufau, M. L., Charreau, E. H., Ryan, D., Catt, K. J. 1974. Soluble gonadotropin receptors of the rat ovary. *FEBS Lett.* 39:149–53

46. Dufau, M. L., Ryan, D., Catt, K. J. 1974. Disulphide groups of gonadotropin receptors are essential for specific binding of human chorionic gonadotropin. *Biochim. Biophys. Acta* 343:417–22

47. Dufau, M. L., Catt, K. J. 1975. High-affinity binding sites in detergent-solubilized gonadotropin receptors. *FEBS Lett.* 52:273–77

48. Dufau, M. L., Podesta, E. J., Catt, K. J. 1975. Physical characteristics of the gonadotropin-receptor complex formed in vivo and in vitro. *Proc. Natl. Acad. Sci. USA* 72:1272–75

49. Dufau, M. L., Ryan, D. W., Baukal, A. J., Catt, K. J. 1975. Gonadotropin receptors. Solubilization and purification by affinity chromatography. *J. Biol. Chem.* 250:4822–24

50. Dufau, M. L., Catt, K. J. 1976. See Reference 11, pp. 135–63

51. Dufau, M. L., Baukal, A., Ryan, D., Catt, K. J. 1976. Properties of detergent-solubilized adenylate cyclase and gonadotropin receptors of testis and ovary. *Mol. Cell. Endocrinol.* In press

52. Eldefrawi, M. E., Eldefrawi, A. T., Shamoo, A. E. 1975. Molecular and functional properties of the acetylcholine receptor. *Ann. NY Acad. Sci.* 264:183–202

53. Fishman, P. H., Moss, J., Vaughan, M. 1976. Uptake and metabolism of ganglioside in transformed mouse fibroblasts. *J. Biol. Chem.* 251:4490–94

54. Flier, J. S., Kahn, C. R., Roth, J., Bar, R. S. 1975. Antibodies that impair insulin receptor binding in an unusual diabetic syndrome with severe insulin resistance. *Science* 190:63–65

55. Franklin, T. J., Foster, S. J. 1973. Hormone-induced desensitization of hormonal control of cyclic AMP in human coupled fibroblasts. *Nature* 246:146–48

56. Freychet, P., Kahn, C. R., Roth, J., Neville, D. M. 1972. Insulin interactions with liver plasma membranes: Independence of binding of the hormone and its degradation. *J. Biol. Chem.* 247:3953–61

57. Freychet, P., Laudat, M. H., Laudat, P., Rosselin, G., Kahn, C. R., Gorden, P., Roth, J. 1972. Impairment of insulin binding to the fat cell membrane in the obese hyperglycemic mouse. *FEBS Lett.* 25:339–32

58. Freychet, P., Brandenburg, D., Wollmer, A. 1974. Receptor-binding assay of chemically modified insulins: Comparison with in vitro and in vivo bioassays. *Diabetologia* 10:1–5

59. Gammeltoft, S., Gliemann, J. 1973. Binding and degradation of ^{125}I-labelled insulin by isolated rat fat cells. *Biochim. Biophys. Acta* 320:16–32

60. Gardner, J. D., Klaeveman, H. L., Bilezikian, J. P., Aurbach, G. D. 1973. Effect of beta-adrenergic catecholamines on sodium transport in turkey erythrocytes. *J. Biol. Chem.* 248:5590–97

61. Gavin, J. R., Gorden, P., Roth, J. 1973. Characteristics of the human lymphocyte insulin receptor. *J. Biol. Chem.* 248:2202–7
62. Gavin, J. R., Roth, J., Neville, D. M., De Meyts, P. D., Buell, D. N. 1974. Insulin-dependent regulation of insulin receptor concentrations: A direct demonstration in cell culture. *Proc. Natl. Acad. Sci. USA* 71:84–88
63. Giorgio, N. A., Johnson, C. B., Blecher, M. 1974. Hormone receptors. III. Properties of glucagon-binding proteins isolated from liver plasma membranes. *J. Biol. Chem.* 249:428–37
64. Gliemann, J., Gammeltoft, S. 1974. The biological activity and the binding affinity of modified insulin determined on isolated rat cells. *Diabetologia* 10:105–13
65. Glossmann, H., Baukal, A. J., Catt, K. J. 1974. Properties of angiotensin II receptors in the bovine and rat adrenal cortex. *J. Biol. Chem.* 249:825–34
66. Glossmann, H., Baukal, A. J., Catt, K. J. 1974. Angiotensin II receptors in bovine adrenal cortex. Modifications of angiotensin II binding by guanyl nucleotides. *J. Biol. Chem.* 249:664–66
67. Glossmann, H., Baukal, A. J., Catt, K. J. 1974. Cation dependence of high-affinity angiotensin II binding to adrenal cortex receptors. *Science* 185:281–83
68. Goldfine, I. D., Gardner, J. D., Neville, D. M. 1972. Insulin action in isolated rat thymocytes. Binding of ^{125}I-insulin and stimulation of α-aminoisobutyric acid transport. *J. Biol. Chem.* 247:6919–26
69. Goldfine, I. D. 1975. Binding of insulin to thymocytes from suckling and hypophysectomized rats: Evidence for two mechanisms regulating insulin sensitivity. *Endocrinology* 97:948–54
70. Goldfine, I. D., Roth, J., Birnbaumer, L. 1972. Glucagon receptors in β-cells. Binding of ^{125}I-glucagon and activation of adenylate cyclase. *J. Biol. Chem.* 247:1211–18
71. Gorden, P., Lesniak, M. A., Hendricks, C. M., Roth, J. 1973. "Big" growth hormone components from human plasma: Decreased reactivity demonstrated by radioreceptor assay. *Science* 182:829–31
72. Gorden, P., Gavin, J. R., Kahn, C. R., Archer, J. A., Lesniak, M., Hendricks, C., Neville, D. M., Roth, J. 1973. Application of radioreceptor assay to circulating insulin, growth hormone, and

to their tissue receptors in animals and man. *Pharmacol. Rev.* 25:179–87
73. Grahame-Smith, D. G., Butcher, R. W., Ney, R. L., Sutherland, E. W. 1967. Adenosine 3', 5'-monophosphate as the intracellular mediator of the action of adrenocorticotropic hormone on the adrenal cortex. *J. Biol. Chem.* 242:5535–41
74. Haynes, R. C., Sutherland, E. W., Rall, T. W. 1960. The role of cyclic adenylic acid in hormone action. *Rec. Prog. Horm. Res.* 16:121–38
75. Hofmann, K., Wingender, W., Finn, F. M. 1970. Correlation of adrenocorticotropic activity of ACTH analogs with degree of binding to an adrenal cortical particulate preparation. *Proc. Natl. Acad. Sci. USA* 67:829–36
76. Hofmann, K., Montibeller, J. A., Finn, F. M. 1974. ACTH antagonists. *Proc. Natl. Acad. Sci. USA* 71:80–83
77. Holmgren, J., Lonnroth, I., Svennerholm, L. 1972. Tissue receptor for cholera exotoxin: Postulated structure from studies with G_{MI} ganglioside and related glycolipids. *J Infect. Immunol.* 8:208–14
78. Holmgren, J., Lonnroth, I., Mansson, J-E., Svennerholm, L. 1975. Interaction of cholera toxin and membrane G_{MI} ganglioside of small intestine. *Proc. Natl. Acad. Sci. USA* 72:2520–24
79. Hsueh, A. J. W., Dufau, M. L., Catt, K. J. 1976. Regulation of luteinizing hormone receptors in testicular interstitial cells by gonadotropin. *Biochem. Biophys. Res. Commun.* 72:1145–52
80. Hunzicker-Dunn, M., Birnbaumer, L. 1976. Adenylyl cyclase activities in ovarian tissues. IV. Gonadotropin-induced desensitization of the luteal adenylyl cyclase throughout pregnancy and pseudopregnancy in the rabbit and the rat. *Endocrinology* 211–22
81. Jarett, L., Smith, R. M. 1976. See Reference 11, pp. 91–104
82. Kahn, C. R. 1975. In *Methods in Membrane Biology*, ed. E. D. Korn. 3:81–156. New York: Plenum
83. Kahn, C. R. 1976. Membrane receptors for hormones and neurotransmitters. *J. Cell. Biol.* 70:261–86
84. Kahn, C. R., Flier, J. S., Bar, R. S., Archer, J. A., Gorden, P., Martin, M. M., Roth, J. 1976. The syndromes of insulin resistance and acanthosis nigricans. Insulin-receptor disorders in man. *New Engl. J. Med.* 294:739–45
85. Kahn, C. R., Neville, D. M., Roth, J. 1973. Insulin-receptor interaction in the

obese-hyperglycemic mouse. *J. Biol. Chem.* 248:244–50

86. Kahn, C. R., Roth, J. 1975. Cell membrane receptors for polypeptide hormones. Applications to disease states in mice and men. *Am. J. Clin. Pathol.* 63:656–68

87. Kahn, C. R., Roth, J. 1967. In *Isolation of Hormone Receptors,* ed. G. S. Levey, pp. 1–29. New York: Dekker

88. Katzen, H. M., Vlahakes, G. J. 1973. Biological activity of insulin-sepharose. *Science* 179:1142–43

89. Kebabian, J. W., Zatz, M., Romero, J. A., Axelrod, J. 1975. Rapid changes in rat pineal β-adrenergic receptor: Alterations in [³H] alprenolol binding and adenylate cyclase. *Proc. Natl. Acad. Sci. USA* 72:3735–39

90. Ketelslegers, J.-M., Catt, K. J. 1974. Receptor binding properties of ¹²⁵I-hFSH prepared by enzymatic iodination. *J. Clin. Endocrinol. Metab.* 39:1159–62

91. Ketelslegers, J.-M., Knott, G. D., Catt, K. J. 1975. Kinetics of gonadotropin binding by receptors of the rat testis: Analysis by a non-linear curve-fitting method. *Biochemistry* 14:3075–83

92. Kono, T. 1969. Destruction and restoration of the insulin effector system in isolated fat cells. *J. Biol. Chem.* 244:5777–84

93. Kono, T., Barham, F. W. 1971. The relationship between the insulin-binding capacity of fat cells and the cellular response to insulin. Studies with intact and trypsin-treated cells. *J. Biol. Chem.* 246:6210–16

94. Kono, T. 1972. In *Insulin Action,* ed. I. B. Fritz, p. 171. New York: Academic

95. Korenman, S. G., Perrin, L. E., McCallum, T. P. 1969. A radioligand binding assay for oestradiol measurement in human plasma. *J. Clin. Endocrinol. Metab.* 29:879–83

96. Lefkowitz, R. J., Roth, J., Pricer, W., Pastan, I. 1970. ACTH-receptors in the adrenal: Specific binding of ACTH-¹²⁵I and its relation to adenyl cyclase. *Proc. Natl. Acad. Sci. USA* 65:745–52

97. Lefkowitz, R. J., Roth, J., Pastan, I. 1970. Radioreceptor assay of adrenocorticotropic hormone: New approach to assay of polypeptide hormones in plasma. *Science* 170:633–35

98. Lefkowitz, R. J., Roth, J., Pastan, I. 1971. ACTH-receptor action in the adrenal: A model for the initial step of hormones that stimulate adenylate cyclase. *Ann. NY Acad. Sci.* 185:195–209

99. Lefkowitz, R. J., Caron, M. G., Mukherjee, C., Mickey, J., Tate, R. 1976. See Reference 11, pp. 49–65

100. Lefkowitz, R. J., Mullikin, D., Caron, M. G. 1976. Regulation of beta-adrenergic receptors by guanyl-5'-yl imidodiphosphate and other purine nucleotides. *J. Biol. Chem.* 251:4686–92

101. Lesniak, M. A., Roth, J., Gorden, P., Gavin, J. R. 1973. Human growth hormone radioreceptor assay using cultured human lymphocytes. *Nature New Biol.* 241:20–22

102. Lesniak, M. A., Roth, J., Gorden, P., Gavin, J. R. 1974. Binding of human growth hormone to specific receptors in human cultured lymphocytes. *J. Biol. Chem.* 249:1661–67

103. Lesniak, M. A., Roth, J. 1976. Regulation of receptor concentration by homologous hormone. Effect of human growth hormone on its receptor in IM-9 lymphocytes. *J. Biol. Chem.* 251:3720–29

104. Levey, G. S., Fletcher, M. A., Klein, I. 1975. In *Advances in Cyclic Nucleotide Research,* ed. G. J. Drummond, P. Greengard, G. A. Robison, 5:53. New York: Raven

105. Levitzki, A. 1974. Negative cooperativity in clustered receptors as a possible basis for membrane action. *J. Theor. Biol.* 44:367–72

106. Levitzki, A., Atlas, D., Steer, M. L. 1974. The binding characteristics and number of β-adrenergic receptors on the turkey erythrocyte. *Proc. Natl. Acad. Sci. USA* 72:2773–76

107. Limbird, L. E., De Meyts, P., Lefkowitz, R. J. 1975. Beta-adrenergic receptors: Evidence for negative cooperativity. *Biochem. Biophys. Res. Commun.* 64:1160–68

108. Lin, S.-Y., Goodfriend, T. L. 1970. Angiotensin receptors. *Am. J. Physiol.* 218:1319–28

109. Londos, C., Salomon, Y., Lin, M. C., Harwood, J. P., Schramm, M., Wolff, J., Rodbell, M. 1974. 5'-Guanylylimidodiphosphate, a potent activator of adenylate cyclase systems in eukaryotic cells. *Proc. Natl. Acad. Sci. USA* 71:3087–90

110. Manley, S. W., Bourke, J. R., Hawker, R. W. 1974. The thyrotropin receptor in guinea-pig thyroid homogenate: Interaction with the long-acting thyroid stimulator. *J. Endocrinol.* 61:437–45

111. Marchesi, V. T., Furthmayer, F., Tomita, M. 1976. See Reference 11, pp. 217–22

112. Marinetti, G. V., Shatz, L., Reilly, K. 1972. In *Insulin Action*, ed. I. B. Fritz, pp. 207–76, New York: Academic

113. Marsh, J. 1975. The role of cyclic AMP in gonadal function. *Adv. Cyclic Nucleotide Res.* 6:137–99

114. McGuffin, W. L., Gavin, J. R., Lesniak, M. A., Gorden, P., Roth, J. 1976. Water-soluble specific growth hormone binding sites from cultured human lymphocytes: Preparation and partial characterization. *Endocrinology* 98:1401–7

115. McIlhinney, R. A. J., Schulster, D. 1975. Studies on the binding of ^{125}I-labeled corticotrophin in isolated rat adrenocortical cells. *J. Endocrinol.* 64:175–84

116. McIntosh, C., Warnecke, J., Nieger, M., Barner, A., Kobberling, J. 1976. Solubilization and partial purification of a growth hormone receptor from rabbit liver. *FEBS Lett.* 66:149–54

117. Means, A. R., Huckins, C. 1974. In *Hormone Binding and Target Cell Activation in the Testis*, ed. M. L. Dufau, A. R. Means, pp. 145–65. New York: Plenum. 371 pp.

118. Megyesi, K., Kahn, C. R., Roth, J., Gorden, P. 1974. Hypoglycemia in association with extrapancreatic tumors: Demonstration of elevated plasma NSILA-s by a new radioreceptor assay. *J. Clin. Endocrinol. Metab.* 38:931–34

119. Megyesi, K., Kahn, C. R., Roth, J., Neville, D. M., Nissley, S. P., Humbel, R. E., Froesch, E. R. 1975. The NSILA-s receptor in liver plasma membranes. Characterization and comparison with the insulin receptor. *J. Biol. Chem.* 250:8990–96

120. Mendelson, C., Dufau, M. L., Catt, K. J. 1975. Gonadotropin binding and stimulation of cyclic AMP and testosterone production in isolated Leydig cells. *J. Biol. Chem.* 250:8818–23

121. Menon, K. M. J., Kiburz, J. 1974. Isolation of plasma membranes from bovine corpus luteum possessing adenylate cyclase, ^{125}I-hCG binding and Na-K-ATPase activities. *Biochem. Biophys. Res. Commun.* 56:363–71

122. Meunier, J-C., Olsen, R. W., Changeux, J.-P. 1972. Studies on the cholinergic receptor protein from *Electrophorus electricus*. *FEBS Lett.* 24:63–68

123. Meunier, J-C., Sealock, R., Olsen, R., Changeux, J.-P 1974. Purification and properties of the cholinergic receptor protein from *Electrophorus electricus* electric tissue. *Eur. J. Biochem.* 45:371–94

124. Mickey, J., Tate, R., Lefkowitz, R. J. 1975. Subsensitivity of adenylate cyclase and decreased β-adrenergic receptor binding after chronic exposure to (-)-isoproterenol vitro. *J. Biol. Chem.* 250:5727–29

125. Moyle, W. R., Ramachandran, J. 1973. Effect of LH on steroidogenesis and cyclic AMP accumulation in rat Leydig cell preparations and mouse tumor Leydig cells. *Endocrinology* 93:127–34

126. Moyle, W. R., Bahl, O. P., Marz, L. 1975. Role of the carbohydrate of human chorionic gonadotropin in the mechanism of hormone action. *J. Biol. Chem.* 250:9163–69

127. Mukherjee, C., Caron, M. G., Coverstone, M., Lefkowitz, R. 1975. Identification of adenylate cyclase-coupled β-adrenergic receptors in frog erythrocytes with (-)[^{3}H] alprenolol. *J. Biol. Chem.* 250:4869–76

128. Mukherjee, C., Caron, M. G., Lefkowitz, R. J. 1975. Catecholamine-induced subsensitivity of adenylate cyclase-coupled beta adrenergic receptor binding sites. *Proc. Natl. Acad. Sci. USA* 72:1945–49

129. Mukhtar, E. D., Smith, B. R., Pyle, G. A., Hall, R., Vice, P. 1975. Relation of thyroid-stimulating immunoglobulins to thyroid function and effects of surgery, radioiodine and antithyroid drugs. *Lancet* 1:713–15

130. Mullin, B. R., Fishman, P. H., Lee, G., Aloj, S. M., Ledley, F. D., Winand, R. J., Kohn, L. D., Brady, R. A. 1976. Thyrotropin-ganglioside interactions and their relationship to the structure and function of thyrotropin receptors. *Proc. Natl. Acad. Sci. USA* 73:842–46

131. Nakamura, M., Ide, M., Okabayashi, T., Tanaka, A. 1972. Relationship between steroidogenesis and cyclic AMP production in isolated adrenal cells. *Endocrinol. Jpn.* 19:443–48

132. Neer, E. J. 1973. Vasopressin-responsive, soluble adenylate cyclase from the rat renal medulla. *J. Biol. Chem.* 218:3742–44

133. Orci, L., Rufener, C., Malaisse-Lagae, F., Blondel, B., Amherdt, M., Bataille, D., Freychet, P., Perrelet, A. 1975. A morphological approach to surface receptors in islet and liver cells. *Isr. J. Med.* 11:639–55

134. Pastan, I., Roth, J., Macchia, V. 1966. Binding of hormone to tissue: The first step in polypeptide hormone action. *Proc. Natl. Acad. Sci. USA* 56:1802–9

135. Patrick, J., Lindstrom, J. M. 1973. Autoimmune response to acetylcholine receptor. *Science* 180:871–72

136. Perkins, J. P. 1973. Adenyl cyclase. *Adv. Cyclic Nucleotide Res.* 3:1–64

137. Podesta, E. J., Dufau, M. L., Catt, K. J. 1976. Characterization of two forms of cyclic 3', 5'-adenosine monophosphate-dependent protein kinase in rat testicular interstitial cells. *Mol. Cell Endocrinol.* 5:109–22

138. Pohl, S. L., Krans, H. M. J., Kozyreff, V., Birnbaumer, L., Rodbell, M. 1971. The glucagon-sensitive adenyl cyclase system in plasma membrane of rat liver. Evidence for a role of membrane lipids. *J. Biol. Chem.* 246:4447–54

139. Posner, B. I., Kelly, P. A., Friesen, H. G. 1974. Induction of a lactogenic receptor in rat liver: Influence of estrogen and the pituitary. *Proc. Natl. Acad. Sci. USA* 71:2407–10

140. Posner, B. I. 1975. Polypeptide hormone receptors: Characteristics and applications. *Can. J. Physiol. Pharmacol.* 53:689–703

141. Pullen, R. A., Lindsay, D. G., Wood, S. P., Tickle, I. J., Blundell, T. L., Wollmer, A., Krail, G., Brandenburg, D., Zahn, H., Gliemann, J., Gammeltoft, S. 1976. Receptor-binding region of insulin. *Nature* 259:369–73

142. Queener, S. F., Fleming, J. W., Bell, N. H. 1975. Solubilization of calcitonin-responsive renal cortical adenylate cyclase. *J. Biol. Chem.* 250:7586–7601

143. Remold-O'Donnell, E. 1974. Stimulation and desensitization of macrophage adenylate cyclase by prostaglandins and catecholamines. *J. Biol. Chem.* 249:3615–27

144. Robison, G. A., Butcher, R. W., Sutherland, E. W. 1967. Adenyl cyclase as an adrenergic receptor. *Ann. NY Acad. Sci.* 139:703–23

145. Robison, G. A., Butcher, R. W., Sutherland, E. W., eds. 1971. *Cyclic AMP.* New York: Academic. 529 pp.

146. Rodbell, M., Birnbaumer, L., Pohl, S. L., Sundby, F. 1971. The reaction of glucagon with its receptor: Evidence for discrete regions of activity and binding in the glucagon molecule. *Proc. Natl. Acad. Sci. USA* 68:909–13

147. Rodbell, M., Lin, M. C., Salomon. Y. 1974. Evidence for interdependent action of glucagon and nucleotides on the hepatic adenylate cyclase system. *J. Biol. Chem.* 249:59–65

148. Rodbell, M., Lin, M. C., Salomon, Y., Londos, C., Harwood, J. P., Martin, B. R., Rendell, M., Berman, M. 1975. Role of adenine and guanine nucleotides in the activity and response of adenylate cyclase systems to hormones. Evidence for multisite transition states. *Adv. Cyclic Nucleotide Res.* 5:3–29

149. Roth, J. 1973. Peptide hormone binding to receptors. A review of direct studies in vitro. *Metabolism* 22:1059–73

150. Roth, J., Kahn, C. R., Lesniak, M. A., Gorden, P., De Meyts, P., Megyesi, K., Neville, D. M., Gavin, J. R., Soll, A. H., Freychet, P., Goldfine, I. D., Bar, R. S., Archer, J. A. 1975. Receptors for insulin, NSILA-s and growth hormone: Applications to disease states in man. *Rec. Progr. Horm. Res.* 31:95–139

151. Ryan J., Storm, D. R. 1974. Solubilization of glucagon and epinephrine sensitive adenylate cyclase from rat liver plasma membrane. *Biochem. Biophys. Res. Commun.* 60:304–11

152. Saltman, S., Baukal, A., Waters, S., Bumpus, F. M., Catt, K. J. 1975. Competitive binding activity of angiotensin II analogues in an adrenal cortex radioligand-receptor assay. *Endocrinology* 97:275–82

153. Saltman, S., Fredlund, P., Catt, K. J. 1976. Actions of angiotensin II antagonists upon aldosterone production by isolated adrenal glomerulosa cells. *Endocrinology* 98:894–903

154. Sasaki, K., Dockerill, S., Adamiak, D. A., Tickle, I. J., Blundell, T. 1975. X-ray analysis of glucagon and its relationship to receptor binding. *Nature* 257:751–57

155. Schramm, M. 1975. The catecholamine-responsive adenylate cyclase system and its modification by 5'-guanylylimidodiphosphate. *Adv. Cyclic Nucleotide Res.* 5:105–15

156. Schwartz, R. H., Bianco, A. R. Handwerger, B. S., Kahn, C. R. 1975. A demonstration that monocytes rather than lymphocytes are the insulin binding cells in human peripheral blood mononuclear leukocyte preparations: Implications for studies of insulin-resistant states in man. *Proc. Natl. Acad. Sci. USA* 72:474–78

157. Shiu, R. P. C., Kelly P. A., Friesen, H. G. 1973. Radioreceptor assays for prolactin and other lactogenic hormones. *Science* 180:968–71

158. Shiu, R. P. C., Friesen, H. G. 1974. Solubilization and purification of a prolactin receptor from the mammary gland. *J. Biol. Chem.* 249:7902–11

159. Shiu, R. P. C., Friesen, H. G. 1976. Blockade of prolactin action by an antibody to its receptors. *Science* 192:259–61

160. Singer, S. J., Nicholson, G. L. 1972. The fluid mosaic model of the structure of cell membranes. *Science* 175:720–31

161. Smith, B. R., Hall, R. L. 1974. Thyroid-stimulating immunoglobulins in Graves disease. *Lancet* 2:427–31

162. Soll, A. H., Goldfine, I. D., Roth, J., Kahn, C. R., Neville, D. M. 1974. Thymic lymphocytes in obese (ob/ob) mice: A mirror of the insulin receptor defect in liver and fat. *J. Biol. Chem.* 249:4127–31

163. Soll, A. H., Kahn, C. R., Neville, D. M. 1975. Insulin binding to liver plasma membranes in the obese hyperglycemic mouse (ob/ob) mouse: Demonstration of a decreased number of functionally normal receptors. *J. Biol. Chem.* 250:4702–7

164. Stadie, W. C., Haugaard, N., Marsh, J. B. 1951. Factors influencing the combination of insulin with muscle from normal rats. *J. Biol. Chem.* 189:53–58

165. Stadie, W. C., Haugaard, N., Vaughan, M. 1953. The quantitative relation between insulin and its biological activity. *J. Biol. Chem.* 200:745–51

166. Stephenson, R. P. 1956. A modification of receptor theory. *Br. J. Pharmacol.* 11:379–93

167. Sutherland, E. W., Oye, I., Butcher, R. W. 1965. The action of epinephrine and the role of the adenyl cyclase system in hormone action. *Rec. Progr. Horm. Res.* 21:623–46

168. Tate, R. L., Holmes, J. M., Kohn, L. D., Winand, R. J. 1975. Characteristics of a solubilized thyrotropin receptor from bovine thyroid plasma membranes. *J. Biol. Chem.* 250:6527–33

169. Tate, R. L., Schwartz, H. I., Holmes, J. M., Kohn, L. D., Winand, R. J. 1975. Thyrotropin receptors in thyroid plasma membranes. *J. Biol. Chem.* 250:6509–15

170. Tsuruhara, T., Dufau, M. L., Hickman, J., Catt, K. J. 1972. Biological properties of hCG after removal of terminal sialic acid and galactose residues. *Endocrinology* 91:296–301

171. Tsuruhara, T., Van Hall, E. V., Dufau, M. L., Catt, K. J. 1972. Ovarian binding of intact and desialylated hCG in vivo and in vitro. *Endocrinology* 91:463–69

172. Tsushima, T., Friesen, H. G. 1973. Radioreceptor assay for growth hormone. *J. Clin. Endocrinol. Metab.* 37:334–37

173. Van Wyk, J. J., Underwood, L. E., Hintz, R. L., Voina, S. J., Weaver, R. P. 1974. The somatomedins: A family of insulin-like hormones under growth hormone control. *Rec. Progr. Horm. Res.* 30:259–95

174. Verrier, B., Fayet, G., Lissitzky, S. 1974. Thyrotropin-binding properties of isolated thyroid cells and their plasma membranes. Relation of thyroid-specific binding to adenylate-cyclase activation. *Eur. J. Biochem.* 42:355–65

175. Williams, J. A. 1972. Cyclic AMP formation and thyroid secretion by incubated mouse thyroid glands. *Endocrinology* 91:1411–17

176. Williams, L. T., Snyderman, R., Lefkowitz, R. J. 1975. Identification of β-adrenergic receptors in human lymphocytes by (–)[³H]alprenolol binding. *J. Clin. Invest.* 57:149–55

177. Wolff, J., Cook, G. H. 1975. Charge effects in the activation of adenylate cyclase. *J. Biol. Chem.* 250:6897–6903

178. Wood, S. P., Blundell, T. L., Wollmer, A., Lazarus, N. R., Neville, R. W. J. 1975. The relationship of conformation and association of insulin to receptor binding: X-ray and circular dichroism studies on bovine and hystricomorph insulins. *Eur. J. Biochem.* 55:531–42

179. Zeleznik, A. J., Midgley, A. R., Reichert, L. E. 1974. Granulosa cell maturation in the rat: Increased binding of human chorionic gonadotropin following treatment with follicle-stimulating hormone in vivo. *Endocrinology* 95:818–25

Ann. Rev. Physiol. 1977. 39:559–86
Copyright © 1977 by Annual Reviews Inc. All rights reserved

THE INTERACTION OF BODY TEMPERATURE AND ACID-BASE BALANCE IN ECTOTHERMIC VERTEBRATES

❖1182

Robert Blake Reeves

Department of Physiology, School of Medicine, State University of New York, Buffalo, New York 14214

INTRODUCTION

Sir Joseph Barcroft began his 1934 volume *Features in the Architecture of Physiological Function* (9) with two essays illustrating Claude Bernard's dictum: "La fixité du milieu intérieur est la condition de la vie libre." The first essay noted the sensitivity of cellular activities to hydrogen ion concentrations, observing that due to life processes there is "... every opportunity for the hydrogen ion concentration of the internal environment to be inconstant; yet it remains remarkably constant" within narrow limits in man and other mammals. Concerning the application of this principle to "lower animals," Barcroft stated: "The extreme limits of hydrogen ion concentrations in the blood of sub-mammalian forms are given differently by different authors and are quite obscure." In his second essay Barcroft dealt with temperature, noting that "the temperature of man is approximately constant," and mused on the remarkable proposition "that at any one temperature all the reactions of the body should progress at velocities suitable to one another." He went on to ask: "How does the body of the animal of variable temperature so control its reactions as to keep them in step over a great range of temperature?"

It has taken many decades since Barcroft wrote to perceive that, for all vertebrates, a direct relationship exists between the subjects dealt with in these essays, i.e. between regulated hydrogen ion activity and temperature, a relationship only clarified through the study of many "animals of variable temperature." It is more accurate, as we see later, to substitute for hydrogen ion activity (or pH) that happy phrase of Henderson's (42), the "acid-base balance," which is preserved upon changing body temperature. More recently it has been recognized that the particular balance achieved is not the constancy of blood pH that Barcroft sought, but is rather

559

the preservation of protein net charge states in extra- and intracellular compartments. Regulation of acid-base state as temperature varies can now be related to preservation of cellular activities dependent upon protein function, inasmuch as the binding of substrates, activators, and inhibitors to protein enzyme and transport molecules, as well as their conformation and activity, are directly affected by charge distribution. Furthermore, Donnan equilibria, key factors in ion and water distribution, also depend on protein (and other polyelectrolyte) net charge states. These considerations suggest that the fixity of the internal environment as now perceived did not suddenly emerge with the achievement of homeothermism; rather the milieu intérieur has been carefully regulated throughout vertebrate development so as to preserve protein activities, changing temperature and blood pH notwithstanding.

The number of published investigations dealing in some measure with comparative studies of blood pH and temperature is large; consequently, this review can only highlight the development of experimental evidence and hypotheses concerning the interaction of temperature and acid-base balance in ectothermic vertebrates. It commences with the air-breathing vertebrates because the evidence regarding them is, in most cases, more plentiful, and proceeds to the less straightforward, experimentally more difficult problems of acid-base balance in water breathers. During the short history of this field, many illuminating review and summarizing papers have appeared (2, 47, 70, 77, 84). Ectotherm acid-base regulation is also ably presented in a more general context in a welcome new text on principles of comparative respiratory physiology (24).

ACID-BASE RESPONSES OF AIR-BREATHING ECTOTHERMS

Blood pH and P_{CO_2} In Vivo

EARLY WORK   Comparative studies on the interaction of temperature and acid-base regulation are not new. Four important studies made during 1927–1935 were carried out by investigators of mammalian acid-base chemistry whose names read like a listing from a *Who Was Who in Physiological Chemistry*. Austin et al (6) found blood pH (pH_B) in *Alligator* to be 7.72 at 9°C and 7.27 at 35°C; L. J. Henderson (43) reported values of pH_B for the turtle *Chelydra* of 8.02 at 5°C and 7.60 at 20°C; Dill et al (27) found pH_B values in the lizard *Sauromalus* ranging from 7.76 at 20°C to 6.78 at 38°C; and Dill & Edwards (26) in *Alligator* found pH_B to be 7.74 at 5° to 7.47 at 37.5°C. As these investigators recognized, these values were clearly unlike pH_B values for man and mammals. Austin et al (6) concluded in part that the "decrease in serum pH (in vivo) with rise in (body) temperature is perhaps the most interesting finding." These results were in large part ignored by later workers, partially because the pH determinations had been carried out with colorimetric method for determining blood pH of Hastings & Sendroy (40) which was replaced soon after by the glass electrode. Those who have seen the colorimetric method used by skilled investigators can hardly doubt that the accuracy was sufficient for the large pH_B changes occurring in the blood of ectothermic vertebrates. Also modern calibration buffers (11) had not then been agreed upon; this too could hardly introduce a correction large enough to affect the validity of the basic observations.

It is really unclear why these important observations were ignored for almost three decades; meanwhile the prevailing assumption, unsubstantiated in experiment, grew that the pH of mammalian blood at 37°C, 7.4 was a universal constant which ought to apply to all vertebrates. The very large number of investigations that uncritically used pH 7.4 for Ringer's solutions at any temperature in experiments on frog and other ectothermic tissues attests to how cherished misinformation can be even in the scientific community.

RECENT INVESTIGATION   To Professor Eugene D. Robin and to Professor Hermann Rahn must go the credit for the rediscovering, and reawakening interest in, problems of acid-base regulation in ectothermic vertebrates. In 1962 Robin (83) reported blood pH and Pco_2 measurements carried out on the freshwater turtle *Pseudemys scripta;* he was led to make measurements because he earlier noted a large discrepancy between pH_B values in Pittsburgh, Pennsylvania and similar measurements carried out later at Salisbury Cove, Maine. Robin correctly attributed the discrepancy to a difference in body temperature. He therefore set out to measure pH_B and the partial pressure of CO_2 in arterial blood ($Paco_2$) with modern electrometric blood gas techniques and calibration in unanesthetized animals kept at least 24 hr at temperatures of 10°, 24°, and 37°C. Mean values from these data are included among other measurements on this species in Figure 1. His data affirmed the conclusion of Austin et al (6) that normal blood pH of these animals is not constant but varies inversely with temperature; carbon dioxide partial pressure also was not constant in *Pseudemys* but increased with body temperature.

Pseudemys represents the most completely investigated species for acid-base behavior among air-breathing ectotherms. Figure 1 presents mean values for blood pH_B and Pco_2 taken from six independent investigations and shows excellent correspondence between them. These data demonstrate that at each body temperature *Pseudemys* defends a different pH_B and Pco_2 value. Additional investigations [summarized in Howell et al (46) in a definitive study on three species, bullfrogs (*Rana catesbeiana*), toads (*Bufo marinus,*) and snapping turtles (*Chelydra serpentina*), and illustrated in Figure 2] indicate similar behavior. The change in blood pH with temperature in vivo in unanesthetized animals was found to be about –0.016U/°C between 5 and 37°C. The partial pressure of carbon dioxide increased with body temperature in all species even though specific values varied widely from species to species. This pattern of temperature dependent blood acid-base status has now been observed in many species [see Howell & Rahn (47) for data from 16 reptilian species also (18, 39)]; no exceptions to this pattern are known for air-breathing ectothermic vertebrates.

The similarity of pattern of acid-base regulation as body temperature changes in different ectotherm species should not, however, be taken as evidence that identical values for pH_B or for Pco_2 occur from species to species at a given body temperature. Rahn & Garey (72), using the waters of the Amazon River as their field 28°C constant temperature water bath, compared blood acid-base values from unanesthetized representatives derived from 14 species. The average pH_B found was 7.61 ± 0.10 standard deviation (range 7.50–7.77); Pco_2 varied from 3.5 to 38 torr and plasma bicarbonate concentration from 4 to 45 mM/*l* respectively.

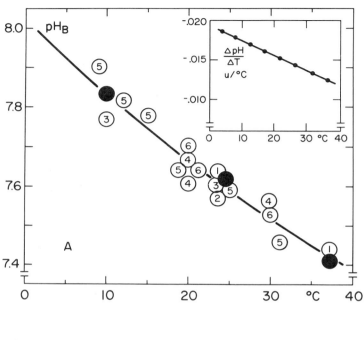

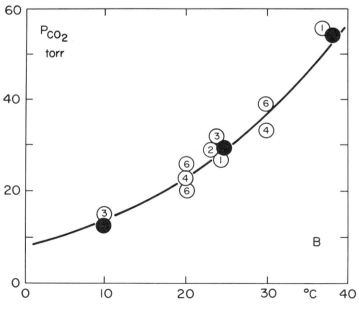

Acid-base Responses of Blood in Vitro

Robin (83) in his initial study of *Pseudemys* acid-base balance included data on pH and P_{CO_2} obtained when turtle blood at constant gas content was warmed or cooled in a syringe. These in vitro data are indicated on Figure 1; the striking fact is not their similarity to, but their identity with, values obtained in vivo. Provided only that one commences with a normal blood sample at a given temperature, the change in pH and P_{CO_2} on changing temperature for that sample at constant carbon dioxide content accurately indicates the acid-base responses of the open metabolizing regulated system in vivo. Similar experimental comparisons of blood pH in vivo with blood in vitro under conditions of changing temperature are shown for *Rana* and *Chelydra* (47) in Figure 2.

ROSENTHAL TEMPERATURE CORRECTION FACTORS   Blood from cold-blooded species is not unique in showing in vitro a large pH decrease ($\sim$–0.0147 U/°C) with increasing temperature and a simultaneous increase in the partial pressure of carbon dioxide (approximately $\Delta\log P_{CO_2}/\Delta T = 0.020$); Rosenthal (85) in 1948 first described these changes in human and laboratory animal blood as an aid to measuring blood pH in vivo when the glass electrode measuring system was not thermostatted at body temperature. Their practical utility soon gave rise to a series of empirical temperature correction factors for blood pH (1, 7, 58) and P_{CO_2} (7, 14, 58, 63) for human blood warmed or cooled at constant carbon dioxide content. The chemical basis for these changes has now been determined (79). These systems consist of binary mixtures of protein and CO_2-bicarbonate buffers with protein buffering quantitatively predominant. It is the change of pK' of the principal buffer group (in the physiological pH range) in protein, the imidazole group (IM) of peptide histidine, that dominates the change in pH of the solution as temperature changes. The change in pK'_{IM} with temperature is large (approximately –0.017 U/°C for the ΔT 20–30°C) with an enthalpy of ionization of about 7 kcal/mol (79). The pH change resulting from the temperature-altered dissociation strength of histidine imidazole groups affects the carbonic acid-bicarbonate equilibrium, together with the effect of temperature on carbon dioxide solubility. These simultaneous changes can be described and quantitatively predicted from simple chemical equilibrium and mass conservation equations (15, 79).

◄ ───

Figure 1   The change in blood pH (pH_B) in panel *A* and carbon dioxide tension (P_{CO_2}) in panel *B* as a function of temperature for blood in vivo and in vitro from the turtle, *Pseudemys scripta*. Numbered open circles represent mean values in vivo reported from the following: 1. Robin (83); 2. Jackson (49); 3. Jackson & Silverblatt (54); 4. Jackson et al (53); 5. Malan et al (60); 6. Jackson & Kagen (34, 52). Filled circles are in vitro data of Robin (83). Solid curves are computed for blood of constant carbon dioxide content after Reeves (78) for following conditions: $pH_B = 7.60$, $P_{CO_2} = 28$ torr at $T_B = 24°C$ with imidazole concentration (c_B) 0.030 M/*l*, true plasma carbon dioxide content (C_{CO_2}) .032 M/*l*, strong ion concentration difference ($c_a - c_c$) – 0.026 Eq/*l*. Inset in panel *A* shows $\Delta pH/\Delta T$ of solid curve for temperature intervals of 5° over the range 0–40°C.

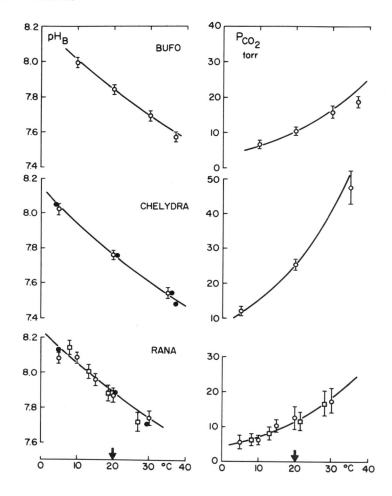

Figure 2 Blood pH (pH$_B$) and carbon dioxide partial pressure (P$_{CO_2}$) in toads (*Bufo marinus*), snapping turtles (*Chelydra serpentina*), and bullfrogs (*Rana catesbeiana*). Open circles are in vivo data and filled circles, in vitro data from Howell et al (46, 90). The open square data are from Reeves (60, 78). Curves drawn in each case are binary buffer model solutions (78, 79) at constant carbon dioxide content; for each species pH$_B$ and P$_{CO_2}$ data at 20°C were used to calculate a strong ion concentration difference ($c_a - c_c$). For *Bufo*: $c_B = 0.020$ M/l, ($c_a - c_c$) = –0.0192 Eq/l, $C_{CO_2} = 0.022$ M/l. For *Chelydra*: $c_B = 0.050$ M/l, ($c_a - c_c$) = –0.039 Eq/l, $C_{CO_2} = 0.038$ M/l. For *Rana*: $c_B = 0.020$ M/l, ($c_a - c_c$) = –0.024 Eq/l, $C_{CO_2} = 0.027$ M/l.

PROTEIN NET CHARGE STATES   Of special interest for this analysis is the effect on blood protein net charge as pH and P_{CO_2} vary when blood changes temperature at constant CO_2 content. For simple illustrative purposes, mean net charge ($\bar{Z}$) for a hypothetical peptide can be computed following Edsall & Wyman (28). Suppose this peptide contains n_1 free carboxyl groups, all alike and ionizing independently, with a pK'_{COOH} of 4.3 (25°C), n_2 imidazole groups of histidine with a pK'_{IM} of 7.0 and n_3 ϵ-ammonium groups of lysine, $pK'_{\epsilon\text{-}NH_2}$ of 10.0. The number of negatively charged $-COO^-$ groups at any pH is then $n_1\,\alpha_{COOH}$, where α_{COOH} is the fractional dissociation of total carboxyl groups given by pH $=$ pK'_{COOH} $+$ log $\alpha_{COOH}/1-\alpha_{COOH}$. The number of positively charged imidazolium groups is $n_2(1 - \alpha_{IM})$, where α_{IM} (the fractional dissociation of total imidazole groups) is calculated similarly for a pK'_{IM} of 7.0. Analogously, the number of positively charged ammonium groups is $n_3(1 - \alpha_{\text{-}NH_2})$. The total mean net charge summing cationic and anionic groups then is

$$\bar{Z} = n_2\,(1 - \alpha_{IM}) + n_3(1 - \alpha_{\text{-}NH_2}) - n_1\,\alpha_{COOH}.$$

However the physiological pH range (6–8) is so far distant from pK'_{COOH} and $pK'_{\epsilon\text{-}NH_2}$, that $\alpha_{COOH} \longrightarrow 1.0$ and $\alpha_{\text{-}NH_2} \longrightarrow 0$, and our equation for $\bar{Z}$ simplifies to:

$$\bar{Z} = n_2(1 - \alpha_{IM}) + n_3 - n_1.$$

Hence $\bar{Z}$, for a given polypeptide composition, n_1, n_2, n_3, is solely a function in the pH 6–8 range of α_{IM}, the fractional dissociation of histidine imidazole groups.

Proteins contain only one additional ionizing group titratable in the physiological pH range, the N-terminal α-amino group, $pK_{\alpha\text{-}NH_2}$ 7.8 (29), in addition to the histidine imidazolium group. However, the small number of α-amino groups compared to histidine imidazole groups, combined with a similar large enthalpy of ionization, and $\Delta H° = 8.4\,kcal/mol$ (25°)(30), permits all proteins for our simplified purposes to be treated as though only histidine imidazole is changing contribution to $\bar{Z}$ when pH varies in the physiological range. Thus, if α_{IM} can be computed for the conditions occurring for blood in a syringe, a measure of the change in mean net protein charge can be obtained. Despite recognized microscopic variability of pK'_{IM} and $\Delta H°$ in proteins (82), all peptide histidine imidazole dissociations may be arbitrarily assigned a uniform pK'_{IM} (6.96 at 25°C) with an average $\Delta H°$ of 7 kcal/mol (79) for purposes of computing α_{IM}.

For human blood treated as though it were a single phase binary buffer, an approximation which permits prediction of changes of pH and P_{CO_2} in this system as temperature varies, the calculated variation of α_{IM} over the temperature range 0–45°C is almost negligible, 0.79–0.82 (79). In this system, protein net charge is essentially invariant as temperature changes at constant CO_2 content. Reeves (80) experimentally tested this conclusion by measuring the Donnan distribution between human red cells and plasma for $^{36}Cl^-$ under in vitro conditions; even though pH changed from 7.3 to 7.95 as temperature changed, chloride ion distribution between red cell and plasma water remained constant. Had such a change in pH been carried out isothermally, r_{Cl^-} would have changed from 0.7 to 0.45. This experiment establishes that the protein CO_2- bicarbonate binary buffer mixture of plasma and whole blood has the remarkable property at constant CO_2 content of maintaining a protein charge state invariant when temperature changes, even though pH and P_{CO_2} vary significantly.

BINARY BUFFER THEORY APPLIED TO IN VIVO BEHAVIOR   In vitro analysis of temperature effects on blood at constant CO_2 content has found application in describing the behavior in vivo of pH_B and P_{CO_2} as body temperature changes. The data for *Pseudemys* in Figure 1 and three additional species in Figure 2 have each been fitted to theoretical binary buffer curves. In each species, the observed pH_B and P_{CO_2} at a single temperature have been used along with an assumed imidazole concentration (c_B), to calculate a strong ion concentration difference (nonbuffer anion minus nonbuffer cation concentration difference, $c_a - c_c$) and total CO_2 content. Simultaneous solution of proton equilibrium and mass conservation equations (78, 79) at all temperatures by reiterative digital computation permits simultaneous solution for pH and P_{CO_2} as a function of temperature. The only fitted parameter in these calculations is the effective imidazole (protein) buffer concentration. A property of all these calculated curves derived from in vitro model calculations applied to in vivo data is the constancy of α_{IM} (see Figure 3 for values in vivo for blood α_{IM}). Thus these computations establish that in the open metabolizing system, α_{IM} is regulated by the animal so as to maintain constant protein charge state. To contrast this system of acid-base regulation with the constant pH system of homeotherms (i.e. a pH-stat), the ectotherm pattern of acid-base control has been termed *alphastat regulation* (78). This term is meant to convey the fact that by whatever means the intact animal regulates his acid-base balance as body temperature changes, α_{IM}, and thus mean protein net charge, are protected and maintained constant.

BLOOD CARBON DIOXIDE CONTENT IN VIVO   The equations whose solutions provide the theoretical values for pH and P_{CO_2} as a function of temperature expressed as the curves indicated on Figure 1 and Figure 2, are solved for a condition of constant CO_2 content. Blood enclosed in vitro in the absence of gas exchange must necessarily have a constant carbon dioxide content. Does blood, or more accurately, true plasma, in vivo have a constant CO_2 content? Since most (98%) of the carbon dioxide in true plasma is in the chemical form of bicarbonate ions, one can ask the equivalent question: Are plasma bicarbonate concentrations unchanged as air-breathing ectotherms change body temperature?

Robin (83) found an increase in bicarbonate concentration as body temperature rose in *Pseudemys*. Howell et al (46) reported that bicarbonate concentrations fell as body temperature rose in *Rana, Chelydra,* and *Bufo.* In both cases the bicarbonate concentrations were calculated by the Henderson equation from measured pH and P_{CO_2} data; the pK_1' for the first dissociation of carbonic acid used in these calculations (87) appears to be increasingly in error at temperatures below 20°C, as discussed further below. Hence these reported changes are probably spurious, as has been subsequently recognized by Howell & Rahn (47). In experiments in which total carbon dioxide content was measured directly by Van Slyke analysis (65), plasma CO_2 content did not change significantly in *Rana* (78) or in *Pseudemys* (52, 53) as

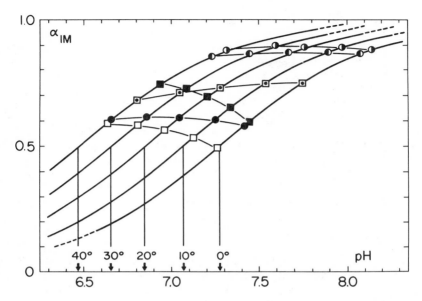

Figure 3   Alpha imidazole (α_{IM}) values for blood and intracellular compartments as a function of measured pH for selected tissues of *Rana* and *Pseudemys* (60). Dissociation curves for protein imidazole groups are depicted at five temperatures over the range 0–40°C. Value of pK'$_{IM}$ at each temperature is indicated along pH abscissa. On each dissociation curve tissue values for α_{IM} are plotted; points are computed from pH$_i$ values of regression line for tissue pH$_i$ versus body temperature. *Rana:* blood (◐), striated muscle, (□); *Pseudemys:* blood (○), striated muscle (●), cardiac muscle (■), liver (▣).

body temperature was altered. Thus in air-breathing ectotherms, neither loading nor unloading of blood carbon dioxide stores takes place during alteration of body temperature (78).

IS BLOOD pH A LINEAR FUNCTION OF TEMPERATURE?   In vitro analysis of acid-base balance as blood changes temperature suggests that characterization of the pH dependence on temperature in vivo as a linear function may be inappropriate. Many investigators describe blood pH versus temperature data by fitting a linear regression and characterizing the dependence by the slope of the regression line, i.e. values reported for ΔpH/ΔT have ranged from –0.010 to –0.021 U/°C (47). The inset in Figure 1, panel *A*, shows the computed ΔpH/ΔT for 5° ΔT intervals of the calculated constant CO_2 content curve. These calculated ΔpH/ΔT values decrease significantly as temperature increases. If acid-base regulation in vivo is based on regulation of α_{IM}, description of the nonlinear dependence of blood pH on temperature by use of a single ΔpH/ΔT will neither describe the regulation observed nor assist in comparing one system with another. However, characterization by a ΔpH/ΔT does allow description within the limits of experimental error without commitment to a particular mechanism of regulation.

What is the Regulated Parameter in Air-Breathing Ectotherms?

ALPHASTAT HYPOTHESIS   Measurements on ectotherm blood acid-base balance unquestionably indicate that unlike the situation well-documented for homeotherms, neither pH nor P_{CO_2} is kept constant as these animals pursue their normal activities where body temperature varies. It has already been indicated that one parameter which appears invariant over a wide range of temperatures is the fractional dissociation of protein histidine imidazole groups, the critical protein R-group dissociation affecting protein net charge in the physiological pH range. In order for α_{IM} to remain constant, the difference $(pH_B - pK'_{IM})$ must remain constant. For in vitro systems this is accomplished by virtue of the factors affecting change in plasma (or blood) pH with temperature (79):

$$\frac{dpH}{dT} = \frac{\beta_{HCO_3^-} \cdot dpK'_1/dT + \beta_{IM} \cdot dpK'_{IM}/dT}{\beta_{HCO_3^-} + \beta_{IM}},$$

where $\beta_{HCO_3^-}$ and β_{IM} are buffer values (in slykes or MEq base $L^{-1} U^{-1}$) of CO_2-bicarbonate and protein histidine imidazole buffers respectively and pK'_1 is the first dissociation of carbonic acid. For mammalian plasma at 20°C β_{IM} is 6.2 times greater than $\beta_{HCO_3^-}$ while dpK'_{IM}/dT is large (–0.018 U/°C) compared to dpK'_1/dT (–0.007 U/°C). Under in vitro conditions, the protein buffering dominates and $dpH/dT \approx dpK'_{IM}/dT$, permitting nearly constant $(pH_B - pK'_{IM})$ and α_{IM}, a general feature of acid-base response in all vertebrate bloods.

In vivo the system depends on physiological controls, not on buffer properties, because the organism constantly produces carbon dioxide. There are only two independent variables in acid-base control, P_{CO_2} and the strong ion concentration difference, once the total amount and composition of the buffers have been specified. If the strong ion concentration difference were regulated to control α_{IM}, total CO_2 (as bicarbonate) would not be maintained constant as experimental data indicate it is. This leaves then the P_{CO_2} as the independent variable by which observed acid-base balance in air-breathing ectotherms must be physiologically regulated.

CONSTANT RELATIVE ALKALINITY   Rahn (46, 67, 68) pointed out that at first analysis it hardly appears that acid-base balance regulation occurs in ectotherms because of the dependence of pH_B and P_{CO_2} on body temperature. He noted however that the observed change in pH_B is exactly what one would predict if the OH^-:H^+ ratio were the defended parameter. Water is by definition neutral when $(OH^-) = (H^+)$, or $(OH^-):(H^+) = 1$ or pH = pOH. Since pH + pOH = pK_w, at neutrality (pN) $2pN = pK_w$ or $pN = \frac{1}{2} pK_w$. The dissociation of water as expressed by pK_w is a function of temperature ranging from 14.94 at 0° to 13.53 at 40°C; thus pN is also temperature dependent, with neutrality being 7.47 at 0° and 6.77 at 40°C.

Extracellular fluids, including blood, are alkaline solutions, $pH_B > pN$. Rahn (47, 69–71) documented the parallel between pH_B and pN as body temperature changes; under these conditions $pH_B = pN + K$ where the constant K is about 0.6–0.8 units. When $pH_B - pN$ remains constant, the OH^-:H^+ ratio, or relative alkalinity, is also constant.

As already discussed for calculated pH_B as a function of temperature at constant α_{IM} or constant CO_2 content, the pH_B curve describing a constant relative alkalinity at all temperatures is not a straight line function. The slope of this curve decreases with temperature from -0.020 U/°C (0–10°C) to -0.0149 U/°C (30–40°C). Over the 0–40°C range, the mean $\Delta pN/\Delta T$ averages -0.0176 U/°C.

Just as in alphastat control, constant relative alkalinity would have to be actively regulated by physiological processes; for the same reasons as already advanced for the alphastat regulation, Pco_2 control in air-breathing vertebrates would necessarily be the means of effecting a constant relative alkalinity.

Albery & Lloyd (4) pointed out that alphastat and constant relative alkalinity hypotheses are not mutually exclusive nor contradictory; from a physical chemical point of view all that is required for α_{IM} and $OH^-:H^+$ each to be a valid potential candidate for the regulated variable is for the $\Delta H°$ for imidazole dissociation to be equal to $\frac{1}{2} \Delta H°_w$, the enthalpy for the dissociation of water. This is indeed the case; $\Delta H°_{IM}$ and $\frac{1}{2} \Delta H°_w$ are each approximately 7 kcal/mol. Hence as Albery & Lloyd (4) emphasized, it is entirely possible for the parallelism between a temperature invariant α_{IM} and preservation of a constant relative alkalinity to arise by accident. Several considerations may be pertinent in attempting to decide whether constant $OH^-:H^+$ ratio or a constant α_{IM} are equivalent candidates for the role of controlled parameter in acid-base regulation in ectotherms. In the physical chemical description of the purely chemical factors affecting change in pH_B in vitro with temperature, the effect of changing pK_w is quantitatively insignificant; the large buffer values of the other buffer components, CO_2–HCO_3^- and protein, completely overwhelm any effect changes in pK_w could contribute (79). Also, many reactions, if not most, in living systems are sensitive to changes in $[H^+]$; none is yet known to be specifically sensitive to $OH^-:H^+$ ratio. However, the effect of preservation of protein net charge state would potentially exert effects on all protein activities in the organism.

Ventilatory Control of Acid-Base State

The previous summaries of blood data have shown that open regulated systems in vivo and closed systems in vitro (at constant CO_2 content), have essentially identical pH and Pco_2 variation with temperature. In the open system, the metabolizing animal continually producing carbon dioxide, the pattern of acid-base regulation requires that the animal's ventilation be adjusted at each temperature to provide the proper Pco_2. From the alveolar equation appropriate to lung breathing animals:

$$\frac{\dot{V}_A}{\dot{V}_{CO_2}} = k \, \frac{1}{Pco_2},$$

where $\dot{V}_A$ is alveolar ventilation, $\dot{V}_{CO_2}$ carbon dioxide production, and k is a constant. From this relation it is evident that for carbon dioxide tension to decrease as body temperature falls, it is necessary for the ratio $\dot{V}_A:\dot{V}_{CO_2}$ to increase; that is, the ventilation per unit of metabolism, or relative ventilation, must increase as temperature falls (70). Experimental data in accord with this analysis have been provided by Jackson (50, 51, 53). In *Pseudemys* chronically catheterized for blood measurement of $Paco_2$ and utilizing ingenious methods for measurement of tidal volume and frequency, Jackson et al (53) determined expired minute volume, $\dot{V}_E$, an approximation to $\dot{V}_A$, and by inflow-outflow gas analysis were able to measure oxygen consumption, $\dot{V}_{O_2}$. The measured ratio $\dot{V}_E : \dot{V}_{O_2}$ bears a fixed relation to $\dot{V}_E : \dot{V}_{CO_2}$ for a constant gas exchange ratio, $R = \dot{V}_{CO_2} : \dot{V}_{O_2}$. At 30°C when Pa_{CO_2} was 32 torr, the $\dot{V}_E : \dot{V}_{O_2}$ (ml BTPS/ml STPD) was 23. At a body temperature of 10°C, blood CO_2 tension had decreased to 14 torr, while relative ventilation, $\dot{V}_E : \dot{V}_{O_2}$ had increased to 62. Hence the ventilation per unit oxygen consumption increased as body temperature fell, essentially hyperventilating as temperature decreased. The most remarkable observation in these experiments was that $\dot{V}_E$ was essentially constant over the 20° range; the value of the ratio $\dot{V}_E : \dot{V}_{O_2}$ changed due to changes in oxygen consumption. Davies (20) has reported a similar increase in $\dot{V}_E : \dot{V}_{O_2}$ in the alligator as body temperature falls; this species however, shows a marked increase in $\dot{V}_E$ as body temperature increases. By adding carbon dioxide to the inspired air, Jackson et al (53) in *Pseudemys* and Davies et al (21) in *Alligator* were able to establish the $\dot{V}_E$ sensitivity to Pa_{CO_2} at several body temperatures; increased Pa_{CO_2} produced a marked hyperventilation at all temperatures.

Jackson & Silverblatt (54, see also 49) followed the response of *Pseudemys* to long-lasting (2–4 hr) experimental dives at constant body temperature (24°C); these experiments produced severe respiratory and lactate acidosis. During recovery studies it was found that normal blood pH and bicarbonate levels were achieved after 24 hrs. Immediately post-dive, a brisk hyperventilation restored blood pH to normal in 2 hr despite a continuing metabolic acidosis. These experiments indicate the power of ventilatory control of blood carbon dioxide tensions to maintain a normal blood pH set-point both when temperature is the experimental variable and when a metabolic acidosis from a prolonged apnea challenges the regulated acid-base balance.

TEMPERATURE-SENSITIVE VENTILATION RECEPTOR   How is ventilation regulated in these circumstances? What is the receptor which controls ventilation and establishes the correct $\dot{V}_E$ for the challenge imposed, i. e. temperature change or isothermal metabolic acidosis? Reeves in (70, 78) suggested that both types of regulation could be achieved if the ventilation receptor had two fundamental properties: 1. the receptor must contain a dissociable group with a pK' in the physiological range conferring pH responsiveness; and 2. the change in pK' with temperature for that group must be similar to the in vivo pH_B temperature curve, i. e. a $\Delta H°$ of 7 kcal/mol (4). It is then possible to envisage the receptor site as a specific amino acid in a protein component whose charge-state and conformation are sensitive to the animal's acid-base status at any body temperature. The protein might be considered as an "ion-gating protein" in the membrane of a respiratory pacemaker neuron; the dissociation of the receptor site is written in terms of a histidine imidazole group in peptide linkage, unique among biological compounds for satisfying the two important conditions already mentioned. The model proposes that the pacemaker neuronal activity for ventilation is governed by α_{IM} at a specific protein locus, and that a set-point is defended over all physiological temperatures (i. e. the system functions as an alphastat for a specific imidazole locus or loci). The difference between expressing ventilation control classically as pH sensitive, and according to the model as α_{IM} sensitive, can only be detected in systems where comparisons at different body temperatures are made. By virtue of alphastat regulation for the membrane elements of the ventilatory receptor, all imidazole group dissociations in proteins throughout the organism would be entrained.

Intracellular pH Responses to Changing Body Temperature

If the central function of ectotherm acid-base balance is protection of protein charge states, and thus protein activity, as body temperature varies, how does extracellular acid-base regulation affect the bulk of protein function in the organism, i. e. intracellular proteins? First attempts at an experimental answer to this question are now at hand. Malan et al (60) applied the DMO weak acid distribution method to measurement of intracellular pH in a series of tissues in *Rana* and *Pseudemys* in vivo over a wide range of steady-state temperatures. Their results indicate that even though intracellular pH values are not equilibrium distributions for H^+ (and/or HCO_3^- and OH^-) but are actively maintained near neutrality, the change in pH_i with changing body temperature follows the path of near constant α_{IM}. Figure 3 summarizes calculations of α_{IM} in these tissues. Blood α_{IM} is constant, falling between 0.85 and 0.9 in both species. Tissue values fall in the 0.5–0.75 range, and each tissue α_{IM} is maintained within close limits over wide temperature excursions. In the case of *Pseudemys* striated muscle, for instance, α_{IM} is maintained at about 0.6; if the imidazole $\Delta H°$ were not 7 kcal/mol, but instead near zero, i. e. if pK'_{IM} were unaffected by temperature, α_{IM} would decrease to about 0.2 for a rise in temperature of 40°C. These findings emphasize that the observed pattern of regulation of CO_2 partial pressure when body temperature changes, not only regulates and preserves peptide histidine imidazole dissociation in the extracellular compartment, but also within cells as well. Hence Donnan states and protein activities are shielded from rather than disrupted by temperature fluctuations.

Protection from Acid-Base Transients during Step-Change in Temperature

If a major function of acid-base regulation is the preservation of protein charge state, how are rapid near step-changes in body and tissue temperature accommodated without producing disruptive transients in α_{IM}? Instances of body temperature changes of remarkable rapidity and magnitude in air-breathing vertebrates are now well documented (see Figure 4).

Blood in vitro at constant CO_2 content shows no transient changes in pH and P_{CO_2}, which departs from the steady-state temperature behavior already described; the proton equilibria and even CO_2 hydration reaction are so rapid compared to observed rates of temperature change that steady-state behavior is seen as quickly as the imposed heat flux and heat capacity limitations permit temperature change. In vivo there are two important investigations of blood acid-base response to temperature transients. Baumgardner (12) studied the blood pH and P_{CO_2} variation of unanesthetized 300 g *Bufo marinus* subjected to a diurnal rhythm of 12 hr at 15°C followed by 12 hr at 30°C repeated for periods of over twenty days before measurements commenced. The temperature-cycled animals remained on the same pH_B-temperature curve as did steady-state temperature-adapted animals. Hence no acid-base transient could be detected.

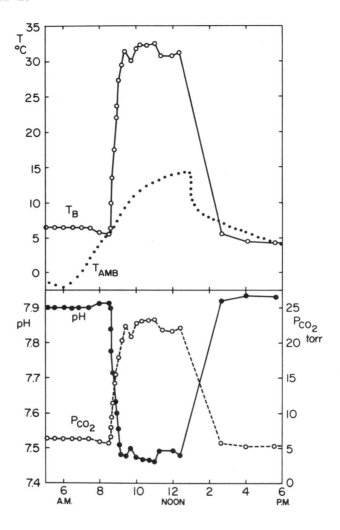

Figure 4   Body temperature (T_B) changes of a free-ranging lizard, *Liolaemus multiformis,* and ambient temperature (T_{AMB}) plotted over a 12-hr period from Pearson & Bradford (64). Shown below along same time scale are computed changes in blood pH and carbon dioxide tension (P_{CO_2}) based on data from *Iguana iguana* (92, 93); values are computed using $pH_B = 7.55$, $P_{CO_2} = 18$ torr at $T_B = 27°C$ for a $c_B = 0.030$ M/l and $C_{CO_2} = 0.018$ M/l as described by Reeves (78).

Jackson & Kagen (52) measured ventilatory and blood parameters in *Pseudemys* maintained at a water temperature of 20°C and subjected to a single 1-hr exposure at 30°C. Ventilatory state ($\dot{V}_E/\dot{V}_{O_2}$ and $\dot{V}_E/\dot{V}_{CO_2}$) and metabolic rate adjusted promptly to temperature change, stabilizing at values similar to those observed previously in turtles following one or more days at each temperature. Mean blood pH and P_{CO_2} values also conformed both in absolute values and in temperature-dependence to previously obtained values from animals with steady-state body temperature. Jackson & Kagen (52) concluded that physiological control of blood acid-base status adjusts rapidly to body temperature variation resulting in little or no disturbance to CO_2 balance. These results also indicate that temperature change in vivo does not require significant alteration in total body CO_2 stores; that is, stores need not be loaded nor unloaded to permit full temperature adjustment of acid-base status.

Reeves & Malan (81) attempted to approach the question of how intracellular compartment proteins avoid disrupting transients in response to a step change in temperature by computation on model systems. These studies assessed the passive intracellular buffer system response to a combined change in body temperature and CO_2 partial pressure as occurs in vivo. The cell compartment was simulated by a closed volume of ternary buffer solution, containing protein imidazole (0.05 M/l), phosphates (0.015 M/l) and CO_2–HCO_3^- buffer components, permeable only to CO_2 and permitted no change in strong ion concentrations. Excursions from a steady-state non-equilibrium pH_i were computed for step changes in temperature/P_{CO_2}. These responses in general tended to move along a path closely similar to the steady-state temperature relationship. No transient away from steady-state α_{IM} and carbon dioxide content of significant magnitude was observed. Such calculations lend credence to the view that intracellular acid-base state in air-breathing ectotherm cells requires essentially no period of adaptation (i.e. by pH_i modification resulting from active transport activity) to respond to sudden alteration of body temperature. These systems, by virtue of their passive physical chemical properties, can change temperature rapidly, preserving protein charge state and keeping intracellular CO_2 content nearly constant.

A Day in the Acid-Base Regulation of an Ectotherm

Ectothermic vertebrates in nature undergo surprisingly large changes in body temperature, frequently with great rapidity. The consequences of such temperature fluctuations for acid-base balance can be estimated with reasonable confidence. Pearson (64) recently reported noteworthy measurements of body temperature (T_b) by means of radio telemetry on a small 18 g iguanid lizard, *Liolaemus multiformis*, under free ranging conditions in the field. These lizards live on the altiplano of Peru at an altitude of 13,000 ft (4300 m). Ambient air temperatures vary from -2 to 15°C over the course of 24 hr; mornings are clear with sunshine but the afternoons develop storms of hail, snow, or freezing rain. Figure 4 excerpts a 12 hr portion of a 3-day continuous body temperature record and shows *Liolaemus* body temperature (6.5°C) well above ambient air temperature throughout the early morning; between 8 and 9 AM the lizard emerges from a ground burrow to bask in direct sunlight. The direct radiation input raises body temperature rapidly; in this record

T_b goes from 5° to 33°C in approximately half an hour. Pearson measured rates of change in body temperature of 0.4 to 0.8° per minute. Once at the 32–34°C temperature level the lizard regulates body temperature behaviorally. When afternoon hail storms commence between noon and 1 PM, body temperature falls precipitously as the animal again enters the cool ground burrow. This record shows almost a 30° temperature excursion in body temperature occurring in a very short period of time.

Direct acid-base data on *Liolaemus* are not available; we may for illustrative purposes use the acid-base temperature relationship from another lizard *(Iguana iguana)* of Wood & Moberly (93) to express the acid-base responses to a 30° body temperature change. Figure 2 also depicts the time course of calculated blood pH and carbon dioxide partial pressure over the diurnal temperature cycle of *Liolaemus*. The 30° rise of body temperature is associated with a change in pH_B from 7.93 (5°C) to 7.47 (33°C); despite these dramatic changes in blood pH, protein histidine dissociation and relative alkalinity remain constant. The corresponding change in partial pressure of CO_2 is 5.8–23.7 torr; when temperature and carbon dioxide partial pressure change simultaneously under these conditions, no titration of protein buffers forming additional bicarbonate occurs. These acid-base changes can be accomplished quickly and reversibly because they require no extensive loading or unloading of carbon dioxide either from tissue or blood stores. Dramatic changes in body temperature can be accommodated with essentially no change in blood or intracellular protein net charge state. The special properties of CO_2-HCO_3^- and protein binary buffer systems as well as the regulation of ventilation permit the animal the freedom to change body temperature rapidly and not suffer transients of α_{IM} in either direction. It is this protection from large changes in net charge of cellular proteins which, in part at least, permits *Liolaemus,* in Barcroft's words, to "so control its reactions as to keep them in step over a great range of temperature."

ACID-BASE RESPONSES IN WATER-BREATHING VERTEBRATES

The development of our understanding of acid-base balance in air-breathing ectotherms, once the concept of a temperature-dependent blood pH and Pa_{CO_2} had been firmly established experimentally, has been relatively straightforward. The natural extension of concepts derived from air breathers to include water-breathing ectotherms has, however, not been as readily accomplished for a number of reasons. There are important theoretical physiological consequences of respiratory exchange in a water medium, only recently clarified (66), that bear directly on the regulation of arterial carbon dioxide tension and hence on acid-base regulation mechanisms. Furthermore, water breathers apparently possess respiratory adaptations to optimize oxygen extraction from a medium of low and frequently variable oxygen content. Compounding the problems presented by these new elements are a series of experimental handicaps to the investigator who seeks to make acid-base measurements on these organisms.

Constraints Imposed by Aquatic Gas Exchange

Fundamental limitations for acid-base balance of water-breathing organisms have been elegantly identified by Rahn (66, 67, 71) in an extension of the O_2-CO_2 diagram analysis of Fenn et al (33). Large gill ventilations, necessary to extract sufficient oxygen as a consequence of breathing a medium with low oxygen solubility, place new boundary conditions upon acid-base regulation in water breathers. One such boundary condition is a theoretical upper limit to the gill blood (arterial) $P_{G_{CO_2}}$ of about 5 torr at 20°C for organisms in air-saturated water. In water, the ratio of CO_2 solubility (q'_{CO_2}) to oxygen solubility (q'_{O_2}) is about 28 (20°C); thus a fish with a gas-exchange ratio (R) of 1.0 must have a decrease in gill effluent water oxygen tension of 28 torr for each increment of 1 torr in CO_2 partial pressure. For inspired gill water that is air-saturated ($P_{I_{O_2}} = 150$ torr), complete extraction of all oxygen in that water would result in an effluent gill water $P_{G_{CO_2}}$ of 150/28 = 5.4 torr. Since oxygen extraction is, practically speaking, never complete and R<1, a maximum for arterial blood carbon dioxide tension under these conditions is about 5 torr. Thus water breathers are compelled by the physical solubilities of respiratory gases in water to maintain blood carbon dioxide tensions at very low levels, at values well below those obtaining in air-breathing vertebrates.

Furthermore, for a given carbon dioxide production (or O_2 consumption), the partial pressure of carbon dioxide in gill blood ($P_{G_{CO_2}}$) varies inversely with gill ventilation ($\dot{V}_G$) (71):

$$P_{G_{CO_2}} = \dot{V}_{CO_2}/(\dot{V}_G q'_{CO_2}).$$

Carbon dioxide solubility (q'_{CO_2}) is close to unity ($q'_{CO_2} = 1$ at 25°C). As emphasized in a later section, gill ventilation is inversely affected by the oxygen tension of inspired water. Hence, for the water breather, the oxygen tension of inspired water is a further important determinant of gill ventilation and thus of blood carbon dioxide tension. The consequence of this limitation for acid-base balance in fishes is that blood P_{CO_2} is determined by environmental conditions, denying the possibility of physiological control of acid-base status by regulating $P_{a_{CO_2}}$ through control of ventilation. In fishes it thus becomes important to examine acid-base balance as a function of hypoxic, normoxic, and hyperoxic environmental states.

Special Problems in Experimentation on Water Breathers

BLOOD SAMPLE COLLECTION TECHNIQUES   The need for measurements on chronically catheterized unrestrained fish if normal acid-base state is to be studied has been graphically illustrated by Garey (35, 36). He compared blood pH values obtained on rapidly netted fish immediately subjected to heart puncture with data from the same fish chronically catheterized by the technique of Smith & Bell (89), permitted 2–3 days for recovery, and sampled in an unrestrained, free-swimming state. In data from three species, char (3°C), pink salmon (14°C), and electric eel (28°C), Garey showed that blood samples obtained from the chronically catheterized animals had pH values from 0.39 to 0.77 units higher. Clearly, stresses of netting, handling, and sampling induced a prompt and severe acidosis whose presence obscured the normal acid-base status being studied. Dejours (25) emphasized the direct effect of the commonly used anesthetic agent MS222 in stimulating respiration in fishes, again obscuring normal acid-base control mechanisms. If only blood acid-base data from fishes having a chronically implanted catheter permitting measurements on unrestrained animals are judged acceptable, the number of experimental studies providing information on the processes governing normal acid-base control in fish is sharply reduced. Uncritical acceptance of nonsteady-state heart-puncture blood data can lead to conclusions directly contradictory to studies based solely on steady-state data from chronically catheterized fish (44).

NEED FOR CO_2 SOLUBILITY AND pK_1' VALUES AT LOW TEMPERATURES
Frequent use is made in acid-base studies of calculated bicarbonate concentrations based on directly measured glass electrode pH values and CO_2 partial pressure determinations by the Astrup technique (5) made at the animal's body temperature; Cameron (16) noted that fish blood P_{CO_2} values are "below levels that can be conveniently measured with CO_2 electrodes (usually 1–5 mm Hg)." Bicarbonate estimates based on the relation, $[HCO_3^-] = q' \cdot P_{CO_2} \cdot 10^{pH \cdot pK_1'}$, also require values for the solubility of carbon dioxide (q') as well as a value for the pK_1' for the first dissociation of carbonic acid. Both constants are functions of temperature and ionic strength. For the solubility of carbon dioxide in human plasma (ionic strength 0.15 M, an appropriate approximate value for many teleosts) measurements are available over the continuous temperature range 15–38°C (8, 10); extrapolation is, however, required to estimate carbon dioxide solubility at temperatures frequently encountered in studies on fish. In the case of pK_1', the values recommended (2) and widely used for fish at temperatures in the range 5–15°C are extrapolations based on measurements made only at two temperatures, 24 and 37.5°C, by Severinghaus et al (88). These primary data have been recalculated, extrapolated to cover the range 10–40°C, and separately published in tabular form (86, 87). Apparently many users of these pK_1' data are unaware that these "constants" lack experimental verification in the temperature range below 20°C.

Some measure of how seriously these solubility and pK_1' values can be in error when employed at low temperatures can be seen in Figure 5, which presents a calculated carbon dioxide content for a sample of separated dog plasma based on pH and P_{CO_2} measurements made at four temperatures. The plasma sample after equilibration at 37°C was kept within a glass syringe and no gas exchange was permitted during temperature change. Thus this sample remained at constant carbon dioxide content. pH measurements were made with a glass electrode calibrated at the temperature of the sample; P_{CO_2} was measured by the Astrup technique (5). Calculation of carbon dioxide content as the sum of dissolved CO_2 and bicarbonate, and using Severinghaus' constants (87), seriously overestimates the true value at lower temperatures. At a temperature of 8°C, total carbon dioxide content is overestimated by nearly 23%. These calculations are included here only to emphasize the need for caution in the application of extrapolated pK_1' and q' data; they also underline an urgent need in fish acid-base balance studies for new experimental determinations of q' and pK_1' over the temperature range appropriate to many such studies, particularly 0–15°C. In addition, if, as Albers (2) suggested, the need for pH correction of pK_1' arises because of the combined effects of the bicarbonate/carbonate equilibrium as well as the formation of ion complexes such as $NaCO_3^-$, it is likely that pH-corrected pK_1' are even more important at temperatures below 10°C than they are for studies at mammalian body temperature.

For studies on organisms possessing body fluids of high-ionic strengths such as elasmobranchs (19) and marine invertebrates (48), the need for experimental determinations of CO_2 solubility and pH-corrected pK_1' is less imperative. Albers & Pleschka (3) and Truchot (91) suggested pK_1' values appropriate for these organisms, but in each case an assumed carbon dioxide solubility has been used. However, new determinations for both CO_2 solubility and pK' at three temperatures (10, 15, 20°C) in seawater are provided in Randall et al (76).

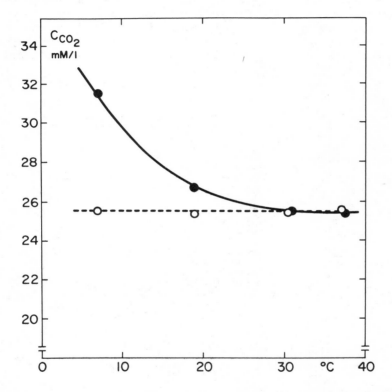

Figure 5 Comparison of calculated and measured carbon dioxide content in dog plasma as a function of temperature. Plasma was equilibrated in a tonometer at 37°C and a sample anaerobically drawn; as temperature was changed no gas exchange was permitted. Carbon dioxide tension and pH were measured at each temperature; carbon dioxide content (mMl^{-1}) was calculated as sum of dissolved CO_2 and bicarbonate from the relation $C_{CO_2} = q' \cdot P_{CO_2} \cdot [1 + 10^{(pH - pK_1')}]$ where q' is the carbon dioxide solubility ($mMl^{-1}torr^{-1}$) and pK_1' is first dissociation constant of carbonic acid. Closed circles pK_1' data of Severinghaus (87); open circles, pK_1' extrapolated values of Reeves (79); dotted line, measured Van Slyke analysis value.

Acid-Base Behavior of Fish under Normoxic Conditions

Blood pH data as a function of body temperature taken from reports of 14 investigators on ten species of fish are presented in Figure 6; these pH_B data span a body-temperature range of over 25°. Most of these investigations present results gathered from cannulated, unrestrained fish in the steady state. Since the number of animals being averaged at each experimental temperature is not always specified in the reference of origin, it is not possible to compute accurately a best fitting regression line. To offer some perspective for evaluating the dependence of blood pH on body temperature in these species, however, the curve for a constant $\alpha_{IM} = 0.85$ is indicated; this curve roughly corresponds to a $\Delta pH/\Delta T$ value of –0.018 U/°C. On the basis of evidence thus far available, fish blood pH from properly sampled animals under normoxic conditions shows a similar response to the acid-base behavior exhibited by air-breathing ectothermic vertebrates. Under normoxic conditions, fish,

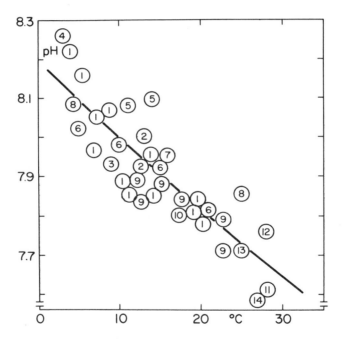

Figure 6   Steady state arterial blood pH of normoxic fish. Key: 1. *Salmo gairdneri,* Randall & Cameron (75); 2. *Salmo gairdneri,* Cameron & Randall (17); 3. *Salmo gairdneri,* Janssen & Randall (55); 4. *Salvelinus alpinus,* Garey (36); 5. *Oncorhynchus gorbuscha,* Garey (36); 6. *Cyprinus carpio,* Baumgardner (13); 7. *Cyprinus carpio,* Dejours (23); 8. *Cyprinus carpio,* Dejours & Armand (25); 9. *Scyliorhinus stellaris,* Heisler et al (41); 10. *Scyliorhinus stellaris,* Randall et al (76); 11. *Clarius botrachus,* Rahn & Garey (72); 12. *Phractocephalus hemiliopterus,* Rahn & Garey (72); 13. *Protopterus aethiopicus,* Lenfant & Johansen (59); 14. *Electrophorus electricus,* Garey & Rahn (38).

like other ectotherms, regulate their acid-base status in such a way that blood α_{IM} (or $OH^-:H^+$ ratio) is essentially preserved invariant with changing body temperature.

Of the investigations so far complete, greatest detail is presented in the landmark study of Randall & Cameron (75) of rainbow trout (*Salmo gairdneri*) with chronically implanted cannulae in the dorsal aortae. Body temperature in this study was varied over a range of 4.5–20°C. The steady-state pH of blood decreased as temperature increased with a $\Delta pH/\Delta T$ of –0.017 U/°C. Concomitant with this change in blood pH was the complete absence of change in the blood partial pressure of carbon dioxide; between 5 and 19°C the mean Pa_{CO_2} was 2.1 torr. As these authors rightly emphasized, accurate measurements of Pa_{CO_2} are not easily carried out at the low tensions found in fish especially when low temperatures are involved; neither the Astrup technique (5) nor P_{CO_2} electrode methods are optimal for accurate reproducible measurements under these conditions. Application by Randall & Cameron of total plasma CO_2 measurement using Cameron's method (16) only partly circumvented these difficulties; total CO_2 values increased as temperature decreased, but variability in the data and lack of agreement between calculated and measured values only served to emphasize the formidable experimental problems and again point up the need for better physical constant data. Randall & Cameron's work, however, is clearly the first to show that fish do not regulate blood pH by ventilatory adjustments of the $\dot{V}_G/\dot{V}_{CO_2}$ ratio. In this species, and presumably other water breathers as well, acid-base regulation, as temperature changes under normoxic conditions, is achieved by regulation of plasma bicarbonate ion concentration levels (or more accurately, the strong ion concentration difference). Thus, compared with air breathers which regulate their acid-base balance as temperature changes by ventilatory adjustments of Pa_{CO_2}, water breathers, by virtue of having Pa_{CO_2} dependent on the gill ventilation required for adequate oxygen extraction, must vary total carbon dioxide content in the plasma. Randall & Cameron further pointed out that adjustment of plasma bicarbonate concentration to achieve a new steady-state blood pH requires several hours after the onset of temperature change. From known observations on gill anion-exchange mechanisms for the ions chloride and bicarbonate (61), it is tempting to ascribe an acid-base regulatory function to active gill ion transport processes. The tissue sites and mechanisms by which plasma carbon dioxide content is adjusted as body temperature varies constitute a major area for investigation in future water-breather acid-base regulation studies.

Heisler et al (41) reported the first DMO intracellular pH measurements on water breathers in experiments carried out on dogfish, *Scyliorhinus stellaris*, over a range of temperatures from 10–23°C. In these animals $\Delta pH_i/\Delta T$ (U/°C) values for white muscle (–0.018), red muscle (–0.033), and heart muscle (–0.010) were found. Interpretation of these results is complicated, however, by differences in blood pH and P_{CO_2} between the adult and juvenile members of the mixed age population used in these studies. Intracellular data reported were averaged from both groups in this study. Further measurements will be required before it is possible to answer the question of whether intracellular compartments of water-breathers, maintain α_{IM} constant.

Hypoxic, Hyperoxic, and Hypercapnic Effects on Acid-Base Balance

Dejours (23) discussed the "respiratory ecology" of water breathers surveying the wide variation of partial pressures and concentrations of O_2 and CO_2 found in natural waters; he concluded that the variation is so great that "no two natural waters have the same composition or undergo the same changes when submitted to a given O_2 extraction and a given CO_2 addition due to fish respiration." Air breathers, on the other hand, have a respiratory medium which is homogeneous and of constant composition the world over.

A consequence of the variable O_2 content of natural waters is that achievement of an adequate O_2 supply for metabolism requires gill ventilation, $\dot{V}_G$, to vary inversely with O_2 content (22, 23, 56, 62); $\dot{V}_G$ increases in hypoxia (23) and decreases in hyperoxia (23), as can be found in waters with a high rate of photosynthetic oxygen production (37). Change in gill ventilation with inspired oxygen tension necessarily alters blood Pa_{CO_2} and other acid-base parameters.

Dejours's striking results (23) from long-term blood acid-base measurements on carp (*Cyprinus*) at 15°C exposed to normoxic, hypoxic and hyperoxic inspired gill water are shown in Figure 7. Hypoxic exposure increasing $\dot{V}_G$ decreased blood

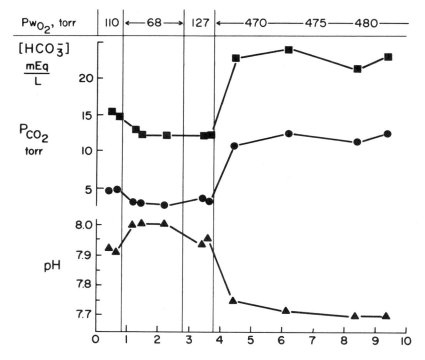

Figure 7   Bicarbonate concentration, arterial carbon dioxide tension, and pH in a chronic catheterized carp (*Cyprinus carpio*) at 15°C [after Dejours (23)]. The partial pressure of oxygen in the water (Pw_{O_2}) is given at the top of the figure. Abscissa is time in days.

P_{CO_2}, bicarbonate concentration, and hydrogen ion activity; hyperoxic exposure, by inducing a decrease in $\dot{V}_G$, gave the opposite response, resulting in increases in P_{CO_2}, bicarbonate concentration, and hydrogen ion activity. In the case of the hypoxic to hyperoxic transition, the magnitude of the effects is impressive with P_{CO_2} increasing from 3 to 12 torr and pH decreasing from 8.0 to 7.7. The changes were complete in 24 hr and were sustained for long periods. These observations emphasize that acid-base regulation as typified by the behavior seen in normoxic fish can be overridden to satisfy the organism's oxygen demand. Changes in ambient oxygen content of water can apparently reset the regulated acid-base state in these organisms.

The responses to hypercapnia found by Janssen & Randall (55) on *Salmo* and by Randall et al (76) on *Scyliorhinus* stand in marked contrast to the responses to hyperoxic challenge described by Dejours (23) for *Cyprinus*. In each of the hypercapnia studies the inspired water P_{ICO_2} was increased 5 torr; in each case the P_{aCO_2} rose promptly by a like amount. Both species eventually returned plasma pH to prehypercapnic values; in *Salmo*, the compensatory processes required 3 days, in *Scyliorhinus*, compensation was complete in several hours. In both studies, gill epithelial chloride efflux linked with simultaneous bicarbonate influx may have been responsible. Hypercapnia produced a transient respiratory acidosis but was fully compensated after a period of time. In the hyperoxic challenge to *Cyprinus*, P_{aCO_2} also increased, due in this case to a decrease in $\dot{V}_G$; but little significant acid-base compensation occurred over a period of many days. One is left with the puzzling question of how the normoxic acid-base state set-point is defended in the case of hypercapnia while a wholly new and apparently steady-state acid-base state results from alteration in oxygen content of inspired gill water.

Transition from Water- to Air-Breathing

Air-breathing fishes have held a special place of interest in investigations exploring respiratory adaptations of water breathing versus air breathing. Among the adaptations required for the transition to air breathing is an intriguing acid-base regulatory problem (45, 73). In moving into an oxygen-rich gaseous respiratory medium, the ventilation required to extract sufficient O_2 to satisfy oxygen demands is greatly diminished. A reduced ventilation requires a higher expired P_{CO_2} to permit elimination of sufficient CO_2; higher expired P_{CO_2} tensions are necessarily reflected in similar increases in arterial blood carbon dioxide tension, typically some 2–5-fold higher in air breathers than in water-breathing organisms at the same temperature. If a profound respiratory acidosis is to be avoided, plasma bicarbonate concentration must also be increased. Rahn et al (74) studied this transition in the garfish (*Lepisosteus osseus*), a species completely dependent on gill exchange at low water temperatures in winter, but one which can extract 70–80% of its total oxygen requirement by use of lung ventilation at higher summer water temperatures. In winter at 10°C the garfish maintains blood pH, P_{CO_2}, and bicarbonate concentration at 7.83, 3.2 torr, and 7.3 mM/*l* falling within the range of acid-base values of typical fishes as shown in Figure 6. In summer at a water temperature of 25°C, pH, P_{CO_2}, and bicarbonate concentration are 7.44, 13.2 torr, and 10.4 mM/*l*. The arterial blood carbon dioxide tension clearly exceeds the range of normal water breathers at warmer temperatures. The blood samples in this study were obtained by heart puncture; the low blood pH values found, particularly at higher fish temperatures, suggest some degree of acidosis may have resulted from the catching, handling, and sampling procedures used. It seems likely that sampling from undisturbed animals would show an even higher bicarbonate concentration under the air-breathing warm water conditions.

Obligatory air-breathing fishes also show a high P_{CO_2} compared to water-breathing fishes. Lung carbon dioxide tensions of about 30 torr are reported for the African lungfish (59) and the electric eel (32). These values are some fivefold greater than could occur under water-breathing circumstances.

The transformation of the tadpole form into the adult frog at constant temperature (20°C) is another example of the transition from water breathing to air breathing. Erasmus et al (31) presented blood pH and blood buffer value data from the bullfrog, *Rana catesbeiana*, at these two stages of development. In the tadpole, a blood pH of 7.72 and a Pa_{CO_2} of 3.2 torr are reported with a calculated bicarbonate concentration of 5.5 mM/l. In the adult frog at the same temperature arterial pH is somewhat higher 7.9 with a Pa_{CO_2} of 13 torr and a bicarbonate ion concentration of 30 mM/l. In this case the blood pH is apparently defended by maintaining an increased bicarbonate concentration when higher carbon dioxide partial pressures are required to ensure adequate rates of CO_2 loss in the air medium. Just et al (57) made acid-base measurements on a series of defined stages of bullfrog metamorphosis and presented more extensive data which, in general, sustain the original observations of Erasmus et al (31).

CONCLUSION

Ectothermic vertebrates exhibit a "fixité du milieu intérieur" no less striking than the functionally related regulation of blood pH by mammalian and avian species. The pattern of ectotherm regulation of acid-base state is obscured when attention is focused solely on classical parameters such as blood pH, because air-breathing ectotherms as well as normoxic fish show a uniquely defended hydrogen ion activity or pH_B at each temperature. When, however, the factors affecting protein charge state, the dissociation of protein imidazole groups (α_{IM}), are examined, each uniquely defended pH_B at each body temperature is precisely that required to maintain protein charge states constant. The implications of a strategy of defending protein charge state in an organism whose biochemical apparatus is composed of protein components, the functions of which critically depend on charge state, are evident. At a single temperature, i.e. 37°C, defense of protein imidazole charge state, alphastat regulation, cannot be distinguished from regulation of blood pH. Hence homeotherms are not exceptions to alphastat control; they are isothermal examples of the same phenomenon.

Evidence, as yet preliminary and limited, suggests that the pattern of alphastat control of blood carbon dioxide partial pressure to maintain blood protein imidazole dissociation constant has a like effect on proteins within the intracellular compartments. Viewed from this perspective, acid-base regulation as seen in ectothermic vertebrates also serves as a protection for intracellular protein function.

Mechanisms by which alphastat control is effected differ between air-breathing and water-breathing ectotherms. Air breathers regulate α_{IM} principally by rapid adjustment of ventilation to secure the required CO_2 partial pressure at each temperature. Water breathers, constrained by the limited solubilities of respiratory gases in water, must resort to slower mechanisms such as gill ion exchange processes in order to change the bicarbonate concentration of plasma. Provided normoxic conditions prevail, blood pH values follow similar patterns in water breathers and air breathers—patterns consistent with protein charge state regulation.

The buffer systems of blood and tissue fill a special role in air-breathing ectotherm acid-base responses to temperature change. Tissue buffers, because of the predominance of protein (histidine imidazole) buffering, change P_{CO_2} (at constant gas content) when temperature is varied with α_{IM} maintained essentially constant. The P_{CO_2} passively generated by temperature change closely matches the P_{CO_2} which must be provided by ventilatory control when the tissue functions as an open CO_2-producing system. This special property of passively responding to a temperature change in a way that maintains protein charge state constant obviates the need for filling or emptying tissue carbon dioxide stores. These passive tissue buffering properties permit steady-state acid-base conditions to prevail as rapidly as tissue temperature can be altered.

ACKNOWLEDGMENTS

It is a pleasure to express my gratitude to Professor Hermann Rahn for his continuous interest and helpful criticism. This work was supported in part by National Institutes of Health Grant HL-14414–05.

Literature Cited

1. Adamsons, K. Jr., Daniel, S., Gandy, G., James, L. 1964. Influence of temperature on blood pH of the human adult and newborn. *J. Appl. Physiol.* 19:897–900
2. Albers, C. 1970. Acid-base balance. In *Fish Physiology,* ed. W. S. Hoar, D. J. Randall, 4:173–208. New York: Academic. 532 pp.
3. Albers, C., Pleschka, K. 1967. Effect of temperature on CO_2 transport in elasmobranch blood. *Respir. Physiol.* 2:261–73
4. Albery, W. J., Lloyd, B. B. 1967. Variation of chemical potential with temperature. In *Development of the Lung,* ed. A. De Reuck, R. Porter, pp. 30–33. Boston: Little, Brown. 408 pp.
5. Astrup, P. 1956. A simple electrometric technique for determination of P_{CO_2} in blood and plasma. *Scand. J. Clin. Lab. Invest.* 8:33–43
6. Austin, J. H., Sunderman, F. W., Camack, J. G. 1927. The electrolyte composition and the pH of serum of a poikilothermous animal at different temperatures. *J. Biol. Chem.* 72:677–85
7. Austin, W. H., Lacombe, E. H., Rand, P. W. 1964. pH-temperature conversion factors and P_{CO_2} factors for hypothermia. *J. Appl. Physiol.* 19:893–96
8. Austin, W. H., Lacombe, E., Rand, P. W., Chatterjee, M. 1963. Solubility of carbon dioxide in serum from 15 to 38°C. *J. Appl. Physiol.* 18:301–4
9. Barcroft, J. 1934. *Features in the Architecture of Physiological Function.* Cambridge, England: Univ. Press. 368 pp.
10. Bartels, H., Wrbitzky, R. 1960. Bestimmung des CO_2-Absorptionskoeffizienten zwischen 15 and 38°C in Wasser und Plasma. *Pfluegers Arch. Gesamte Physiol. Menschen Tiere* 271:162–68
11. Bates, R. G. 1964. *Determination of pH: Theory and Practice.* New York: Wiley. 435 pp.
12. Baumgardner, F. W. 1968. *The effect of temperature on acid-base balance in the*

toad. MA thesis. State Univ. New York, Buffalo, New York. 65 pp.

13. Baumgardner, F. W. 1971. *Acid-base balance in vertebrates.* PhD thesis. State Univ. New York, Buffalo, New York. 141 pp.

14. Bradley, A. F., Stupfel, M., Severinghaus, J. W. 1956. Effect of temperature on P_{CO_2} and P_{O_2} in blood in vitro. *J. Appl. Physiol.* 9:201–4

15. Burton, R. F. 1973. The roles of buffers in body fluids: Mathematical analysis. *Respir. Physiol.* 18:34–42

16. Cameron, J. N. 1971. Rapid method for determination of total carbon dioxide in small blood samples. *J. Appl. Physiol.* 31:632–34

17. Cameron, J. N., Randall, D. J. 1972. The effects of increased ambient CO_2 on arterial CO_2 tension, CO_2 content and pH in rainbow trout. *J. Exp. Biol.* 57:673–80

18. Crawford, E. C., Gatz, R. N. 1973. Acid-base status of the blood of a desert lizard at different temperatures. *Pfluegers Arch.* 343 (Suppl.): R3

19. Cross, C. E., Packer, B. S., Linta, J. M., Murdaugh, H. V. Jr., Robin, E. D. 1969. H^+ buffering and excretion in response to acute hypercapnia in the dogfish *Squalus acanthias. Am. J. Physiol.* 216:440–52

20. Davies, D. G. 1975. The effect of temperature on ventilation and gas exchange in the American alligator. *Fed. Proc.* 34(3):431 (Abstr.)

21. Davies, D. G., Kopetzky, M. T. 1976. Effect of body temperature on the ventilatory response to hypercapnia in the awake alligator. *Fed. Proc.* 35(3):840 (Abstr.)

22. Davis, J. C., Cameron, J. N. 1970. Water flow and gas exchange at the gills of rainbow trout, *Salmo gairdneri. J. Exp. Biol.* 54:1–18

23. Dejours, P. 1973. Problems of control of breathing in fishes. In *Comparative Physiology,* ed. L. Bolis, K. Schmidt-Nielsen, S. H. P. Maddrell, pp. 117–33. Amsterdam: North-Holland. 634 pp.

24. Dejours, P. 1975. *Principles of Comparative Respiratory Physiology.* New York: American Elsevier. 253 pp.

25. Dejours, P., Armand, J. 1973. L'equilibre acide-base du sang chez la Carpe en fonction de la temperature. *J. Physiol. Paris* 67:264A

26. Dill, D. B., Edwards, H. T. 1935. Properties of reptilian blood. IV. The alligator (*Alligator mississippiensis*). *J. Cell Comp. Physiol.* 6:243–54

27. Dill, D. B., Edwards, H. T., Bock, A. V. Talbott, J. H. 1935. Properties of reptilian blood. III. The chuckwalla (*Sauromalus obesus*). *J. Cell. Comp. Physiol.* 6:37–42

28. Edsall, J. T., Wyman, J. 1958. *Biophysical Chemistry,* p. 509. New York: Academic. 699 pp.

29. Ellenbogen, E. 1952. Dissociation constants of peptides. I. A survey of the effect of optical configuration. *J. Am. Chem. Soc.* 74:5198–201

30. Ellenbogen, E. 1956. Dissociation constants of peptides. IV. The isomeric alanylalanines. *J. Am. Chem. Soc.* 78:369–72

31. Erasmus, B. DeW., Howell, B. J., Rahn, H. 1970. Ontogeny of acid-base balance in the bullfrog and the chicken. *Respir. Physiol.* 11:46–53

32. Farber, J., Rahn, H. 1970. Gas exchange between air and water and the ventilation pattern in the electric eel. *Respir. Physiol.* 9:151–61

33. Fenn, W. O., Rahn, H., Otis, A. B. 1946. A theoretical study of the composition of the alveolar air at altitude. *Am. J. Physiol.* 146:637–54

34. Frankel, H. M., Steinberg, G., Gordon, J. 1966. Effects of temperature on blood gases, lactate and pyruvate in turtles, *Pseudemys scripta elegans in vivo. Comp. Biochem. Physiol.* 19:279–83

35. Garey, W. F. 1967. *Gas exchange, cardiac output and blood pressure in free swimming carp* (*Cyprinus carpio*). PhD thesis. State Univ. New York, Buffalo, New York. 123 pp.

36. Garey, W. F. 1972. Determination of the normal blood pH of fishes. *Respir. Physiol.* 14:180–82

37. Garey, W. F., Rahn, H. 1970. Gas tensions in tissues of trout and carp exposed to diurnal changes in oxygen tension of the water. *J. Exp. Biol.* 52:575–82

38. Garey, W. F., Rahn, H. 1970. Normal arterial gas tensions and pH and the breathing frequency of the electric eel. *Respir. Physiol.* 9:141–50

39. Giordano, R. V., Jackson, D. C. 1973. The effect of temperature on ventilation in the green iguana (*Iguana iguana*). *Comp. Biochem. Physiol. A* 45:235–38

40. Hastings, A. B., Sendroy, J. Jr. 1924. The colorimetric determination of blood pH at body temperature without buffer standards. *J. Biol. Chem.* 61:695–710

41. Heisler, N., Weitz, H., Weitz, A. M. 1976. Extracellular and intracellular

pH with changes of temperature in the dogfish *Scyliorhinus stellaris. Respir. Physiol.* 26:249–63

42. Henderson, L. J. 1909. Das Gleichgewicht zwischen Basen und Sauren in Tierischen Organismus. *Ergebn. Physiol.* 8:254–325

43. Henderson, L. J. 1928. *Blood. A Study in General Physiology.* New Haven: Yale Univ. Press. 397 pp.

44. Houston, A. M. 1971. Some comments upon acid-base balance in teleost fishes and its relationship to environmental temperature. *Comp. Biochem. Physiol. A* 40:535–42

45. Howell, B. J. 1970. Acid-base balance in transition from water breathing to air breathing. *Fed. Proc.* 29:1130–34

46. Howell, B. J., Baumgardner, F. W., Bondi, K., Rahn, H. 1970. Acid-base balance in poikilotherms as a function of body temperature. *Am. J. Physiol.* 218:600–6

47. Howell, B. J., Rahn, H. 1976. Regulation of acid-base balance in reptiles. In *Biology of the Reptilia,* ed. C. Gans, W. R. Dawson, 5A:335–63. London: Academic. 556 pp.

48. Howell, B. J., Rahn, H., Goodfellow, D., Herreid, C. 1973. Acid-base regulation and temperature in selected invertebrates as a function of temperature. *Am. Zool.* 13:557–63

49. Jackson, D. C. 1969. The response of the body fluids of the turtle to imposed acid-base disturbances. *Comp. Biochem. Physiol.* 29:1105–10

50. Jackson, D. C. 1971. The effect of temperature on ventilation in the turtle, *Pseudemys scripta elegans. Respir. Physiol.* 12:131–40

51. Jackson, D. C. 1973. Ventilatory response to hypoxia in turtles at various temperatures. *Respir. Physiol.* 18:178–87

52. Jackson, D. C., Kagen, R. D. 1976. Effects of temperature transients on gas exchange and acid-base status of turtles. *Am. J. Physiol.* 230:1389–93

53. Jackson, D. C., Palmer, S. E., Meadow, W. L. 1974. The effects of temperature and carbon dioxide breathing on ventilation and acid-base status of turtles. *Respir. Physiol.* 20:131–46

54. Jackson, D. C., Silverblatt, H. 1974. Respiration and acid-base status of turtles following experimental dives. *Am. J. Physiol.* 226:903–9

55. Janssen, R. G., Randall, D. J. 1975. The effects of changes in pH and Pco_2 in blood and water on breathing in rainbow trout, *Salmo gairdneri. Respir. Physiol.* 25:235–45

56. Johansen, K., Maloiy, G. M., Lykkeboe, G. 1975. A fish in extreme alkalinity. *Respir. Physiol.* 24:159–62

57. Just, J. J., Gatz, R. N., Crawford, E. C. Jr. 1973. Changes in respiratory functions during metamorphosis of the bullfrog. *Respir. Physiol.* 17:276–82

58. Kelman, G. R., Nunn, J. F. 1966. Nomograms for correction of blood Po_2, Pco_2, pH and base excess for time and temperature. *J. Appl. Physiol.* 21:1484–90

59. Lenfant, C., Johansen, K. 1968. Respiration in the African lungfish *Protopterus aethiopicus. J. Exp. Biol.* 49:437–52

60. Malan, A., Wilson, T. L., Reeves, R. B. 1976. Intracellular pH in cold-blooded vertebrates as a function of body temperature. *Respir. Physiol.* 28:29–47

61. Maetz, J. 1971. Fish gills: Mechanisms of salt transfer in fresh water and sea water. *Philos. Trans. R. Soc. London Ser. B* 262:209–49

62. Milne, R. S., Randall, D. J. 1976. Regulation of arterial pH during fresh water to sea water transfer in the rainbow trout, *Salmo gairdneri. Comp. Biochem. Physiol. A* 53:157–60

63. Nunn, J. F., Bergman, N. A., Bunatyan, A., Coleman, A. J. 1965. Temperature coefficients for Pco_2 and Po_2 of blood in vitro. *J. Appl. Physiol.* 20:23–36

64. Pearson, O. P., Bradford, D. F. 1976. Thermoregulation of lizards and toads at high altitudes in Peru. *Copeia* 1976:155–70

65. Peters, J. P., Van Slyke, D. D. 1932. *Quantitative Clinical Chemistry, Volume II. Methods.* Baltimore: Williams & Wilkins. 981 pp.

66. Rahn, H. 1966. Aquatic gas exchange: Theory. *Respir. Physiol.* 1:1–12

67. Rahn, H. 1966. Evolution of the gas transport system in vertebrates. *Proc. R. Soc. Med.* 59:493–94

68. Rahn, H. 1967. Gas transport from the external environment to the cell. See Reference 4, pp. 3–23

69. Rahn, H. 1974. Body temperature and acid-base regulation. *Pneumonologie* 151:87–94

70. Rahn, H. 1974. Pco_2, pH and body temperature. In *Carbon Dioxide and Metabolic Regulations,* ed. G. Nahas, K. E. Smith, pp. 152–62. Heidelberg: Springer. 372 pp.

71. Rahn, H., Baumgardner, F. W. 1972.

Temperature and acid-base regulation in fish. *Respir. Physiol.* 14:171–82

72. Rahn, H., Garey, W. F. 1973. Arterial CO_2, O_2, pH and HCO_3^- values of ectotherms living in the Amazon. *Am. J. Physiol.* 225:735–38

73. Rahn, H., Howell, B. J. 1976. Bimodal gas exchange. In *Respiration of Amphibious Vertebrates,* ed. G. Hughes, pp. 271–86. New York: Academic. 402 pp.

74. Rahn, H., Rahn, K. B., Howell, B. J., Gans, C., Tenney, S. M. 1971. Air breathing of the garfish (*Lepisosteus osseus*). *Respir. Physiol.* 11:285–307

75. Randall, D. J., Cameron, J. N. 1973. Respiratory control of arterial pH as temperature changes in rainbow trout, *Salmo gairdneri. Am. J. Physiol.* 225:997–1002

76. Randall, D. J., Heisler, N., Drees, F. 1976. Ventilatory response to hypercapnia in the larger spotted dogfish *Scyliorhinus stellaris. Am. J. Physiol.* 230:590–94

77. Reeves, R. B. 1969. Role of body temperature in determining the acid-base state in vertebrates. *Fed. Proc.* 28:1204–8

78. Reeves, R. B. 1972. An imidazole alphastat hypothesis for vertebrate acid-base regulation: Tissue carbon dioxide content and body temperature in bullfrogs. *Respir. Physiol.* 14:219–36

79. Reeves, R. B. 1976. Temperature-induced changes in blood acid-base status: pH and P_{CO_2} in a binary buffer. *J. Appl. Physiol.* 40:752–61

80. Reeves, R. B. 1976. Temperature induced changes in blood acid-base status: Donnan r_{Cl} and red cell volume. *J. Appl. Physiol.* 40:762–67

81. Reeves, R. B., Malan, A. 1976. Model studies of intracellular acid-base temperature responses in ectotherms. *Respir. Physiol.* 28:49–63

82. Roberts, G., Meadows, D., Jardetzky, O. 1969. Solvent and temperature effects on the ionization of histidine residues of ribonuclease. *Biochemistry* 8:2053–56

83. Robin, E. D. 1962. Relationship between temperature and plasma pH and carbon dioxide tension in the turtle. *Nature* 195:249–51

84. Robin, E. D., Bromberg, P. A., Cross, C. E. 1969. Some aspects of the evolution of vertebrate acid-base regulation. *Yale J. Biol. Med.* 41:448–67

85. Rosenthal, T. B. 1948. The effect of temperature on the pH of blood and plasma in vitro. *J. Biol. Chem.* 173:25–30

86. Severinghaus, J. W. 1965. Blood gas concentrations. In *Handb. Physiol., Sect. 3, Vol. II,* ed. W. O. Fenn, H. Rahn, pp. 1475–87. Wash. DC: Am. Physiol. Soc. 1696 pp.

87. Severinghaus, J. W. 1971. Carbon dioxide solubility and first dissociation constant (pK') of carbonic acid in plasma and cerebrospinal fluid: Man. In *Respiration and Circulation,* ed. P. L. Altman, D. S. Dittmer, Table 83, pp. 218–19. Bethesda, Md: Fed. Am. Soc. Exp. Biol. 930 pp.

88. Severinghaus, J. W., Stupfel, M., Bradley, A. F. 1956. Variations of serum carbonic acid pK' with pH and temperature. *J. Appl. Physiol.* 9:197–220

89. Smith, L. S., Bell, G. R. 1964. A technique for prolonged blood sampling in free-swimming salmon. *J. Fish. Res. Board Canada* 21:711–17

90. Torre, C. M. 1967. *The effect of temperature on CO_2 clearance in frogs.* MA thesis. State Univ. New York, Buffalo, New York. 72 pp.

91. Truchot, J. P. 1973. Temperature and acid-base regulation in the shore crab *Carcinus maenus. Respir. Physiol.* 17:11–20

92. Tucker, V. A. 1966. Oxygen transport by the circulatory system of the green iguana (*Iguana iguana*) at different body temperatures. *J. Exp. Biol.* 44:77–92

93. Wood, S. C., Moberly, W. R. 1970. The influence of temperature on the respiratory properties of iguana blood. *Respir. Physiol.* 10:20–29

AUTHOR INDEX

SUBJECT INDEX

CUMULATIVE INDEXES

CONTRIBUTING AUTHORS VOLUMES 35-39

CHAPTER TITLES VOLUMES 35-39